Competency Based

BD Chaurasia's

Human Anatomy

Tenth Edition

Volume 2

Regional and Applied **Dissection and Clinical**

As per the latest NMC Guidelines | Competency Based Medical Education (CBME) Curriculum under Graduate Medical Education Regulation

Lower Limb

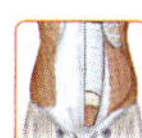

Abdomen and Pelvis

Dr BD Chaurasia (1937–1985)

was Reader in Anatomy at GR Medical College, Gwalior.
He received his MBBS in 1960, MS in 1965 and PhD in 1975.
He was elected fellow of National Academy of Medical Sciences (India) in 1982.
He was a member of the Advisory Board of the *Acta Anatomica* since 1981,
member of the editorial board of *Bionature*, and in addition
member of a number of scientific societies.
He had a large number of research papers to his credit.

Competency Based

BD Chaurasia's Human Anatomy

Tenth Edition

Volume 2

Regional and Applied | Dissection and Clinical

As per the latest NMC Guidelines | Competency Based Medical Education (CBME) Curriculum under Graduate Medical Education Regulation

 Lower Limb

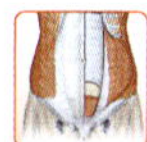 Abdomen and Pelvis

Chief Editor

Krishna Garg
MBBS MS PhD FIMSA FIAMS FAMS FASI
Legend of Anatomy; Nation's Who's Who
Fellow, Anatomical Society of India
Lifetime Achievement Awardee
DMA Distinguished Service Awardee
Ex-Professor and Head, Department of Anatomy
Lady Hardinge Medical College, New Delhi

Executive Editor

Yogesh Ashok Sontakke MBBS MD
Additional Professor
Department of Anatomy
Jawaharlal Institute of Postgraduate Medical Education and Research (JIPMER)
(An Institute of National Importance under the Ministry of Health and Family Welfare, Government of India)
Puducherry

Editors

Pragati Sheel Mittal MBBS MS
Professor, Department of Anatomy
Government Institute of Medical Sciences
Greater Noida, Uttar Pradesh

Mrudula Chandrupatla MBBS MD
Professor and Head, Department of Anatomy
All India Institute of Medical Sciences
Bibinagar, Hyderabad, Telangana

CBS Publishers & Distributors Pvt Ltd

New Delhi • Bengaluru • Chennai • Kochi • Kolkata • Lucknow • Mumbai
Hyderabad • Jharkhand • Nagpur • Patna • Pune • Uttarakhand

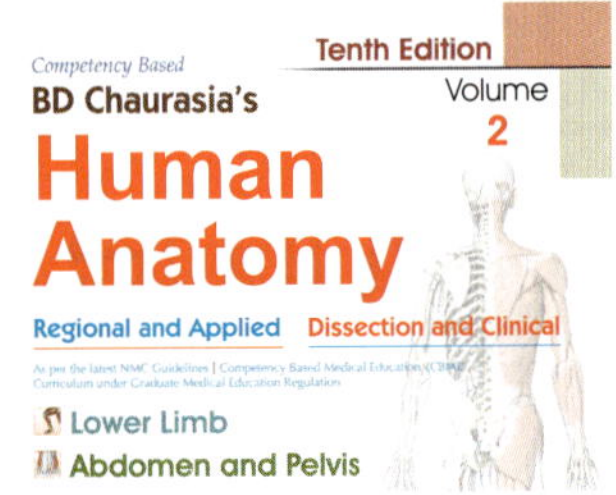

ISBN: 978-93-5466-967-5

Tenth Edition: 2025

First Edition: 1979
Reprint: 1980, 1981, 1982, 1983, 1984, 1985, 1986, 1987, 1988
Second Edition: 1989
Reprint: 1990, 1991, 1992, 1993, 1994
Third Edition: 1995
Reprint: 1996, 1997, 1998, 1999, 2000, 2001, 2002, 2003, 2004
Fourth Edition: 2004
Reprint: 2005, 2006, 2007, 2008, 2009
Fifth Edition: 2010
Reprint: 2011, 2012
Sixth Edition: 2013
Reprint: 2014, 2015
Seventh Edition: 2016
Reprint: 2017, 2018, 2019
Eighth Edition: 2020
Reprint: 2021, 2022
Ninth Edition: 2023
Reprint: 2024

Published by Satish Kumar Jain and produced by Varun Jain for

CBS Publishers & Distributors Pvt Ltd
4819/XI Prahlad Street, 24 Ansari Road, Daryaganj, New Delhi 110 002, India
Ph: 011-23289259, 23266838 Website: www.cbspd.com
e-mail: delhi@cbspd.com

Corporate Office: 204 FIE, Industrial Area, Patparganj, Delhi 110 092, India
Ph: 011-4934 4934 Fax: 011-4934 4935 e-mail: publishing@cbspd.com; publicity@cbspd.com

Branches

- **Bengaluru:** Seema House 2975, 17th Cross, K.R. Road, Banasankari 2nd Stage, Bengaluru 560 070, Karnataka, India
Ph: +91-80-26771678/79 Fax: +91-80-26771680 e-mail: bangalore@cbspd.com
- **Chennai:** 7, Subbaraya Street, Shenoy Nagar, Chennai 600 030, Tamil Nadu, India
Ph: +91-44-26680620, 26681266 Fax: +91-44-42032115 e-mail: chennai@cbspd.com
- **Kochi:** 42/1325, 1326, Power House Road, Opposite KSEB, Power House, Ernakulum 682 018, Kochi, Kerala, India
Ph: +91-484-4059061–65, 67 Fax: +91-484-4059065 e-mail: kochi@cbspd.com
- **Kolkata:** 147, Hind Ceramics Compound, 1st Floor, Nilgunj Road, Belghoria, Kolkata 700 056, West Bengal, India
Ph: +91-33-25633055/56 e-mail: kolkata@cbspd.com
- **Lucknow:** Basement, Khushnuma Complex, 7 Meerabai Marg (behind Jawahar Bhawan), Lucknow 226 001, UP, India
Ph: +91-522-4000032 e-mail: tiwari.lucknow@cbspd.com
- **Mumbai:** PWD Shed, Gala No. 25/26, Ramchandra Bhatt Marg, Next JJ Hospital Gate No. 2, Opp. Union Bank of India, Noorbaug, Mumbai 400 009, Maharashtra, India
Ph: +91-22-66661880/89 e-mail: mumbai@cbspd.com

Representatives

• **Hyderabad**	0-9885175004	• **Jharkhand**	0-9811541605	• **Nagpur**	0-8692091830
• **Patna**	0-9334159340	• **Pune**	0-9664372571	• **Uttarakhand**	0-9716462459

Printed at: Thomson Press (India) Ltd., Faridabad, Haryana, India

to

---

my teacher
Shri Uma Shankar Nagayach

— BD Chaurasia

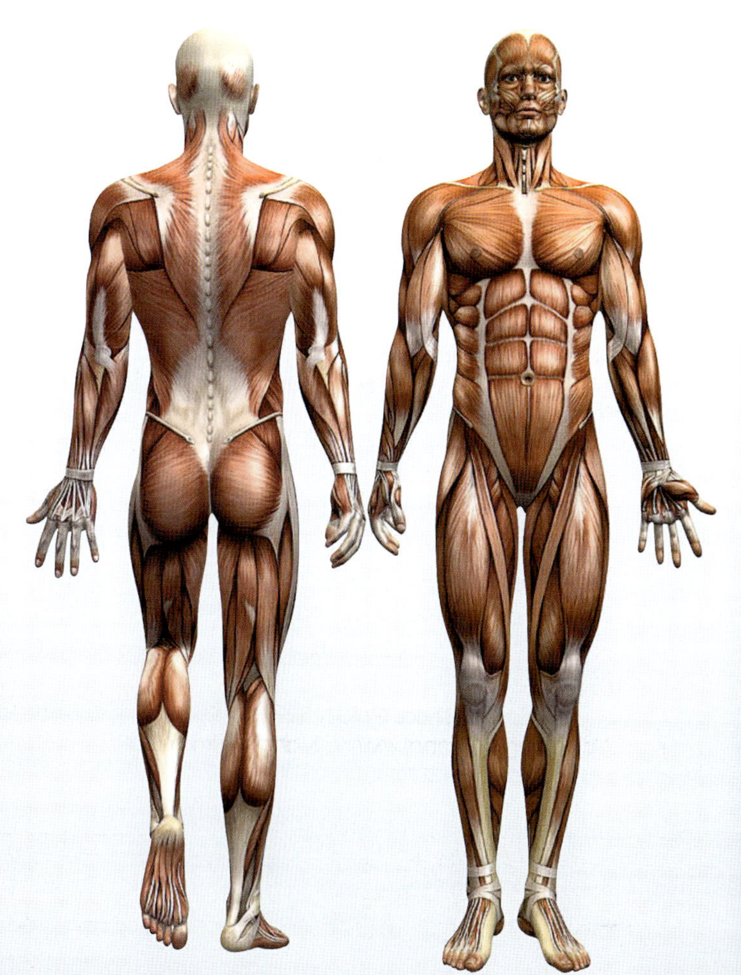

UPPER LIMB and **THORAX**

LOWER LIMB, ABDOMEN and **PELVIS**

Volume 2

HEAD and **NECK**

BRAIN–NEUROANATOMY

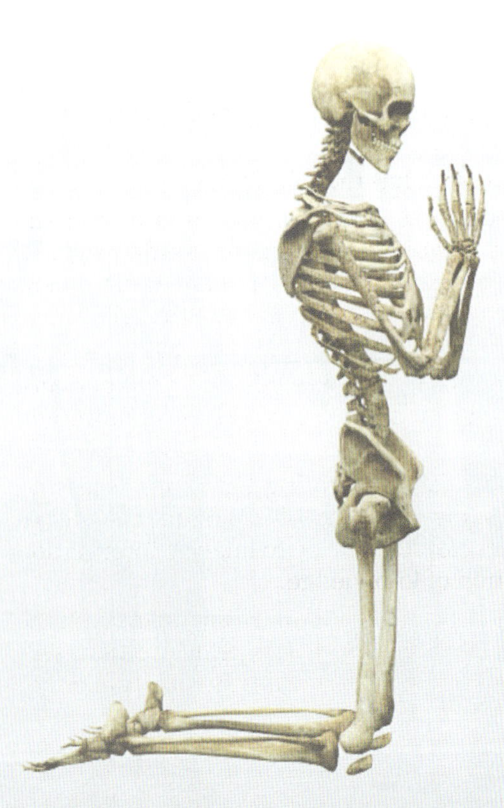

Preface to the Tenth Edition

With the change in time, the needs of the students and curriculum are continuously changing. The science is continuously evolving. To integrate the solutions to common problems faced by the students and to follow the latest NMC guidelines for the CBME curriculum, the most widely accepted and read book has been revised thoroughly to maintain the standards of the last half-century. The primary goal of this book is to help the students for easy understanding and rapid grasping of knowledge for their higher academic achievements, to prepare them for all academic formative, summative and entrance examinations and to make it extremely student-friendly.

Anatomy forms the foundation of the clinical knowledge. This book has been made more clinically oriented with the following salient features:

- **Complete** and **time-tested textbook** boasting unparalleled **quality content** designed to enrich both fundamental and clinical understanding for students.
- **Simple text** is the main feature of the book. It will facilitate easier understanding for students. Small sentences minimize effort, enhancing readability and accessibility. This approach ensures clarity of information, aiding students in grasping complex concepts effortlessly.
- **3D colour illustrated plates** will aid the students in comprehending anatomical structures and their relationships with clarity. These visual aids offer a dynamic perspective, enhancing spatial understanding and facilitating the identification of anatomical features.
- **Simple line diagrams** are incorporated. These diagrams will allow students to easily redraw them during examinations. These diagrams are designed for clarity and simplicity, ensuring that students can accurately reproduce anatomical structures in assessments and examinations efficiently.
- **Flowcharts** will facilitate rapid revision and memorizing of facts, alleviating students' concerns about time constraints during the subject review. These visuals will enhance comprehension and retention. Students can quickly navigate through key concepts, optimizing study time and effectively addressing time limitations in their revision process.
- **Clinical anatomy** sections are integrated at the end of each topic to maintain the purpose towards **early clinical exposure** (ECE). By seamlessly merging theoretical knowledge with practical application, this approach ensures students gain valuable insights into clinical contexts, enhancing their understanding and readiness for real-world clinical scenarios.
- **Dissection boxes** will guide the students in the step-wise dissection of the human cadaver.
- **Tables** are used to summarise essential facts for clear understanding and retention.
- ***QR codes*** for ***eSmartQuiz*** are embedded in the text, which will grant access to online MCQ tests for self-assessment at the end of each chapter. This interactive feature will enhance engagement and facilitate convenient self-evaluation. Students can assess their understanding, reinforce learning, and identify areas for improvement, facilitate a dynamic and effective learning experience.
- ***Free Workbook:*** The main textbook is supported with a workbook, which has the following:
    1. **Clinicoanatomical problems** emphasize early clinical exposure and vertical integration in medical education. By integrating anatomical knowledge with clinical practice from the outset, students gain a holistic understanding of medical concepts. This approach fosters practical skills, enhances diagnostic abilities, and promotes a deeper comprehension of the human body's complexities within clinical contexts.
    2. **Practice figures** aid in preparing students for academic examinations by providing hands-on experience with exam-style preparation. It will help to build confidence in tackling the challenges commonly encountered in academic assessments.
    3. **Multiple choice questions (MCQs)** will serve as potent tools for reinforcing learning, assessing comprehension, and enhancing attention and critical thinking skills. Through MCQs, students engage actively with the curriculum, consolidate understanding, and develop the ability to analyse information critically, ultimately fostering deeper comprehension and retention of knowledge.
    4. **Spotters** and **question bank** introduce students to the examination system by familiarising them with the format and types of questions commonly encountered in assessments. These wide ranges of questions will aid the students in preparing for examinations and gaining confidence in tackling examination challenges effectively.

- *Free access to BDC's Anatomy eBook (digital content through CBSiCentral app):* It includes the following:
  a. Additional topics and clinical aspects
  b. *Viva voce* questions, and
  c. Topics for further reference and reading.

  This digital resource will enhance the book's utility, providing students with expanded knowledge and resources for comprehensive learning. Accessible supplementary materials will enhance understanding and facilitate deeper exploration, empowering students to excel in their studies and clinical practice.
- **Free Access to CBSiCentral App:** It includes videos of osteology and soft parts and chapter-wise self-assessment MCQ tests. The videos of the dissection will give three-dimensional image descriptions of tissues and organs, which get effectively registered in the brain for a longer time.
- **Wall charts:** Each volume is provided with meticulously crafted wall charts, elegantly designed and tailored to enhance students' comprehension of anatomy. These visually engaging aids can be easily affixed to walls to grasp the visual impressions of anatomy.

Always remember that success is achieved only through diligent effort and hard work.

Chief Editor
Krishna Garg

Executive Editor
Yogesh Ashok Sontakke

Editors
Pragati Sheel Mittal
Mrudula Chandrupatla

Preface to the First Edition (excerpts)

The necessity of having a simple, systematized and complete book on anatomy has long been felt. The urgency for such a book has become all the more acute due to the shorter time now available for teaching anatomy, and also to the falling standards of English language in the majority of our students in India. The national symposium on 'Anatomy in Medical Education' held at Delhi in 1978 was a call to change the existing system of teaching the unnecessary minute details to the undergraduate students.

This attempt has been made with an object to meet the requirements of a common medical student. The text has been arranged in small classified parts to make it easier for the students to remember and recall it at will. It is adequately illustrated with simple line diagrams which can be reproduced without any difficulty, and which also help in understanding and memorizing the anatomical facts that appear to defy memory of a common student. The monotony of describing the individual muscles separately, one after the other, has been minimised by writing them out in tabular form, which makes the subject interesting for a lasting memory. The relevant radiological and surface anatomy have been treated in separate chapters. A sincere attempt has been made to deal, wherever required, the clinical applications of the subject. The entire approach is such as to attract and inspire the students for a deeper dive in the subject of anatomy.

The book has been intentionally split in three parts for convenience of handling. This also makes a provision for those who cannot afford to have the whole book at a time.

It is quite possible that there are errors of omission and commission in this mostly single-handed attempt. I would be grateful to the readers for their suggestions to improve the book from all angles.

I am very grateful to my teachers and the authors of numerous publications, whose knowledge has been freely utilised in the preparation of this book. I am equally grateful to my professor and colleagues for their encouragement and valuable help. My special thanks are due to my students who made me feel their difficulties, which was a great incentive for writing this book. I have derived maximum inspiration from Prof. Inderbir Singh (Rohtak), and learned the decency of work from Shri SC Gupta (Jiwaji University, Gwalior).

I am deeply indebted to Shri KM Singhal (National Book House, Gwalior) and Mr SK Jain (CBS Publishers & Distributors, Delhi), who have taken unusual pains to get the book printed in its present form. For giving it the desired get-up, Mr VK Jain and Raj Kamal Electric Press are gratefully acknowledged. The cover page was designed by Mr Vasant Paranjpe, the artist and photographer of our college; my sincere thanks are due to him. I acknowledge with affection the domestic assistance of Munne Miyan and the untiring company of my Rani, particularly during the odd hours of this work.

BD Chaurasia

Acknowledgements

We have the blessings and good wishes of Prof NA Faruqi (Aligarh); Dr DC Naik (Rewa); Dr SD Joshi and Dr SS Joshi (Indore); Dr (Brig) Rakesh Gupta (Greater Noida); Dr DR Singh (Lucknow); Dr M Kaul; Dr C Anand and Dr I Bahl (Delhi); Dr Mohsin Azmi (Kanpur); Dr Medha Joshi (Ghaziabad); Dr Surbhi Gupta (Delhi); Dr Nitin Nagarkar (Raipur); Dr CK Shukla (Raipur); Dr Shakuntala Pai (Manipal); Manik Chatterjee (Raipur) and Dr SN Kazi (Pune).

We are thankful to Dr Surjit Ghatak (Jodhpur); Dr Vinay Sharma (Muzzafarnagar); Dr Deepu Singh Kataria and Dr Anup Singh Gurjar (Pali); Dr Jagmohan Sharma, Dr Deepak Sharma, Dr Rajesh Arora and Dr Pooja Garg (Jaipur); Dr Sumit Gupta (Kota); Dr Gopal Sharma and Dr Manoj Sharma (Jhalawar); Dr Rekha Parashar (Chittorgarh); Dr Santosh Kumar (Dholpur); Dr BK Aghera (Sirohi); Dr Isha Srivastav, Dr Aprajita Raizada, Dr Sajan Skaria, Dr Anjali Jain and Dr Kalpana Sharma (Udaipur); for giving feedback for various sections of the volumes. We are greatful to Dr K Aravindhan, Dr V Gladwin, Dr Raveendranath V, Dr Suman Verma, Dr Sulochana Sakthivel, Dr Rajasekhar SSSN and Dr Vidhya G (Puducherry) for their support.

We are grateful to Dr Anupma Mahajan (Amritsar); Dr Vanita Gupta (Jammu); Dr Vikas Verma (Lucknow) and Dr Tripta Bhagat (Ghaziabad) for editing chapters to enhance the value of the volumes. We are grateful to Dr Ravikant (Amritsar); Dr Sangeeta and Dr Nusrat Jabeen (Jammu); Dr Gurdeep Singh Kalyan and Dr Rajan Singla (Patiala); Dr Aprajita Sikka (Ludhiana); Dr Bashir (Srinagar); Dr Seema and Dr Ritu (Rajouri); Dr Mubeen (Kathua); Dr RK Srivastava (Kanpur); Dr Punita Manik (Lucknow); Dr Binod Kumar; Dr Sunita Nayak and Dr Shambhu Prasad (Patna); Dr AK Dubey (Ranchi); Dr Satyam Khare, Dr Shilpi Jain and Dr Alok Tripathi (Meerut), for promoting the volumes.

We have been getting constant encouragement and support from Dr Ranjana Verma, Dr Muthukrishnan P, Dr Yogesh Yadav, Dr Pullimi Vineel and Dr Nirupma Gupta (Greater Noida); Dr Nisha Kaul (Ghaziabad); Dr Vinay Singhal (Saharanpur); Dr RK Ashoka (Mathura); Dr Vineet Guhia (Khandwa); Dr Manisha Sinha (Raipur); Dr Jahan Shirin (Kanpur); Dr Damyanti (Manipur) and Dr MK Anand (Bhuj).

Our regards and affection to Dr Rewa Choudhry, Dr Shilpa Paul, Dr Smita Kakar, Dr Anita Tuli, Dr Gayatri Rath, Dr Shashi Raheja, Dr Shyama Rajdan, Dr Mangala Kohli, Dr A Shariff, Dr SB Ray, Dr Vandana Mehta, Dr Sabita Mishra, Dr Renu Chauhan, Dr Jyoti Arora, Dr Sneh Aggarwal, Dr TS Roy, Dr Ruchi Dhuria and Dr Shaifaly Madan Rustagi (Delhi) for going through the volumes.

We would like to thank Dr Pritha Bhuiyan (Mumbai); Dr Brijendra Singh (Rishikesh); Dr (Col.) Sushil Kumar (Pune); Dr AK Srivastava (Lucknow); Dr MK Pant (Dehradun); Dr Simmi Mehra (Rajkot); Dr Fatima M De Souza (Goa); Dr Mukesh Mittal (Shivpuri); Dr Priti Sinha (Saharanpur); Dr Rashmi Malhotra (Rishikesh); Dr Simmi Soni (Aziznagar); Dr Sunita Gupta (Ahmedabad); Dr Raghunandan Ramanathan (Chennai) and many-many other teachers all over the globe, for giving us good wishes.

We also acknowledge Drs Neetu Sivadasan, Rituraj Majumdar, Nandhini R, Nithya D, Kalaivani K, Jakkula Akhil, Ambiga R, S Nikilesh, Udit Narayan, Jayasree S, Bharathy Mohan P, Nandhini S, Aakriti Mehrotra, Sancy Charly, Madhusingh Thakur, Tarakeshwari RB, Dhivyaa Shree R, Thaiyal Nayagi and Prasanna Raj AV (Puducherry) for their support.

Videos of bones and soft parts of human body, prepared at Kathmandu University School of Medical Sciences, have now been added with the respective chapters and are available at our mobile App CBSiCentral. We are grateful to Dr R Koju, CEO of Kathmandu University School of Medical Sciences (KUSMS) and Dhulikhel Hospital, for his generosity.

The moral support of my (chief editor) family members, Late Dr DP Garg, Dr Suvira Gupta, Dr JP Gupta, Mr Manoj, Ms Rekha, Mr Sanjay, Ms Meenakshi, Dr Manish, Dr Shilpa Garg, Dr Naveen Garg, Dr Manoj, Dr Nalini Shukla, Dr Vikas Verma and Dr Swati Gupta, is appreciated.

The magnanimity shown by Mr SK Jain (Chairman) and Mr Varun Jain (Director), CBS Publishers & Distributors, has been always forthcoming. The unquestionable support of Mr YN Arjuna (Senior Vice President—Publishing, Editorial and Publicity) and his entire team comprising Ms Ritu Chawla (GM—Production), Mr Neeraj Prasad (Graphic Artists), Mr Binay Kumar (Proofreader) and Mr Vikrant Sharma (DTP operator) has made an excellent contribution to bring out this edition. We are really obliged to them and pray for their prosperity.

Editors

Acknowledgements

We extend our heartfelt thanks to the following teachers of anatomy for their consistent academic support, encouragement, and well wishes.

- Dr A B Mishra (Mathura, UP)
- Dr A Hima Bindu (Visakhapatnam, AP)
- Dr Aaditya Madhusudan Tarnekar (Nagpur, Maharashtra)
- Dr Aarushi Jain (Kota, Rajasthan)
- Dr Abhijeet Joshi (Barmer, Rajasthan)
- Dr Abhilasha Priya (Jamshedpur, Jharkhand)
- Dr Abhinav Kumar Mishra (Sitapur, UP)
- Dr Abid Ali (Yenkapally, Telangana)
- Dr Abraham Joseph (Nandyal, AP)
- Dr Ajay Kumar (Ludhiana, Punjab)
- Dr Ajay Nene (Alwar, Rajasthan)
- Dr Ajay Rathva (Vadodara, Gujarat)
- Dr AK Singh (Almora, Uttarakhand)
- Dr AK Srivastava (Lucknow, UP)
- Dr Alka Singh (Ayodhya, UP)
- Dr Alka Udainia (Surat, Gujarat)
- Dr Alka V Bhingardeo (Bibinagar, Hyderabad)
- Dr Alok Saxena (Dehradun, Uttarakhand)
- Dr Amar Jayanthi A (Idukki, Kerala)
- Dr Amarappa S Nagalikar (Belagavi, Karnataka)
- Dr Ambica Wadhwa (Jalandhar, Punjab)
- Dr Amit Kumar (Bilaspur, CG)
- Dr Amit Mehta (Chindwada, MP)
- Dr Amol Durgkar (Chindwada, MP)
- Dr Amol Shinde (Pune, Maharashtra)
- Dr Amrita Kumari (Patna, Bihar)
- Dr Amrut Mahajan (Jalgaon, Maharashtra)
- Dr Amrutha Roopa Ramagalla (Siddipet, Telangana)
- Dr Amudha Mohan Ram (Chilakaluripet, Guntur, AP)
- Dr Angela A Viswasom (Kollam, Kerala)
- Dr Anil Agrawal (Bilaspur, CG)
- Dr Anil Kumar (Kothagudem, Telangana)
- Dr Anil Kumar Dwivedi (Srinagar, Uttarakhand)
- Dr Anil Rahule (Ramagundam, Telangana)
- Dr Anita (Bharatpur, Rajasthan)
- Dr Anita Fating (Amaravati, Maharashtra)
- Dr Anitha V (Kanyakumari, TN)
- Dr Anjali Aggarwal (Chandigarh)
- Dr Anjali Jain (Ludhiana, Punjab)
- Dr Anjali Jain (Udaipur, Rajasthan)
- Dr Anjali Prasad (Muzaffarpur, Bihar)
- Dr Anjali Sabnis (Navi Mumbai, Maharashtra)
- Dr Anju Partap (Shimla, HP)
- Dr Ankur Kumar (Karauli, Rajasthan)
- Dr Anne George (Kottayam, Kerala)
- Dr Annie Doley (Tezpur, Assam)
- Dr Anshu Sharma (Chandigarh)
- Dr Anshu Soni (Ludhiana, Punjab)
- Dr Anterpreet Arora (Amritsar, Punjab)
- Dr Anu Sharma (Ludhiana, Punjab)
- Dr Anuj Ram Sharma (Muzaffarnagar, UP)
- Dr Anup Singh Gurjar (Pali, Rajasthan)
- Dr Anupama Doddappaiah Panagar (Hosur, TN)
- Dr Anupama Mahajan (Amritsar, Punjab)
- Dr Anuradha (Amritsar, Punjab)
- Dr Anurag (Dehradun, Uttarakhand)
- Dr Anwar Unisa Sabry (Siricilla, Telangana)
- Dr Aparna (Vijayawada, AP)
- Dr Aparna Dixit (Unnao, UP)
- Dr Aparna K Vedapriya (Siddipet, Telangana)
- Dr Aparna Muraleedharan (Puducherry)
- Dr Aprajita Raizada (Udaipur, Rajasthan)
- Dr Aprajita Sikka (Ludhiana, Punjab)
- Dr APS Batra (Sonipat, Haryana)
- Dr Archana (Alzapur, Telangana)
- Dr Archana Goel (Shahbad, Haryana)
- Dr Archana Kalyankar (Aurangabad, Maharashtra)
- Dr Archana Kannamwar (Yavatmal, Maharashtra)
- Dr Arindam Banerjee (Durgapur, WB)
- Dr Arun Arya (Muzaffarnagar, UP)
- Dr Arun Kasote (Nagpur, Maharashtra)
- Dr Arun Prasad Singh (Patna, Bihar)
- Dr Arun Pundlikrao Kasote (Jalgaon, Maharashtra)
- Dr Arunabha Tapadar (Uluberia, WB)
- Dr Arvinder Pal Singh Batra (Sonipat, Haryana)
- Dr Asha Latha (Nellore, AP)
- Dr Ashok Kumar Singh (Nalanda, Bihar)
- Dr Ashok Patil (Sangamner, Ahmednagar, Maharashtra)
- Dr Ashutosh Mangalagiri (Bhopal, MP)
- Dr Ashwani K Sharma (Jammu, J&K)
- Dr Ashwini Jadhav (Mumbai, Maharashtra)
- Dr AV Kulkarni (Dharwad, Karnataka)
- Dr Avanish Kumar (Patna, Bihar)
- Dr Avinash Abhaya (Chandigarh)
- Dr Avinash Rudrajwar (Durg, CG)
- Dr Azhar Ahmed Siddiqui (Badnapur, Jalna, Maharashtra)
- Dr B Naveen Kumar (Bachupally, Hyderabad, Telangana)
- Dr Babu Rao (Hyderabad, Telangana)
- Dr Badal Singh (Prayagraj, UP)
- Dr Banani Kundu (Uluberia, WB)
- Dr Bandi Sirisha (Telangana)
- Dr Bashir Ahmad Shah (Srinagar, J&K)
- Dr Beena Nambiar (Pariyaram, Kannur, Kerala)
- Dr Bertha AD Rathinam (Bhopal, MP)
- Dr Bhagyashree (Bilaspur, HP)
- Dr Bharat Patel (Ahmedabad, Gujarat)
- Dr Bhaskar Pal (Haldia, WB)
- Dr Bhaudas Khanderao Jadhav (Mumbai, Maharashtra)
- Dr Bhavan Junagade (Mumbai, Maharashtra)
- Dr Bhavik Doshi (Ahmedabad, Gujarat)
- Dr Bindu Singh (Gorakhpur, UP)
- Dr Binod Kumar (Muzzafarpur, Bihar)
- Dr Bipinchandra Khade (Bhopal, MP)
- Dr Biswabina Ray (Kalyani, WB)
- Dr BR Singh (Nagpur, Maharashtra)
- Dr Brijendra Singh (Rishikesh, Uttarakhand)
- Dr BS Lala (Indore, MP)
- Dr BS Patil (Vijayapura, Karnataka)
- Dr C Kishan Reddy (Karimnagar, Telangana)
- Dr C Lalitha (Bengaluru, Karnataka)
- Dr Chandan Kumar Yadav (Lucknow, UP)
- Dr Charulata A Satpute (Nagpur, Maharashtra)
- Dr Chetan Sahni (Varanasi, UP)
- Dr Chetna Thakur (Agra, UP)
- Dr Chitti Narasamma (Kurnool, AP)
- Dr D Asha Latha (Machlipatnam, AP)
- Dr D Sudhakar Babu (Nizamabad, Telangana)
- Dr Daizy Singh (Ludhiana, Punjab)
- Dr DAVS Sesi (Kakinada, AP)
- Dr Debjani Roy (Midinapore, WB)
- Dr Deepa Bently (Coimbatore, TN)
- Dr Deepa Deopa (Haldwani, Uttarakhand)
- Dr Deepak Joshi (Mumbai, Maharashtra)
- Dr Deepak Sharma (Jaipur, Rajasthan)
- Dr Deepali G Vidhale (Amaravati, Maharashtra)
- Dr Deepali Onkar (Nagpur, Maharashtra)
- Dr Deepanshu Shukla (Lucknow, UP)
- Dr Deepti Shastri Deputy (Salem, TN)
- Dr DH Gopalan (Chennai, TN)
- Dr Dibyendu Dutta (Kolkata, WB)
- Dr Dimpal Patel (Ahmedabad, Gujarat)
- Dr Dipali Trivedi (Ahmedabad, Gujarat)
- Dr Dipti Gautam (Mahasamund, CG)
- Dr Dipti Nimje (Nagpur, Maharashtra)
- Dr Divya Mahajan (Chandigarh)
- Dr DV Singh (Bareilly, UP)
- Dr Faizal Mohammad (Siddipet, Telangana)
- Dr Fatima M De Souza (Goa)
- Dr Fazal Ur Rehman (Aligarh, UP)
- Dr Firoz Hossain (Guwahati, Assam)
- Dr G Sundar (Vellore, TN)
- Dr GA Jos Hemalatha (Virudhunagar, TN)
- Dr Gajanan L Maske (Yavatmal, Maharashtra)
- Dr Ganesh Khemnar (Kurnool, AP)
- Dr Ganesh Trivedi (Shri Ganganagar, Rajasthan)
- Dr Garima Pardhi (Vidisha, MP)
- Dr Garima Shivhare (Shahbad, Haryana)
- Dr Gaurav Agnihotri (Amritsar, Punjab)
- Dr Gautam A Shroff (Aurangabad, Maharashtra)
- Dr Gayatri Muthiyan (Nagpur, Maharashtra)
- Dr Geetha KN (Mumbai, Maharashtra)

- Dr Ghanshyam Gupta (Jaipur, Rajasthan)
- Dr Ghulam Mohammad Bhat (Srinagar, J&K)
- Dr Gitanjali Arora (Bhubaneswar, Odisha)
- Dr Gnanavel A (Kanchipuram, TN)
- Dr Gopal Mondal (Barasat, WB)
- Dr Gopal Sharma (Jhalawar, Rajasthan)
- Dr Gouri Shankar Jha (Laheriasarai, Darbhanga, Bihar)
- Dr Gunapriya Raghunath (Chennai, TN)
- Dr Gunwant Chaudhari (Dahod, Gujarat)
- Dr Gursharan S Dhindsa (Faridkot, Punjab)
- Dr Gyan Prakash Mishra (Basti, UP)
- Dr Gyanraj Singh (Jaipur, Odisha)
- Dr Hari Narayan Yadav (Mathura, UP)
- Dr Haritha Nimmagadda (Navi Mumbai, Maharashtra)
- Dr Harpreet Singh Gulati (Jalandhar, Punjab)
- Dr Harsh Chawre (Datia, MP)
- Dr Harsh Mishrikoti P (Belagavi, Karnataka)
- Dr Harsimrajit Kaur (Patiala, Punjab)
- Dr Harsimran Gerewal (Patiala, Punjab)
- Dr Hemlata Ambade (Nagpur, Maharashtra)
- Dr Hina Sharma (Udaipur, Rajasthan)
- Dr Hitant Vohra (Ludhiana, Punjab)
- Dr Hrishikesh Jadhav (Sola, Ahmedabad, Gujarat)
- Dr I Gowri (Chevella, Telangana)
- Dr Indra Kumar Patel (Bahraich, UP)
- Dr Indushri (Kannauj, UP)
- Dr Isha Srivastav (Udaipur, Rajasthan)
- Dr Israr Ahmed Khan (Shahdol, MP)
- Dr J P Yadav (Churu, Rajasthan)
- Dr J S Kullar (Amritsar, Punjab)
- Dr J Sreevidya (Chennai, TN)
- Dr Jaba Rajguru (Vadodra, Gujarat)
- Dr Jaedeo Ughade (Parbhani, Maharashtra)
- Dr Jagmohan Sharma (Jaipur, Rajasthan)
- Dr Jagriti Agrawal (Raipur, CG)
- Dr Jaita Chowdhury (Haldia, WB)
- Dr Jami Sagar Prusty (Berhampur, Odisha)
- Dr Jasmeen Shaikh (Hyderabad, Telangana)
- Dr Jasween Kaur (Jalandhar, Punjab)
- Dr Jaswinder Kaur (Ambala, Haryana)
- Dr Javed Akhtar (Patna, Bihar)
- Dr Jaya Prakash (Kamareddy, Telangana)
- Dr Jayasree K (Kozhikode, Kerala)
- Dr Jayasree Reddy (Siddipet, Telangana)
- Dr Jessy Rose George (Kozhikode, Kerala)
- Dr Jeyanthi G (Thirunelveli, TN)
- Dr Jitendra Patel (Ahmedabad, Gujarat)
- Dr Jolly Agarwal (Dehradun, Uttarakhand)
- Dr Joy Ghoshal (Mangalagiri, AP)
- Dr Jwalant Waghmare (Sevagram, Maharashtra)
- Dr Jyoti Gaiwad (Mumbai, Maharashtra)
- Dr Jyoti Ramling Gaikwad (Sanpada, Maharashtra)
- Dr Jyoti Rohilla (Mohali, Punjab)
- Dr Jyotsna Singh (Chandigarh)
- Dr K Manivanan (Kuppam, AP)
- Dr K Shanmuganathan (Puducherry)
- Dr K Udhaya (Tiruchengode, TN)
- Dr Kalpana Ramachandran (Chennai, TN)
- Dr Kalpana Sharma (Udaipur, Rajasthan)
- Dr Kalu Ram Meena (Jodhpur, Rajasthan)
- Dr Kalyan Bhattacharya (Kolkata, WB)
- Dr Kamaljeet Kaur (Jalandhar, Punjab)
- Dr Kanan Shah (Ahmedabad, Gujarat)
- Dr Kanchan Kapoor (Chandigarh)
- Dr Kanika Sachdeva (Amritsar, Punjab)
- Dr Kavita Nanda (Hamirpur, HP)
- Dr Kiran Kalloor (Palakkad, Kerala)
- Dr Kiran V Padeyappanavar (Belagavi, Karnataka)
- Dr Kirti Nemade (Nagpur, Maharashtra)
- Dr KK Thakur (Doda, J&K)
- Dr KKP Singh (Ranchi, Jharkhand)
- Dr Komala B (Bengaluru)
- Dr Krishnaiah M (Suryapet, Telangana)
- Dr Kulbir Kaur (Amritsar, Punjab)
- Dr Kumar Satish Ravi (Gorakhpur, UP)
- Dr Kunal Chawla (Shimla, HP)
- Dr L Hema (Nellore, AP)
- Dr Lakshmikantha (Meppadi, Wayanad, Kerala)
- Dr Lalatendu Swain (Puri, Odisha)
- Dr Lency Davis (Thrissur, Kerala)
- Dr Lenin S (Kanyakumari, TN)
- Dr Lola Das (Thrissur, Kerala)
- Dr M Chatterjee (Raipur, CG)
- Dr M Prasad (Dhanbad, Jharkhand)
- Dr M Siva Kumar (Thiruvannamalai, TN)
- Dr M Sivakumar (Trichi, TN)
- Dr MA Doshi (Karad, Maharashtra)
- Dr Madasi Pranay Kumar (Karimnagar, Telangana)
- Dr Madhusmita Panda (Balasore, Odisha)
- Dr Mahendra Kumar Pant (Dehradun, Uttarakhand)
- Dr Mahesh GM (Chitradurga, Karnataka)
- Dr Mahesh K Sharma (Chandigarh)
- Dr Mahesh Ugale (Latur, Maharashtra)
- Dr Mahita Bojja (Nagarkurnool, Telangana)
- Dr Malamoni Dutta (Kokrajhar, Assam)
- Dr Mallela Padmavati (Hyderabad, Telangana)
- Dr Mamata Sar (Burla, Odisha)
- Dr Mamta Kumari (Pawapuri, Nalanda, Bihar)
- Dr Mamta Sharma (Jalandhar, Punjab)
- Dr Maneesha (Mohali, Punjab)
- Dr Mangesh Lone (Mumbai, Maharashtra)
- Dr Mangesh Selukar (Latur, Maharashtra)
- Dr Mani Kathapillai (Chengalpattu, TN)
- Dr Maninder Kaur (Patiala, Punjab)
- Dr Manish Patil (Ujjain, MP)
- Dr Manisha Nakhate (Navi Mumbai, Maharashtra)
- Dr Manisha R Gaikwad (Bhubaneswar, Odisha)
- Dr Manisha Upadhyay (Azamgarh, UP)
- Dr Manjunath V Motagi (Indore, MP)
- Dr Manjusha Tabhane (Nagpur, Maharashtra)
- Dr Manjushree Chakroborty (Nagaon, Assam)
- Dr Manoj Sharma (Jhalawar, Rajasthan)
- Dr Maria Kala (Siddipet, Telangana)
- Dr Martin Lucas A (Bengaluru)
- Dr Md Jawed Akhtar (Patna, Bihar)
- Dr Meenakshi Aggarwal (Ludhiana, Punjab)
- Dr Meenakshi Borkar (Mumbai, Maharashtra)
- Dr Meenakshi Khullar (Faridkot, Punjab)
- Dr Meenakshi Parthsarathy (Bengaluru, Karnataka)
- Dr Meetu Agarwal (Faridabad, Haryana)
- Dr Meghana Mishra (Reva, MP)
- Dr Mehandi V Mahajan (Thiruvallur, TN)
- Dr Mehera Bhoir (Mumbai, Maharashtra)
- Dr MG Puranik (Pune, Maharashtra)
- Dr Mini Kariappa (Thrissur)
- Dr Mini Mol (Mumbai, Maharashtra)
- Dr MM Peerzade (Solapur, Maharashtra)
- Dr Mohammad Mujahid Ansari (Shahdol, MP)
- Dr Mohd Ajmal (Siddharthnagar, UP)
- Dr Monica Jain (Agroha, Haryana)
- Dr Monika Gupta (Bathinda, Punjab)
- Dr Monika Lalit Piplani (Amritsar, Punjab)
- Dr MP Sultana (Nellore, AP)
- Dr Mrinal Barua (Rishikesh, Uttarakhand)
- Dr Mrityunjay Pandey (Deoria, UP)
- Dr MS Arathi (Chennai, TN)
- Dr Mubeen Rashid (Kathua, J&K)
- Dr Mukesh Mittal (Shivpuri, MP)
- Dr Mukesh Singhla (Rishikesh, Uttarakhand)
- Dr Mukul Sarma (Tinsukia, Assam)
- Dr Muthukumaravel Narayanaswamy (Ariyur, Puducherry)
- Dr N Bhanu Sudha Parimala (Mangalagiri, AP)
- Dr Nagraj S (Mahabubnagar, Telangana)
- Dr Naina Wakode (Vidisha, MP)
- Dr Namdeo Y Kamdi (Chandrapur, Maharashtra)
- Dr Nandita Dutta (Jalpaiguri, WB)
- Dr Natwar Agrawal (Jabalpur, MP)
- Dr Nava Kalyani (Mahabubnagar, Telangana)
- Dr Navita Aggarwal (Bhatinda, Punjab)
- Dr Neelam Bala (Amritsar, Punjab)
- Dr Neelam Jit Kaur (Patiala, Punjab)
- Dr Neeru Goyal (Ludhiana, Punjab)
- Dr Neeta Chhabra (Faridabad, Haryana)
- Dr Neetu Arora (Nalhar, Nuh, Haryana)
- Dr Neha Rai (Bhopal, MP)
- Dr Neha Vijay (Alwar, Rajasthan)
- Dr Nidhi Puri (Bilaspur, HP)
- Dr Nilesh Rakate (Bhopal, MP)
- Dr Nilofer Mulla (Mumbai, Maharashtra)
- Dr Nimisha Madhu (Gaya, Bihar)
- Dr Nirmal Kumar K (Vikarabad, Telangana)
- Dr Nirmaladevi M (Coimbatore, TN)
- Dr Nirmalya Saha (Agartala, Tripura)
- Dr Nirupama Gupta (Greater Noida, UP)

- Dr Nishigandha Sadamate (Vadodara, Gujarat)
- Dr Nita Gathe (Gondia, Maharashtra)
- Dr Nitin R Mudiraj (Sangali, Maharashtra)
- Dr Nivedita Pandey (Israna, Panipat, Haryana)
- Dr Niyati Airen (Srinagar, Uttarakhand)
- Dr Nusrat Jabeen (Jammu, J&K)
- Dr P Ashok (Hyderabad, Telangana)
- Dr P Bapuji (Eluru, AP)
- Dr P David Anand Kumar (Telangana)
- Dr P Sasikala (Tiruchengode, TN)
- Dr Padamjeet Panchal (Patna, Bihar)
- Dr Padmasini S (Chennai, TN)
- Dr Pankaj Maheria (Valsad, Gujarat)
- Dr Pankaj Singh (Jaipur, Rajasthan)
- Dr Pankaj Soni (Mandi, HP)
- Dr Patil Shrish (Chitradurga, Karnataka)
- Dr Payal Kasat (Kharagpur, WB)
- Dr Peter Ericson (Hyderabad, Telangana)
- Dr PG Khanwalkar (Bhopal, MP)
- Dr Phalguni Srimani (Kolkata, WB)
- Dr Piyush Kumar (Dehradun, Uttarakhand)
- Dr PK Ramakrishnan (Palakkad, Kerala)
- Dr PN Panshewdikar (Palghar, Maharashtra)
- Dr Poonam Delmotra (Shahbad, Haryana)
- Dr Poonam Verma (Amritsar, Punjab)
- Dr PP Kulkarni (Islampur, Maharashtra)
- Dr Prabhakaran K (Ahmedabad, Gujarat)
- Dr Pradeep Bokariya (Sevagram, Maharashtra)
- Dr Pradeep Kumar (Gaya, Bihar)
- Dr Pradeep Pawar (Mumbai, Maharashtra)
- Dr Prafulla Pralhadrao Nikam (Wardha, Maharashtra)
- Dr Prajakta Kishve (Hyderabad, Telangana)
- Dr Prajna Paramita Samanta (Bhubaneswar, Odisha)
- Dr Prakash Baburao Hosmani (Solapur, Maharashtra)
- Dr Prakash KG (Udaipur, Rajasthan)
- Dr Pranab Deb Barma (Tripura)
- Dr Prasanna MB (Ernakulam, Kerala)
- Dr Prashant Chaware (Bhopal, MP)
- Dr Prashant Munjamkar (Bibinagar, Hyderabad)
- Dr Prateek Singha (Nahan, HP)
- Dr Pratibha Shakya (Lucknow, UP)
- Dr Pratima Jaiswal (Kota, Rajasthan)
- Dr Praveen B Iyer (Mumbai, Maharashtra)
- Dr Praveen Kurrey (Raipur, CG)
- Dr Praveen Ojha (Udaipur, Rajasthan)
- Dr Praveen Singh (Karamsad, Gujarat)
- Dr Preeti Chaudhary (Bhatinda, Punjab)
- Dr Prerna Gupta (Amausi, Lucknow, UP)
- Dr Pritha S Bhuiyan (Mumbai, Maharashtra)
- Dr Priti Chaudhary (Bhatinda)
- Dr Priti Nemade (Nagpur, Maharashtra)
- Dr Priti Sinha (Meerut, UP)
- Dr Priya P Roy (Karad, Maharashtra)
- Dr Priya Ranganath (Bengaluru, Karnataka)
- Dr PS Chitra (Ariyalur, TN)
- Dr Pulipati Anil Kumar (Vizianagaram, AP)
- Dr Punita Sharma (Amritsar, Punjab)
- Dr Purushotam Rao (Vikarabad, Telangana)
- Dr PV Satya Kumar (Vijayawada, AP)
- Dr R Azhagiri (Chennai, TN)
- Dr R Manoranjitham (Perambalur, TN)
- Dr R Sarah (Madurai, TN)
- Dr Rachna Agarwal (Bharatpur, Rajasthan)
- Dr Rajan Singla (Patiala, Punjab)
- Dr Rajashree Biswal (Cuttack, Odisha)
- Dr Rajashree S Raut (Kolhapur, Maharashtra)
- Dr Rajasri Chunder (Budge, Kolkata, WB)
- Dr Rajeev Panwar (KK Nagar, Chennai, TN)
- Dr Rajeev Ranjan (Ranchi, Jharkhand)
- Dr Rajendra Prasad (Gaya, Bihar)
- Dr Rajendrakumar D Virupaxi (Belagavi, Karnataka)
- Dr Rajesh Dehankar (Nagpur, Maharashtra)
- Dr Rajesh Maurya (Dehradun, Uttarakhand)
- Dr Rajkumar KR (Gulbarga, Karnataka)
- Dr Rajlaxmi Panda (Berhampur, Odisha)
- Dr Rajveer Singh Chourasia (Bhawanipatna, Odisha)
- Dr Rakesh Kumar Verma (Lucknow, UP)
- Dr Rakesh Mani (Bikaner, Rajasthan)
- Dr Rakesh Mishra (Lucknow, UP)
- Dr Rakesh Shukla (Mirzapur, UP)
- Dr Ram Kumar Singhal (Bharatpur, Rajasthan)
- Dr Ram Prakash Gupta (Greater Noida, UP)
- Dr Randhir S Chauhan (Solan, HP)
- Dr Randhir Sigh Chauhan (Solan, Himachal Pradesh)
- Dr Rani Raphael M (Alappuzha, Kerala)
- Dr Ranjana Barjatya (Ajmer, Rajasthan)
- Dr Ranjeet Kumar (Deoghar, Jharkhand)
- Dr Ranjneet Guha (Patna, Bihar)
- Dr Rashmi Deopujari (Vidisha, MP)
- Dr Rashmi Malhotra (Rishikesh, Uttarakhand)
- Dr Rashmi Prasad (Patna, Bihar)
- Dr Rashmi S Sinha (Mumbai, Maharashtra)
- Dr Rashmoni Jana (Delhi)
- Dr Ravi Kant Sharma (Solan, Himachal Pradesh)
- Dr Raviendra Marathe (Akola, Maharashtra)
- Dr Reeha Mahajan (Vijaypur, Jammu, J&K)
- Dr Reena Singla (Mohali, Punjab)
- Dr Rekha More (Mumbai, Maharashtra)
- Dr Rekha Parashar (Dausa, Rajasthan)
- Dr Renu Agarwal (Agra, UP)
- Dr Renuka Ahankari (Pune, Maharashtra)
- Dr Richa Gupta (Chandigarh)
- Dr Richa Niranjan (Srinagar, Uttarakhand)
- Dr Rimpi Gupta (Karnal, Haryana)
- Dr Rimple Bansal (Patiala, Punjab)
- Dr Ritesh Shah (Ahmedabad, Gujarat)
- Dr Ritika Gaddewar (Nagpur, Maharashtra)
- Dr Ritika Sharma (Amritsar, Punjab)
- Dr Ritu Gothwal (Churu, Rajasthan)
- Dr Ritu Saloi (Diphu, Assam)
- Dr Ritu Slathia (Rajouri, J&K)
- Dr Rohini Karambelkar (Islampur, Maharashtra)
- Dr Rohini Motwani (Bibinagar, Telangana)
- Dr Roli Joshi (Unnao, UP)
- Dr Romi S (Kollam, Kerala)
- Dr Roonmoni Deka (Guwahati, Assam)
- Dr RS Bulagouda (Vijayapura, Karnataka)
- Dr Rubi Saikia (Jorhat, Assam)
- Dr Ruchi Dhuria (Delhi)
- Dr Ruchi Ratnesh (Deoghar, Jharkhand)
- Dr Rup Sekhar Deka (Nalbari, Assam)
- Dr Rupa Chaparrwal (Indore, MP)
- Dr Rupali Kavitake (Alibagh, Maharashtra)
- Dr Ruta Bapat (Navi Mumbai, Maharashtra)
- Dr S Archana (Chengalpattu, TN)
- Dr S Babu Rao (Hyderabad, Telangana)
- Dr S Bharathi Rani (Sivagangai, TN)
- Dr S Diwya Lakshmi (Virudhunagar, TN)
- Dr S Karthick Selvaraj (Kanchipuram, TN)
- Dr S Naveen Kumar (Hyderabad, Telangana)
- Dr S Satish Kumar (Dharmapuri, TN)
- Dr S Satishkumar (Kalakuruchi, TN)
- Dr S Sundarapandian (Chengalpattu, TN)
- Dr Sabin Malik (Ernakulam, Kerala)
- Dr Sachendra Mittal (Jaipur, Rajasthan)
- Dr Sachin Soni (Bilaspur, HP)
- Dr Sadakat Ali (Dehradun, Uttarakhand)
- Dr Sagun Shukla (Shahjanpur, UP)
- Dr Saif Umar (Behita, Bihar)
- Dr Saikat Roy (Kalyani, Nadia, WB)
- Dr Sajan Skaria (Udaipur, Rajasthan)
- Dr Sajey PS (Alappuzha, Kerala)
- Dr Saju Bina Cherian (Hyderabad, Telangana)
- Dr Saleena N Ali (Alappuzha, Kerala)
- Dr Samala Niveditha (Hyderabad, Telangana)
- Dr Samatha Roshini Padala (Siddipet, Telangana)
- Dr Sambhu Prasad (Sasaram, Bihar)
- Dr Samta Gaur (Pali, Rajasthan)
- Dr Sandeep K Sharma (Ambedkar Nagar, UP)
- Dr Sandeep S Mohite (Karad, Maharashtra)
- Dr Sandhya Kurup (Kolanchery, Kerala)
- Dr Sangeeta Gupta (Jammu, J&K)
- Dr Sangeeta M (Bengaluru)
- Dr Sangeeta Naik (Hyderabad, Telangana)
- Dr Sanjana (Bhatinda, Punjab)
- Dr Sanjay Sharma (Sri Ganganagar, Rajasthan)
- Dr Sanjeev Kolagi (Bagalkot, Karnataka)
- Dr Santhini Arulselvi (Karaikal, Puducherry)
- Dr Santosh Kumar (Dholpur, Rajasthan)
- Dr Santoshkumar A Dope (Latur, Maharashtra)
- Dr Sarada Devi (Moinabad, Telangana)
- Dr Saritha S (Hyderabad, Telangana)
- Dr Saryu Sen (Sikar, Rajasthan)
- Dr Sashi Bhushan (Kuppam, AP)
- Dr Satheesha KS (Mangaluru, Karnataka)
- Dr Satyashree Ray (Koraput, Odisha)
- Dr Saurabh Kulkarni (Aurangabad, Maharashtra)

- Dr Saurjya Ranjan Das (Bhubaneswar, Odisha)
- Dr Savithri Krishnan (Kollam, Kerala)
- Dr Sayantan Das (Kishanganj, Bihar)
- Dr Seema Gupta (Jaipur, Rajasthan)
- Dr Seema Gupta (Ludhiana, Punjab)
- Dr Seema Prakash (Udaipur, Rajasthan)
- Dr Seema Sharma (Rajouri, J&K)
- Dr Seema SR (Bengaluru, Karnataka)
- Dr Shaheen Rizvi (Mumbai, Maharashtra)
- Dr Shaifaly Madan Rustagi (Delhi)
- Dr Shailaja Shetty (Bengaluru, Karnataka)
- Dr Shailendra Singh (Banda, UP)
- Dr Shakuntala Pai (Manipal, Karnataka)
- Dr Shalni Kumar (Delhi)
- Dr Shantanu Nandy (Bankura, WB)
- Dr Shanthini S (Puducherry)
- Dr Sharad Saant (Mumbai, Maharashtra)
- Dr Sharmisttha Biswas (Kolkata WB)
- Dr Shashi Munjal (Dehradun, Uttarakhand)
- Dr Shavi Garg (Faridabad, Haryana)
- Dr Sheela Sivan (Perinthalmanna, Malappuram, Kerala)
- Dr Shema Nair (Bhopal, MP)
- Dr Sherry Sharma (Jalandhar, Punjab)
- Dr Shibanee Jena (Jaipur, Odisha)
- Dr Shikha Sharma (Agra, UP)
- Dr Shilpa Bhimalli (Belagavi, Karnataka)
- Dr Shilpa Sonare (Nagpur, Maharashtra)
- Dr Shivaji B Sukre (Parbhani, Maharashtra)
- Dr Shobha Ramnarayan (Kolenchery, Ernakulum, Kerala)
- Dr Shrikant Verma (Raipur, CG)
- Dr Shruthi BN (Bengaluru, Karnataka)
- Dr Shruti Mamidwar (Chandrapur, Maharashtra)
- Dr Shubhangi Bhagwat Ghule (Jalgaon, Maharashtra)
- Dr Shubhpreet Sodhi (Nahan, HP)
- Dr Shweta Asthana (Udaipur, Rajasthan)
- Dr Shweta Swami (Karnal, Haryana)
- Dr Simmi Mehra (Rajkot, Gujarat)
- Dr Simmi Soni (Aziznagar, Telangana)
- Dr Sindhu Chaudhary (Almora, Uttarakhand)
- Dr Sirikonda Parimala (Telangana)
- Dr SK Chavan (Pune, Maharashtra)
- Dr SM Belsare (Talgaon, Pune, Maharashtra)
- Dr Smruti Rekha Mohanty (Bhubaneswar, Odisha)
- Dr Sonali Thomas (Haldwani, Uttarakhand)
- Dr Sonia Singh (Ludhiana, Punjab)
- Dr Soumitra Trivedi (Raipur, CG)
- Dr Soumya Chakraborty Bhattachrya (Kohima, Nagaland)
- Dr Sreevidya J (Chennai, TN)
- Dr SS Saiyad (Nadiad, Gujarat)
- Dr Subhash Gujar (Vadnagar, Gujarat)
- Dr Subhash K Deshpande (Dharwad, Karnataka)
- Dr Subhasis Chakraborty (Kolkata, WB)
- Dr Subodh Kumar (Patna, Bihar)
- Dr Suchetra Chaudhary (Ahmadabad, Gujarat)
- Dr Suchit Kumar (Dehradun, Uttarakhand)
- Dr Sudha R (Salem, TN)
- Dr Sudha Rani (Hazaribagh, Jharkhand)
- Dr Sujata K (Kuppam, AP)
- Dr Sujithaa N (Villupurum, TN)
- Dr Sukhinder Baidwain (Nahan, HP)
- Dr Sumalatha Thimmaraju (Hyderabad, Telangana)
- Dr Suman Kumari (Gaya, Bihar)
- Dr Suman Yadav (Tanda, HP)
- Dr Sumedha Anjankar (Raipur, CG)
- Dr Sumit Gupta (Kota, Rajasthan)
- Dr Sumit Patil (Bhopal, MP)
- Dr Sumita Agrawal (Dehradun, Uttarakhand)
- Dr Sumita Shukla (Ayodhya, UP)
- Dr Sundar Lal Jethani (Dehradun, Uttarakhand)
- Dr Sunita Bharti (Navi Mumbai, Maharashtra)
- Dr Sunita Gupta (Ahmedabad, Gujarat)
- Dr Sunita Nayak (Patna, Bihar)
- Dr Surajit Ghatak (Jodhpur, Rajasthan)
- Dr Surekha Patil (Jaipur, Rajasthan)
- Dr Surekha W Meshram (Gondia, Maharashtra)
- Dr Suresh Kumar (Vellore, TN)
- Dr Suresh Sharma (Sri Ganganagar, Rajasthan)
- Dr Susan Varghese (Kollam, Kerala)
- Dr Sushant Swaroop Das (Bilaspur, HP)
- Dr Susheela Rana (Mandi, HP)
- Dr Sushil Jiwane (Bhopal, MP)
- Rt. Brig (Dr) Sushil Kumar (Faridabad, Haryana)
- Dr Sushma Kushal Kataria (Jodhpur, Rajasthan)
- Dr SVV Nagarajamannar (Rajahmundry, AP)
- Dr Swati Bansal (Karnal, Haryana)
- Dr Swati Saxena (Dehradun, Uttarakhand)
- Dr Sweta Singh (Barabanki, UP)
- Dr T Anitha (Villupurum, TN)
- Dr T Rajan (Puducherry)
- Dr T Sreekanth (Peerancheru, Telangana)
- Dr Tapan Kumar Jana (Murshidabad, WB)
- Dr Taqiuddin Mohammed (Hyderabad, Telangana)
- Dr Tarkeshwar Golghate (Nagpur, Maharashtra)
- Dr TC Singel (Dahod, Gujarat)
- Dr Tejaswi HL (Mandya, Karnataka)
- Dr Teresa Rani (AP)
- Dr Thanuja Kumari (Telangana)
- Dr Thuslima M (Chennai, TN)
- Dr TK Rajashree (Hyderabad, Telangana)
- Dr Tom J Nallikuzhy (Idukki, Kerala)
- Dr Trupti Balwir (Nagpur, Maharashtra)
- Dr Uday Kumar (Telangana)
- Dr Ujwala Bhanarkar (Kalyani, WB)
- Dr UK Kulkarni (Belagavi, Karnataka)
- Dr Upendra M (Vikarabad, Telangana)
- Dr Usha KK (Manjeri, Kerala)
- Dr V Anandhi (Trichy, TN)
- Dr V Dharani (Villupuram, TN)
- Dr V Rajapriya (Omandurar, TN)
- Dr V Ravi Kumar (Shimoga, Karnataka)
- Dr V Subhashini (Amalapuram, AP)
- Dr Vaishali Inamdar (Nanded, Maharashtra)
- Dr Vandana Mehta (New Delhi)
- Dr Vandana Sidhu (Amritsar, Punjab)
- Dr Vandana Tiwari (Haldwani, Uttarakhand)
- Dr Vanita Gupta (Udhampur, J&K)
- Dr Varsha Dahiphale (Ambajogai, Maharashtra)
- Dr Varsha Mokhasi (Bengaluru)
- Dr Vasant Vaniya (Vadodra, Gujarat)
- Dr Vashali Kadam (Mumbai, Maharashtra)
- Dr Vasi Padmaja (Telangana)
- Dr Vedula Sailaja (Hyderabad, Telangana)
- Dr Venkateshwar Reddy (Mehboobnagar, Telangana)
- Dr Vijay Anand S Nagdeve (Raipur, CG)
- Dr Vijay Nayak (Bundi, Rajasthan)
- Dr Vijayamma KN (Kerala)
- Dr Vijisha Phalgunan (Puducherry)
- Dr Vikas Saxena (Ajmer, Rajasthan)
- Dr Vikram Ephram (Hyderabad, Telangana)
- Dr Vinay Kumar (Saharanpur, UP)
- Dr Vinay Sharma (Muzaffarnagar, UP)
- Dr Vineet Gohiya (Khandwa, MP)
- Dr Vinod Kumar (Turky, Bihar)
- Dr Vinodini (Secunderabad, Telangana)
- Dr Vinoth S (Chennai, TN)
- Dr Virendra Bhdhiraja (Karnal, Haryana)
- Dr Vishal Bhadkaria (Sagar, MP)
- Dr Vishnu Gupta (Muzaffarnagar, UP)
- Dr VK Chimurkar (Wardha, Maharashtra)
- Dr VP Rukhmode (Gondia, Maharashtra)
- Dr X Chandra Philip (Puducherry)
- Dr Yogendra Singh (Gorakhpur, UP)
- Dr Yogesh Diwan (Shimla, HP)
- Dr Yogesh Shridhar Ganorkar (Pune, Maharashtra)
- Dr Yuvraj Bhosale (Mumbai, Maharashtra)
- Dr Zafar Sultana (Hyderabad, Telangana)
- Dr Zeba Alam (Patna, Bihar)
- Dr Zeba Khan (Mumbai, Maharashtra)
- Dr Zeenat Akhtar (Jammu, J&K)
- Dr Zuberi Hussain Riyaz (Badnapur, Jalna, Maharashtra)
- Pulkit Jain (Ludhiana, Punjab)

Editors

Reviewers

We extend our gratitude to the following anatomy teachers for their unwavering support and for reviewing various topics in the field.

- Dr Aga Ammar Murthuza (Bengaluru, Karnataka)
- Dr Angela (Kollam, Kerala)
- Dr Anjali Jain (Ludhiana, Punjab)
- Dr Anu Sharma (Ludhiana, Punjab)
- Dr Aparna K Vedapriya (Siddipet, Telangana)
- Dr Archana Rani (Lucknow, UP)
- Dr Arvind Kumar Pankaj (Lucknow, UP)
- Dr Ashok KL (Bengaluru, Karnataka)
- Dr Benjamin W (Palakkad, Kerala)
- Dr Dharmaraj Tamgire (Puducherry)
- Dr Dibyendu Dutta (Kolkata, WB)
- Dr Dinesh Kumar V (Puducherry)
- Dr Gaurav Agnihotri (Amritsar, Punjab)
- Dr Gitanjali Arora (Bhubaneswar, Odisha)
- Dr Gunapriya Raghunath (Chennai, Tamil Nadu)
- Dr Hitant Vohra (Ludhiana, Punjab)
- Dr Indira CK (Ernakulam, Kerala)
- Dr Jahira Banu T (Puducherry)
- Dr Jaswinder Kaur (Ambala, Haryana)
- Dr Juned Labbai (Mumbai, Maharashtra)
- Dr K Chandra Kumari (Trivandrum, Kerala)
- Dr Komala B (Bengaluru, Karnataka)
- Dr Kumari TK (Kollam, Kerala)
- Dr Mubeena Sheikh (Palakkad, Kerala)
- Dr Nagaraja V Pai (Mumbai, Maharashtra)
- Dr Nusrat Jabeen (Jammu, J&K)
- Dr Payal Kasat (Kharagpur, WB)
- Dr PK Ramakrishnan (Palakkad, Kerala)
- Dr Prajna Paramita Samanta (Bhubaneswar, Odisha)
- Dr Pratibha Shakya (Lucknow, UP)
- Dr Pretty Rathnakar (Mangaluru, Karnataka)
- Dr R Gomathi (Puducherry)
- Dr R Sarah (Madurai, Tamil Nadu)
- Dr Rajashree Biswal (Cuttack, Odisha)
- Dr Rakesh Kumar Diwan (Lucknow, UP)
- Dr Rakesh Kumar Verma (Lucknow, UP)
- Dr Rakhi More (Mumbai, Maharashtra)
- Dr Rashmi Sinha (Mumbai, Maharashtra)
- Dr Ravikiran Gole (Mumbai, Maharashtra)
- Dr Rohini K (Bengaluru, Karnataka)
- Dr S Arivu Selvan (Calicut, Kerala)
- Dr S Naveen Kumar (Hyderabad, Telangana)
- Dr Sabin Malik (Guildford, UK)
- Dr Saleena N Ali (Alappuzha, Kerala)
- Dr Sandhya Kurup (Kolanchery, Kerala)
- Dr Sajay PS (Alappuzha, Kerala)
- Dr Saurjya Ranjan Das (Bhubaneswar, Odisha)
- Dr Shantanu Nandy (Kolkata, WB)
- Dr Sharmila Pal (Jadavpur, Kolkata, WB)
- Dr Sheela Sivan (Perimthalmanna, Kerala)
- Dr Smrutirekha Mohanty (Bhubaneswar, Odisha)
- Dr Sneha John (Mumbai, Maharashtra)
- Dr Sreekumar R (Thiruvananthapuram, Kerala)
- Dr Sreevidya J (Chennai, TN)
- Dr Srividya Sreenivasan (Mumbai, Maharashtra)
- Dr Surendra Babu T (Bengaluru, Karnataka)
- Dr Swapna Chavan Thakur (Mumbai, Maharashtra)
- Dr Swetha B (Bengaluru, Karnataka)
- Dr T Rajini (Bengaluru, Karnataka)
- Dr Taquiuddin Mohammed (Hyderabad, Telangana)
- Dr Ujwala Bhanarkar (Kalyani, WB)
- Dr V Lokanayaki (Chennai, Tamil Nadu)
- Dr Vandana LR (Thiruvananthapuram, Kerala)
- Dr Vasrha R Bhivate (Mumbai, Maharashtra)
- Dr WMS Johnson (Chennai, Tamil Nadu)
- Dr Yogitha R (Bengaluru, Karnataka)

Editors

Contents

eSmartQuiz – Online MCQ Test

After attending the class, students should go through the "*eSmartQuiz* – Online MCQ test" for the following reasons:

- *Reinforcement of Learning*: The "*eSmartQuiz* – Online MCQ test" provide an opportunity to reinforce learning after attending a class or reading a book. It helps to assess understanding and retention of concepts, to solidify knowledge and identify areas that need further revision or clarification.
- *Assessment of Comprehension*: The "*eSmartQuiz* – Online MCQ test" is an effective tool to assess comprehension of the subject matter and to demonstrate the ability to apply the concepts learned in the class.
- *Enhancement of Attention and Critical Thinking*: The "*eSmartQuiz* – Online MCQ test" will help to make students attentive for the class and to enhance critical thinking skills by selecting the most appropriate answer among the given options.

Each *eSmartQuiz* test consists of 10 MCQs, mostly image-based, and the students can see their scores at the end of each test. These questions will be modified after a certain interval. Use the given links or scan the QR code (given in each chapter) for the test. One student can solve each test only one time.

Chapter	*Link for* ***eSmartQuiz***
Lower Limb	
1. Introduction	https://forms.gle/NRD1x2JNDTgRCKP8A
2. Bones of Lower Limb	https://forms.gle/h5Q9mGxpUd6QyGXA6
3. Front of Thigh	https://forms.gle/hDFsJd1Z7Bb2srAYA
4. Medial Side of Thigh	https://forms.gle/SMJp1NN4pEvhjKXAA
5. Gluteal Region	https://forms.gle/fHLmnxN4AQri9yWQA
6. Popliteal Fossa	https://forms.gle/ZWaNVwwx1bSCbmt78
7. Back of Thigh	https://forms.gle/ycdgWXengkHBGf1U6
8. Front of Leg with Dorsum of Foot; Lateral and Medial Sides of Leg	https://forms.gle/MXUuoohUSG78axgC9
9. Back of Leg	https://forms.gle/fQDyryQMFrj8wd367
10. Sole of Foot	https://forms.gle/FNMDK27oq214B5HM9
11. Venous and Lymphatic Drainage; Segmental and Sympathetic Innervation	https://forms.gle/GGerj5QhwaXTHEE79
12. Joints of Lower Limb	https://forms.gle/h1tsJyw7LHPjoorp8
13. Arches of Foot	https://forms.gle/knQU4jRtBTJtZB4q6
14. Surface and Radiological Anatomy of Lower Limb	https://forms.gle/XKF5AnXCuVma6GAK7
Abdomen and Pelvis	
15. Introduction and Osteology of Abdomen	https://forms.gle/Hp4nkwjwCMvj4EzL9
16. Anterior Abdominal Wall	https://forms.gle/EJK7Jfbu98HURPTe7
17. Male External Genital Organs	https://forms.gle/cdzkugyBMuY6Kcgb8
18. Abdominal Cavity and Peritoneum	https://forms.gle/1oFckyZQrFMukRAY8
19. Abdominal Part of Oesophagus and Stomach	https://forms.gle/LEuZcnnGYthhX3X57
20. Small and Large Intestines	https://forms.gle/MLheERXtp6DaKmM27
21. Large Blood Vessels of the Gut	https://forms.gle/wvcrmtfwwRNc6qa78
22. Extrahepatic Biliary Apparatus	https://forms.gle/wqF56B31VuCcmAVf8
23. Spleen, Pancreas and Liver	https://forms.gle/hbBKKRzMGtdgfhej9
24. Kidney and Ureter	https://forms.gle/X9ciDTSfZFrSrH8x5

(Contd.)

(Contd.)

Chapter	*Link for* ***eSmartQuiz***
25. Suprarenal Gland and Chromaffin System	https://forms.gle/NQ8NZMHXV6rv4Mgw9
26. Thoracoabdominal Diaphragm	https://forms.gle/hbweRURskHBGxxaT6
27. Posterior Abdominal Wall	https://forms.gle/r5LpaZxDTJttJssQA
28. Perineum	https://forms.gle/T7ubgYmw4sGJZM9o8
29. Preliminary Consideration of Boundaries and Contents of Pelvis	https://forms.gle/gwzfqVVg3ch3MvcM8
30. Urinary Bladder and Urethra	https://forms.gle/WNPbBLGFfAh5GKKd7
31. Female Reproductive Organs	https://forms.gle/XD6GirCZd1g1g2Ht7
32. Male Internal Genital Organs	https://forms.gle/c6RzPMqBkYZHWkg86
33. Rectum and Anal Canal	https://forms.gle/8hcohRy1S84wzVyk7
34. Walls of Pelvis	https://forms.gle/q9NoHXkiZ9SNcASn9
35. Surface Marking of Abdomen and Pelvis	https://forms.gle/dL7zyQVdjdFTXjkHA
36. Radiological and Imaging Procedures	https://forms.gle/mMyvGuXv6pdccaKPA

Index of Competencies

As per the latest NMC Guidelines | Competency Based Medical Education (CBME)
Curriculum under Graduate Medical Education Regulation

(Contd.)

(Contd.)

Code	Competency	Chapter	Page no.
AN19.5	Describe factors maintaining important arches of the foot with its importance	13	164
AN19.6	Explain the anatomical basis of flat foot and club foot	13	167
AN19.7	Explain the anatomical basis of plantar fasciitis	10	121
AN20.1	Describe and demonstrate the type, articular surfaces, capsule, synovial membrane, ligaments, relations, movements and muscles involved, blood and nerve supply of tibiofibular and ankle joint	12	155
AN20.2	Describe the subtalar and transverse tarsal joints	12	159
AN20.3	Describe and demonstrate, venous drainage, lymphatic drainage and dermatomes of lower limb	11	131
AN20.4	Explain anatomical basis of enlarged inguinal lymph nodes	11	136
AN20.5	Explain anatomical basis of varicose veins and deep vein thrombosis	11	133
AN20.6	Identify the bones and joints of lower limb seen in anteroposterior and lateral view radiographs of various regions of lower limb	14	175
AN20.7	Identify and demonstrate important bony landmarks of lower limb: Vertebral levels of highest point of iliac crest, posterior superior iliac spines, iliac tubercle, pubic tubercle, ischial tuberosity, adductor tubercle, tibial tuberosity, head of fibula, medial and lateral malleoli, condyles of femur and tibia, sustentaculum tali, tuberosity of fifth metatarsal, tuberosity of the navicular	14	170
AN20.9	Identify and demonstrate palpation of vessels (femoral, popliteal, dorsalis pedis, post-tibial), mid-inguinal point, surface projection of: Femoral nerve, saphenous opening, sciatic, tibial, common peroneal and deep peroneal nerves, great and small saphenous veins	14	172
AN44.1	Describe and demonstrate the planes (transpyloric, transtubercular, subcostal, lateral vertical, linea alba, linea semilunaris), regions and quadrants of abdomen	18	236
AN44.2	Describe and identify the fascia, nerves and blood vessels of anterior abdominal wall	16	205
AN44.3	Describe the formation of rectus sheath and its contents	16	214
AN44.4	Describe and demonstrate extent, boundaries, contents of inguinal canal including Hesselbach's triangle	16	216
AN44.5	Explain the anatomical basis of inguinal hernia	16	219
AN44.6	Describe and demonstrate attachments of muscles of anterior abdominal wall	16	207
AN44.7	Enumerate common abdominal incisions	16	212
AN45.1	Describe thoracolumbar fascia	27	360
AN45.2	Describe and demonstrate lumbar plexus for its root value, formation and branches	27	367
AN45.3	Mention the major subgroups of back muscles, nerve supply and action	27	357
AN46.1	Describe and demonstrate coverings, internal structure, side determination, blood supply, nerve supply, lymphatic drainage and descent of testis with its applied anatomy	17	229
AN46.2	Describe parts of epididymis	17	234
AN46.3	Describe penis under following headings: Parts, components, blood supply and lymphatic drainage	17	223
AN46.4	Explain the anatomical basis of varicocele	17	229
AN46.5	Explain the anatomical basis of phimosis and circumcision	17	227
AN47.1	Describe and identify boundaries and recesses of lesser and greater sacs	18	246
AN47.10	Enumerate the sites of portosystemic anastomosis	21	294
AN47.11	Explain the anatomic basis of hematemesis and caput medusae in portal hypertension	21	294
AN47.12	Describe important nerve plexuses of posterior abdominal wall	27	368
AN47.13	Describe and demonstrate the attachments, openings, nerve supply and action of the thoracoabdominal diaphragm	26	351
AN47.14	Describe the abnormal openings of thoracoabdominal diaphragm and diaphragmatic hernia	26	354
AN47.2	Name and identify various peritoneal folds and pouches with its explanation	18	250

(Contd.)

(Contd.)

Code	Competency	Chapter	Page no.
AN47.3	Explain anatomical basis of ascites and peritonitis	18	238
AN47.4	Explain anatomical basis of subphrenic abscess	18	252
AN47.5	Describe and demonstrate major viscera of abdomen under the following headings: Anatomical position, external and internal features, important peritoneal and other relations, blood supply, nerve supply, lymphatic drainage and applied aspects	19, 20	254, 267
AN47.6	Explain the anatomical basis of splenic notch, accessory spleens, Kehr's sign, different types of vagotomy, liver biopsy (site of needle puncture), referred pain in cholecystitis, obstructive jaundice, referred pain around umbilicus, radiating pain of kidney to groin and lymphatic spread in carcinoma stomach	22, 23,	302, 309, 325
AN47.7	Mention the clinical importance of Calot's triangle	22	300
AN47.8	Describe and identify the formation, course, relations and tributaries of portal vein, inferior vena cava and renal vein	21, 27	292, 364
AN47.9	Describe and identify the origin, course, important relations and branches of abdominal aorta, coeliac trunk, superior mesenteric, inferior mesenteric and common iliac artery	21, 27	287, 361, 363
AN48.1	Describe and identify the muscles of pelvic diaphragms	34	448
AN48.2	Describe and demonstrate the position, features, important peritoneal and other relations, blood supply, nerve supply, lymphatic drainage and clinical aspects of important female pelvic viscera	31, 32	409, 427
AN48.3	Describe and demonstrate the origin, course, important relations and branches of internal iliac artery	34	452
AN48.4	Describe the branches of sacral plexus	34	454
AN48.5	Explain the anatomical basis of suprapubic cystostomy, urinary obstruction in benign prostatic hypertrophy, retroverted uterus, prolapse uterus, internal and external haemorrhoids, anal fistula, tubal pregnancy and tubal ligation	31, 32	414, 422, 428
AN48.6	Describe the neurological basis of automatic bladder	30	398
AN48.7	Mention the lobes involved in benign prostatic hypertrophy and prostatic cancer	32	434
AN48.8	Mention the structures palpable during vaginal and rectal examination	31, 33	422, 439
AN49.1	Describe and demonstrate the superficial and deep perineal pouch (boundaries and contents)	28	377
AN49.2	Describe and identify perineal body	28	381
AN49.3	Describe and demonstrate perineal membrane in male and female	28	375
AN49.4	Describe and demonstrate boundaries, content and applied anatomy of ischioanal fossa	28	383
AN49.5	Explain the anatomical basis of perineal tear, episiotomy, perianal abscess and anal fissure	28, 33	385, 445
AN50.2	Describe and demonstrate the type, articular ends, ligaments and movements of intervertebral joints, sacroiliac joints and pubic symphysis	34	458
AN50.4	Explain the anatomical basis of scoliosis, lordosis, prolapsed disc, spondylolisthesis and spina bifida	15	191
AN52.1	Describe and identify the microanatomical features of fundus and pylorus of stomach	19, 20, 22, 23, 25	265, 273, 275, 285, 302, 309, 316, 325, 348
AN52.2	Describe and identify the microanatomical features of penis	17, 24, 30, 31, 32	223, 229, 234, 342, 398, 411, 414, 421, 425, 428, 433
AN52.5	Describe the development and congenital anomalies of thoracoabdominal diaphragm	26	354
AN52.6	Describe the development of foregut	19, 20, 22, 23, 33	265, 280, 282, 304, 309, 316, 325, 445

(Contd.)

(Contd.)

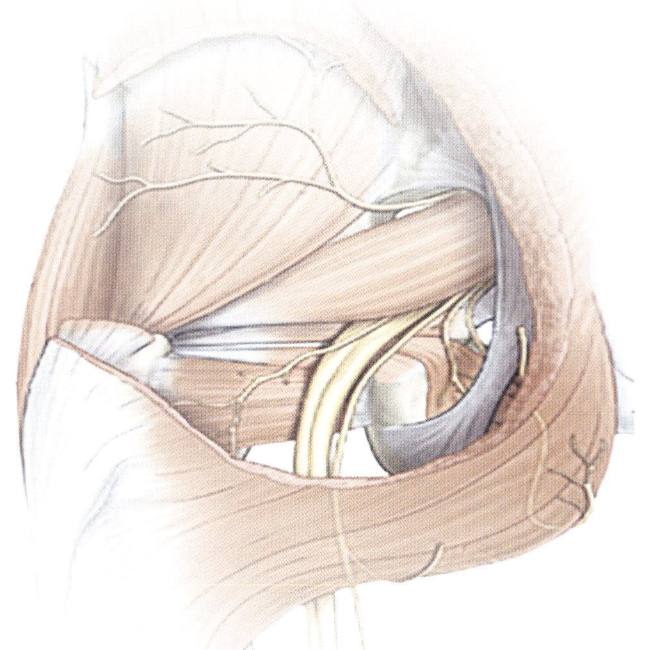

Section 1

Lower Limb

1. Introduction
2. Bones of Lower Limb
3. Front of Thigh
4. Medial Side of Thigh
5. Gluteal Region
6. Popliteal Fossa
7. Back of Thigh
8. Front of Leg with Dorsum of Foot; Lateral and Medial Sides of Leg
9. Back of Leg
10. Sole of Foot
11. Venous and Lymphatic Drainage; Segmental and Sympathetic Innervation
12. Joints of Lower Limb
13. Arches of Foot
14. Surface and Radiological Anatomy of Lower Limb

Appendix 1: Major Nerves and Arteries of Lower Limb

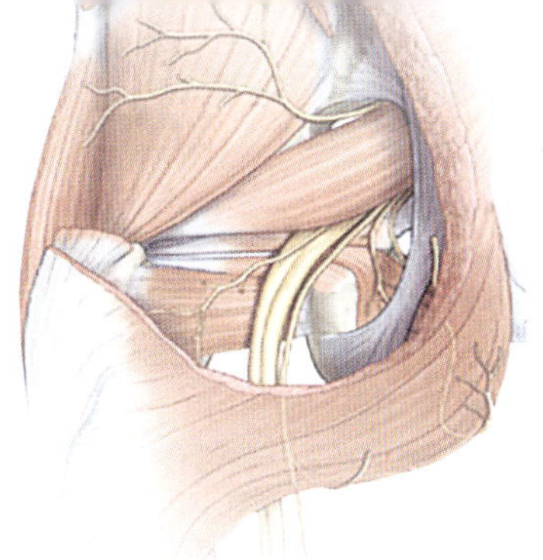

Chapter

1

Introduction

The lower limb or extremities are modified in the human body for weight transmission and bipedal locomotion. The lower limb, in its basic structure, is slightly different from the upper limb. The emancipated upper limb is specialised for prehension and free mobility, whereas the lower limb is specialised for support and locomotion.

In general, the lower limbs attain stability at the cost of some mobility, and the upper limbs attain freedom of mobility at the cost of some stability. Thus, the lower limbs are bulkier and stronger than the upper limbs.

PARTS OF THE LOWER LIMB

The lower limb consists of four parts (Table 1.1 and Plate 1.1):

1. Gluteal region
2. Thigh
3. Leg or crus
4. Foot or pes.

Gluteal Region

The *gluteal region*, overlying the side and back of the pelvis, includes the hip and the buttock, which are not sharply distinguished from each other.

Hip or *coxa* is the superolateral part of the gluteal region presented in a side view, while the ***buttock*** or *natis* is the inferomedial rounded bulge of the region presented in a back view.

The ***hip bone*** is made up of three elements—ilium, pubis and ischium; which are fused at the acetabulum. Two hip bones form the *hip girdle*, which articulates posteriorly with the sacrum at the sacroiliac joints. The bony *pelvis* includes the two hip bones—a sacrum and a coccyx. *Hip joint* is an articulation between the hip bone and femur.

Thigh

The thigh extends from hip to the knee joint. ***Femur*** and patella are bones of thigh. The junction of thigh and anterior abdominal wall is indicated by the groove of groin or inguinal region. The *gluteal fold* is the upper limit of the thigh posteriorly. *Ham* or *poples* is the lower part of the back of thigh and the back of the knee.

Leg

Leg lies between the ***knee joint*** and the ankle joint. It comprises tibia and fibula including their three tibiofibular joints.

Foot

The foot or *pes* has an upper surface, called the *dorsal surface,* and a lower surface, called the ***sole*** or *plantar surface.* Sole is homologous with the palm of the hand.

TABLE 1.1: Parts of the lower limb

Regions	*Bones*	*Joints*
Gluteal region (covers the side and back of the pelvis)	Hip bone	Hip joint
Thigh (from hip to knee)	Femur Patella	Knee joint
Leg or crus (from knee to ankle)	Tibia Fibula	Tibiofibular joints
Foot or pes (from heel to toe)	Tarsus: 7 tarsal bones Metatarsus: 5 metatarsals 14 phalanges: Two for great toe, three for each of the four toes	Ankle joint Subtalar and transverse tarsal (TT) joints Tarsometatarsal (TM) joints Intermetatarsal (IM) joints Metatarsophalangeal (MP) joints Interphalangeal (IP) joints

Plate 1.1: Parts and bones of lower limb

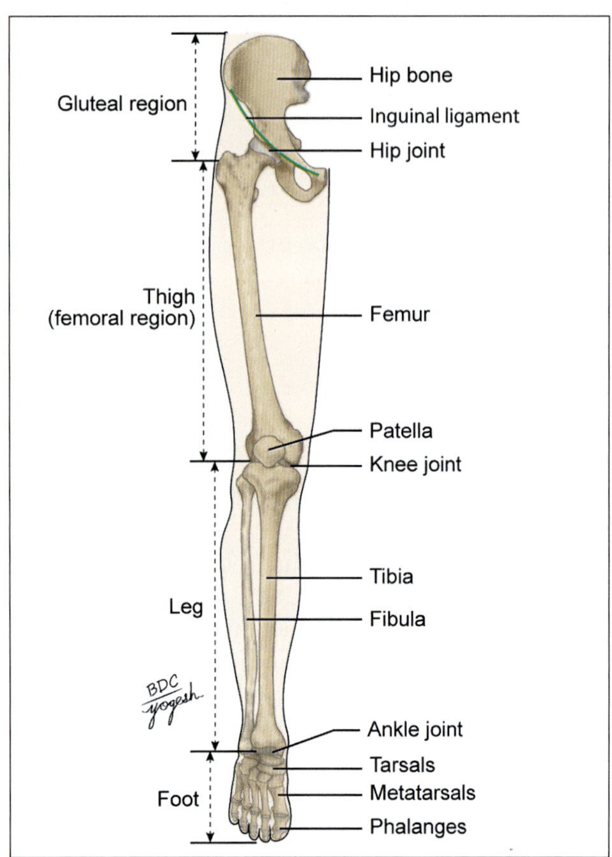

Line of Gravity

The line of gravity passes through cervical and lumbar vertebrae. In the lower limbs, it passes behind the hip joint and in front of knee and ankle joints (Fig. 1.1).

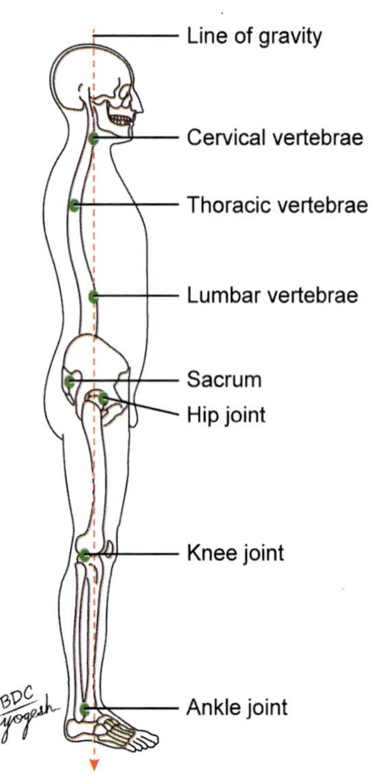

Fig. 1.1: Line of gravity

Weight Transmission in Lower Limb

The weight of a person of 60 kg gets divided into two parts of 30 kg each and descends to respective ankle joint. At ankle joint, 30 kg is divided into two equal parts; 15 kg goes to ground via calcaneal tuberosity, and other 15 kg reaches forepart of the foot. At the metatarsophalangeal joints of foot, 15 kg is divided into six parts of 2.5 kg each; two parts pass to the big toe, and one part each passes to 2nd–5th toes. Since the big toe on its head articulates with two sesamoid bones, each transmits 2.5 kg to the ground (Figs 1.2 and 1.3).

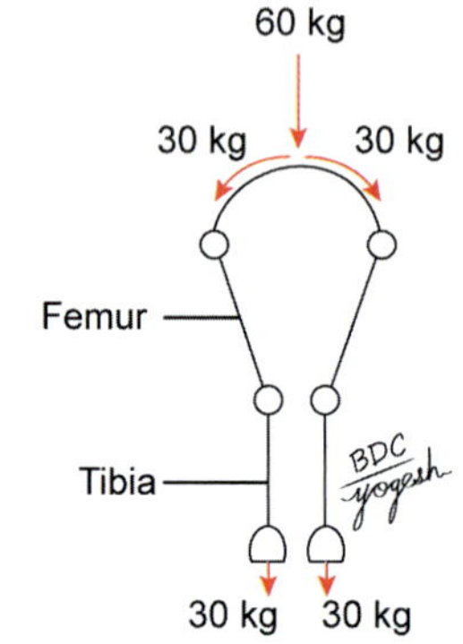

Fig. 1.2: Distribution of weight

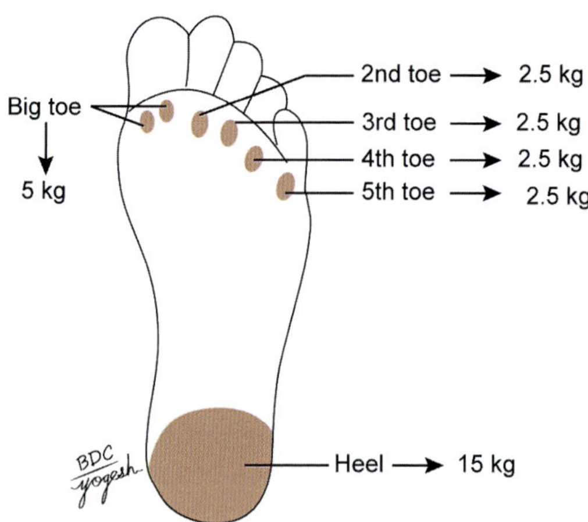

Fig. 1.3: Weight transmission

Peculiarities of Lower Limb

1. Longest and heaviest bone—femur
2. Most complicated joint—knee joint. There are 12 bursae in this joint.
3. Longest muscle—sartorius
4. Largest muscle—gluteus maximus
5. Strongest tendon—tendo calcaneus
6. Thickest nerve—sciatic nerve
7. Longest vein—great saphenous vein
8. Arches—foot with well-developed arches
9. Muscle with maximum heads—quadriceps femoris
10. Biggest sesamoid bone—patella
11. Longest cutaneous nerve—saphenous nerve.

CLINICAL ANATOMY

Intramuscular injection: The commonest sites for intramuscular injections in the lower limb are gluteal region in adults (gluteus medius muscle) and the anterolateral aspect of thigh in children (vastus lateralis muscle).

Arterial pulse palpation**:** The commonly used arterial pulse in the lower limb is as follows:

a. Femoral pulse
b. Popliteal pulse
c. Posterior tibial pulse
d. Dorsalis pedis pulse

Varicose veins: The superficial veins of the lower limb often become enlarged, swollen, and tortuous, called varicose veins. It occurs mostly in individuals with prolonged standing jobs such as bus conductors, traffic police, doctors and teachers.

BDC's Anatomy *e*-book

1. Development of lower limb
2. Molecular regulation of limb development
3. Viva voce questions

Chapter

2

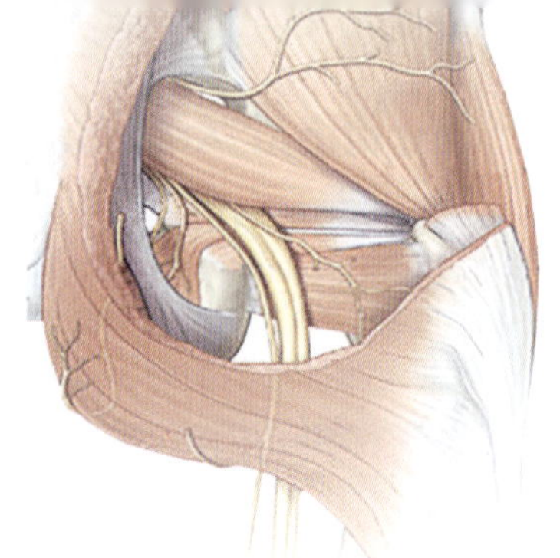

Bones of Lower Limb

Each lower limb is supported with 31 bones. They are as follows:

Pelvic girdle	
Hip bone	1
Bone of thigh	
Femur	1
Knee cap	
Patella	1
Bones of leg	
Tibia	1
Fibula	1
Bones of foot	
Tarsals	7
Metatarsals	5
Phalanges	14
Total	**31 bones**

Hip bone (pelvic girdle) connects the lower limb with axial skeleton. This chapter discusses features of hip bone.

Competencies:

AN14.1 Identify the given bone, its side, important features and keep it in anatomical position.

AN14.2 Identify and describe joints formed by the given bone.

Plate 2.1: Hip bone: Anterior view (Right, male)

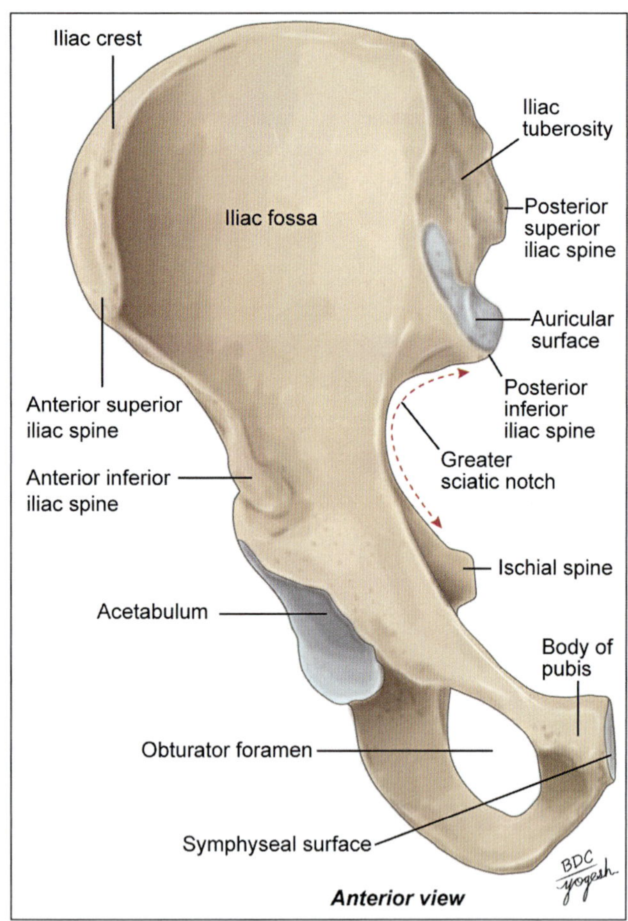

HIP BONE

Hip/innominate bone is a large irregular bone (Plates 2.1 and 2.2).

It is made up of three parts:

1. *Ilium* (Latin *loin*) superiorly
2. *Pubis* (Latin *genital area*) anteroinferiorly
3. *Ischium* (Greek *hip joint*) posteroinferiorly.

The three parts are joined to each other at a cup-shaped hollow, called the *acetabulum (*Latin *vinegar cup)*. The pubis and ischium are separated by a large oval opening, called the *obturator foramen.* The acetabulum articulates with the head of the femur to form the *hip joint*. The pubic parts of the two hip bones meet anteriorly to form the *pubic symphysis*. The two hip bones form the *pelvic* or hip girdle. The bony pelvis is formed by the two hip bones along with the sacrum and coccyx.

Side Determination and Anatomical Position

Hold the bone in such a way that—

1. Large cup-shaped acetabulum lies laterally and looks vertically downward.
2. Flat expanded ilium projects upward.
3. Obturator foramen lies below the acetabulum.

Plate 2.2: Hip bone: Medial and lateral views (Right, male)

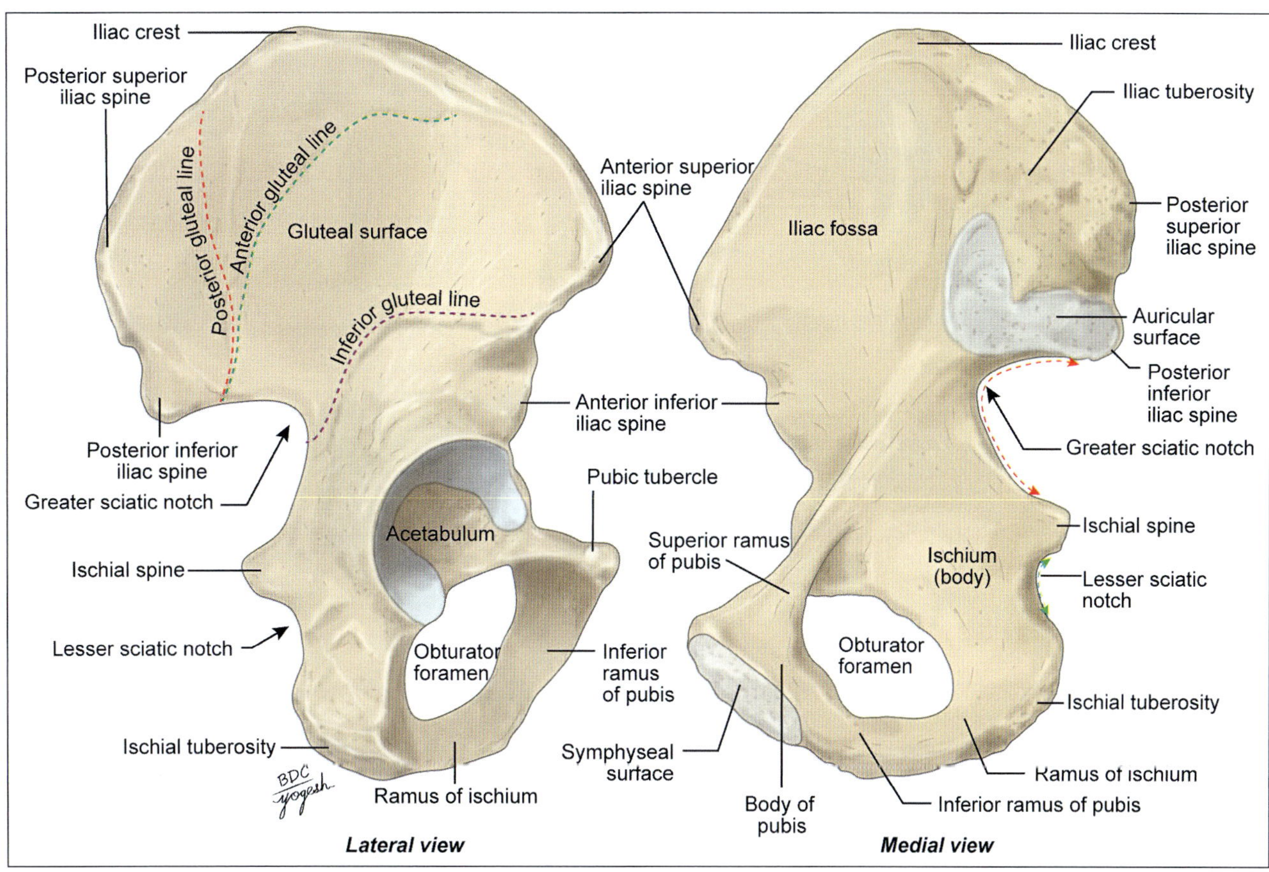

4. Thin pubis lies anteromedial to the obturator foramen and thick ischium lies posterolateral to the foramen.

Tilt the bone in such a way that the anterior superior iliac spine and pubic tubercle lie in the same coronal plane.

Note: Acetabulum determines the side to which the bone belongs; for example, for the right hip bone, the acetabulum lies on the right.

ILIUM

The ilium or *flank* forms the upper expanded plate-like part of the hip bone. Its lower part forms the upper 2/5th of the acetabulum.

Parts of Ilium

The ilium has the following parts (Plates 2.1, 2.2 and Figs 2.1, 2.2):

1. *Two ends:* Upper end (iliac crest) and lower end
2. *Three borders:* Anterior, posterior and medial
3. *Three surfaces:* Gluteal surface, iliac surface or iliac fossa and a sacropelvic surface.

Features of Ilium (Flowchart 2.1)

Upper end or Iliac Crest

The upper end of the ilium is called *iliac crest*. It (Fig. 2.1) is a broad convex ridge forming the upper end of the ilium. It can be felt in the living at the lower limit of the flank.

Curvatures

Vertically, it is convex upwards, anteroposteriorly; concave inwards in front and concave outwards behind (Fig. 2.1).

The highest point of the iliac crest is situated a little behind the midpoint of the crest. It lies at the level of the interval between the spines of vertebrae L3 and L4.

Ends of iliac crest

1. The anterior end of the iliac crest is called the ***anterior superior iliac spine*** (ASIS). This is a prominent landmark that is easily felt in the living.
2. The posterior end of the crest is called the ***posterior superior iliac spine***. Its position on the surface of the body is marked by a *dimple* 5 cm lateral of the second sacral spine (S2).

Morphological divisions

Morphologically, the iliac crest is divided into a long *ventral segment* and a short *dorsal segment*.

1. ***Ventral segment*:** It forms more than the anterior 2/3rd of the crest. It has an outer lip, an inner lip and an intermediate area. The ***tubercle of the iliac crest*** is an elevation that lies on the outer lip about 5 cm behind the anterior superior iliac spine (Fig. 2.1).
2. ***Dorsal segment*:** It forms less than the posterior 1/3rd of the crest. It has a lateral and a medial slope separated by a ridge.

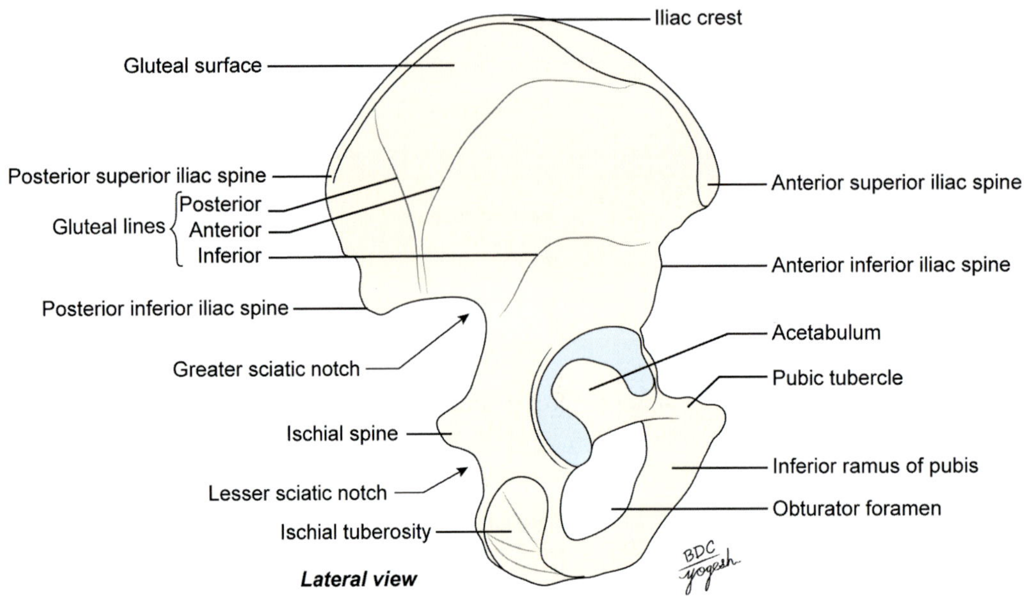

Fig. 2.1: Outer surface of right hip bone

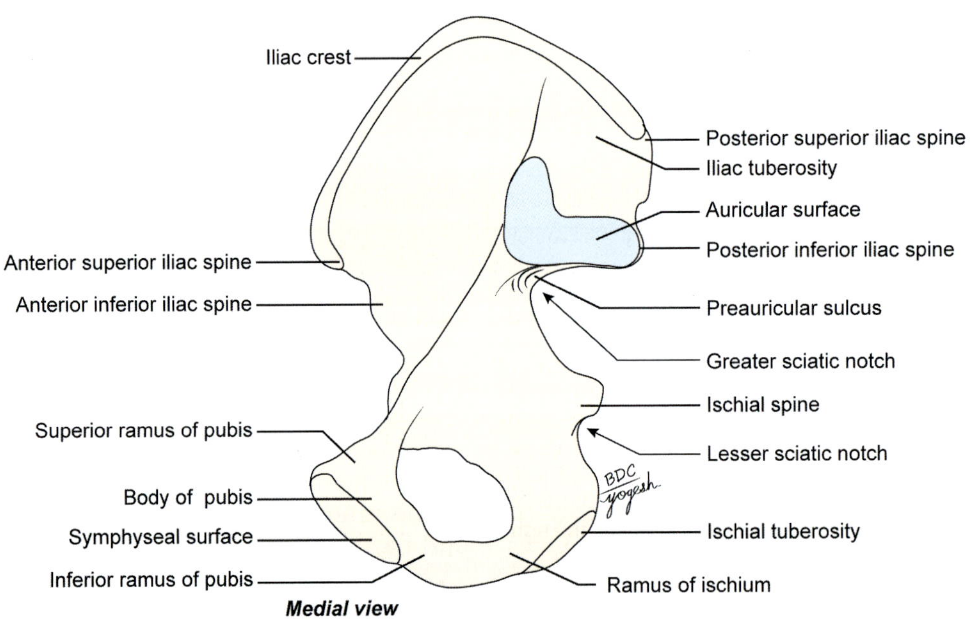

Fig. 2.2: Inner surface of right hip bone

Lower End of Ilium

The lower end of the ilium is smaller. It fuses with ischium and pubis at the acetabulum. It forms upper 2/5th of the acetabulum.

Anterior Border

Anterior border starts at the *anterior superior iliac* spine and runs downwards to the acetabulum. The upper part of the border presents a notch, while its lower part shows an elevated area called the ***anterior inferior iliac spine***. The lower half of this spine is large, triangular and rough.

Posterior Border

Posterior border extends from the *posterior superior iliac spine* to the upper end of the posterior border of the ischium. A few centimetres below the posterior superior iliac spine, it presents another prominence which is called the ***posterior inferior iliac spine***. Still lower down the posterior border is marked by a large deep notch, called the ***greater sciatic notch*** (Fig. 2.1).

Medial Border

Medial border extends on the inner or pelvic surface of the ilium from the iliac crest to the ***iliopubic eminence***. It separates the iliac fossa from the sacropelvic surface.

Its lower rounded part forms the iliac parts of the ***arcuate line*** or inlet of pelvis.

Gluteal Surface

Gluteal surface is the outer surface of the ilium, which is convex in front and concave behind, like the iliac crest.

Flowchart 2.1: Ilium

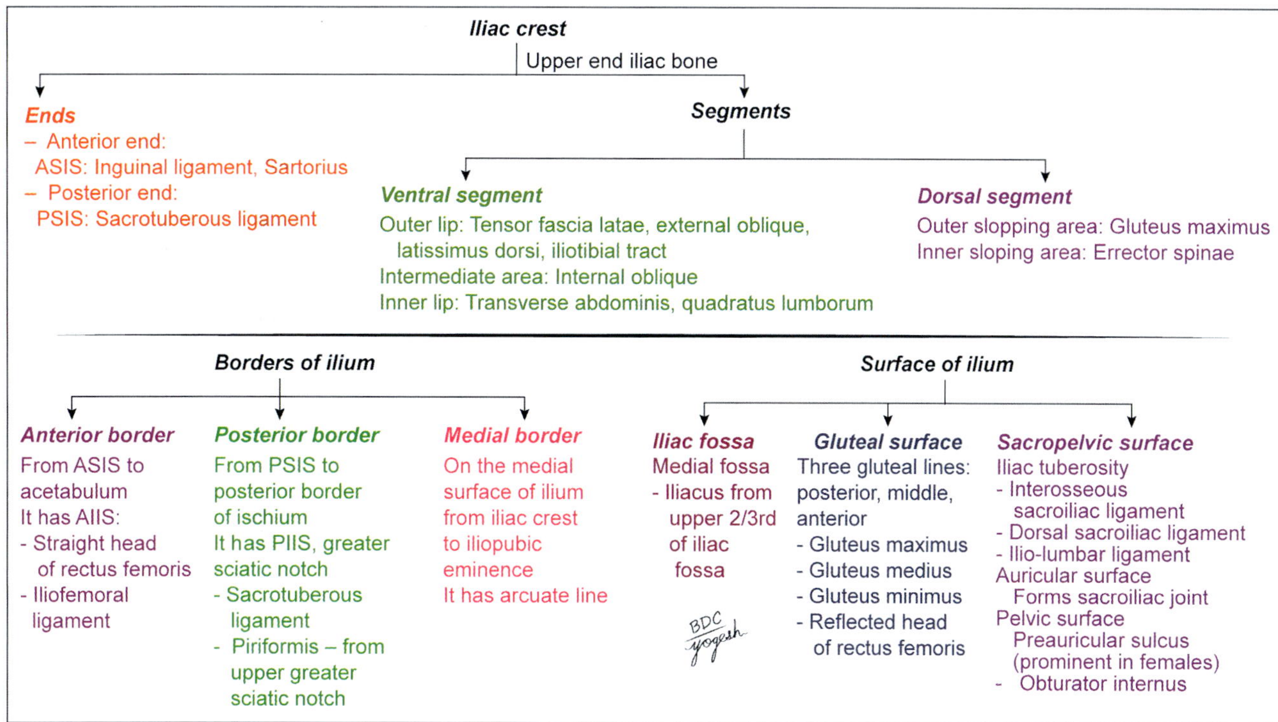

It is divided into four areas by three gluteal lines (Fig. 2.1).

1. ***Posterior gluteal line***: It is the shortest, begins 5 cm in front of the posterior superior iliac spine and runs downwards to end at upper part of greater sciatic notch.
2. ***Anterior gluteal line***: It is the longest, begins about 4 cm behind the anterior superior iliac spine, runs backwards and then downwards to end at the middle of the upper border of the greater sciatic notch.
3. ***Inferior gluteal line***: It is the most ill-defined, begins a little above and behind the anterior inferior iliac spine, and runs backwards and downwards to end near the apex of the greater sciatic notch.

Iliac Fossa

Iliac fossa is the large concave area on the inner surface of the ilium, situated in front of its medial border. It forms the lateral wall of the ***false pelvis***.

Sacropelvic Surface

Sacropelvic surface is the uneven area on the inner surface of the ilium, situated behind its medial border. It is subdivided into three parts—the iliac tuberosity, the auricular surface and the pelvic surface.

1. ***Iliac tuberosity***: It is the upper, large, roughened area, lying just below the dorsal segment of the iliac crest. It is raised in the middle and depressed both above and below (Fig. 2.2).
2. ***Auricular surface***: It is articular but pitted. It lies anteroinferior to the iliac tuberosity. It articulates with the sacrum to form the *sacroiliac joint*.
3. ***Pelvic surface***: It is smooth and lies anteroinferior to the auricular surface. It forms a part of the lateral wall of the true pelvis. Along the upper border of the greater sciatic notch, this surface is marked by the ***preauricular sulcus***. This sulcus is deeper in females than in males.

Attachments (Figs 2.3 and 2.5)

1. ***Anterior superior iliac spine***: It gives attachment to the lateral end of the inguinal ligament. It also gives origin to the sartorius muscle; the origin extends onto the upper half of the notch below the spine.
2. The upper half of the ***anterior inferior iliac spine*** gives origin to the straight head of the rectus femoris. The rough lower part of this spine gives attachment to the iliofemoral ligament.
3. ***Posterior border of the ilium***: It provides:
   a. Attachment to upper fibres of the sacrotuberous ligament above the greater sciatic notch.
   b. Origin to few fibres of the piriformis from upper margin of the greater sciatic notch.
4. ***Iliac crest*** (Fig. 2.5)
   The *outer lip of the ventral segment of iliac crest* provides:
   a. Attachment to the fascia lata in its whole extent.
   b. Origin to the tensor fasciae latae in front of the tubercle.
   c. Insertion to the external oblique muscle in its anterior 2/3rd.
   d. Origin to latissimus dorsi just behind the highest point of the crest. Tubercle of crest gives attachment to the iliotibial tract.

   The *intermediate area of the iliac crest* gives origin to the internal oblique muscle in its anterior 2/3rd.

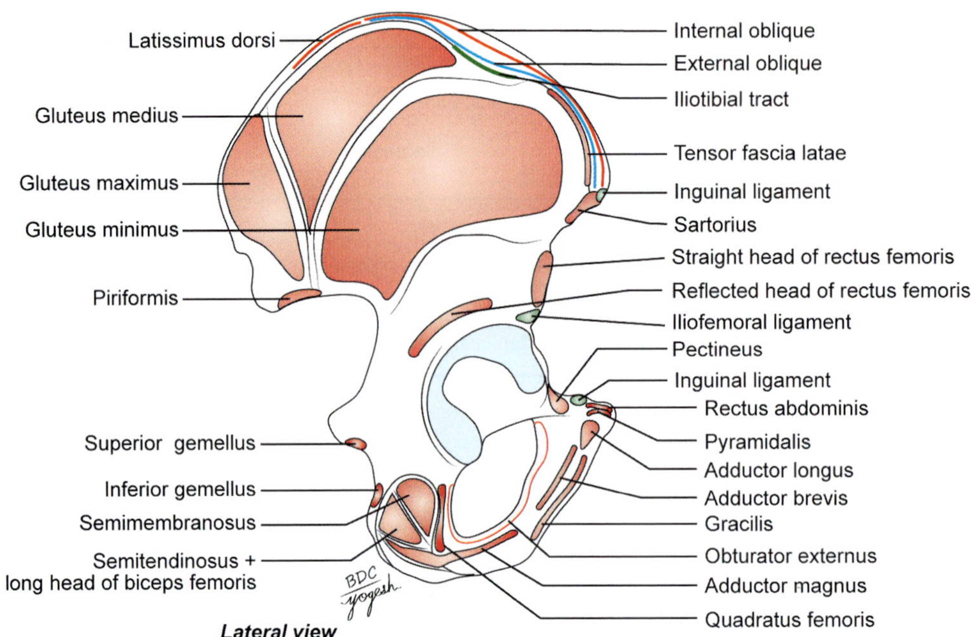

Fig. 2.3: Attachments on the outer surface of the right hip bone

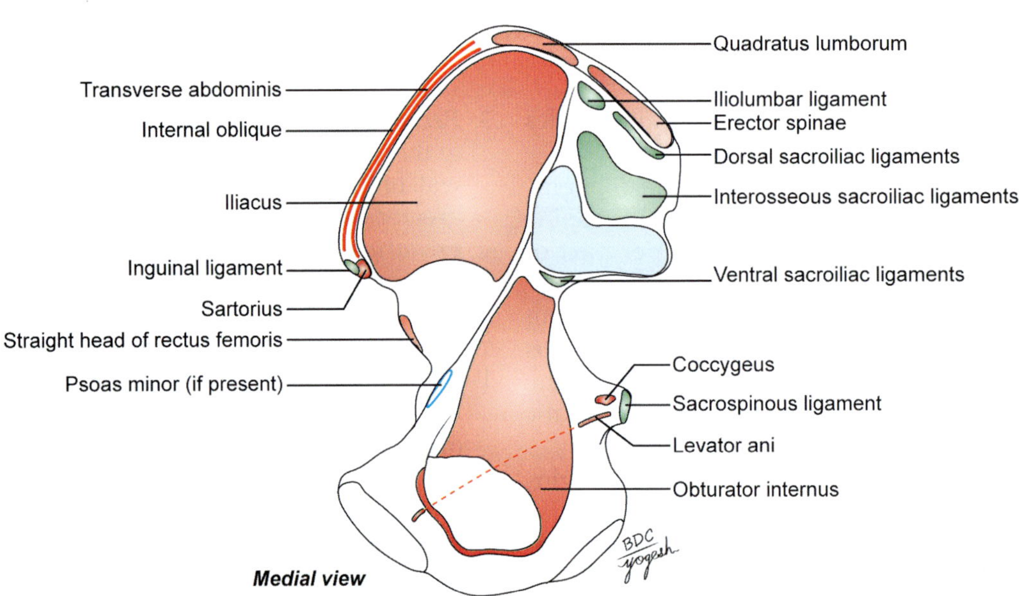

Fig. 2.4: Attachments on the inner surface of the right hip bone

The *inner lip of the iliac crest* provides:

a. Origin to the transversus abdominis in its anterior 2/3rd.

b. Attachment to the fascia transversalis and to the fascia iliaca in its anterior two-thirds, deep to the attachment of the transversus abdominis.

c. Origin to the quadratus lumborum in its posterior 1/3rd.

d. Attachment to the thoracolumbar fascia around the attachment of the quadratus lumborum.

The attachments on the *dorsal segment of the iliac crest* are as follows:

a. The lateral slope gives origin to the gluteus maximus.

b. The medial slope gives origin to the *erector spinae*.

c. The interosseous and dorsal sacroiliac ligaments are attached to the medial margin deep to the attachment of the erector spinae.

5. ***Gluteal surface***:

a. The area behind the posterior gluteal line gives origin to upper fibres of the gluteus maximus.

b. The gluteus medius arises from the area between the anterior and posterior gluteal lines.

c. The gluteus minimus arises from the area between the anterior and inferior gluteal lines.

d. Below the inferior gluteal line, the reflected head of the rectus femoris arises from the groove above the acetabulum.

e. The capsular ligament of the hip joint is attached along the margin of acetabulum.

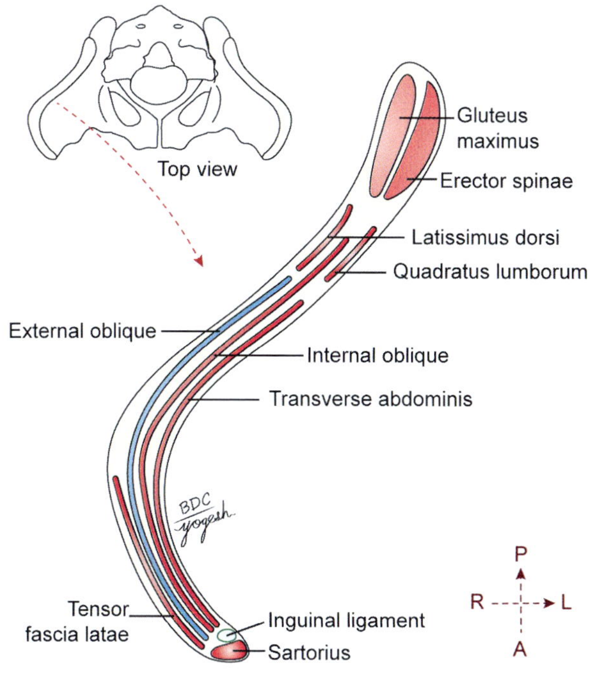

Fig. 2.5: Attachments on the right iliac crest (as seen from above)

6. *Iliac fossa:* It gives origin to the iliacus from its upper 2/3rd). The lower grooved part of the fossa is covered by the iliac bursa.
7. *Iliac tuberosity:* It provides attachment to:
   a. The interosseous sacroiliac ligament in its greater part.
   b. The dorsal sacroiliac ligament posteriorly.
   c. The iliolumbar ligament superiorly.
8. The convex margin of the *auricular surface* gives attachment to ventral sacroiliac ligament.
9. *Pelvic surface*:
   a. The preauricular sulcus provides attachment to the lower fibres of the ventral sacroiliac ligament.
   b. The part of the pelvic surface lateral to the preauricular sulcus gives origin to a few fibres of the piriformis.
   c. The rest of the pelvic surface gives origin to the upper half of the obturator internus.

PUBIS

Pubis forms the anteroinferior part of the hip bone and the anterior on 1/5th of the acetabulum, forms the anterior boundary of the obturator foramen. It has:

a. A *body* anteriorly.
b. A *superior ramus* superolaterally.
c. An *inferior ramus* inferolaterally (Plates 2.1–2.3, Figs 2.1 and 2.2, Flowchart 2.2).

Features of Pubis

Body

Body of pubis is flattened from before backwards and has:

1. A superior border called the *pubic crest*.
2. *A pubic tubercle* at the lateral end of the pubic crest.
3. Three surfaces, viz. anterior, posterior and medial.

The ***pubic tubercle*** is the lateral end of the pubic crest, forming an important landmark.

The ***anterior surface*** is directed downwards, forwards and slightly laterally. It is rough superomedially and smooth elsewhere.

The ***posterior*** or ***pelvic surface*** is smooth. It is directed upwards and backwards. It forms the anterior wall of the true pelvis and is related to the urinary bladder.

The ***medial*** or ***symphyseal surface*** articulates with the opposite pubis to form the pubic symphysis.

Superior Ramus

Superior ramus extends from the body of the pubis to the acetabulum, above the obturator foramen. It has three borders and three surfaces.

1. Borders of superior ramus
   a. The *superior border* is called the ***pectineal line*** or ***pecten pubis***. It is a sharp crest extending from just behind the pubic tubercle to the posterior part of the iliopubic eminence. With the pubic crest it forms the pubic part of the arcuate line (Plate 2.3).
   b. The *anterior border* is called the ***obturator crest***. The border is a rounded ridge, extending from the pubic tubercle to the acetabular notch.
   c. The *inferior border* is sharp and forms the upper margin of the obturator foramen.

Flowchart 2.2: Pubis: Body and superior ramus

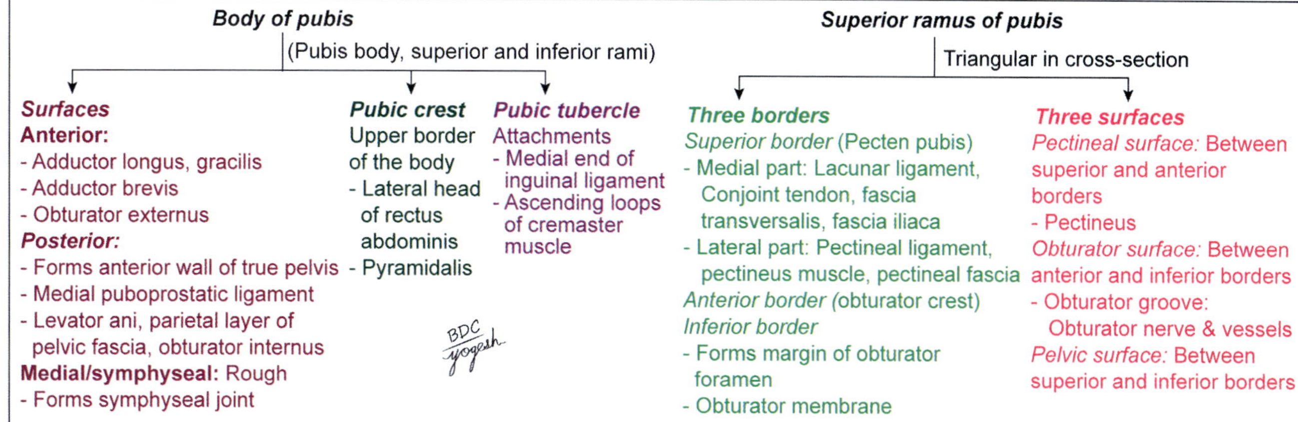

Plate 2.3: Features of pubis: Medial and lateral views

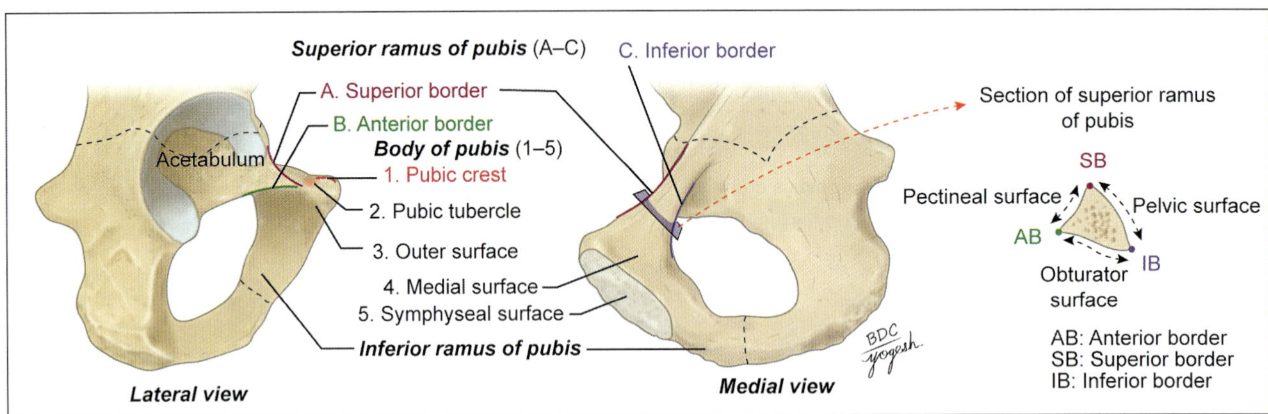

2. Surfaces of superior ramus (Plate 2.3)
   a. The ***pectineal surface*** is a triangular area between the anterior and superior borders, extending from the pubic tubercle to the iliopubic eminence.
   b. The ***pelvic surface*** lies between the superior and inferior borders. It is smooth and is continuous with the pelvic surface of the body of the pubis.
   c. The ***obturator surface*** lies between the anterior and inferior borders. It presents the obturator groove.

Inferior Ramus

Inferior ramus extends from the body of the pubis to the ramus of the ischium, medial to the obturator foramen. It unites with the ramus of the ischium to form the ***conjoined ischiopubic rami***. For convenience of description, the conjoined rami will be considered together at the end.

Attachments and Relations (Figs 2.3 and 2.4)

1. The ***pubic tubercle*** provides attachment to the medial end of the inguinal ligament and to ascending loops of the cremaster muscle.
   In males, the tubercle is crossed by the spermatic cord.
2. The medial part of the ***pubic crest*** is crossed by the medial head of the rectus abdominis. The lateral part of the crest gives origin to the lateral head of the rectus abdominis and to the pyramidalis.
3. The ***anterior surface*** of the body of the pubis provides:
   a. Attachment to the anterior pubic ligament medially.
   b. Origin to the adductor longus in the angle between the crest and the symphysis.
   c. Origin to the gracilis, from the margin of symphysis, and from the inferior ramus.
   d. Origin to the adductor brevis lateral to the origin of the gracilis.
   e. Origin to the obturator externus near the margin of the obturator foramen.
4. The ***posterior surface*** of the body of the pubis provides:
   a. Origin to the *levator ani* from its middle part.
   b. Origin to the obturator internus laterally.
   c. Attachment to the puboprostatic/pubovesical ligaments medial to the attachment of the levator ani.
5. The *medial surface* forms pubic symphysis.
6. The ***pectineal line*** or superior border of superior ramus provides attachment to:
   a. The conjoint tendon at the medial end.
   b. The lacunar ligament at the medial end, in front of the attachment of the conjoint tendon.
   c. The pectineal ligament of Cooper along the whole length of the line lateral to the attachment of the lacunar ligament.
   d. The pectineus muscle that arises from the whole length of the line.
   e. The fascia covering the pectineus.
   f. The psoas minor, which is inserted here when present.
7. The upper part of the ***pectineal surface*** gives origin to the pectineus.
8. The ***pelvic surface*** is crossed by round ligament of the uterus in females and by the ductus deferens in males.
9. The *obturator groove* on obturator surface transmits the obturator vessels and nerve.

Note: Attachments of conjoined ischiopubic rami are given separately at the end of this section.

ISCHIUM

The ischium forms the posteroinferior part of the hip bone and the adjoining 2/5th of the acetabulum. It forms the posterior boundary of the obturator foramen. The ischium has a body and a ramus (Plates 2.4 and Flowchart 2.3).

Features of Ischium

Body

This is a thick and massive mass of bone that lies below and behind the acetabulum. It has:

Two ends: Upper and lower;
Three borders: Anterior, posterior and lateral;
Three surfaces: Femoral, dorsal and pelvic.

Plate 2.4: Features of body of ischium: Medial and lateral views

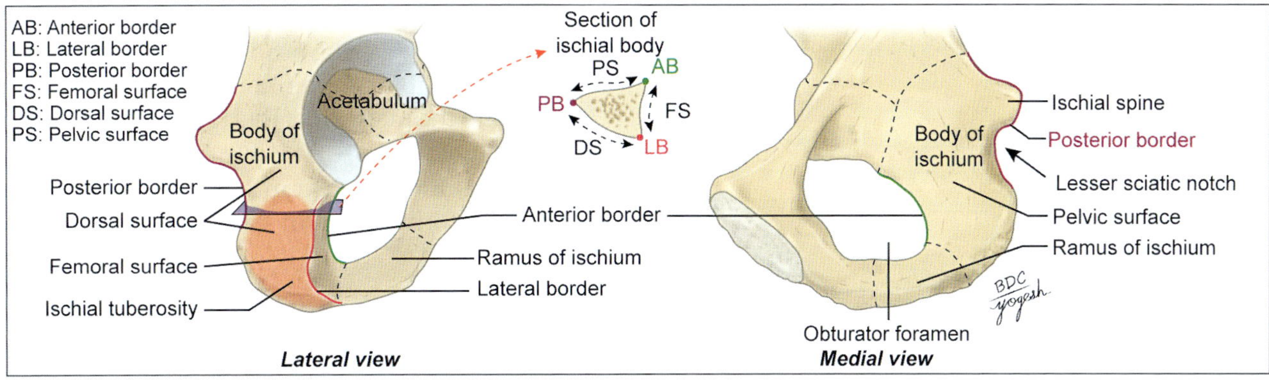

Flowchart 2.3: Ischium: Body and ischial tuberosity

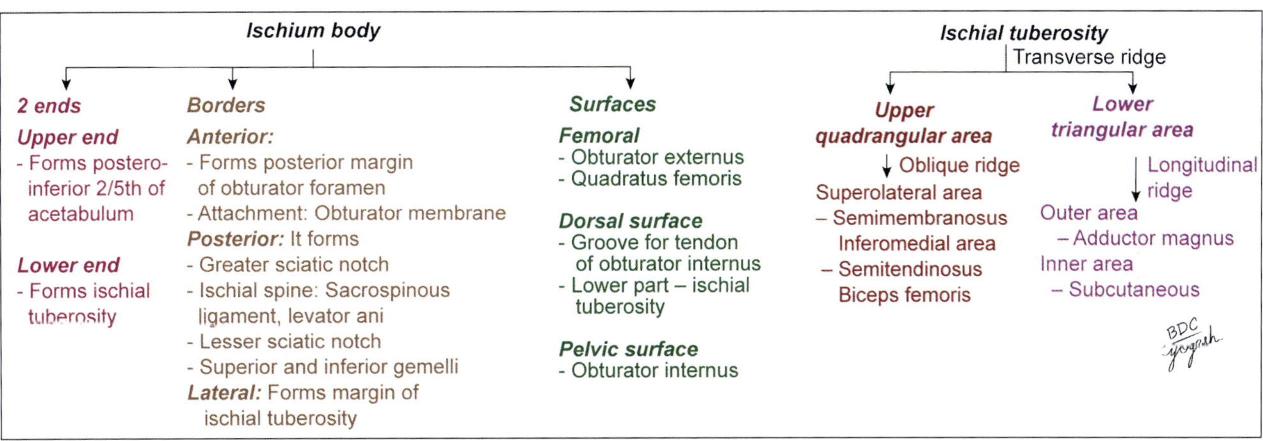

Ends

1. ***Upper end***: It forms the posteroinferior 2/5th of the acetabulum. The ischium, ilium and pubis fuse with each other in the acetabulum.
2. ***Lower end***: It forms the ***ischial tuberosity***. It gives off the ramus of the ischium which forms an acute angle with the body.

Borders

1. ***Anterior border*** forms the posterior margin of the obturator foramen.
2. ***Posterior border*** is continuous above with the posterior border of the ilium. Below, it ends at the upper end of the ischial tuberosity. It also forms part of the lower border of the *greater sciatic notch*. Below the notch, the posterior margin shows a projection called the ***ischial spine***. Below the spine, the posterior border shows a concavity, called the ***lesser sciatic notch***.
3. ***Lateral border*** forms the lateral margin of the ischial tuberosity, except at the upper end where it is rounded.

Surfaces

1. ***Femoral surface*** lies between the anterior and lateral borders (Plate 2.4).
2. ***Dorsal surface*** is continuous above with the gluteal surface of the ilium. From above downwards, it presents a convex surface adjoining the acetabulum, a wide shallow groove and the upper part of the ischial tuberosity.

   The ***ischial tuberosity*** is divided by a *transverse ridge* into an upper and a lower area. The upper area is subdivided by an *oblique ridge* into a superolateral area and an inferomedial area. The lower area is subdivided by a *longitudinal ridge* into outer and inner area (Fig. 2.6).
3. ***Pelvic surface*** is smooth and forms part of the lateral wall of the true pelvis.

Attachments and Relations (Figs 2.3, 2.4 and 2.6)

1. ***Ischial spine*** provides:
   a. Attachment to the sacrospinous ligament along its margins.
   b. Origin for the posterior fibres of the levator ani from its pelvic surface. Its dorsal surface is crossed by pudendal nerve, the internal pudendal vessels and by the nerve to the obturator internus.
2. ***Lesser sciatic notch*** is occupied by the tendon of the obturator internus. There is a bursa deep to the tendon. The notch is lined by hyaline cartilage. The upper and lower margins of the notch give origin to the superior and inferior gemelli, respectively. Gemellus is derived from Gemini, which means 'twin'. Gemini is a sun sign.

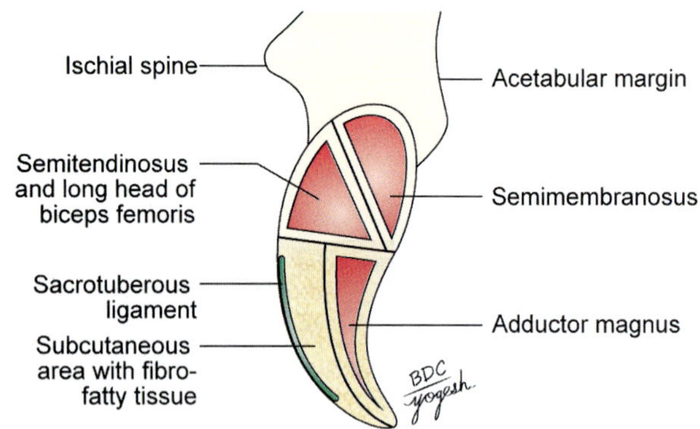

Fig 2.6: Posterior view of the right ischial tuberosity and its attachments

3. ***Femoral surface*** of the ischium gives origin to:
   a. The obturator externus along the margin of the obturator foramen.
   b. The quadratus femoris along the lateral border of the upper part of the ischial tuberosity.
4. ***Dorsal surface*** of the ischium has the following relationships. The upper convex area is related to the piriformis, the sciatic nerve and the nerve to the quadratus femoris.
5. ***Ischial tuberosity*** (Fig. 2.6)
   a. The superolateral area gives origin to the semimembranosus.
   b. The inferomedial area to the semitendinosus and the long head of the biceps femoris.
   c. The outer lower area to the adductor magnus.
   d. The inner lower area is covered with fibrofatty tissue and a bursa which supports body weight in the sitting position. While standing, this area is covered by gluteus maximus muscle.
   e. The sharp medial margin of the tuberosity gives attachment to the sacrotuberous ligament.
   f. The lateral border of the ischial tuberosity provides attachment to the ischiofemoral ligament, just below the acetabulum.
6. The greater part of the ***pelvic surface*** of the ischium gives origin to the obturator internus. So this muscle arises from all 3 components of hip bone. The lower end of this surface forms part of the lateral wall of the ischioanal fossa (Fig. 2.4).

ACETABULUM

1. Acetabulum is a deep cup-shaped hemispherical cavity on the lateral aspect of the hip bone, about its centre (Plate 2.2, Fig. 2.1).
2. It is directed laterally, downwards and forwards.
3. The margin of the acetabulum is deficient inferiorly, this deficiency is called the ***acetabular notch*** (Fig. 2.3). It is bridged by the transverse ligament.
4. The non-articular roughened floor is called the ***acetabular fossa***. It contains a mass of fat which is lined by synovial membrane.
5. A horseshoe-shaped articular surface or lunate surface is seen on the anterior, superior and posterior parts of the acetabulum. It is lined with hyaline cartilage and articulates with the head of the femur to form the *hip joint*. The fibrocartilaginous ***acetabular labrum*** is attached to the margins of the acetabulum; it deepens the acetabular cavity.
6. Ilium and ischium both form 2/5th each of acetabulum. Pubis only forms 1/5th of acetabulum.

OBTURATOR FORAMEN

1. This is a large gap in hip bone, lying anteroinferior to acetabulum, between pubis and ischium.
2. It is large and oval in males, and small and triangular in females (Fig. 2.2).
3. It is closed by the obturator membrane which is attached to its margins, except at the ***obturator groove*** where the obturator vessels and nerve pass out of the pelvis.

CONJOINED ISCHIOPUBIC RAMUS

The inferior ramus of the pubis unites with the ramus of the ischium on the medial side of the obturator foramen. The site of union may be marked by a localized thickening (Flowchart 2.4, Plate 2.5).

The conjoined rami have:

Two borders: Upper and lower

Two surface: Inner and outer.

Features of Conjoint Ramus

Borders

1. The *upper border* forms part of the margin of the obturator foramen.
2. The *lower border* forms the pubic arch along with the corresponding border of the bone of the opposite side.

Flowchart 2.4: Conjoint ischiopubic ramus

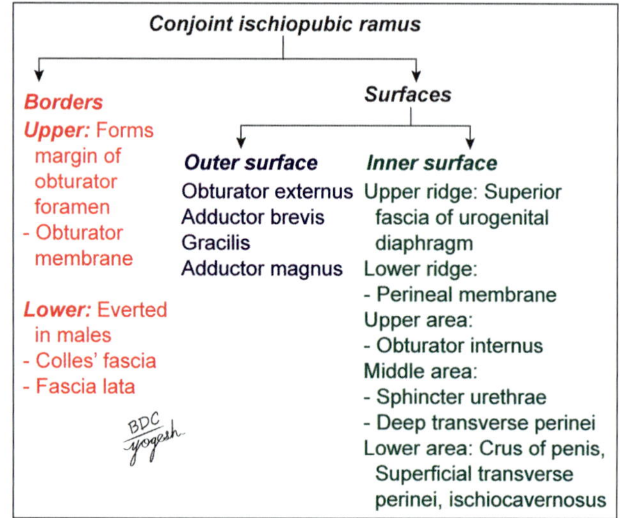

Plate 2.5: Conjoint ischiopubic ramus

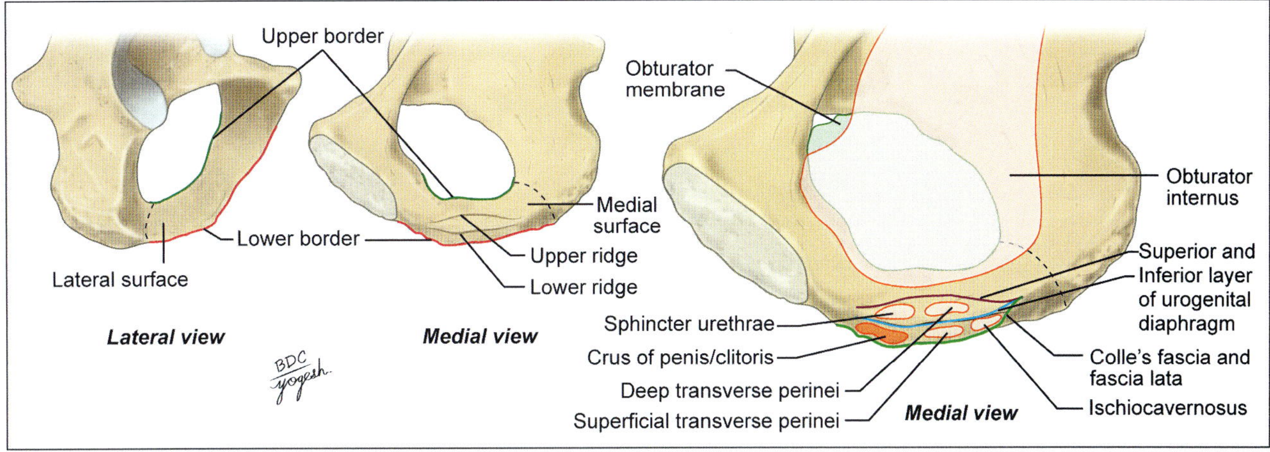

Surfaces

1. The *inner surface* is convex and smooth. It is divided into three areas, upper, middle and lower, by two ridges.
2. The *outer surface* is rough for the attachment of muscles.

Attachments and Relations

1. The upper border gives attachment to the obturator membrane.
2. The lower border provides attachment to the fascia lata and to the membranous layer of superficial fascia or Colles' fascia of the perineum.
3. The muscles taking origin from the outer surface are:
   a. The obturator externus, near the obturator margin of both rami.
   b. The adductor brevis, chiefly from the pubic ramus.
   c. The gracilis, chiefly from the pubic ramus.
   d. The adductor magnus, chiefly from the ischial ramus.
4. The attachments on the inner surface are as follows:
   a. The perineal membrane is attached to the lower ridge.
   b. The upper area gives origin to the obturator internus.
   c. The middle area gives origin to the deep transversus perinei and is related to the dorsal nerve of the penis clitoris and to the internal pudendal vessels.
   d. The lower area provides attachment to crus penis/clitoris and gives origin to the ischiocavernosus and to superficial transversus perinei.

OSSIFICATION

- The hip bone ossifies in cartilage from three primary centres and five secondary centres (Fig. 2.7).
- Primary centres are as follows:
  - 1 for ilium – appears by the 2nd month of intra-uterine life (IUL)
  - 1 for ischium – appears by the 4th month of IUL
  - 1 for pubis – appears by the 4th month of IUL
- Fusion of primary centres results in a Y-shaped triradiate cartilage in the floor of acetabulum. Ischium and pubis fuse to form conjoined ramus from 7th to 8th year of age.
- Secondary centres appear at puberty as follows:
  - 1 for the iliac crest
  - 2 for the Y-shaped cartilage of the acetabulum
  - 1 for the ischial tuberosity.
- Ossification in the acetabulum is complete at 16th–17th year, and the rest of the bone is ossified by 20th–25th year.
- The anterior superior iliac spine, pubic tubercle and crest, and the symphyseal surface may have separate secondary centres of ossification.

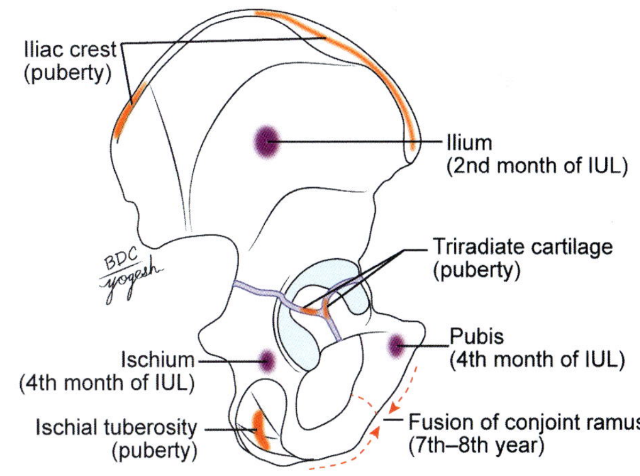

Fig. 2.7: Ossification of the hip bone

CLINICAL ANATOMY

- Iliac crest is used for taking bone marrow biopsy in cases of anaemia or leukaemia.
- Weaver's bottom—persons sitting for a long period of time may get inflammation of their ischial tuberosity bursa.
- The differences between male and female hip bone are listed in Table 2.1.

TABLE 2.1: Differences between the male and female hip bones

Features	*Male hip bone*	*Female hip bone*
Bony features	Heavier bone with prominent muscular impressions	Lighter bone with less prominent muscular impressions
Greater sciatic notch	Narrower	Wider
Obturator foramen	Large, oval	Small, triangular
Ischial spine	Inverted	Not inverted
Preauricular sulcus	Less marked	Very prominent and well-marked
Ischiopubic ramus	Everted and thick	Not everted and thin
Acetabulum	Larger (diameter >5 cm)	Smaller (diameter <5 cm)
Iliac fossa	Deeper	Shallower

FEMUR

The femur (Latin *thigh*) or thigh bone is the longest and the strongest bone of the body. Like any other typical bone (Fig. 2.8, Plate 2.6, Flowchart 2.5), femur has an upper rounded end, a lower bicondylar end and a long shaft which is convex forwards.

Side Determination and Anatomical Position

Hold the bone vertically in such a way that:
- Spherical head looks upward, medially and slightly forward.
- The convex anterior surface of body looks forward.
- The long axis of the body is directed downward medially so that both condyles lie in the same horizontal plane.

Note: The head faces to the side opposite to the bone. For example, the head of right femur faces left. Balance the neck of the femur on index finger to hold the femur for holding it in the anatomical position.

Features of Femur

Upper End

The upper end of the femur includes (Plate 2.7):
1. Head
2. Neck
3. Two trochanters (Greek *runner*): Greater trochanter, lesser trochanter.

Head

1. The head forms more than half a sphere and is directed medially, upwards and slightly forwards.
2. It articulates with the acetabulum to form the ***hip joint***.
3. A roughened pit is situated just below and behind the centre of the head. This pit is called the ***fovea***.

Neck

1. It connects the head with the shaft and is about 5 cm long.
2. The neck has two borders and two surfaces (Plate 2.7).
   a. The ***upper border***, concave and horizontal, meets the shaft at the greater trochanter.

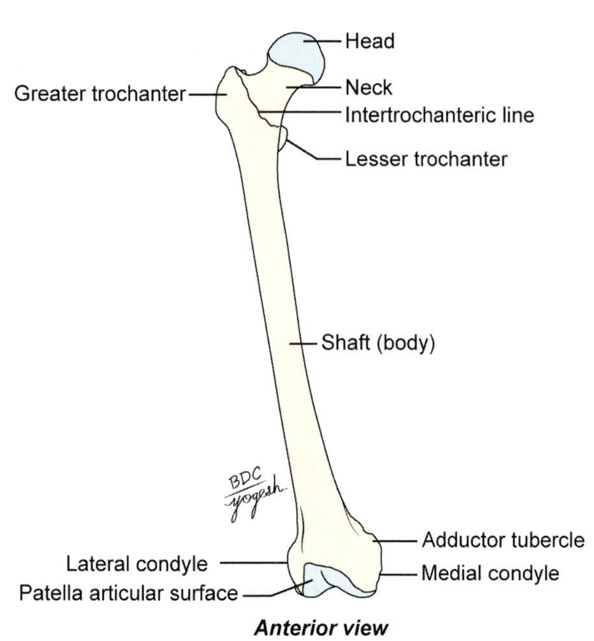

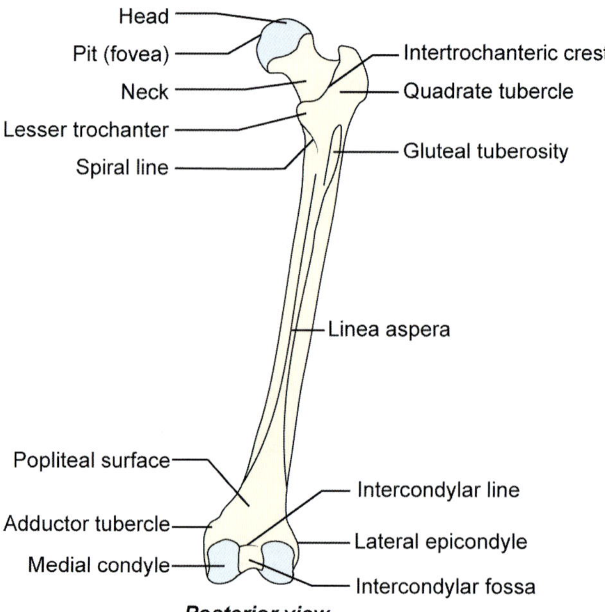

Fig. 2.8: Right femur

Plate 2.6: Femur

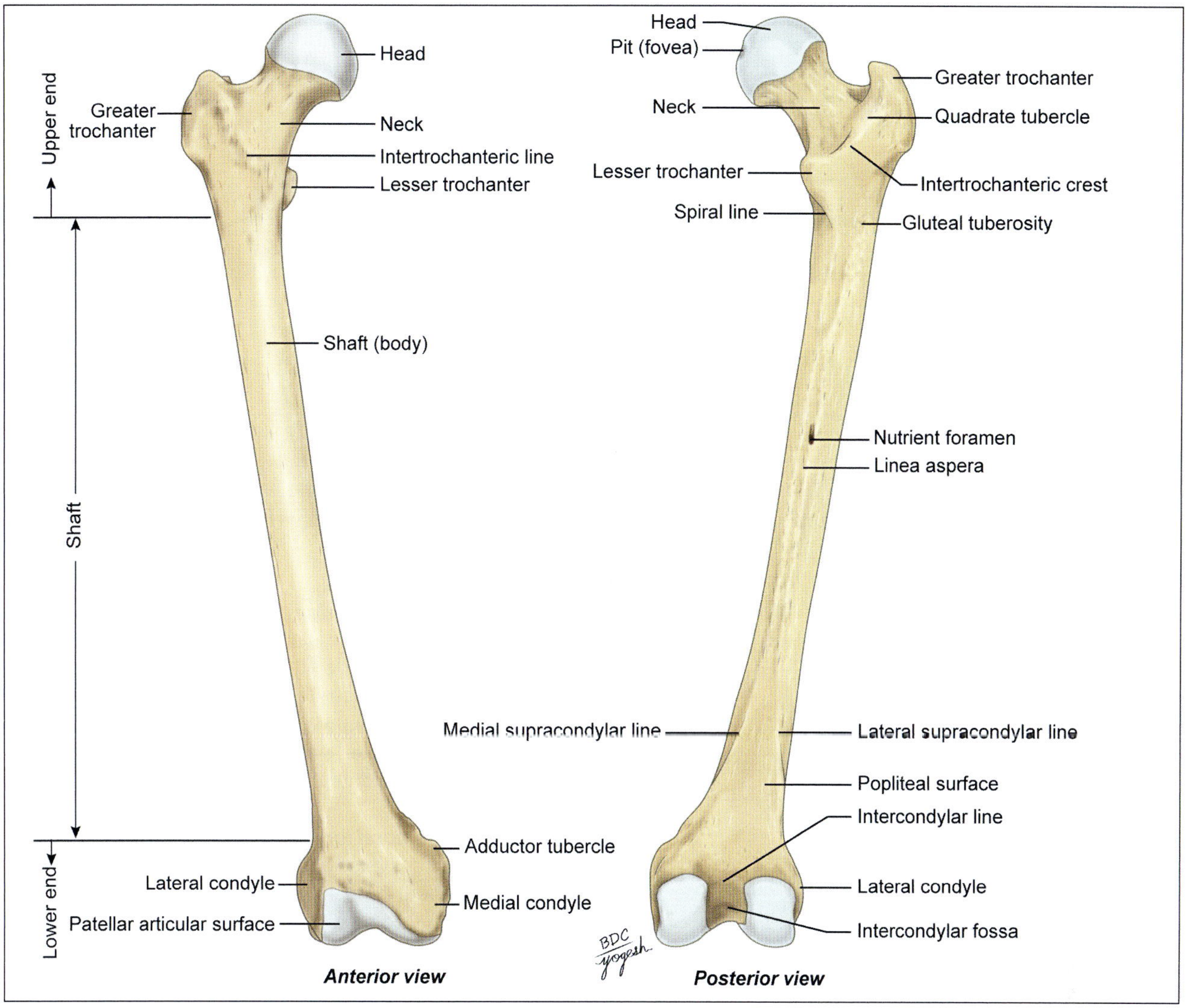

Upper end
Shaft
Lower end
Head
Greater trochanter
Neck
Intertrochanteric line
Lesser trochanter
Shaft (body)
Adductor tubercle
Lateral condyle
Medial condyle
Patellar articular surface
Anterior view

Head
Pit (fovea)
Greater trochanter
Quadrate tubercle
Neck
Lesser trochanter
Intertrochanteric crest
Spiral line
Gluteal tuberosity
Nutrient foramen
Linea aspera
Medial supracondylar line
Lateral supracondylar line
Popliteal surface
Intercondylar line
Lateral condyle
Intercondylar fossa
Posterior view

Flowchart 2.5: Femur

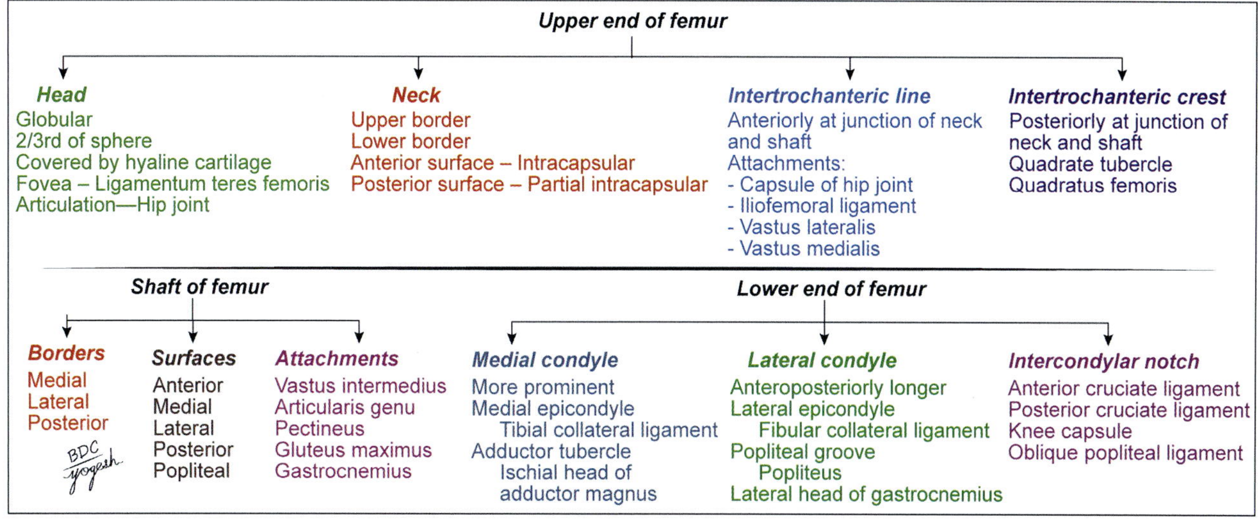

b. The ***lower border***, straight and oblique, meets the shaft near the lesser trochanter.

c. The ***anterior surface*** is flat. It meets the shaft at the intertrochanteric line. It is entirely intracapsular.

The articular cartilage of the head may extend to this surface.

d. The ***posterior surface*** is convex from above downwards and concave from side to side. It

Plate 2.7: Features of upper end of femur

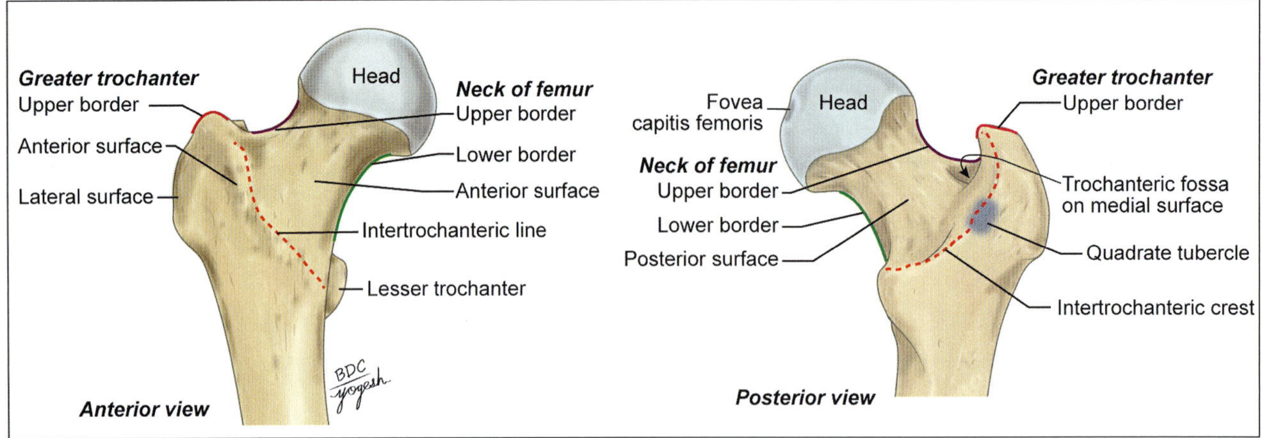

meets the shaft at the ***intertrochanteric crest***. Only a little more than its medial half is intracapsular. The posterior surface is crossed by a horizontal groove for the tendon of the obturator externus to be inserted into the trochanteric fossa.

3. *Blood supply:* The intracapsular part of the neck is supplied by the ***retinacular arteries*** derived chiefly from the ***trochanteric anastomoses***. The vessels produce longitudinal grooves and foramina directed towards the head, mainly on the anterior and posterosuperior surfaces. The extracapsular part of the neck is supplied by the *ascending branch of the medial circumflex femoral artery* (Fig. 2.9).

Fig. 2.9: Blood supply of head of femur

Note:
- The neck makes an angle with the shaft. The ***neck–shaft angle (angle of inclination)*** is about 127° in adults. It is less in females due to their wider pelvis (Fig. 2.10). The angle facilitates movements of the hip joint. It is strengthened by a thickening of bone called the ***calcar femorale*** present along its concavity.
- ***Trochanter-shaft angle*** is about 8° in adults. It is an important radiological parameter which provides the idea of direction of medullary canal and its alignment with the greater trochanter (Fig. 2.10).
- The ***angle of femoral torsion*** or ***angle of anteversion*** is formed between the transverse axes of the upper and lower ends of the femur. It is about 10 to 15° (Fig. 2.10).

Greater Trochanter

1. This is a large quadrangular prominence located at the upper part of the junction of neck with the shaft.
2. The greater trochanter has an upper border with an apex and three surfaces, anterior, medial and lateral.
   a. The ***apex*** is the inturned posterior part of the upper border.
   b. The ***anterior surface*** is rough in its lateral part.
   c. The ***medial surface*** presents a rough impression above and a deep ***trochanteric fossa*** below.
   d. The ***lateral surface*** is crossed by an oblique ridge directed downwards and forwards.

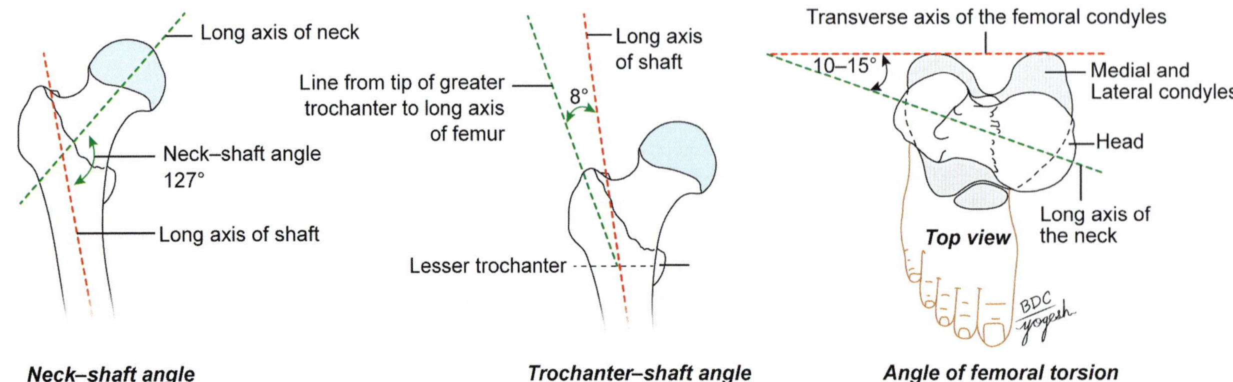

Fig. 2.10: Neck–shaft angle, trochanter–shaft angle and angle of femoral torsion

Lesser Trochanter

It is a conical eminence directed medially and backwards from the junction of the posteroinferior part of the neck with the shaft.

Intertrochanteric Line

It marks the junction of the anterior surface of the neck with the shaft of the femur. It is a prominent roughened ridge which begins above, at the anterosuperior angle of the greater trochanter as a tubercle, and is continuous below with the ***spiral line*** in front of the lesser trochanter. The spiral line winds around the shaft below the lesser trochanter to reach the posterior surface of the shaft.

Intertrochanteric Crest

It marks the junction of the posterior surface of the neck with the shaft of the femur. It is a smooth-rounded ridge. It extends from the tip of greater trochanter to the lesser trochanter posteriorly. The rounded elevation, a little above its middle, is called the ***quadrate tubercle***.

Shaft

The shaft is more or less cylindrical. It is the narrowest in the middle and is more expanded inferiorly than superiorly. It is convex forwards and is directed obliquely downwards and medially (Fig. 2.8, Plate 2.8).

Middle 1/3rd of shaft: In the *middle 1/3rd*, the shaft has three borders—medial, lateral and posterior, and three surfaces—anterior, medial and lateral.

The medial and lateral borders are rounded and ill-defined, but the posterior border is in the form of a broad roughened ridge, called the ***linea aspera*** (Latin *rough line*). The linea aspera has distinct medial and lateral lips.

Upper 1/3rd of the shaft: In the *upper 1/3rd of the shaft*, the two lips of the linea aspera diverge to enclose an additional posterior surface. Thus, this part has:

- Four borders—medial, lateral, spiral line and the lateral lip of the gluteal tuberosity
- Four surfaces—anterior, medial, lateral and posterior. The gluteal tuberosity is a broad roughened ridge on the lateral part of the posterior surface.

Lower 1/3rd of shaft: In the *lower 1/3rd of the shaft* also, the two lips of the linea aspera diverge as ***supracondylar lines*** to enclose an additional, ***popliteal surface*** (Fig. 2.8). Thus, this part of the shaft has:

- Four borders—medial, lateral, medial supracondylar line and lateral supracondylar line.
- Four surfaces—anterior, medial, lateral and popliteal.
- The medial border and medial supracondylar line meet inferiorly to obliterate the medial surface. Similarly, the lateral border and lateral supracondylar line also meet inferiorly to obliterate the lateral surface.

Note: ***Nutrient artery to the femur*** is derived from the *second perforating artery*, branch of profunda femoris artery. The nutrient foramen is located on the medial side of the linea aspera and is directed upwards (Plate 2.6).

Plate 2.8: Features of shaft of femur

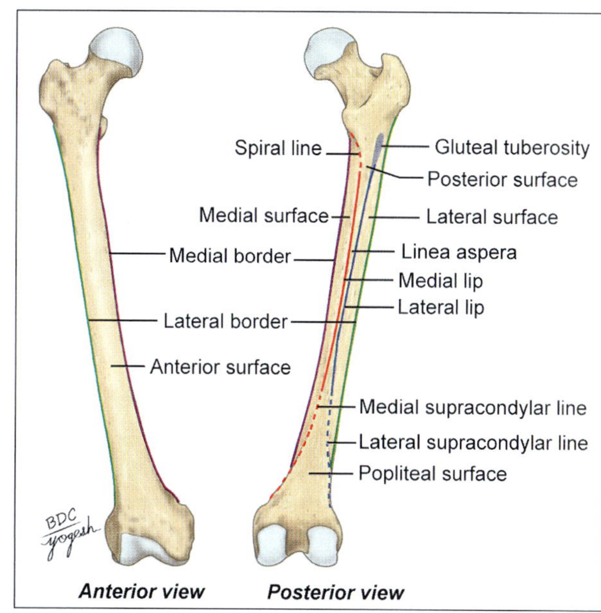

Lower End

The lower end of the femur is widely expanded to form two large condyles—one medial and one lateral. These form articular surface for the knee joint. Anteriorly, the two condyles are united and are in line with the front of the shaft. Posteriorly, they are separated by a deep gap, termed the ***intercondylar fossa*** or intercondylar notch, and project backwards much beyond the plane of the popliteal surface (Plate 2.9).

Articular Surface

The lower end of the femur has V-shaped articular surface. The articular surface is covered by hyaline cartilage. The articular surface is divided into two parts: Patellar and tibial parts. Patellar articular surface articulates with the patella, and tibial articular surface articulates with corresponding tibial condyles and menisci of knee joint.

1. ***Patellar articular surface:*** It covers the anterior surface of both condyles. It extends more on the lateral condyle than medial condyle. It is separated from tibial articular surface by two faint grooves.
2. ***Tibial articular surface:*** It covers the inferior and posterior surfaces of both condyles. Tibial articular surfaces of both the condyles are separated from each other by intercondylar notch.

Lateral Condyle

The lateral condyle is flat laterally and is more in line with the shaft. It, therefore, takes greater part in the transmission of body weight to the tibia. Though it is less prominent than the medial condyle, it is stouter and stronger. The lateral aspect presents the following.

1. A prominence called the ***lateral epicondyle***.
2. The ***popliteal groove*** that lies just below the epicondyle. It has a deeper anterior part and a shallower posterior part.
3. A *muscular impression* posterosuperior to the epicondyle.

Plate 2.9: Features of lower end of femur

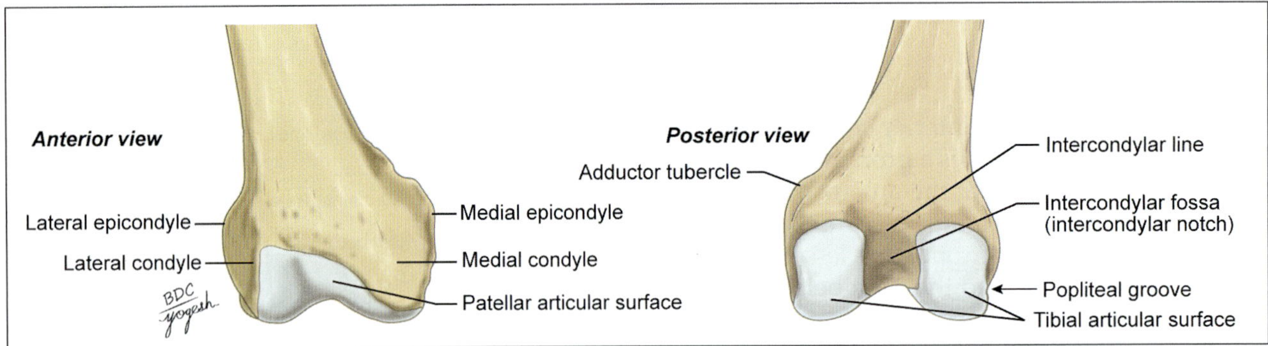

Medial Condyle

This condyle is convex medially. The most prominent point on it is called the ***medial epicondyle***.

Posterosuperior to the epicondyle, there is a projection, the ***adductor tubercle***. This tubercle is an important landmark. The epiphyseal line for the lower end of the femur passes through it.

Intercondylar Fossa or Intercondylar Notch

This notch separates the lower and posterior parts of the two condyles. It is limited anteriorly by the patellar articular surface, and posteriorly by the intercondylar line which separates the notch from the popliteal surface.

Attachments on the Femur

Upper End of Femur (Figs 2.11 and 2.12)

1. The ***fovea*** on the head of the femur (Fig. 2.11) provides attachment to the ligament of the head of femur or round ligament, or ligamentum teres/femoris (Fig. 2.12).
2. ***Greater trochanter***
   a. The piriformis is inserted into the apex.
   b. The gluteus minimus is inserted into the rough lateral part of the anterior surface.
   c. The obturator internus and the two gemelli are inserted into the upper rough impression on medial surface.
   d. The obturator externus is inserted into the trochanteric fossa.
   e. The gluteus medius is inserted into the ridge on the lateral surface. The trochanteric bursa of the gluteus maximus lies behind the ridge.
3. ***Lesser trochanter***
   a. The psoas (Greek *loin*) major is inserted on the apex and medial part of the rough anterior surface.
   b. The iliacus is inserted on the anterior surface of the base of the trochanter and on the area below it.
   c. The smooth posterior surface of the lesser trochanter is covered by a bursa that lies deep to the upper horizontal fibres of the adductor magnus.
4. ***Intertrochanteric line*** provides:
   a. Attachment to the capsular ligament of the hip joint.
   b. Attachment to the upper band of the iliofemoral ligament in its upper part.
   c. Attachment to the lower band of iliofemoral ligament in its lower part.
   d. Origin to the highest fibres of the vastus lateralis from the upper end.
   e. Origin to the highest fibres of the vastus medialis from the lower end of the line.
5. ***Quadrate tubercle*** on intertrochanteric crest receives the insertion of the quadratus femoris.

Shaft of Femur (Figs 2.12 and 2.13)

1. The medial and popliteal surfaces are bare, except for a little extension of the origin of the medial head of the gastrocnemius to the medial part of popliteal surface.
2. The vastus intermedius arises from the upper three-fourths of the anterior and lateral surfaces.
3. The articularis genu arises just below the vastus intermedius.
4. The lower 5 cm of the anterior surface is related to *suprapatellar bursa*.
5. The vastus lateralis arises from the upper part of the intertrochanteric line, anterior and inferior aspects of the greater trochanter, the lateral margin of the gluteal tuberosity and the upper half of the lateral lip of the linea aspera.
6. The vastus medialis arises from the lower part of intertrochanteric line, the spiral line, medial lip of the linea aspera and the medial supracondylar line.
7. The deeper fibres of the lower half of the gluteus maximus (i.e. 1/4th) are inserted into the gluteal tuberosity.
8. The pectineus is inserted on a line extending from the lesser trochanter to the linea aspera.
9. The adductor longus is inserted along the medial lip of the linea aspera between the vastus medialis and the adductors brevis and magnus.
10. The adductor brevis is inserted below and behind pectineus and upper part of the adductor longus.
11. The adductor magnus is inserted into medial margin of the gluteal tuberosity, linea aspera, medial supracondylar line and adductor tubercle, leaving a gap/opening for the popliteal vessels. Insertion is behind adductor brevis.
12. The short head of the biceps femoris arises from lateral lip of the linea aspera upper two-thirds of

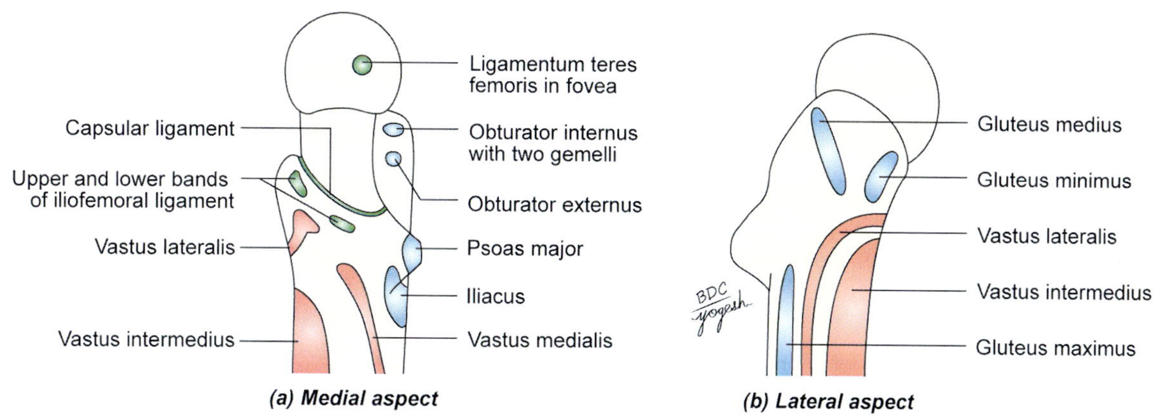

Figs 2.11a and b: Upper end of the right femur

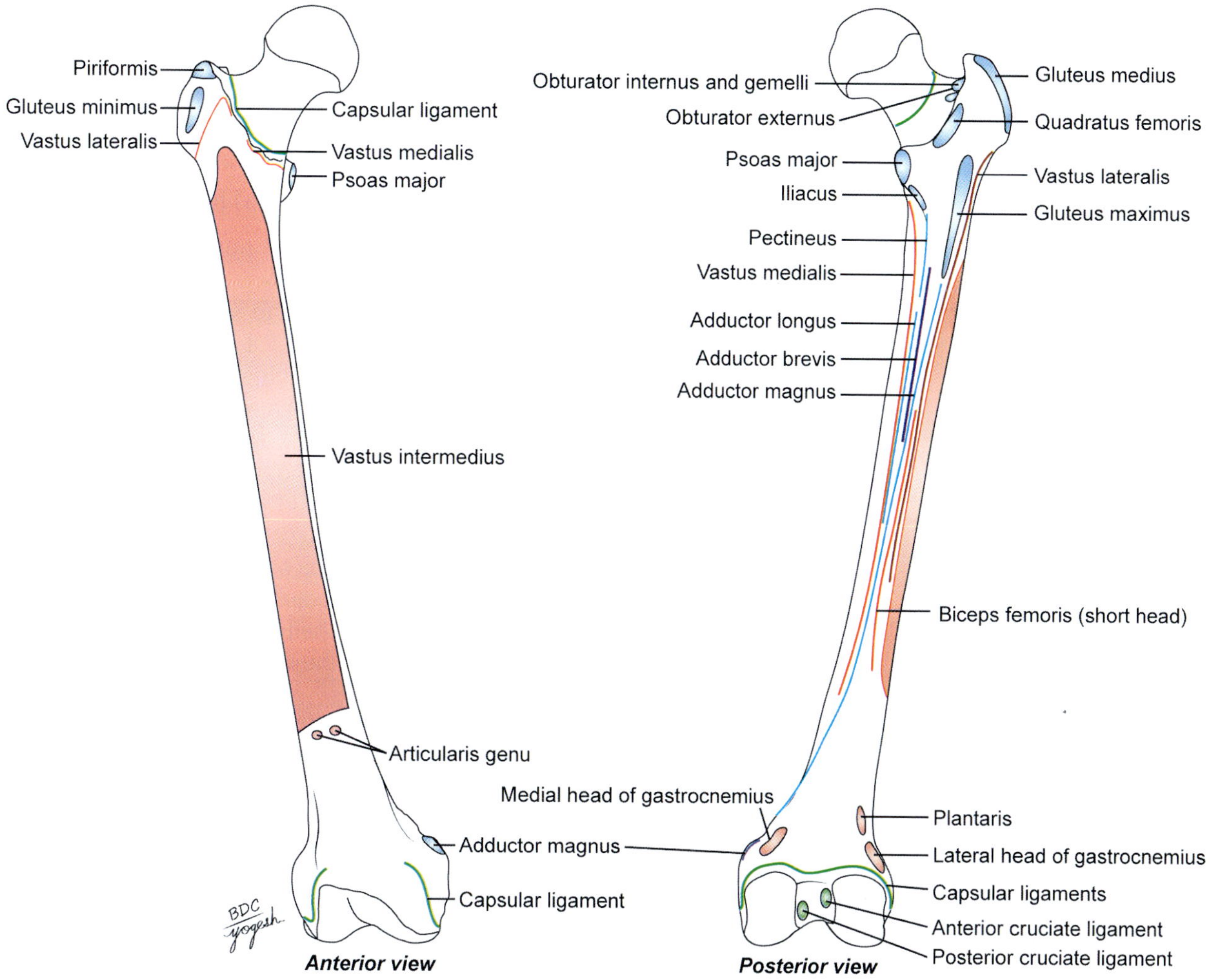

Fig. 2.12: Attachments on the right femur

the lateral supracondylar line. Origin lies between adductor magnus and vastus lateralis.

13. The medial and lateral intermuscular septa are attached to the lips of the linea aspera and to the supracondylar lines. They separate the extensor muscles of anterior compartment from the adductors of medial compartment and from the flexors in posterior compartment.
14. The lower end of the lateral supracondylar line gives origin to the plantaris above and the upper part of the lateral head of the gastrocnemius below.
15. The ***popliteal surface*** is covered with fat and forms the floor of the popliteal fossa. The origin of the medial head of the gastrocnemius from lower part of medial supracondylar line extends to the popliteal surface just above the medial condyle.

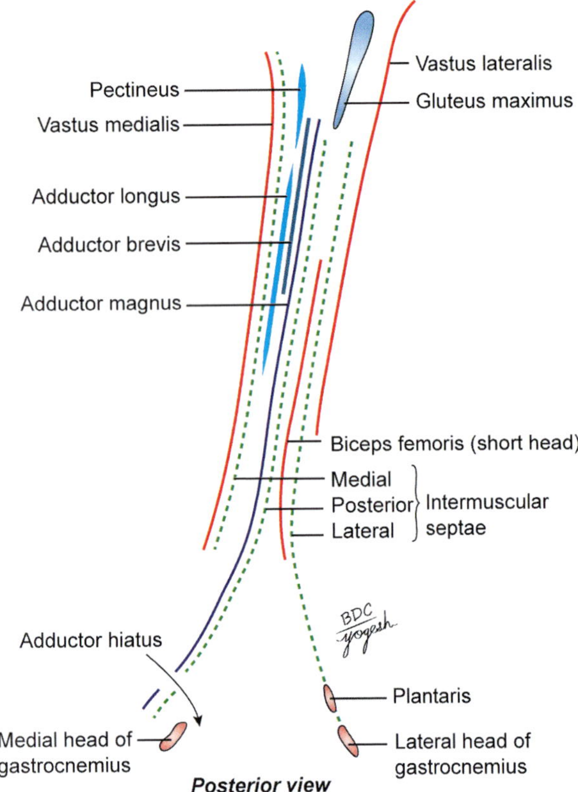

Fig. 2.13: Magnified view of structures attached to linea aspera

Lower End of Femur (Figs 2.11 and 2.14)

1. ***Lateral condyle***
   a. The fibular collateral ligament of the knee joint is attached to the lateral epicondyle (Fig. 2.16).
   b. The popliteus arises from the deep anterior part of the popliteal groove. When the knee is flexed, the tendon of this muscle lies in the shallow posterior part of the groove.
   c. The muscular impression near the lateral epicondyle gives origin to the lateral head of the gastrocnemius (Fig. 2.16).
2. ***Medial condyle***
   a. The tibial collateral ligament of the knee joint is attached to the medial.
   b. The adductor tubercle receives the insertion of the hamstring part or the ischial head of the adductor magnus.

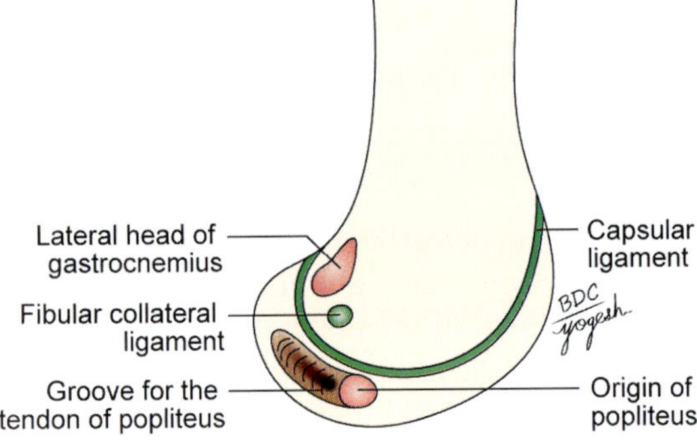

Fig. 2.14: Attachments on the lateral surface of the lateral condyle of the femur

3. ***Intercondylar notch***
   a. The anterior cruciate ligament is attached to the posterior part of the medial surface of the lateral condyle, on a smooth impression.
   b. The posterior cruciate ligament is attached to the anterior part of the lateral surface of medial condyle, on a smooth impression.
   c. The *intercondylar line* provides attachment to the capsular ligament and laterally to the oblique popliteal ligament.
   d. The *infrapatellar synovial fold* is attached to the anterior border of the intercondylar fossa.

[*Mnemonic (for attachment of linea aspera, from lateral to medial side)*: **L**ovely **B**utterflies, **M**aking **B**eautiful **M**emories, **L**ike **P**layful **M**usic: Vastus **l**ateralis, Short head of **b**iceps femoris, Adductor **m**agnus, Adductor **b**revis, Adductor **l**ongus and **p**ectineus, Vastus **m**edialis]

Competency:
AN14.3 Describe the importance of ossification of lower end of femur and upper end of tibia.

OSSIFICATION

- The femur ossifies from 1 primary and 4 secondary centres.
- The primary centre for the shaft appears in the 7th week of intrauterine life (IUL).
- The secondary centres appear—one for the lower end at the end of the 9th month of IUL, one for the head during the 1st year, one for the greater trochanter during the 4th year and one for the lesser trochanter during the 12th year (Fig. 2.15).
- There are three epiphyses at the upper end and one epiphysis at the lower end. The upper epiphyses—lesser trochanter, greater trochanter and head, in that order, fuse with the shaft at about 18th year. The lower epiphysis fuses by the 20th year.

Note: The following points are noteworthy.

1. The neck represents the upper end of the shaft because it ossifies from the primary centre.
2. Ossification of the lower end of the femur is of medicolegal importance. Presence of its centre in a newborn child found dead indicates that the child was viable, i.e. it was capable of independent existence.
3. The lower end of the femur is the growing end.
4. The lower epiphyseal line passes through the adductor tubercle.
5. The epiphyseal line of the head coincides with the articular margins, except superiorly where a part of the non-articular area is included in the epiphysis for passage of blood vessels to the head. In addition, the plane of this epiphysis changes with age from an oblique to a more vertical one.

CLINICAL ANATOMY

- ***Medicolegal significance of femur ossification:*** The lower end of femur ossifies from the secondary centre that appears by the 9th month of intrauterine life, irrespective of the birth of the baby. It is the

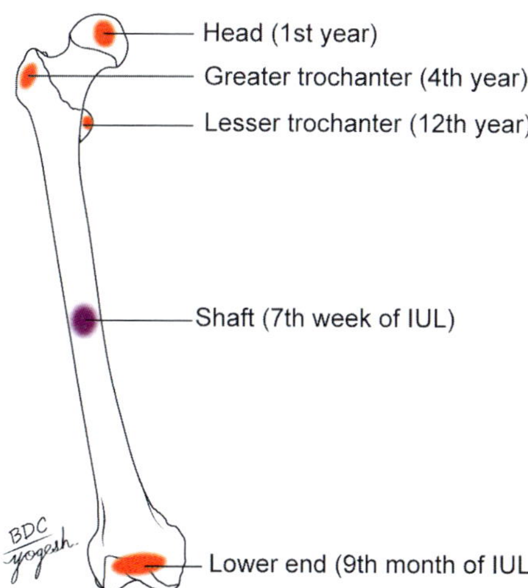

Fig. 2.15: Ossification of femur (IUL: Intrauterine life)

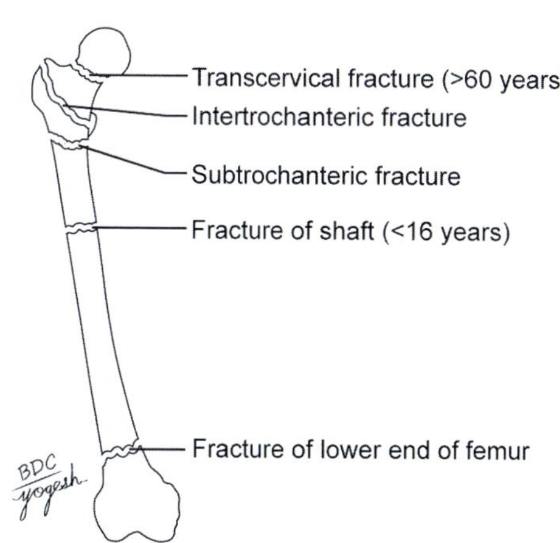

Fig. 2.16: Common sites of fracture

only secondary centre that appears before birth if pregnancy continues beyond the 9th month of intrauterine life. Hence, radiological appearance of secondary centre indicates that the newborn baby found dead was capable of survival (viable) and it was full term (completed 9 months of pregnancy). The centre of ossification in lower end of femur and even in upper end of tibia seen by X-ray is used as a medicolegal evidence to prove that the newborn (found dead) was nearly full term and was viable.

- Tripping over minor obstructions or other accidents causing forced medial rotation of the thigh and leg during the fall results in (Fig. 2.16):
  a. The fracture of the shaft of femur in persons below the age of 16 years.
  b. Bucket-handle tear of the medial meniscus between the ages of 14 and 40 years.
  c. Pott's (British surgeon, 1713–88) fracture of the leg bones between the ages of 40 and 60 years.
  d. Fracture of neck of the femur over the age of 60 years. This is common in females due to osteoporosis and degeneration of calcar femorale. There is shortening and lateral rotation of the affected limb. Adductors now become lateral rotators of hip joint.
- The head of femur is partly supplied by a branch of obturator artery along the ligamentum teres. Main arterial supply is from retinacular arteries, branches of medial circumflex femoral artery. These arteries get injured in intracapsular fracture of neck of femur, leading to ***avascular necrosis of the head***.
- ***Legg-Calvé-Perthes disease or Perthes disease:*** It is a childhood disorder that results from avascular necrosis of the head of femur [George Perthes, German surgeon, 1869–1927]. It is also called pseudocoxalgia. It can be diagnosed by X-ray of hip region.
- In normal knee, the obliquity of the line of quadriceps muscle and its insertion into the tibia results in an angle called '***Q angle***'. It is normally 15°–20°. If the angle is increased, there may be lateral subluxation of the patella.

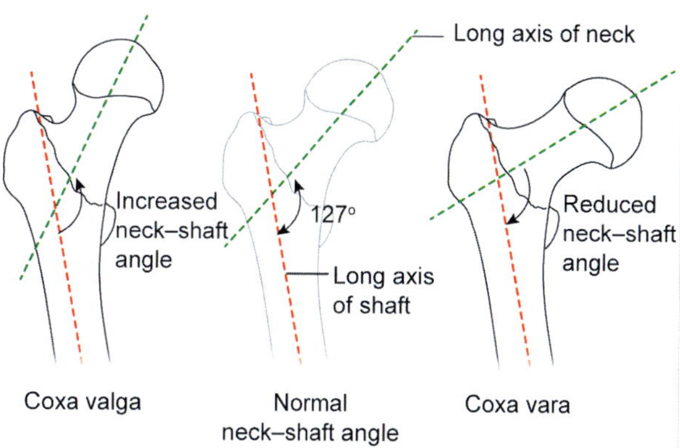

Fig. 2.17: Coxa vara and coxa valga

- ***Coxa vara and coxa valga:*** The normal neck–shaft angle of femur is 127°. Coxa valga is an abnormal increase in the neck–shaft angle (above 135°). Coxa vara is an abnormal decrease in the neck–shaft angle (less than 120°) (Fig. 2.17).

PATELLA

The patella (Latin *small plate*) is the largest sesamoid bone in the body, developed in the tendon of the quadriceps femoris. It is situated in front of the lower end of the femur about 1 cm above the knee joint (Plate 2.10, Fig. 2.18).

Side Determination and Anatomical Position

Hold the patella in such a way that:

1. Its pointed apex faces downward.
2. Its rough convex anterior surface faces forward.
3. The larger articular portion on the posterior surface lies on the side to which the bone belongs (for example, larger articular portion of right patella lies on the right).

Note: Keep the patella on the table in such a way that its articular surface faces table-top, base is directed towards you and its apex away. The patella tilts towards the side to which it belongs.

Plate 2.10: Patella (right, anterior and posterior views)

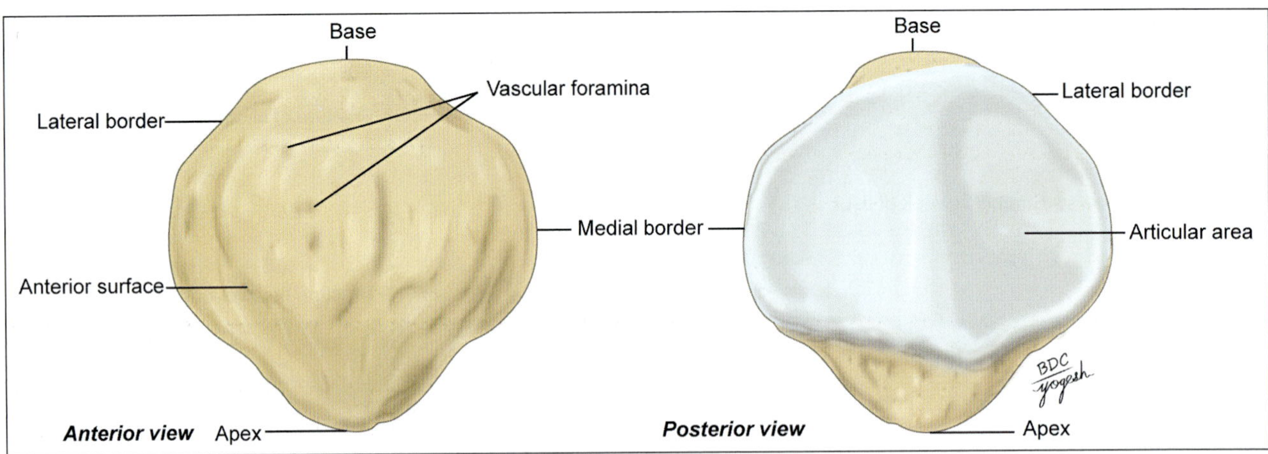

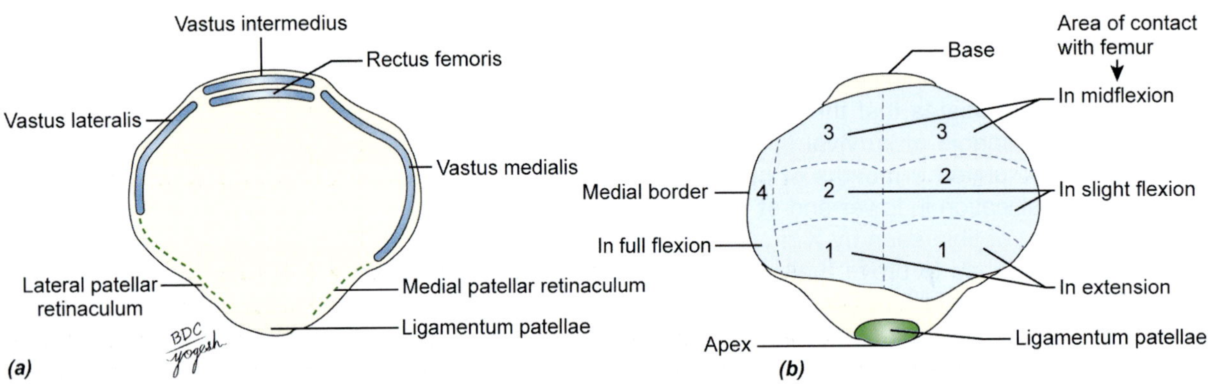

Figs 2.18a and b: Features of the right patella: (a) Anterior view and (b) posterior view

Features of Patella

Patella is a triangular bone, and it has the following (Flowchart 2.6):

1. Apex
2. Three borders: Superior, lateral and medial
3. Two surfaces: Anterior and posterior

The ***apex*** directed downwards is rough and vertically ridged. It is covered by an expansion from the tendon of the rectus femoris and is separated from the skin by the prepatellar bursa.

The ***posterior surface*** is articular in its upper 3/4th and non-articular in its lower 1/4th.

The ***articular area*** is divided by a vertical ridge into a larger lateral and smaller medial area. Another vertical ridge separates a medial strip from the medial area. The rest of the medial portion and the lateral portion of the articular surface are divided by two transverse lines into three pairs of facets.

Note: During various phases of movements of the knee, different portions of the patella articulate with the femur as follows:

a. Medial strip of articular surface articulates with a reciprocal strip on the medial side of the intercondylar notch of the femur during full flexion.
b. The lower pair of articular facets articulate during extension; middle pair during beginning of flexion; upper pair during midflexion; and the medial strip during full flexion of the knee.

Attachments of Patella (Fig. 2.18)

1. The *superior border* or base provides insertion to the rectus femoris in front and to the vastus intermedius behind.
2. The *lateral border* provides insertion to vastus lateralis in its upper one-third or half.
3. The *medial border* provides insertion to the vastus medialis in its upper two-thirds.
4. The non-articular area on the posterior surface provides attachment to the ligamentum patellae below and is related to infrapatellar pad of fat above.
5. The quadriceps femoris muscle is inserted into patella, from where ligamentum patellae arises which ends into the tibial tuberosity.

OSSIFICATION

The patella ossifies from several centres which appear during 3 to 6 years of age. Fusion is complete at puberty.

One or two centres at the superolateral angle of the patella may form separate pieces of bone. Such a patella is known as ***bipartite*** or ***tripartite patella***. The condition is bilateral and symmetrical (Fig. 2.19).

Flowchart 2.6: Patella

- ***Patella***
  - Largest sesamoid bone
  - Develops in the tendon of quadriceps femoris
  - ***Apex***
    - Directed downward
    - Attachment
      - Ligamentum patellae
  - ***Borders***
    - ***Superior***
      - Rectus femoris
      - Vastus intermedius
    - ***Lateral***
      - Vastus lateralis
      - Lateral patellar retinaculum
    - ***Medial***
      - Vastus medialis
      - Medial patellar retinaculum
  - ***Surfaces***
    - ***Anterior***
      - Convex
      - Nonarticular
      - Related to subcutaneous prepatellar bursa
    - ***Posterior***
      - Upper 3/4th: Articular
      - Lower 1/4th: Nonarticular
        - Ligamentum patellae

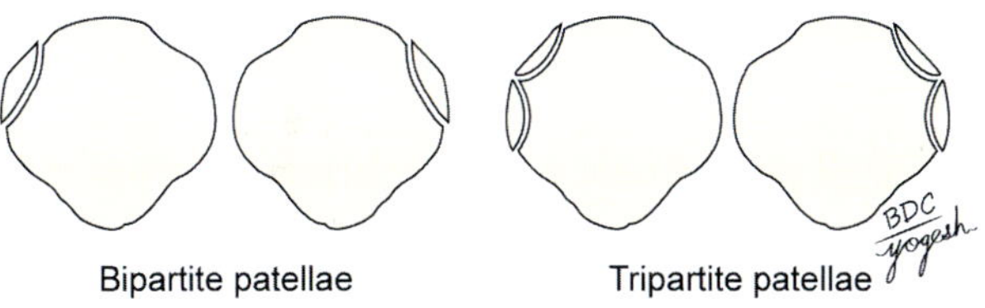

Fig. 2.19: Bipartite and tripartite patella

CLINICAL ANATOMY

- ***Fracture of the patella*** should be differentiated from a bipartite or a tripartite patella. Patella may get fractured into multiple pieces or 2 pieces (Fig. 2.20).
- ***Dislocation of patella***: The patella has a natural tendency to dislocate outwards because of the outward angulation between the long axes of the thigh and leg. Stability of patella is maintained by
  1. tension of the medial patellar retinaculum,
  2. contraction of vastus medialis and
  3. forward bulging of the lateral condyle of femur.
- Bursitis occurs in prepatellar and subcutaneous infrapatellar bursae.

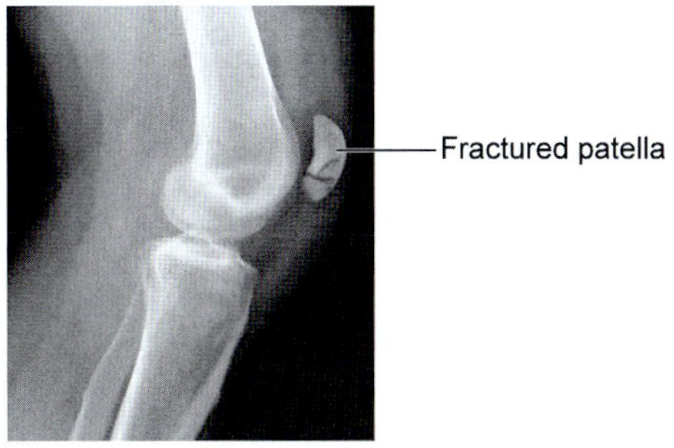

Fig. 2.20: Fracture of the patella

TIBIA

The tibia (Latin *shin bone*) is the medial and larger bone of the leg. It is homologous with the radius of the upper limb. Its upper end comprises two large flat condyles. Its lower end has a prominent medial malleolus. The shaft in between the two ends is prismoid in shape.

Side Determination and Anatomical Position

Hold the bone in such a way that (Plate 2.11)

1. The broad upper end faces upward.
2. The tibial tuberosity and sharp anterior border look forward.
3. ***Medial malleolus*** project from medial side of lower end and helps to determine the side of the bone. For example, the medial malleolus of the right tibia is directed on the left.

Features of Tibia

The tibia comprises an upper end, lower end and a shaft in between the two ends (Plates 2.1 and 2.2, Fig. 2.21, Flowchart 2.7).

Upper End

The upper end of the tibia is markedly expanded from side to side, to form two large condyles which overhang the posterior surface of the shaft. The upper end includes (Plate 2.12):

1. Two condyles: Medial and lateral
2. Intercondylar area
3. Tibial tuberosity.

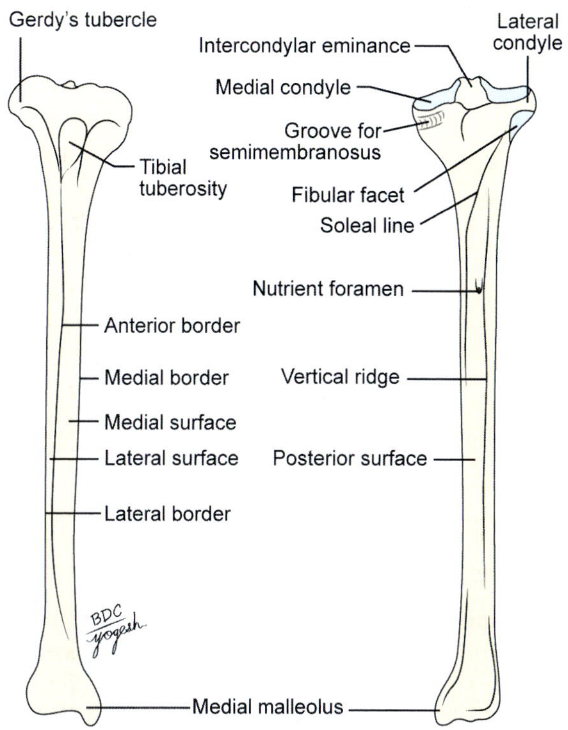

Fig. 2.21: Right tibia

Plate 2.11: Tibia (right, anterior and posterior views)

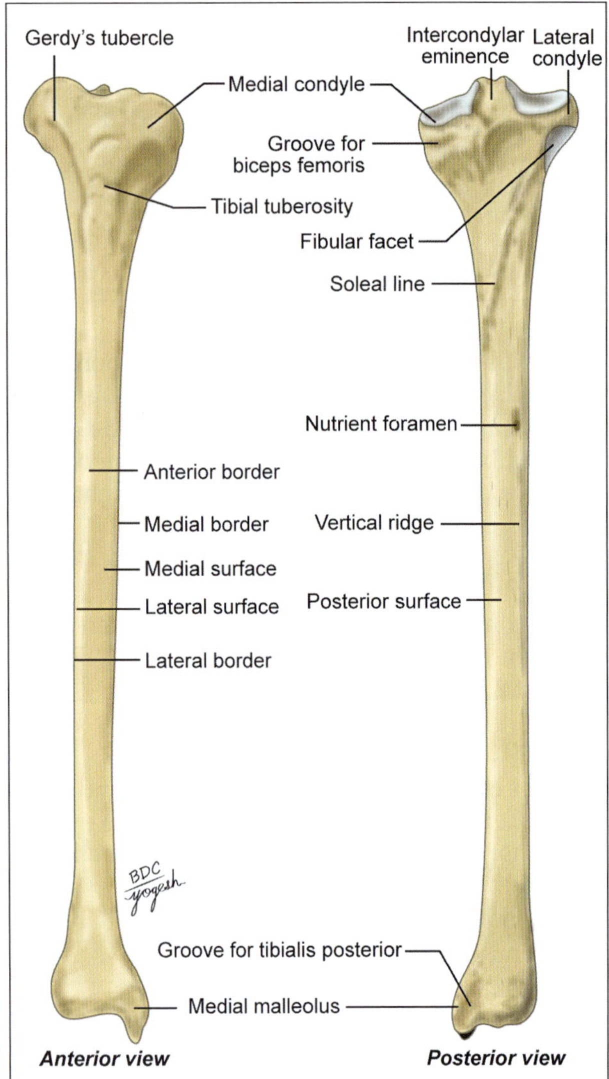

Plate 2.12: Superior view of right tibia

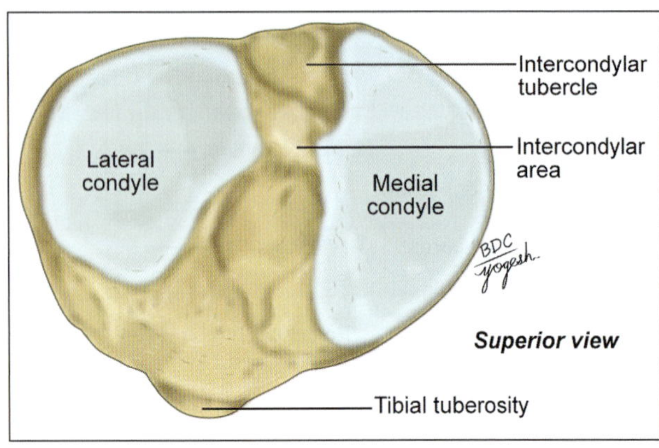

Medial Condyle

Medial condyle is larger than the lateral condyle. Its *superior surface* articulates with the medial condyle of the femur. The articular surface is oval and its long axis is anteroposterior. The *posterior surface* of the medial condyle has a *groove*. The *anterior* and *medial surfaces* are marked by numerous vascular foramina.

Lateral Condyle

The lateral condyle overhangs the shaft more than the medial condyle. The *superior surface* of the condyle articulates with the lateral condyle of the femur. The articular surface is nearly circular.

The posteroinferior aspect of the lateral condyle articulates with the fibula. The ***fibular facet*** is flat, circular and is directed downwards, backwards and laterally. Superomedial to the fibular facet, the posterior surface of the condyle is marked by a *groove*.

The anterior aspect of the condyle bears a flattened impression known as ***Gerdy's tubercle***.

Intercondylar Area

Intercondylar area is the roughened area on the superior surface, between the articular surfaces of the two condyles. The area is the narrowest in its middle part. This part is elevated to form the ***intercondylar eminence*** which is flanked by the ***medial*** and ***lateral intercondylar tubercles*** (Plate 2.12).

Tuberosity

Tuberosity of the tibia is a prominence located on the anterior aspect of the upper end of the tibia. The tuberosity is divided into an upper smooth area and a lower rough area. The epiphyseal line for the upper end of the tibia passes through the junction of these two parts.

Shaft

The shaft of the tibia is prismoid in shape. It has (Plate 2.13)

- *3 borders*: Anterior, medial and interosseous
- *3 surfaces*: Lateral, medial and posterior.

Borders

1. The ***anterior border*** is sharp and S-shaped being convex medially in the upper part and convex laterally in the lower part. It extends from the tibial tuberosity above to the anterior border of the medial malleolus below. It is subcutaneous and forms the ***shin***.
2. The ***medial border*** is rounded. It extends from the medial condyle, above, to the posterior border of the medial malleolus, below.
3. The ***interosseous*** or ***lateral border*** extends from the lateral condyle a little below and in front of the fibular facet, to the anterior border of the fibular notch.

Surfaces

1. The ***lateral surface*** lies between the anterior and interosseous borders. In its upper 3/4th, it is concave and is directed laterally. In its lower 1/4th, it is directed forwards.
2. The ***medial surface*** lies between the anterior and medial borders. It is broad, and most of it is subcutaneous.
3. The ***posterior surface*** lies between the medial and interosseous borders. It is the widest in its upper part. This part is crossed obliquely by a rough ridge called the ***soleal line***. The soleal line begins just behind the fibular facet, runs downwards and medially and terminates by joining the medial border at the junction of its upper and middle thirds.

Plate 2.13: Borders and surfaces of the shaft of tibia and fibula

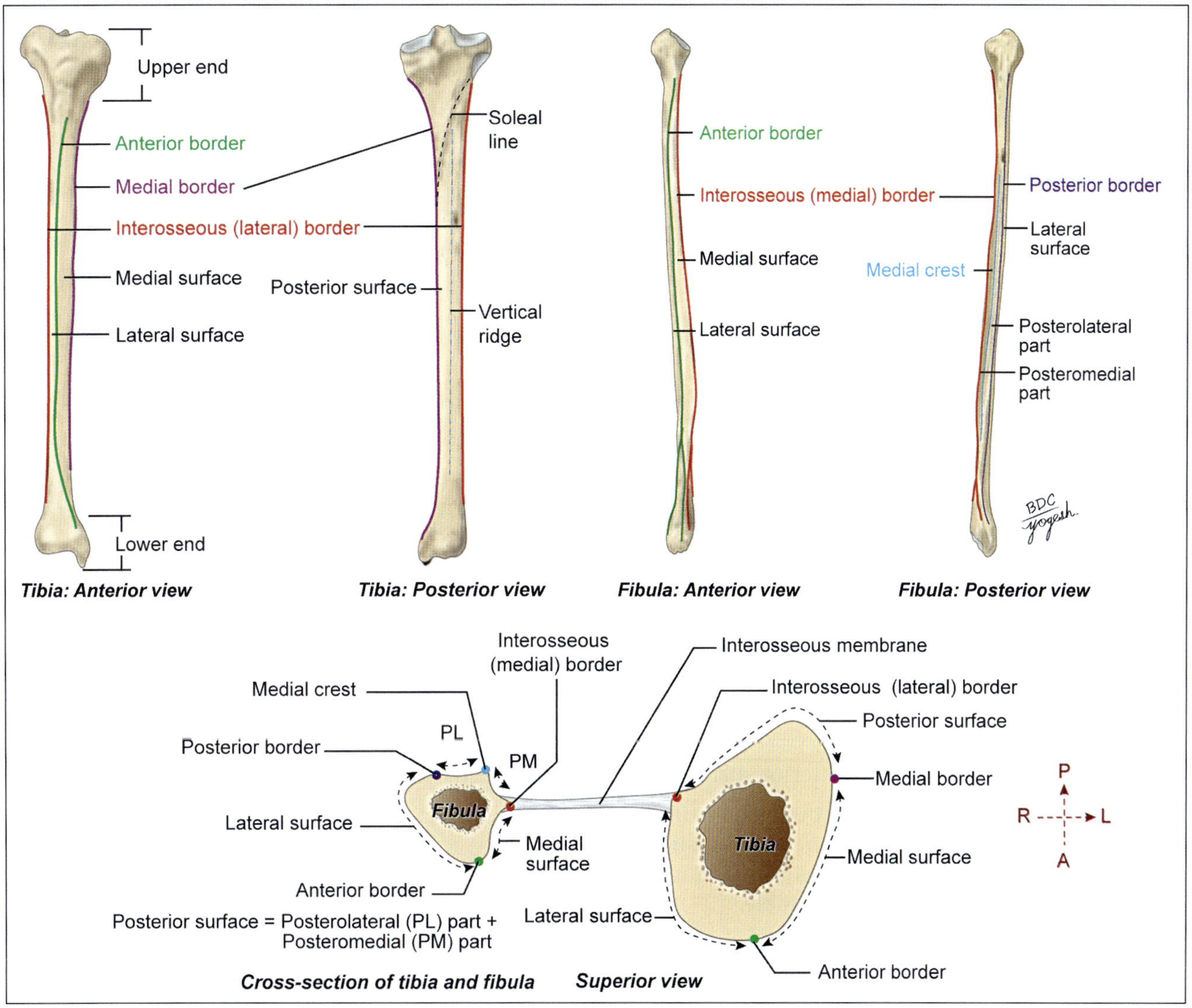

Upper end
Anterior border
Medial border
Interosseous (lateral) border
Medial surface
Lateral surface
Lower end
Soleal line
Posterior surface
Vertical ridge
Anterior border
Interosseous (medial) border
Medial surface
Lateral surface
Posterior border
Lateral surface
Medial crest
Posterolateral part
Posteromedial part
BDC yogesh

Tibia: Anterior view *Tibia: Posterior view* *Fibula: Anterior view* *Fibula: Posterior view*

Interosseous (medial) border
Medial crest
Posterior border
PL
PM
Lateral surface
Fibula
Medial surface
Anterior border
Posterior surface = Posterolateral (PL) part + Posteromedial (PM) part
Interosseous membrane
Interosseous (lateral) border
Posterior surface
Medial border
Tibia
Medial surface
Lateral surface
Anterior border
P
R
L
A

Cross-section of tibia and fibula *Superior view*

Flowchart 2.7: Tibia

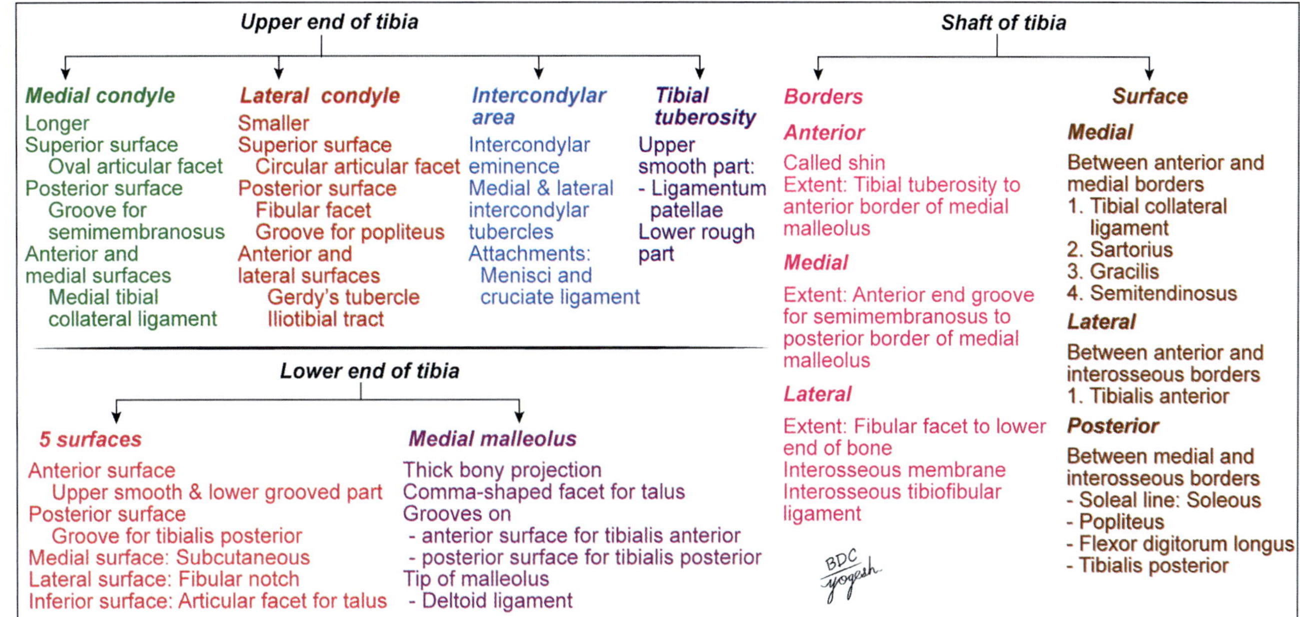

Above the soleal line, the posterior surface is in the form of a triangular area. The area below the soleal line is elongated. It is divided into medial and lateral parts by a ***vertical ridge***. A ***nutrient foramen*** is situated near the upper end of this ridge. It is directed downwards and transmits the nutrient artery which is a branch of the *posterior tibial artery*.

Lower End

The lower end of the tibia is slightly expanded. It has five surfaces. Medially, it is prolonged downwards as the medial malleolus.

1. The larger *anterior surface* of the lower end has an upper smooth part and a lower rough and grooved part.
2. The *medial surface* is subcutaneous and is continuous with the medial surface of the medial malleolus.
3. The *lateral surface* of the lower end presents a triangular ***fibular notch*** to which the lower end of the fibula articulates to form ***inferior tibiofibular joint***. The upper part of the notch is rough. The lower part is smooth and may be covered with hyaline cartilage.
4. The *inferior surface* of the lower end is articular. It articulates with the superior trochlear surface of the talus and thus takes part in forming the *ankle joint*. Medially, the articular surface extends onto the medial malleolus.
5. *Posterior surface* is smaller than anterior surface.

The ***medial malleolus*** is a short but strong process which projects downwards from the medial surface of the lower end of the tibia. It forms a subcutaneous prominence on the medial side of the ankle.

Attachments of Tibia

Figures 2.22 to 2.24 show the attachments on the tibia.

Attachments on the Medial Condyle

1. The capsular ligament of the knee joint is attached to the upper border, which also gives attachment to the deeper fibres of the tibial collateral ligament.
2. The semimembranosus is inserted into the groove on the posterior surface.
3. The medial patellar retinaculum is attached to the anterior surface.

Attachments on the Lateral Condyle

1. The iliotibial tract is attached to the flattened impression on the anterior surface.
2. The capsular ligament of the superior tibiofibular joint is attached around the margins of the fibular facet.
3. The groove on the posterior surface of the lateral condyle is occupied by the tendon of the popliteus with a bursa intervening.

Attachments on the Intercondylar Area

The following are attached from before backwards (Fig. 2.24):

1. The anterior horn of the medial meniscus (Greek *small moon*) just in front of the medial articular surface.

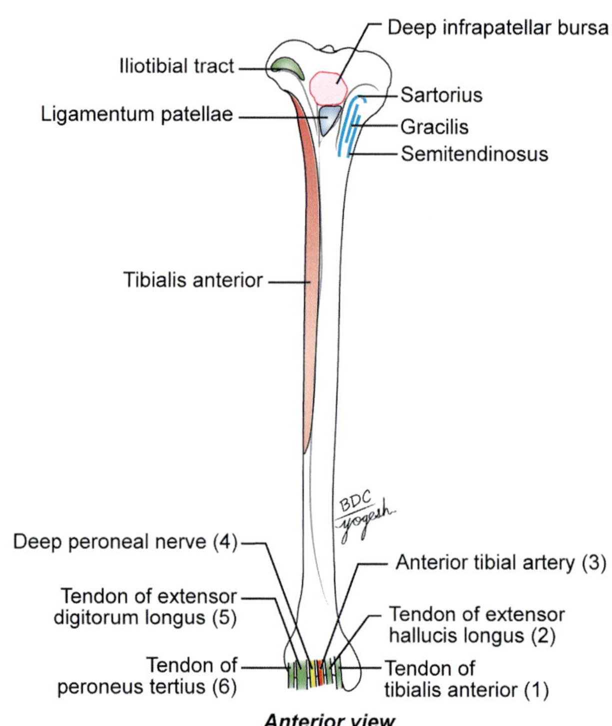

Fig. 2.22: Attachments and relations on the anterior aspect of the right tibia

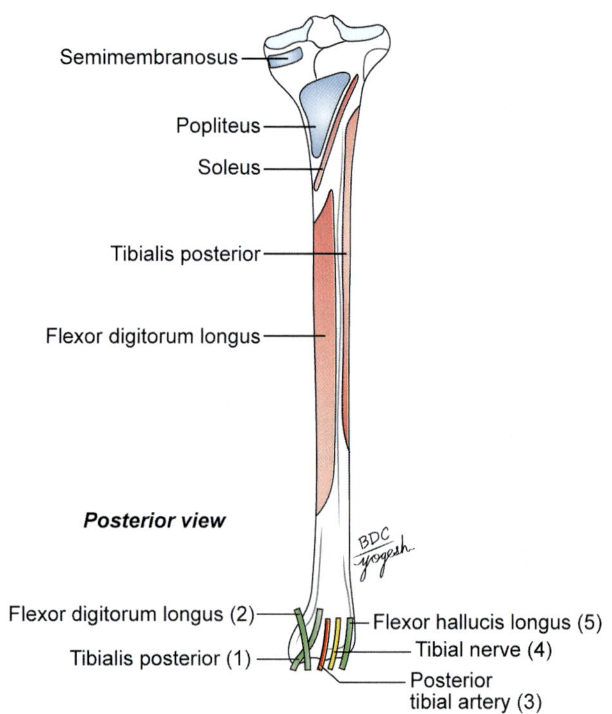

Fig. 2.23: Attachments and relations on the posterior aspect of the right tibia

2. The anterior cruciate (Latin *cross*) ligament on a smooth area just behind the previous attachment.
3. The anterior horn of the lateral meniscus, to the front of the intercondylar eminence, and lateral to the anterior cruciate ligament.
4. The posterior horn of the lateral meniscus, to the posterior slope of the intercondylar eminence.

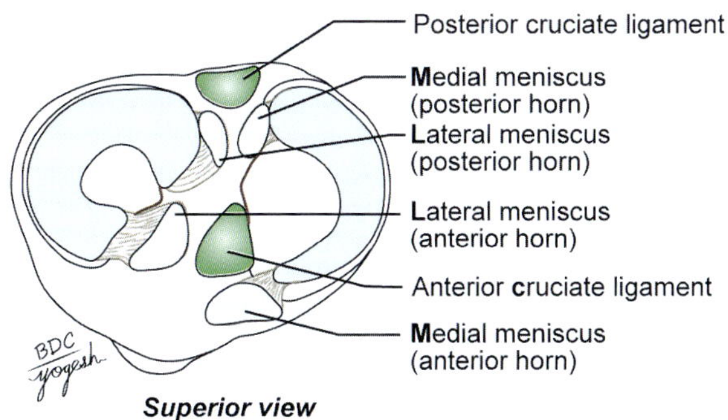

Fig. 2.24: Superior view of the upper end of the right tibia

5. The posterior horn of the medial meniscus, to the depression behind the base of the medial intercondylar tubercle.
6. The posterior cruciate ligament to the posterior-most smooth area.

[*Mnemonic*: **M**edical **C**ollege **L**ucknow, **L**ucknow **M**edical **C**ollege]

Attachment on the Tibial Tuberosity

The *ligamentum patellae* is attached to the upper smooth part of the *tibial tuberosity.* The lower rough area of the tuberosity is subcutaneous but is separated from the skin by the subcutaneous infrapatellar bursa.

Attachments on the Shaft

1. The anterior border of the tibia gives attachment to the deep fascia of the leg and, in its lower part, to the superior extensor retinaculum. Medial border also gives attachment to deep fascia. Interosseous border gives attachment to interosseous membrane. Vertical ridge gives attachment to deep transverse fascial septum.
2. The tibialis anterior arises from the upper 2/3rd of the lateral surface.
3. The upper part of the medial surface receives the insertions of the sartorius, the gracilis and the semitendinosus, from before backwards. Still further posteriorly this surface gives attachment to the tibial collateral ligament along the medial border.
4. The soleus arises from the soleal line. The soleal line also gives attachment to the fascia covering the soleus, the fascia covering the popliteus and the superficial transverse fascial septum. The tendinous arch for origin of the soleus is attached to a tubercle at the upper end of the soleal line.
5. The popliteus is inserted on the posterior surface, into the triangular area above the soleal line.
6. The medial area of the posterior surface below the soleal line gives origin to the flexor digitorum longus, while the lateral area gives origin to the tibialis posterior.
7. The rough upper part of the fibular notch gives attachment to the interosseous tibiofibular ligament.
8. The capsular ligament of the ankle joint is attached to the lower end along the margins of articular surface. The deltoid ligament of the ankle joint is attached to the lower border of the *medial malleolus*.

Relations

Apart from the relations mentioned above, the following may be noted:

1. The lower part of the anterior surface of the shaft and the anterior aspect of the lower end are crossed from medial to lateral side by the tibialis anterior, the extensor hallucis longus, the anterior tibial artery, the deep peroneal nerve, the extensor digitorum longus and the peroneus tertius (Fig. 2.27).
2. The lower most part of the posterior surface of the shaft and the posterior aspect of the lower end are related from medial to lateral side to the tibialis posterior, which lies in a groove, the flexor digitorum longus, the posterior tibial artery, the tibial nerve and the flexor hallucis longus. The groove for the tendon of the tibialis posterior continues downwards on the posterior surface of the medial malleolus (Fig. 2.23).
3. The lower 1/3rd of the medial surface of the shaft is crossed by the great saphenous vein (*see* Fig. 8.1a).

Blood Supply

The nutrient artery to the tibia is the largest nutrient artery in the body. It is a branch of the posterior tibial artery which enters the bone on its posterior surface at the upper end of vertical ridge. It is directed downwards.

OSSIFICATION

1. The tibia ossifies from one primary and two secondary centres.
2. The primary centre appears in the shaft during the 7th week of intrauterine life.
3. A secondary centre for the upper end appears just *before birth* (at the end of 9th month) and fuses with the shaft at 16th–18th year. The upper epiphysis is prolonged downwards to form the tibial tuberosity.
4. A secondary centre for the lower end appears during the 1st year, forms the medial malleolus by the 7th year and fuses with the shaft by 15th–17th year (Fig. 2.25).

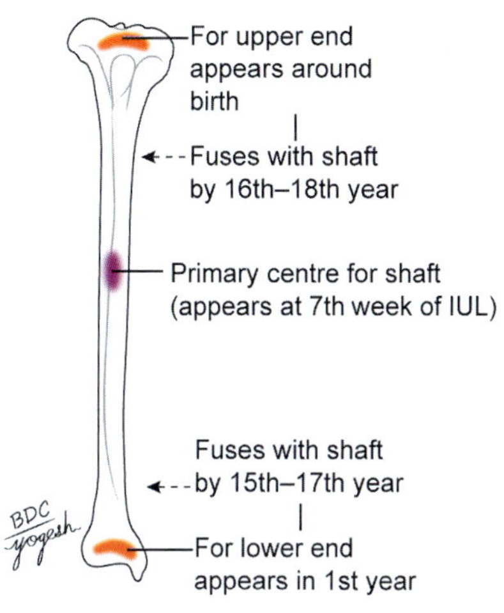

Fig. 2.25: Ossification of tibia

CLINICAL ANATOMY

- ***Osteomyelitis***: Osteomyelitis is an infectious inflammation of the bone. Upper end of tibia is one of the commonest site of osteomyelitis (Fig. 2.26).
- ***Fracture of tibia***: The tibia is commonly fractured at the junction of upper 2/3rd and lower 1/3rd of shaft (this is a narrow and weak zone of the bone). As this zone has poor blood supply, fractures here may not unite.
- ***Transverse march (stress) fracture***: It occurs in soldiers, bikers, hospital doctors (usually in people performing long standing duties; it occurs at the upper part of the shaft of tibia and/or in distal part of metatarsals).
- ***Boot top fracture***: In people wearing rigid ski boot, a forward fall may result in low transverse fractures of tibia and fibula (Fig. 2.27).
- ***Osgood-Schlatter disease***: It is an inflammation of tibial tuberosity in young athletes; traction over the tibial tuberosity before it fuses with shaft (by 16–18 years) causes inflammation and painful swelling over tibial tuberosity (Fig. 2.28).
- Forward dislocation of the tibia on the talus produces a characteristic prominence of the heel. This is the most common type of injury to the ankle.

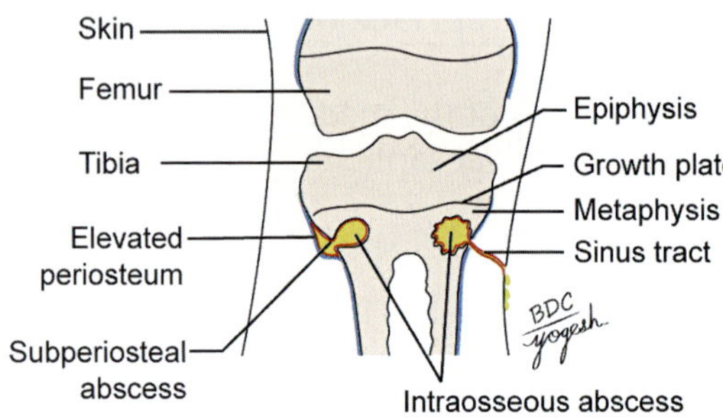

Fig. 2.26: Osteomyelitis (commonest site: tibia)

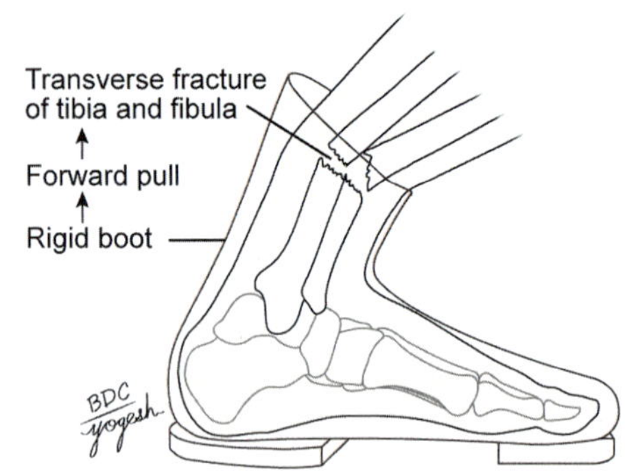

Fig. 2.27: Boot top fracture

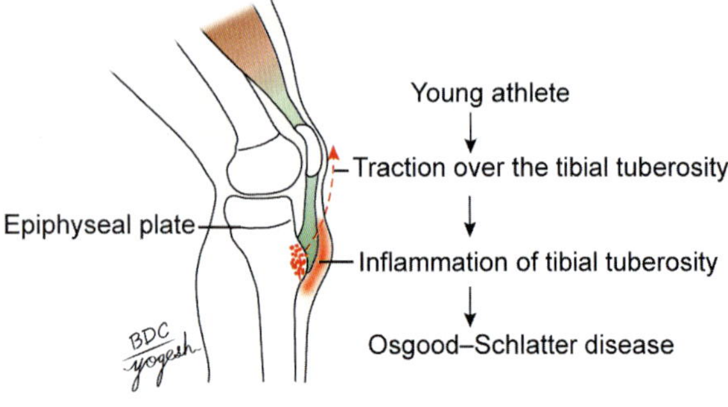

Fig. 2.28: Osgood–Schlatter disease

FIBULA

The fibula (Latin *clasp/pin*) is the lateral and smaller bone of the leg. It is very thin as compared to the tibia. It is homologous with the ulna of the upper limb (Plate 2.14, Fig. 2.29). The fibula comprises an upper end or head with a circular articular facet and a small styloid process; a lower end with prominent lateral malleolus and a thin shaft between the two ends.

Side Determination and Anatomical Position

Hold the fibula vertical in such a way that—

1. Head is directed upward.
2. Triangular articular facet at lower end faces medially.
3. Malleolar fossa lies below and behind the triangular articular facet.
4. The non-articular lateral surface of lower end faces the side of the bone and helps to determine the side of the bone to which it belongs.

Features of Fibula

The fibula has an upper end, a shaft (Fig. 2.29) and a lower end.

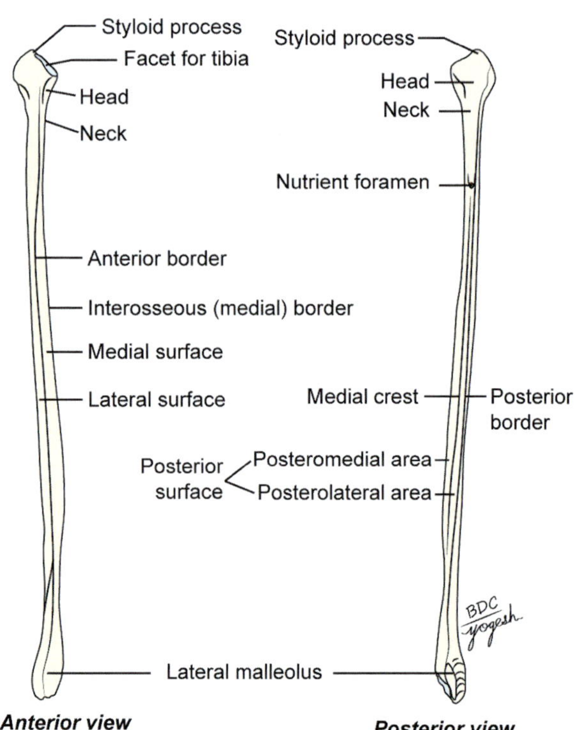

Fig. 2.29: Fibula (right, schematic representation, anterior and posterior views)

Plate 2.14: Fibula

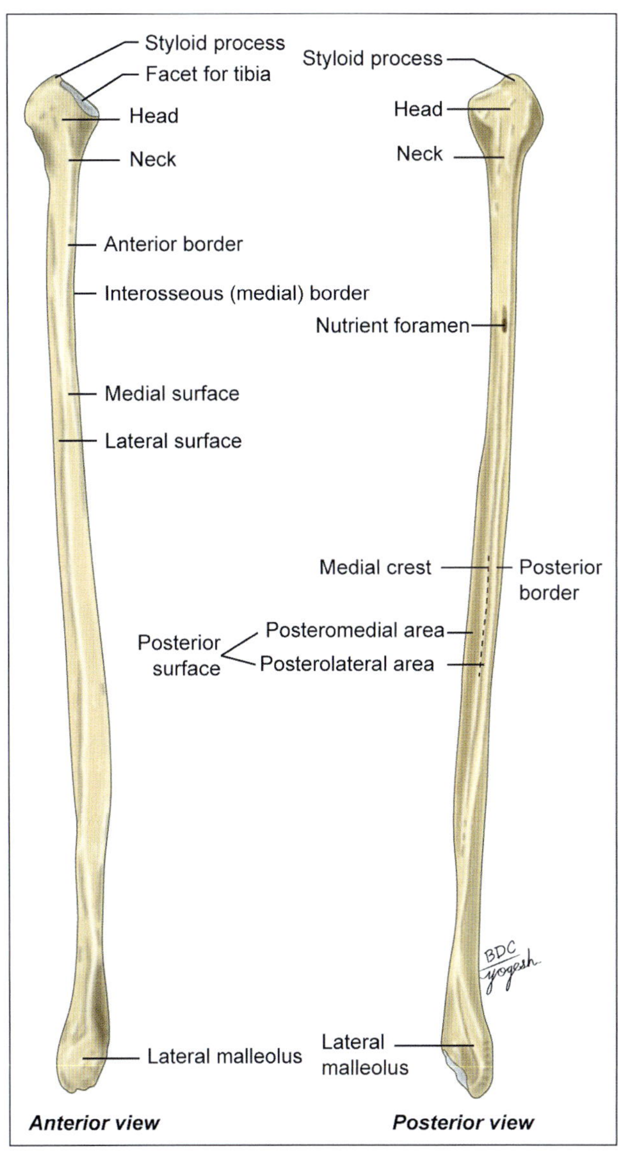

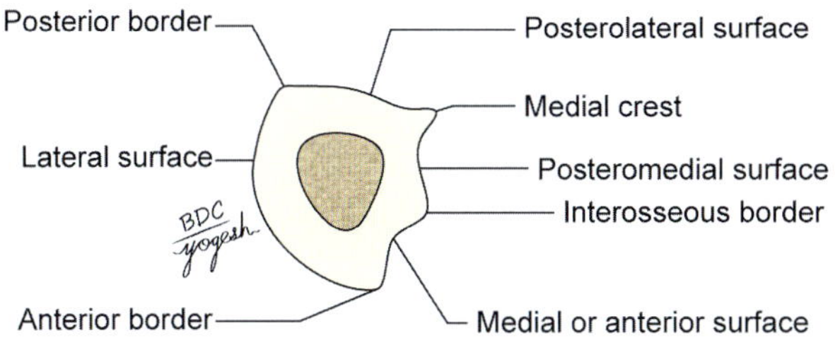

Fig. 2.30: Transverse section through shaft of middle 2/4th of fibula to show its borders and surfaces

Upper End or Head

Upper end/head is slightly expanded in all directions. The superior surface bears a ***circular articular facet*** which articulates with the lateral condyle of the tibia.

The *apex* of the head or the ***styloid process*** projects upwards from its posterolateral aspect.

The constriction immediately below the head is known as the ***neck*** of the fibula.

Shaft

The shaft shows considerable variation in its form because it is moulded by the muscles attached to it. It has
- *3 borders*: Anterior, posterior and interosseous
- *3 surfaces*: Medial, lateral and posterior (Fig. 2.30).

Borders

1. The ***anterior border*** begins just below the anterior aspect of the head. At its lower end, it divides to enclose an elongated triangular area which is continuous with the lateral surface of the lateral malleolus (Fig. 2.30).
2. The ***posterior border*** is rounded. Its upper end lies in line with the styloid process. Below, the border is continuous with the medial margin of the groove on the back of the lateral malleolus (Fig. 2.35).
3. The ***interosseous*** or ***medial border*** lies just medial to the anterior border, but on a more posterior plane. It terminates below at the upper end of a roughened area above the talar facet of the lateral malleolus. In its upper 2/3rd, the interosseous border lies very close to the anterior border and may be indistinguishable from it.

Surfaces

1. The ***medial surface*** lies between the anterior and interosseous borders. In its upper 2/3rd, it is very narrow, measuring 1 mm or less (Fig. 2.30).
2. The ***lateral surface*** lies between the anterior and posterior borders. It is twisted backwards in its lower part.
3. The ***posterior surface*** is the largest of the three surfaces. It lies between the interosseous and posterior borders. In its upper two-thirds, it is divided into two parts by a vertical ridge called the ***medial crest***.

Lower End or Lateral Malleolus

The lower end is prolonged to form lateral malleolus. Its medial surface articulates with talus. The tip of the lateral malleolus is 0.5 cm lower than that of the medial malleolus, and its anterior surface is 1.5 cm posterior to that of the medial malleolus. It has the following four surfaces:
1. The *anterior surface* is rough and rounded.
2. The *posterior surface* is marked by a groove.
3. The *lateral surface* is subcutaneous.
4. The *medial surface* bears a triangular articular facet for the talus anteriorly and the malleolar fossa posteriorly.

Attachments and Relations (Figs 2.31–2.34)

Head

1. It receives the insertion of the biceps femoris on the anterolateral slope of the apex. This insertion is C-shaped.
2. The fibular collateral ligament of knee joint is attached within this C-shaped area. The origins of extensor digitorum, peroneus longus and soleus, below, extend onto the corresponding aspects of the head.
3. The capsular ligament of the superior tibiofibular joint is attached around the articular facet.

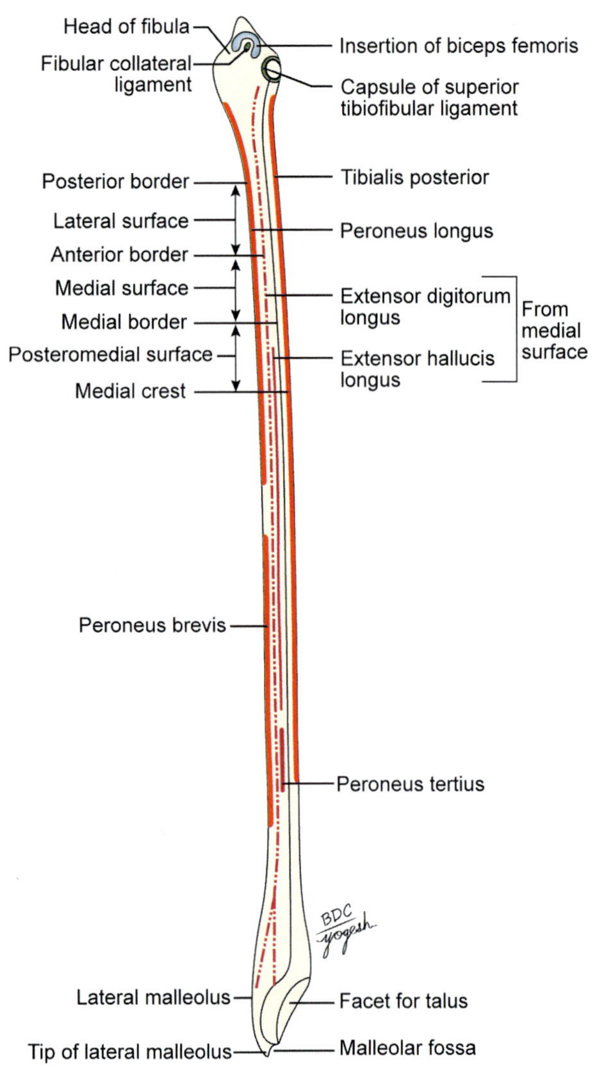

Fig. 2.31: Right fibula: Anterior aspect

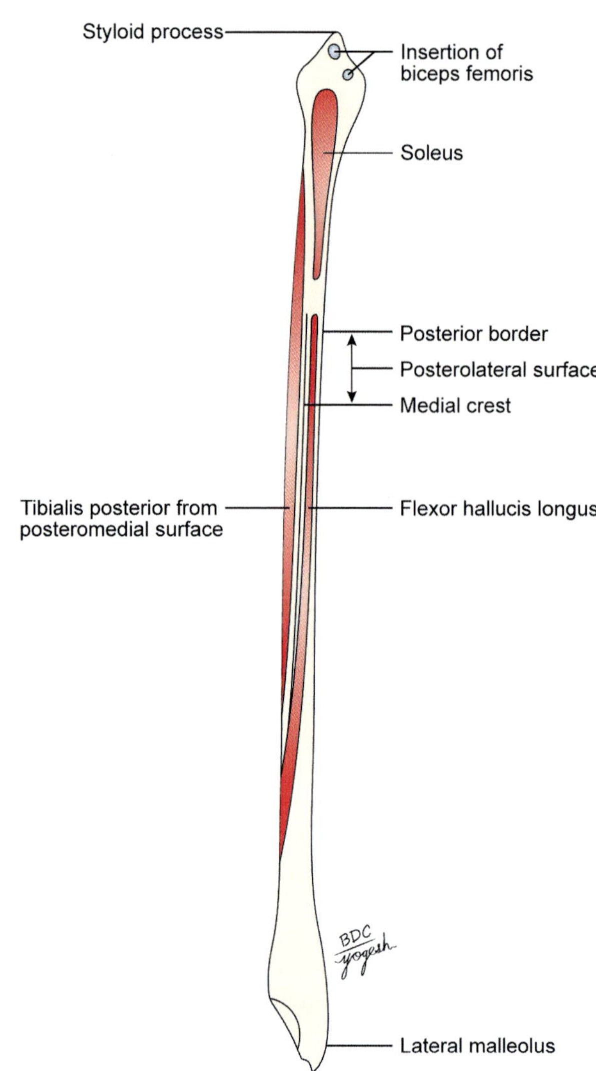

Fig. 2.32: Right fibula: Posterior aspect

Neck

1. Neck of fibula is related to common peroneal nerve.

Shaft

1. The ***anterior border*** of fibula gives attachment to:
   a. Anterior intermuscular septum of the leg.
   b. Superior extensor retinaculum, to lower part of the anterior margin of triangular area.
   c. Superior peroneal retinaculum, to the lower part of the posterior margin of triangular area.
2. The ***posterior border*** gives attachment to the posterior intermuscular septum.
3. The ***interosseous border*** gives attachment to the interosseous membrane. The attachment leaves a gap at the upper end for passage of the *anterior tibial vessels* and a gap at lower end for passage of perforating branch of peroneal artery.
4. ***Medial crest*** on posterior surface gives attachment to deep transverse fascial septum.
5. The ***medial surface*** of the shaft gives origin to:
   a. The extensor digitorum longus, from the whole of the upper 1/4th, and from the anterior half of the middle 2/4th.

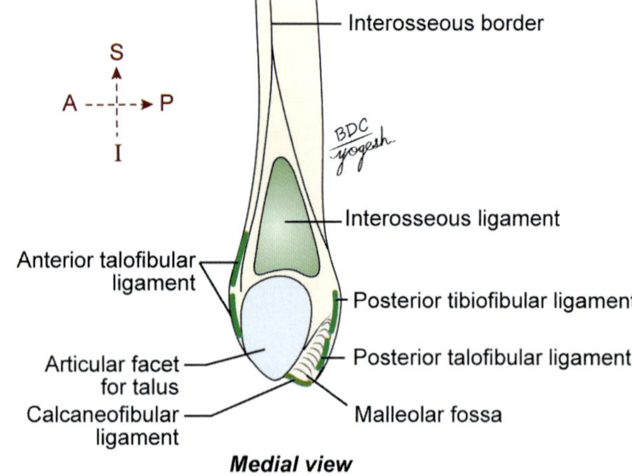

Fig. 2.33: Ligaments attached on the medial aspect of lower end of fibula

   b. The extensor hallucis longus, from the posterior half of its middle 2/4th.
   c. The peroneus tertius, from its lower 1/4th.
6. The lateral surface of the shaft gives origin to:
   a. Peroneus longus (*PL*) from its upper 1/3rd, and posterior half of the middle 1/3rd

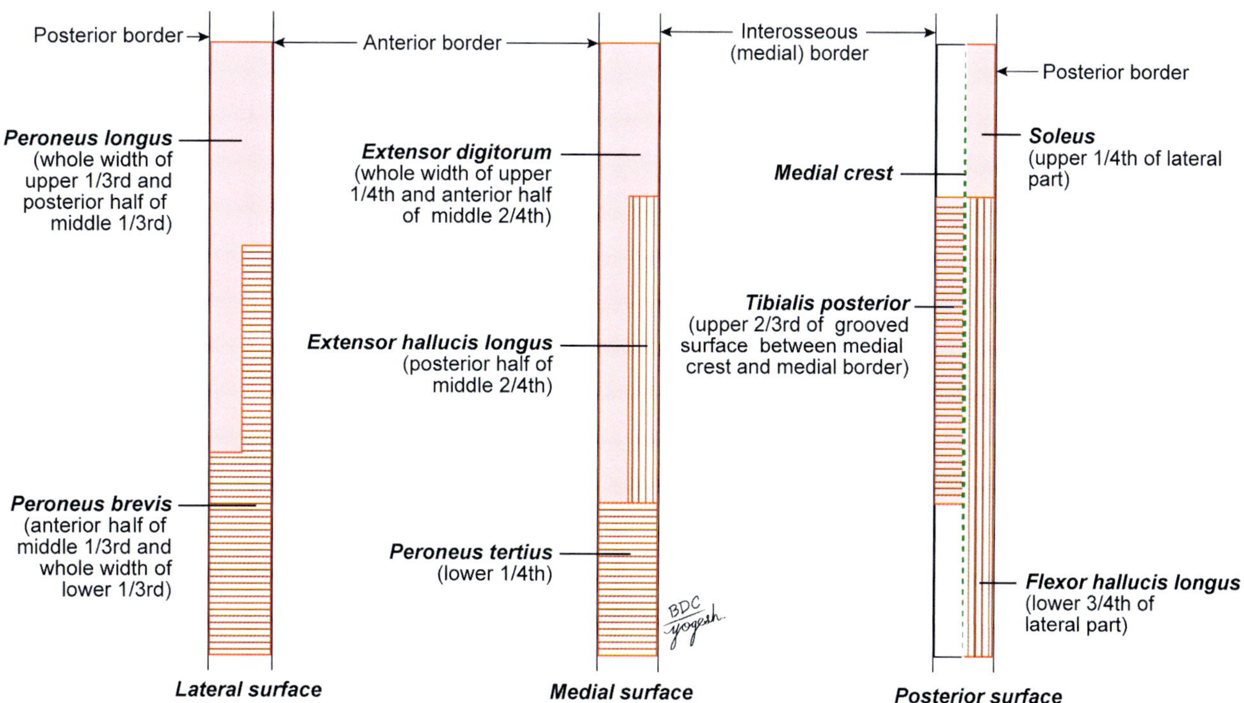

Fig. 2.34: Attachments of right fibula (schematic)

   b. The peroneus brevis (*PB*) from the anterior half of its middle 1/3rd and the whole of lower 1/3rd. The common peroneal nerve terminates in relation to the neck of fibula.
7. The part of the posterior surface between the medial crest and the posterior border gives origin to:
   a. Soleus from the upper 1/4th
   b. Flexor hallucis longus from its lower 3/4th of area of posterior surface between medial crest and posterior border (except lowest 2.5 cm).
8. The part of the posterior surface between the medial crest and the interosseous border (medial border), the grooved part, gives origin to the tibialis posterior.
9. The triangular area above the medial surface of the lateral malleolus gives attachment to:
   a. The interosseous tibiofibular ligament, in the middle. The joint between lower ends of tibia and fibula is called *syndesmoses* (Greek *binding together*).
   b. The anterior tibiofibular ligament, anteriorly.
   c. The posterior tibiofibular ligament, posteriorly.

Lateral malleolus

1. The attachments on the lateral malleolus are as follows:
   a. Anterior talofibular ligament to the anterior surface.
   b. Inferior transverse tibiofibular (a part of posterior tibiofibular) ligament above and posterior talofibular ligament below the *malleolar fossa*.
   c. The capsule of the ankle joint along the edges of the malleolar articular surface.
   d. Slight notch on the lower border gives attachment to calcaneofibular ligament.
2. The groove on the posterior surface of the malleolus lodges the tendons of the *peroneus brevis*, which is deep, and of the *peroneus longus*, which is superficial.

Blood Supply

The peroneal artery gives off the nutrient artery for the fibula, which enters the bone on its posterior surface. The nutrient foramen is directed downwards.

OSSIFICATION

- The fibula ossifies from 1 primary and 2 secondary centres.
- The primary centre for the shaft appears during the 8th week of IUL.
- A secondary centre for the lower end appears during the 1st year and fuses with the shaft by about 16th years. A secondary centre for the upper end appears during the 4th year and fuses with the shaft by about 18th year (Fig. 2.35).

Note: The fibula violates the law of ossification because the secondary centre which appears first in the lower end fuses earlier and not later. The reasons for this violation are as follows:
1. The secondary centre appears first in the lower end because it is a pressure epiphysis (law states that pressure epiphysis appears before the traction epiphysis).
2. The upper epiphysis fuses last because this is the growing end of the bone. It continues to grow afterwards along with the upper end of tibia which is a growing end.

CLINICAL ANATOMY

- Sometimes a surgeon takes a piece of bone from the part of the body and uses it to repair a defect in some other part. This procedure is called a ***bone graft***. For this purpose, pieces of bone are easily obtained from the subcutaneous medial aspect of tibia and shaft of fibula. Fibula is an ideal spare bone for a bone graft.

- ***Fracture of fibula:*** The most common type of fibular fracture is located at the distal end of fibula. Avulsion fracture of the head of fibula involves the fracture of head and displacement of part of bone due to the pull of biceps femoris muscle. It may result in non-union (Fig. 2.36).
- The common peroneal nerve can be rolled against the neck of fibula. This nerve is commonly injured here resulting in ***foot drop***.

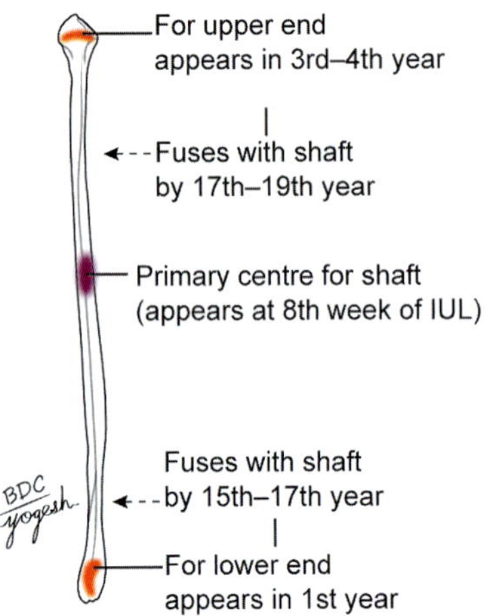

Fig. 2.35: Ossification of fibula

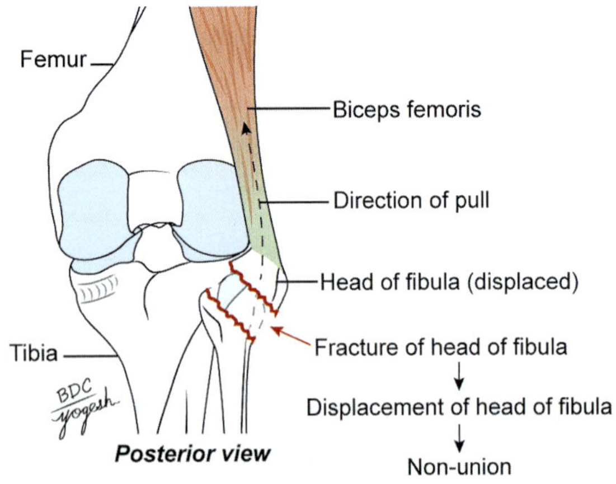

Fig. 2.36: Avulsion fracture of the head of fibula

Competency:
AN14.4 Identify and name various bones in the articulated foot with individual muscle attachment.

BONES OF THE FOOT

TARSUS/TARSALS

The tarsus is made up of 7 tarsal bones, arranged in rows as follows (Fig. 2.37):

Proximal row
- Talus (superior bone)
- Calcaneum (inferior bone)

Middle row
- Navicular (wedge-shaped)

Distal row (medial to lateral)
- Medial cuneiform
- Intermediate cuneiform
- Lateral cuneiform
- Cuboid bone

[*Mnemonic*: Tiger Cub Needs Medical Interventional Life Care.]

For major attachments and relations of all tarsal bones, *see* Table 2.2. For ossification of all tarsal bones, *see* Table 2.3.

TALUS

The talus (Latin *ankle*) is the 2nd largest tarsal bone. It lies between the tibia above and the calcaneum below, gripped on the sides by the two malleoli (Plate 2.15, Fig. 2.38).

It has a head, a neck and a body.

Side Determination and Anatomical Position

Hold the talus in such a way that
1. The rounded head is directed forward, slightly downward and medially.
2. Superior convex articular surface of body faces upward.
3. Large triangular facet on the lateral surface of body is directed towards the side of the bone to which the bone belongs.

Features

Head

1. It is directed forward and slightly downwards and medially.
2. Its *anterior surface* is oval and convex and articulates with the posterior surface of the navicular bone.
3. The *inferior surface* is marked by 3 articular areas separated by indistinct ridges as follows:
   a. The ***posterior facet*** is largest, oval and gently convex; it articulates with the middle facet on sustentaculum tali of the calcaneum.
   b. The ***anterolateral facet*** articulates with the anterior facet of the calcaneum.
   c. The ***medial facet*** with the spring ligament.

Neck

1. This is the constricted part of the bone between the head and the body.
2. When viewed from dorsal side, the long axis of the neck is directed downwards, forwards and medially. The ***neck–body angle*** is 130–140° in infants and 150° in adults. The smaller angle in young children accounts for the inverted position of their feet.
3. The medial part of its plantar surface is marked by a deep groove termed the ***sulcus tali***. The sulcus tali lies opposite the sulcus calcanei on the calcaneum, the two together enclosing a space called the ***sinus tarsi***.

Body

The body is cuboidal in shape and has 5 surfaces.
1. The ***superior surface*** bears an articular surface, which articulates with the lower end of the tibia to form the

Plate 2.15: Right talus

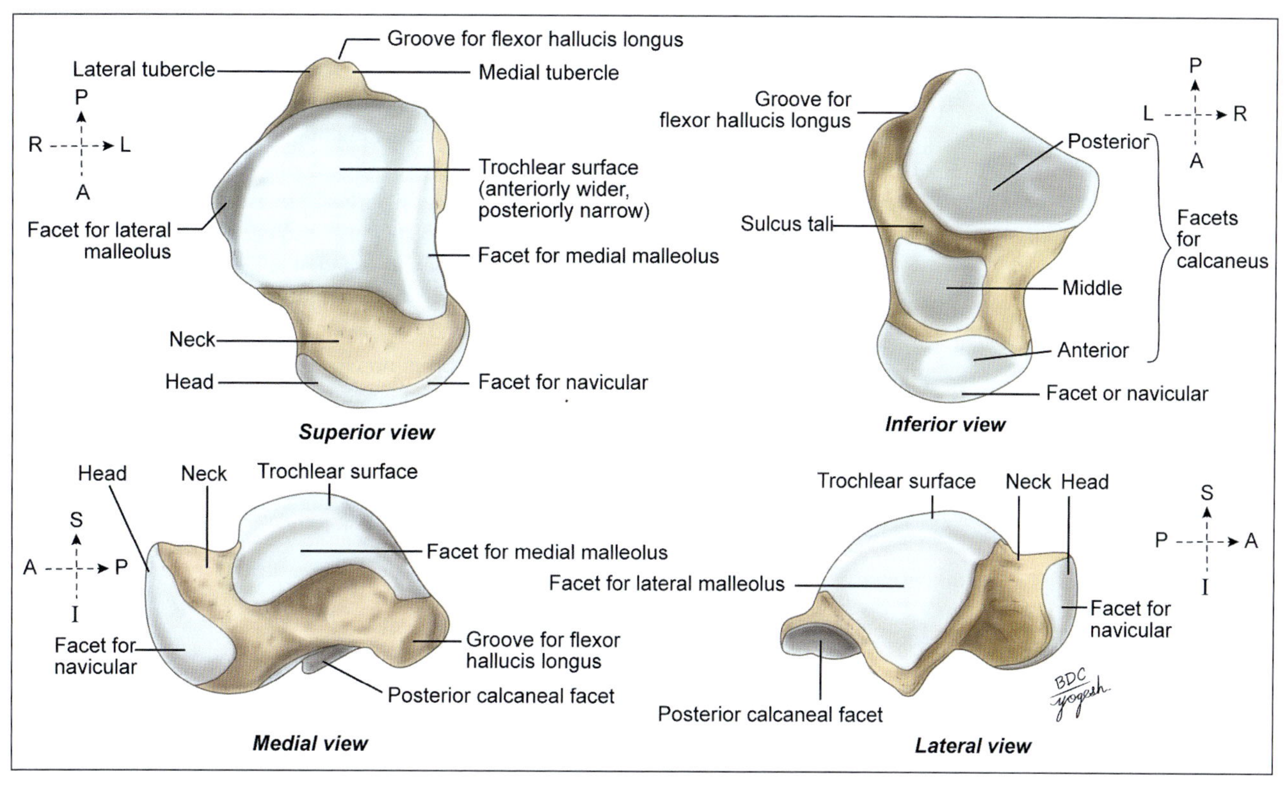

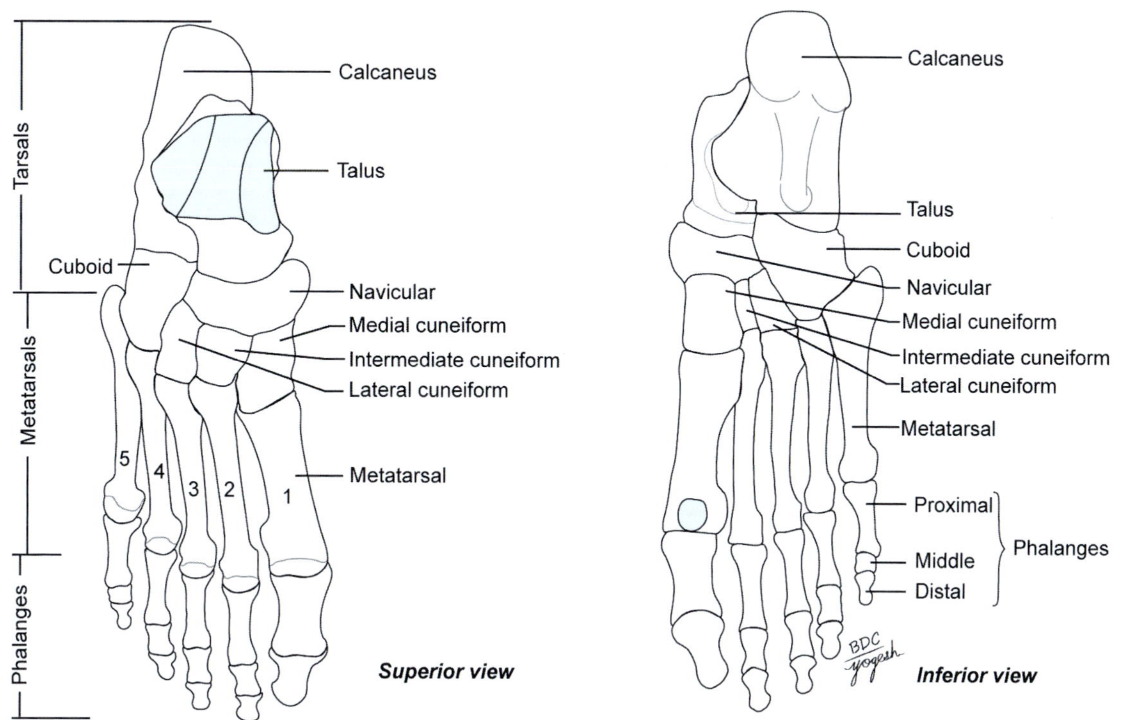

Fig. 2.37: Bones of the right foot

ankle joint. This surface is also called the ***trochlear surface***.

2. The ***inferior surface*** bears an oval, concave articular surface which articulates with the posterior facet of the calcaneum to form the subtalar joint.
3. The ***medial surface*** is articular above and non-articular below. The articular surface is ***comma-shaped*** and articulates with the medial malleolus of tibia.
4. The ***lateral surface*** bears a ***triangular articular surface*** for the lateral malleolus.

TABLE 2.2: Major attachments and relations of tarsal bone (Figs 2.40 and 2.41)

Tarsal bone	*Part*	*Attachments and relations*
Talus (no muscle attachment)	*Neck*	*Superior surface*: Capsular ligament of the ankle joint, dorsal talonavicular ligament *Inferior surface*: Interosseous talocalcaneal and cervical ligaments *Lateral surface*: Anterior talofibular ligament
	Body	*Superior surface*: Dorsal talonavicular ligament *Medial surface*: Anterior tibiotalar ligament, posterior tibiotalar ligament *Inferior surface*: Interosseous talocalcaneal and cervical ligaments *Posterior surface*: At medial tubercle—medial talocalcaneal ligament, groove lodges the tendon of the flexor hallucis longus
Calcaneus	Posterior surface	Middle rough area gives insertion of the tendo calcaneus and of the plantaris
	Superior surface	1. Origin to the extensor digitorum brevis 2. Stem of the inferior extensor retinaculum 3. Stem of the bifurcate ligament 4. Interosseous talocalcaneal ligament 5. Cervical ligament
	Superior or plantar surface	*Medial tubercle*: 1. Origin for the abductor hallucis 2. Flexor retinaculum 3. Origin to the flexor digitorum brevis 4. Plantar aponeurosis *Lateral tubercle*: Origin to the abductor digiti minimi *Anterior tubercle*: Short plantar ligament Rough strip between the three tubercles: Long plantar ligament
	Lateral surface	Calcaneofibular ligament *Peroneal tubercle*: 1. Lies between the tendons of the peroneus brevis above and the peroneus longus below 2. Attachment to inferior peroneal retinaculum
	Medial surface	Sustentaculum tali • Groove on its lower surface occupies the tendon of the flexor hallucis longus • *Medial margin*: 1. Spring ligament 2. A slip from the tibialis posterior 3. Deltoid ligament 4. Medial talocalcanean ligament 5. Origin of medial head of the flexor digitorum accessories
	Anterior surface	Articulates with cuboid
Navicular	Tuberosity	Insertion of the tibialis posterior
	Groove below the tuberosity	Transmits a part of the tendon of tibialis posterior
	Plantar surface	Spring ligament or plantar calcaneonavicular ligament
	Lateral surface	Calcaneonavicular part of the bifurcate ligament
	Dorsal surface	Talonavicular, cuneonavicular and cubonavicular ligaments
Medial cuneiform	Medial surface	Insertion of tibialis anterior
	Plantar surface	Insertion of tibialis posterior
	Lateral surface	Insertion of peroneus longus
Intermediate cuneiform	Plantar surface	Insertion of tibialis posterior
Lateral cuneiform	Plantar surface	Insertion of tibialis posterior
Cuboid	Lateral surface	Groove transmits tendon of the *peroneus longus*
	Plantar surface	Groove transmits tendon of the *peroneus longus* Ridge posterior to the groove – Long plantar ligament Posterior border – Short plantar ligament Posteromedial part a. Insertion to a slip from the tibialis posterior Origin to the flexor hallucis brevis
	Medial surface	Lateral limb of the bifurcate ligament

Note: All the metatarsals except talus receive insertion to a slip from the tibialis posterior.

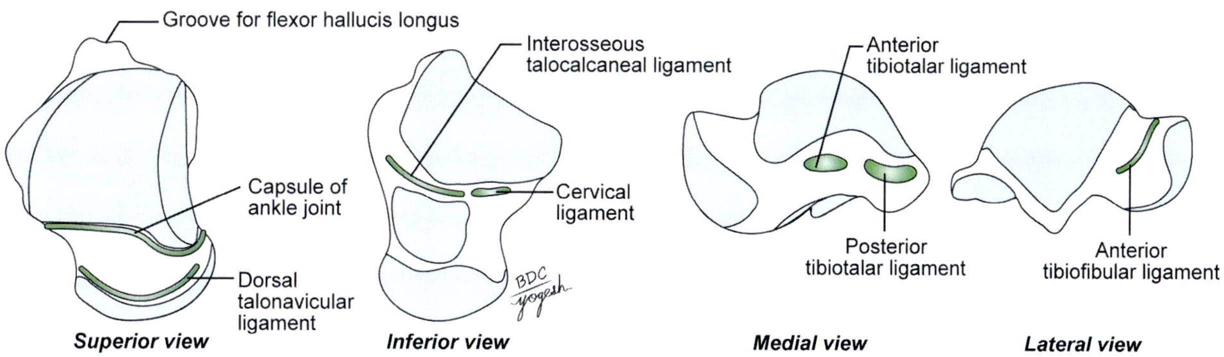

Fig. 2.38: Attachments of right talus

TABLE 2.3: Ossification of tarsal bones	
Tarsal bone	***Ossification***
Talus	1 primary centre: 6th month of intra-uterine life
Calcaneus	1 primary centre: 3rd month of intra-uterine life 1 secondary centre: between 6th and 8th year Fuses by 14th–16th year
Navicular	1 secondary centre: 3rd year of life
Medial cuneiform	1 secondary centre: 2nd year
Intermediate cuneiform	1 secondary centre: 3rd year
Lateral cuneiform	1 secondary centre: 1st year
Cuboid	1 primary centre: Appears just before birth

5. The ***posterior process*** is small and is marked by an oblique groove for tendon of *flexor hallucis longus*. The groove is bounded by medial and lateral tubercles. The lateral tubercle is occasionally separate (5%) and is then called the ***os trigonum***.

*Note: The **talus is devoid of muscular attachments**.*

CLINICAL ANATOMY

- ***Fracture of talus***: Forced dorsiflexion may cause fracture of the neck of the talus.
- ***Avascular necrosis of talus:*** If arteries to body of talus go through the neck only as occurs in some cases, the body would get avascular necrosis in fracture of its neck (Fig. 2.39). Normally, each artery goes through neck and body separately.

CALCANEUS OR CALCANEUM

The calcaneus (Latin *heel*) is the largest tarsal bone. It forms the prominence of the heel. Its long axis is directed forward, upward and laterally. It is roughly cuboidal and has six surfaces (Plate 2.16, Figs 2.42a to d).

Side Determination and Anatomical Position

Hold the calcaneus in such a way that:

1. Its anterior surface with a triangular facet looks forward, upward and laterally.

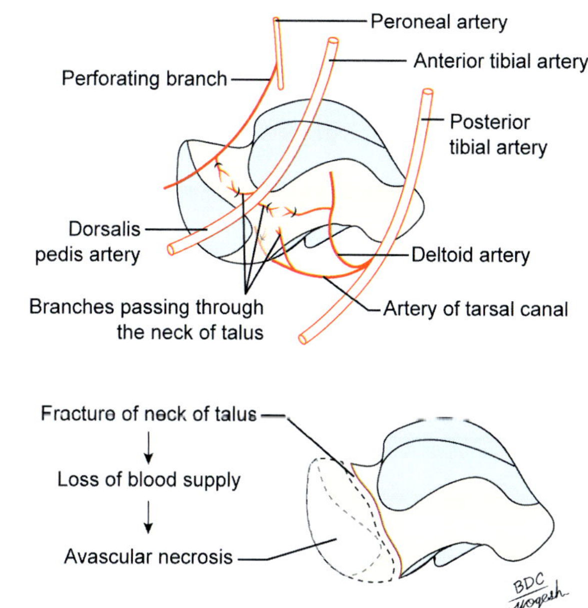

Fig. 2.39: Avascular necrosis of body of talus in some cases

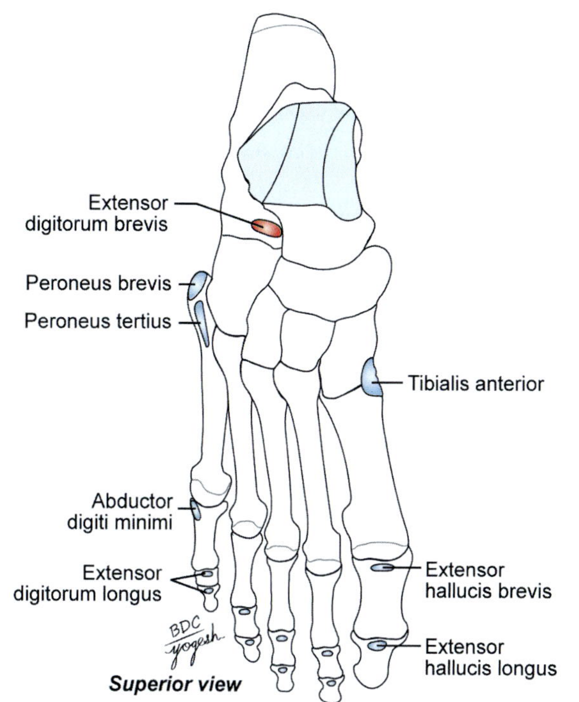

Fig. 2.40: Attachment of muscles to skeleton of the foot (dorsal aspect) except interossei

Plate 2.16: Right calcaneus

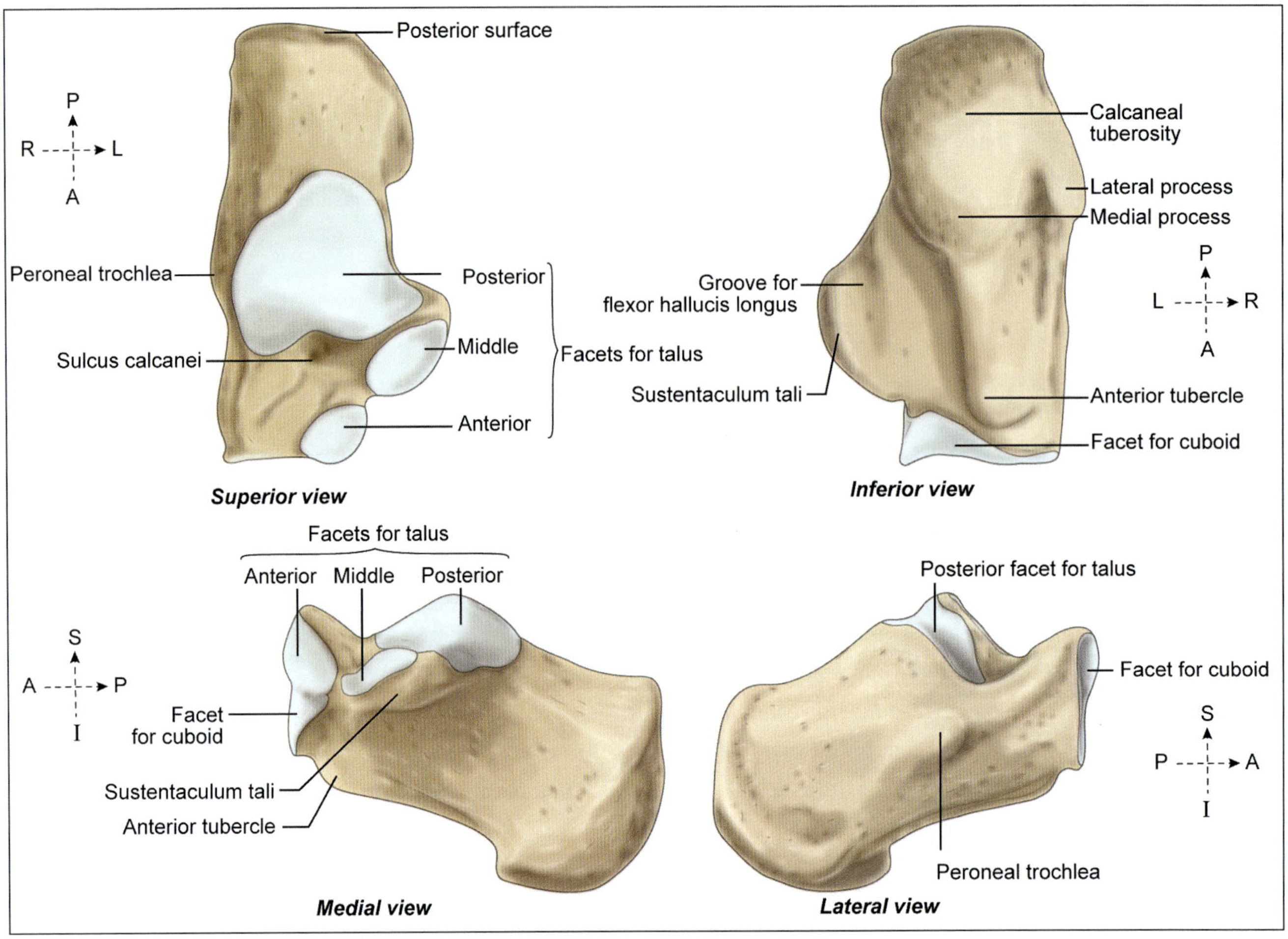

Posterior surface
P
R
L
A
Peroneal trochlea
Posterior
Middle
Facets for talus
Sulcus calcanei
Anterior
Superior view
Calcaneal tuberosity
Lateral process
Medial process
P
L
R
A
Groove for flexor hallucis longus
Sustentaculum tali
Anterior tubercle
Facet for cuboid
Inferior view
Facets for talus
Anterior
Middle
Posterior
S
A
P
I
Facet for cuboid
Sustentaculum tali
Anterior tubercle
Medial view
Posterior facet for talus
Facet for cuboid
S
P
A
I
Peroneal trochlea
Lateral view

Abductor hallucis
Flexor digitorum brevis
Flexor digitorum accessorius
Abductor digiti minimi
Long plantar ligament
Short plantar ligament
Tibialis posterior
Peroneus brevis
Flexor hallucis brevis
Flexor digiti minimi brevis
Tibialis anterior
Peroneus longus
Adductor hallucis (oblique head)
Adductor digiti minimi + flexor digiti minimi brevis
Abductor hallucis + medial part of flexor hallucis brevis
Adductor hallucis + lateral part of flexor hallucis brevis
Flexor digitorum brevis
Flexor digitorum longus
Flexor hallucis longus
Inferior view

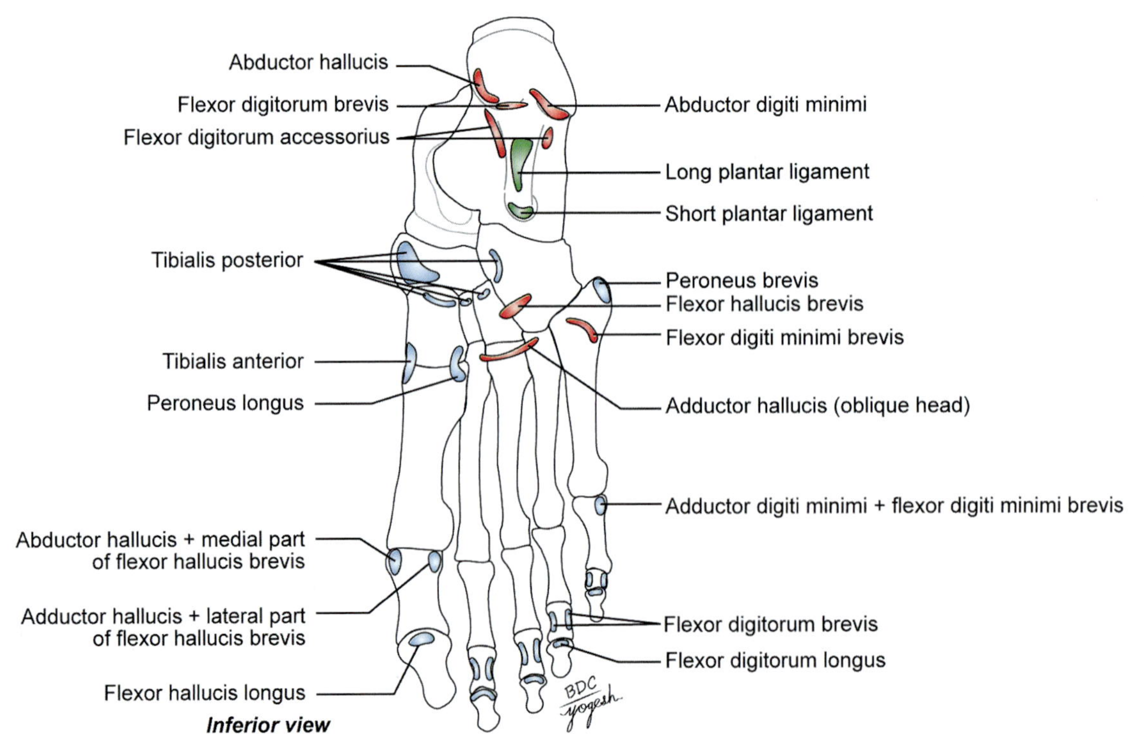

Fig. 2.41: Attachment to skeleton of the foot (plantar aspect) except interossei

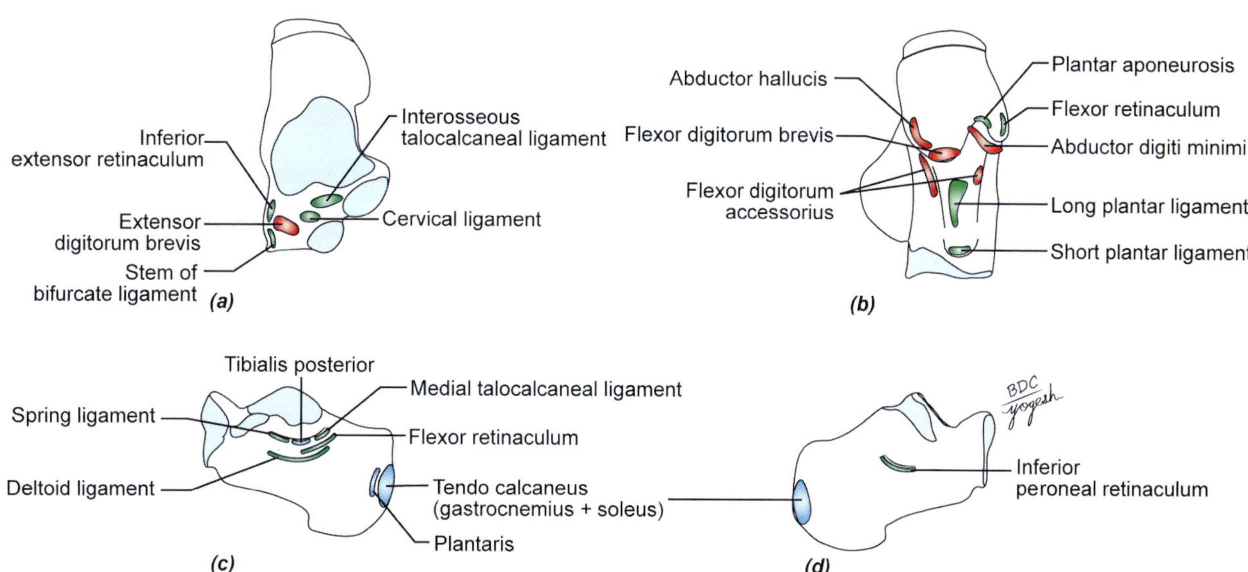

Figs 2.42a to d: Right calcaneus: (a) Superior view, (b) inferior view, (c) medial view, and (d) lateral view

2. Superior surface with an oval articular facet in its intermediate area looks upward.
3. Shelf-like bony projection sustentaculum tali on medial surface is directed to the side to which the bone belongs.

Features of Calcaneus

1. The ***anterior surface*** is the smallest surface of the bone. It is covered by a concavo-convex articular facet for the cuboid.
2. The ***posterior surface*** is divided into three areas—upper, middle and lower. The *upper area* is smooth and related to synovial bursa while the others are rough.
3. The *dorsal* or ***superior surface*** can be divided into three areas.
   a. The *posterior* 1/3rd is rough.
   b. The *middle* 1/3rd has the ovel, *posterior facet for talus.*
   c. The *anterior* 1/3rd is articular in the anteromedial part and non-articular in its posterolateral part. The articular part has *middle facet* present on the sustentaculum tali and an *anterior facet for talus.*
4. The ***plantar surface*** is rough and marked by three tubercles—medial, lateral and anterior tubercles. Medial and lateral tubercles are parts of ***calcaneum tuberosity***.
5. The ***lateral surface*** is flat. It presents in its anterior part, a small elevation termed the ***peroneal trochlea*** or *tubercle.*
6. The ***medial surface*** is concave from above downwards. The concavity is accentuated by the presence of a shelflike projection of bone, called the ***sustentaculum tali***, which projects medially from its anterosuperior border. The upper surface of this projection assists in the formation of the *talocalcaneonavicular joint*. Its lower surface is grooved.

CLINICAL ANATOMY

- Fracture of the calcaneum results by a fall from a height. Sustentaculum tali may get fractured in forced inversion of the foot.
- Calcaneum may develop a 'spur', which is painful (Fig. 2.43).

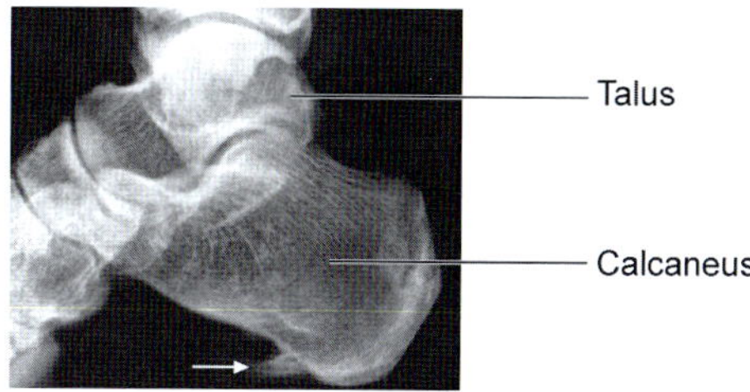

Fig. 2.43: Calcanean spur

NAVICULAR BONE

The navicular bone is boat-shaped. It is situated on the medial side of the foot, in front of the head of the talus and behind the three cuneiform bones (Figs 2.37, 2.40 and 2.41).

Anatomical Position

Hold the navicular bone in such a way that:

1. Its convex anterior surface carrying three articular facets face forward and concave posterior surface faces backwards.
2. Inferior surface with groove and bony projection points downwards.
3. Navicular tuberosity faces (medially) to the opposite side to which the bone belongs and helps to determine the side of the bone.

Features

1. The ***anterior surface*** is convex and is divided into three facets for the three cuneiform bones.

2. The ***posterior surface*** is concave and oval for articulation with the head of the talus.
3. The ***dorsal surface*** is broad and convex from side-to-side. It is rough for the attachment of ligaments.
4. The ***plantar surface*** is small and slightly concave from side to side. It is rough and non-articular.
5. The ***medial surface*** has a blunt and prominent *tuberosity*, directed downwards, the tuberosity is separated from the plantar surface by a *groove.*
6. The ***lateral surface*** is rough and irregular, but frequently has a facet for the cuboid.

CUNEIFORM BONES

Common Features

1. There are three cuneiform bones—medial, intermediate and lateral. The medial cuneiform is the largest and the intermediate cuneiform is the smallest (Figs 2.37, 2.40 and 2.41).
2. As their name suggests, these are ***wedge-shaped*** bones. In the medial cuneiform, the edge of the wedge forms the dorsal surface. In the intermediate and lateral cuneiforms, the thin edge of wedge forms the plantar surface. Medial cuneiform articulates proximally with navicular and distally with base of 1st metatarsal.
3. The anterior parts of the medial and lateral cuneiforms project further forwards than the intermediate cuneiform. This forms a deep recess for the base of second metatarsal bone.

MEDIAL CUNEIFORM

Features

1. *Dorsal surface* is formed by the rough edge of the wedge (Figs 2.37, 2.40 and 2.41).
2. *Plantar surface* is formed by the base of the wedge.
3. *Distal surface* has a large kidney-shaped facet for the base of the first metatarsal bone, with its hilum directed laterally.
4. *Proximal surface* is a pyriform facet for the navicular.
5. *Medial surface* is rough and subcutaneous.
6. *Lateral surface* is marked by an inverted L-shaped facet along the posterior and superior margins for the intermediate cuneiform bone. The anterosuperior part of the facet is separated by a vertical ridge. This part is for the base of second metatarsal bone. The anteroinferior part of the lateral surface is roughened.

INTERMEDIATE CUNEIFORM

Features

1. The *proximal* and *distal surfaces* bear triangular articular facets (Figs 2.37, 2.40 and 2.41).
2. The *lateral surface* is marked by a vertical facet along its posterior margin. This facet is for the lateral cuneiform bone. It is indented in the middle.
3. The *plantar surface* is formed by the edge of the wedge.

LATERAL CUNEIFORM

Features

1. The *proximal surface* is rough in its lower 1/3rd and has a triangular facet in its upper two-thirds for the navicular bone (Figs 2.37, 2.40 and 2.41).
2. The *lateral surface* is marked in its posterosuperior part by a triangular or oval facet for the cuboid.
3. Medially, it articulates with the intermediate cuneiform bone.
4. The *plantar surface* is formed by the edge of the wedge.

CUBOID

The cuboid is the lateral bone of the distal row of the tarsus, situated in front of the calcaneum and behind the fourth and fifth metatarsal bones. It has six surfaces (Figs 2.37, 2.40 and 2.41).

Anatomical Position

Hold the cuboid bone in such a way that:
1. Inferior surface carrying groove faces downwards.
2. Anterior surface carrying large facets faces forwards.
3. Notch on the lateral surface is directed to the side to which the bone belongs.

Features

1. The *proximal surface* is concavo-convex for articulation with the calcaneum.
2. The *distal surface* is also articular. It is divided by a vertical ridge into two areas for the fourth and fifth metatarsal bones.
3. The *dorsal surface* is rough for the attachment of ligaments. It is directed upwards and laterally.
4. The *plantar surface* is crossed anteriorly by an *oblique groove*. The groove is bounded posteriorly by a prominent ridge.
5. The *lateral surface* is short and notched.
6. The *medial surface* is extensive, being partly articular and partly non-articular. An oval facet in the middle articulates with the lateral cuneiform bone. Proximal to this a small facet may present for the navicular bone.

METATARSUS

1. The metatarsus is made up of 5 metatarsal bones, which are numbered from medial to lateral side.
2. Each metatarsal is a miniature long bone and has the following parts (Figs 2.37, 2.40 and 2.41).
   a. The ***shaft*** which is slightly convex dorsally and concave ventrally in its longitudinal axis. It is prismoid in form and tapers from base to the head.
   b. The ***base*** or proximal end is set obliquely in such a way that it projects backwards and laterally.
   c. The ***head*** or distal end is flattened from side-to-side.

Identification

First Metatarsal

1. First metatarsal is the *shortest, thickest* and *stoutest* of all metatarsal bones and is adapted for transmission of the body weight.
2. The proximal surface of the base has a kidney-shaped facet, which is concave outwards.

Second Metatarsal

1. Second metatarsal is the *longest* metatarsal. It has a wedge-shaped base.
2. The lateral side of the base has two articular facets—a larger dorsal and a smaller plantar—each of which is subdivided into a proximal part for the lateral cuneiform bone and a distal part for the third metatarsal.
3. The medial side of the base bears one facet, placed dorsally, for the medial cuneiform.

Third Metatarsal

1. The lateral side of the base has one facet, placed dorsally, for the fourth metatarsal bone.
2. The medial side of the base has two facets, dorsal and plantar, for second metatarsal bone.

Fourth Metatarsal

1. The proximal surface of the base is quadrangular. It articulates with the cuboid bone.
2. The lateral side of the base has one facet, placed dorsally, for the fifth metatarsal bone.
3. The medial side of the base has one facet, placed dorsally, which is subdivided into a proximal part for the lateral cuneiform and a distal part for third metatarsal bone.

Fifth Metatarsal

1. The lateral side of the base has a large tuberosity or styloid process projecting backwards and laterally.
2. The medial side of the base has one facet for the fourth metatarsal bone.
3. The plantar surface of the base is grooved by the tendon of the *abductor digiti minimi.*

Important Attachments (Figs 2.40 and 2.41)

1. A part of the tibialis anterior is inserted on the medial side of the base of the 1st metatarsal bone.
2. The greater part of the peroneus longus is inserted on a large impression at the inferior angle of the lateral surface of the base of the 1st metatarsal bone.
3. The peroneus brevis is inserted on the dorsal surface of the tuberosity of the 5th metatarsal bone.
4. The peroneus tertius is inserted on the medial part of the dorsal surface of the base and the medial border of the shaft of the 5th metatarsal bone.
5. The flexor digiti minimi brevis arises from the plantar surface of the base of the 5th metatarsal bone.
6. The shafts of metatarsal bones give origin to 4 bipennate dorsal and 3 unipennate plantar interossei muscles.

OSSIFICATION

- Each metatarsal bone ossifies from one primary and one secondary centre.
- The primary centre appears in the shaft during the 10th week of foetal life in the 1st metatarsal and during the 9th week of foetal life in the rest of the metatarsals.
- A secondary centre appears for the base of the 1st metatarsal during the 3rd year and for the heads of the other metatarsals between 3rd and 4th years. All secondary centres unite with the shaft by 18th year. A separate centre for the tuberosity of the 5th metatarsal bone may be present.

METACARPALS VERSUS METATARSALS

The metatarsals are quite similar to metacarpals. The differences between the metacarpals and metatarsals are shown in Table 2.4.

TABLE 2.4: Differences between metacarpals and metatarsals

Metacarpals	*Metatarsals*
1. The head and shaft are prismoid	1. The head and shaft are flattened from side to side
2. The shaft of uniform thickness	2. The shaft tapers distally
3. The dorsal surface of the shaft has an elongated, flat triangular area	3. The dorsal surface of the shaft is uniformly convex
4. The base is irregular	4. The base appears to be cut sharply and obliquely

PHALANGES

There are 14 phalanges in each foot; 2 for the great toe and 3 for each of the other toes. As compared to the phalanges of the hand, these are much smaller in size, and the shafts particularly of first row are compressed from side to side. Otherwise, their arrangement and features are similar in two limbs (Figs 2.37, 2.40 and 2.41).

Attachments (Figs 2.40 and 2.41)

1. On bases of distal phalanges
   a. Lateral four toes: Flexor digitorum longus on the plantar surface and the dorsal digital expansion on the dorsal surface.
   b. Great toe: Flexor hallucis longus on the plantar surface and part of the extensor hallucis longus on the dorsal surface.
2. On shaft and bases of middle phalanges flexor digitorum brevis on each side of the shaft on plantar surface; and part of extensor expansion on the dorsal surface.
3. On bases of proximal phalanges
   a. Second, third and fourth toes: A lumbrical muscle on the medial side and an interosseous muscle on each side.
   b. Fifth toe: A plantar interosseous muscle on the medial side and the abductor digiti minimi and the flexor digiti minimi brevis on the lateral side.

c. Great toe, abductor hallucis and part of the flexor hallucis medially, adductor hallucis and the remaining part of the flexor hallucis brevis laterally.

4. The fibrous flexor sheath is attached to the margins of the proximal and middle phalanges of the lateral four toes.

OSSIFICATION

Phalanx ossifies by one primary centre for the shaft which appears in tenth week of foetal life. The single secondary centre appears in the base. It appears in the proximal phalanx in 2nd year, middle phalanx in 3rd year and in distal phalanx in the 6th year.

These fuse with the respective shafts by 18th year. The big toe has two phalanges and their secondary centres appear in 2nd and 3rd years and fuse with shaft in 18th year.

CLINICAL ANATOMY

- Adventitious bursae develop due to excessive or abnormal friction, for example, bursa over tendo calcaneus due to ill-fitting shoes.
- Bunion is an adventitious bursa on the medial side of the head of 1st metatarsal bone.
- Fracture of tuberosity of 5th metatarsal bone may occur due to the pull of peroneus brevis muscle.
- Fracture of 2nd, 3rd, 4th or 5th metatarsal bones is common in soldiers and policemen and is called '***march fracture***' (Fig. 2.44).

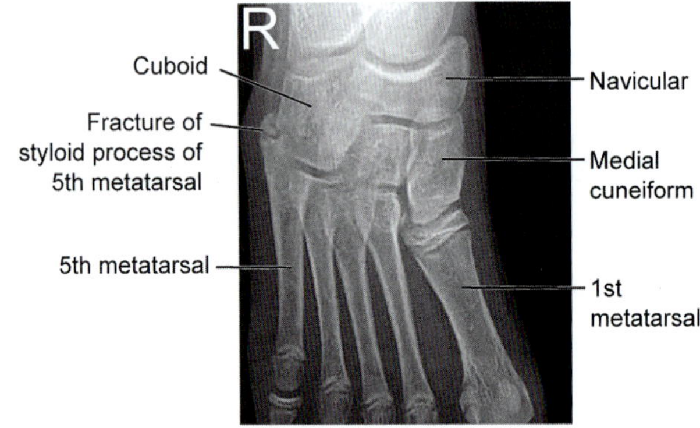

Fig. 2.44: Fracture of styloid process of 5th metatarsal

Video 2.2.1 Hip Bone ▶ Introduction ▶ Side identification ▶ Attachments and relations
Video 2.2.2 Femur ▶ General features and side identification ▶ Attachments and relations
Video 2.2.3 Patella
Video 2.2.4 Tibia ▶ Introduction and general features ▶ Attachments and relations of upper end, shaft, lower end
Video 2.2.5 Fibula ▶ Introduction and general features ▶ Attachments and relations ▶ Muscles attached to fibula and bones of foot
Video 2.2.6 Tarsus ▶ Introduction and general features
Video 2.2.7 Metatarsals and Phalanges ▶ Introduction and attachments
Video 2.2.8 Joints of the Foot

Facts to Remember

- Ossification of the lower end of the femur is of medicolegal importance. Presence of its centre in a newborn child found dead indicates that the child was viable, i.e. it was capable of independent existence.
- Iliac crest of hip bone is used for bone marrow biopsy.
- Femur is the longest and strongest bone.
- Fibula is mostly used for bone graft.
- Tibia has the largest nutrient artery in the body.
- Talus bone has no muscle attachment.
- First metatarsal has two sesamoid bones on the plantar surface of its head for transmitting double the amount of weight to the ground as compared to second to fifth metatarsal bones
- The metatarsal bones give origin to the dorsal and plantar interossei muscles.
- Lateral tubercle of posterior process of talus is an atavistic epiphysis.
- Calcaneus is the first tarsal bone to start ossification, and it is the largest and strongest bone of the foot.

BDC's Anatomy *e*-book

1. Structures of femur
2. Blood supply of head of femur
3. Fractures of femur
4. Sesamoid bones in lower limb
5. Further reading
6. Viva voce questions

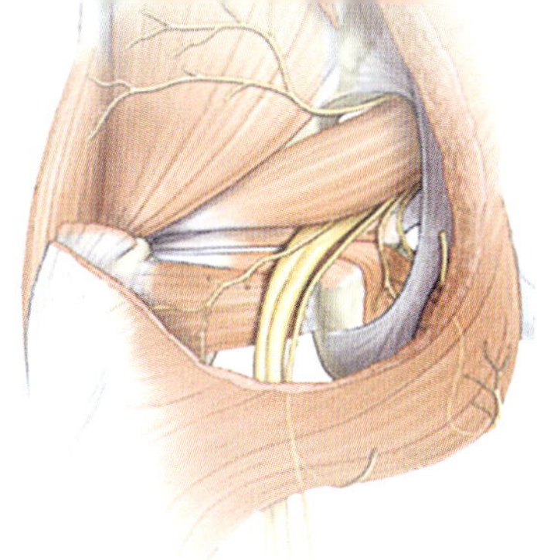

Chapter

3

Front of Thigh

For study purposes, the thigh is divided into three regions – front of the thigh, medial side of the thigh, and the back of the thigh. The front of thigh extends between the hip and knee joints.

SURFACE LANDMARKS

1. ***Iliac crest*** is a thick, curved bony margin, forming laterally the lower margin of the waist. The hands are often supported on the iliac crests in a relaxed standing posture. ***Anterior superior iliac spine*** (ASIS) is the anterior end of the iliac crest (Fig. 3.1). ***Tubercle of the iliac crest*** is a low bony prominence situated on the outer lip of the iliac crest about 5 cm behind the anterior superior iliac spine.
2. ***Fold of groin*** is a shallow curved groove extending from anterior superior iliac spine to the pubic tubercle. It overlies the inguinal ligament and separates the front of the thigh from the anterior abdominal wall.
3. ***Pubic tubercle*** is a small bony projection felt at the medial end of the fold of groin. ***Pubic crest*** is a short bony ridge between the pubic tubercle and pubic symphysis (Fig. 3.2).
4. ***Greater trochanter*** of femur lies a hand breadth below the ***tubercle of iliac crest***, forming a wide prominence just in front of the hollow on the side of the hip.
5. ***Midinguinal point*** lies midway between the anterior superior iliac spine and the pubic symphysis (Fig. 3.2). The femoral artery and the head of the femur lie beneath the midinguinal point.
6. ***Midpoint of inguinal ligament*** lies slightly lateral to midinguinal point. It is the middle point of inguinal ligament, at the midway between ASIS and pubic tubercle. Femoral nerve lies beneath it.
7. ***Patella*** (knee cap) is the largest sesamoid bone of the body and develops in the tendon of quadriceps femoris. It is easily seen and felt in front of the knee. It can be moved freely in a fully extended knee.
8. ***Ligamentum patellae*** can be felt as a strong fibrous band extending from the patella to tibial tuberosity.

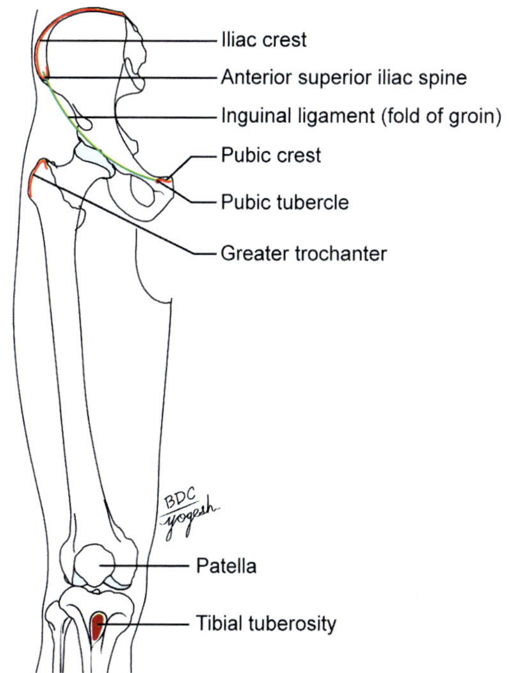

Fig. 3.1: Surface landmarks of the thigh

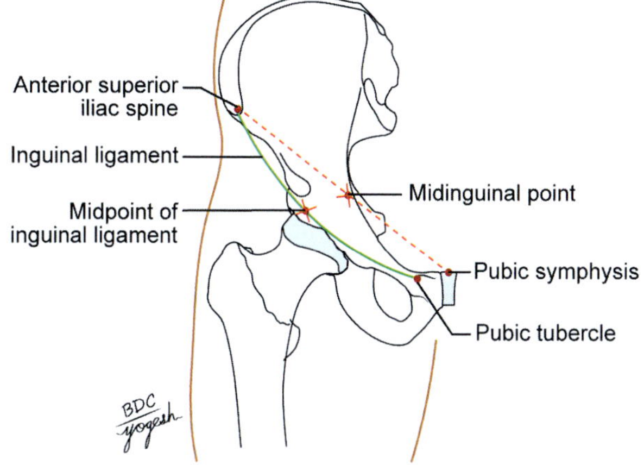

Fig. 3.2: Midinguinal point and midpoint of inguinal ligament

9. ***Tibial tuberosity*** is a blunt prominence in front of the upper end of tibia, marking the upper end of the shin.

10. The medial and lateral ***condyles of the femur*** and ***of the tibia*** form large bony masses at the sides of the knee. The most prominent points on the sides of the femoral condyles are called the medial and lateral ***epicondyles***. Vastus medialis forms a fleshy prominence above the medial condyle of femur, particularly in an extended knee.
11. ***Adductor tubercle*** is a bony projection from the uppermost part of the medial condyle of femur to which the tendon of adductor magnus is attached. To palpate the tubercle, flex the knee partly and note the wide, shallow groove that appears posterior to the mass of vastus medialis. The tendon of adductor magnus can be felt in this groove. The tendon can be traced down to the adductor tubercle.

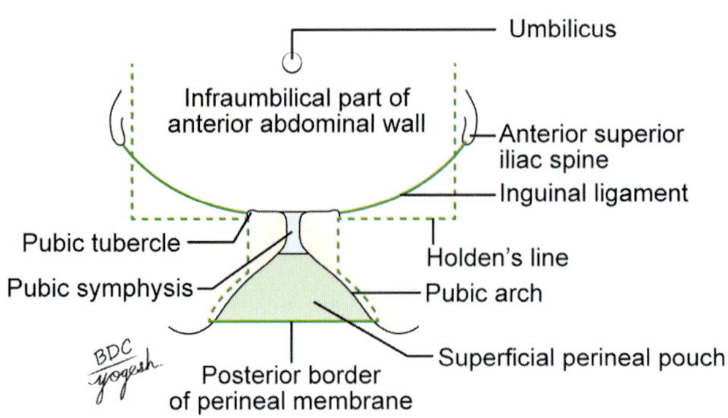

Fig. 3.3: Superficial area into which urine may pass when urethra is injured. The areas within the interrupted lines have a well-defined membranous layer of superficial fascia

SKIN AND SUPERFICIAL FASCIA

SKIN

The skin of thigh, in the region around pubic symphysis, is studded with hair. The presence of few stitches indicates that embalming for preservation of the body has been done from this site.

SUPERFICIAL FASCIA

The superficial fascia has *two layers*—a superficial fatty layer and a deep membranous layer, which are continuous with the corresponding layers of the anterior abdominal wall.

The ***membranous layer*** is loosely attached to the deep fascia of the thigh except near the inguinal ligament, where it is firmly attached along a horizontal line. The line of firm attachment is called ***Holden's line***. It begins a little lateral to the pubic tubercle and extends laterally for about 8 cm (Fig. 3.3).

Contents: The superficial fascia contains:
1. Cutaneous nerves
2. Cutaneous arteries
3. Great saphenous vein and its tributaries
4. Superficial inguinal lymph nodes.

CLINICAL ANATOMY

When the urethra is injured in the perineum, urine may flow out or extravasate into the interval deep into the membranous layer of superficial fascia. This urine can pass up into the anterior abdominal wall from where it can enter the upper part of the thigh. However, the firm attachment of the membranous layer of superficial fascia to the deep fascia along Holden's line prevents urine from descending into the thigh beyond the line.

Cutaneous Nerves

The skin of the front of the thigh is supplied by following cutaneous nerves (Figs 3.4 to 3.6):
1. Ilioinguinal nerve
2. Femoral branch of the genitofemoral nerve

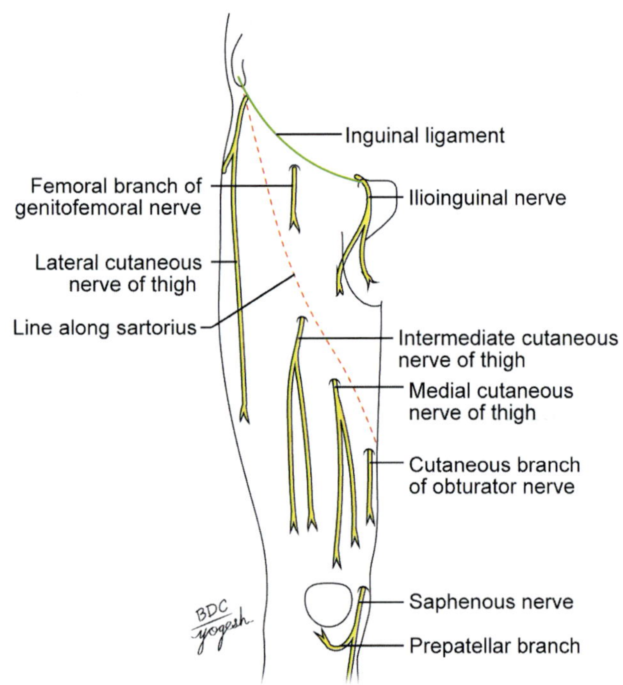

Fig. 3.4: Cutaneous nerves on the front of the thigh

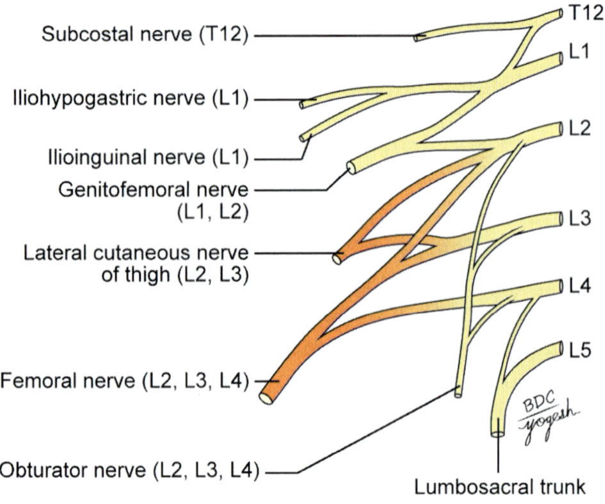

Fig. 3.5: Lumbar plexus and its branches

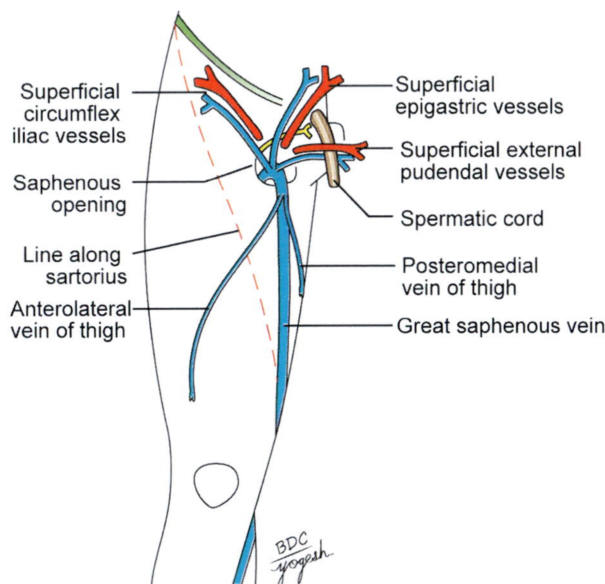

Fig. 3.6: Superficial nerves and vessels seen on the front of the thigh

3. Lateral cutaneous nerve of the thigh
4. Intermediate cutaneous nerve of the thigh
5. Medial cutaneous nerve of the thigh
6. Saphenous nerve
7. Cutaneous branch of the obturator nerve.

Note:

Ilioinguinal nerve (L1): It emerges at the superficial inguinal ring, and supplies the skin at the root of the penis or over the mons pubis in the female, the anterior 1/3rd of the scrotum or labium majus, and the superomedial part of the thigh (Fig. 3.5).

Femoral branch of genitofemoral nerve (L1, L2): It pierces the femoral sheath and the overlying deep fascia 2 cm below the midinguinal point, and supplies most of the skin over the femoral triangle.

Lateral cutaneous nerve of thigh (L2, L3): It is a branch of the lumbar plexus. It emerges behind the lateral end of the inguinal ligament, divides into anterior and posterior branches, and supplies the skin on the anterolateral side of the thigh and the anterior part of the gluteal region.

Intermediate cutaneous nerve of thigh (L2, L3): It is a branch of the anterior division of the femoral nerve. It pierces the deep fascia at the junction of the upper 1/3rd and middle 1/3rd of the thigh. It divides into two or more branches and supplies a strip of skin on the front of the thigh, extending from the sartorius to the knee.

Medial cutaneous nerve of the thigh (L2, L3): It is a branch of the anterior division of the femoral nerve. It divides into anterior and posterior divisions. The nerve supplies the skin on the medial side of the lower 2/3rd of the thigh.

Saphenous nerve (L3, L4): It is a branch of the posterior division of the femoral nerve. It pierces the deep fascia on the medial side of the knee, runs down in front of the great saphenous vein, and supplies the skin on the medial side of the leg and foot up to the ball of the big toe. Before piercing the deep fascia, the saphenous nerve gives off the ***infrapatellar branch***, which runs downwards and laterally, and supplies the skin over the ligamentum patellae.

Cutaneous branch of obturator nerve (L2, L3): It is a small branch that arises from the anterior division of the obturator nerve. It supplies the lower 1/3rd of medial aspect of the thigh.

Patellar Plexus

Patellar plexus is a plexus of fine nerves situated in front of the patella, the ligamentum patellae and the upper end of the tibia. It is formed by contributions from:

1. The anterior division of the lateral cutaneous nerve
2. The intermediate cutaneous nerve
3. The anterior division of the medial cutaneous nerve
4. The infrapatellar branch of the saphenous nerve.

CLINICAL ANATOMY

- Injury to femoral nerve results in sensory loss on the anterior aspect of thigh and front of leg including medial border of foot till the ball of big toe—positions A1 and A2 in Fig. 3.7.
- Lateral cutaneous nerve of thigh may get entangled in the inguinal ligament. This leads to pain on lateral side of thigh. It is called ***'meralgia paraesthetica'***—position B in Fig. 3.7.

Cutaneous Arteries

Three small arteries arising from the femoral artery can be seen a little below the inguinal ligament (Fig. 3.6).

1. *Superficial external pudendal artery* pierces the cribriform fascia, runs medially in front of the spermatic cord, and supplies the external genitalia.
2. *Superficial epigastric artery* pierces the cribriform fascia, runs towards the umbilicus, and supplies the lower part of anterior abdominal wall.
3. *Superficial circumflex iliac artery* pierces the fascia lata lateral to saphenous opening, runs upwards below the inguinal ligament, and anastomoses at the anterior superior iliac spine with deep circumflex iliac, superior gluteal and lateral circumflex femoral arteries.

Great or Long Saphenous Vein

This is the largest and longest superficial vein of the lower limb (*Saphes* = easily seen) (Fig. 3.6).

Beginning and course: It begins on the dorsum of the foot from the medial end of the dorsal venous arch, and runs upwards in front of the medial malleolus, along the medial side of the leg and behind the knee.

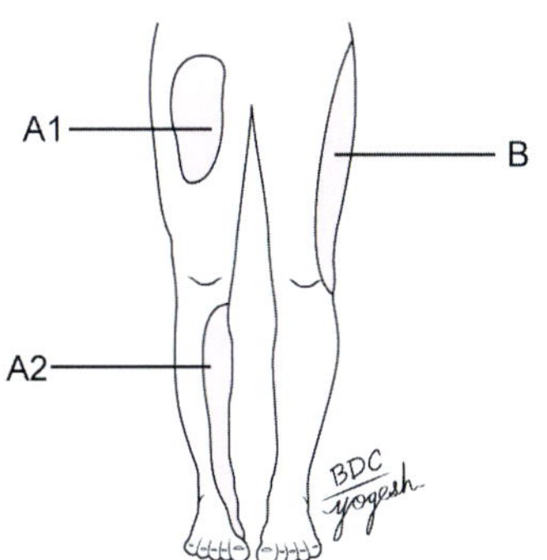

Fig. 3.7: (A1, A2) Sensory loss due to injury to femoral nerve, and (B) meralgia paraesthetica

Termination: In the thigh, it inclines forwards to reach the saphenous opening, where it pierces the cribriform fascia and opens into the femoral vein.

Tributaries: Before piercing the cribriform fascia, it receives three named tributaries corresponding to the three cutaneous arteries, and also many unnamed tributaries. It also receives blood from the anterolateral vein of thigh, posteromedial vein of thigh and deep external pudendal vein.

Superficial Inguinal Lymph Nodes

The superficial inguinal lymph nodes are variable in their number and size. Their arrangement is T-shaped, there being a lower vertical group and an upper horizontal group. The upper nodes can be subdivided into the upper lateral and upper medial groups (Fig. 3.8).

1. *Lower vertical group* drains lymph from most of the lower limb.
2. *Upper lateral group* drains lymph from lateral parts of infraumbilical part of anterior abdominal wall and gluteal region.
3. *Upper medial group* drains lymph from medial parts of infraumbilical part of anterior abdominal wall and external genital organs including the terminal ends of the *urethra, anal canal* and *vagina.*

Subcutaneous Bursae

Bursae are lubricating mechanisms that are provided at sites of friction to smoothen movement. Undue pressure on them may cause their pathological enlargement. Bursae present in relation to the patella are described here.

Prepatellar Bursa

Prepatellar bursa lies in front of the lower part of the patella and the upper part of the ligamentum patellae.

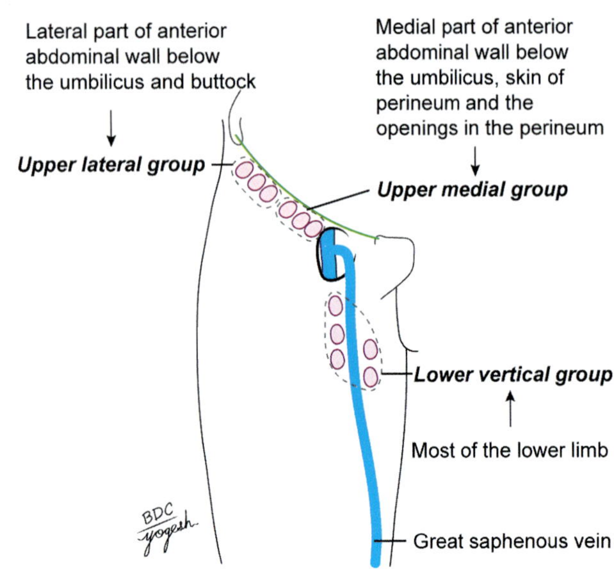

Fig. 3.8: Superficial inguinal lymph nodes

Subcutaneous Infrapatellar Bursa

Subcutaneous infrapatellar bursa lies in front of lower part of the tibial tuberosity and of the lower part of the ligamentum patellae.

Deep Bursae

Two deep bursae are also present. These are suprapatellar bursa and deep infrapatellar bursa.

DISSECTION

Make a curved incision from anterior superior iliac spine to the pubic tubercle.

Give a curved incision around the scrotum/pudendal cleft towards upper medial side of thigh. Extend it vertically down below the medial condyle of tibia till the level of tibial tuberosity.

Now make a horizontal incision below the tibial tuberosity till the lateral side of leg (Fig. 3.9).

Reflect the skin laterally, exposing the superficial fatty and deeper membranous layers of superficial fascia. Remove the fatty layer.

Identify the great saphenous vein in the medial part of anterior surface of thigh. Draining into its upper part are its three superficial tributaries, namely superficial circumflex iliac, superficial epigastric and superficial external pudendal. The vertical group of superficial inguinal lymph nodes lies along the upper part of great saphenous vein.

Dissect the superficial inguinal ring 1 cm above and lateral to the pubic tubercle. The spermatic cord and ilioinguinal nerve leave the abdomen through this ring.

Trace the great saphenous vein backwards till it pierces the specialised deep fascia known as cribriform fascia to drain into the femoral vein enclosed in the femoral sheath.

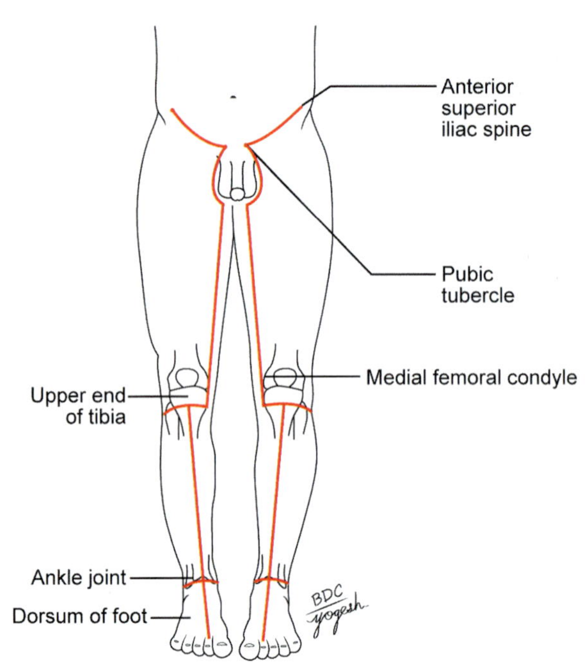

Fig. 3.9: Lines of dissection

DEEP FASCIA

DEEP FASCIA/FASCIA LATA

The *fascia lata* is a tough fibrous sheath that envelops the whole of the thigh like a sleeve (Fig. 3.10).

Attachments: Its attachments are as follows:

1. *Superiorly*, it is attached to the boundary line between the lower limb and the pelvis. Thus, anteriorly, it is attached to the inguinal ligament; laterally to the iliac crest; posteriorly, through the gluteal fascia to the sacrum, coccyx and sacrotuberous ligament; and medially to the pubis, the pubic arch and the ischial tuberosity.
2. *Inferiorly*, on the front and sides of the knee, the fascia lata is attached to subcutaneous bony prominences and the capsule of the knee joint. Posteriorly, it forms the strong popliteal fascia, which is continuous below with the fascia of the back of the leg.

CLINICAL ANATOMY

The fascia lata is attached to the inguinal ligament. Extension of the thighs pulls the abdominal wall downwards and makes it tense. To relax the abdomen fully for palpation by an examining physician, the patient is asked to draw the legs up. This overcomes the pull of the fascia lata on the abdominal wall. Iliotibial tract is used to replace the dura mater or a ruptured tendon of a muscle.

Modifications of Fascia Lata

Iliotibial Tract

The fascia lata is thickened laterally where it forms a 5 cm wide band called the iliotibial tract (Fig. 3.10).

Attachments: *Superiorly,* the tract splits into two layers. The superficial, lamina is attached to tubercle of iliac crest and deep lamina to the capsule of hip joint. *Inferiorly,* the tract is attached to a smooth area on anterior surface of the lateral condyle of tibia.

Functional significance: The importance of the iliotibial tract is as follows:

1. *Site for muscle insertion:* Two important muscles are inserted into its upper part, between the superficial and deep laminae. These are the 3/4th part of the *gluteus maximus*; and the *tensor fasciae latae*.
2. *Stabilization of knee:* The iliotibial tract stabilizes the knee both in extension and in partial flexion; and is, therefore, used constantly during walking and running. In leaning forwards with slightly flexed knees, the tract is the main support of the knee against gravity.

Saphenous Opening

This is an oval opening in the fascia lata. The centre of the opening is 4 cm below and 4 cm lateral to the pubic tubercle (Plate 3.1).

Plate 3.1: Right saphenous opening

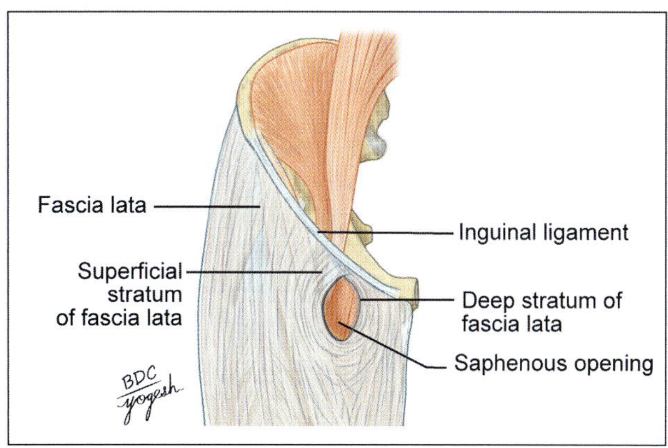

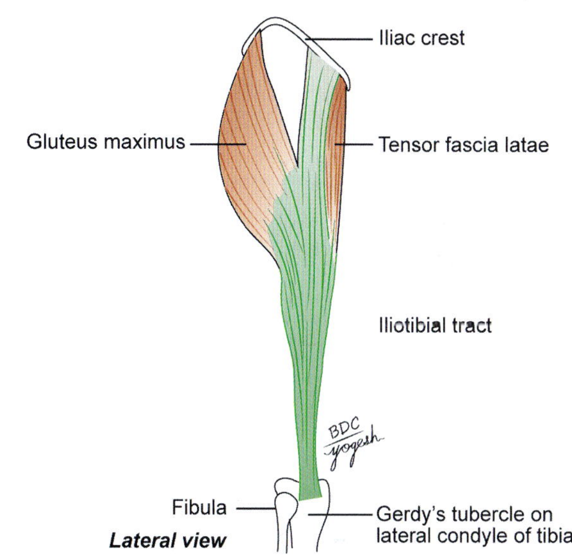

Fig. 3.10: Iliotibial tract with insertion of two muscles

It is about 2.5 cm long and 2 cm broad. The opening has a sharp crescentic lateral margin or *falciform margin*, which lies in front of the femoral sheath. The medial ill-defined margin of the opening lies at a deeper level. It is formed by the fascia overlying the pectineus. The fascia passes behind the femoral sheath (Fig. 3.6).

The saphenous opening is closed by the ***cribriform fascia*** formed by modification of superficial fascia, which covers the opening.

Structures passing through saphenous opening—

1. Great saphenous vein
2. Superficial epigastric and superficial external pudendal vessels
3. Lymphatics from superficial to deep inguinal nodes

Intermuscular Septa

Three intermuscular septa divide the thigh into three compartments (Fig. 3.11).

1. The *lateral intermuscular septum* is the thickest of these septa. It extends from the iliotibial tract to

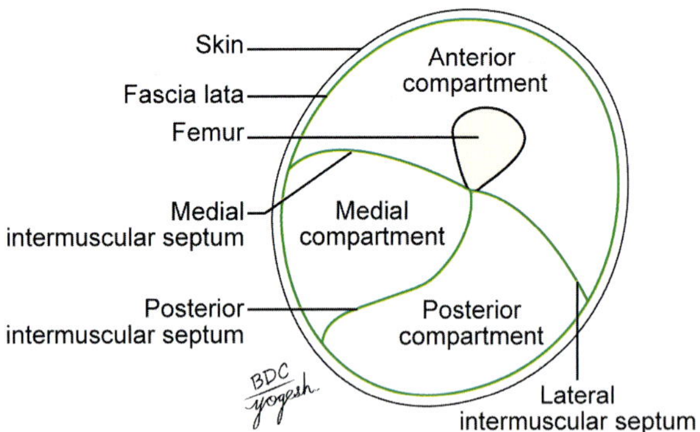

Fig. 3.11: Intermuscular septa and compartments of thigh

the lateral lip of the linea aspera. It separates the anterior compartment of the thigh from the posterior compartment.

2. The *medial intermuscular septum* is attached to the medial lip of the linea aspera, and separates the anterior compartment of the thigh from the medial compartment.
3. The *posterior intermuscular septum* is poorly defined. It separates the medial compartment of the thigh from the posterior compartment.

DISSECTION

After the reflection of the superficial fascia, the deep fascia of thigh is visible. Study its attachments, modifications and extensions.

Follow the great saphenous vein through the cribriform fascia and the anterior wall of femoral sheath into the femoral vein. The femoral vein occupies the intermediate compartment of the femoral sheath. Medial compartment of femoral sheath is the femoral canal occupied by a lymph node, while the lateral compartment is occupied by the femoral artery.

Give a vertical incision in the deep fascia of thigh from tubercle of iliac crest to the lateral condyle of femur and remove the deep fascia or fascia lata in lateral part of thigh. This will expose the tensor fasciae latae muscle and gluteus maximus muscle getting attached to iliotibial tract. Identify the four heads of quadriceps femoris muscle.

Remove the entire deep fascia from upper 1/3rd of the front of thigh. Identify the sartorius muscle stretching gently across the thigh from lateral to medial side and the adductor longus muscle extending from medial side of thigh towards lateral side into the femur, being crossed by the sartorius. This triangular depression in the upper 1/3rd of thigh is the femoral triangle. The medial border of sartorius forms lateral boundary and medial border of adductor longus forms medial boundary. The base of this triangle is formed by the inguinal ligament. Dissect its boundaries, and contents, e.g. femoral nerve, artery and vein and accompanying structures.

Expose the sartorius muscle till its insertion into the upper medial surface of shaft of tibia.

Competency:

AN15.3 Describe and demonstrate boundaries, floor, roof and contents of femoral triangle.

FEMORAL TRIANGLE

Femoral triangle is a triangular depression on the front of the upper 1/3rd of the thigh immediately below the inguinal ligament (Figs 3.12 to 3.16, Plates 3.2 and 3.3, Flowchart 3.1).

Boundaries

***Lateral*:** Medial border of *sartorius*.

***Medial*:** Medial border of the *adductor longus*.

***Base*:** Inguinal ligamtent.

***Apex*:** It is directed downwards and is formed by the point where the medial and lateral boundaries cross. The apex is continuous, below with the adductor canal.

***Roof*:**

a. Skin
b. *Superficial fascia* containing the superficial inguinal lymph nodes, the femoral branch of the genitofemoral nerve, branches of the ilioinguinal nerve, superficial

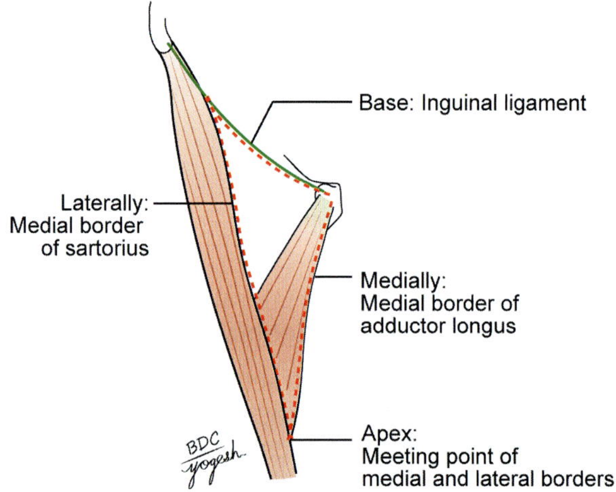

Fig. 3.12: Boundaries of the right femoral triangle

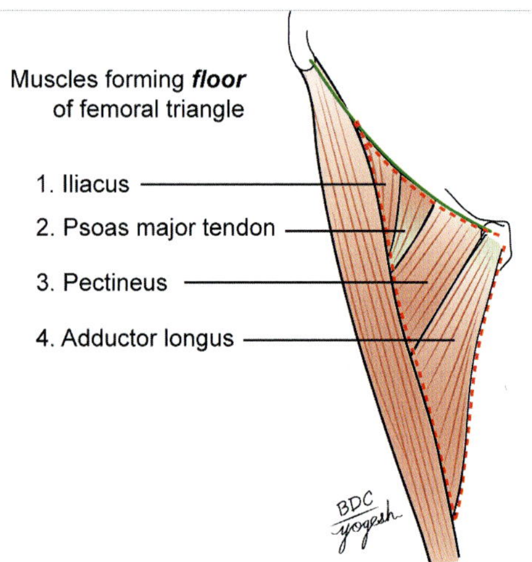

Fig. 3.13: Muscles forming the floor of the right femoral triangle

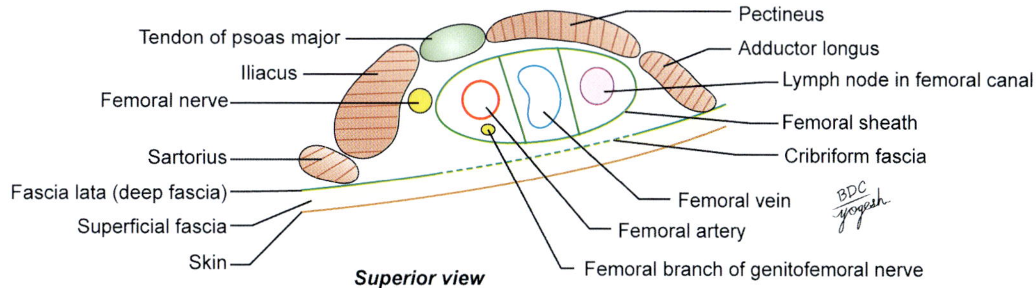

Fig. 3.14: Content of the right femoral triangle (transverse section)

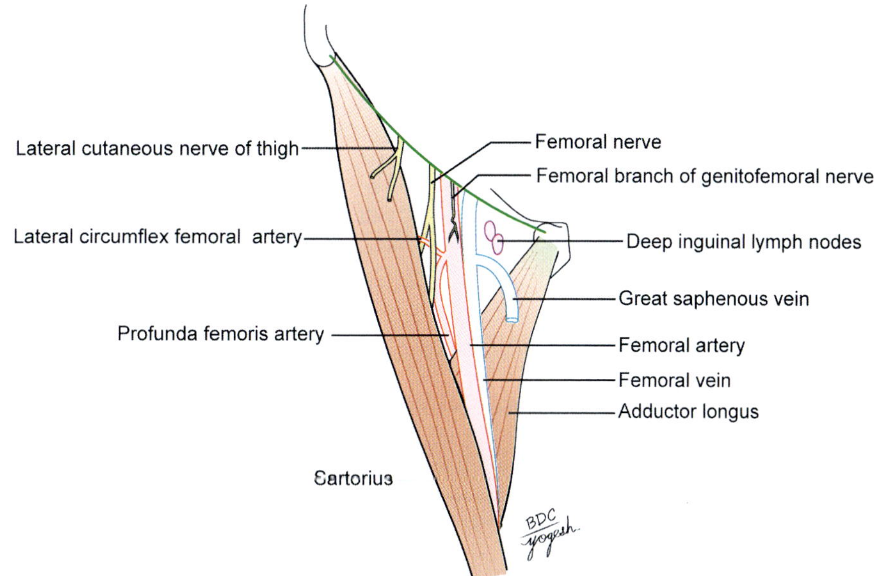

Fig. 3.15: Contents of the right femoral triangle

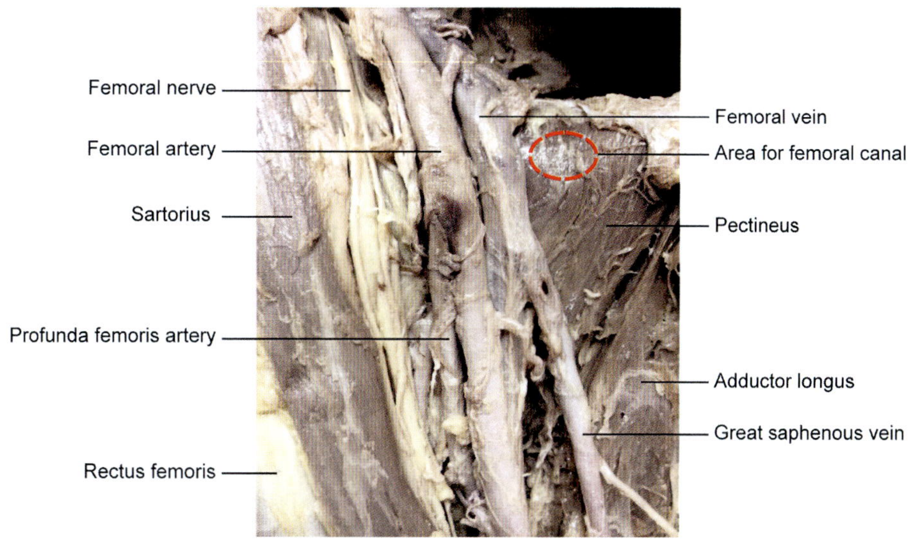

Fig. 3.16: Dissection of main contents of femoral triangle

branches of the femoral artery with accompanying veins, and the upper part of the great saphenous vein.

c. *Deep fascia*, including the cribriform fascia covering the saphenous opening.

Floor:

The floor of the femoral triangle is gutter-shaped and formed by four muscles from lateral to medial:

1. Iliacus
2. Psoas major tendon
3. Pectineus
4. Adductor longus.

Contents (Figs 3.15 and 3.16)

1. Femoral artery and its branches
2. Femoral vein and its tributaries
3. Femoral nerve

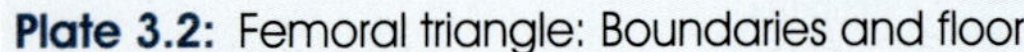

Plate 3.2: Femoral triangle: Boundaries and floor

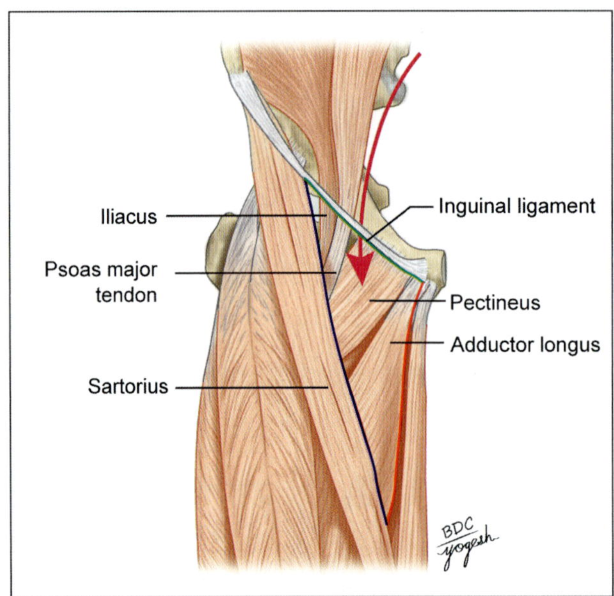

Plate 3.3: Contents of femoral triangle

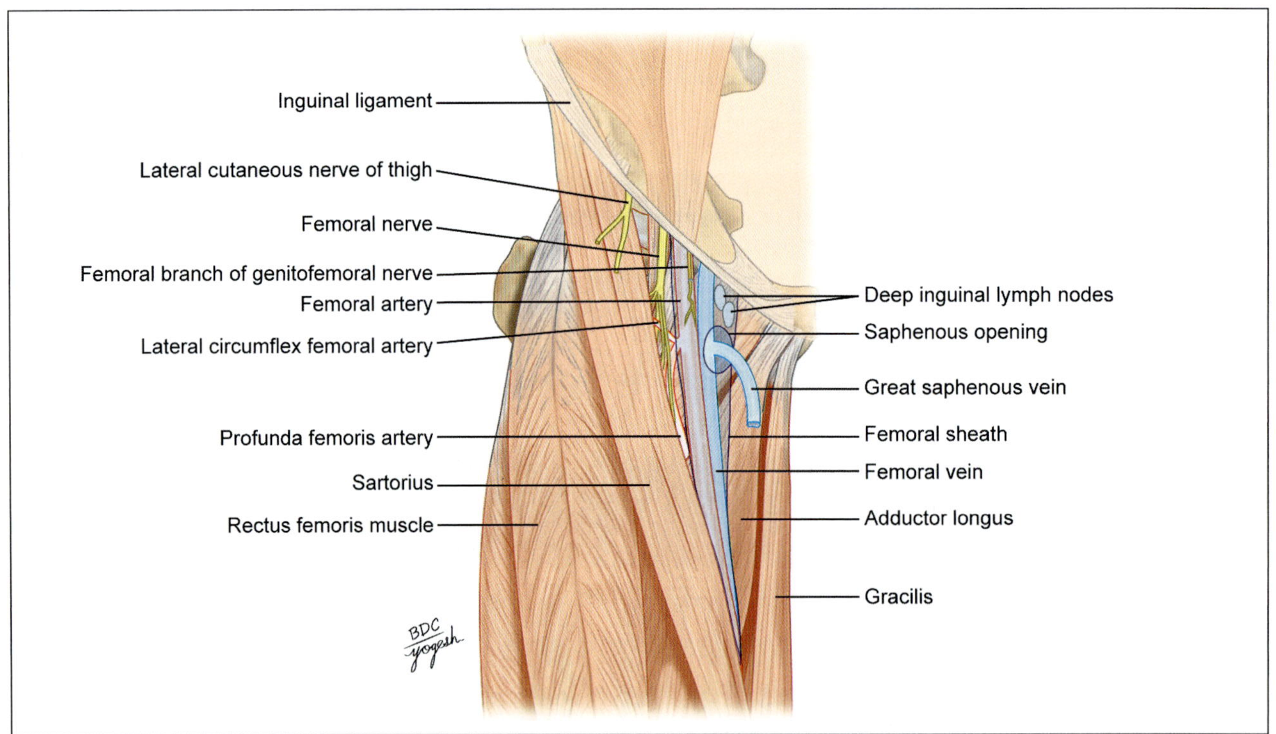

Flowchart 3.1: Femoral triangle

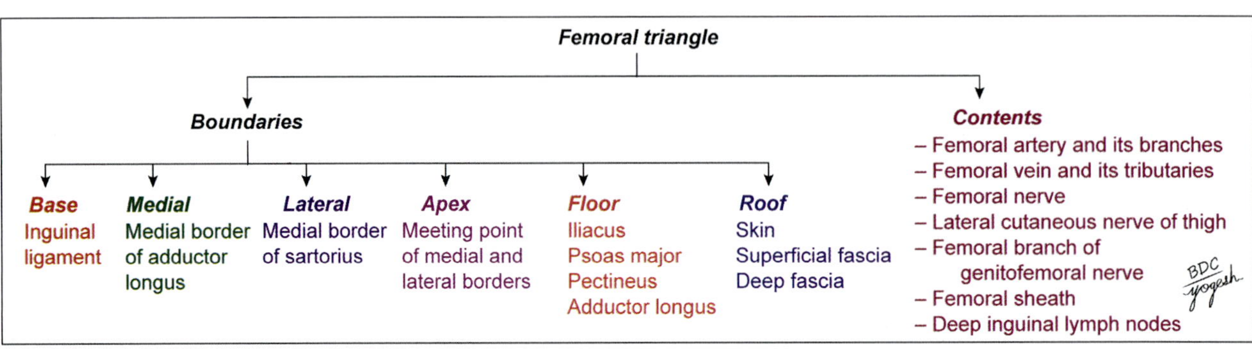

4. Deep inguinal nodes
5. Lateral cutaneous nerve of thigh
6. Femoral branch of genitofemoral nerve
7. Femoral sheath
8. Fibrofatty tissue

Note:

1. The ***femoral artery*** traverses the triangle from the base of the femoral triangle at the midinguinal point to the apex. In the triangle, it gives off six branches—three superficial and three deep.
2. The ***femoral vein*** accompanies the femoral artery. The vein is medial to the artery at base of triangle, but posteromedial to artery at the apex. The femoral vein receives the great saphenous vein, circumflex veins and veins corresponding to the branches of femoral artery.
3. The ***femoral sheath*** encloses the upper 4 cm of the femoral vessels (Fig. 3.12a).
4. The ***femoral nerve*** lies lateral to the femoral artery *outside the femoral sheath*, in the groove between the iliacus and the psoas major muscles. It is described later.
5. The *nerve to the pectineus* arises from the femoral nerve just above the inguinal ligament. It passes behind femoral sheath to reach the anterior surface of pectineus.
6. The ***femoral branch of the genitofemoral nerve*** occupies the lateral compartment of the femoral sheath along with the femoral artery. It supplies most of the skin over the femoral triangle.
7. The ***lateral cutaneous nerve of the thigh*** crosses the lateral angle of the triangle. Runs on the lateral side of thigh and ends by dividing into anterior and posterior branches. These supply anterolateral aspect of front of thigh and lateral aspect of gluteal region, respectively.
8. The ***deep inguinal lymph nodes*** lie deep to the deep fascia. These lie medial to upper part of femoral vein and receive lymph from superficial inguinal lymph nodes, from glans penis or clitoris and deep lymphatics of lower limb.

Femoral Sheath

This is a funnel-shaped sleeve of fascia enclosing the upper 3 to 4 cm of the femoral vessels. The femoral sheath is asymmetrical. Its lateral wall is vertical, and the medial wall is oblique, being directed downwards and laterally (Fig. 3.17, Flowchart 3.2).

Formation

The sheath is formed by downward extension of two layers of the fascia of the abdomen. The anterior wall of the sheath is formed by the *fascia transversalis*, which lies in the anterior abdominal wall deep to the transversus abdominis; and the posterior wall is formed by the fascia iliaca, which covers the iliacus muscle (Figs 3.17 and 3.18). Inferiorly, the sheath merges with connective tissue around the femoral vessels.

Compartments

The sheath is divided into the following three compartments by septa (Fig. 3.19).

1. The *lateral compartment* contains the *femoral artery* and the *femoral branch of the genitofemoral nerve.*
2. The *intermediate compartment* contains the *femoral vein.*
3. The *medial compartment* is the smallest of all, and is known as the *femoral canal*, which is described below.

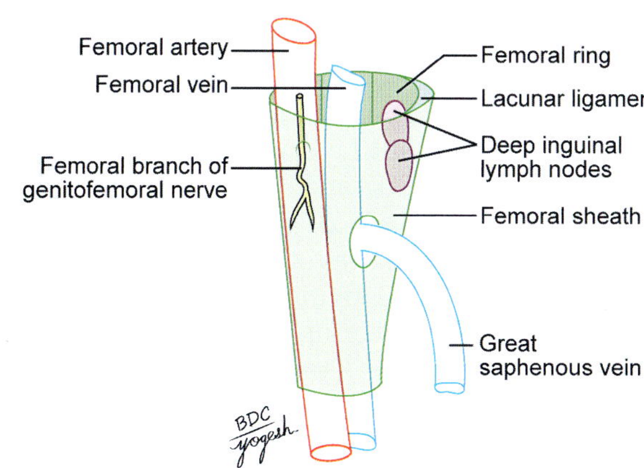

Fig. 3.17: Femoral sheath enclosing the upper parts of the femoral vessels

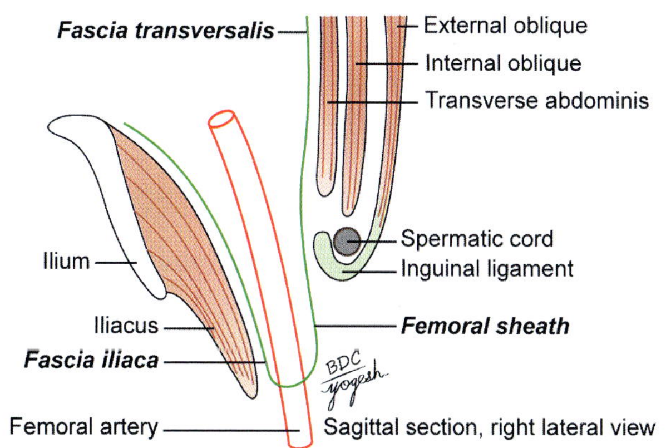

Fig. 3.18: Formation of the femoral sheath by extension of the fascia transversalis and the fascia iliaca into the thigh

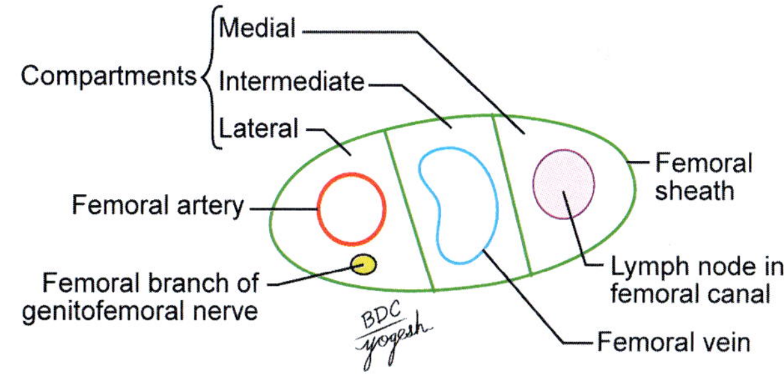

Fig. 3.19: Transverse section of the right femoral sheath with its contents

Flowchart 3.2: Femoral sheath

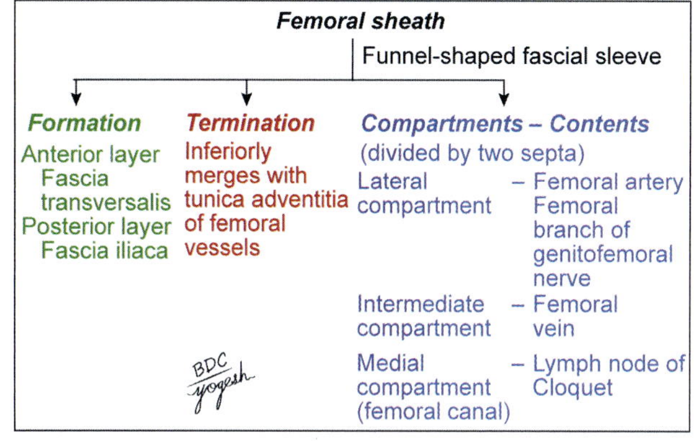

Femoral Canal

This is the medial compartment of the femoral sheath. It is conical in shape, being wide above or at base and narrow below. It is about 1.5 cm long and about 1.5 cm wide at the base (Figs 3.17 and 3.19, Flowchart 3.3).

The base or upper end of femoral canal is called ***femoral ring***. The boundaries of ring are important. It is *bounded* anteriorly by the inguinal ligament, posteriorly by pectineus and its covering fascia, medially by the concave margin of *lacunar ligament*, and laterally by the septum separating it from femoral vein.

The *inferior epigastric vessels* are closely related to junction of the anterior and lateral walls of ring. The femoral ring is closed by a condensation of extraperitoneal connective tissue, called the *femoral septum*.

The parietal peritoneum covering septum from above shows a depression which is called *femoral fossa*.

The femoral canal contains a lymph node of *Cloquet* or *Rosenmüller*, lymphatics, and a small amount of areolar tissue. The lymph node drains the glans penis in males and the clitoris in females.

Flowchart 3.3: Femoral canal

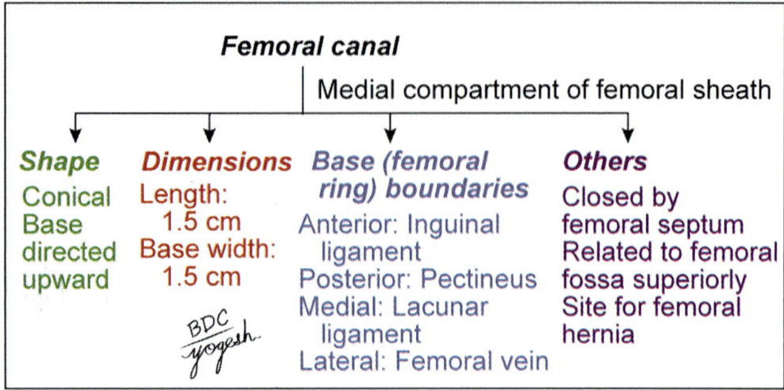

Competency:

AN15.4 Explain anatomical basis of psoas abscess and femoral hernia.

CLINICAL ANATOMY

- ***Femoral hernia***
  - The femoral canal is an area of potential weakness in the abdominal wall through which abdominal contents may bulge out forming a femoral hernia. *Note*: It is never congenital.
  - A femoral hernia is more common in females because the femoral canal is wider. This is associated with the wider pelvis, and the smaller size of the femoral vessels, in the female (Fig. 3.20).
  - ***Parts and contents***: Hernia comprises a neck and a sac. Coverings are the various layers on the sac. Mostly the content of hernial sac is a loop of bowel (Fig. 3.20).
  - ***Course of femoral hernia***: The course of an enlarging hernial sac is typical. First it passes downwards through the femoral canal, then forwards through the saphenous opening, and finally upwards along with the superficial epigastric and superficial circumflex iliac vessels. For reduction of such a hernia the reverse course has to be followed (Fig. 3.20).
  - In cases of ***strangulation of a femoral hernia***, the surgeon has to enlarge the femoral ring. This is possible only by cutting the lacunar ligament, which forms the medial boundary of the ring. Normally, this can be done without danger. Occasionally, however, an abnormal obturator artery may lie along the edge of the lacunar ligament; and cutting it may cause alarming haemorrhage (Fig. 3.20).
- ***Abnormal obturator artery***: The normal obturator artery is a branch of the internal iliac. It gives a pubic branch, which anastomoses with the pubic branch of the inferior epigastric artery. Occasionally, this

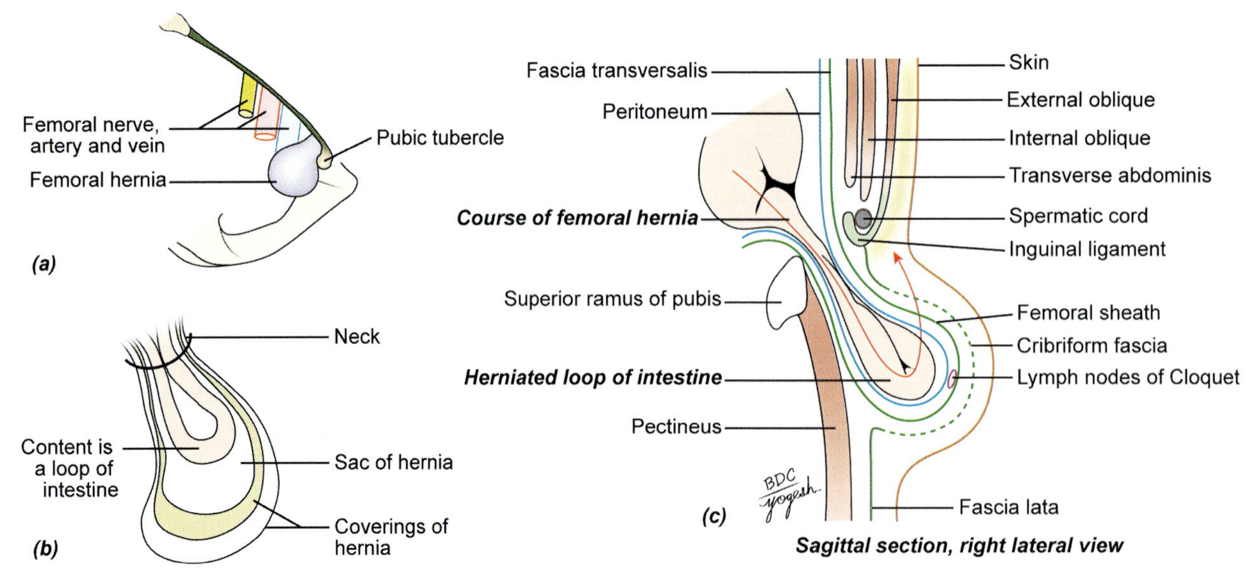

Figs 3.20a to c: Femoral hernia: (a) Location of femoral hernia, (b) hernial sac with loop of bowel, and (c) femoral canal and the course of a femoral hernia

anastomosis is large and the obturator artery then appears to be a branch of the inferior epigastric. Usually, the abnormal artery passes lateral to the femoral canal in contact with the femoral vein and is safe in an operation to enlarge the femoral ring. Sometimes, however, the abnormal obturator artery may lie along the medial margin of the femoral ring, i.e. along the free margin of the lacunar ligament. Such an artery is likely to be cut if an attempt is made to enlarge the femoral ring by cutting lacunar ligament (Fig. 3.21).

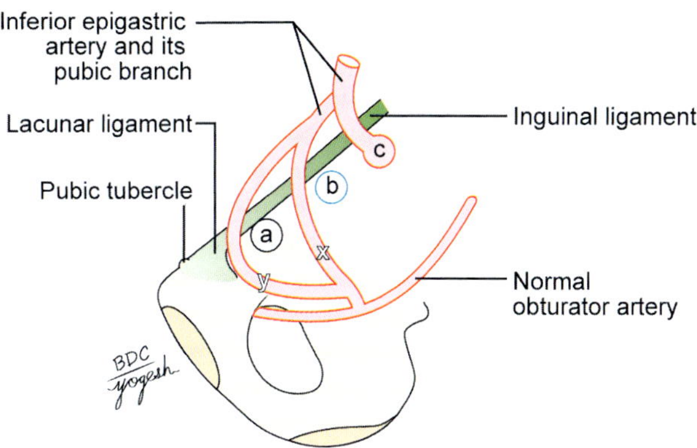

Fig. 3.21: Pubic region seen from behind to show the course of an abnormal obturator artery a. Femoral canal; b. femoral vein; c. junction of external iliac and femoral arteries; x. usual safe course of abnormal obturator artery; y. occasional dangerous position of artery

Competency:
AN15.2 Describe and demonstrate major muscles with their attachment, nerve supply and actions.

MUSCLES OF THE FRONT OF THE THIGH

The muscles of the anterior compartment of the thigh are (Plates 3.4 to 3.6, Fig. 3.22, Flowchart 3.4, Tables 3.1 and 3.2):

1. Sartorius
2. Quadriceps femoris: Rectus femoris, vastus lateralis, vastus medialis, vastus intermedius
3. Articularis genu
4. Muscles of iliac region extended to the front of thigh: Iliacus and psoas major.

The ***sartorius*** (Latin *tailor*) is long, narrow and ribbon like. It runs downwards and medially across the front of the thigh. It is the longest muscle in the body.

Quadriceps femoris

The *quadriceps femoris* consists of four parts: Rectus femoris, vastus lateralis, vastus medialis and vastus intermedius. The rectus femoris is fusiform. It runs more or less vertically on the front of the thigh superficial to the vasti. The three vasti are wrapped around the shaft of the femur in the positions indicated by their names.

Note: All the quadriceps femoris muscles are supplied by femoral nerve. They produce extension at knee joint and helps for rising from sitting or squatting position by extending the knee.

Plate 3.4: Muscles of anterior compartment of thigh

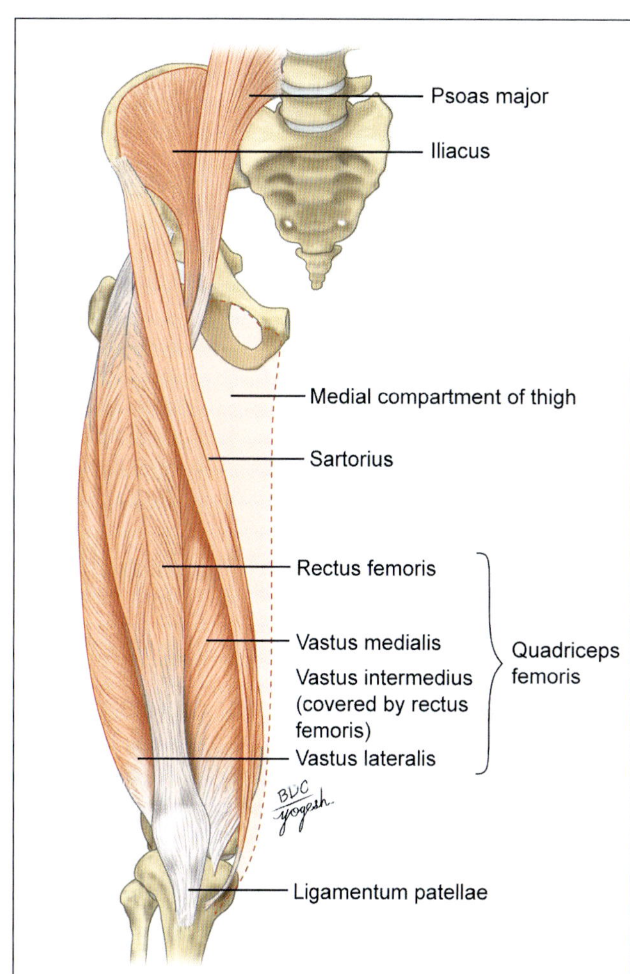

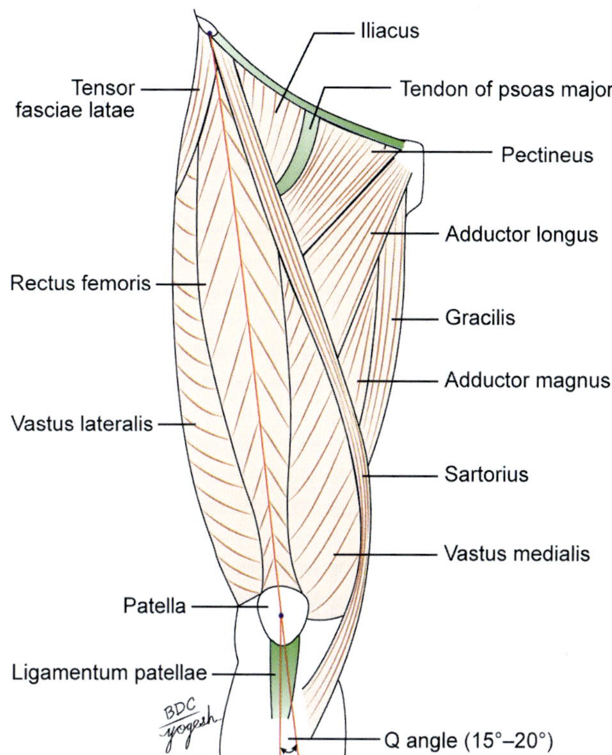

Fig. 3.22: Muscles seen on the front of the thigh

TABLE 3.1: Origin and insertion of muscles of the anterior or extensor compartment of thigh		
Muscle	***Origin***	***Insertion***
1. **Sartorius** (Latin *tailor*)	Anterior superior iliac spine Upper half of the notch below the spine	Upper part of the medial surface of the shaft of the tibia in front of the insertions of the gracilis and semitendinosus
2. **Quadriceps femoris**		
A. Rectus femoris (Fusiform, superficial fibres bipennate and deep fibres straight)	***Straight head*** from the upper half of the anterior inferior iliac spine ***Reflected head*** from the groove above the margin of the acetabulum and the capsule of the hip joint	Base of patella
B. Vastus lateralis	Upper part of intertrochanteric line Anterior and inferior borders of greater trochanter Lateral lip of gluteal tuberosity Upper half of lateral lip of linea aspera	Lateral part of the base of patella Upper one-third of the lateral border of patella Expansion to the capsule of knee joint, tibia and iliotibial tract
C. Vastus medialis	Lower part of intertrochanteric line Spiral line Medial lip of linea aspera Upper 1/4th of medial supracondylar line	Medial 1/3rd of the base and upper 2/4th of the medial border of the patella, expansion to the capsule of knee joint
D. Vastus intermedius	Upper 3/4th of the anterior and lateral surfaces of the shaft of femur	Base of patella*
3. **Articularis genu**	Anterior surface of femur	Suprapatellar bursa/synovial membrane of knee joint

*The patella is a sesamoid bone in the tendon of the quadriceps femoris. The ligamentum patellae is the actual tendon of the quadriceps femoris, which is inserted into the upper part of tibial tuberosity.

TABLE 3.2: Nerve supply and actions of muscles of anterior/extensor compartment of thigh		
Muscle	***Nerve supply***	***Actions***
1. **Sartorius**	Femoral nerve	Abductor and lateral rotator of thigh Flexor of leg at knee joint These actions are involved in assuming the position in which a tailor work, i.e. ***palthi posture*** used during prayer sessions also
2. **Quadriceps femoris**		
A. Rectus femoris	Femoral nerve, this branch also supplies hip joint	Extensor of knee joint, and flexor of hip joint, also called ***'kicking muscle'.***
B. Vastus lateralis	Femoral nerve, this branch also supplies knee joint	Extends knee joint, helps in standing, walking and running
C. Vastus medialis	Same as above	Extends knee joint, prevents lateral displacement of patella. Rotates femur medially during locking stage of extension of knee joint. Action is extremely important for ***stability of patella.***
D. Vastus intermedius	Same as above	Extends knee joint
3. **Articularis genu**	Femoral nerve	Pulls the synovial membrane upwards during extension of the knee, thus preventing damage to it

The ***articularis genu*** consists of a few muscular slips that arise from the anterior surface of the shaft of the femur, a few centimetres above the patellar articular margin. They are inserted into the upper part of the synovial membrane of the knee joint. They pull the synovial membrane upwards during extension of the knee, thus preventing damage to it.

Iliacus and Psoas Major

Iliacus and psoas major muscles form the lateral part of the floor of the femoral triangle. They are classified as muscles of the iliac region, and also among the muscles of the posterior abdominal wall (For details, *see* Chapter 27, Plate 27.2).

Plate 3.5: Sartorius and rectus femoris muscles

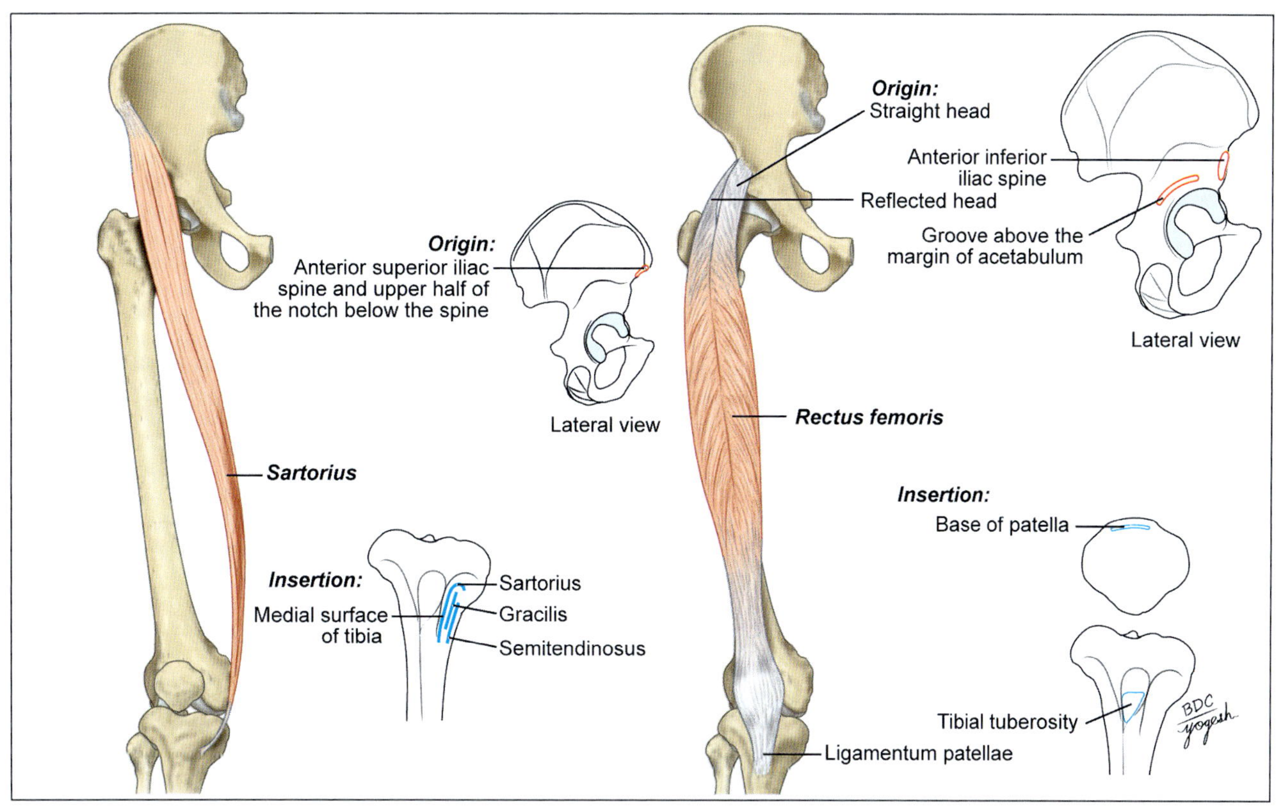

Plate 3.6: Vastus lateralis, medialis and intermedius

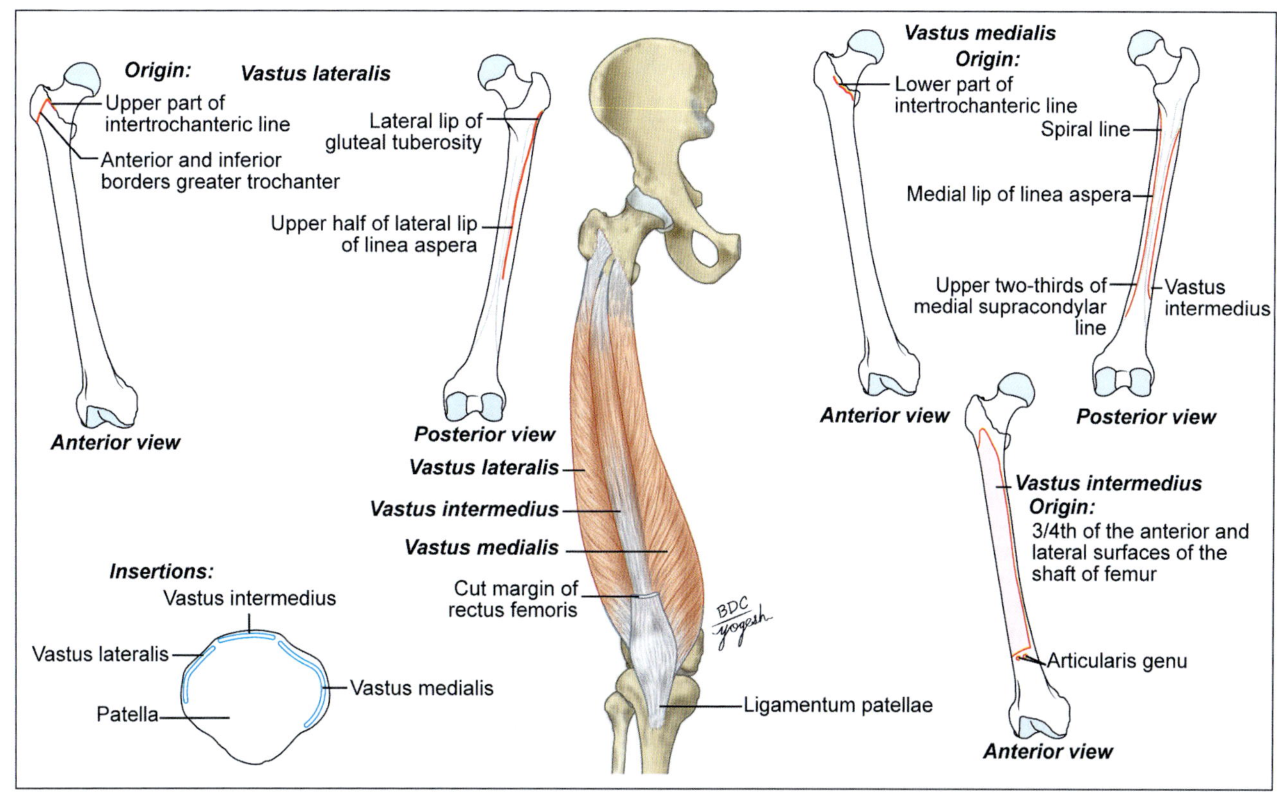

These muscles have a common insertion on the lesser trochanter of the femur and are the chief and powerful flexors of the hip joint. Because of their common insertion and action, the two muscles are often referred to by a common name, the ***iliopsoas***. Both are supplied by spinal segments L2, L3. The psoas is supplied by the branches from the nerve roots, whereas the iliacus is supplied by the femoral nerve.

Flowchart 3.4: Muscles of front of the thigh

Muscles of front of the thigh

	Origin	Insertion	Actions
Sartorius Longest muscle	Anterior superior iliac spine Upper 1/2 of notch below ASIS	Upper part of medial surface of tibia	Flexion of hip and knee joints Lateral rotation of thigh
Rectus femoris Kicking muscle	Straight head: AIIS Reflected head: Groove above acetabulum	Base of patella	Extension of knee Flexion of hip
Vastus lateralis Largest vastus	Upper part of intertrochanteric line Anterior and inferior borders of greater trochanter, lateral lip of gluteal tuberosity Upper ½ of linea aspera	Base and lateral border of patella	Extension at knee joint
Vastus medialis	Intertrochanteric line, spiral line Medial lip of linea aspera Medial supracodylar line	Base and medial border of patella	Extension of knee, locking of knee joint by medial rotation of femur, prevents lateral displacement of patella
Vastus intermedius	Upper 3/4th of anterior and lateral surface of femur	Base of patella	Extension of knee joint

Innervation: All these muscles are supplied by posterior division of femoral nerve except sartorius (supplied by anterior division)

Competency:
AN15.4 Explain anatomical basis of psoas abscess and femoral hernia.

CLINICAL ANATOMY

- ***Testing for quadriceps femoris***: Ask the person to extend the knee against the resistance and palpate the contracting muscle (Fig. 3.23).
- ***Patellar tendon reflex*** or ***knee jerk*** (L3, L4). The knee joint gets extended on tapping the ligamentum patellae.
- ***Psoas abscess*** formed due to tubercular infection of lumbar vertebrae can track down between psoas major muscles and its fascia to reach behind the inguinal ligament into the femoral triangle. It may be mistaken for enlarged lymph nodes.
- ***Intramuscular injection*** can be given in anterolateral region of thigh in the vastus lateralis muscle.

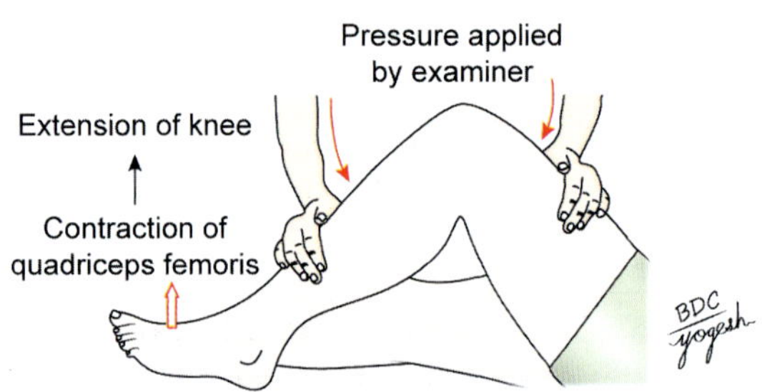

Fig. 3.23: How to test the quadriceps femoris muscle

Competency:
AN15.1 Describe and demonstrate origin, course, relations, branches (or tributaries), termination of important nerves and vessels of anterior thigh.

FEMORAL ARTERY

This is the chief artery of the lower limb. Developmentally, it is not derived from the axis artery. The original axis artery in the uppermost part of the limb is represented by the inferior gluteal artery (Fig. 3.24, Flowchart 3.5).

Beginning

Femoral artery is the continuation of external iliac artery. It begins behind the inguinal ligament at the midinguinal point.

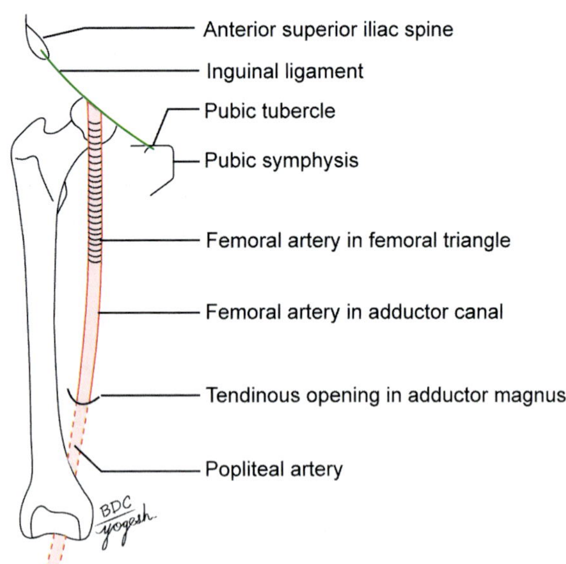

Fig. 3.24: Course and extent of the femoral artery

Extent, Course and Termination

Femoral artery passes downwards and medially, first in the femoral triangle, and then in the adductor canal.

At the lower end of the adductor canal, i.e. at the junction of the middle and lower thirds of the thigh, it passes through an opening in the adductor magnus to become continuous with the popliteal artery.

Major Relations of Femoral Artery in Femoral Triangle

Anterior: Skin, fasciae, anterior wall of the femoral sheath.

Posterior: Posterior wall of femoral sheath, psoas major, the pectineus, and the adductor longus.

Medial: Femoral vein in the upper part of femoral triangle.

Lateral: Femoral nerve and its branches.

Note: Femoral vein lies medial to the femoral artery at the base of femoral triangle but gradually shifts posterior to the artery towards the apex of the triangle.

Branches (Fig. 3.25)

In the femoral triangle

The 3 superficial branches are:

1. Superficial external pudendal supplies the skin of external genital organs.
2. Superficial epigastric for skin and fasciae of lower part of anterior abdominal wall.
3. Superficial circumflex iliac for skin along the iliac crest.

The 3 deep branches are:

1. Profunda femoris
2. Deep external pudendal supplies the external genital organs, e.g. scrotum, penis.
3. Muscular branches.

In the adductor canal

1. Descending genicular artery
2. Muscular branches.

Profunda Femoris Artery

Profunda femoris is the largest branch of the femoral artery (Fig. 3.22). It is the chief artery of supply to all the three compartments of the thigh. It arises from the lateral side of the femoral artery about 4 cm below the inguinal ligament.

As the artery descends, it passes posterior to the femoral vessels. It leaves the femoral triangle by passing deep to the adductor longus. Continuing downwards, it passes first between the adductor longus and the adductor brevis, and then between the adductor longus and the adductor magnus. Its terminal part pierces the adductor magnus to anastomose with upper muscular branches of the popliteal artery.

Branches

1. Medial circumflex femoral artery
2. Lateral circumflex femoral artery
3. Four perforating arteries (described in Chapter 7)
4. Muscular branches.

Note:

1. ***Medial circumflex femoral artery*** leaves the femoral triangle by passing posteriorly, between the pectineus and the psoas major muscles. It gives an acetabular branch and divides into an ascending branch and a transverse branch.
2. ***Lateral circumflex femoral artery*** runs laterally between the anterior and posterior divisions of the femoral nerve (Fig. 3.11b), passes behind the sartorius and the rectus femoris, and divides into ascending, transverse and descending branches (*see* Figs 7.12a and 7.13a).
3. The ***ascending branch*** runs deep to the tensor fasciae latae and anastomoses with the superior gluteal artery.

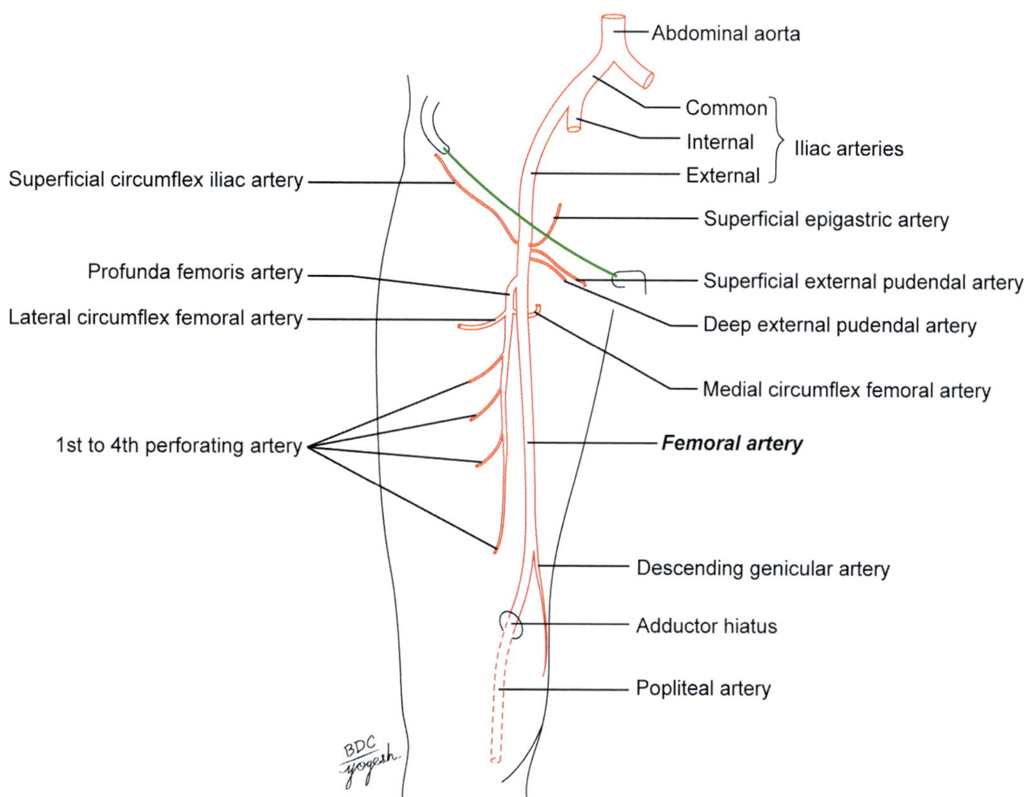

Fig. 3.25: Branches of femoral artery

4. The ***transverse branch*** pierces the vastus lateralis and takes part in the cruciate anastomosis.
5. The ***descending branch*** runs down along the anterior border of the vastus lateralis, accompanied by the nerve to that muscle.
6. ***Deep external pudendal artery*** passes deep to the spermatic cord, or the round ligament of the uterus, and supplies the scrotum or the labium majus.

CLINICAL ANATOMY

- ***Femoral pulse*:** Pulsations of the femoral artery can be felt at the midinguinal point, against the head of the femur and the tendon of the psoas major (Fig. 3.26). A bilateral absence or feebleness of the femoral pulse may result from coarctation or narrowing of the aorta, or thrombosis, i.e. clotting of blood within the aorta.
- ***Compression of femoral artery*:** The femoral artery can be compressed at the midinguinal point against the head of the femur or against the superior ramus of the pubis to control bleeding from the distal part of the limb in the thigh or leg.
- ***Femoral artery cannulation*:** Since the femoral artery is quite superficial in the femoral triangle, it can be easily exposed for ligation, i.e. tying, or for passing a cannula or a thick needle. Catheters are passed upwards till the heart for certain minor operation (Fig. 3.27).
- In cases of posterior dislocation of hip, the femoral artery cannot be palpated as the head of the femur is displaced. This is termed as a positive vascular ***sign of Narath***.

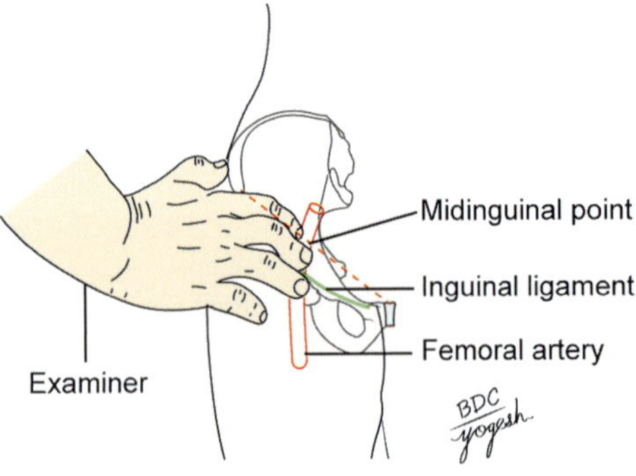

Fig. 3.26: Palpation of femoral pulse at midinguinal point

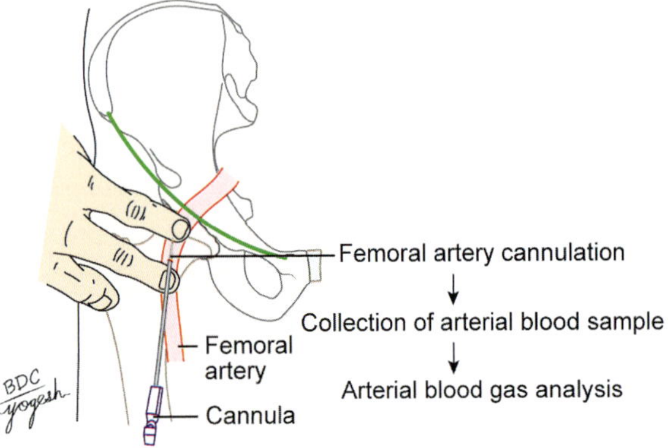

Fig. 3.27: Catheterisation of femoral artery

Flowchart 3.5: Femoral artery

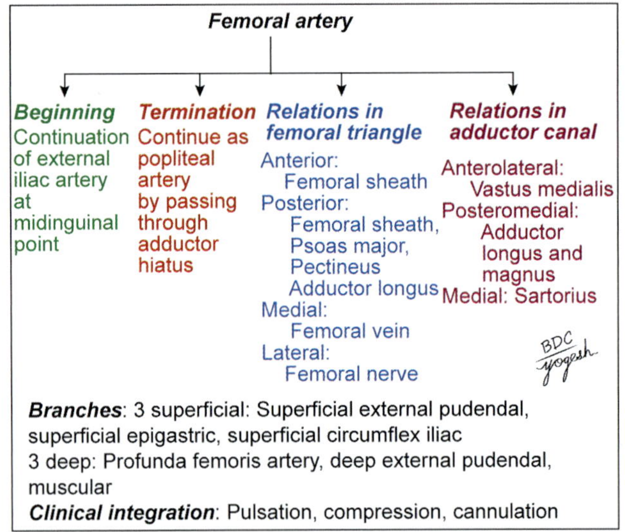

FEMORAL VEIN

Femoral vein begins as an upward continuation of the popliteal vein at the lower end of the adductor canal, and ends by becoming continuous with the external iliac vein behind the inguinal ligament, medial to the femoral artery.

Tributaries: It receives:

1. Great saphenous vein
2. Medial and lateral circumflex femoral veins
3. Deep external pudendal vein
4. Profunda femoris vein
5. Veins accompanying the muscular branches of femoral artery
6. Formative tributary – popliteal vein.

CLINICAL ANATOMY

- ***Intravenous infusion*:** Femoral vein is commonly used for intravenous infusions in infants, children, and in patients with peripheral circulatory failure.
- ***Right heart catheterisation*:** Femoral vein is also used for right heart catheterisation. The catheter inserted from the femoral vein.

FEMORAL NERVE

The femoral nerve is the chief nerve of the anterior compartment of the thigh (Fig. 3.28, Flowchart 3.6).

Origin and Root Value

Femoral nerve is the largest branch of the lumbar plexus.

It is formed by the dorsal divisions of the anterior primary rami of spinal nerves L2, L3, L4.

Course

Femoral nerve enters the femoral triangle by passing behind the inguinal ligament just lateral to the femoral artery.

Flowchart 3.6: Femoral nerve

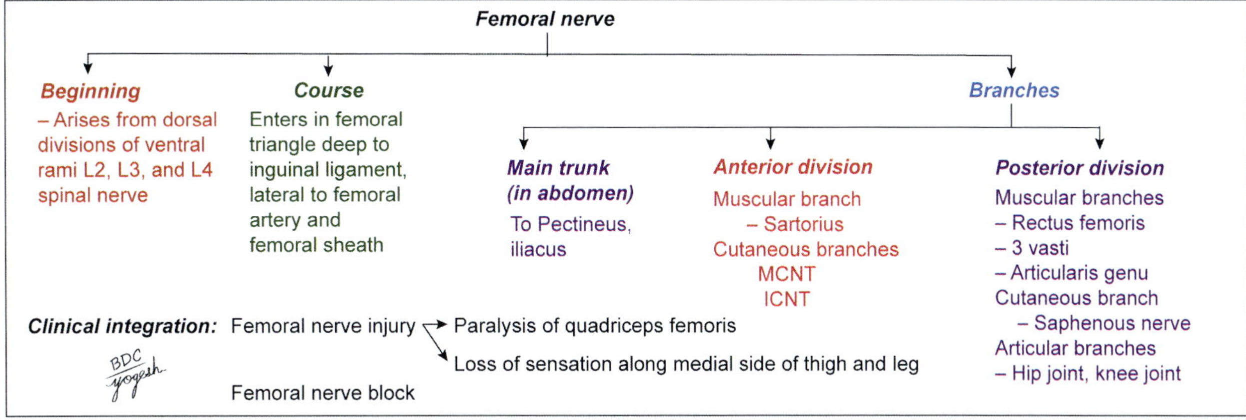

MCNT: Medial cutaneous nerve of thigh; ICNT: Intermediate cutaneous nerve of thigh

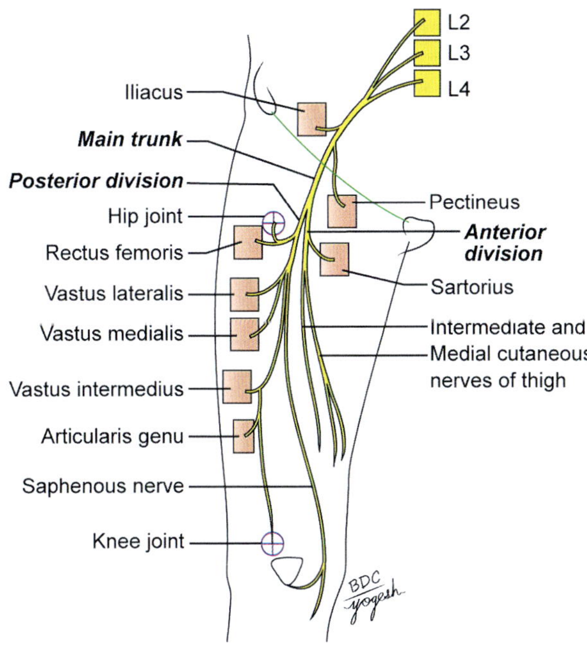

Fig. 3.28: Branches and distribution of femoral nerve

In the thigh, it lies in the groove between the iliacus and the psoas major, outside the femoral sheath, and lateral to the femoral artery. The nerve is not included in the femoral sheath as its formation is behind the fascia iliaca, which is forming posterior wall of the sheath.

After a short course of about 2.5 cm below the inguinal ligament, the nerve divides into anterior and posterior divisions, which are separated by the lateral circumflex femoral artery.

BRANCHES AND DISTRIBUTION

In Abdomen

Main trunk: Muscular branches from main trunk for
- Iliacus
- Pectineus

In Thigh

Anterior division
- Muscular branch for sartorius
- Cutaneous branches
  - Medial cutaneous nerve of thigh
  - Intermediate cutaneous nerve of thigh.

Posterior division
- Muscular branches for:
  - Rectus femoris
  - Vastus medialis
  - Vastus lateralis
  - Vastus intermedius
  - Articularis genu through branch to vastus intermedius
- Cutaneous branch
  - Saphenous nerve (largest cutaneous branch of femoral nerve)
- Articular branches
  - Nerve to rectus femoris supplies hip joint
  - Nerve of all vasti muscles supply knee joint.

Note: Lateral cutaneous nerve of the thigh is a separate branch of lumbar plexus. Vascular branches of femoral nerve supply femoral artery. Femoral nerve gives vascular branches to the femoral artery and its branches.

CLINICAL ANATOMY

- ***Femoral nerve injury***: It may result due to wounds in groin. It results in paralysis of quadriceps femoris and sensory loss over the anterior and medial side of thigh, and medial side of leg.
- ***Femoral nerve block***: Local anaesthetic agent is injected around the femoral nerve to achieve the femoral nerve block.

Competency:
AN15.5 Describe and demonstrate adductor canal with its content.

ADDUCTOR/HUNTER'S/SUBSARTORIAL CANAL

Features

Adductor canal is also called the subsartorial canal or Hunter's canal. John Hunter (Scottish surgeon, 1728–1793) was an anatomist and surgeon at London. Hunter's operation for the treatment of popliteal aneurysm by ligating the femoral artery in the adductor canal is a landmark in the history of vascular surgery.

The adductor canal is an intermuscular space situated on the medial side of the middle 1/3rd of the thigh (Figs 3.29 and 3.30, Flowchart 3.7, Plate 3.7).

Extent

The canal extends from the apex of the femoral triangle, above; to the tendinous opening in the adductor magnus, below.

Shape

The canal is triangular on cross-section.

Boundaries

The adductor canal has anterolateral, posteromedial and medial walls.

Anterolateral wall: It is formed by the vastus medialis.

Posteromedial wall or floor: It is formed by the adductor longus, above and the adductor magnus, below.

Medial wall or roof: It is formed by a strong fibrous membrane joining the anterolateral and posteromedial walls. The roof is overlapped by the sartorius.

Contents of Adductor Canal

1. Femoral artery
2. Femoral vein
3. Saphenous nerve
4. Nerve to vastus medialis
5. Branches of anterior and posterior divisions of obturator nerve
6. Descending genicular artery.

Note:

1. The ***femoral artery*** enters the adductor canal at the apex of the femoral triangle. Within the canal, it gives off muscular and a descending genicular branches. The *descending genicular artery* divides into a *superficial saphenous branch* that accompanies the saphenous nerve, and a *deep muscular branch* that enters the vastus medialis and reaches the knee. Femoral artery leaves the adductor canal through the opening in adductor magnus muscle to continue as popliteal artery in the popliteal fossa.
2. ***Femoral vein*** begins as the upward continuation of popliteal vein from the popliteal fossa. The femoral vein lies posterior to the femoral artery in the upper part, and lateral to the artery in the lower part of the canal.
3. The ***saphenous nerve*** crosses the femoral artery anteriorly from lateral to medial side. It leaves the canal with the saphenous artery by piercing the fibrous roof.
4. The ***nerve to the vastus medialis*** lies lateral to the femoral artery, and enters the vastus medialis in the upper part of the canal.
5. ***Branches of two divisions of obturator nerve***: The anterior division emerges at the lower border of the adductor longus, gives branches to the subsartorial plexus and ends by supplying the femoral artery. The posterior division of the obturator nerve runs on the anterior surface of the adductor magnus, accompanies the femoral and popliteal arteries, and ends by supplying the knee joint.
6. ***Subsartorial plexus of nerves***: It lies on the fibrous roof of the canal under cover of the sartorius. The plexus is formed by branches from the medial cutaneous nerve of the thigh, the saphenous nerve and the anterior division of the obturator nerve. It supplies the overlying fascia lata and the neighbouring skin.

Flowchart 3.7: Adductor canal

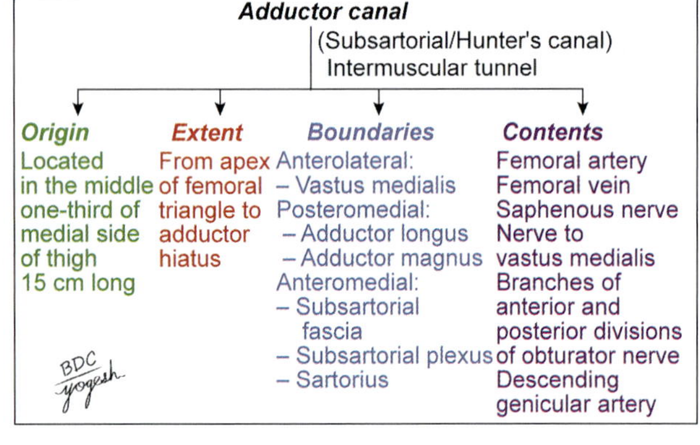

CLINICAL ANATOMY

Adductor canal block: Local anaesthetic is injected in the adductor canal to block the saphenous nerve.

Adductor canal compression syndrome: Hypertrophy of adjacent muscles may cause compression of neurovascular bundle in the adductor canal. It may result in claudication symptoms due to femoral artery compression or neurological symptoms due to saphenous nerve compression.

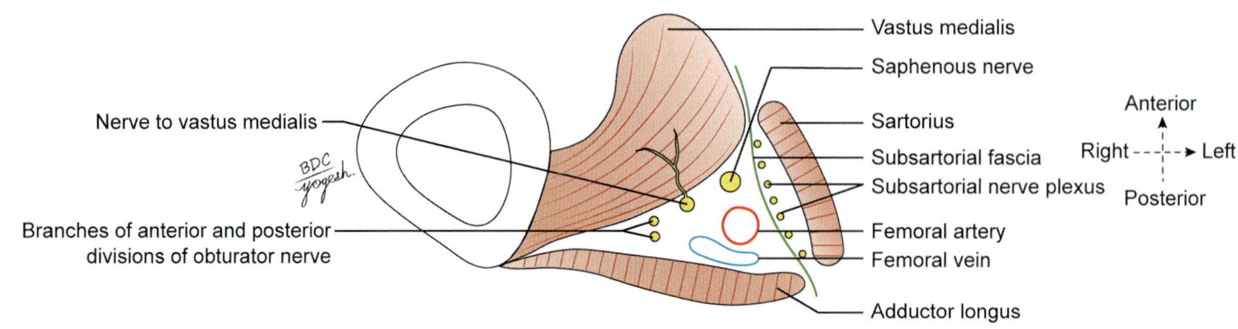

Fig. 3.29: Transverse section through the middle of the right adductor canal, seen from above. Note the boundaries and contents of the canal

Plate 3.7: Location of adductor canal

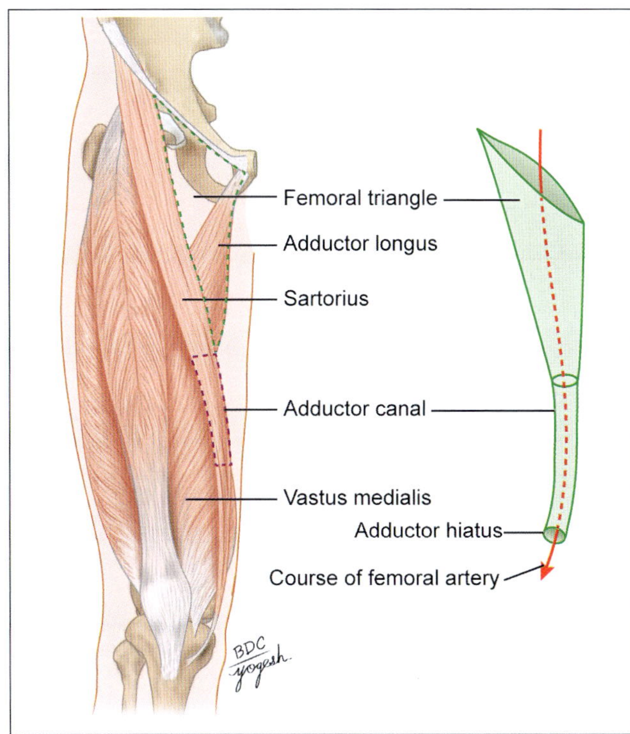

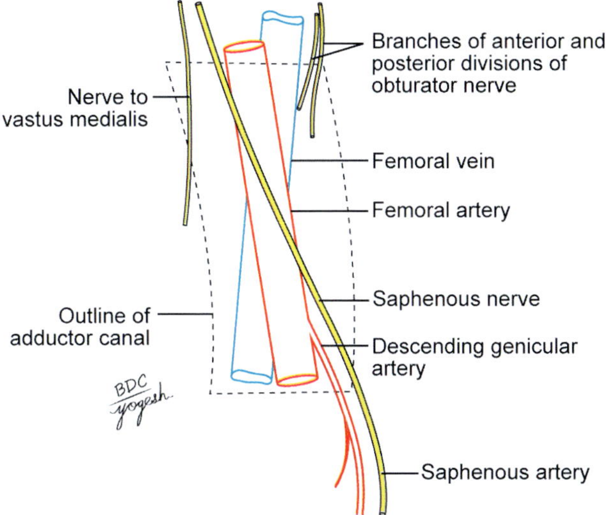

Fig. 3.30: Contents of the adductor canal

DISSECTION

Upper 1/3rd of sartorius forms the lateral boundary of the femoral triangle.

On lifting the middle 1/3rd of sartorius, a part of deep fascia stretching between vastus medialis and adductor muscles is exposed. On longitudinal division of this strong fascia, the adductor canal is visualised.

Dissect its contents, e.g. femoral vessels, saphenous nerve and nerve to vastus medialis, and distal parts of both divisions of obturator nerve.

Video 2.3 Front of Thigh: Muscles of the front of thigh, Femoral triangle, Subsartorial canal.

Facts to Remember

- Peculiarities of muscles of thigh:
  - Sartorius – Longest muscle of the body, Tailor's muscle
  - Rectus femoris – Kicking muscle
  - Vastus lateralis – Useful for intramuscular injections
- Saphenous is the longest cutaneous nerve.
- Femoral hernia is common in female, while inguinal hernia is common in male.
- Insertion of vastus medialis extends to lower level on patella than that of vastus lateralis to stabilise the patella.

BDC's Anatomy *e*-book

1. Procedure for embalming
2. Femoral nerve
3. Applied aspects of femoral vein
4. Femoral nerve and Hilton's law
5. Femoral hernia
6. Transverse section through the upper third of the thigh
7. Anterior and posterior relations of the femoral artery
8. Psoas abscess
9. Further reading
10. Viva voce questions

Chapter

4

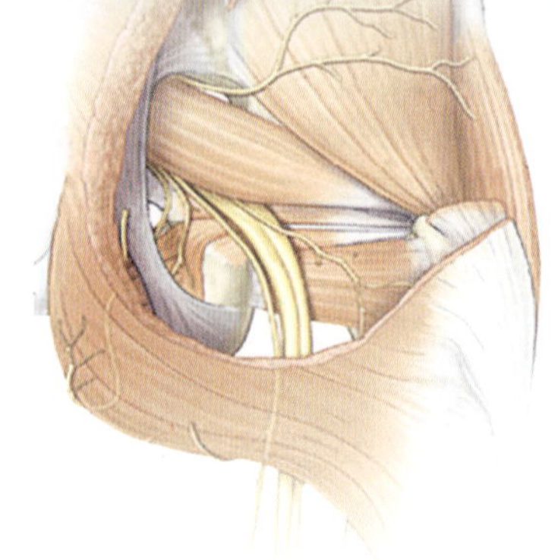

Medial Side of Thigh

The adductor or medial compartment of thigh is very well developed and is derived, as indicated by its nerve supply, from both the flexors and extensors between which it lies. Its counterpart in the arm is represented only by coracobrachialis muscle, as the arm can be adducted by pectoralis major and latissimus dorsi muscles.

ADDUCTOR COMPARTMENT

Boundaries

The adductor or medial compartment of the thigh is bounded anteriorly by the medial intermuscular septum, which separates it from the extensor (anterior) compartment, and posteriorly by an ill-defined posterior intermuscular septum, which separates it from the flexor (posterior) compartment (*see* Fig. 3.9).

Contents

- ***Muscles***
  - *Intrinsic:* Adductor longus, adductor brevis, adductor magnus, gracilis and pectineus (Plate 4.1, Fig. 4.1).
  - *Extrinsic:* The obturator externus lies deep in this region. It is functionally related to the gluteal region.
- ***Nerves***: Obturator nerve, accessory obturator nerve.
- ***Arteries***: Obturator artery, medial circumflex femoral artery.

Competency:
AN15.2 Describe and demonstrate major muscles with their attachment, nerve supply and actions.

Plate 4.1: Muscles of medial compartment of thigh

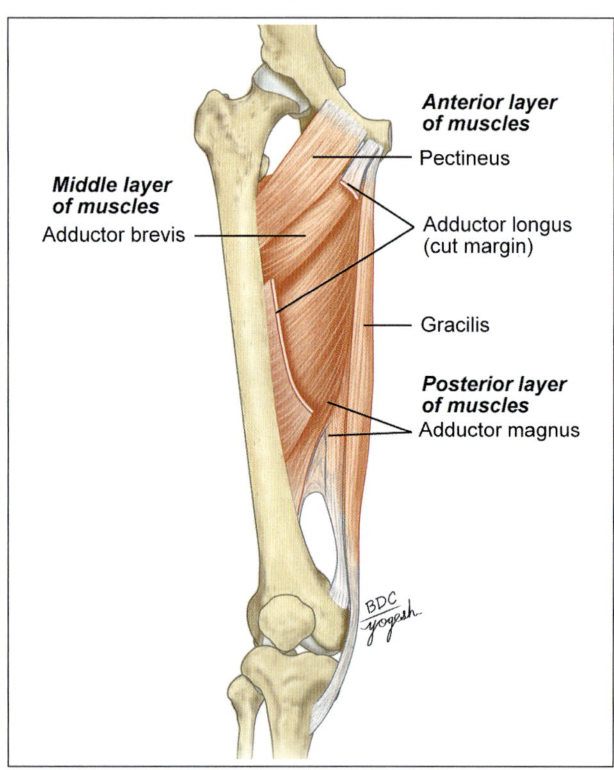

DISSECTION

The triangular adductor longus was seen to form the medial boundary of femoral triangle (*see* Fig. 3.12). Cut this muscle 3 cm below its origin and reflect the distal part laterally. On its deep surface, identify the anterior division of obturator nerve which supplies both adductor longus and gracilis muscles.

Lateral to adductor longus on the same plane is the pectineus muscle. Cut it close to its origin and reflect laterally, tracing the branch of anterior division of obturator nerve to this muscle. Obturator nerve is accompanied by the branches of obturator artery and medial circumflex femoral arteries.

Deeper to adductor longus and pectineus is the adductor brevis. Look for its nerve supply either from anterior/posterior division.

Divide adductor brevis close to its origin. Deepest plane of muscles comprises adductor magnus and obturator externus, both are supplied by posterior division of obturator nerve.

Lying vertically along the medial side of thigh is the 'graceful' gracilis. Study these muscles and the course of obturator nerve.

Look for accessory obturator nerve. If present, it supplies pectineus.

Lastly, remove the obturator externus from its origin to expose the obturator artery and its branches.

MUSCLES OF ADDUCTOR COMPARTMENT OF THIGH

The adductor or medial compartment of the thigh has five intrinsic muscles: Adductor longus, adductor brevis, adductor magnus, gracilis and pectineus (Tables 4.1, 4.2, Plates 4.2 and 4.3, Figs 4.2 and 4.3, Flowchart 4.1).

Peculiarities of Adductor Muscles

1. All the muscles of the adductor compartment of the thigh are supplied by the obturator nerve.
2. ***Composite muscles*:** Pectineus and adductor magnus are composite muscles as they have dual innervations. The pectineus is supplied by the femoral and obturator nerves while the adductor magnus is supplied by the

TABLE 4.1: Origin and insertion of muscles of the medial compartment of thigh

Muscle	*Origin*	*Insertion*
1. **Adductor longus** This is a triangular muscle, forming the medial part of the floor of the femoral triangle. It lies in the plane of the pectineus	It arises by a narrow, flat tendon from the front of the *body of the pubis* in the angle between the pubic crest and the pubic symphysis	The *linea aspera* in middle 1/3rd of the shaft of the femur between the vastus medialis and the adductor brevis and magnus
2. **Adductor brevis** The muscle lies behind the pectineus and adductor longus	a. Anterior surface of *body of the pubis* b. Outer surface of *inferior ramus of the pubis* between the gracilis and obturator externus c. Outer surface of *ramus of the ischium* between gracilis and the adductor magnus	Line extending from the lesser trochanter to upper part of linea aspera, behind the upper part of adductor longus
3. **Adductor magnus** This is the largest muscle of this compartment. Because of its double nerve supply, it is called a hybrid muscle	a. Inferolateral part of the *ischial tuberosity* b. Ramus of the ischium c. Lower part of inferior ramus of the pubis	a. Medial margin of *gluteal tuberosity* b. Linea aspera c. Medial supracondylar line d. Adductor tubercle
4. **Gracilis** (Greek *slender*)	a. Medial margin of the lower half of the body of the pubis b. Inferior ramus of the pubis c. Adjoining part of the ramus of the ischium	Upper part of the medial surface of *tibia* behind the sartorius and in front of the semitendinosus
5. **Pectineus** This is flat, quadrilateral muscle; it forms a part of the floor of the femoral triangle	a. Pecten pubis b. Upper half of the pectineal surface of superior ramus of the pubis c. Fascia covering the pectineus	Line extending from lesser trochanter to the linea aspera

TABLE 4.2: Nerve supply and actions of muscles of medial compartment of thigh

Muscle	*Nerve supply*	*Actions*
1. **Adductor longus**	Anterior division of obturator nerve	Powerful adductor of thigh at hip joint The adductor muscles act as posture controllers
2. **Adductor brevis**	Anterior or posterior division of obturator nerve	Adductor longus, adductor brevis help in adduction and flexion of thigh
3. **Adductor magnus** (Hybrid muscle)	Double nerve supply: Adductor part by posterior division of obturator nerve Hamstring part by tibial part of sciatic nerve	Adductor part causes adduction and medial rotation of thigh and hamstring part helps in extension of thigh at the hip joint
4. **Gracilis**	Anterior division of obturator nerve	Flexor and medial rotator of thigh. It is a weak adductor of thigh. It is used for transplantation of any damaged muscles, e.g. external anal sphincter
5. **Pectineus** (Hybrid or composite muscle)	Double nerve supply: Anterior fibres by femoral nerve Posterior fibres by anterior division of obturator nerve	Flexor of thigh Adductor of thigh

Plate 4.2: Adductor longus, brevis and magnus muscles

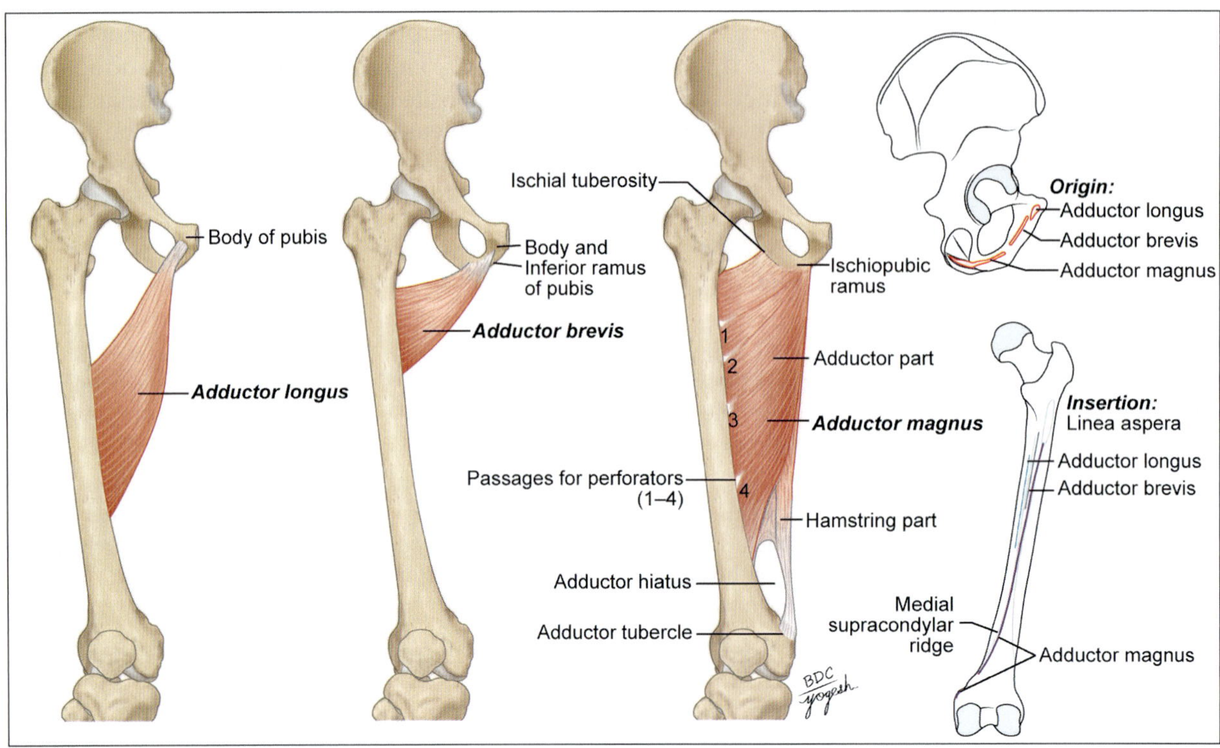

Plate 4.3: Pectineus and gracilis muscles

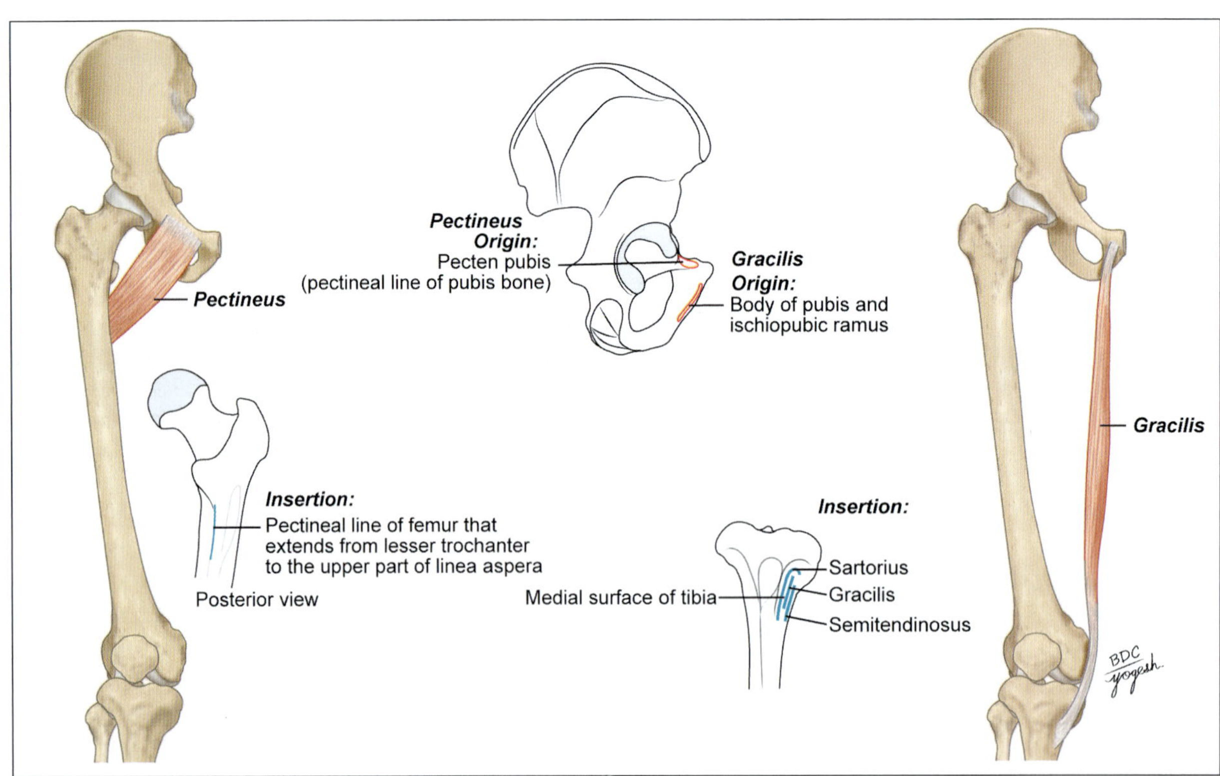

obturator nerve (posterior division) and tibial part of sciatic nerve.

3. ***Rider's bone*:** In horse riders, the rounded tendon of adductor longus often gets calcified due to its friction with the horseback. This calcified tendon is called rider's bone.
4. ***Custodian of virginity*:** The adductor muscles of the thigh have been known collectively as custodes virginitatis.
5. ***Clinical testing of adductors*:** Adductors of thigh are usually tested as group by adduction of thigh against resistance.

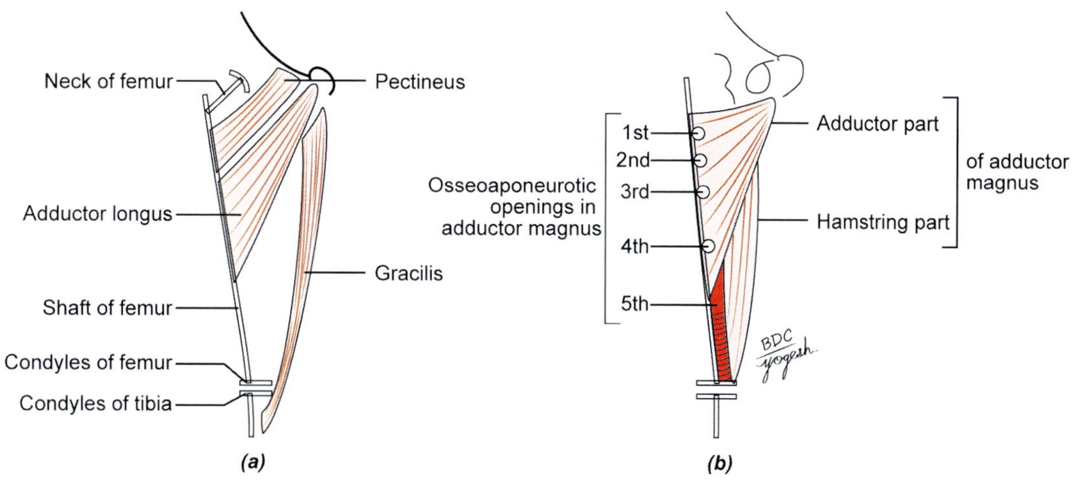

Figs 4.1a and b: Insertion of muscles of the medial compartment of thigh

Flowchart 4.1: Muscles of medial compartment of thigh

Muscles of medial compartment of thigh

	Origin	*Insertion*	*Actions*
Adductor longus	Front of the body of pubis	Linea aspera between vastus medialis, and adductor brevis and magnus	Adduction and flexion of thigh
Adductor brevis	Body of pubis, inferior ramus of pubis Part of ischial ramus	Line extending from lesser trochanter to upper part of linea aspera	Adduction and flexion of thigh
Adductor magnus	Adductor part: Outer surface of ischiopubic ramus Hamstring part: inferolateral part of ischial tuberosity	Adductor part: Medial margin of gluteal tuberosity, linea aspera, medial supracondylar ridge Hamstring part: Adductor tubercle	Adduction of thigh, Extension of thigh
Gracilis	Body of pubis, inferior ramus of pubis Part of ischial ramus	Upper part of medial surface of tibia	Adduction of thigh, flexion and medial rotation of leg
Pectineus	Pecten pubis, pectineal surface of pubis	On femur at line extending from lesser trochanter to linea aspera	Flexion and adduction of thigh

Innervation: All these muscles are supplied by obturator nerve (pectineus is additionally supplied by femoral nerve, and adductor magnus by tibial part of sciatic nerve

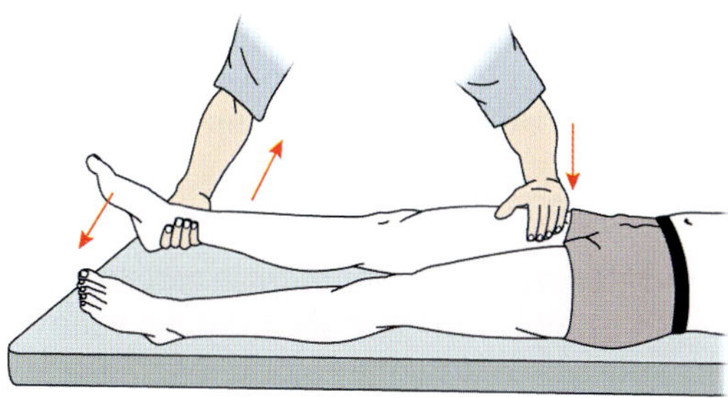

Fig. 4.2: Testing the adductors of thigh

6. The gracilis muscle is most superficial muscle of the adductor compartment. Gracilis is commonly used for muscle transplantation and reconstructive surgery. This muscle is often used for transplantation of external anal sphincter.
7. ***Adductor hiatus***: This is the large lowest osseoaponeurotic gap between the adductor magnus and shaft of femur. It gives passage to femoral vessels from adductor canal to popliteal fossa. Upper four osseoaponeurotic openings give passage to perforating branches of profunda femoris artery. This is main supply of adductor compartment.

CLINICAL ANATOMY

Testing the adductors: The patient lies supine with right lower limb abducted. The right hand of physician holds the leg in abducted position. Patient is requested to bring the thigh medially against the resistance of the physician's right hand, while his left hand feels the contracting adductor muscles (Fig. 4.2).

Competency:

AN15.1 Describe and demonstrate origin, course, relations, branches (or tributaries), termination of important nerves and vessels of medial side of thigh.

OBTURATOR NERVE

The obturator nerve is the chief nerve of the medial compartment of the thigh.

Origin and Root Value

It is a branch of the lumbar plexus. It is formed by the ***ventral divisions*** of the anterior primary rami of spinal nerves **L2–L4**. The proximal part of the nerve lies in the pelvis. It enters the thigh by passing through the obturator canal (Figs 4.3 and 4.4, Flowchart 4.2).

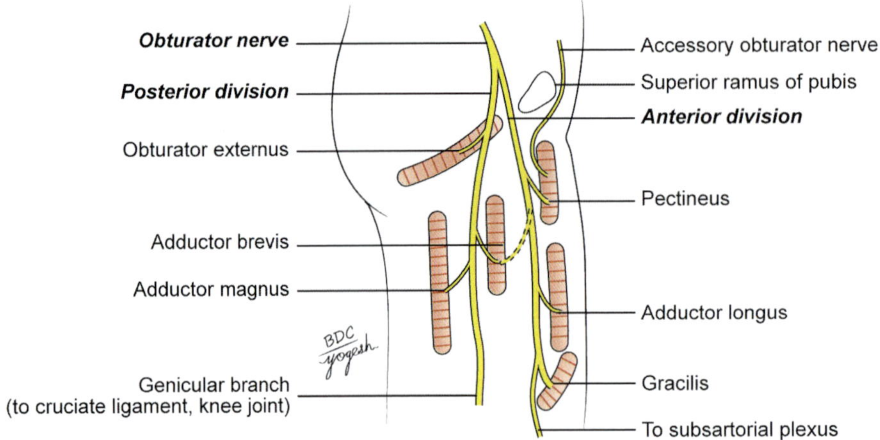

Fig. 4.3: Course and distribution of the obturator nerve

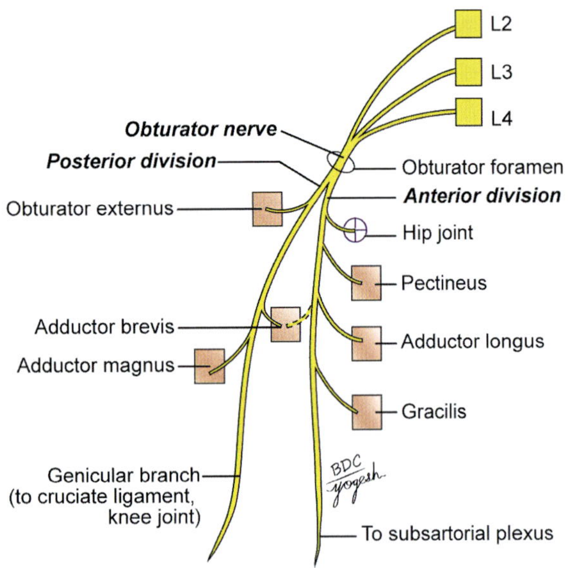

Fig. 4.4: Branches of obturator nerve

Flowchart 4.2: Obturator nerve

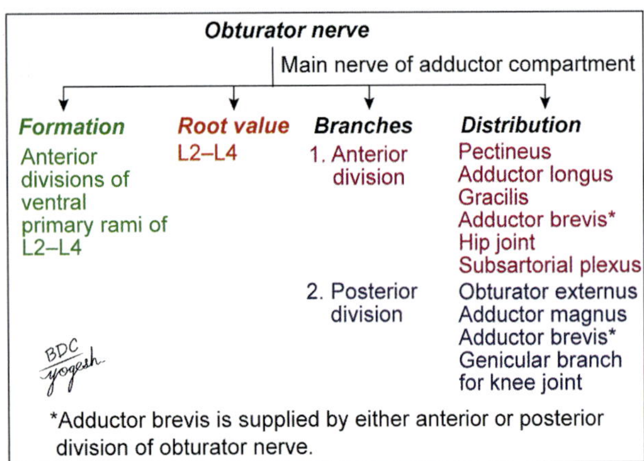

Obturator nerve

Main nerve of adductor compartment

Formation	Root value	Branches	Distribution
Anterior divisions of ventral primary rami of L2–L4	L2–L4	1. Anterior division	Pectineus Adductor longus Gracilis Adductor brevis* Hip joint Subsartorial plexus
		2. Posterior division	Obturator externus Adductor magnus Adductor brevis* Genicular branch for knee joint

*Adductor brevis is supplied by either anterior or posterior division of obturator nerve.

Course and Relations in Thigh

Within the obturator canal, the nerve divides into anterior and posterior divisions.

Anterior division: It passes downwards in front of the obturator externus being separated from the posterior division by a few fibres of this muscle. It then descends behind the pectineus and the adductor longus and in front of the adductor brevis. The anterior division supplies the following structures:

a. Pectineus
b. Adductor longus
c. Gracilis
d. Adductor brevis, if not supplied by the posterior division.
e. The anterior division also gives a branch to the *hip joint*.
f. Below the lower border of the adductor longus, it supplies a twig to the *subsartorial plexus* and ends by supplying the femoral artery in the adductor canal.

Posterior division: It enters the thigh by piercing the upper border of the obturator externus muscle. It descends behind the adductor brevis and in front of the adductor magnus. It gives branches to the following structures:

a. Obturator externus
b. Adductor magnus
c. Adductor brevis, if not supplied by the anterior division.
d. In the adductor canal, it is reduced to a thin *genicular branch* which enters the popliteal fossa, pierces the oblique popliteal ligament and ends by supplying the capsule and the cruciate ligaments of the *knee joint*. Some of its fibres end by innervating the popliteal artery.

CLINICAL ANATOMY

- ***Spasm of the adductors of thigh*** in certain intractable cases of spastic paraplegia may be relieved by surgical division of the obturator nerve.
- A disease of the hip joint may cause ***referred pain*** in the knee and on the medial side of the thigh because of their common nerve supply by the obturator nerve.
- Obturator nerve may be involved with femoral nerve in retroperitoneal tumours. A nerve entrapment syndrome leading to chronic pain on the medial side of thigh may occur in athletes with big adductor muscles.

ACCESSORY OBTURATOR NERVE

This nerve is present in about 30% of subjects. It is a branch of the lumbar plexus and is formed by the ventral divisions of the anterior primary rami of spinal nerves L3 and L4. It descends along the medial border of the psoas major, crosses the superior ramus of the pubis behind the pectineus and terminates by dividing into three branches.

1. For pectineus from its deep surface,
2. To the hip joint,
3. A communicating branch for the anterior division of the obturator nerve.

Sometimes the nerve is very small and ends by supplying the pectineus only (Fig. 4.5).

OBTURATOR ARTERY

1. The obturator artery is a branch of the internal iliac and accompanies (lies below) the obturator nerve in the pelvis.
2. At the upper margin of the obturator foramen, the obturator artery divides into ***anterior*** or ***medial*** and ***posterior*** or ***lateral branches*** which form a circle over the obturator membrane and anastomoses with the medial circumflex femoral artery.
3. Both branches supply the neighbouring muscles.
4. The posterior branch also gives an *acetabular branch* which passes through the acetabular notch to supply the fat in the acetabular fossa and sends a twig to the head of the femur along the round ligament (***foveolar artery***) (Fig. 4.6).

MEDIAL CIRCUMFLEX FEMORAL ARTERY

1. This artery arises from the profunda femoris (Fig. 4.7).
2. It leaves the femoral triangle by passing backwards and ends by dividing into ascending and transverse branches (Fig. 4.7).
3. ***Ascending branch*** of medial circumflex femoral anastomoses with ascending branch of lateral circumflex femoral and superior gluteal artery to form '***trochanteric anastomoses***'. This gives *retinacular branches* which lie along the retinacula of capsule of hip joint to supply head of femur.
4. ***Transverse branch*** anastomoses with transverse branch of lateral circumflex femoral, inferior gluteal and first perforating branch of profunda femoris to form '*cruciate anastomoses*'.

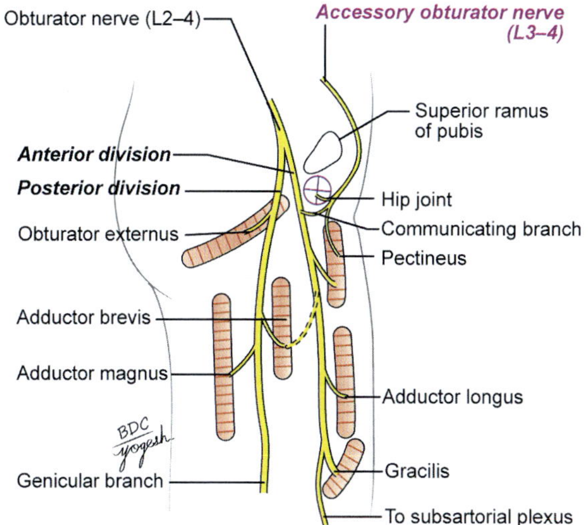

Fig. 4.5: Accessory obturator nerve

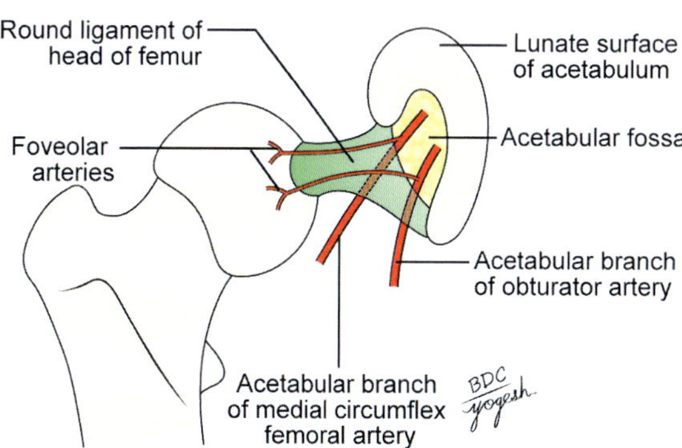

Fig. 4.6: Acetabular arteries and their foveolar branches

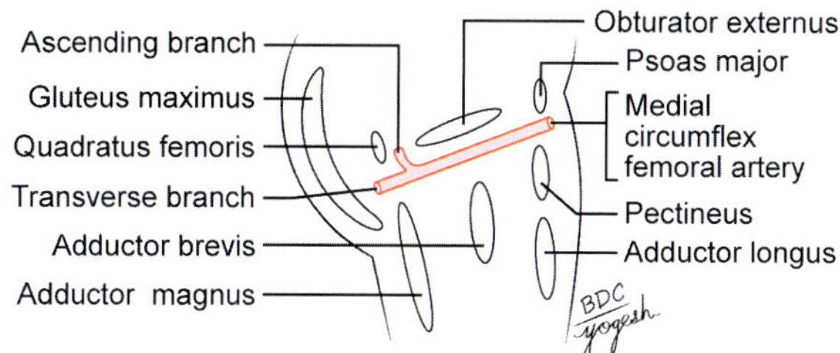

Fig. 4.7: Course of medial circumflex femoral artery

5. Before giving off the terminal branches, the artery gives off many muscular branches and an ***acetabular branch*** which passes through the acetabular notch to supply fat in the acetabular fossa. It also sends a twig to the head of the femur along the round ligament (foveolar artery).

Video 2.4 **Medial Side of Thigh:** Muscles of medial side of thigh.

Facts to Remember

- Obturator nerve arises from ventral divisions of ventral primary rami of L2–L4 segments of spinal cord; whereas femoral nerve arises from dorsal divisions of ventral primary rami of the same segments.
- Special muscles of medial compartment of thigh:
  1. Adductor magnus and pectineus – Hybrid or composite muscles.
  2. Adductors of thigh – Custodian of virginity
  3. Calcified tendon of adductor longus – Rider's bone.
- Since femoral and obturator nerves supply both the hip joint and knee joint, pain from one joint may be referred to the other joint.
- Obturator artery, branch of internal iliac and medial circumflex femoral, branch of profunda femoris are seen on the medial side of the thigh.

BDC's Anatomy *e*-book

1. Relations of adductor longus
2. Comparison between femoral and obturator nerves
3. Further reading
4. Viva voce questions

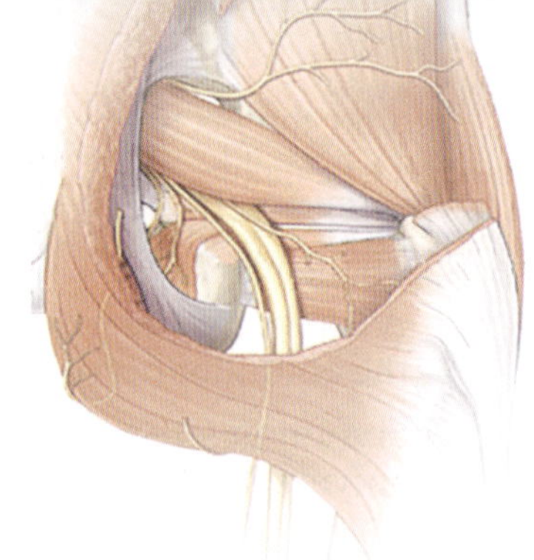

Chapter

5

Gluteal Region

The gluteal (Greek *rump*) region overlies the side and back of the pelvis, extending from the iliac crest above to the gluteal fold below. The lower part of the gluteal region which presents a rounded bulge due to excessive amount of subcutaneous fat is known as the ***buttock*** or ***natis***. The anterosuperior part of the region seen in a side view is called the ***hip***. Gluteus maximus is one of the most powerful and bulkiest muscles of the body. This region is commonly used for intramuscular injections.

SURFACE LANDMARKS

1. ***Buttock*** is the rounded bulge in the lower part of the gluteal region. The two buttocks are separated from each other in the posterior median line by the ***natal cleft***.
2. ***Gluteal fold*** marks the lower limit of the buttock. Note that the *gluteal fold* is the transverse skin crease of the hip joint and that it does not correspond to the lower border of gluteus maximus which crosses the fold obliquely downwards and laterally (Fig. 5.1).
3. ***Ischial tuberosity*** is a large bony prominence which lies deep to the lower border of gluteus maximus about 5 cm from the median plane and about the same distance above the gluteal fold. It can be felt by placing the fingers in the medial part of the gluteal fold and pressing them upwards.
4. ***Greater trochanter*** of femur is a large bony prominence situated immediately in front of the hollow on the side of the hip and about a hands breadth below the tubercle of iliac crest.
5. ***Iliac crest*** is a thick curved bony ridge felt in a groove in the lower margin of the waist. The hands spanning the waist are often supported by the iliac crest. The *highest point* of iliac crest corresponds to the interval between the spines for the L3 and L4 vertebrae; this is the site of the lumbar puncture.
6. The posterior end of iliac crest is known as the ***posterior superior iliac spine***. It lies in the floor of a dimple about 5 cm from the median plane and at the level of S2 spine opposite the middle of sacroiliac joint.
7. ***Sacrum*** lies posteriorly between the two hip bones. The upper three sacral spines are usually palpable in the median plane. The lower part of sacrum and the coccyx lie on the floor of the natal cleft.
8. ***Coccyx*** lies just behind the anus. It is slightly mobile under pressure.
9. The ***sacrotuberous ligament*** lying deep to the lower border of gluteus maximus can be felt by a firm pressure between the lower part of sacrum and ischial tuberosity.

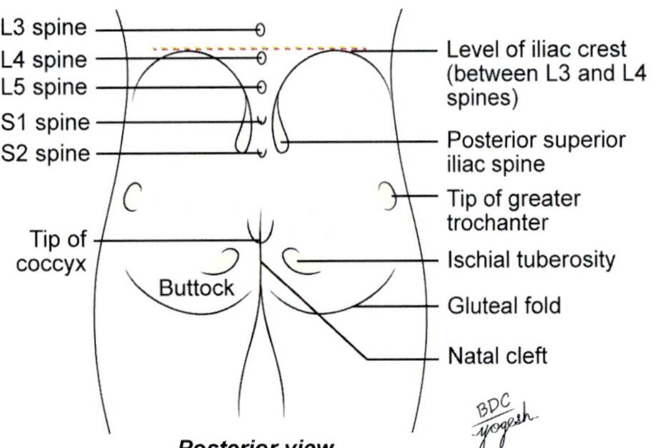

Fig. 5.1: Landmarks of the gluteal region

Note: **Nelaton's line** is an imaginary line between anterior superior iliac spine (ASIS) and ischial tuberosity (Fig. 5.2). This line crosses the tip of the greater trochanter of femur. In case of coxa vara (reduced angle between head and shaft of femur, <120°), fracture of neck of femur and posterior dislocation of hip joint, the greater trochanter lies above the Nelaton's line.

Bryant's triangle is a triangle that is drawn by using the following lines (Fig. 5.3): Horizontal line from anterior superior iliac spine (ASIS), vertical line from tip of greater trochanter and a line joining the anterior superior iliac spine and the tip of greater trochanter. The decrease in distance between tip of greater trochanter and junction of two perpendicular lines (point 3) is called supratrochanteric shortening. It may occur in dislocation of hip joint, fracture of neck of femur, destruction of femur head or acetabulum and coxa vara deformity.

DISSECTION

Make a curved incision from spine of second sacral vertebra (i); along the iliac crest till its tubercle (ii); make a vertical incision from the second sacral spine downwards till the natal cleft (iii); taking it further laterally with downward convexity till the middle of the back of thigh (iv) are shown in Fig. 5.4. For points v, vi, vii, viii and ix, *refer* to Chapters 6, 7 and 9.

Reflect the thick skin and fascia towards the lateral aspect. The cutaneous nerves and vessels are difficult to find. Study them from the text. After removing the deep fascia from gluteus maximus muscle, define the attachments of this muscle.

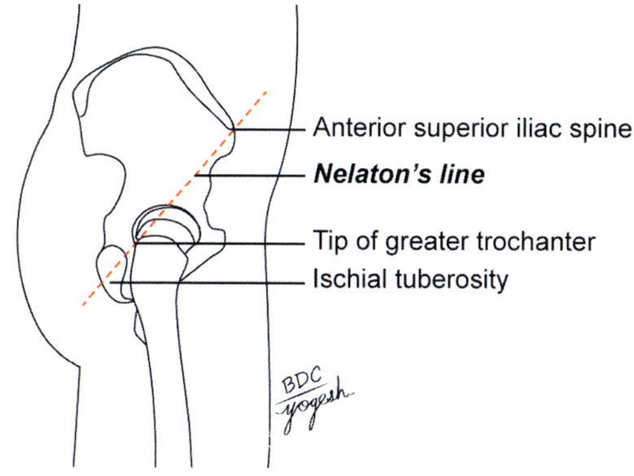

Fig. 5.2: Nelaton's line

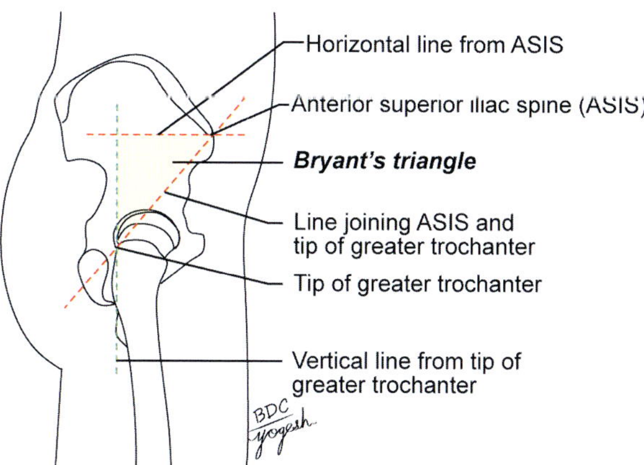

Fig. 5.3: Bryant's triangle

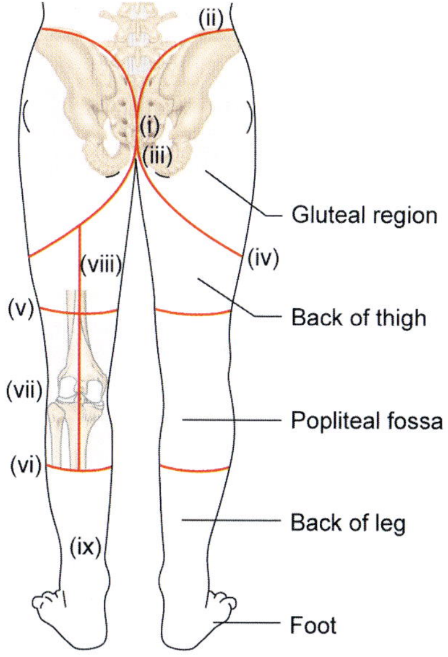

Fig. 5.4: Lines for dissection

SUPERFICIAL AND DEEP FASCIAE

SUPERFICIAL FASCIA

Superficial fascia is heavily laden with fat, more so in females, and is tough and stringy over the ischial tuberosity where it forms an efficient cushion for supporting the body weight in the sitting posture. It contains cutaneous nerves, vessels and lymphatics.

Cutaneous Nerves

The cutaneous nerves converge on the gluteal region from all directions (Figs 5.5a and b).

1. The ***upper anterior part*** is supplied by:
   - Lateral cutaneous branch of the subcostal T12
   - Lateral cutaneous branch of iliohypogastric L1 nerves.
2. The ***upper posterior part*** is supplied by the posterior primary rami of spinal nerves L1–L3 and S1–S3.
3. The ***lower anterior part*** is supplied by branches from the posterior division of the lateral cutaneous nerve of the thigh (L2, L3).
4. The ***lower posterior part*** is supplied by branches from:
   - Posterior cutaneous nerve of the thigh (S1–S3)
   - Perforating cutaneous nerve (S2, S3).

Cutaneous Vessels and Lymphatics

The *blood supply* of the skin and subcutaneous tissue is derived from branches of the superior and inferior gluteal arteries.

The *lymphatics* from the gluteal region drain into the lateral group of the superficial inguinal lymph nodes.

DEEP FASCIA

The deep fascia above and in front of the gluteus maximus, i.e. over the gluteus medius, is thick, dense, opaque and pearly white. Over the gluteus maximus, however, it is thin and transparent (Figs 5.6a and b). The deep fascia splits and encloses the gluteus maximus muscle.

SACROTUBEROUS AND SACROSPINOUS LIGAMENTS

These two ligaments convert the greater and lesser sciatic notches of the hip bone into foramina of the same name.

The ***sacrotuberous ligament*** is a long and strong ligament extending between the medial margin of ischial tuberosity and the posterior iliac spines. It forms the posterolateral boundary of the outlet of the pelvis (Plate 5.1).

The ***sacrospinous ligament*** is a short, thick, triangular band situated deep in the sacrotuberous ligament. It is attached:

a. Laterally to the ischial spine.
b. Medially to the sacrococcygeal junction.

Plate 5.1: Sacrotuberous and sacrospinous ligament

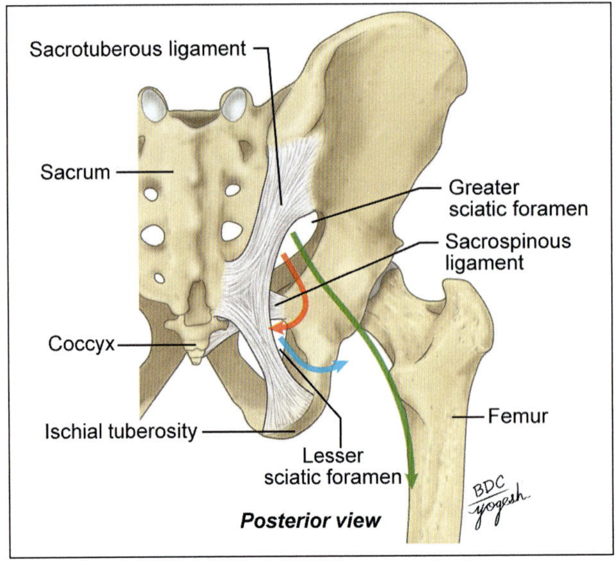

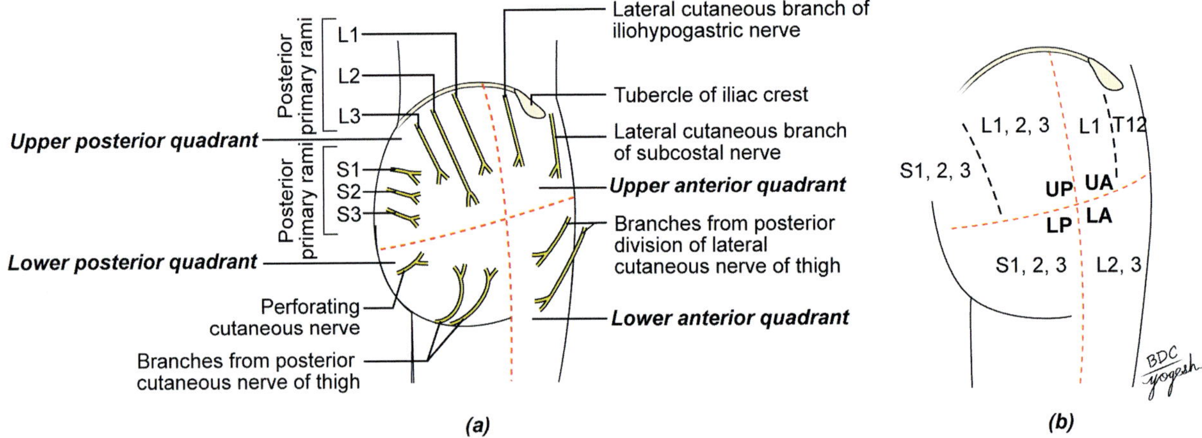

Figs 5.5a and b: Cutaneous innervation of the gluteal region: (a) Cutaneous nerves and (b) root values of the nerves in the four quadrants

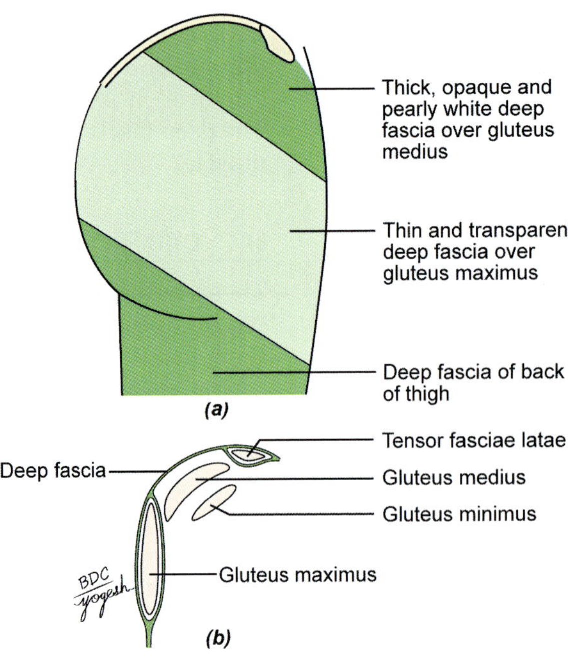

Figs 5.6a and b: Deep fascia overlying some muscles of the gluteal region

MUSCLES OF GLUTEAL REGION

Features

- The muscles of gluteal region are the gluteus maximus, the gluteus medius, the gluteus minimus, the piriformis, the superior and inferior gemelli, the obturator internus, obturator externus and quadratus femoris (Plate 5.2, Figs 5.7 to 5.9, Tables 5.1 and 5.2). The tensor fasciae latae which lies on the lateral side of thigh, just in front of gluteal region, is also considered here.
- The gluteus maximus is the chief extensor of the thigh at the hip joint. This action is very important in rising from a sitting position. It is essential for maintaining the erect posture. Along with the tensor fasciae latae, the muscle stabilises the knee through the iliotibial tract. It supports both the hip and the knee when these joints are slightly flexed. It is an antigravity muscle as well.
- For the gluteus medius and minimus, the most important action is to maintain the balance of the body when the opposite foot is off the ground, as in walking and running. They do this by preventing the opposite side of the pelvis from tilting downwards under the influence of gravity.
- The tendon of the obturator internus leaves the pelvis through the lesser sciatic foramen. Here it bends at a right angle around the lesser sciatic notch and runs laterally to be inserted into the medial surface of the ***greater trochanter*** of the femur.
- The obturator externus muscle ends in a tendon which runs upwards and laterally behind the neck of the femur to reach the gluteal region where it is inserted into the trochanteric fossa (on medial side of the greater trochanter).
- Structures under cover of the gluteus maximus are listed in Table 5.3 (Figs 5.10 and 5.11).
- Structures deep to the gluteus medius are:
  1. Superior gluteal nerve
  2. Deep branch of the superior gluteal artery
  3. Gluteus minimus
  4. Trochanteric bursa of the gluteus medius
- Structures deep to the gluteus minimus are the reflected head of the rectus femoris and the capsule of the hip joint.

Fig. 5.7: Gluteus maximus muscle

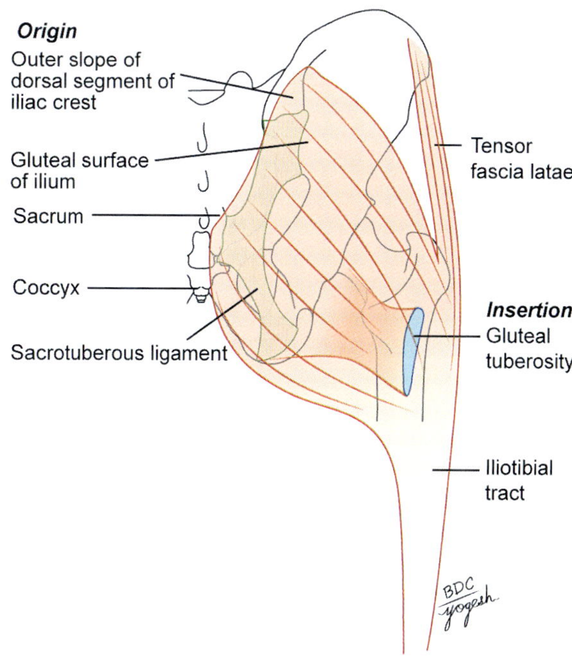

Fig. 5.8: Origin and insertion of the gluteus maximus muscle

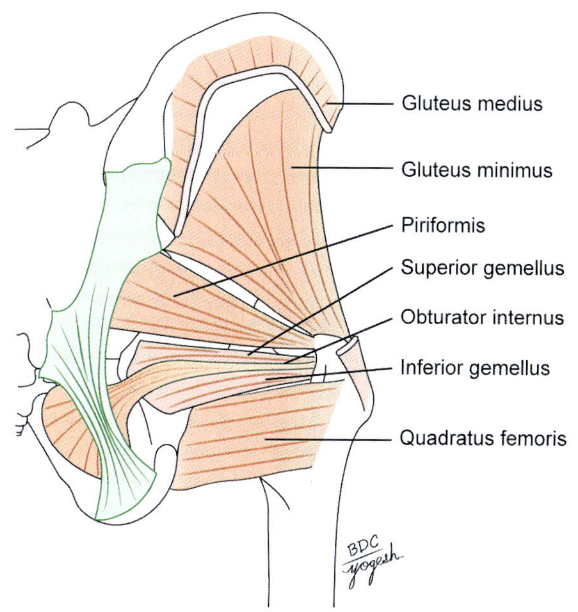

Fig. 5.9: Muscles of right gluteal region

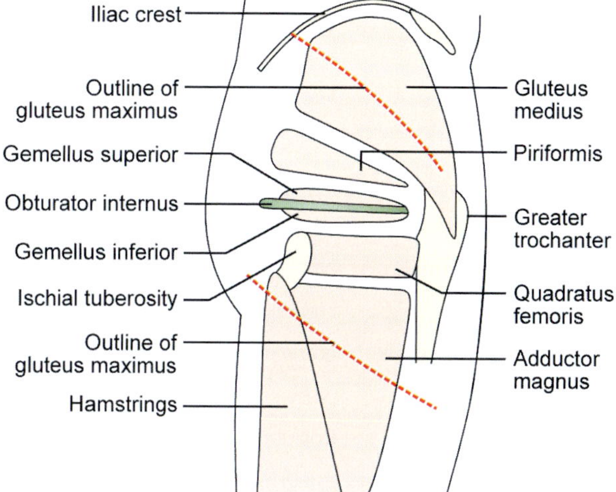

Fig. 5.10: Muscles under cover of the gluteus maximus

TABLE 5.1: Origin and insertion of muscles of the gluteal region

Muscle	Origin	Insertion
1. Gluteus maximus Quadrilateral powerful muscle. It comprises red muscle fibres	• Outer slope of the dorsal segment of iliac crest • Posterior gluteal line • Posterior part of gluteal surface of ***ilium*** behind the posterior gluteal line • Aponeurosis of erector spinae • Dorsal surface of lower part of sacrum • Side of coccyx • Sacrotuberous ligament	• The deep fibres of the lower part of the muscle are inserted into the ***gluteal tuberosity*** (1/4th part) • The greater part of the muscle is inserted into the ***iliotibial tract*** (3/4th part)
2. Gluteus medius Fan-shaped muscle	Gluteal surface of ***ilium*** between the anterior and posterior gluteal lines	On oblique ridge at the lateral surface of the ***greater trochanter*** of femur
3. Gluteus minimus Fan-shaped	Gluteal surface of ***ilium*** between the anterior and inferior gluteal lines	Into ***greater trochanter*** of femur, on a ridge on its anterior surface
4. Piriformis	It arises within the pelvis from: • Pelvic surface of the middle three pieces of the ***sacrum***, by three digitations • Upper margin of the greater sciatic notch	The rounded tendon is inserted into the apex of the ***greater trochanter*** of the femur (*see* Fig. 2.12)
5. Gemellus superior	Upper part of ***lesser sciatic notch***	Blends with tendon of obturator internus, and gets inserted into medial surface of ***greater trochanter*** of femur
6. Gemellus inferior	Lower part of ***lesser sciatic notch***	Same as above
7. Obturator internus Fan-shaped muscle	Pelvic surface of ***obturator membrane*** and surrounding bones	Medial surface of the ***greater trochanter*** of the femur
8. Quadratus femoris Quadrilateral muscle	Upper part of the outer border of ***ischial tuberosity***	***Quadrate tubercle*** and the area below it
9. Obturator externus Triangular in shape	Outer surface of obturator membrane and adjacent bony margins of obturator foramen	***Trochanteric fossa*** (on medial side of the greater trochanter)
10. Tensor fasciae latae	Anterior 5 cm of the outer lip of the ***iliac crest*** up to the tubercle of iliac crest	***Iliotibial tract*** 3–5 cm below the level of greater trochanter

TABLE 5.2: Nerve supply and actions of muscles of the gluteal region

Muscle	Nerve supply	Actions
1. Gluteus maximus	Inferior gluteal nerve (L5, S1, 2)	• Chief extensor of the hip joint • Assists in rising from a sitting position and maintaining an erect posture • Lateral rotation of the thigh • Abduction of the thigh (by upper fibres) • Along with the tensor fasciae latae, it stabilises the knee
2. Gluteus medius	Superior gluteal nerve (L4, 5, S1)	The *gluteus medius* and *gluteus minimus* are: • Powerful abductors of the thigh • Their anterior fibres are also medial rotators • Prevents the sagging of pelvis on the unsupported side
3. Gluteus minimus	Superior gluteal nerve (L4, 5, S1)	
4. Piriformis	Ventral rami of S1, 2	Lateral rotators of thigh at the hip joint
5. Gemellus superior	Nerve to obturator internus (L5, S1, 2)	
6. Gemellus inferior	Nerve to quadratus femoris (L4, 5, S1)	
7. Obturator internus	Nerve to obturator internus (L5, S1, 2)	
8. Quadratus femoris	Nerve to quadratus femoris (L4, 5, S1)	
9. Obturator externus	Posterior division of obturator nerve (L2, 3, 4)	
10. Tensor fasciae latae	Superior gluteal nerve (L4, 5, S1)	Abductor and medial rotator of thigh and an extensor of knee joint

Plate 5.2: Muscles of the gluteal region

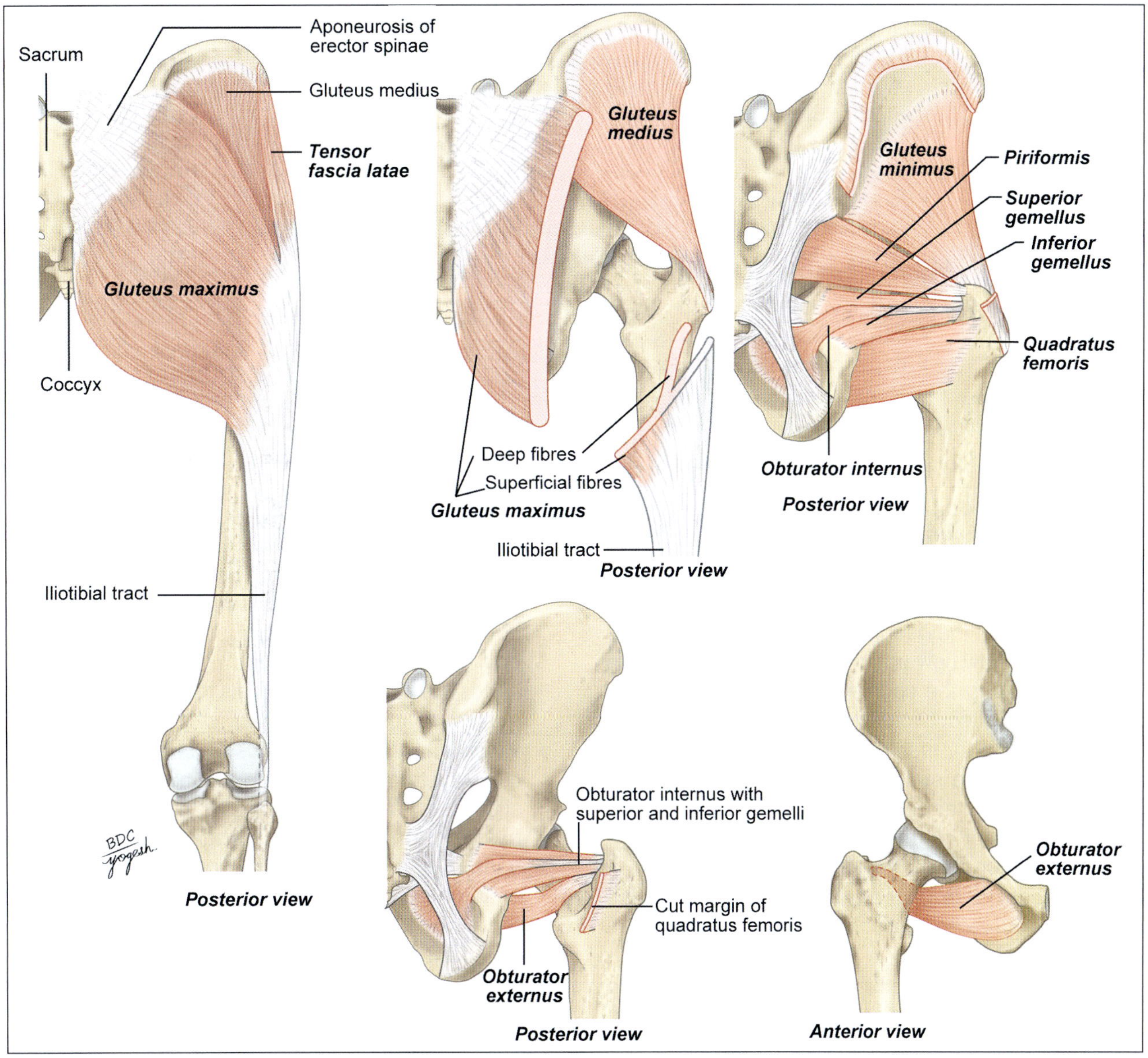

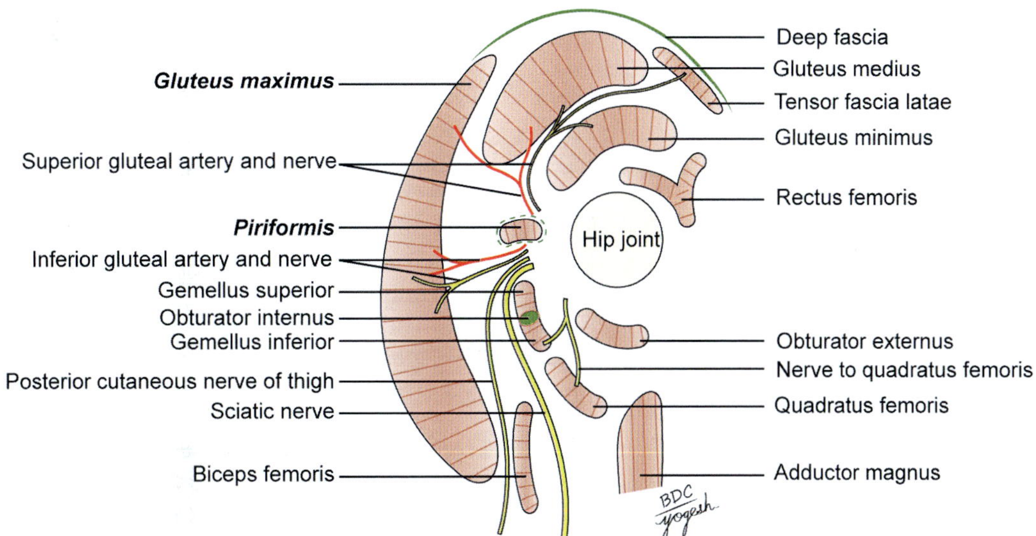

Fig. 5.11: Scheme of an oblique vertical section showing structures under cover of the gluteus maximus

TABLE 5.3: Structures under cover of the gluteus maximus

Muscles	*Vessels*	*Nerves*	*Bones, joints and ligaments*	*Bursae*
• Gluteus medius • Gluteus minimus • Reflected head of the rectus femoris • Piriformis • Obturator internus with two gemelli • Quadratus femoris • Obturator externus • Origin of the four hamstrings from the ischial tuberosity • Insertion of the upper or pubic fibres of the adductor magnus	• Superior gluteal vessels • Inferior gluteal vessels • Internal pudendal vessels • Ascending branch of the medial circumflex femoral artery • Trochanteric anastomoses • Cruciate anastomoses • The first perforating artery	• Superior gluteal • Inferior gluteal • Sciatic • Posterior cutaneous nerve of thigh • Nerve to the quadratus femoris • Pudendal nerve • Nerve to the obturator internus • Perforating cutaneous nerves	• Ilium • Ischium with ischial tuberosity • Upper end of femur with the greater trochanter • Sacrum • Coccyx • Hip joint • Sacroiliac joint • Sacrotuberous ligament • Sacrospinous ligament • Ischiofemoral ligament	• Trochanteric bursa of gluteus maximus • Bursa over the ischial tuberosity • Bursa between the gluteus maximus and vastus lateralis

DISSECTION

Reflect the gluteus maximus to examine the underlying structures. For this, identify the lower border of muscle. Insert a forceps on the deep surface of muscle which is to be cut from below upwards midway between its origin and insertion along the course of posterior cutaneous nerve of thigh. Reflect two parts on either side.

Piriformis is *key muscle* of the region, define its margins. Identify the structures above and below this muscle, most important being the sciatic nerve. Above piriformis—superior gluteal vessels and nerve. Below piriformis—inferior gluteal vessels and nerve.

The thickest nerve of the body, sciatic nerve also enters the gluteal region through the greater sciatic notch below piriformis muscle.

Pudendal nerve and vessels appear here through greater sciatic notch and disappear through the lesser sciatic notch (Fig. 5.11).

Under the lower and medial part of the gluteus maximus muscle, ischial tuberosity is easily palpable. Separate the hamstring muscles from the ischial tuberosity.

Identify long vertical sacrotuberous ligament and smaller horizontal sacrospinous ligament to demarcate the greater and lesser sciatic foramina and structures entering and leaving them. Greater sciatic notch is the 'gateway' of the gluteal region.

Define the borders of the gluteus medius muscle. Cut through the muscle 5 cm above its insertion into the greater trochanter of femur. The superior gluteal vessels and nerve are now exposed which are to be traced into gluteus minimus and tensor fasciae latae.

Reflect gluteus minimus from its origin towards the insertion to expose the straight and reflected heads of rectus femoris muscle and the capsule of the hip joint.

Competency:

AN16.2 Describe anatomical basis of sciatic nerve injury during gluteal intramuscular injections.

CLINICAL ANATOMY

- *Testing gluteus maximus:* The patient lies prone. The right hand of physician presses the patient's right leg downwards. Patient is requested to extend his hip against resistance provided by the physician's right hand; while his left hand feels the contracting gluteus maximus muscle (Fig. 5.12).
- *When the gluteus maximus is paralysed* as in muscular dystrophy, the patient cannot stand up from a sitting posture without support. Such patients, while trying to stand up, rise gradually, supporting their hands first on legs and then on the thighs; they climb on themselves (Fig. 5.13).
- *Intramuscular injections* are given in the upper lateral quadrant of the gluteal region, i.e. in the gluteus medius muscle, to avoid injury to large vessels and nerves which pass through the lower part of this region (Fig. 5.14). Gluteal region is not the prominence of the buttock only. It is a very big area over the iliac bone. This is known as positive Gower's sign.
- *When the glutei medius and minimus (of right side) are paralysed,* the patient cannot walk normally. She bends or lurches on the right side or paralysed side to clear the opposite foot, i.e. left, off the ground. This is known as *lurching gait* (Fig. 5.15)*;* when bilateral, it is called *waddling gait.*
- The normal gait depends on the proper abductor mechanism at both hips (Fig. 5.16). This mechanism comprises:
  a. The adequate power, provided by the glutei medius and minimus.
  b. The fulcrum, formed by a normal relationship of the head of the femur with the acetabulum.
  c. The weight transmitted by the head and neck of the femur.
- Normally when the body weight is supported on one (say right) limb, the glutei of the supported (right) side raise the opposite and unsupported (left) side of the pelvis. However, if the abductor mechanism

is defective, the unsupported (left) side of the pelvis drops, and this is known as a positive *Trendelenburg's sign* (Figs 5.17a to c).

- The sign is positive in defects of power, i.e. paralysis of the glutei medius and minimus; defects of the fulcrum, i.e. congenital or pathological dislocation of the hip; and defects of the weight, i.e. ununited fracture of the neck of femur.

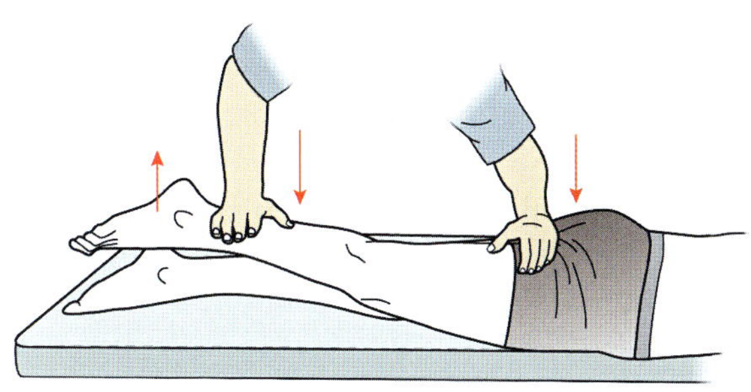

Fig. 5.12: How to test the gluteus maximus

Fig. 5.13: Trying to stand up in paralysis of gluteus maximus muscle

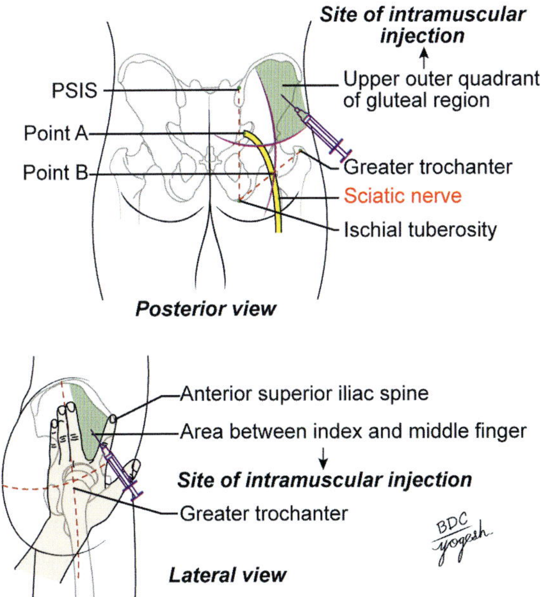

Fig. 5.14: Site of intramuscular injection in the gluteal region (Point A: 2.5 cm lateral to the midpoint of the line joining posterior superior iliac spine and ischial tuberosity; Point B: Midpoint of line joining greater trochanter and ischial tuberosity

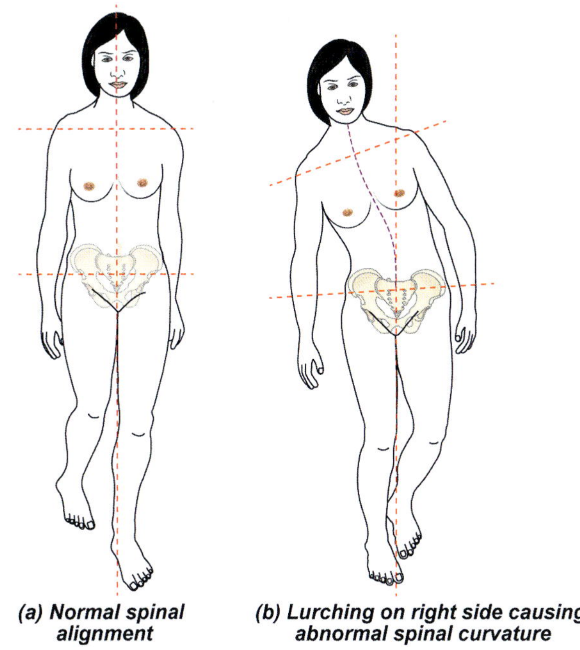

Figs 5.15a and b: Differences between normal gait and lurching gait

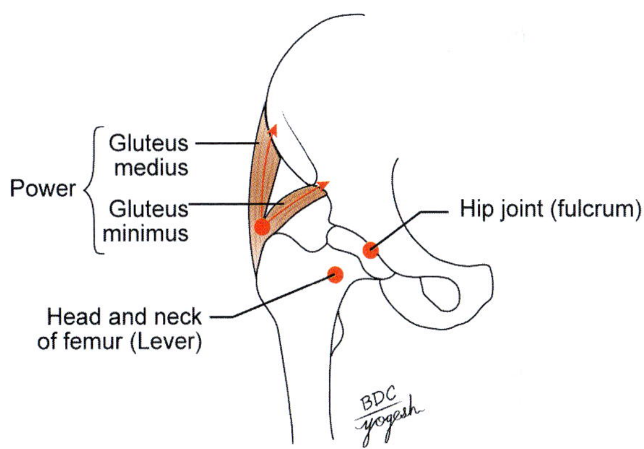

Fig. 5.16: Abductor mechanism at the hip joint

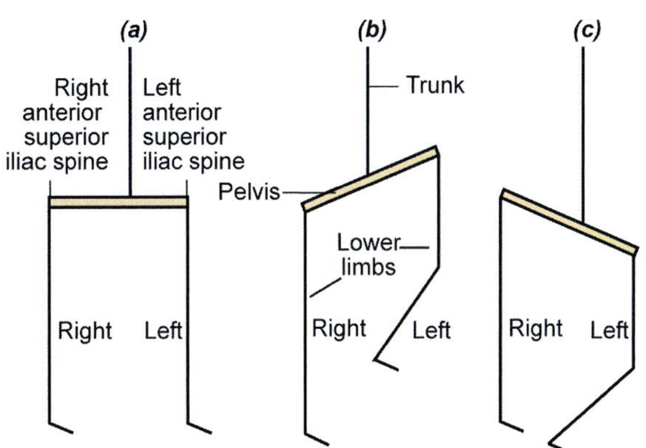

Figs 5.17a to c: Trendelenburg's sign. a and b normal: (a) When both feet are supporting the body weight, the pelvis (anterior superior iliac spine) on the two sides lie in the same horizontal plane, (b) when only the right foot is supporting the body weight, the unsupported side of the pelvis is normally raised by the opposite gluteal medius and minimus, and (c) if the right glutei medius and minimus are paralysed, the unsupported left side of the pelvis drops. This is a positive Trendelenburg's sign

- Gluteus medius and gluteus minimus can be tested together by doing internal rotation of thigh against resistance. The person lies in supine position with the hip and knee flexed.
- Gluteus medius, gluteus minimus and tensor fasciae latae are tested by the abducting lower limb against resistance. The person lies in the supine position and the knee is extended (Fig. 5.18).

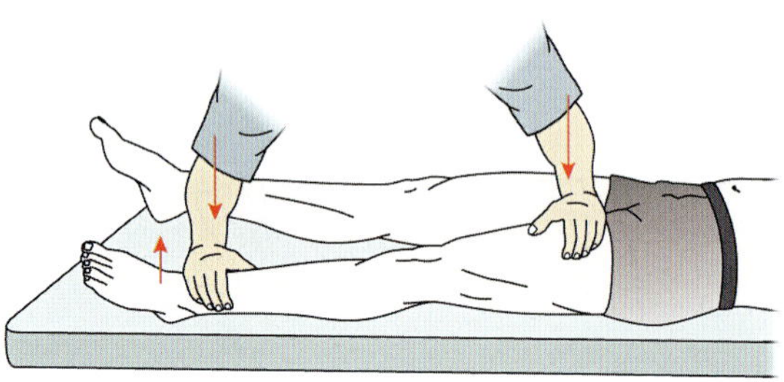

Fig. 5.18: How to test the gluteus medius, gluteus minimus and tensor fasciae latae

Competencies:

AN16.1 Describe and demonstrate origin, course, relations, branches (or tributaries), termination of important nerves and vessels of gluteal region.

AN16.3 Explain the anatomical basis of Trendelenburg sign.

NERVES OF THE GLUTEAL REGION

Superior Gluteal Nerve (L4, 5, S1)

The superior gluteal nerve is a branch of the lumbosacral plexus. It enters the gluteal region through the greater sciatic foramen, above the piriformis, runs forwards between the gluteus medius and minimus and supplies three muscles, viz. the *gluteus medius*, the *gluteus minimus* and the *tensor fasciae latae* (Plate 5.3).

Inferior Gluteal Nerve (L5, S1, 2)

The inferior gluteal nerve is also a branch of the sacral plexus given off in the pelvis. It enters the gluteal region through the greater sciatic foramen below the piriformis and ends by supplying the *gluteus maximus* only, to which it is fully committed (Plate 5.3).

Sciatic Nerve (L4, 5, S1–S3)

The sciatic nerve is the thickest nerve in the body. It is the main continuation of the sacral plexus. It enters the gluteal region through the greater sciatic foramen below the piriformis, runs downwards between the greater trochanter and the ischial tuberosity and enters the back of the thigh at the lower border of the gluteus maximus. ***It does not give any branches in the gluteal region*** (Plate 5.3). It is described in detail in Chapter 7, page 90.

Posterior Cutaneous Nerve of the Thigh (S1–S3)

Posterior cutaneous nerve is a branch of the sacral plexus. It enters the gluteal region through the greater sciatic foramen, below the piriformis, and runs downwards medial or posterior to the sciatic nerve. It continues in the back of the thigh immediately deep to the deep fascia (Plate 5.3).

The nerve gives:

a. A ***perineal branch*** crosses the ischial tuberosity enters the urogenital triangle of the perineum and supplies the skin of the posterior 2/3rd of the scrotum, or labium majus.

b. ***Gluteal branches*** wind upwards around the lower border of the gluteus maximus and supply the skin of the posteroinferior quadrant of the gluteal region.

Nerve to Quadratus Femoris (L4, 5, S1)

Nerve to quadratus femoris arises from the sacral plexus, enters the gluteal region through the greater sciatic foramen below the piriformis and runs downwards deep to the sciatic nerve, the obturator internus and the gemelli. It supplies the *quadratus femoris*, the *gemellus inferior* and the hip joint.

Nerve to the Obturator Internus (L5, S1, 2)

This is a branch of the sacral plexus. It enters the gluteal region through the greater sciatic foramen and crosses the ischial spine, lateral to the internal pudendal vessels, to re-enter the pelvis. It supplies both the *obturator internus* and the *gemellus superior* muscles.

Pudendal Nerve (S2, 3, 4)

Pudendal nerve is a branch of the sacral plexus. Only a small part of this nerve is seen in the gluteal region. It enters this region through the greater sciatic foramen. It then crosses the apex or lateral end of the sacrospinous ligament, medial to the internal pudendal vessels. It leaves the gluteal region by passing into the lesser sciatic foramen through which it enters the ischioanal fossa. It does not supply any structure in the gluteal region.

Perforating Cutaneous Nerve (S2, 3)

Perforating cutaneous nerve is a branch of the sacral plexus. It pierces the lower part of the sacrotuberous ligament, winds round the lower border of the gluteus maximus and supplies the skin of the posteroinferior quadrant of the gluteal region.

CLINICAL ANATOMY

- ***'Sciatic nerve block'*** is done by injecting an anaesthetic agent 1.5 cm below the midpoint of the line joining posterior superior iliac spine and upper border of greater trochanter.
- ***Sciatic nerve compression*:** Sciatic nerve lies on the femur for a very short distance between lower border of quadratus femoris and upper border of adductor magnus muscles. At this site it may get compressed when one sits on a stool or a bench; leading to harmless condition, the sleeping foot.
- ***Piriformis syndrome*** occurs, if sciatic nerve gets compressed by piriformis muscle. It leads to pain in the buttock.

Plate 5.3: Structures in the gluteal region

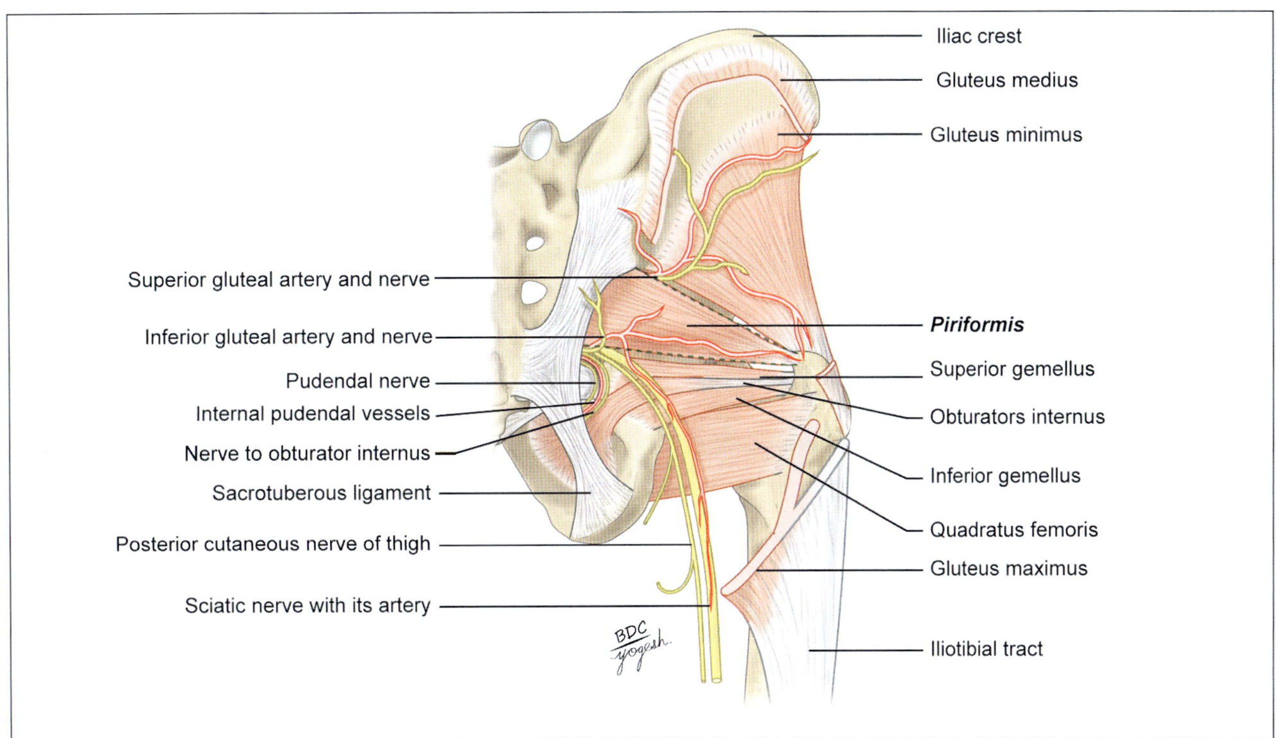

ARTERIES OF GLUTEAL REGION

Superior Gluteal Artery

Superior gluteal artery is a branch of the posterior division of the internal iliac artery. It enters the gluteal region through the greater sciatic foramen passing above the piriformis along with the superior gluteal nerve. In the foramen, it divides into superficial and deep branches.

Branches

1. Superficial branch supplies gluteus maximus.
2. Deep branch divides into:
   - *Superior division*: It runs between gluteus medius and gluteus minimus and ends at anterior superior iliac spine in spinous anastomosis.
   - *Inferior division*: It forms trochanteric anastomosis.

Inferior Gluteal Artery

Inferior gluteal artery is a branch of the anterior division of the internal iliac artery. It enters the gluteal region by passing through the greater sciatic foramen, below the piriformis, along with the inferior gluteal nerve. It supplies:

Branches

1. Muscular branches to gluteal muscles
2. Cutaneous branches
3. Articular branches to hip joint
4. Anastomotic branches to cruciate and trochanteric anastomosis.
5. ***Arteria nervi ischiadici*** – artery to sciatic nerve. It represents axial artery of the lower limb. Coccygeal branch to supply area over coccyx.

Internal Pudendal Artery

Internal pudendal artery is a branch of the anterior division of the internal iliac artery.

It enters the gluteal region through the greater sciatic foramen. It has a very short course in the gluteal region.

It crosses the ischial spine and leaves the gluteal region by passing into the lesser sciatic foramen through which it reaches the ischioanal fossa.

Trochanteric Anastomosis

It is situated near the trochanteric fossa. It is a chief source of arterial supply to the head of femur (Fig. 5.19, Flowchart 5.1).

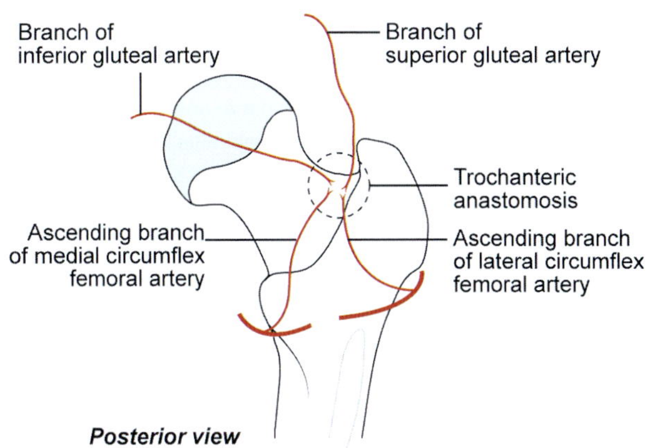

Fig. 5.19: Trochanteric anastomosis

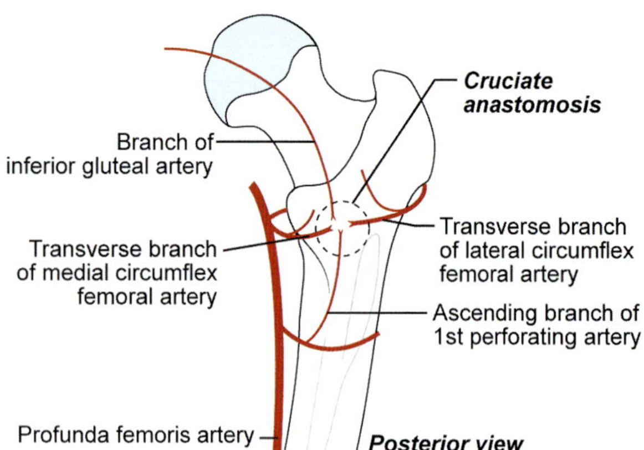

Fig. 5.20: Cruciate anastomosis

Flowchart 5.1: Trochanteric anastomosis

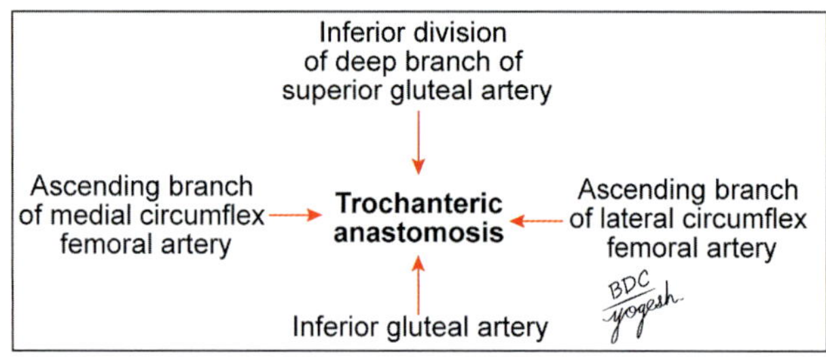

Flowchart 5.2: Cruciate anastomosis

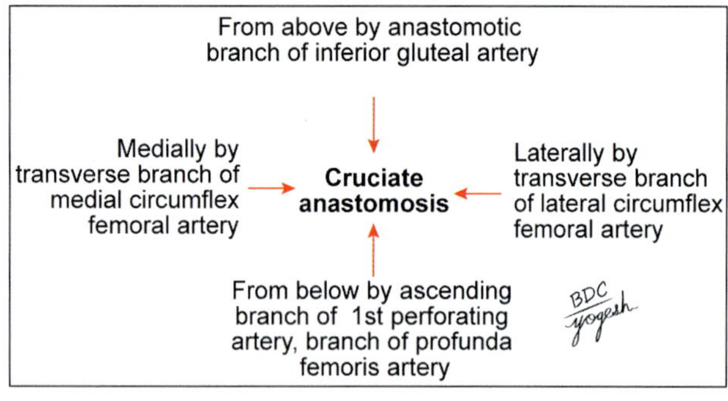

Formation

It is formed by the following arteries:

1. Inferior division of deep branch of superior gluteal artery.
2. Ascending branch of medial circumflex femoral artery.
3. Ascending branch of lateral circumflex femoral artery.
4. Inferior gluteal artery.

Cruciate Anastomosis

It is situated over the upper part of the back of the femur. It establishes collateral circulation between branches of internal iliac and external iliac arteries (femoral artery → profunda femoris artery) (Fig. 5.20, Flowchart 5.2).

Formation

It is formed by the following arteries:

1. *Superiorly*: Branch of inferior gluteal artery.
2. *Inferiorly*: Ascending branch of 1st perforating artery (branch of profunda femoris artery).
3. *Medially*: Transverse branch of medial circumflex femoral artery.
4. *Laterally*: Transverse branch of lateral circumflex femoral artery.

STRUCTURES PASSING THROUGH THE GREATER SCIATIC FORAMEN (GATEWAY OF GLUTEAL REGION)

1. The piriformis, emerging from the pelvis fills the foramen almost completely. It is the key muscle of the region (Fig. 5.21).
2. Structures passing above the piriformis are:
   a. Superior gluteal nerve
   b. Superior gluteal vessels
3. Structures passing below the piriformis from medial to lateral side are as follows:
   a. Pudendal nerve
   b. Internal pudendal vessels
   c. Nerve to obturator internus
   d. Inferior gluteal vessels
   e. Inferior gluteal nerve
   f. Posterior cutaneous nerve of thigh
   g. Sciatic nerve
   h. Nerve to quadratus femoris

Note: Structures passing through the lesser sciatic foramen (*Mnemonic*: PIN–T

1. **P**udendal nerve
2. **I**nternal pudendal vessels
3. **N**erve to obturator internus
4. **T**endon of obturator internus)

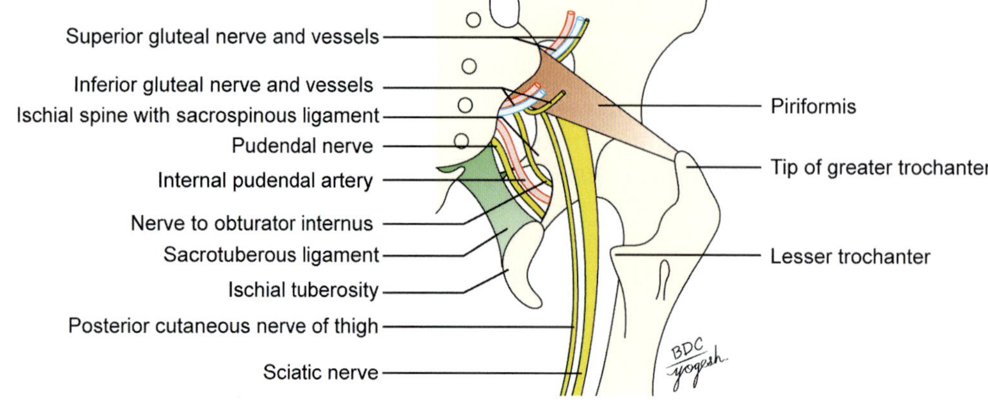

Fig. 5.21: Structures passing through greater and lesser sciatic notches

Video 2.5 **Gluteal Region**

Facts to Remember

- Gluteus maximus is the antigravity, postural thickest muscle of the body. It contains red fibres.
- Sciatic nerve is the thickest nerve in the body.
- Intramuscular injections are given in the upper lateral quadrant of the gluteal region into gluteus medius.
- Sciatic nerve and pudendal nerve do not supply any structure in the gluteal region.
- Piriformis is the key muscle of the gluteal region.
- Sciatic nerve and its branches supply the hamstring muscles, muscles of the three compartments of the leg and the muscles of the sole.
- Sciatic nerve is accompanied by a thin artery, the sciatic artery, which is part of the axial artery of the lower limb.
- Lesser sciatic foramen is the gateway of the perineal region.

BDC's Anatomy *e*-book

1. Gluteal bursae
2. Further reading
3. Viva voce questions

Chapter

6

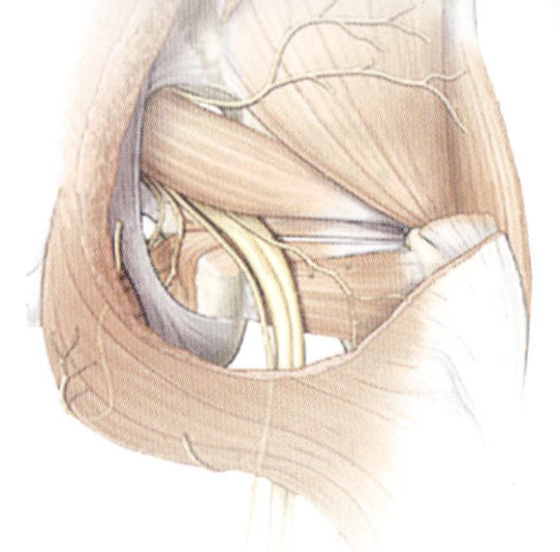

Popliteal Fossa

Competency:

AN16.6 Describe and demonstrate the boundaries, roof, floor, contents and relations of popliteal fossa.

Popliteal (Latin *hamstring of knee*) fossa is a shallow diamond-shaped depression felt best at the back of knee joint, when the joint is semiflexed. It corresponds to the cubital fossa of the forearm.

LOCATION

The popliteal fossa is a diamond-shaped depression lying behind the knee joint, the lower part of the femur, and the upper part of the tibia (Plate 6.1).

BOUNDARIES

The popliteal fossa has four boundaries as follows:

Superolaterally: Biceps femoris (Figs 6.1 and 6.2, Flowchart 6.1).

Superomedially: Semitendinosus and the semimembranosus, supplemented by the gracilis, the sartorius and the adductor magnus.

Inferolaterally: Lateral head of the gastrocnemius supplemented by the plantaris.

Inferomedially: Medial head of the gastrocnemius.

Roof

It is formed by deep fascia or popliteal fascia (Fig. 6.3). The superficial fascia over the roof contains:

1. Small saphenous vein and cutaneous nerves.
2. Three cutaneous nerves:
   a. Branches and terminal part of the posterior cutaneous nerve of the thigh.
   b. Posterior division of the medial cutaneous nerve of the thigh.
   c. Peroneal or sural communicating nerve.

Floor

It is formed from above downwards by (Figs 6.4 a and b):

a. Popliteal surface of the femur.
b. Capsule of the knee joint and the oblique popliteal ligament.
c. Popliteus muscle covered by its fascia.

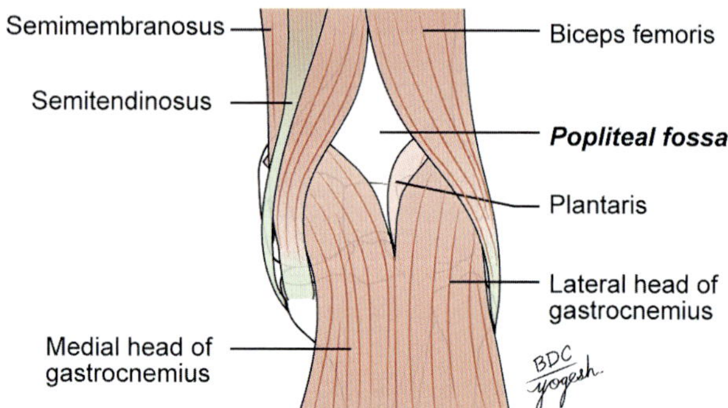

Fig. 6.1: Boundaries of the right popliteal fossa

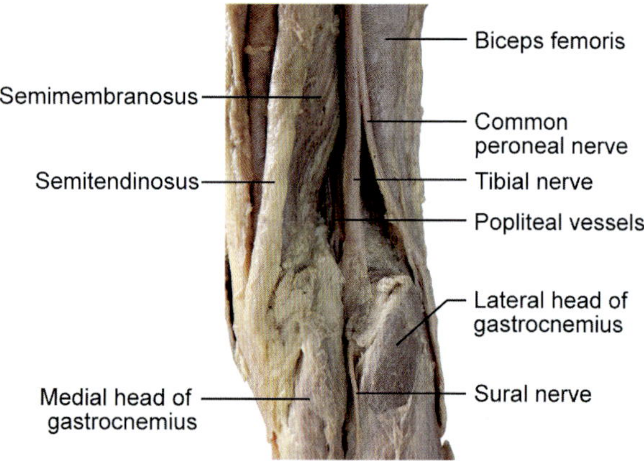

Fig. 6.2: Superficial dissection of the popliteal fossa

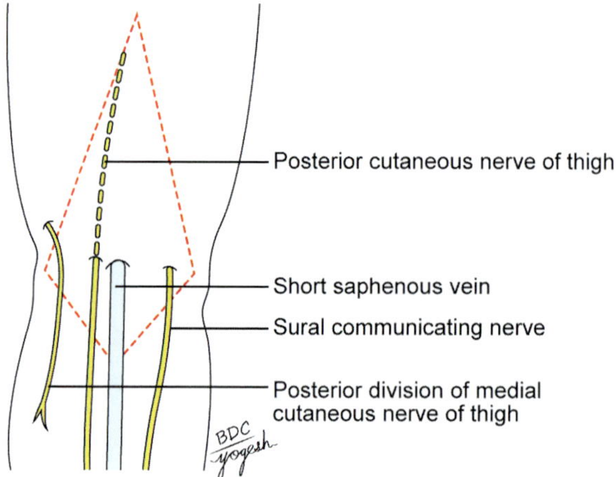

Fig. 6.3: Structures in the roof of the popliteal fossa

Plate 6.1: Boundaries and floor of the right popliteal fossa

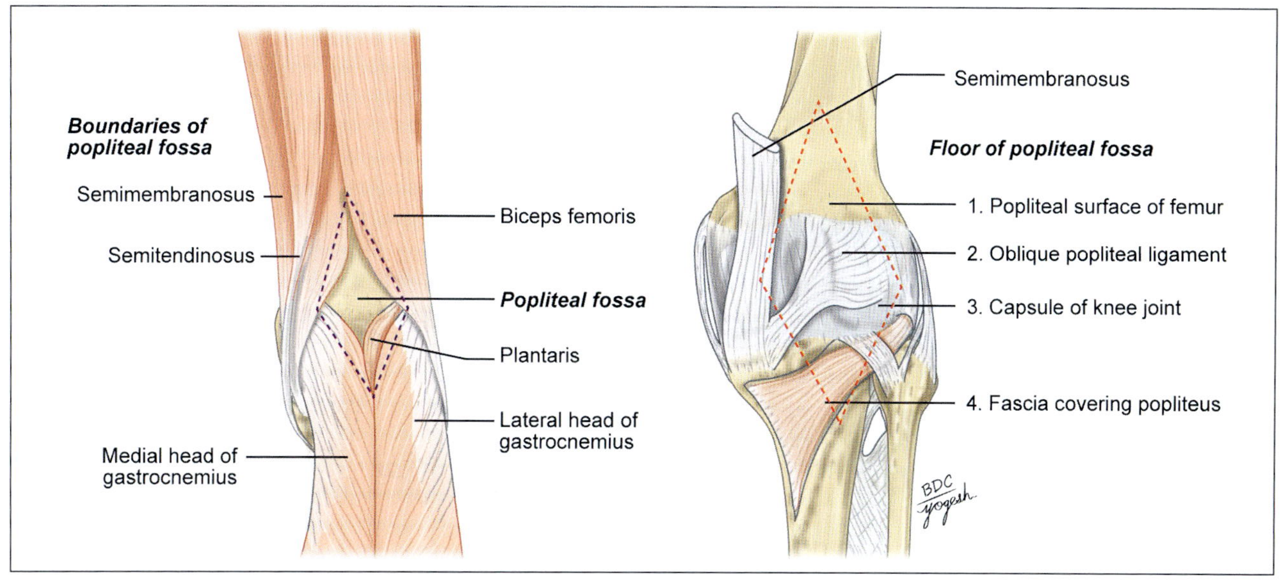

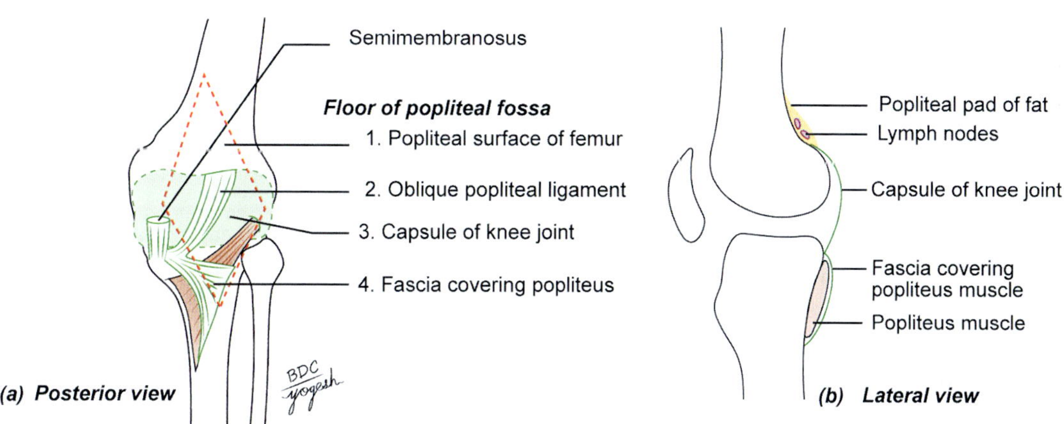

Figs 6.4a and b: Floor of the popliteal fossa: (a) Posterior view and (b) lateral view

Flowchart 6.1: Popliteal fossa

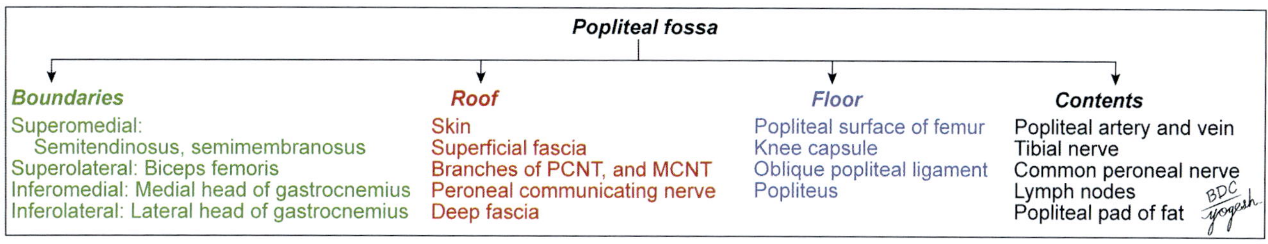

CONTENTS

1. Popliteal artery and its branches (Fig. 6.5)
2. Popliteal vein and its tributaries
3. Tibial nerve and its branches
4. Common peroneal nerve and its branches
5. Posterior cutaneous nerve of the thigh
6. Genicular branch of the obturator nerve
7. Popliteal lymph nodes
8. Fat: Surrounds and supports all the above structures.

Note: Relations of popliteal artery popliteal vein and tibial nerve: In the popliteal fossa, the tibial nerve is most superficial; the popliteal vein lies deep or anterior to tibial nerve; and the popliteal artery is deepest of all. The artery is crossed posteriorly by the vein and by the nerve. The relative position of these structures (Fig. 6.4a) is as follows.

- In the upper part of the fossa, from medial to lateral side – artery, vein and nerve (A, V, N).
- In the middle part, from behind forwards – nerve, vein and artery (N, V, A).
- In the lower part, from medial to lateral side – nerve, vein and artery (N, V, A).

The common peroneal nerve crosses the fossa obliquely from the superior angle to the lateral angle, along the medial border of the biceps femoris, lying in the same superficial plane as the tibial nerve (Fig. 6.4b).

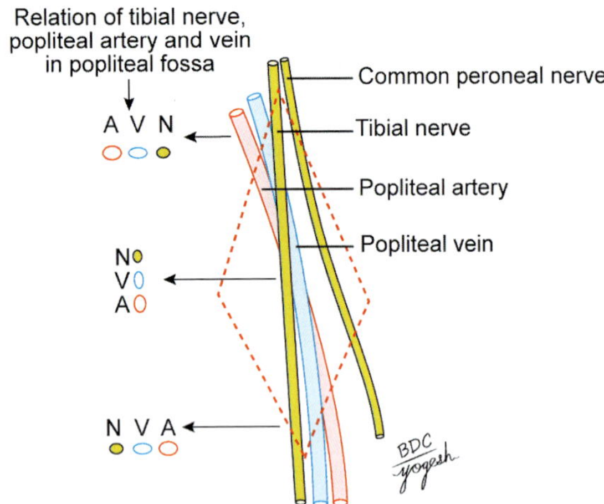

Fig. 6.5: The arrangement of the main nerves and vessels in the popliteal fossa. (AVN: artery–vein–nerve; NVA: nerve–vein–artery)

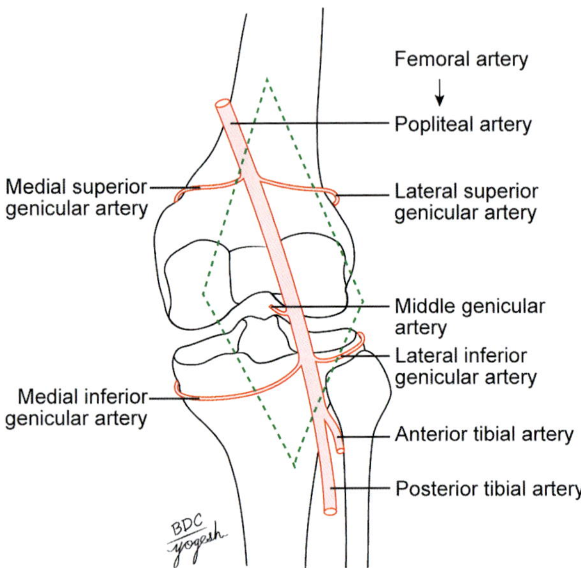

Fig. 6.6: Course of the genicular branches of the popliteal artery

DISSECTION

Make a horizontal incision across the back of thigh at its junction of upper 2/3rd with lower one-third and another horizontal incision at the back of leg at its junction of upper one-third and lower two-thirds (v), (vi) (*see* Fig. 5.4).

Draw a vertical incision joining the midpoints of the two horizontal incisions made (vii) (*see* Fig. 5.4). Reflect the skin and fascia on either side.

Find the cutaneous nerves, e.g. posterior cutaneous nerve of thigh, posterior division of medial cutaneous nerve, sural communicating nerve and short saphenous vein. Cut and clean the deep fascia.

Identify the boundaries and contents of the fossa (*see* Figs 6.1 and 6.2).

Trace the tibial nerve as it courses through the centre of the popliteal fossa. Its three delicate articular branches are given off in the upper part of the fossa, cutaneous branch in the middle part and muscular branches in lower part of the fossa.

Common peroneal nerve is lying just medial to the tendon of biceps femoris muscle. Trace its branches.

Popliteal vein is deep to the tibial nerve and popliteal artery is the deepest, as seen from the back. Trace all the muscular, cutaneous, genicular and terminal branches of the popliteal artery.

POPLITEAL ARTERY

Beginning, Course and Termination

Popliteal artery is the continuation of the femoral artery. It begins at the opening in the adductor magnus or hiatus magnus, i.e. at the junction of middle 1/3rd with the lower 1/3rd of thigh.

It runs downwards and slightly laterally to reach the lower border of the popliteus.

It terminates at the lower border of popliteus by dividing into the anterior and posterior tibial arteries (Fig. 6.6, Flowchart 6.2).

Flowchart 6.2: Popliteal artery

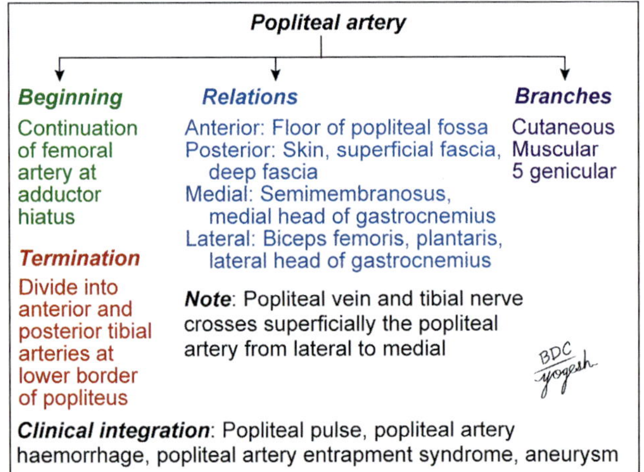

Relations

The popliteal artery is the deepest structure in the popliteal fossa. It has the following relations.

Anterior or deep: To the artery, from above downwards, there are:
- Popliteal surface of the femur
- Back of the knee joint
- Fascia covering the popliteus muscle.

Posterior or superficially: To the tibial nerve.

Medially:
- Semimembranosus and the medial condyle of the femur in the upper part.
- The lower part of the artery is related to the tibial nerve, the popliteal vein, and the medial head of the gastrocnemius in the lower part.

Laterally:
- Biceps femoris and the lateral condyle of the femur in the upper part.
- Plantaris and the lateral head of the gastrocnemius in the lower part.

Branches

Popliteal artery gives the following:
1. Cutaneous branches
2. Muscular branches
3. Five genicular or articular branches: Superior medial, superior lateral, inferior medial, inferior lateral and middle genicular arteries.

Note:

The ***middle genicular artery*** pierces the oblique popliteal ligament of the knee and supplies the cruciate ligaments and the synovial membrane of the knee joint (Fig. 6.6).

The medial and lateral ***superior genicular arteries*** wind around the corresponding sides of the femur immediately above the corresponding condyle and pass deep to the hamstrings.

The medial and lateral ***inferior genicular arteries*** wind around the corresponding tibial condyles, and pass deep to the collateral ligaments of the knee. All these arteries take part in the anastomoses around the knee.

CLINICAL ANATOMY

- ***Popliteal pulse*** is measured in semiflexed knee against the posterior aspect of tibial condyle.
- ***Blood pressure in the lower limb*** is recorded from the popliteal artery (Fig. 6.7). In coarctation of the aorta, the popliteal pressure is lower than the brachial pressure.
- ***Popliteal artery aneurysm:*** It is an abnormal dilation of the popliteal artery (Fig. 6.8). The popliteal artery aneurysm is the most common of the aneurysm of peripheral vessels, accounting for 85% of cases. It presents as a pulsatile midline swelling in the popliteal fossa.

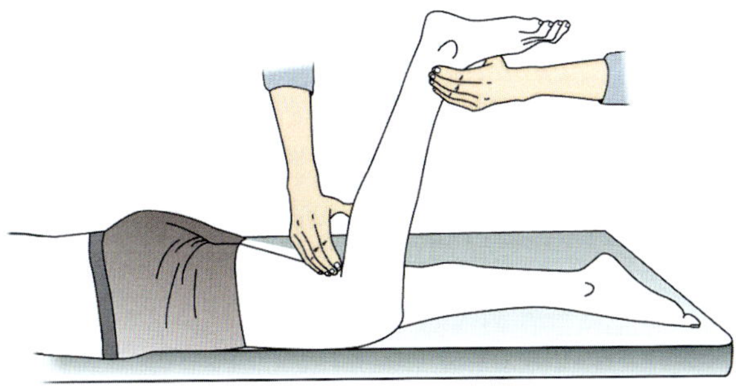

Fig. 6.7: Palpation of left popliteal artery

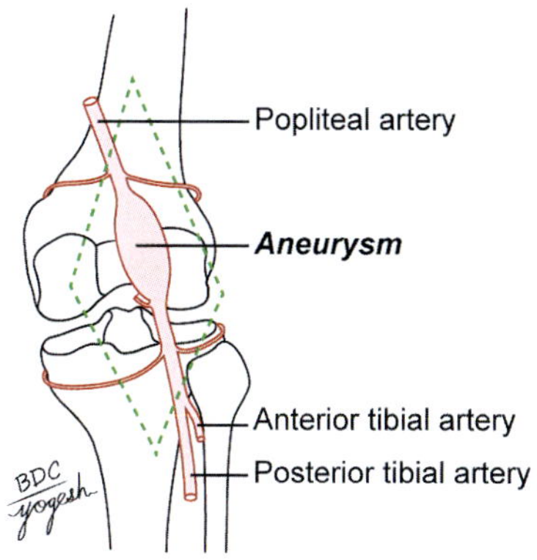

Fig. 6.8: Popliteal artery aneurysm

POPLITEAL VEIN

It begins at the lower border of the popliteus by the union of veins accompanying the anterior and posterior tibial arteries. It is medial to the popliteal artery in the lower part of the fossa; posterior to the artery in the middle and posterolateral to it in the upper part of the fossa. The vein continues as the femoral vein at the opening in the adductor magnus.

Tributaries

1. The small saphenous vein.
2. The veins corresponding to the branches of the popliteal artery.
3. Venae comitantes of anterior tibial artery and posterior tibial artery.

TIBIAL NERVE IN POPLITEAL FOSSA

Root value: Ventral divisions of ventral rami of L4, 5, S1, 2, 3.

Course

This is the larger terminal branch of the sciatic nerve. It lies superficial or posterior to the popliteal vessels (Fig. 6.9). It extends from the superior angle to the inferior angle of the popliteal fossa, crossing the popliteal vessels from the lateral to medial side. It continues in the back of leg.

Branches

1. ***Muscular branches*** arise in the distal part of the fossa for the lateral and medial heads of gastrocnemius, soleus, plantaris and popliteus.

   The ***nerve to the popliteus*** crosses the popliteal artery, runs downwards and laterally, winds round the lower border of the popliteus and supplies it from its deep (anterior) surface.

   Structures supplied by the nerve to popliteus are:
   a. Popliteus muscle
   b. Tibialis posterior
   c. Superior tibiofibular joint
   d. Tibia
   e. Interosseous membrane
   f. Inferior tibiofibular joint.
2. Three genicular or articular branches arise in the upper part of the fossa. These are:
   a. ***Superior medial genicular nerve*** lies above the medial condyle of femur, deep to the muscles.
   b. ***Middle genicular nerve*** pierces the posterior part of the capsule of the knee joint to supply structures in the intercondylar notch of femur (Fig. 6.9).
   c. ***Inferior medial genicular nerve*** lies along the upper border of popliteus and reaches inferior to the medial condyle of tibia.
3. ***Cutaneous nerve*** is called ***sural nerve***, which originates in the middle of the fossa and leaves it at the inferior

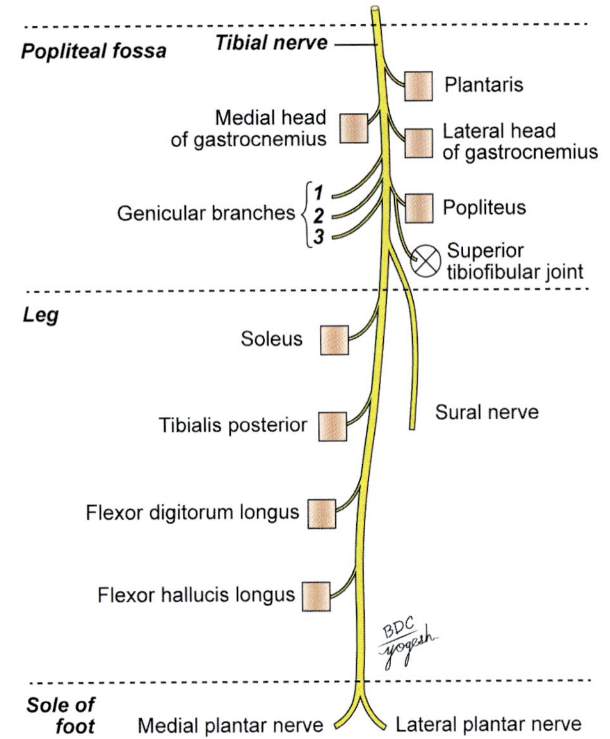

Fig. 6.9: Distribution of right tibial nerve in the popliteal fossa and leg (1: superior medial genicular nerve, 2: middle genicular nerve, 3: inferior medial genicular nerve)

angle. It supplies the skin of lower half of back of leg and whole of lateral border of the foot till the tip of little toe.

Note: ***Surgically safe side***: All the muscular branches of tibial nerve arise from its lateral side, except the nerve to medial head of gastrocnemius that arises from its medial side. Hence, the lateral side of tibial nerve is surgically unsafe (dangerous), whereas the medial side is surgically safe.

CLINICAL ANATOMY

- Most of the muscular branches of tibial nerve arise from its lateral side except to medial head of gastrocnemius. So, the medial side of the nerve is safe.
- Damage to tibial nerve causes motor and sensory loss.
  a. **Motor loss:** Superficial and deep muscles of calf and intrinsic muscles of sole.
  b. **Sensory loss:** Loss of sensation on whole of sole of foot, plantar aspect of digits and nail beds on dorsum of foot.

COMMON PERONEAL NERVE

Root value: Dorsal divisions of ventral rami of L4, 5, S1, 2.

Course

This is the smaller terminal branch of the sciatic nerve. It lies in the same superficial plane as the tibial nerve

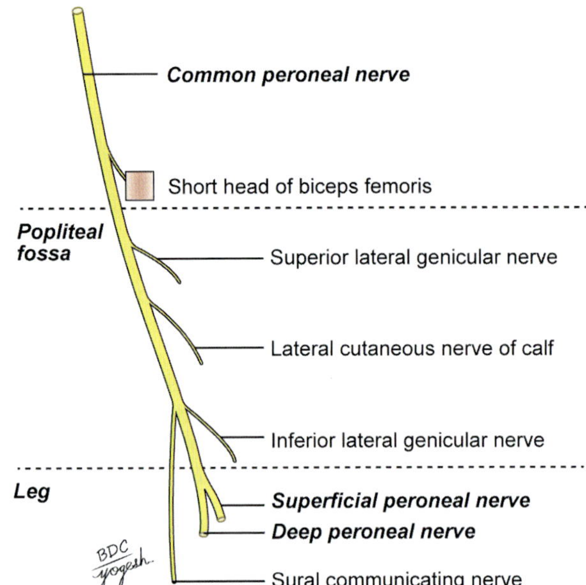

Fig. 6.10: Branches of common peroneal nerve in popliteal fossa and leg

(Fig. 6.10). It extends from the superior angle of the fossa to the lateral angle, along the medial border of the biceps femoris. Continuing downwards and forwards, it ***winds around the neck of the fibula,*** pierces the peroneus longus, and divides into the superficial and deep peroneal nerves.

Branches

1. ***Cutaneous branches*** are two:
   a. ***Lateral cutaneous nerve of the calf*** descends to supply the skin of the upper 2/3rd of the lateral side of the leg.
   b. ***Sural communicating nerve*** arises in the upper part of the fossa. It runs on the posterolateral aspect of calf and joins the sural nerve.
2. ***Articular branches:***
   a. ***Superior lateral genicular nerve*** accompanies the artery of the same name and lies above the lateral femoral condyle.
   b. ***Inferior lateral genicular nerve*** also runs with the artery of the same name to the lateral aspect of knee joint above the head of fibula.
   c. ***Recurrent genicular nerve*** arises where common peroneal nerve divides into superficial and deep peroneal nerves. It ascends anterior to the knee joint and supplies tibialis anterior muscle in addition to the knee joint.

Note: The common peroneal nerve does not give muscular branches in the popliteal fossa. However, it may give a branch to the short head of biceps femoris.

POSTERIOR CUTANEOUS NERVE OF THIGH

It is a content of the upper half of the popliteal fossa. It pierces the deep fascia about the middle of the fossa and supplies the skin up to the middle of the back of the leg.

GENICULAR BRANCH OF OBTURATOR NERVE

This is the continuation of the posterior division of the obturator nerve. It runs on the posterior surface of the popliteal artery, pierces the oblique popliteal ligament, and supplies the capsule of the knee joint.

POPLITEAL LYMPH NODES

These lie deep to the deep fascia near the termination of the small saphenous vein. They receive afferents from lateral part of sole, both superficial and deep parts of back of leg and knee joint. The efferents end in deep inguinal lymph nodes.

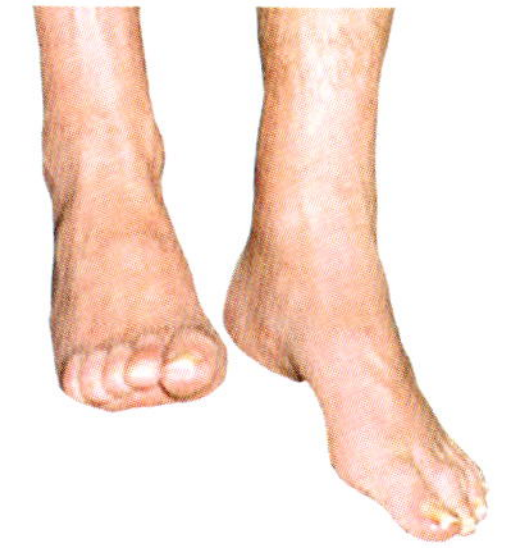

Fig. 6.11: Foot drop on the left side

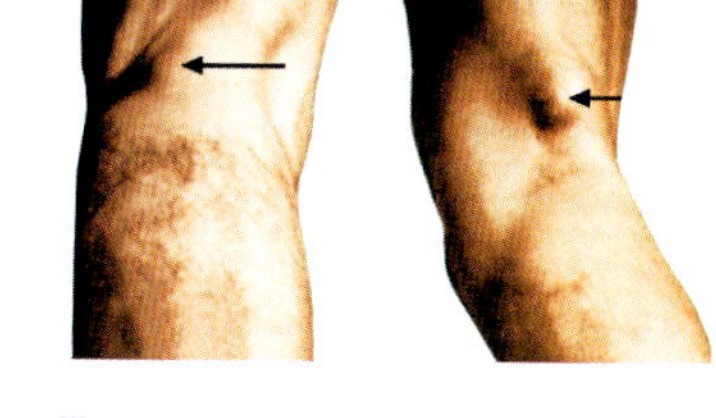

Fig. 6.12: Enlarged popliteal lymph nodes

CLINICAL ANATOMY

- ***Common peroneal nerve injury***: The common peroneal nerve can be palpated against the posterolateral side of the neck of the fibula. It may be injured in this area. It is the most frequently injured nerve in the lower limb. Patients present '*foot drop*', which is usually painless. There is weakness of dorsiflexion of ankle and of eversion of the foot. Inversion and plantar flexion are normal and ankle jerk is intact (Fig. 6.11).
- Popliteal lymph nodes get enlarged in infection on lateral side of sole/foot. These are lying along the short saphenous vein. Short saphenous vein pierces deep fascia to drain into popliteal vein (Fig. 6.12).
- ***Baker's cyst*** (popliteal cyst): It is a fluid-filled swelling of synovial bursa through the fibrous capsule that lies deep to the tendon of knee joint (Fig. 6.13).

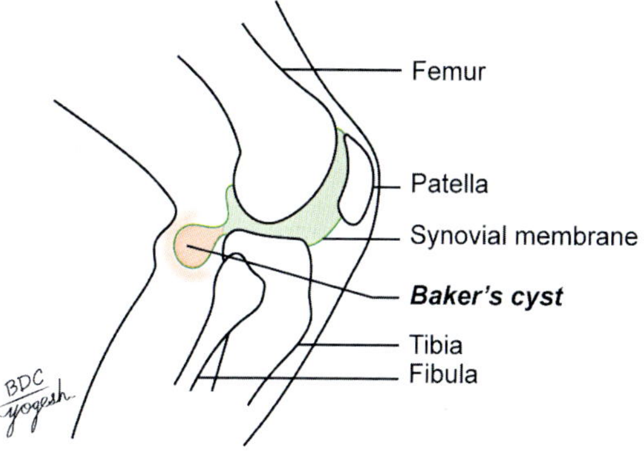

Fig. 6.13: Baker's cyst

ANASTOMOSES AROUND THE KNEE JOINT (GENICULAR ANASTOMOSIS)

The genicular anastomosis is an arterial anastomosis around the knee joint formed by the branches of popliteal, anterior tibial and posterior tibial, femoral and profunda femoris arteries. Anastomosis around the knee joint helps in continuous blood supply during flexion of the knee.

Formation

The following arteries contribute to the anastomosis around the knee joint (Fig. 6.14):

1. Genicular branches:
   a. Descending genicular branch of femoral artery
   b. Superior medial genicular artery
   c. Superior lateral genicular artery
   d. Inferior medial genicular artery
   e. Inferior lateral genicular artery
   f. Middle genicular artery.

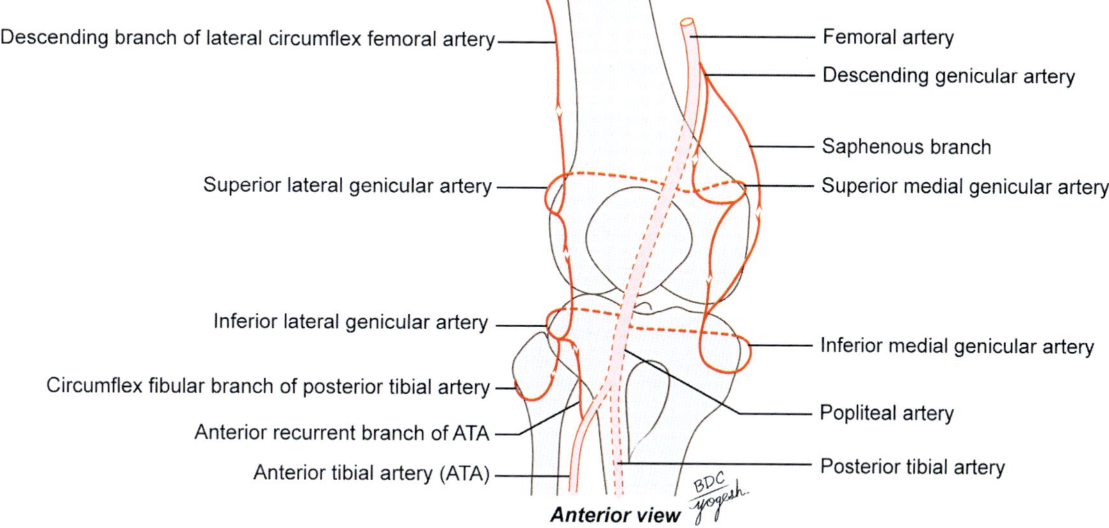

Fig. 6.14: Anastomoses around the knee joint

2. Descending branch of lateral circumflex femoral artery.
3. Anterior tibial recurrent artery.
4. Posterior tibial recurrent artery (branch of anterior tibial artery).
5. Circumflex fibular artery (branch of posterior tibial artery).

Video 2.6 Popliteal Fossa: Boundaries of popliteal fossa, Nerves and vessels of popliteal fossa.

Facts to Remember

- Popliteal artery is used for auscultating while measuring blood pressure in lower limb. It is prone to aneurysm.
- Short saphenous vein starting from the lateral end of the dorsal venous arch drains into the popliteal vein in the popliteal fossa.
- Tibial nerve runs vertically down the popliteal fossa. It gives genicular branches in the upper part, cutaneous branches in the middle part and muscular branches in the lower part of the fossa.
- Common peroneal nerve, as it winds around the neck of fibula, is the most common injured nerve in the lower limb, resulting in foot drop.

BDC's Anatomy *e*-book

1. Surface landmarks of popliteal region
2. Further reading
3. Viva voce questions

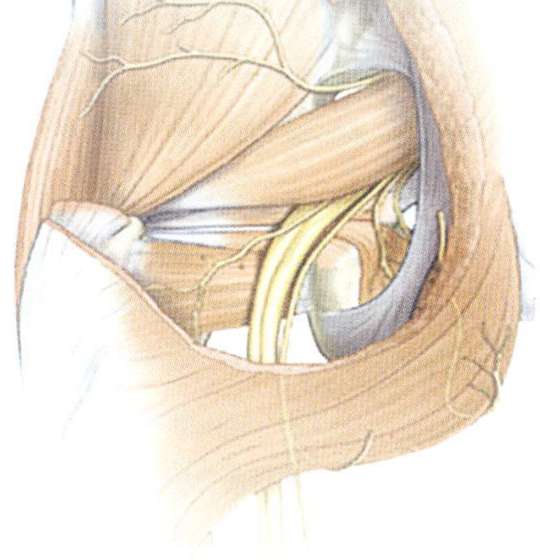

Chapter

7

Back of Thigh

The posterior compartment of the thigh is also called the *flexor compartment*. It is incompletely separated from the medial compartment by the poorly defined posterior intermuscular septum. The adductor magnus is a component of both these compartments.

Cutaneous Innervation

The skin over the back of the thigh is supplied by:
1. Posterior cutaneous nerve of thigh
2. Cutaneous branches of obturator nerve
3. Medial branches of anterior cutaneous nerve of thigh
4. Lateral cutaneous nerve of thigh.

Competency:
AN16.4 Describe and demonstrate the hamstrings group of muscles with their attachment, nerve supply and actions.

MUSCLES OF THE BACK OF THIGH

The muscles of the back of the thigh are called the ***hamstring muscles***. They are the semitendinosus, the semimembranosus, the long head of the biceps femoris and the ischial head of the adductor magnus (Figs 7.1 to 7.3, Plates 7.1 and 7.2, Tables 7.1 and 7.2).

Note: The ***hamstrings*** share the following characters.
a. Origin from the ischial tuberosity.
b. Insertion into one of the bones of the leg: The adductor magnus reaches only up to the adductor tubercle of the femur, but is included amongst the hamstrings because the ***tibial collateral ligament*** of the knee joint morphologically is the degenerated tendon of this muscle. The ligament is attached to medial epicondyle, 2 mm from the adductor tubercle.
c. Nerve supply from the tibial part of the sciatic nerve.
d. The muscles act as flexors of the knee and extensors of the hip.

Semitendinosus is muscular in upper part and has a long tendon of insertion. **Semimembranosus** has a flat tendon of origin. **Biceps femoris** has two heads of origin—long and short. **Adductor magnus** is the largest muscle of this compartment. Because of its double nerve supply, it is called a hybrid muscle.

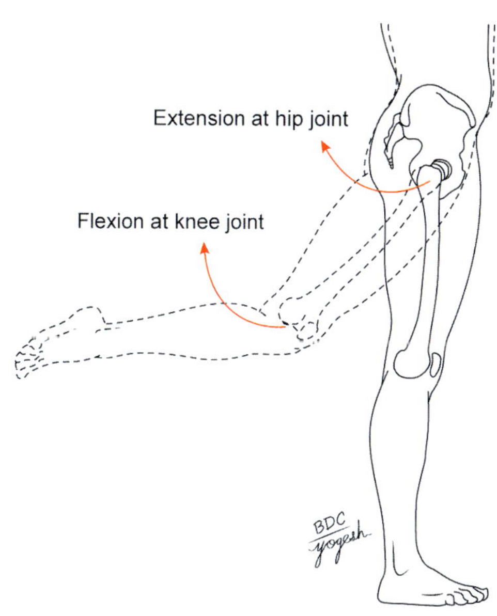

Fig. 7.1: Actions of hamstring muscles

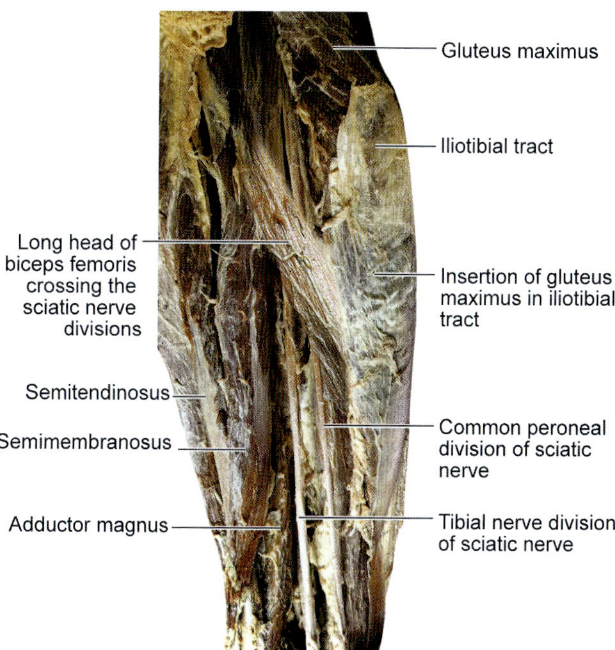

Fig. 7.2: Dissection of hamstring muscles

Plate 7.1: Semitendinosus and semimembranosus

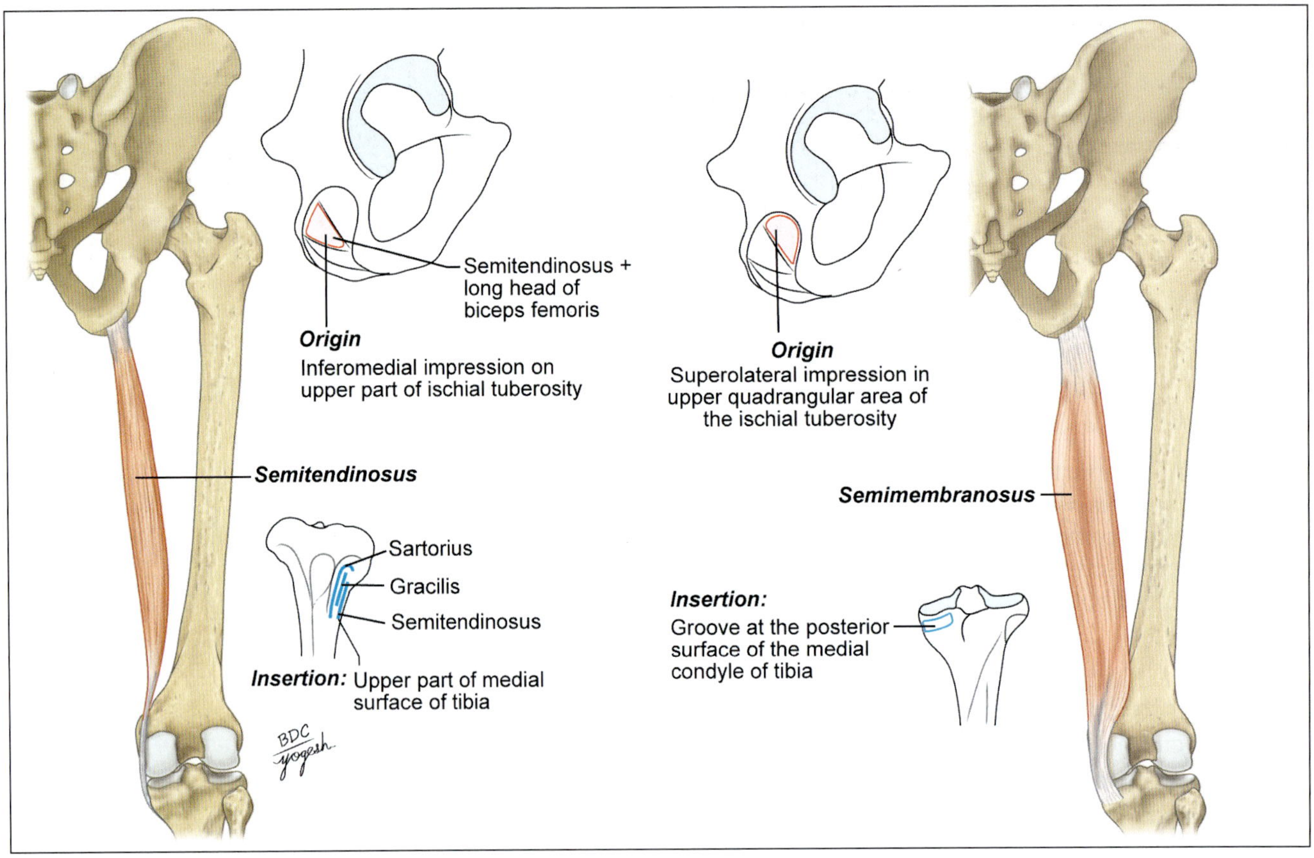

Semitendinosus + long head of biceps femoris
Origin
Inferomedial impression on upper part of ischial tuberosity
Semitendinosus
Sartorius
Gracilis
Semitendinosus
Insertion: Upper part of medial surface of tibia
BDC yogesh
Origin
Superolateral impression in upper quadrangular area of the ischial tuberosity
Semimembranosus
Insertion:
Groove at the posterior surface of the medial condyle of tibia

Plate 7.2: Biceps femoris and adductor magnus

Origin
Long head
Ischial tuberosity
Short head
Lateral lip of linea aspera
Biceps femoris
Insertion:
Head of fibula
BDC yogesh
Origin:
Ischial tuberosity
Conjoint ramus
Adductor magnus
Adductor part
Hamstring part
Adductor magnus
Insertion:
Linea aspera
Adductor tubercle
Medial supracondylar ridge

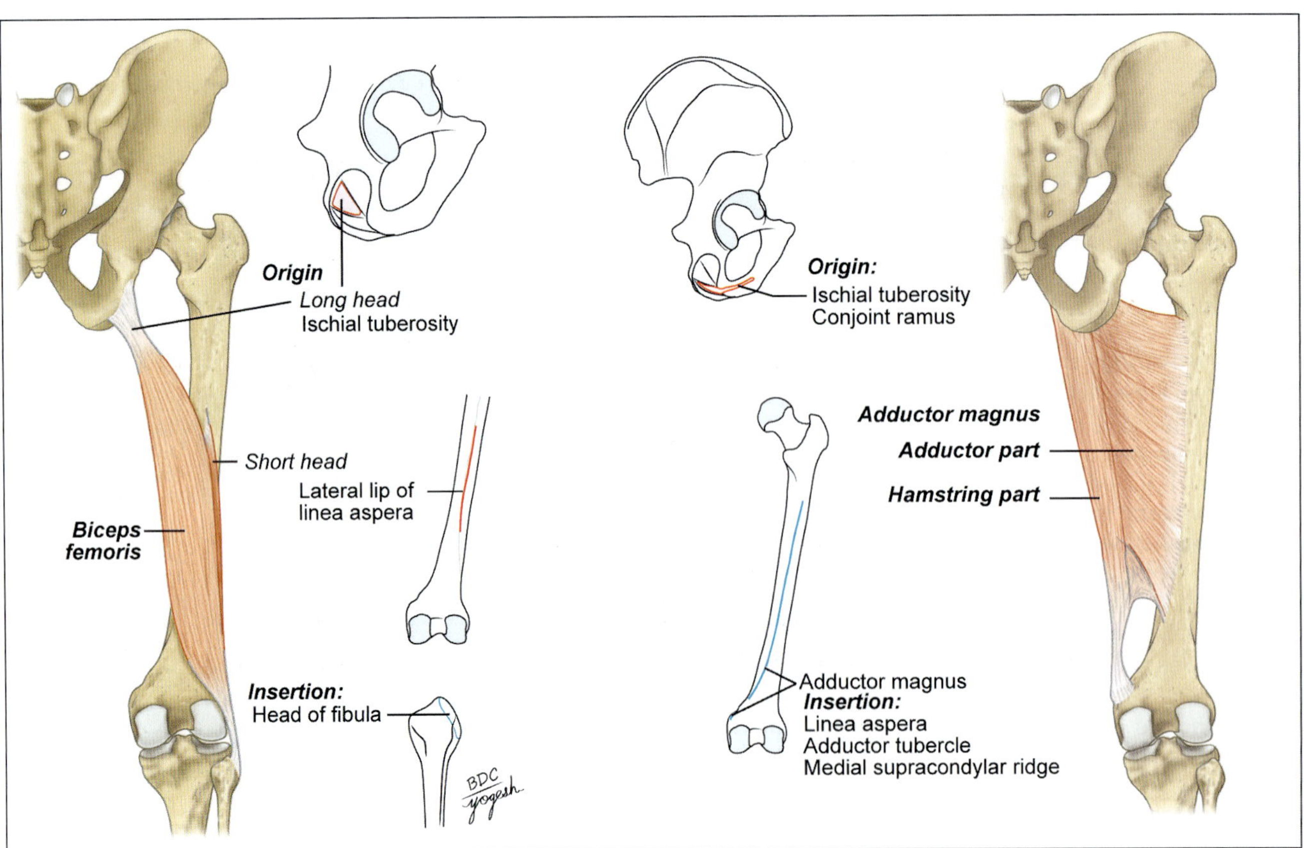

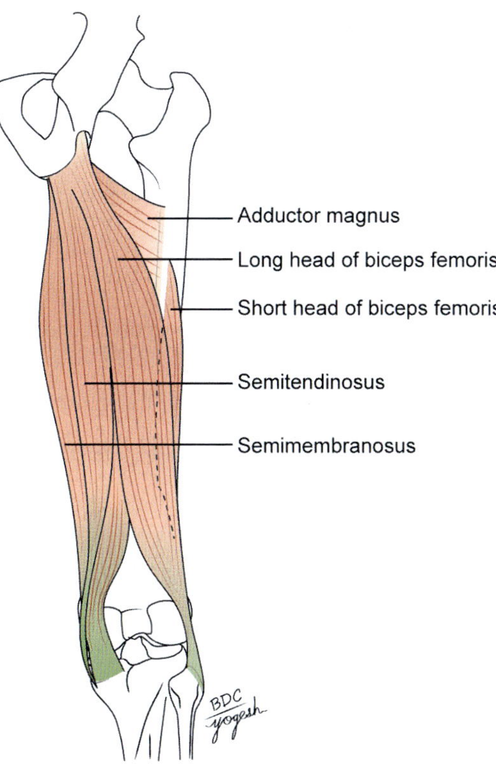

Fig. 7.3: Hamstring muscles

CLINICAL ANATOMY

- ***Testing the hamstring muscles***: Hamstring muscles can be tested by requesting the patient to flex the knee against resistance in prone position (*see* Fig. 7.6).
- The inflammation of semimembranosus bursa is called ***semimembranosus bursitis***. The bursa becomes more prominent during extension of knee and disappears during flexion of knee.

DISSECTION

Give a vertical incision on the back of intact skin left after the dissections of gluteal region and the popliteal fossa (viii) (*see* Fig. 5.4). Reflect the skin and fasciae on either side. Clean the hamstring muscles.

Sciatic nerve is seen in the gluteal region. Identify its branches in back of thigh to each of the hamstring muscles including occasionally for the short head of biceps femoris muscle. Trace the two terminal divisions of this nerve.

Separate the hamstring muscles to expose the ischial part of the composite or hybrid adductor magnus muscle. Look for insertion of adductor longus, into the linea aspera of femur. Trace the profunda femoris vessels behind adductor longus including its perforating branches.

TABLE 7.1: Origin and insertion of muscles of the back of thigh

Muscle	*Origin*	*Insertion*
1. **Semitendinosus**	From the inferomedial impression on the upper part of the ***ischial tuberosity***, in common with the long head of the biceps femoris	Into the upper part of the medial surface of the ***tibia*** behind the sartorius and the gracilis
2. **Semimembranosus**	From the superolateral impression on the upper part of the ***ischial tuberosity***	Into the groove on the posterior surface of the ***medial condyle of the tibia***. Expansions from the tendon form the oblique popliteal ligament, and the fascia covering the popliteus
3. **Biceps femoris**	a. ***Long head:*** From the inferomedial impression on the upper part of the ***ischial tuberosity***; in common with the semitendinosus, and also from the lower part of the sacrotuberous ligament b. ***Short head:*** From the lateral lip of the linea aspera between the adductor magnus and the vastus lateralis, from the upper two-thirds of the lateral supracondylar line, and from the lateral intermuscular septum	Into the ***head of the fibula*** in front of its apex or styloid process
4. **Adductor magnus**	a. Lower lateral part of the ***ischial tuberosity*** b. Conjoint ramus	a. Medial margin of gluteal tuberosity b. Linea aspera c. Medial supracondylar line d. Adductor tubercle

TABLE 7.2: Nerve supply and actions of muscles of the back of thigh

Muscle	*Nerve supply*	*Actions*
1. **Semitendinosus**	Tibial part of sciatic nerve (L5, S1, 2)	Chief flexor of the knee and medial rotator of the leg in semiflexed knee. Weak extensor of the hip
2. **Semimembranosus**	Tibial part of sciatic nerve (L5, S1, 2)	
3. **Biceps femoris**	a. Long head, by tibial part of sciatic nerve b. Short head, by common peroneal part of sciatic nerve (L5, S1, 2)	
4. **Adductor magnus** (hybrid muscle)	Double nerve supply: Adductor part by posterior division of obturator nerve (*see* Fig. 4.4); Hamstring part by tibial part of sciatic nerve	Adductor part causes adduction of thigh; Ischial part helps in extension of hip and flexion of knee

Competency:

AN16.5 Describe and demonstrate the origin, course, relations, branches (or tributaries), termination of important nerves and vessels on the back of thigh.

SCIATIC NERVE

The sciatic nerve is the ***thickest nerve*** in the body. In its upper part, it forms a band about 2 cm wide. It begins in the pelvis and terminates at the superior angle of the popliteal fossa by dividing into the tibial and common peroneal nerves (Figs 7.4 to 7.7).

Origin and Root Value

This is the largest branch of the sacral plexus. Its root value is L4, 5, S1, 2, 3.

It is made up of two parts:

1. ***Tibial part*** is formed by the ventral divisions of the anterior primary rami of L4, 5, S1, 2, 3.
2. ***Common peroneal part*** is formed by the dorsal divisions of the anterior primary rami of L4, 5, S1, 2 (Fig. 7.4).

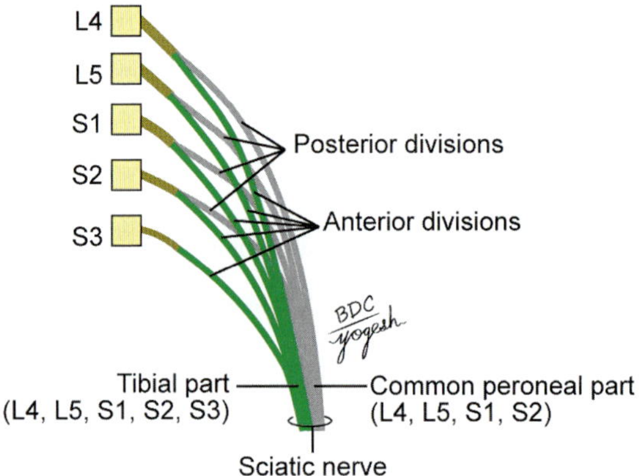

Fig. 7.4: Formation of sciatic nerve

Course

In the pelvis: The nerve lies in front of the piriformis, under cover of its fascia.

In the gluteal region: The sciatic nerve enters the gluteal region through the greater sciatic foramen below the piriformis. It runs downwards with a slight lateral convexity, passing between the ischial tuberosity and the greater trochanter.

In the thigh: The sciatic nerve enters the back of the thigh at the lower border of the gluteus maximus. It runs vertically downwards up to the superior angle of the popliteal fossa, at the junction of the upper 2/3rd and lower 1/3rd of the thigh, where it terminates by dividing into the tibial and the common peroneal nerves (Fig. 7.5).

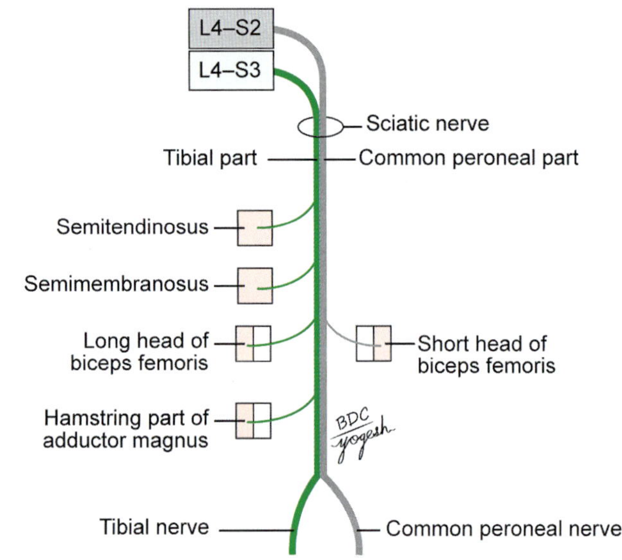

Fig. 7.5: Branches of sciatic nerve

Relations

In the gluteal region

Superficial or posterior: Gluteus maximus.

Deep or anterior:

a. Body of the ischium
b. Tendon of the obturator internus with the gemelli
c. Quadratus femoris, obturator externus
d. Capsule of the hip joint
e. Upper, transverse fibres of the adductor magnus.

Medial: Inferior gluteal nerve and vessels.

In the thigh (Fig. 7.7)

Superficial or posterior: The sciatic nerve is crossed by the long head of the biceps femoris.

Deep or anterior: Adductor magnus

Medial: Semimembranosus and semitendinosus

Lateral: Biceps femoris.

Note: The sciatic nerve is accompanied by a small companion artery – arteria nervi ischiadici. It is a branch of the inferior gluteal artery. The artery runs along the sciatic nerve for some distance before sinking into its substance.

Branches

1. *Articular branches* to the hip joint arise in the gluteal region.
2. *Muscular branches*:
   a. ***Tibial part*** of the sciatic nerve supplies the semitendinosus, the semimembranosus, the long head of the biceps femoris and the ischial head of the adductor magnus from its medial side.
   b. ***Common peroneal part*** supplies only the short head of the biceps femoris.
3. *Terminal branches*: Tibial nerve, and common peroneal nerve.

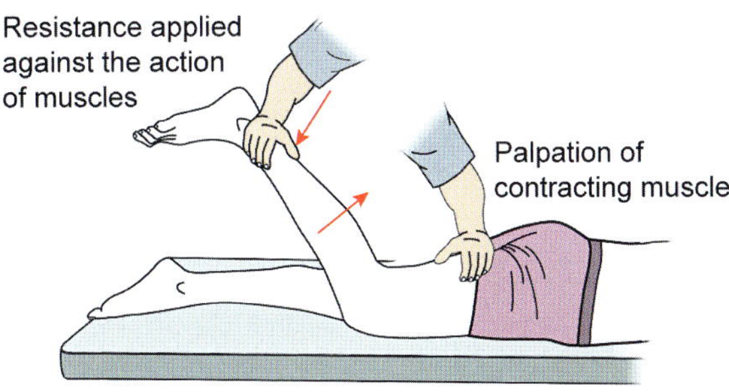

Fig. 7.6: Testing the hamstrings

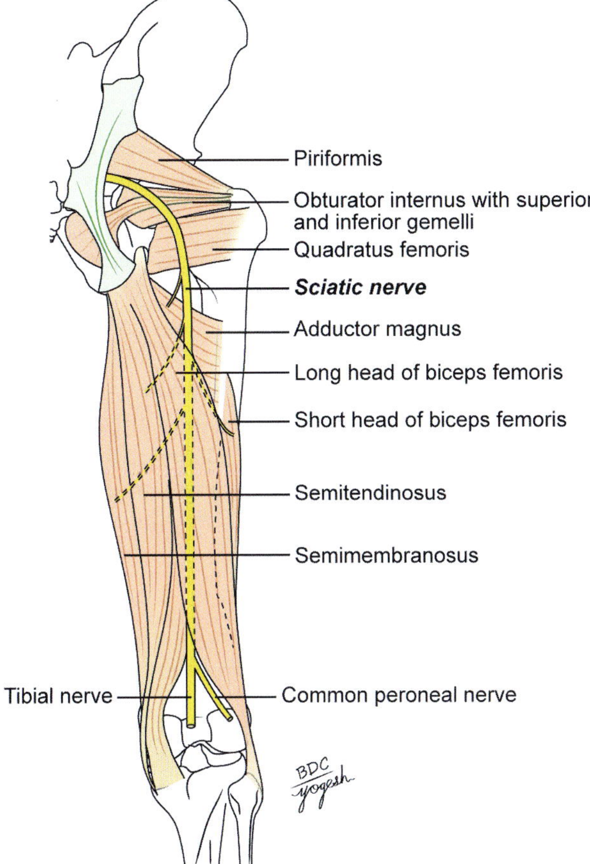

Fig. 7.7: Relations of sciatic nerve in the gluteal region and back of thigh

CLINICAL ANATOMY

- When a person sits on the edge of a hard table/chair, the nerve gets compressed between the edge of table and femur. It results in numbness of lower limb. But the sensations come back when foot is hit on the ground a few times and is called ***sleeping foot***.
- Shooting pain along the cutaneous distribution of the sciatic nerve and its terminal branches, chiefly the common peroneal, is known as ***sciatica***. Pain usually begins in the gluteal region, and radiates along the back of the thigh, and the lateral side of the leg, to the dorsum of the foot. This is usually due to compression of one or more nerve roots forming the sciatic nerve. The cause may be disc prolapse (Fig. 7.8), neuritis, etc.
- ***Sciatic nerve injury:*** The sciatic nerve may be injured by penetrating wounds, dislocation of the hip. This results in:
  a. Loss of all movements below the knee with foot drop – motor loss includes loss of hamstring muscles, loss of dorsiflexors, plantar flexors, evertors and muscles of sole (Fig. 7.9)
  b. Sensory loss on the back of the thigh, the whole of the leg, and the foot except the area innervated by the saphenous nerve (Fig. 7.10).

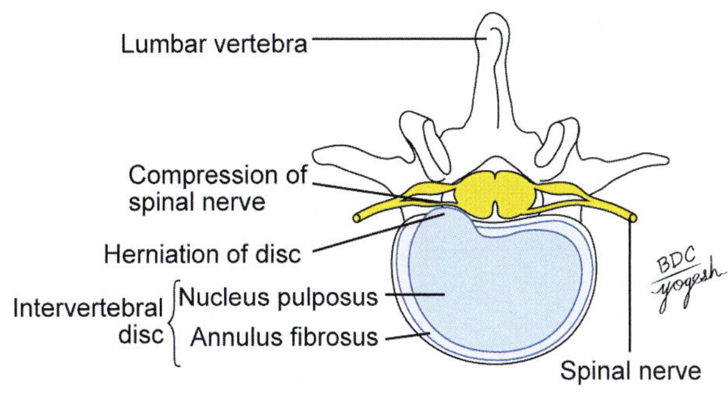

Fig. 7.8: Disc prolapse causing sciatica

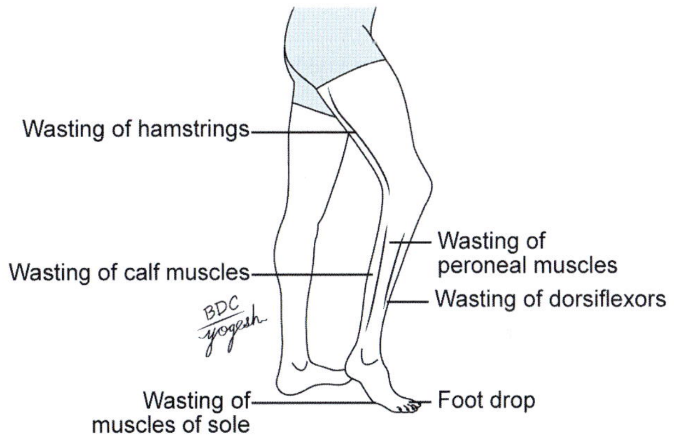

Fig. 7.9: Wasting of various groups of muscles

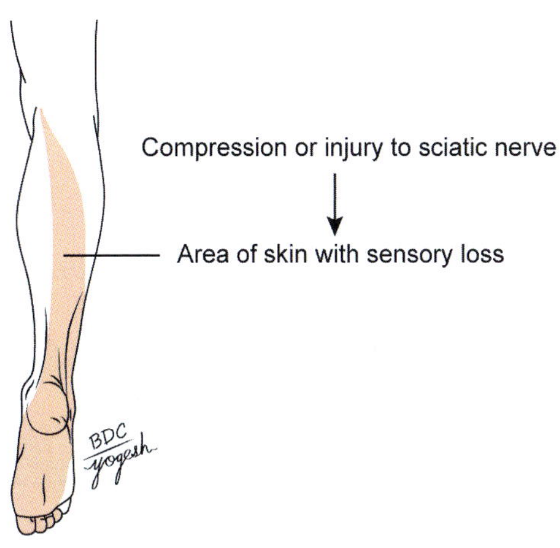

Fig. 7.10: Sensory loss over most of the leg due to injury to sciatic nerve

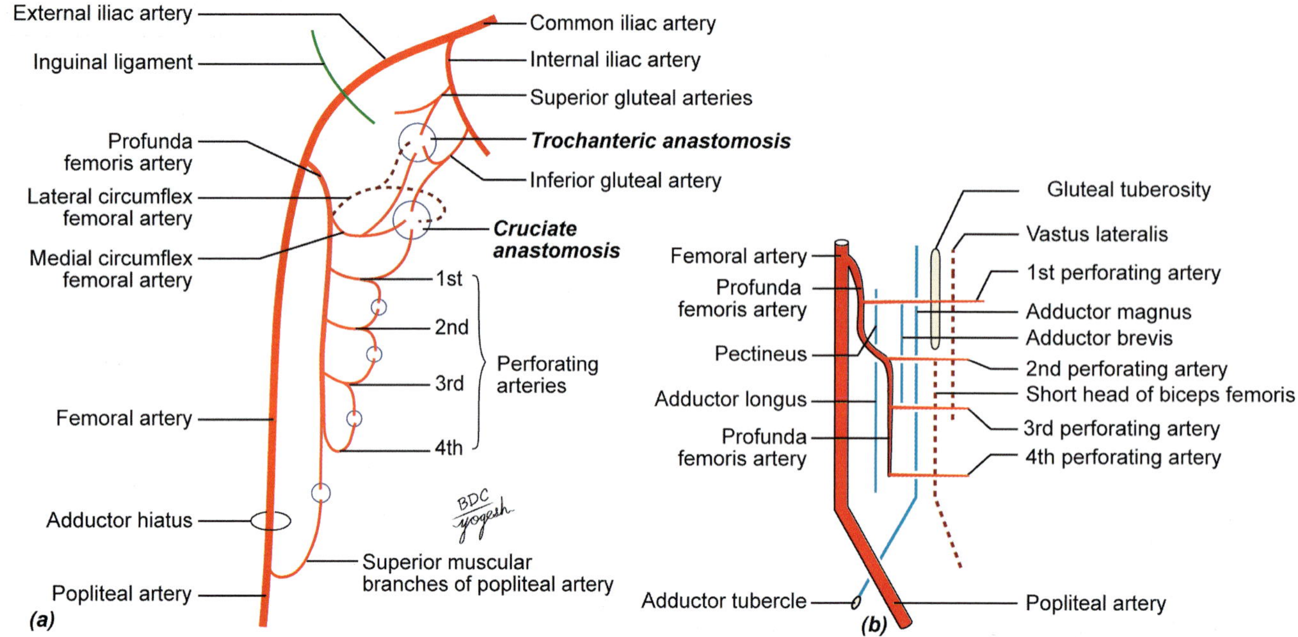

Figs 7.11a and b: (a) Anastomosis on the back of the thigh and (b) branches of profunda femoris artery

ARTERIES OF THE BACK OF THIGH

The back of thigh is supplied by the following arteries:

1. Profunda femoris artery – it gives four perforating branches.
   a. 1st perforating artery passes along upper border of adductor brevis
   b. 2nd through adductor brevis
   c. 3rd at lower border of adductor brevis
   d. 4th is the termination of the profunda femoris artery (Fig. 7.11a).
2. Medial circumflex femoral artery – it divides into ascending, transverse and acetabular branches.
3. Lateral circumflex femoral artery – it divides into ascending, transverse and descending branches.

ANASTOMOSES ON THE BACK OF THIGH

The back of thigh is supplied by the three-arterial anastomosis: Cruciate (*see* Chapter 5), trochanteric (*see* Chapter 5) and longitudinal (Figs 7.11 a and b).

Longitudinal Anastomosis

Longitudinal anastomosis is located near the linea aspera along the insertion of adductor magnus muscle. It is formed by the following arteries:

- Ascending and arteries descending branches of 4 perforating arteries
- Muscular branch of popliteal artery ascending branch.

CLINICAL ANATOMY

- ***Collateral circulation***: The branches of femoral (external iliac) and internal iliac arteries participate in the arterial anastomosis in the thigh.
- In case of blockage of femoral or external iliac artery, the branches of internal iliac artery maintain the blood supply to the lower limb as collateral circulation.
- Excessive bleeding: In case of injuries of the thigh and gluteal region, excessive bleeding may occur owing to the arterial anastomosis.

Video 2.7 Back of the Thigh: Sciatic nerve and muscles of back of the thigh.

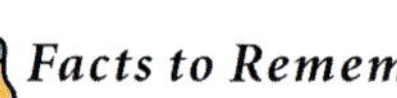

Facts to Remember

- Sciatic nerve is the thickest nerve of the body.
- Sleeping foot is a temporary condition.
- Hamstrings are flexors of knee and weak extensors of hip.
- Adductor magnus is a hybrid muscle.
- Thin artery accompanying sciatic nerve is part of the axial artery of lower limb.

BDC's Anatomy *e*-book

1. Semimembranosus bursitis
2. Oblique popliteal ligament
3. Properties of hamstring muscles
4. Posterior cutaneous nerve of thigh
5. Injury to hamstring muscles
6. Avulsion fracture of ischial tuberosity
7. Sciatica
8. Further reading
9. Viva voce questions

Chapter

8

Front of Leg with Dorsum of Foot; Lateral and Medial Sides of Leg

The leg is the part of the lower limb that extends from the knee to the ankle. The foot lies distal to the ankle. Foot has two surfaces–dorsal or superior surface and plantar or inferior surface. Most of the structures extend from the front of the leg to the dorsum of the foot. Hence, the front of the leg and dorsum of the foot are described together.

SURFACE LANDMARKS

1. ***Medial*** and ***lateral condyles of tibia*** are felt better in a flexed knee with the thigh flexed and laterally rotated (Fig. 8.1).
2. ***Tibial tuberosity*** is a bony prominence on the front of the upper part of tibia, 2.5 cm distal to the knee joint.
3. ***Head of the fibula*** lies posterolaterally at the level of tibial tuberosity. It serves as a guide to common peroneal nerve, which winds around the posterolateral aspect of the neck of fibula.
4. ***Shin*** is the subcutaneous *anterior border of tibia*. It is sinuously curved and extends from the tibial tuberosity to the anterior margin of the medial malleolus.
5. ***Medial surface of tibia*** is mostly subcutaneous. Great saphenous vein crosses lower 1/3rd of the surface (Fig. 8.2).
6. ***Medial border of tibia*** is palpable throughout its whole extent. The saphenous nerve and great saphenous vein run partly along it.
7. ***Gastrocnemius*** and the underlying ***soleus*** form the fleshy prominence of the *calf*. ***Tendo calcaneus*** is the strong, thick tendon of these muscles; it is attached below to the posterior surface of calcaneum.
8. ***Medial malleolus*** is the bony prominence on the medial side of ankle.
9. ***Lateral malleolus*** is the bony prominence on the lateral side of ankle. It is larger but narrower than the medial malleolus, and its tip is 0.5 cm below that of the medial malleolus.
10. ***Peroneal trochlea***, when present, is felt as a little prominence about a finger-breadth below the lateral malleolus. Peroneus brevis passes above and the peroneus longus below the trochlea.

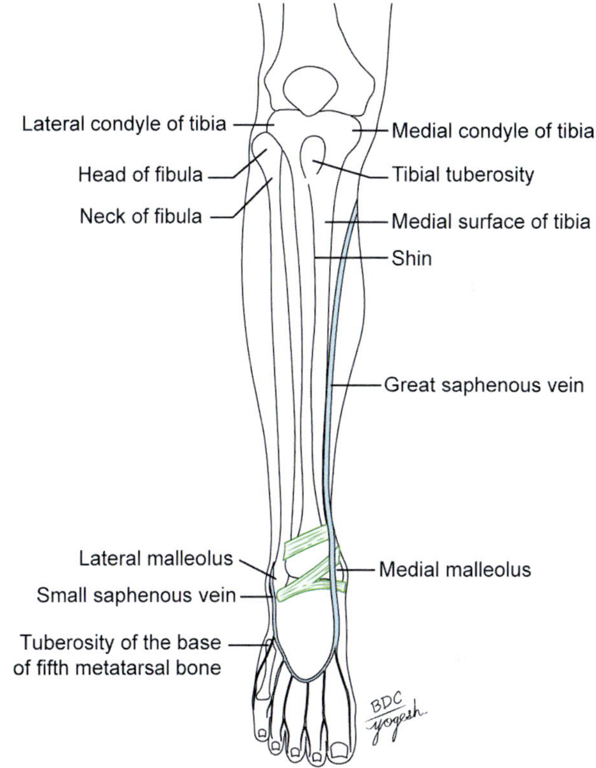

Fig. 8.1: Landmarks on leg and foot with superficial veins on the front; extensor retinacula also seen

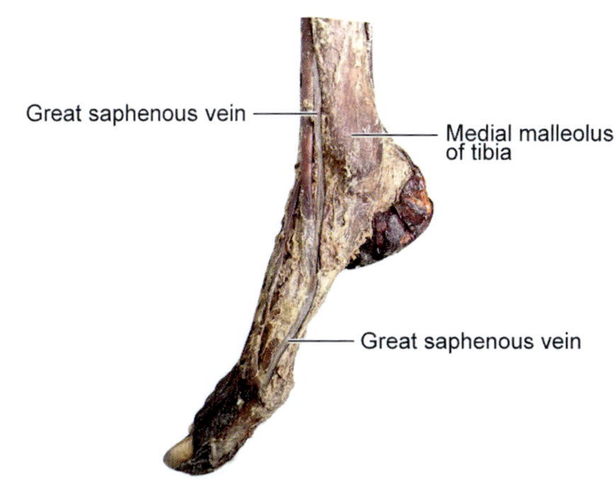

Fig. 8.2: Great saphenous vein

11. ***Sustentaculum tali*** can be felt about a thumb-breadth below the medial malleolus.
12. ***Tuberosity of navicular bone*** is a low bony prominence felt 2.5 to 3.75 cm anteroinferior to the medial malleolus, about midway between the back of the heel and root of the big toe.
13. ***Head of the talus*** lies above the line joining the sustentaculum tali and tuberosity of navicular bone.
14. ***Tuberosity of the base of fifth metatarsal bone*** is the most prominent landmark on the lateral border of the foot. It lies midway between the point of the heel and the root of the little toe.
15. ***Posterior tibial artery pulsations*** can be felt against calcaneum about 2 cm below and behind the medial malleolus.
16. ***Dorsalis pedis artery pulsations*** can be felt best on the dorsum of foot about 5 cm distal to the malleoli, lateral to the tendon of extensor hallucis longus, over the intermediate cuneiform bone.
17. ***Tendon of tibialis anterior*** becomes prominent on active inversion of the foot, passing downwards and medially across the medial part of the anterior surface of ankle.
18. ***Tendon of extensor hallucis longus*** becomes prominent when the foot is dorsiflexed.
19. ***Extensor digitorum brevis*** produces an elevation on the lateral part of the dorsum of foot when the toes are dorsiflexed or extended.
20. ***First metatarsophalangeal joint*** lies a little in front of the centre of the ball of big toe. The *other metatarsophalangeal joints* are placed about 2.5 cm behind the webs of the toes.

SUPERFICIAL FASCIA

The superficial fascia of the front of the leg and the dorsum of the foot contains: The superficial veins, cutaneous nerves, lymphatics and small unnamed arteries.

Superficial Veins

1. ***Dorsal digital veins:*** For each toe, there are two dorsal digital veins. Dorsal digital veins of adjacent toes join to form 4 dorsal metatarsal veins. Dorsal digital vein on the medial side of the great toe continues as *medial marginal vein*. Dorsal digital vein on the lateral side of the little toe continues as *lateral marginal vein*.
2. ***Dorsal venous arch*** lies on the dorsum of the foot over the proximal parts of the metatarsal bones. It receives four dorsal metatarsal veins, each of which is formed by the union of two dorsal digital veins (Fig. 8.1).
3. ***Great*** or ***long saphenous vein*** is formed by the union of the medial end of the dorsal venous arch with the medial marginal vein, which drains the medial side of the great toe. It passes upwards in front of the medial malleolus (Fig. 8.2), crosses the lower 1/3rd of the medial surface of tibia obliquely, and runs along its medial border to reach the back of the knee. The saphenous nerve runs in front of the great saphenous vein.
4. ***Small*** or ***short saphenous vein*** is formed by the union of the lateral end of the dorsal venous arch with the lateral marginal vein, draining the lateral side of the little toe. It passes upwards behind the lateral malleolus to reach the back of the leg. The sural nerve accompanies the small saphenous vein.

Both saphenous veins are connected to the deep veins through the perforating veins.

Cutaneous Nerves

1. ***Infrapatellar branch of the saphenous nerve*** pierces the sartorius and the deep fascia on the medial side of the knee, curves downwards and forwards, and supplies the skin over the ligamentum patellae (Fig. 8.3).
2. ***Saphenous nerve*** (*L3, L4*) is a branch of the posterior division of the femoral nerve (*see* Fig. 3.28). It pierces the deep fascia on the medial side of the knee between the sartorius and the gracilis and runs downwards in front of the great saphenous vein superficial to extensor retinacula. It supplies the skin of the medial side of the leg and the medial border of the foot up to the ball of the great toe.
3. ***Lateral cutaneous nerve of the calf*** is a branch of the common peroneal nerve. It pierces the deep fascia over the lateral head of the gastrocnemius and descends to supply the skin of the upper 2/3rd of the lateral side of the leg (Fig. 8.3).
4. ***Superficial peroneal nerve*** is a branch of the common peroneal nerve. It arises on the lateral side of the neck of the fibula deep to the fibres of the peroneus longus.

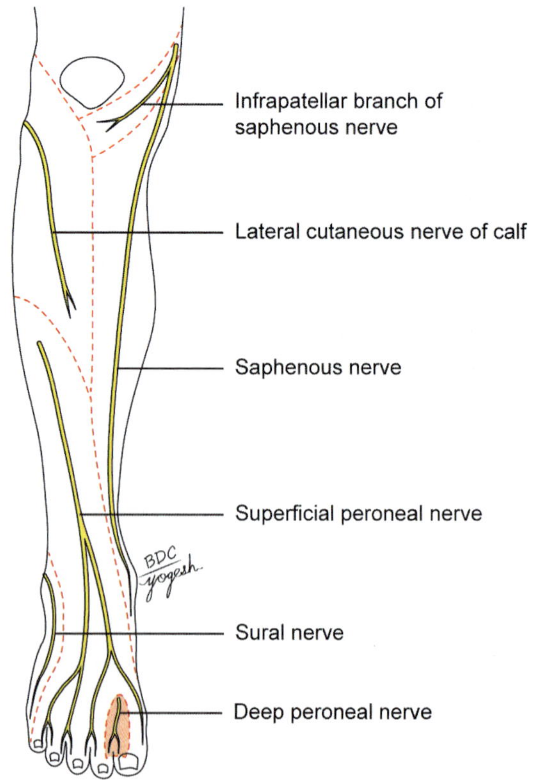

Fig. 8.3: Cutaneous nerves on the front of the leg and dorsum of the foot

It divides into medial and lateral branches, which supply the following areas:

a. The skin over the lower 1/3rd of the lateral side of the leg (Fig. 8.3).
b. The skin over the entire dorsum of the foot with the exception of the following areas.
   - Lateral border, supplied by sural nerve.
   - Medial border up to the base of the great toe, supplied by the saphenous nerve.
   - Cleft between the first and second toes, supplied by the deep peroneal nerve.
   - Distal phalanges including nail beds of 1–5 toes.

5. ***Sural nerve*** is a branch of the tibial nerve. It arises in the middle of the popliteal fossa. It accompanies the small saphenous vein and supplies the skin of the lower half of the back of leg and of the whole of the lateral border of the foot up to the tip of the little toe.
6. ***Deep peroneal nerve*** terminates by supplying the skin adjoining the cleft between the 1st and 2nd toes.
7. ***Digital branches of the medial and lateral plantar nerves*** curve upwards and supply the distal parts of the dorsum of the toes/nail beds. Medial plantar nerve supplies medial 3½ toes; lateral plantar nerve supplies lateral 1½ toes.

CLINICAL ANATOMY

Saphenous nerve may be subjected to entrapment neuropathy as it leaves the adductor canal, leading to pain in the area of its supply.

DISSECTION

1. Make a horizontal incision across the leg at its junction with the foot (*see* Fig. 3.9).
2. Provide a vertical incision up from the centre of incision (1) to the middle of incision drawn just below the level of tibial tuberosity.
3. Carry this vertical incision onto the dorsum of foot till the middle of the second toe.

Reflect the skin on both sides. Look for various veins and cutaneous nerves in the leg and foot according to the description given in the text.

DEEP FASCIA

In the leg, tibia and fibula are partly subcutaneous, the most notable being the medial surface of the tibia and the malleoli. Over these subcutaneous areas, the deep fascia is replaced by *periosteum*.

Extensions of deep fascia form intermuscular septa that divide the leg into compartments (Fig. 8.4).

The *anterior* and *posterior intermuscular septa* are attached to the anterior and posterior borders of the fibula. They divide the leg into three compartments: *Anterior, lateral* and *posterior.* The posterior compartment is subdivided into superficial, intermediate and deep parts by *superficial* and *deep transverse fascial septa.*

RETINACULA

Around the ankle, the deep fascia is thickened to form bands called ***retinacula***. These are so-called because they retain tendons in place. These are as follows (Plate 8.1):

1. On the front of the ankle – *superior and inferior extensor retinacula.*
2. Laterally – *superior and inferior peroneal retinacula.*
3. Posteromedially – *flexor retinaculum.*

The peroneal retinacula is described in the lateral compartment of the leg and the flexor retinaculum in the posterior compartment back of the leg.

Superior Extensor Retinaculum

(Plate 8.1, Figs 8.5 and 8.6, and Flowchart 8.1)

Attachments

Medial: Lower part of the anterior border of the tibia.
Lateral: Lower part of the anterior border of the fibula.

Relations

Medially, it splits to enclose the tendon of tibialis anterior and its synovial sheath. Other structures are deep to the retinaculum.

Inferior Extensor Retinaculum

This is a Y-shaped band of deep fascia, situated in front of the ankle joint and over the posterior part of the dorsum of the foot. The stem of the Y lies laterally, and the upper and lower bands, medially (Plate 8.1, Figs 8.5 and 8.6, and Flowchart 8.1).

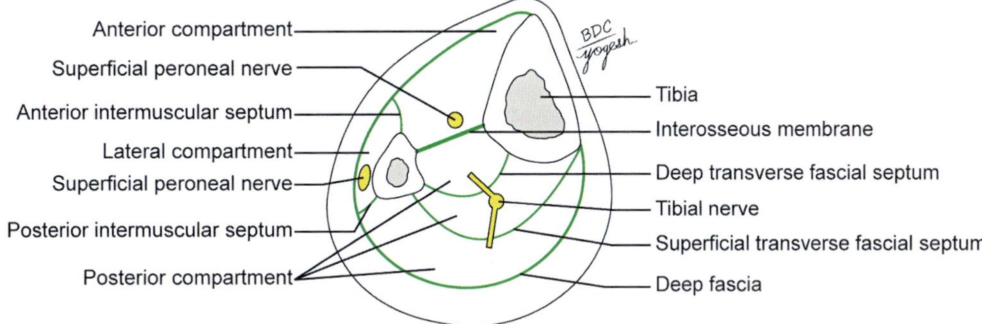

Fig. 8.4: Transverse section through the middle of the leg showing the intermuscular and the transverse fascial septa

Plate 8.1: Right superior and inferior extensor retinacula on the front of the ankle

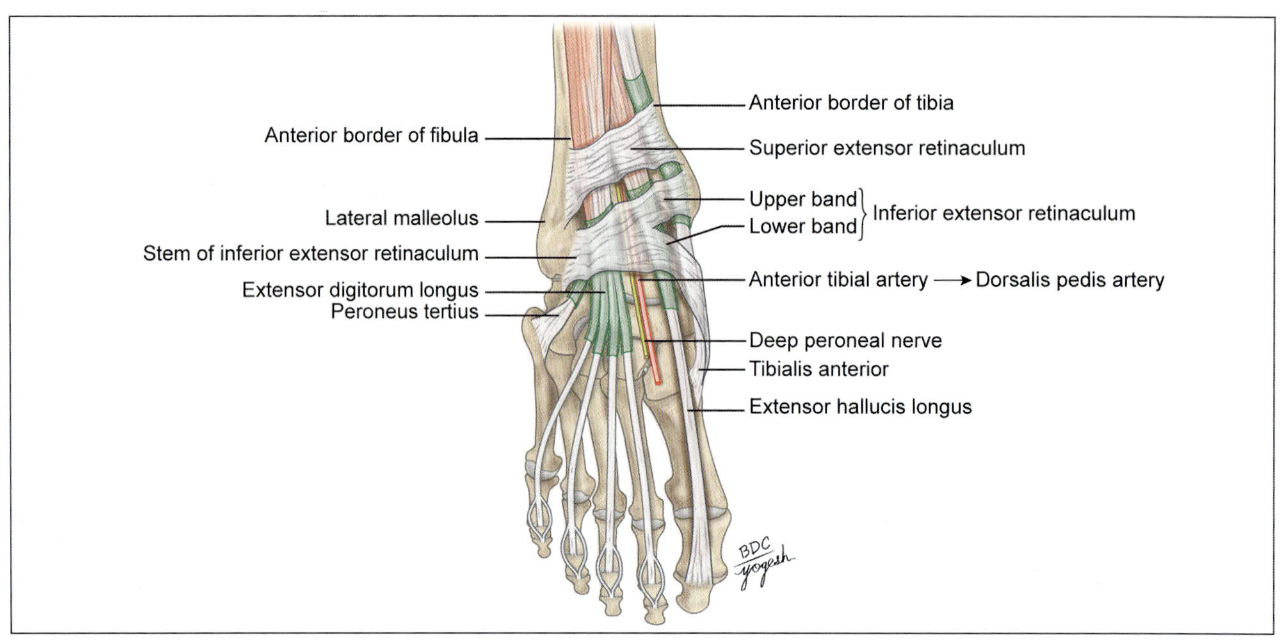

Flowchart 8.1: Extensor retinaculum

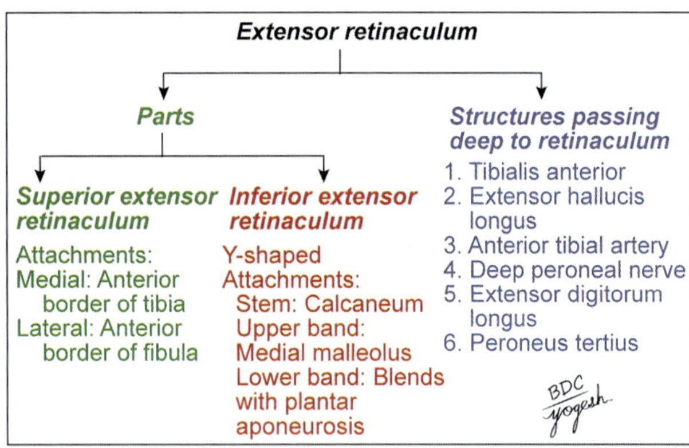

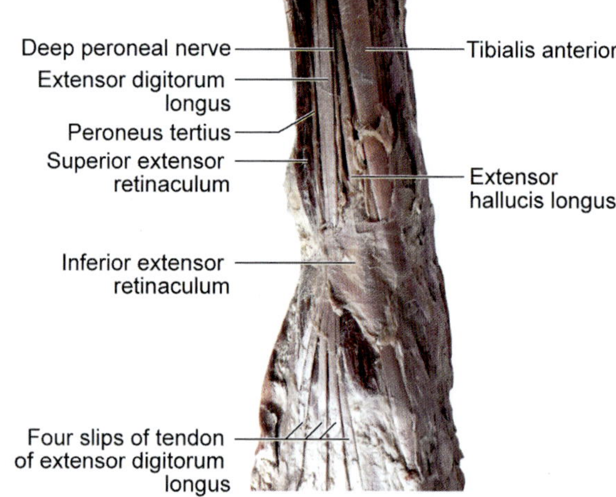

Fig. 8.6: Dissection of the retinacula and structures passing under them

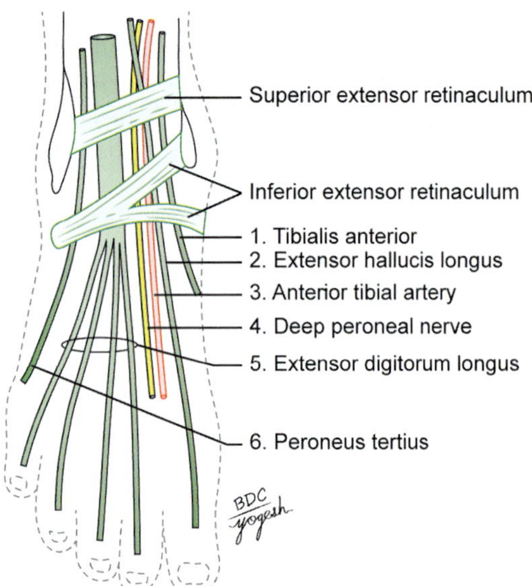

Fig. 8.5: Tendons, vessels and nerves related to the extensor retinacula (numbered 1–6)

Attachments

1. *Stem* is attached to the anterior non-articular part of the superior surface of the calcaneum in front of the sulcus calcanei.
2. *Upper band* passes upwards and medially, and is attached to the anterior border of the medial malleolus.
3. *Lower band* passes downwards and medially and is attached to the plantar aponeurosis.

Relations

The stem of this retinaculum loops around the tendons of extensor digitorum longus and peroneus tertius including their synovial sheaths.

The upper band encloses tendons of tibialis anterior and extensor hallucis longus with their synovial sheaths.

The lower band passes superficial to the tendons of tibialis anterior, extensor hallucis longus, dorsalis pedis artery and deep peroneal nerve.

Structures Passing under the Retinacula

1. **T**ibialis anterior
2. Extensor **h**allucis longus
3. **A**nterior tibial vessels
4. Deep peroneal **n**erve
5. Extensor **d**igitorum longus
6. **P**eroneus tertius.

[*Mnemonics*: **T**he **H**imalayas **A**re **N**ever **D**ry **P**laces.]

CLINICAL ANATOMY

Anterior tibial compartment syndrome/fresher's syndrome: The muscles of the anterior compartment of leg get pain because of too much sudden exercise. The muscles are tender to touch.

DISSECTION

Underlying the superficial fascia is the dense deep fascia of leg. Divide this fascia longitudinally as it stretches between tibia and fibula.

Expose the superior extensor retinaculum 5 cm above the ankle joint and the inferior extensor retinaculum in front of the ankle joint (Fig. 8.3).

Competency:

AN18.1 Describe and demonstrate major muscles of anterior compartment of leg with their attachment, nerve supply and actions.

MUSCLES OF FRONT OF LEG

The muscles of the anterior compartment of the leg are the tibialis anterior, the extensor hallucis longus, the extensor digitorum longus and the peroneus tertius (Figs 8.7 and 8.8, Flowchart 8.2, Plates 8.2 and 8.3, Tables 8.1 and 8.2).

Common Features of Muscles of Anterior Compartment of Leg

1. All these muscles are supplied by deep peroneal nerve.
2. All these muscles originate from fibula except tibialis anterior, which originates from tibia.
3. All of these muscles dorsiflex the ankle. They can pull the body forward when the foot is fixed on the ground during walking.
4. These muscles are tested *by palpation* on the front of leg and requesting the patient to dorsiflex the foot (Fig. 8.9).

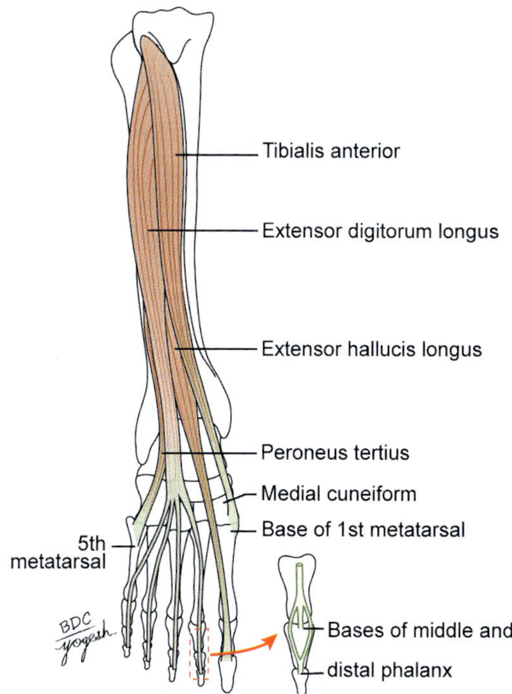

Fig. 8.7: Muscles of anterior compartment of leg

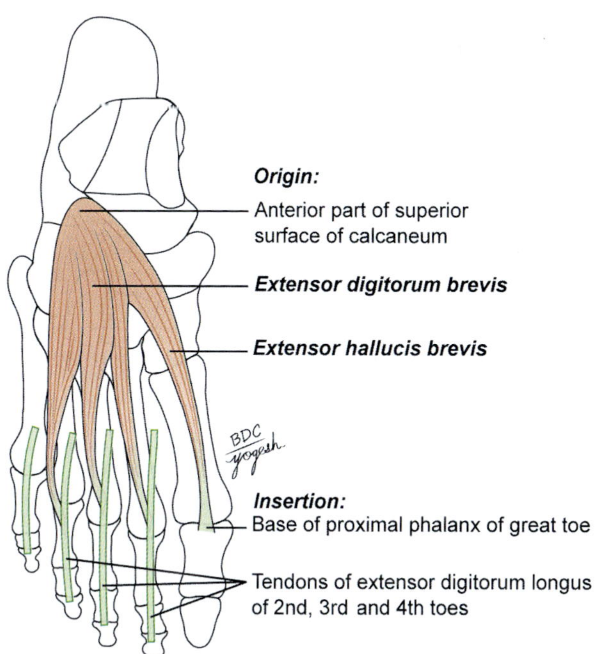

Fig. 8.8: Extensor digitorum brevis and extensor hallucis brevis

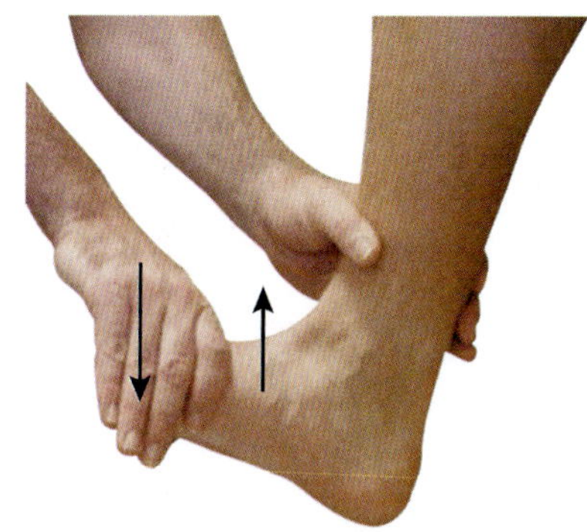

Fig. 8.9: How to test the dorsiflexors of the ankle joint

Plate 8.2: Tibialis anterior, extensor hallucis longus, peroneus tertius

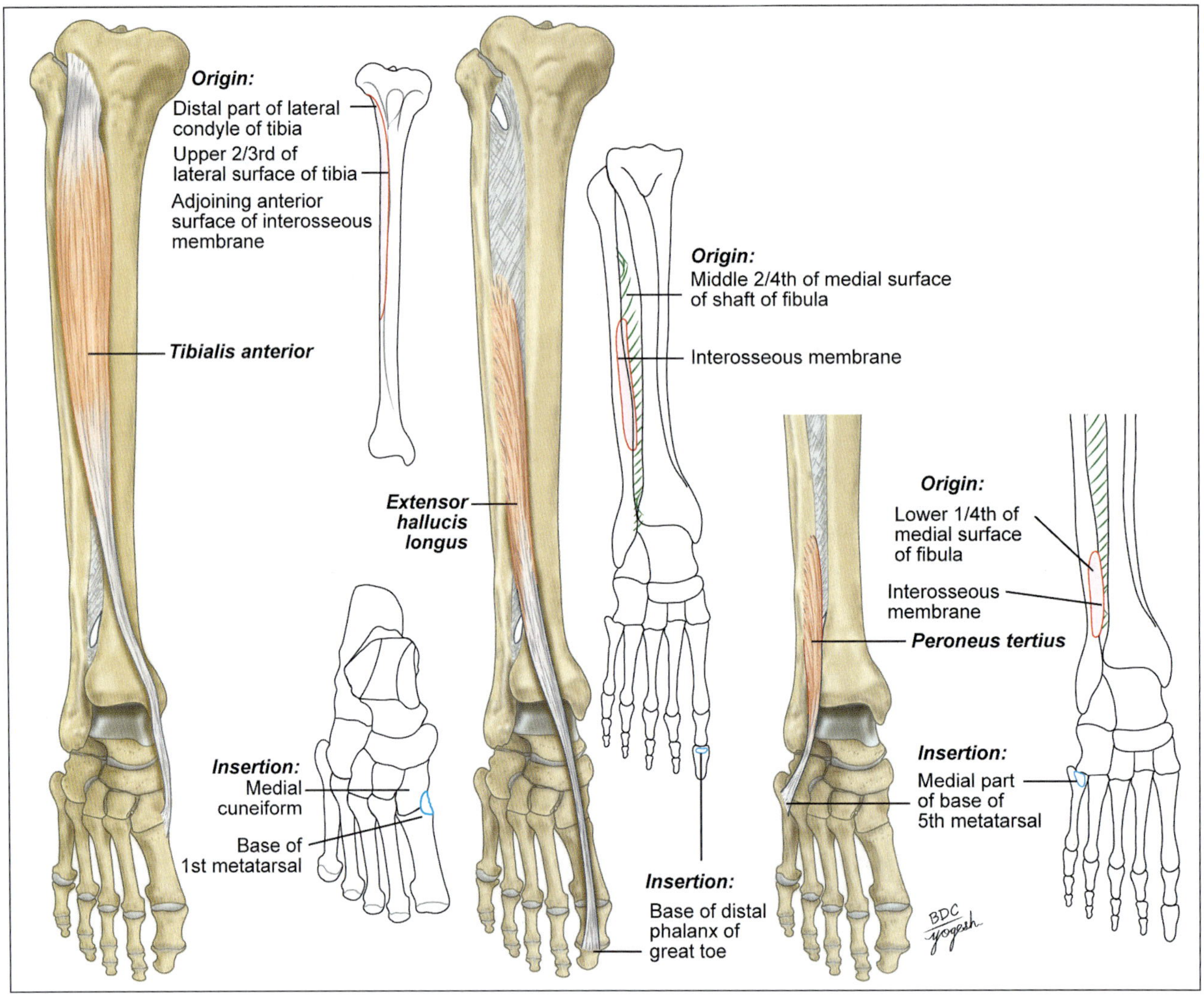

Origin:
Distal part of lateral condyle of tibia
Upper 2/3rd of lateral surface of tibia
Adjoining anterior surface of interosseous membrane
Tibialis anterior
Insertion:
Medial cuneiform
Base of 1st metatarsal

Origin:
Middle 2/4th of medial surface of shaft of fibula
Interosseous membrane
Extensor hallucis longus
Insertion:
Base of distal phalanx of great toe

Origin:
Lower 1/4th of medial surface of fibula
Interosseous membrane
Peroneus tertius
Insertion:
Medial part of base of 5th metatarsal

BDC yogesh

Flowchart 8.2: Muscles of anterior compartment of leg and dorsum of foot

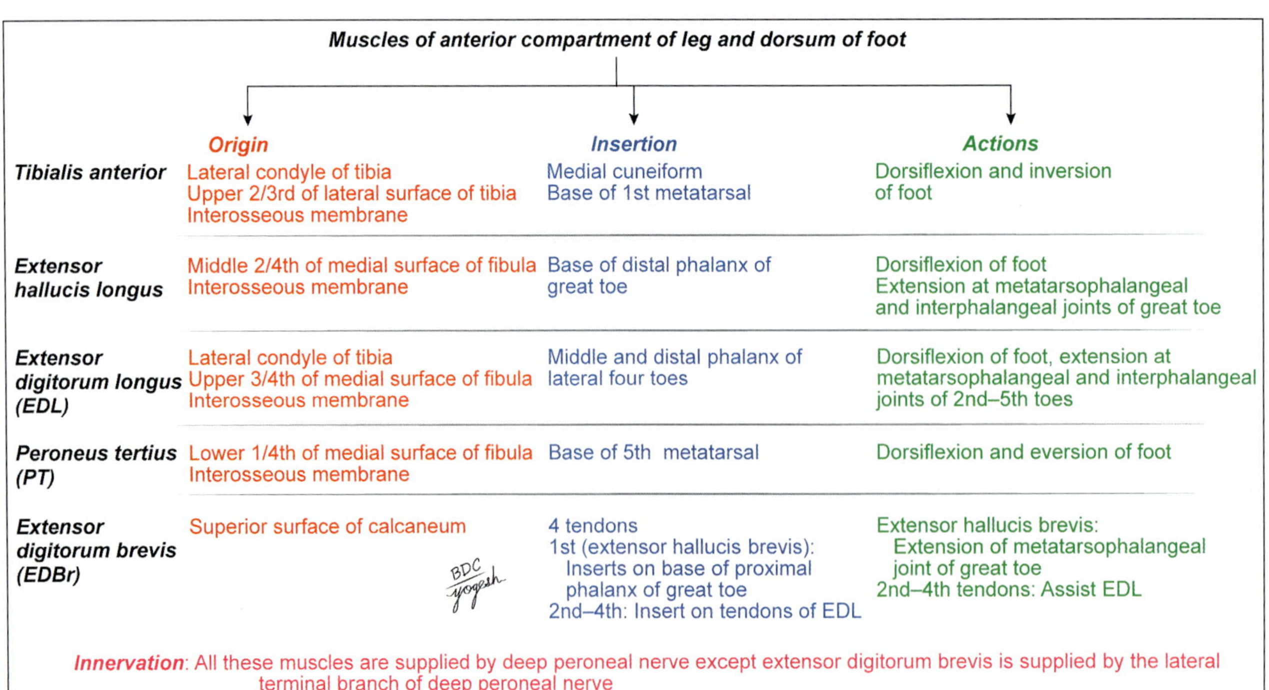

Muscles of anterior compartment of leg and dorsum of foot

	Origin	Insertion	Actions
Tibialis anterior	Lateral condyle of tibia Upper 2/3rd of lateral surface of tibia Interosseous membrane	Medial cuneiform Base of 1st metatarsal	Dorsiflexion and inversion of foot
Extensor hallucis longus	Middle 2/4th of medial surface of fibula Interosseous membrane	Base of distal phalanx of great toe	Dorsiflexion of foot Extension at metatarsophalangeal and interphalangeal joints of great toe
Extensor digitorum longus (EDL)	Lateral condyle of tibia Upper 3/4th of medial surface of fibula Interosseous membrane	Middle and distal phalanx of lateral four toes	Dorsiflexion of foot, extension at metatarsophalangeal and interphalangeal joints of 2nd–5th toes
Peroneus tertius (PT)	Lower 1/4th of medial surface of fibula Interosseous membrane	Base of 5th metatarsal	Dorsiflexion and eversion of foot
Extensor digitorum brevis (EDBr)	Superior surface of calcaneum	4 tendons 1st (extensor hallucis brevis): Inserts on base of proximal phalanx of great toe 2nd–4th: Insert on tendons of EDL	Extensor hallucis brevis: Extension of metatarsophalangeal joint of great toe 2nd–4th tendons: Assist EDL

BDC yogesh

Innervation: All these muscles are supplied by deep peroneal nerve except extensor digitorum brevis is supplied by the lateral terminal branch of deep peroneal nerve

Plate 8.3: Extensor digitorum longus, extensor digitorum brevis and extensor hallucis brevis

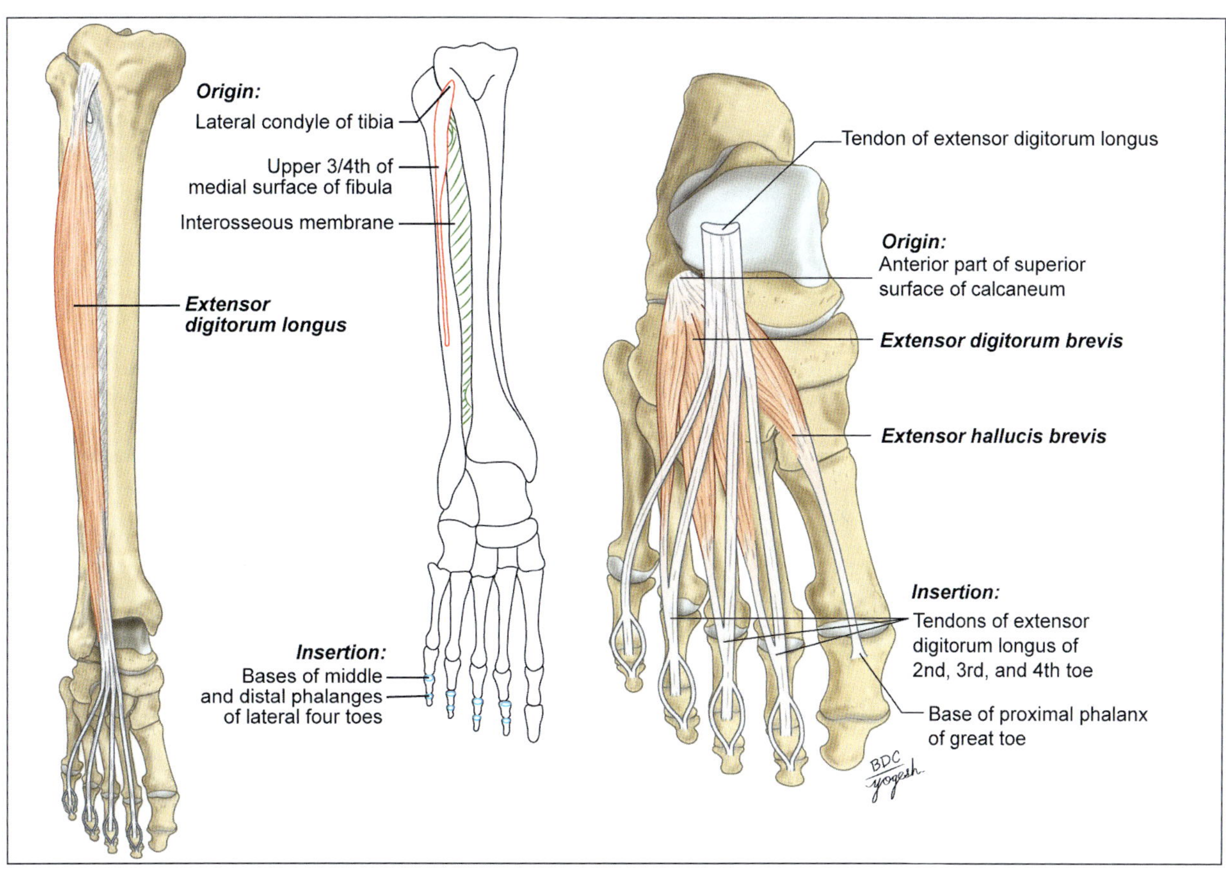

TABLE 8.1: Origin and insertion of muscles of the anterior compartment of the leg and dorsum of foot

Muscle	*Origin*	*Insertion*
1. **Tibialis anterior** Spindle-shaped belly with multipennate fibres	a. Lateral condyle of tibia b. Upper 2/3rd of the lateral surface of the shaft of the tibia c. Adjoining part of interosseous membrane	Inferomedial surface of the medial cuneiform and the adjoining part of the base of 1st metatarsal bone
2. **Extensor hallucis longus**	a. Posterior half of the middle 2/4th of the medial surface of the shaft of the fibula, medial to the extensor digitorum longus b. Adjoining part of the interosseous membrane	Dorsal surface of the base of the distal phalanx of the big toe
3. **Extensor digitorum longus**	a. Lateral condyle of tibia b. Whole of upper one-fourth and anterior half of middle two-fourths of the medial surface of the shaft of the fibula c. Upper part of interosseous membrane	It divides into ***four tendons*** for the lateral four toes. The tendons of 2nd, 3rd and 4th digits are joined on the lateral side by tendon of the extensor digitorum brevis, and form the dorsal digital expansion. It is inserted on the bases of the middle and distal phalanges
4. **Peroneus tertius** Separated part of the extensor digitorum longus, and may be regarded as its 5th tendon	a. Lower 1/4th of the medial surface of the shaft of the fibula b. Adjoining part of the interosseous membrane	Medial part of the dorsal surface of the base of the 5th metatarsal bone
5. **Extensor digitorum brevis**	Anterior part of the superior surface of the calcaneum	The muscle divides into ***four tendons*** for the medial four toes. The medial most part of the muscle, which is distinct, is known as the ***extensor hallucis brevis,*** which is inserted into the dorsal surface of the base of the proximal phalanx of the great toe. The three lateral tendons join the lateral sides of the tendons of the extensor digitorum longus to form the dorsal digital expansion for the 2nd, 3rd and 4th toes.

Note: The above muscles also take origin from the deep surface of the deep fascia, and adjoining intermuscular septa.

TABLE 8.2: Nerve supply and actions of muscles of anterior compartment of the leg and dorsum of foot

Muscle	*Nerve supply*	*Actions*
1. **Tibialis anterior**	Deep peroneal nerve	a. Dorsiflexor of foot b. Invertor of the foot c. Keeps the leg vertical while walking on uneven ground d. Maintains medial longitudinal arch of the foot
2. **Extensor hallucis longus**	Deep peroneal nerve	Dorsiflexor of foot and extends metatarsophalangeal and interphalangeal joints of big toe
3. **Extensor digitorum longus**	Deep peroneal nerve	Dorsiflexor of foot. Extends metatarsophalangeal, proximal and distal interphalangeal joints of 2nd–5th toes
4. **Peroneus tertius**	Deep peroneal nerve	Dorsiflexor of foot and evertor of foot
5. **Extensor digitorum brevis**	Lateral terminal branch of the deep peroneal nerve	Medial tendon, known as extensor hallucis brevis, extends metatarsophalangeal joint of big toe. The other three lateral tendons extend the metatarsophalangeal and interphalangeal joints of 2nd, 3rd and 4th toes particularly in a dorsiflexed foot

Competency:
AN18.2 Describe and demonstrate origin, course, relations, branches (or tributaries), termination of important nerves and vessels of anterior compartment of leg.

VESSELS AND NERVES OF FRONT OF LEG

ANTERIOR TIBIAL ARTERY

This is the main artery of the anterior compartment of the leg (Fig. 8.10, Flowchart 8.3).

Beginning, Course and Termination

The anterior tibial artery is the smaller terminal branch of the popliteal artery.

It begins on the back of the leg at the lower border of the popliteus, opposite the tibial tuberosity. It enters the anterior compartment of the leg by passing forwards close to the fibula, through an opening in the upper part of the interosseous membrane.

In the anterior compartment, it runs vertically downwards to a point midway between the two malleoli, where it changes its name to become the ***dorsalis pedis artery***.

Relations

In the upper 1/3rd of the leg, the artery lies between the *tibialis anterior* and the *extensor digitorum longus* (Fig. 8.11).

In the middle 1/3rd, it lies between the *tibialis anterior* and the *extensor hallucis longus*.

In the lower 1/3rd, it lies between the *extensor hallucis longus* and the *extensor digitorum longus*.

Note: The anterior tibial artery is crossed from lateral to medial side by the tendon of the *extensor hallucis longus*. The deep peroneal nerve is lateral to it in its upper and lower thirds and anterior to it in its middle 1/3rd.

Branches

1. The *anterior* and *posterior tibial recurrent branches* take part in the anastomoses around the knee joint.
2. The *anterior medial malleolar* and *anterior lateral malleolar branches* take part in the anastomoses around the ankle joint.
3. Muscular branches to adjacent muscles.

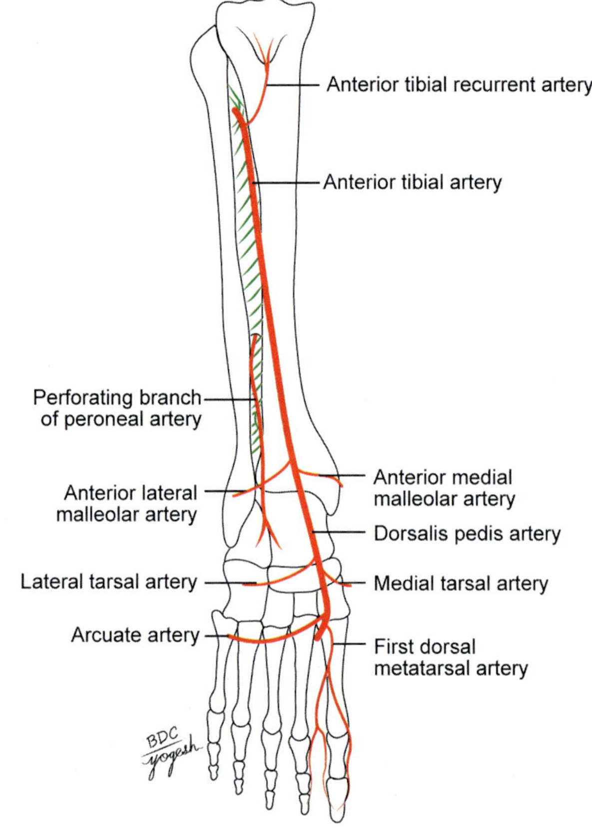

Fig. 8.10: Arteries on the front of the leg and dorsum of the foot

Flowchart 8.3: Anterior tibial artery

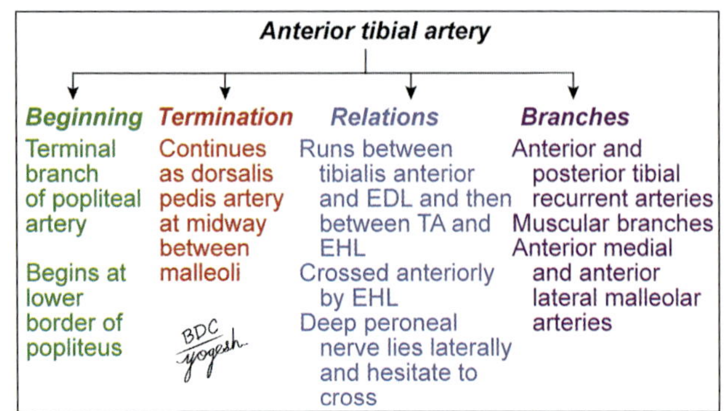

(EDL: Extensor digitorum longus, EHL: Extensor hallucis longus, TA: Tibialis anterior)

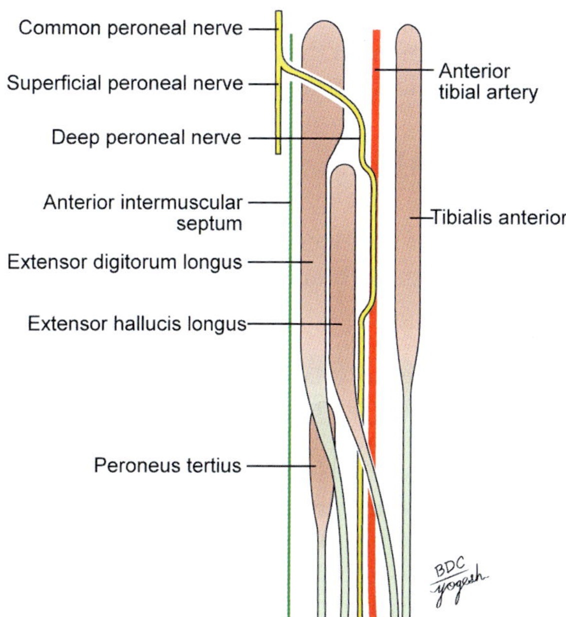

Fig. 8.11: Relations of anterior tibial artery

DEEP PERONEAL NERVE

Deep peroneal nerve is the nerve of the anterior compartment of the leg and the dorsum of the foot. This is one of the two terminal branches of common peroneal nerve (Fig. 8.11, Flowchart 8.4). Its root value is ventral primary rami of L4–5, S1–2 segments of spinal cord.

Beginning, Course and Termination

1. Deep peroneal nerve *begins* on the lateral side of the neck of the fibula (Fig. 8.11). It *enters the anterior compartment* by piercing the anterior intermuscular septum. It then pierces the *extensor digitorum longus* and comes to lie next to the anterior tibial artery.
2. The nerve ends on the dorsum of the foot, close to the ankle joint, by dividing into the lateral and medial terminal branches.
   a. *Lateral terminal branch* turns laterally and ends in a *pseudoganglion* deep to the *extensor digitorum brevis*. Branches proceed from the pseudoganglion and supply the *extensor digitorum brevis* and the *tarsal joints*.
   b. *Medial terminal branch* ends by supplying the skin adjoining the 1st interdigital cleft and the proximal joints of the big toe.

Flowchart 8.4: Deep peroneal nerve

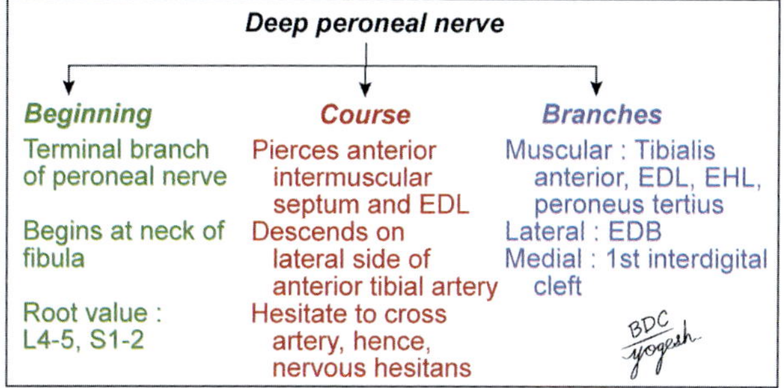

(EDL: Extensor digitorum longus, EHL: Extensor hallucis longus, EDB: Extensor digitorum brevis)

Branches

1. *Muscular branches* supply tibialis anterior, extensor digitorum longus, extensor hallucis longus and peroneus tertius, *extensor digitorum brevis*.
2. *Cutaneous branch* supplies adjacent sides of the 1st and 2nd toes.
3. *Articular branches* supply ankle joints, tarsal joints, tarsometatarsal and metatarsophalangeal joints.

Competency:
AN18.3 Explain the anatomical basis of foot drop.

CLINICAL ANATOMY

Paralysis of the muscles of the anterior compartment of the leg, e.g. tibialis anterior, extensor hallucis longus, extensor digitorum longus and peroneus tertius, due to injury to deep peroneal nerve results in loss of power of dorsiflexion of the foot. As a result, the foot is plantar flexed. The condition is called ***foot drop***. This is usually caused by injury or disease of the common peroneal nerve due to trauma, leprosy or peripheral neuritis (Fig. 8.12). Sensory loss is confined to 1st interdigital cleft.

DISSECTION

Identify the muscles of anterior compartment of leg as these are lying close together on the lateral surface of tibia, adjoining interosseous membrane and medial surface of fibula.

Trace their tendons deep to the two retinacula on the dorsum of foot till their insertion. Learn about these muscles given in Tables 8.1 and 8.2. Look for anterior these lie on the upper part of interosseous membrane of leg. Study their course, relations and branches.

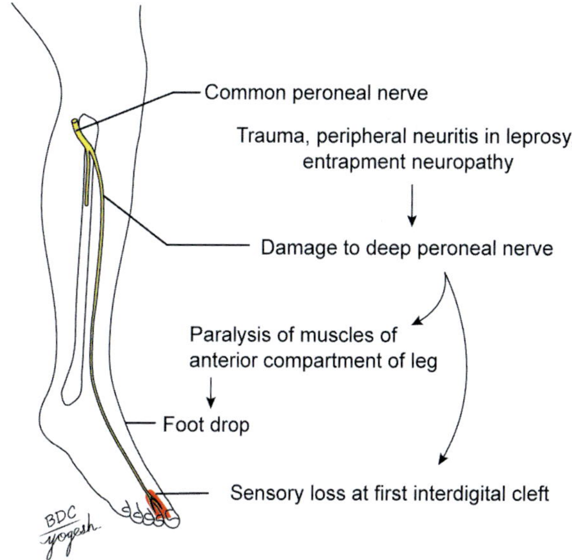

Fig. 8.12: Foot drop on the right side. Sensory loss in the first interdigital cleft

DORSUM OF FOOT

SENSORY INNERVATION OF THE DORSUM OF FOOT

The cutaneous nerves of the dorsum of the foot are as follows (Fig. 8.13):

1. *Superficial peroneal nerve*: It is a branch of common peroneal nerve. It supplies most of the dorsum of the foot except the skin of the cleft between the 1st and 2nd toe.
2. *Deep peroneal nerve*: It is also a branch of common peroneal nerve. It supplies the skin of the cleft between 1st and 2nd toes.
3. *Sural nerve*: It is a branch of tibial nerve. It supplies lateral margin of the dorsum of the foot and little toe.
4. *Saphenous nerve*: It is a branch of femoral nerve. It supplies the medial margin of the dorsum of foot up to the head of the 1st metatarsal.

DORSALIS PEDIS ARTERY
(DORSAL ARTERY OF THE FOOT)

This is the chief palpable artery of the dorsum of foot (Fig. 8.14, Flowchart 8.5).

Beginning, Course and Termination

It is a continuation of the anterior tibial artery onto the dorsum of the foot. The artery begins in front of the ankle between the two malleoli. It passes forwards along the medial side of the dorsum of the foot to reach the proximal end of the first intermetatarsal space. Here, it dips downwards between the two heads of the 1st dorsal interosseous muscle and ends in the sole by completing the plantar arterial arch (Figs 8.8c and d).

Relations

Superficial

1. Skin, fasciae, and inferior extensor retinaculum.
2. Extensor hallucis brevis, which crosses the artery from the lateral to medial side.

Deep

1. Capsular ligament of the ankle joint.
2. The talus, navicular and intermediate cuneiform.

Medial

Extensor hallucis longus.

Lateral

1. First tendon of the extensor digitorum longus.
2. The medial terminal branch of the deep peroneal nerve.

Branches

1. ***Lateral tarsal artery*** is larger than the medial and arises over the navicular bone. It passes deep to the extensor digitorum brevis, supplies this muscle and neighbouring tarsal joints, and ends in the lateral malleolar network.
2. ***Medial tarsal branches*** are two to three small twigs that join the medial malleolar network.
3. ***Arcuate artery*** is a large branch that arises opposite the medial cuneiform bone. It runs laterally over the bases of the metatarsal bones and ends by anastomosing with the lateral tarsal and lateral plantar arteries. It gives off the *2nd, 3rd* and *4th dorsal metatarsal arteries*, each of which divides into dorsal digital branches for adjoining toes.
4. The ***1st dorsal metatarsal artery*** arises just before the dorsalis pedis artery dips into the sole. It gives a branch to the medial side of the big toe, and divides into dorsal digital branches for adjacent sides of the first and second toes.

CLINICAL ANATOMY

Dorsalis pedis pulse: Pulsations of the dorsalis pedis artery are easily felt between the tendons of the extensor hallucis longus and the first tendon of the extensor digitorum longus (Fig. 8.15).

Absence of dorsalis pedis pulse: There may be an absence of dorsalis pedis artery that occurs in 14% of the cases. It indicates that there is a peripheral vascular disease (atherosclerosis, Buerger's disease).

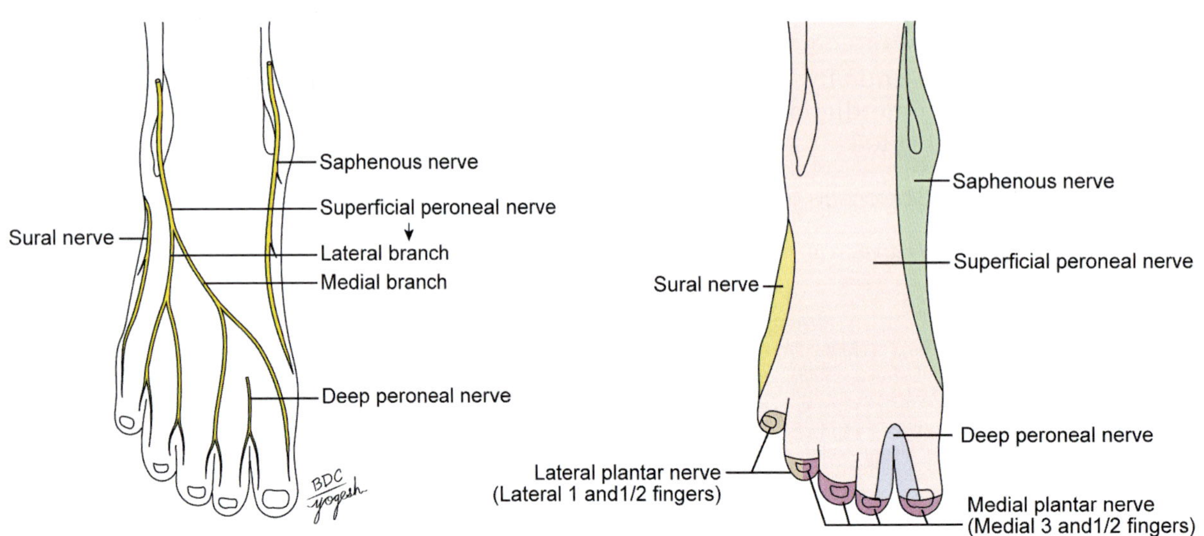

Fig. 8.13: Nerve supply and sensory innervation of the dorsum of the foot

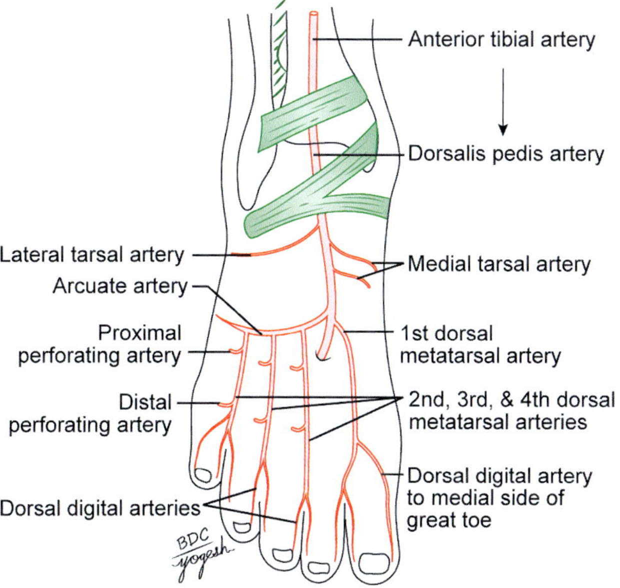

Fig. 8.14: Course of dorsalis pedis artery on dorsum of foot

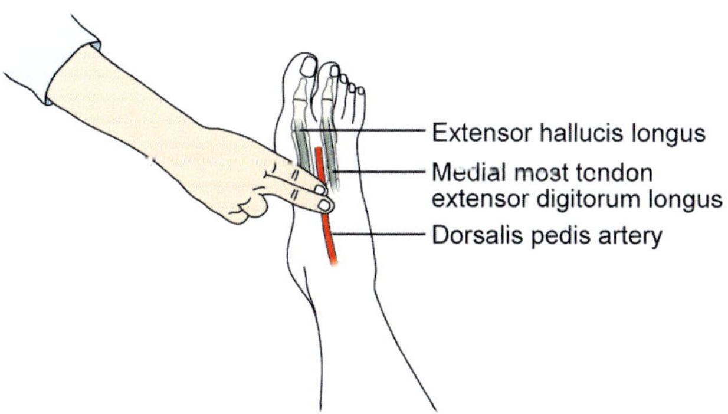

Fig. 8.15: Palpation of dorsalis pedis artery

Flowchart 8.5: Dorsalis pedis artery

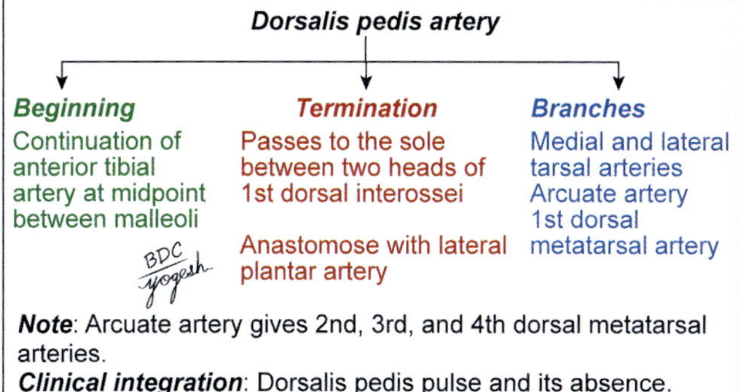

DISSECTION

Identify the small muscle extensor digitorum brevis situated on the lateral side of dorsum of foot. Its tendons are deep to the tendons of extensor digitorum longus. Its most medial tendon is called extensor hallucis brevis (Fig. 8.7). Dissect the dorsalis pedis artery and its branches on the dorsum of the foot.

FASCIA AND MUSCLES OF LATERAL SIDE OF THE LEG

Boundaries

The lateral or peroneal compartment of the leg is bounded:

Anteriorly by the anterior intermuscular septum.
Posteriorly by the posterior intermuscular septum.
Medially by the lateral surface of the fibula.
Laterally by the deep fascia (Fig. 8.4).

Contents

Muscles: Peroneus longus and peroneus brevis.
Nerve: Superficial peroneal nerve.
Artery: Peroneal artery.

Peroneal Retinacula

The peroneal retinacula are two thick bands of deep fascia.

Superior peroneal retinaculum is attached anteriorly to the posterior margin of the lateral malleolus, and posteriorly to the lateral surface of the calcaneum and to the superficial transverse fascial septum of the leg. It holds the peroneal tendons in place against the back of the lateral malleolus.

***Inferior peroneal retinaculum*:** Superiorly, it is attached to the anterior part of the superior surface of the calcaneum, where it becomes continuous with the stem of the inferior extensor retinaculum. Inferiorly, it is attached to the lateral surface of the calcaneum. The peroneal retinacula hold the tendons of the peroneus longus and brevis in place.

DISSECTION

Reflect the lateral skin flap of leg further laterally till peroneal muscles are seen. Divide the deep fascia longitudinally over the peroneal muscles. Clean the superior and inferior peroneal retinacula situated just above and below the lateral malleolus.

Identify the peroneus longus and peroneus brevis muscles. Trace their tendons through the retinacula towards their insertion. Study the deep fascia and peroneal muscles.

CLINICAL ANATOMY

Tenosynovitis of peronei tendon is the inflammation of the tendon sheaths of the peroneal muscles. If superior peroneal retinaculum is torn, the tendons can get dislocated to front of lateral malleolus.

PERONEAL MUSCLES

These are the peroneus longus and the peroneus brevis (Plate 8.4, Figs 8.16 and 8.17, Flowchart 8.6). The origin and insertion of peroneal muscles are described in

Plate 8.4: Peroneus longus, peroneus brevis muscles and peroneal retinacula

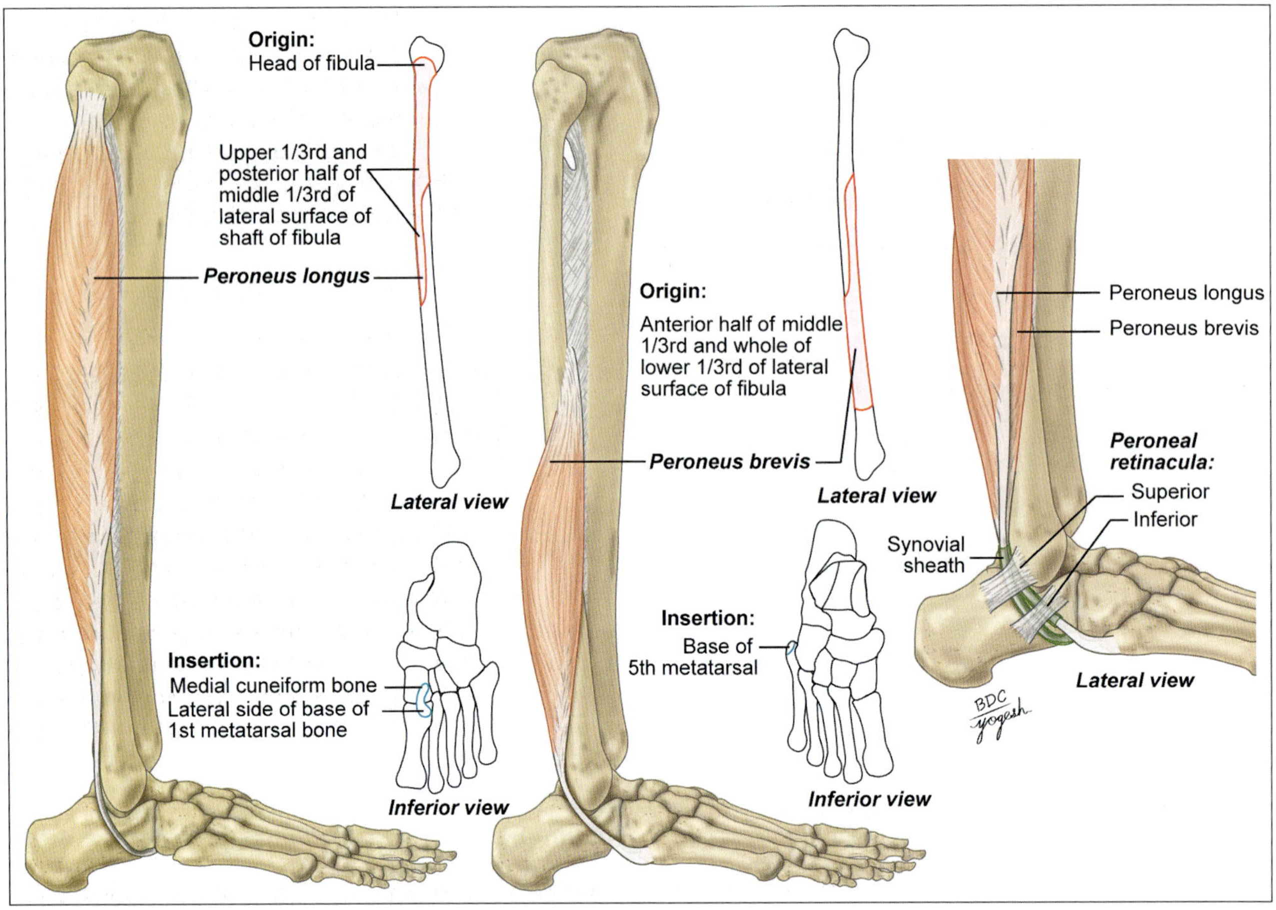

Flowchart 8.6: Muscles of lateral compartment of leg

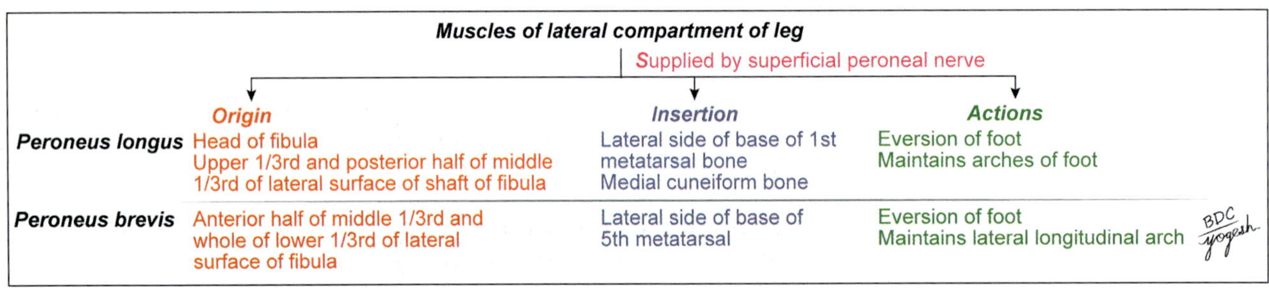

Muscles of lateral compartment of leg — Supplied by superficial peroneal nerve

	Origin	Insertion	Actions
Peroneus longus	Head of fibula Upper 1/3rd and posterior half of middle 1/3rd of lateral surface of shaft of fibula	Lateral side of base of 1st metatarsal bone Medial cuneiform bone	Eversion of foot Maintains arches of foot
Peroneus brevis	Anterior half of middle 1/3rd and whole of lower 1/3rd of lateral surface of fibula	Lateral side of base of 5th metatarsal	Eversion of foot Maintains lateral longitudinal arch

Table 8.3; and their nerve supply and actions are given in Table 8.4.

Note: Peroneus longus tendon changes its direction two times: 1. First below the lateral malleolus; 2. Second at cuboid.

Sesamoid bone is commonly found in the tendon of peroneus longus.

Peroneus longus and tibialis anterior are inserted into the same two bones, and together form a '***stirrup***' beneath the middle of the sole. The presence of the sling keeps the middle of foot pulled up and prevents flattening of its arches.

CLINICAL ANATOMY

Paralysis of peroneus brevis and peroneus longus occurs due to injury to superficial peroneal nerve. The foot cannot be everted at subtalar joint.

SUPERFICIAL PERONEAL NERVE

Superficial peroneal nerve is the main nerve of the lateral compartment of the leg (Fig. 8.18, Flowchart 8.7).

Origin and Root Value

It is a smaller terminal branch of the common peroneal nerve. Its root value is ventral primary rami of L5, S1 segments of spinal cord.

Course

The nerve begins on the lateral side of neck of fibula, runs through the peroneal muscles and becomes superficial at the junction of upper 2/3rd and lower 1/3rd of leg. In the distal part of leg, it becomes cutaneous to supply distal part of leg and most of the dorsum of foot.

TABLE 8.3: Origin and insertion of the peroneal muscles

Muscle	*Origin*	*Insertion*
1. **Peroneus longus**	a. Head of the fibula b. Upper 1/3rd, and posterior half of the middle 1/3rd of the lateral surface of the shaft of the fibula c. Anterior and posterior intermuscular septa of the leg	The tendon passes deep to the peroneal retinacula, runs through a tunnel in the cuboid, and is inserted into: (a) the lateral side of the base of the ***1st metatarsal*** bone, and (b) the adjoining part of the medial cuneiform bone. The tendon changes its direction below the lateral malleolus and again on the cuboid bone.
2. **Peroneus brevis**	a. Anterior half of the middle 1/3rd and whole of the lower 1/3rd of the lateral surface of the shaft of fibula b. Anterior and posterior intermuscular septa of the leg	The tendon passes deep to the peroneal retinacula, and is inserted into the lateral side of the base of the ***5th metatarsal*** bone

TABLE 8.4: Nerve supply and actions of the peroneal muscles

Muscle	*Nerve supply*	*Actions*
1. **Peroneus longus**	Superficial peroneal nerve	a. Evertor of foot especially when foot is off the ground b. Maintain lateral longitudinal arch and transverse arch of the foot
2. **Peroneus brevis**	Superficial peroneal nerve	Evertor of foot

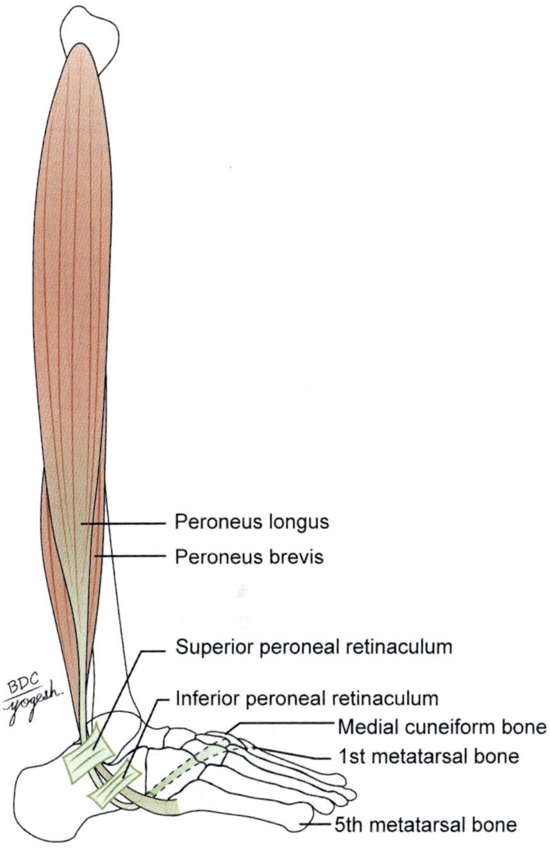

Fig. 8.16: Peroneus longus and brevis muscles

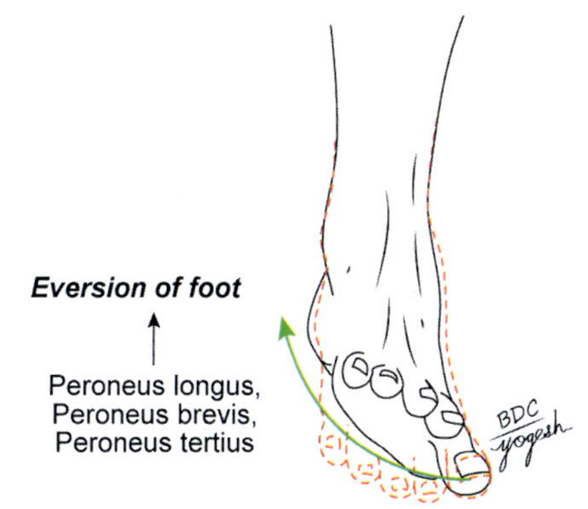

Fig. 8.17: Action of peroneus longus and brevis muscles

Flowchart 8.7: Superficial peroneal nerve

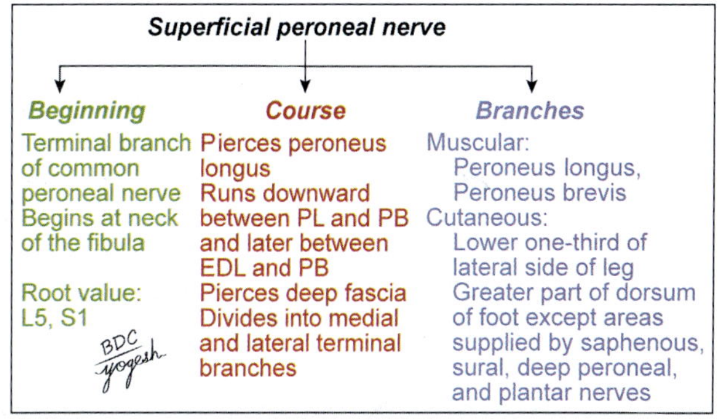

(PL: Peroneus longus, PB: Peroneus brevis, EDL: Extensor digitorum longus)

Relations

1. Superficial peroneal nerve begins on the lateral side of the neck of the fibula, under cover of the upper fibres of the *peroneus longus*.
2. In the upper 1/3rd of the leg, it descends through the substance of the *peroneus longus*. In the middle 1/3rd, it first descends for a short distance between the *peroneus longus* and *brevis* muscles, reaches the anterior border of the *peroneus brevis*, and then descends in a groove between the *peroneus brevis* and the *extensor digitorum longus* under cover of deep fascia.
3. At the junction of the upper 2/3rd and lower 1/3rd of the leg, this nerve pierces the deep fascia to become superficial. It divides into a medial and a lateral branch, which descend into the foot.

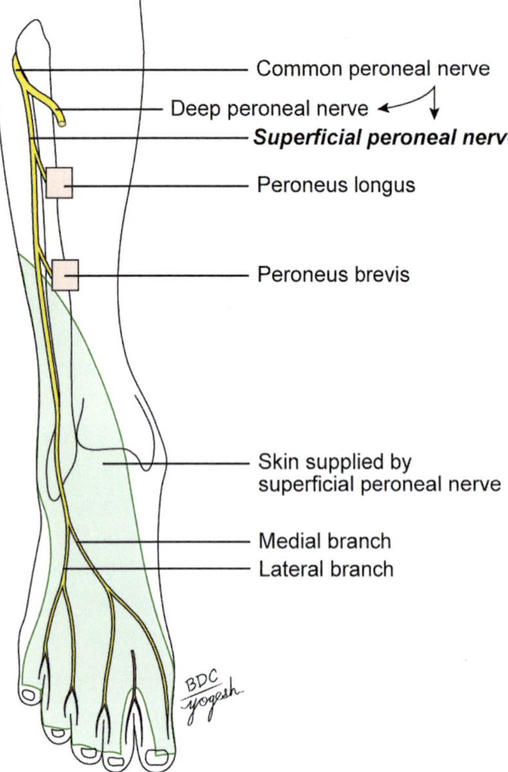

Fig. 8.18: Superficial peroneal nerve

Branches and Distribution

Muscular branches: Peroneus longus and the peroneus brevis.

Cutaneous branches: Through its terminal branches, the superficial peroneal nerve supplies the lower 1/3rd of the lateral side of the leg and the greater part of the dorsum of the foot, except for the territories supplied by the saphenous, sural, deep peroneal and plantar nerves.

Medial branch: It crosses the ankle and divides into two dorsal digital nerves—one for the medial side of the big toe and the other for the adjoining sides of the 2nd and 3rd toes.

Lateral branch: It divides into two dorsal digital nerves for the adjoining sides of the 3rd and 4th, and 4th and 5th toes.

Communicating branches: The medial branch communicates with the saphenous and deep peroneal nerves, and the lateral branch with the sural nerve.

CLINICAL ANATOMY

Injury to the superficial peroneal nerve

1. Superficial peroneal nerve can get entrapped as it penetrates the deep fascia of leg. It may also be involved in ***lateral compartment syndrome***. Its paralysis causes ***loss of eversion*** of foot at subtalar joint.
2. The sensory loss will affect the anterior and lateral aspects of the leg, dorsum of the foot and the toes.

DISSECTION

Carefully look for common peroneal nerve in relation to the neck of fibula.

Superficial peroneal nerve, one of the terminal branches of common peroneal nerve, supplies both the peroneus longus and brevis muscles and in lower 1/3rd of leg, it becomes cutaneous to supply most of the dorsum of foot.

TENDONS ON MEDIAL SIDE OF THE LEG

Features

Medial side of the leg is formed by the medial surface of the shaft of tibia. The greater part of this surface is subcutaneous and is covered only by the skin and superficial fascia (Fig. 8.19).

In the upper part, the tibia provides attachment to tibial collateral ligament near the medial border, and provides insertion to *sartorius, gracilis* and *semitendinosus* in front of the ligament, all of which are covered by a thin layer of deep fascia.

The *great saphenous* vein and the *saphenous nerve* lie in the superficial fascia as they cross the lower 1/3rd of this surface.

Note: The tibial collateral ligament, morphologically, represents a degenerated part of the tendon of adductor magnus.

Guy ropes: The three muscles inserted into the upper part of the medial surface of tibia represent one muscle from each of the three compartments of thigh, corresponding to the three elements of the hip bone.

1. *Sartorius* belongs to anterior compartment of thigh, and is supplied by the nerve of ilium or femoral nerve.
2. *Gracilis* belongs to medial compartment of thigh, and is supplied by the nerve of pubis or obturator nerve.
3. *Semitendinosus* belongs to posterior compartment of thigh, and is supplied by the nerve of ischium or sciatic nerve.

These three muscles are anchored below at one point, and spread out above to span the pelvis, like three strings of a tent. From this arrangement, it appears that they act as 'guy ropes', to stabilise the bony pelvis on the femur (Fig. 8.19).

Anserine bursa: This is a large, complicated bursa, with several diverticula. It separates the tendons of sartorius, gracilis and semitendinosus at their insertion from one another, from the bony surface of tibia, and from the tibial collateral ligament (Fig. 8.20).

DISSECTION

Identify the three tendons of a tripod formed by sartorius, gracilis and semitendinosus at their insertion on the upper medial surface of tibia. Behind these tendons is present the tibial collateral ligament of knee joint. The great saphenous vein is visualised on the lower 1/3rd of tibia. Study these structures.

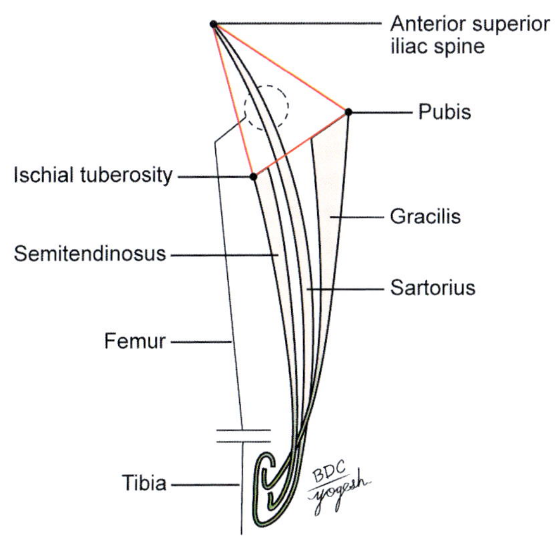

Fig. 8.19: Sartorius, gracilis and semitendinosus form the guy ropes for the tent of pelvis

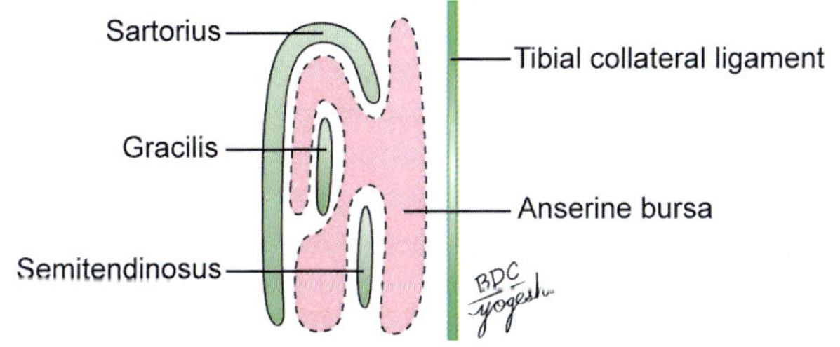

Fig. 8.20: The anserine bursa

CLINICAL ANATOMY

Bursa anserine between insertion of sartorius, gracilis, semitendinosus and tibial collateral ligament may get inflammed. It is called anserine bursitis.

Video 2.8 **Front of Leg:** Muscles of anterior compartment and dorsum of foot, muscles of lateral compartment of leg, medial side of leg.

Facts to Remember

- Tibialis anterior: It is multipennate, most superficial, strongest dorsiflexor of the foot.
- Dorsum of foot contains an extensor digitorum brevis, while dorsum of hand has no muscle of its own.
- The deep peroneal nerve hesitates to cross the anterior tibial artery – hence called nervus hesitans.
- Cleft between the first and second toes which is innervated by the deep peroneal nerve
- Long saphenous vein lying anterior to medial malleolus is used for giving intravenous fluids/blood in case of emergency.
- Guy ropes, formed by sartorius, gracilis and semitendinosus, stabilise the pelvis on the thigh and leg.
- Dorsalis pedis is palpated on the dorsum of foot on medial cuneiform between extensor hallucis longus and extensor digitorum longus.

BDC's Anatomy *e*-book

1. Sensory innervation of the dorsum of foot
2. Relations of the superior and inferior extensor retinacula
3. Further reading
4. Viva voce questions

Chapter

9

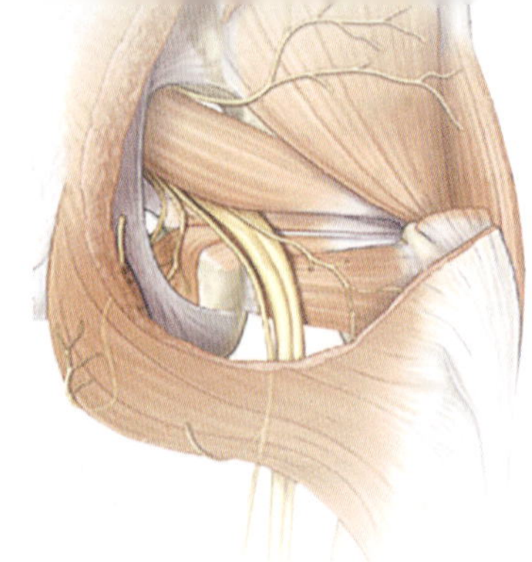

Back of Leg

The back or posterior compartment of the leg, is also called the *calf*, corresponds to the front of forearm. This is the bulkiest of the three compartments of leg, because of the powerful antigravity superficial muscles, e.g. gastrocnemius and soleus, which are quite large in size. They raise the heel during walking.

SUPERFICIAL FASCIA

The superficial fascia of the back of the leg contains the small and great saphenous veins and their tributaries and several cutaneous nerves.

Small or Short Saphenous Vein

The small or short saphenous vein is formed on the dorsum of the foot by the union of the lateral end of the ***dorsal venous arch*** with the ***lateral marginal vein***. It enters the back of the leg by passing behind the lateral malleolus. In the leg, it ascends lateral to the tendo calcaneus, and then along the middle line of the calf, to the lower part of the popliteal fossa. Here, it pierces the deep fascia and opens into the ***popliteal vein***. It drains the lateral border of the foot, the heel, and the back of the leg. It is connected with the deep veins, and is accompanied by the sural nerve (Fig. 9.1).

Great or Long Saphenous Vein

The great or long saphenous vein begins on the dorsum of the foot by union of the medial end of the ***dorsal venous arch*** with the medial marginal vein (*see* Fig. 8.1a). It ascends in front of the medial malleolus. In the lower 1/3rd of the leg, it passes obliquely across the medial surface of the tibia. In the upper 2/3rd of the leg, the vein ascends along the medial border of the tibia, to the posteromedial side of the knee (Figs 9.1a and b). It is accompanied by the saphenous nerve. In the thigh, it inclines forwards to reach saphenous opening and drains into *femoral vein*.

Cutaneous Nerves

The skin of the back of leg is supplied by the following nerves (Figs 9.1a and b):

1. Saphenous nerve
2. Posterior division of medial cutaneous nerve of thigh
3. Posterior cutaneous nerve of thigh
4. Sural nerve
5. Lateral cutaneous nerve of calf
6. Sural communicating nerve
7. Medial calcaneal branch of tibial nerve.

Note:

1. The saphenous nerve lies close to the great saphenous vein. During venesection, this nerve should not be injured.
2. The *posterior division of the medial cutaneous nerve of the thigh* (L2, 3) supplies the skin of the uppermost part of the medial area of the calf.
3. The *posterior cutaneous nerve of the thigh* (S1, 2, 3) is a branch of the sacral plexus and descends along with the small saphenous vein, to supply the skin of the upper half of the central area of the calf.
4. The ***sural nerve*** (L5, S1, 2) is a branch of the tibial nerve in the popliteal fossa. It descends between the two heads of the gastrocnemius. It accompanies the small saphenous vein. It is joined by the *peroneal communicating nerve* about 5 cm above the heel. After passing behind the lateral malleolus, the nerve runs forwards along the lateral border of the foot, and ends at the lateral side of the little toe.
5. The ***lateral cutaneous nerve of the calf*** (L4, 5, S1) is a branch of the common peroneal nerve in the popliteal fossa. It supplies the skin of the upper two-thirds of the lateral area of the leg (both in front and behind).
6. The ***peroneal*** or ***sural communicating nerve*** (L5, S1, 2) is a branch of the common peroneal nerve. It descends to join the sural nerve about 5 cm above the heel. Before joining the latter, it supplies the skin of the lateral area of calf.
7. The *medial calcanean branches* (S1, 2) *of the tibial nerve* perforate the flexor retinaculum and supply the skin of the heel and the medial side of the sole of the foot.

CLINICAL ANATOMY

- Sural nerve has a tendency to form ***painful neuroma***.
- ***Sural nerve graft:*** Sural nerve can be grafted, as it is only sensory, superficial and is easily identified lying between tendon of tendo calcaneus and lateral malleolus.

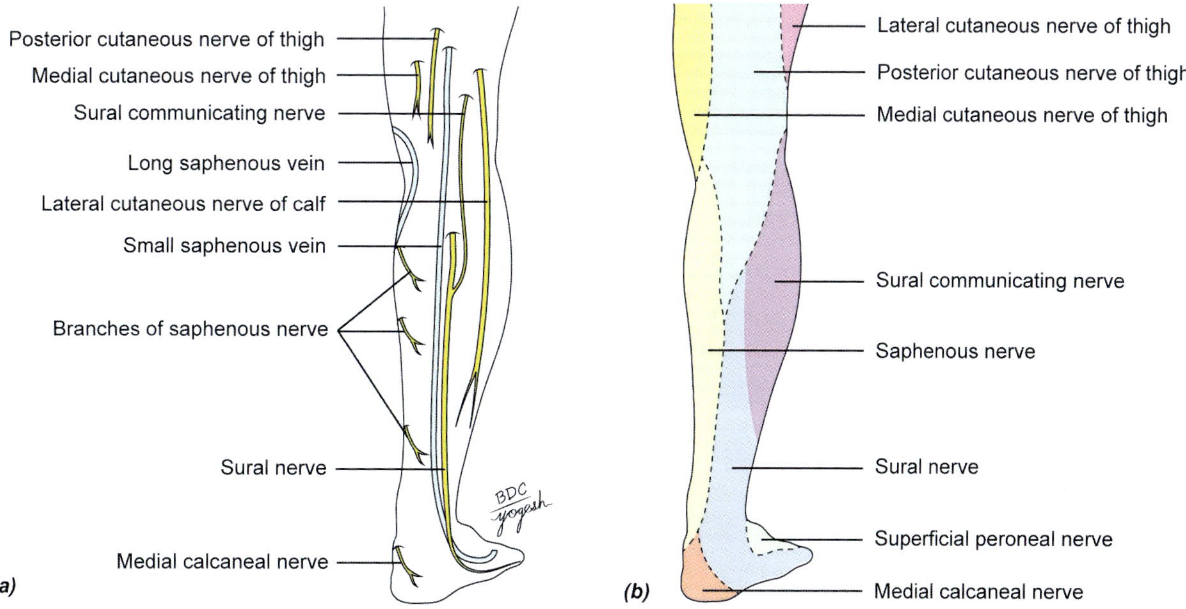

Figs 9.1a and b: The back of leg and heel: (a) Superficial veins and cutaneous nerves and (b) areas supplied by cutaneous nerves

DISSECTION

The horizontal incision (vi) in the skin is already given (*see* Fig. 5.4). Carry this incision along the lateral and medial borders of the leg. Reflect whole skin of the back of leg distally till the heel (ix).

Identify the structures, e.g. great and small saphenous veins, and nerves in the superficial fascia.

DEEP FASCIA

Subdivisions

The posterior compartment of leg is bounded and subdivided by the deep fascia. It is thin above but thick near the ankle, where it forms the flexor and superior peroneal retinacula.

The posterior compartment is subdivided into three parts: Superficial, middle and deep, by two strong fascial septa. These are superficial and deep transverse fascial septa.

Superficial transverse fascial septum (Fig. 9.2): It separates the superficial and deep muscles of the back of the leg and encloses the posterior tibial vessels and tibial nerve. It is attached *medially* to the medial border of the tibia and *laterally*, to the posterior border of the fibula.

Deep transverse fascial septum: It separates the tibialis posterior from the long flexors of the toes. It is attached *medially* to the vertical ridge on the posterior surface of the tibia and *laterally*, to the medial crest of the fibula.

Contents of Posterior Compartments of Leg (Fig. 9.2)

1. *Superficial part*: Gastrocnemius, soleus and plantaris.
2. *Middle part*: Flexor digitorum longus, flexor hallucis longus and posterior tibial nerve and vessels.
3. *Deep part*: Tibialis posterior.

Flexor Retinaculum of Foot (Plate 9.1 and Fig. 9.3)

1. Flexor retinaculum of foot is a thick, 2.5 cm broad band of deep fascia on the medial side of ankle that holds the long flexor tendons of the ankle in position.
2. *Attachments:*

   Anterior: Posterior border and tip of the medial malleolus.

   Posterior and *lateral:* Medial tubercle of the calcaneum.
3. *Structures passing deep to the retinaculum:* These are from medial to lateral side.
   a. Tendon of **t**ibialis posterior
   b. Tendon of flexor **d**igitorum longus
   c. Posterior tibial **a**rtery
   d. Tibial **n**erve
   e. Tendon of flexor **h**allucis longus.

[*Mnemonic*: *Structures under flexor retinaculum:* **T**alented **d**octors **a**re **n**ever **h**ungry]

Note: Each tendon occupies a separate compartment which is lined by a synovial sheath. The nerve and artery share a common compartment. These structures lie in a *tarsal tunnel*. If the nerve gets pressed, it leads to *tarsal tunnel syndrome*.

CLINICAL ANATOMY

Tarsal tunnel syndrome: In this syndrome, the tibial nerve can be injured:

a. In upper part of calf from fracture of tibia
b. In middle of calf from tight plasters
c. Under flexor retinaculum

It results in:

Sensory loss: Distal and middle phalanges including nail beds of all toes. The sensory loss is in the skin over sole of foot.

Plate 9.1: Flexor retinaculum

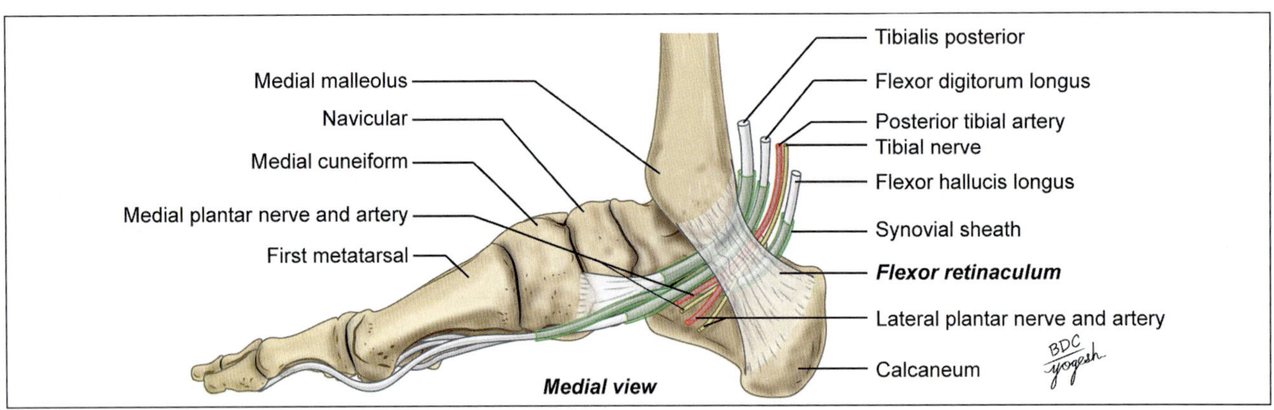

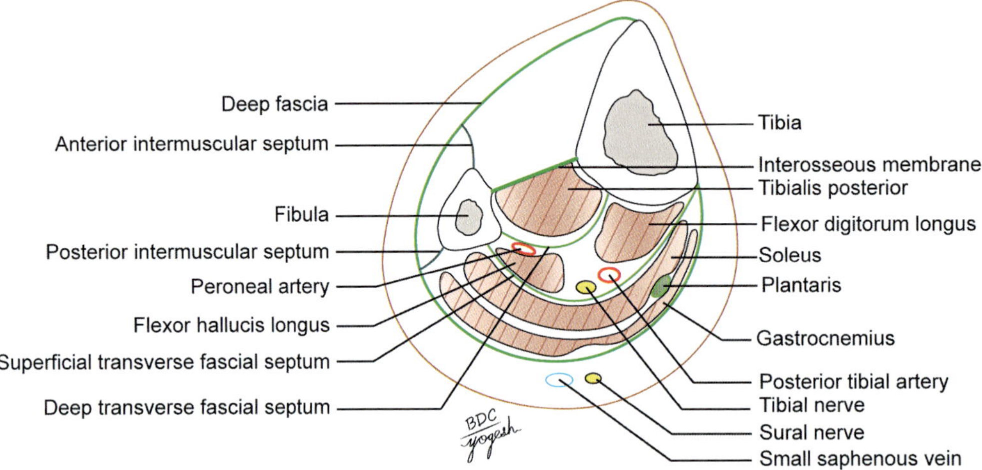

Fig. 9.2: Contents of posterior compartment of leg, section passing through the middle of the leg (right, inferior view)

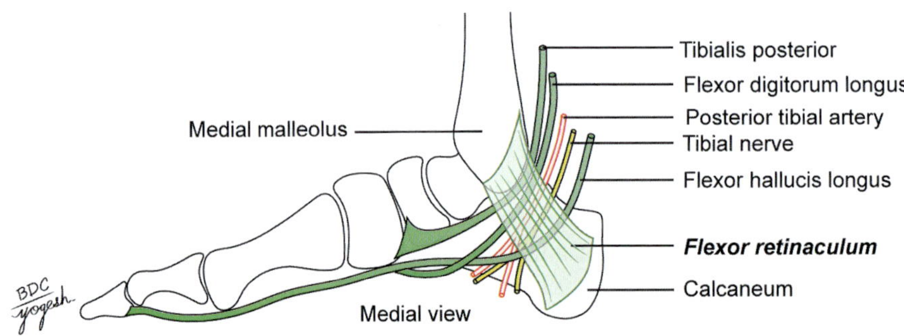

Fig. 9.3: Flexor retinaculum of the ankle and the structures passing deep to it

Motor loss, if injured at upper part of calf:

a. Superficial muscles of calf
b. Deep muscles of calf
c. Intrinsic muscles of sole.

Tinel's sign: Tapping over flexor retinaculum produces tingling and numbness on the skin of medial side of heel and sole of the foot.

DISSECTION

Incise the deep fascia vertically and reflect it. Define the flexor retinaculum posteroinferior to the medial malleolus and identify the tendons enclosed in synovial sheaths passing deep to it.

Identify the medial and lateral bellies of gastrocnemius muscle (Plate 9.2). Cut the medial belly 5 cm distal to the origin. Reflect it laterally to locate the popliteal vessels and tibial nerve. Identify plantaris muscle with its longest tendon situated posteromedial to lateral head of gastrocnemius.

Reflect the lateral head of gastrocnemius 5 cm distal to its origin. Both the bellies now can be turned distally.

Deep to gastrocnemius, expose the strong soleus muscle. The popliteal vessels and tibial nerve travel down to back of leg.

Competencies:

AN19.1 Describe and demonstrate the major muscles of back of leg with their attachment, nerve supply and actions.

AN19.3 Explain the concept of 'peripheral heart'.

SUPERFICIAL MUSCLES OF BACK OF LEG

The superficial muscles are the gastrocnemius, the soleus and the plantaris (Plate 9.2, Figs 9.4 and 9.5, Tables 9.1 and 9.2, Flowchart 9.1).

Features

1. ***Gastrocnemius*** is a large powerful muscle. It has two heads, medial and lateral. It lies superficial to the soleus. The two heads of the gastrocnemius and the soleus are together referred to as the gastro-soleus or the ***triceps surae***. A small sesamoid bone called the ***fabella*** is present in the tendon of origin of the lateral head of the gastrocnemius.
2. A bursa (***Brodie's bursa***) lies deep to the medial head of the gastrocnemius.
3. **Soleus** a sole-shaped multipennate muscle that lies deep to the gastrocnemius. The soleus is more powerful than the gastrocnemius, but the latter is faster acting.
4. The ***tendo calcaneus*** is the thickest and strongest tendon of the body. It is about 15 cm long. It begins near the middle of the leg, but its anterior surface receives fleshy fibres of the soleus almost up to its

Flowchart 9.1: Superficial muscles of back of the leg

Superficial muscles of back of the leg

Supplied by tibial nerve

	Origin	*Insertion*	*Actions*
Gastrocnemius	Medial head: Medial condyle of femur Lateral head: Lateral condyle and lateral supracondylar line of femur	Through tendo calcaneus at middle 1/3rd of posterior surface of calcaneum	Plantar flexion at ankle joint Flexion at knee joint
Soleus	Posterior surface of head and upper 1/4th of posterior surface of fibula Soleal line of tibia	Middle 1/3rd of posterior surface of calcaneum through tendo calcaneus	Plantar flexion at ankle joint
Plantaris	Lateral supracondylar line of femur	Posterior surface of calcaneum, medial to tendo calcaneus	Supports gastrocnemius

BDC yogesh.

TABLE 9.1: Origin and insertion of superficial muscles of back of the leg

Muscle	*Origin*	*Insertion*
1. **Gastrocnemius**	***Medial head*** is larger and arises by a broad flat tendon from: a. Posterosuperior depression on the medial condyle of the femur, behind the adductor tubercle b. Adjoining raised area on the popliteal surface of the femur ***Lateral head*** arises by a broad flat tendon from: a. Lateral surface of the lateral condyle of the femur b. Lateral supracondylar line c. Capsule of the knee joint	The tendons of these muscles fuse to form the ***tendo calcaneus*** or ***tendo-Achilles***, which is inserted into the middle one-third of the posterior surface of the calcaneum
2. **Soleus**	a. Back of head and upper 1/4th of the posterior surface of the shaft of ***fibula*** b. Soleal line and middle 1/3rd of the medial border of the shaft of ***tibia*** c. The tendinous soleal arch that stretches between the tibia and the fibula	
3. **Plantaris**	a. Lower part of the lateral supracondylar line of the femur b. Oblique popliteal ligament	Posterior surface of the calcaneum, medial to the tendo calcaneus.

TABLE 9.2: Nerve supply and actions of superficial muscles of back of the leg

Muscle	*Nerve supply*	*Actions*
1. **Gastrocnemius**	Tibial nerve (S1, 2)	Plantar flexion of the foot at the ankle joint Flexion of the knee
2. **Soleus**	Tibial nerve (S1, 2)	Plantar flexion of the ankle independent of position of the knee Steadies the leg on the foot while standing
3. **Plantaris**	Tibial nerve (S1, 2)	Weak plantar flexion of the ankle

Plate 9.2: Superficial muscles of the back of leg

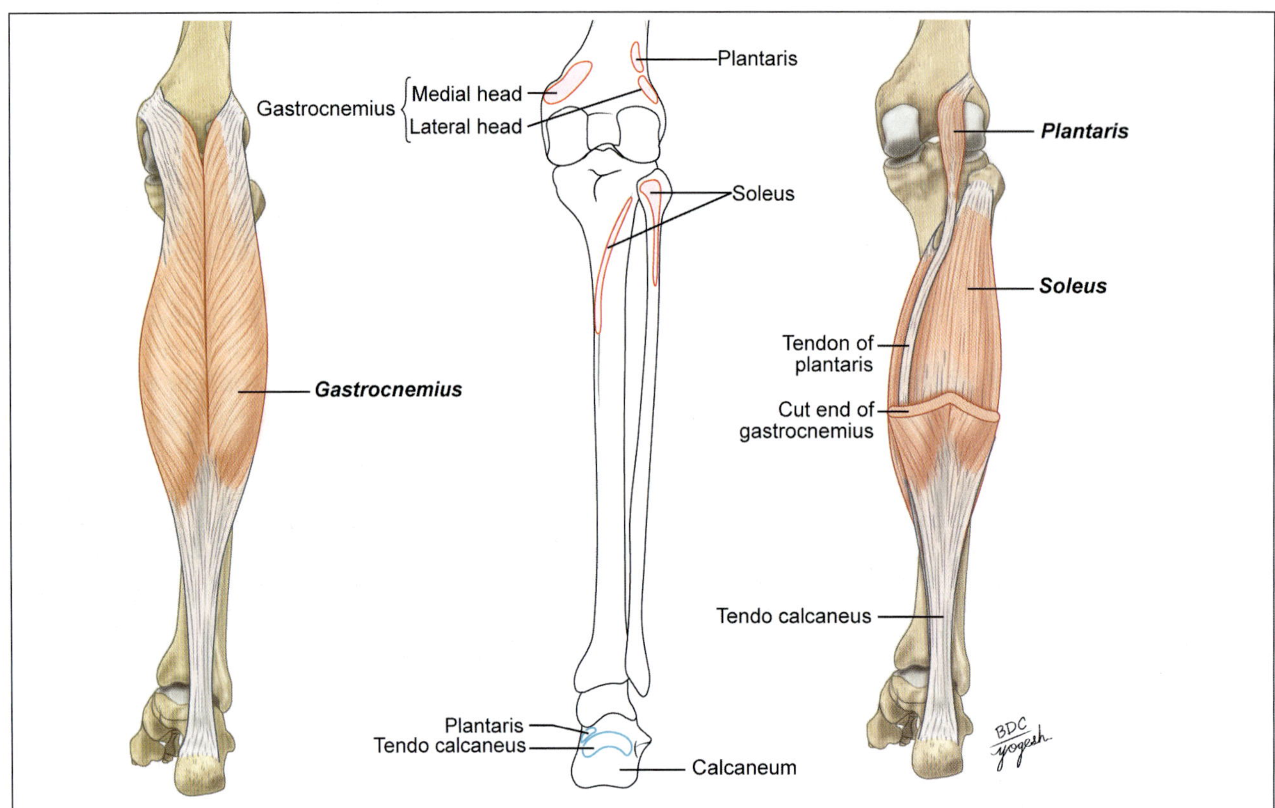

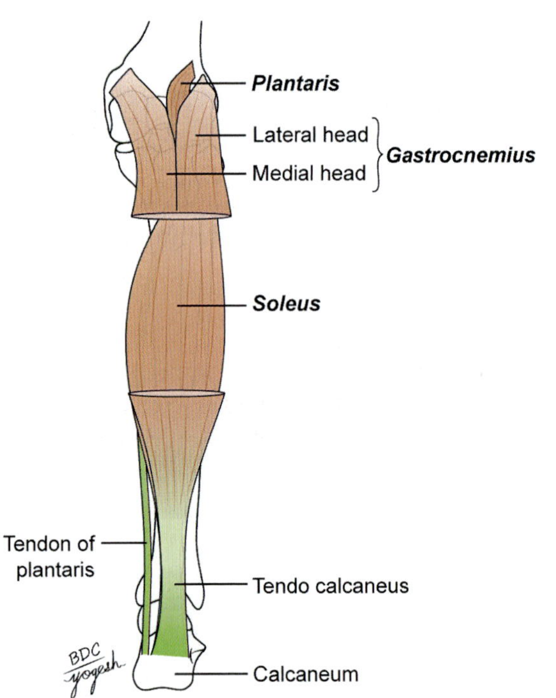

Fig 9.4: Muscles of back of the leg

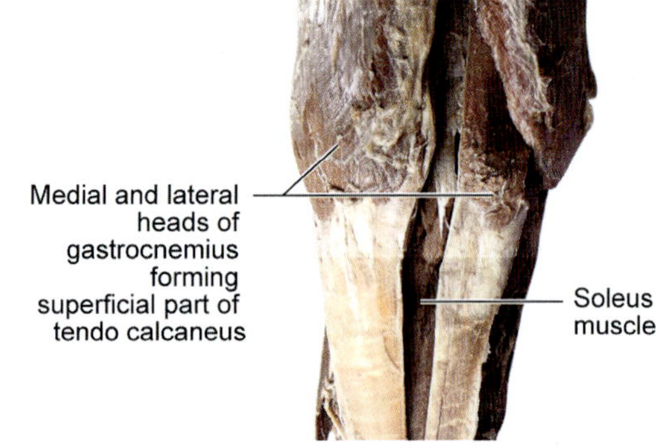

Fig. 9.5: Dissection of superficial muscles of the back of the leg

lower end. It is narrow and thick in the middle, and expanded at both ends and is attached to posterior surface of calcaneum (Fig. 9.4).

Note:

- In walking, the soleus overcomes the inertia of the body weight, like the ***bottom gear of a car***. When movement is underway, the quicker acting gastrocnemius increases the speed like the ***top gear of a car***. Soleus is chiefly a postural muscle, to steady the leg on the foot.
- ***Tendo calcaneus*** is also known as ***tendo-Achilles***. According to a Greek legend, *Achilles* was an irresistible and invincible warrior. His mother, the sea Goddess, had dipped him in the underground river, Styx. No weapon could harm the body, which had been covered by the waters of Styx. But the warrior was ultimately killed in the war of Trojans, by the arrows hitting his vulnerable heel, which was the only unprotected part of his body. His mother had held him by one heel, and the water over this heel had not flowed.
- **Plantaris** is vestigial in human beings. It has a short belly and a long tendon. Its tendon lies between the gastrocnemius and the soleus, crossing from lateral to medial side. It is inserted on the posterior surface of the calcaneum, medial to the tendo calcaneus. ***Plantar aponeurosis*** is the estranged part of the plantaris.

DEEP MUSCLES OF BACK OF LEG

The deep muscles of the back of the leg are the popliteus, the flexor digitorum longus, the flexor hallucis longus, and the tibialis posterior (Plates 9.3 and 9.4, Fig. 9.6, Flowchart 9.2, Tables 9.3 and 9.4).

CLINICAL ANATOMY

- The long tendon of plantaris is used for tendon transplantation in the body.
- The deep muscles are tested by palpating the calf while the foot is being plantar-flexed (Fig. 9.7).
- **Peripheral heart:** The muscles of the calf play an important role in circulation. Contractions of these muscles help in the venous return from the lower limb. The soleus is particularly important in this respect. There are large, valveless, venous sinuses in its substance. When the muscle contracts the blood in these sinuses is pumped upwards. When it relaxes, it sucks the blood from the superficial veins through the perforators. The soleus is, therefore, called the peripheral heart (Fig. 9.8).
- Tendo-Achilles reflex or ***ankle jerk*** (S1, 2): The foot gets plantar-flexed on tapping the tendo calcaneus (Fig. 9.9). Normal reflex is plantar flexion of the ankle joint. The calcaneal tendon reflex tests the S1 and S2 nerve roots. Absence of ankle reflex occurs in S1 nerve root injury.
- ***Tennis leg***: The over stretching of the medial head of gastrocnemius in tennis players results in tear of myotendinous junction of the medial head of gastrocnemius. It results in calf pain and is called tennis leg.
- In long-distance air travel, sitting immobile can lead to thrombosis of ***soleal venous sinuses***. The thrombus may get dislodged to block any other artery. One must stretch the legs frequently.

DISSECTION

Once the soleus has been studied, separate it from its attachment on tibia and reflect it laterally. Look for a number of deep veins that emerge from this muscle.

Plate 9.3: Popliteus

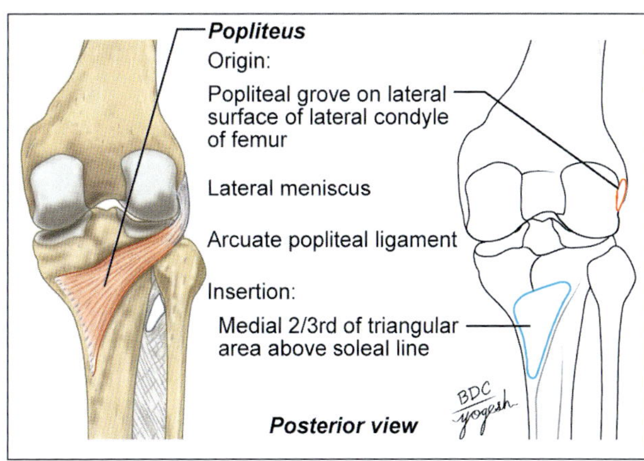

Identify popliteus, situated above the soleus muscle. Deep to soleus is the superficial transverse fascial septum. Incise this septum vertically to reach the long flexors of the toes, e.g. flexor hallucis longus laterally and flexor digitorum longus medially. Trace these tendons till the flexor retinaculum. Turn the flexor hallucis longus laterally and expose the deep transverse fascial septum.

Divide this septum to reveal the deepest muscle of the posterior compartment of leg, e.g. tibialis posterior. Trace its tendon also till flexor retinaculum. Study these deep muscles.

Clean the lowest part of popliteal vessels and trace its two terminal branches—anterior tibial into anterior compartment and posterior tibial into the posterior compartment of leg. Identify posterior tibial vessels and tibial nerve in fibrofatty tissue between the two long flexors of the leg.

Peroneal vessels are identified in the connective tissue of the deep transverse fascial septum. Study their origin, course and branches from the following text.

The nerve to popliteus deserves special mention. Being a branch of tibial nerve, it descends over the popliteus to reach its distal border. There, it supplies the muscle after winding around its distal border. It also supplies a branch to tibialis posterior muscle, both tibiofibular joints and interosseous membrane.

TABLE 9.3: Origin and insertion of deep muscles of posterior compartment of the leg.

Name	*Origin*	*Insertion*
1. **Popliteus**	Lateral surface of lateral condyle of ***femur***; origin is intracapsular Outer margin of ***lateral meniscus*** of the knee joint	Posterior surface of shaft of ***tibia*** above soleal line
2. **Flexor digitorum longus**	Upper 2/3rd of medial part of posterior surface of ***tibia*** below the soleal line	Bases of ***distal phalanges of lateral four toes***. Muscle ends in a tendon which divides into four slips, one for each of the lateral four toes. Each slip is attached to the plantar surface of base of the distal phalanx of the digit concerned
3. **Flexor hallucis longus**	Lower 3/4th area of the posterior surface of the ***fibula*** between medial crest and posterior border (except the lowest 2.5 cm) and interosseous membrane	Plantar surface of base of ***distal phalanx of big toe***
4. **Tibialis posterior**	Upper 2/4th of lateral part of posterior surface of ***tibia*** below the soleal line. Posterior surface of ***fibula*** in front of the medial crest and posterior surface of interosseous membrane	Tuberosity of ***navicular*** bone and ***other tarsal bones except talus***. Insertion is extended into 2nd, 3rd and 4th metatarsal bones at their bases

Plate 9.4: Flexor digitorum longus, flexor hallucis longus and tibialis posterior

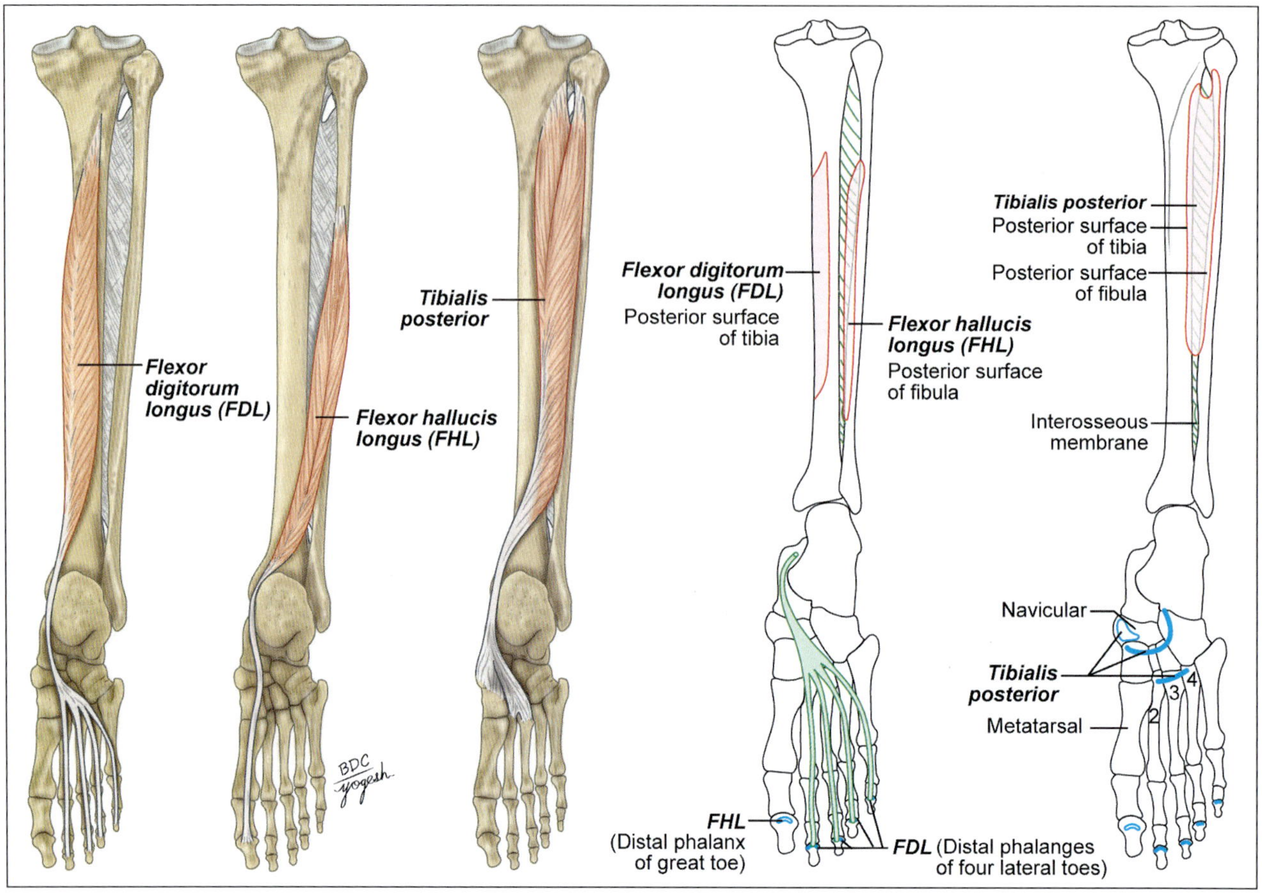

Flowchart 9.2: Deep muscles of posterior compartment of the leg

Deep muscles of posterior compartment of the leg

Supplied by tibial nerve

	Origin	Insertion	Actions
Popliteus	Popliteal groove at the lateral surface of lateral condyle of femur	Triangular area above the soleal line on tibia	Unlocking of knee Flexion of knee
Flexor digitorum longus	Upper 2/3rd of medial part of posterior surface of tibia, below the soleal line	Divide into 4 tendons Plantar surface of base of distal phalanx of 4 lateral toes	Plantar flexion of lateral 4 toes Plantar flexion of ankle Maintain longitudinal arches
Flexor hallucis longus	Lower 3/4th of posterior surface of fibula, behind medial crest Interosseous membrane	Base of distal phalanx of big toe	Plantar flexion of great toe and ankle Maintain longitudinal arches
Tibialis posterior	Upper 2/3rd of lateral part of posterior surface of tibia below soleal line Posterior surface of fibula Interosseous membrane	Tuberosity of navicular All tarsals except talus Bases of 2nd–4th metatarsals	Inversion of foot Plantar flexion of foot Maintain longitudinal arches

TABLE 9.4: Nerve supply and actions of deep muscles of posterior compartment of the leg

Name	*Nerve supply*	*Actions*
1. **Popliteus**	Tibial nerve	***Unlocks knee*** joint by lateral rotation of femur on tibia prior to flexion
2. **Flexor digitorum longus**	Tibial nerve	Flexes distal phalanges Plantar flexor of ankle joint Supports medial and lateral longitudinal arches of foot
3. **Flexor hallucis longus**	Tibial nerve	Flexes distal phalanx of big toe Plantar flexor of ankle joint Supports medial longitudinal arch of foot
4. **Tibialis posterior**	Tibial nerve	Plantar flexor of ankle joint Inverts foot at subtalar joint Supports medial longitudinal arch of foot

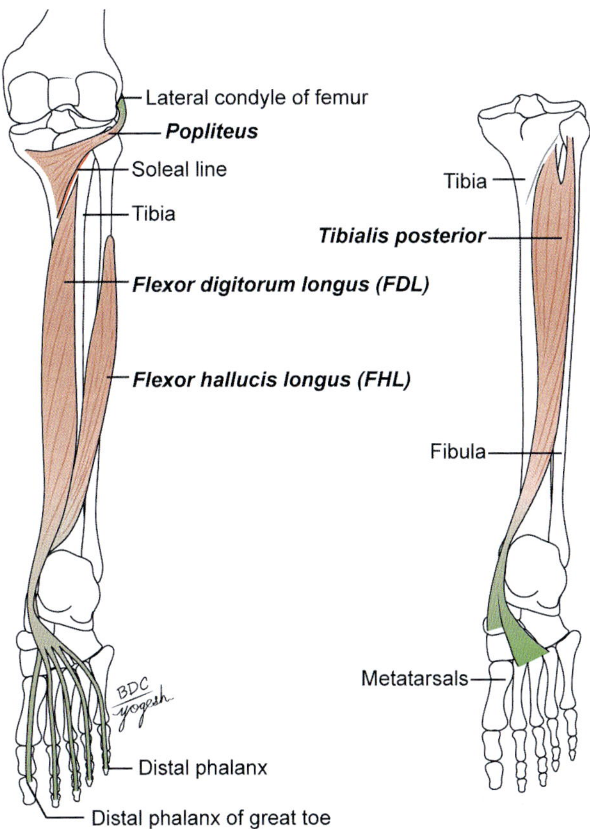

Fig. 9.6: Deep muscles of the back of the leg

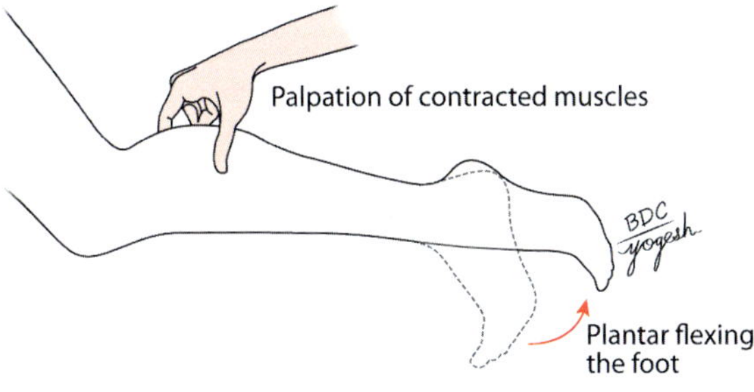

Fig. 9.7: Testing the deep muscles of the calf by plantar flexing the foot

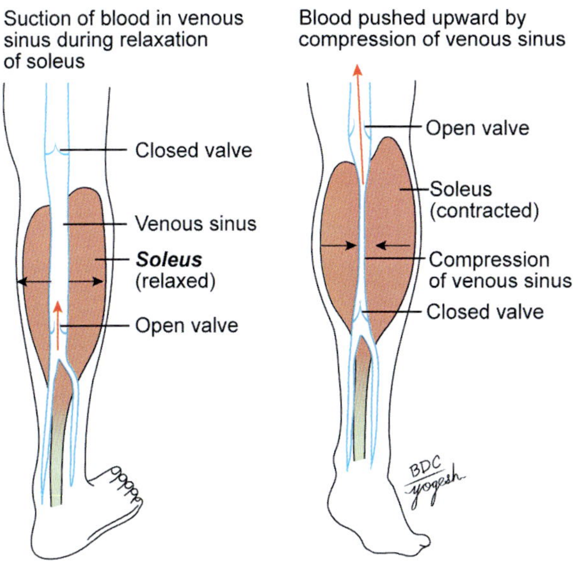

Fig. 9.8: Soleus as peripheral heart

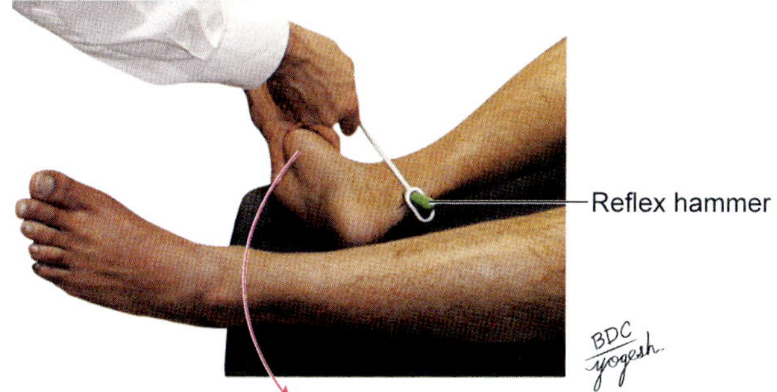

Fig. 9.9: Testing the tendo calcaneus

Competency:

AN19.2 Describe and demonstrate the origin, course, relations, branches (or tributaries) and termination of important nerves and vessels of back of leg.

POSTERIOR TIBIAL ARTERY

Beginning, Course and Termination

It is the main artery and is a *terminal branch of popliteal artery* (Plate 9.5, Fig. 9.10, Flowchart 9.3). It begins at the lower border of the popliteus, between the tibia and the fibula, deep to the gastrocnemius.

In the leg, it runs downwards and slightly medially, to reach the posteromedial side of the ankle, midway between the medial malleolus and the medial tubercle of the calcaneum.

It terminates deep to flexor retinaculum (and the origin of the abductor hallucis) by dividing into the *lateral* and *medial plantar arteries*.

Relations

Superficial

1. In the upper part of the leg, it lies deep to the gastrocnemius and the soleu. It enters the back of leg by passing deep to the *tendinous arch of the soleus*.
2. In the lower part of the leg, it is covered by skin and fasciae.
3. At the ankle, it lies deep to the flexor retinaculum and the abductor hallucis.

Deep

1. In the upper part of the leg, it lies on the tibialis posterior.
2. In the lower part of the leg, it lies on the flexor digitorum longus and on the tibia.
3. At the ankle, it lies directly on the capsule of the ankle joint between the flexor digitorum longus and the flexor hallucis longus.

The artery is *accompanied* by two venae comitantes and by the *tibial nerve*.

Branches

1. *Peroneal artery* is the largest branch of the posterior tibial artery.

Plate 9.5: Posterior tibial artery and tibial nerve

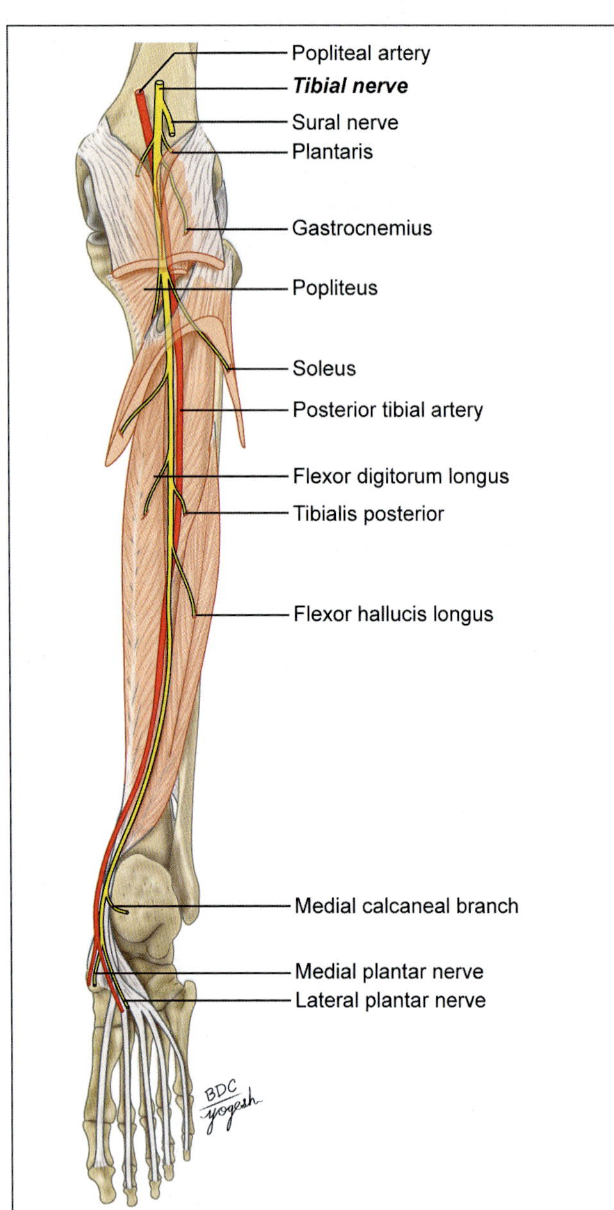

2. Several *muscular branches* are given off to muscles of the back of the leg.
3. *Nutrient artery* to tibia: It is the ***largest nutrient artery*** in the body.
4. *Anastomotic branches:*
   a. The ***circumflex fibular branch*** winds around the lateral side of the neck of the fibula to reach the front of the knee where it takes part in the anastomoses around the knee joint.
   b. A *communicating branch* forms an arch with a similar branch from the peroneal artery about 5 cm above the ankle.
   c. A *malleolar branch* anastomoses with other arteries over the medial malleolus.
   d. *Calcaneal branches* anastomose with other arteries in the region.
5. *Terminal branches:* These are the ***medial*** and ***lateral plantar arteries***.

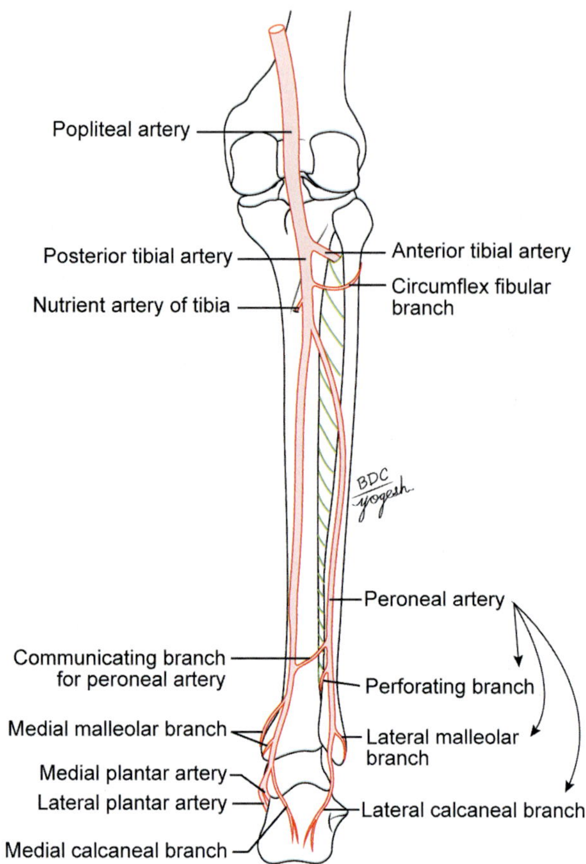

Fig. 9.10: Posterior tibial artery

Flowchart 9.3: Posterior tibial artery

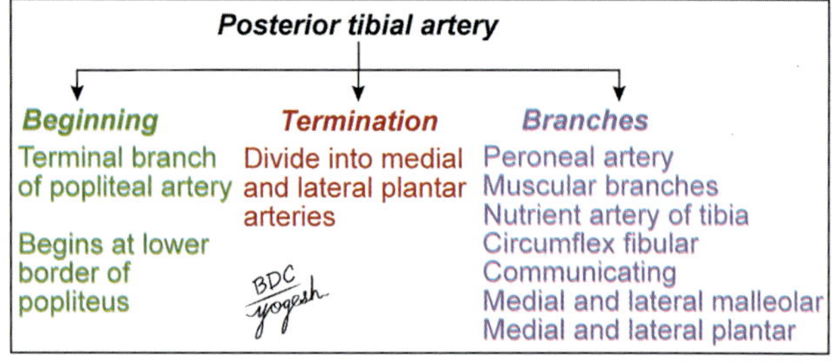

CLINICAL ANATOMY

The ***posterior tibial pulse*** can be felt against the calcaneum about 2 cm below and behind the medial malleolus (Fig. 9.11). It is palpated in doubtful cases of intermittent claudication where a person gets cramps and severe pain in calf muscles due to lack of blood supply.

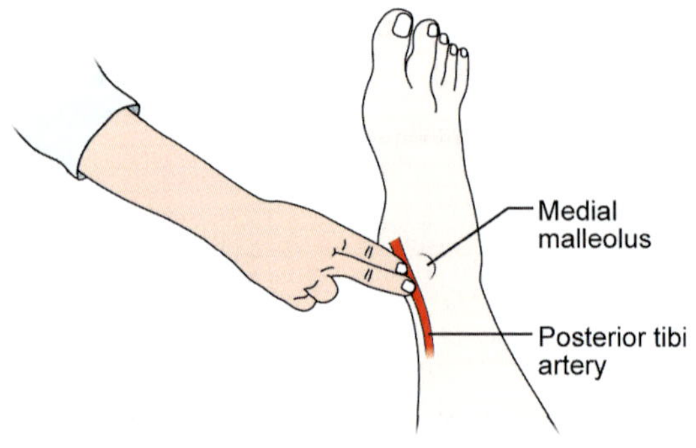

Fig. 9.11: Site of palpation of the posterior tibial artery

PERONEAL ARTERY

Beginning, Course and Termination

This is the largest branch of the posterior tibial artery. It supplies the posterior and lateral compartments of the leg (Fig. 9.10).

It begins 2.5 cm below the lower border of the popliteus.

It runs obliquely towards the fibula, and descends along the medial crest of the fibula, accompanied by the nerve to the flexor hallucis longus. It passes behind the inferior tibiofibular and ankle joints, medial to peroneal tendons. It terminates by dividing into a number of *lateral calcanean branches* (Fig. 9.10).

Branches

1. *Muscular branches*
2. *Nutrient artery* to the fibula
3. *Anastomotic branches:*
   a. The *communicating branch* anastomoses with a similar branch from the posterior tibial artery, about 5 cm above the lower end of the tibia.
   b. The *large perforating branch* pierces the interosseous membrane 4 cm above the ankle.
   c. *Lateral malleolar branches*
   d. The *calcanean branches* join the lateral malleolar network.

Note: The perforating branch of the peroneal artery may reinforce, or even replace the dorsalis pedis artery.

TIBIAL NERVE

Tibial nerve is the longest terminal branch of the sciatic nerve (Plate 9.5, Fig. 9.12).

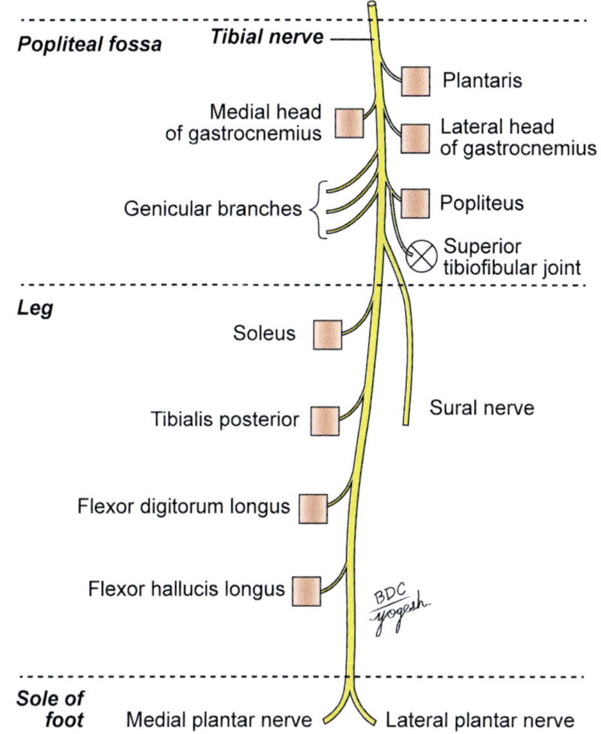

Fig. 9.12: Branches of tibial nerve

Root value: L4, L5, S1, S2, S3. Tibial nerve arises from sciatic nerve at the superior angle of popliteal fossa and runs vertically downward up to the inferior angle for popliteal fossa.

Course

The course and relations of the tibial nerve in the leg are similar to those of the posterior tibial artery. Like the artery, the tibial nerve also terminates by dividing into the medial plantar and lateral plantar nerves.

Branches

1. *Muscular branches* to tibialis posterior, flexor digitorum longus, flexor hallucis longus and deep part of soleus.
2. *Cutaneous branches*: Medial calcaneal nerve pierces the flexor retinaculum and supplies the skin over the heel.
3. *Articular branches* to ankle joint.
4. *Terminal branches*: Medial and lateral plantar nerves.

CLINICAL ANATOMY

- In case of injury to tibial nerve, 'patient will be unable to plantarflex his ankle. There will be clawing of toes due to paralysis of intrinsic muscles of sole'.
- High heels for long periods cause change in posture. Knees are excessively bent, with lumbar vertebrae pushed forwards. There is a lot of stress on the muscles of back and those of the calf. So many fashionable ladies wear high heels for short time and change to flat ones soon (Fig. 9.13).

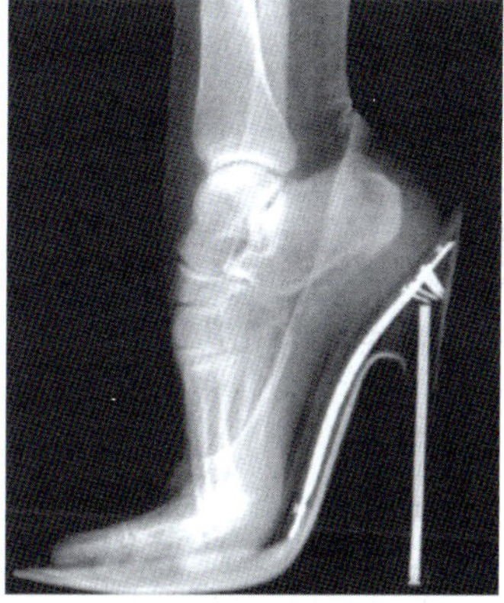

Fig. 9.13: Smart high heels

Video 2.9 Back of Leg: Muscles of the back of leg, flexor retinaculum of ankle.

Facts to Remember

- Triceps surae = Gastrocnemius + Soleus
- Soleus acts as the *peripheral heart*, as it pushes the venous blood upwards
- Soleus acts like first gear (workhouse of the plantar flexion) while gastrocnemius acts like second and third gears during walking.

- Tendo calcaneus is the strongest tendon in the body.
- All the muscles of back of leg/calf are supplied by the tibial nerve.
- Posterior tibial artery is palpated between medial malleolus and calcaneus under the flexor retinaculum.
- Posterior tibial artery ends by dividing into medial and lateral plantar arteries.
- Tendo calcaneus is the strongest tendon in the body.
- Nutrient artery to the tibia is the largest nutrient artery of the body.
- Tendon of plantaris is the fresheman's nerve.
- Sural nerve is the most commonly used for nerve graft.

BDC's Anatomy *e*-book

1. Vein of Giacomini
2. Additional features of superficial muscles of back of leg
3. Fresheman's nerve
4. Additional features of superficial muscles of back of leg
5. Additional features of deep muscles of back of leg
6. Trigger toe
7. Further reading
8. Viva voce questions

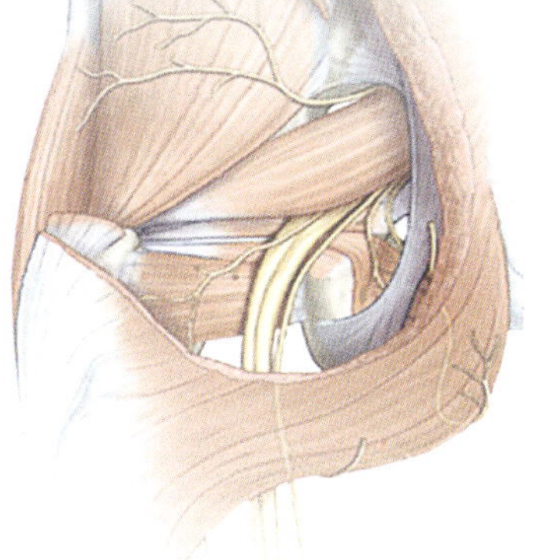

Chapter

10

Sole of Foot

The structure of the sole is similar to that of the palm. The skin, superficial fascia, deep fascia, muscles, vessels and nerves are all comparable in these two homologous parts. However, unlike the hand, the foot is an organ of support and locomotion. Accordingly, the structures of the foot get modified. The great toe has lost its mobility and its power of prehension; the lesser four toes are markedly reduced in size; and the tarsal bones and the first metatarsal are enlarged to form a broad base for better support. The arches of the foot serve as elastic springs for efficient walking, running, jumping and supporting the body weight.

SKIN

The skin of the sole, like that of the palm is:

1. Thick for protection
2. Firmly adherent to the underlying plantar aponeurosis
3. Creased
4. Hairless.

These features increase the efficiency of the grip of the sole on the ground.

FASCIAE

SUPERFICIAL FASCIA

The superficial fascia of the sole is fibrous and dense.

Fibrous bands bind the skin to the deep fascia or *plantar aponeurosis*, and divide the subcutaneous fat into small tight compartments which serve as water-cushions and reinforce the spring-effect of the arches of the foot during walking, running and jumping.

The fascia is very thick and dense over the weight-bearing points. It contains cutaneous nerves and vessels. Thickened bands of superficial fascia stretch across the roots of the toes forming the ***superficial transverse metatarsal ligaments***.

Cutaneous Nerves of Sole of Foot

The skin is mainly supplied by three cutaneous nerves (Figs 10.1 and 10.2). The nerves are:

1. Medial calcaneal branches of the tibial nerve to the posterior and medial portions.
2. Branches from the medial plantar nerve to the larger, anteromedial portion including the medial 3½ toes.
3. Branches from the lateral plantar nerve to the smaller anterolateral portion including the lateral 1½ toes.
4. Small areas on medial and lateral sides are nervated by saphenous and sural nerves.

These nerves are derived from spinal nerves L4, 5 and S1. In eliciting the plantar reflex, the area supplied by segment S1 is stimulated (Fig. 10.2).

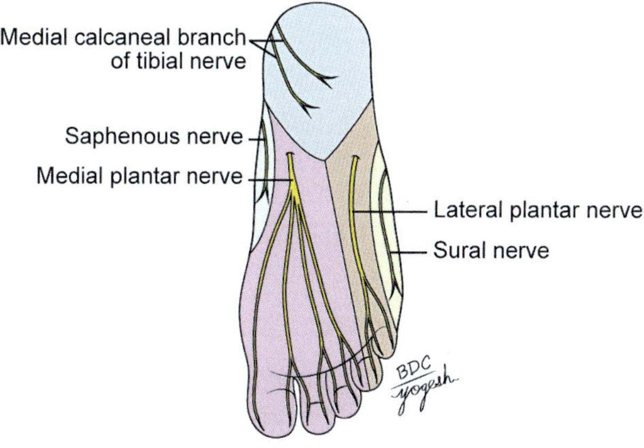

Fig. 10.1: Cutaneous nerves supplying the sole

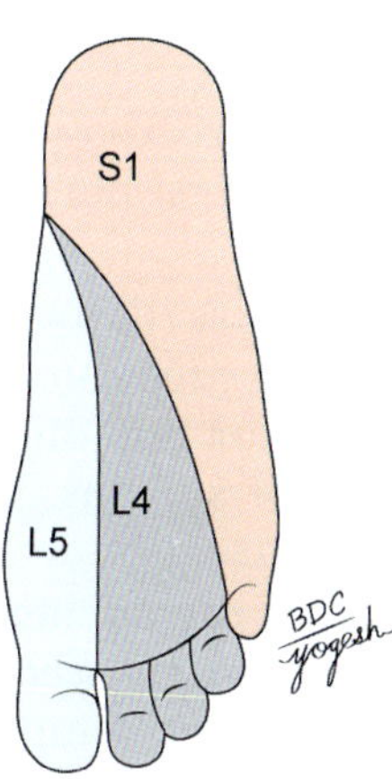

Fig. 10.2: Dermatomes on the sole

DISSECTION

Give the incision from back of heel through the root to the tip of the middle toe. Reflect the skin and fatty superficial fascia to each side of the sole. Look for cutaneous nerves and vessels.

The deep fascia on the plantar aspect of toes is thickened to form fibrous flexor sheaths; proximally, it is continuous with the *plantar aponeurosis* (Plate 10.1).

Identify the cutaneous branches from medial and lateral plantar arteries and nerves on the respective sides of plantar aponeurosis. Between the five distal slips of the aponeurosis, trace the digital nerves and vessels from medial plantar nerve and vessels for 3½ medial toes and from lateral plantar nerve and vessels for lateral 1½ toes.

Divide the plantar aponeurosis 4 cm distal to the heel. Reflect the cut ends both proximally and distally. This exposes the three muscles of the 1st layer of sole. Medial plantar nerve and vessels are easily visualised close to the medial border of sole. Stems of lateral plantar nerve and vessels including its superficial division are also seen.

Plate 10.1: Plantar aponeurosis

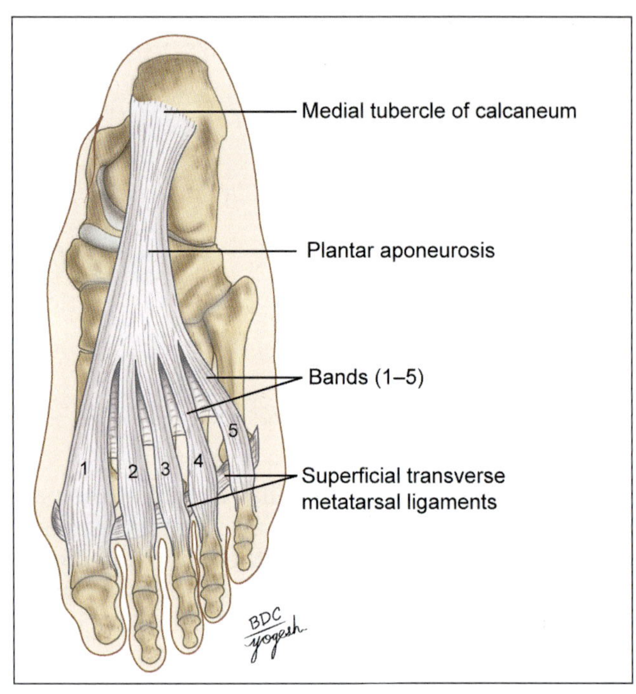

DEEP FASCIA

The deep fascia of the sole is specialized to form:

1. Plantar aponeurosis (Plate 10.1)
2. Deep transverse metatarsal ligaments (Plate 10.1)
3. Fibrous flexor sheaths (Plate 10.2).

Plantar Aponeurosis

The *deep fascia* covering the sole is thick in the centre and thin at the sides. The thickened central part is known as the *plantar aponeurosis* (Plate 10.1, Fig. 10.3, Flowchart 10.1).

Features

1. The aponeurosis is triangular in shape.
2. Its *apex* is proximal. It is attached to the medial tubercle of the calcaneum, proximal to the attachment of the flexor digitorum brevis.
3. Its *base* is distal. It is divided into five processes near the heads of the metatarsal bones. The digital nerves and vessels pass through the intervals between the processes. Each process splits, opposite the metatarsophalangeal joints, into a *superficial and a deep slip*.
   - The superficial slip is attached to dermis of skin.
   - The deep slip divides into two parts, which embrace the flexor tendons, and blend with the fibrous flexor sheaths and with the deep transverse metatarsal ligaments.
4. From the margins of the aponeurosis, lateral and medial *vertical intermuscular septa* pass deeply, and divide the sole into three compartments. Thinner *transverse septa* arise from the vertical septa and divide the muscles of the sole into four layers.

Plate 10.2: Fibrous flexor sheath

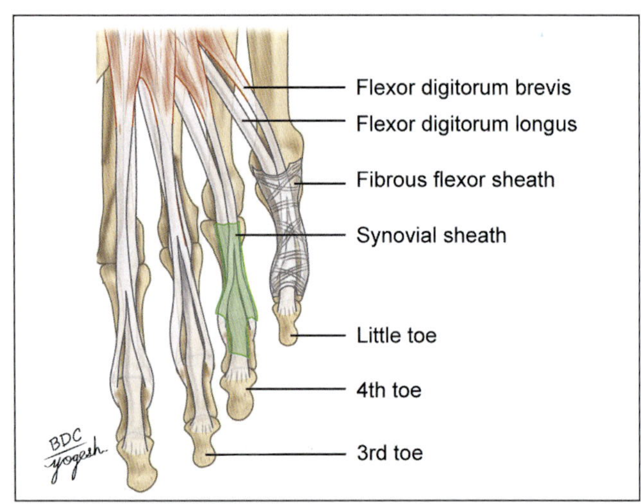

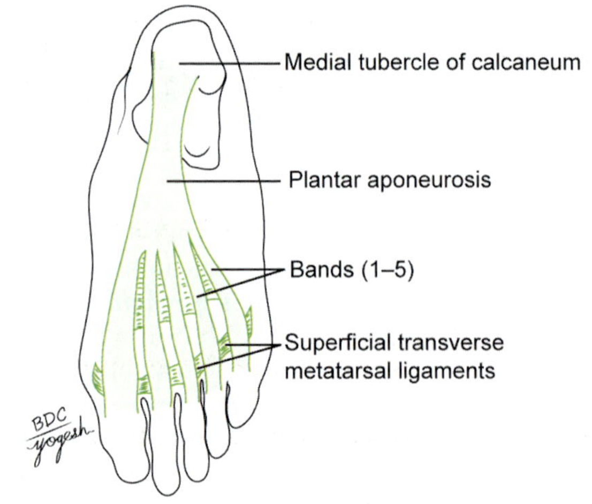

Fig. 10.3: Plantar aponeurosis

Flowchart 10.1: Plantar aponeurosis

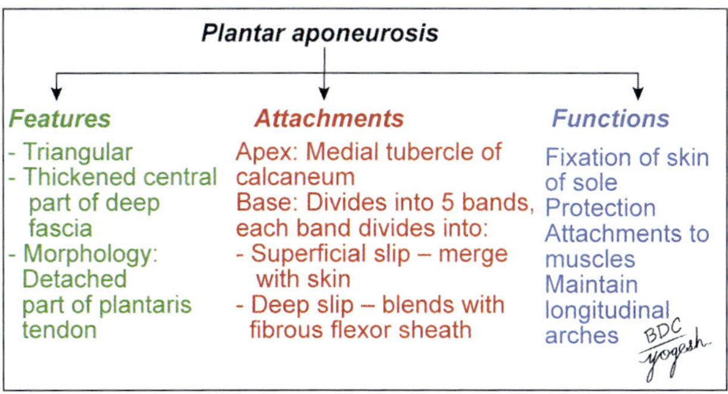

Functions

1. It fixes the skin of the sole.
2. It protects deeper structures.
3. It helps in maintaining the longitudinal arches of the foot.
4. It gives origin to muscles of the 1st layer of the sole.

Note: Plantar aponeurosis represents the distal part of the *plantaris* which has become separated from the rest of the muscle during evolution because of the enlargement of the heel.

The plantar aponeurosis differs from the palmar aponeurosis in giving off an additional process to the great toe, which restricts the movements of the latter.

Deep Transverse Metatarsal Ligaments

These are four short, flat bands that connect the plantar ligaments of the adjoining metatarsophalangeal joints. They are related dorsally to the interossei and ventrally to the lumbricals and the digital vessels and nerves.

Fibrous Flexor Sheaths

These are made up of the deep fascia of the toes. Their structure is similar to that of the fibrous flexor sheaths of the fingers. They retain the flexor tendons in position during flexion of the toes (Plate 10.2).

CLINICAL ANATOMY

Plantar fasciitis occurs in policemen due to stretching of the plantar aponeurosis. This results in pain in the heel region, especially during standing.

Calcaneal spur (heel spur): It is a small calcified bone extension on the inferior aspect of calcaneum or at the site of attachment of tendo calcaneum.

Competency:

AN19.7 Explain the anatomical basis of plantar fasciitis.

MUSCLES OF SOLE

The muscles of the sole (18 intrinsic muscles and 4 extrinsic muscles) are grouped into four layers from superficial to deep as follows:

First layer: This layer covers the whole of the sole. It includes flexor digitorum brevis, abductor hallucis, and abductor digiti minimi.

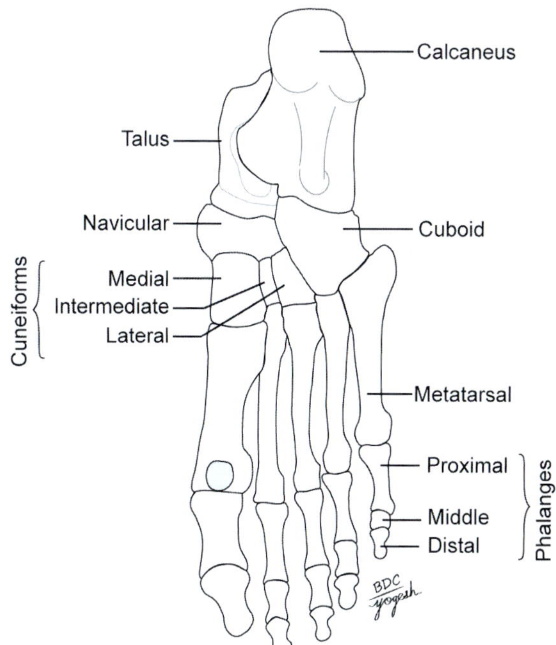

Fig. 10.4: Plantar aspect of skeleton of the foot

Second layer: It includes:

Intrinsic muscles: Flexor digitorum accessories and four lumbricals.

Extrinsic muscles: Tendons of flexor digitorum longus and flexor hallucis longus.

Third layer: The muscles of this layer are confined to metatarsal region only. They are flexor hallucis brevis, flexor digiti minimi brevis, and adductor hallucis.

Fourth layer: The muscles fill up the intermuscular space. They include:

Intrinsic muscles: Three palmar interossei and four dorsal interossei.

Extrinsic muscles: Tendon of tibialis posterior and tendon of peroneus longus.

For revision and understanding, Fig. 10.4, showing the plantar aspect of the skeleton of the foot.

Muscles of First Layer

- The muscles of the first layer are the *flexor digitorum brevis*, the *abductor hallucis*, and the *abductor digiti minimi* (Plate 10.3, Fig. 10.5, Table 10.1).
- **Flexor digitorum brevis** muscle lies deep to the plantar aponeurosis. Its insertion is similar to that of the flexor digitorum superficialis of the hand. The tendon of the flexor digitorum longus (for that digit) passes through the gap between the two slips at the insertion of flexor digitorum brevis.
- **Abductor hallucis** lies along the medial border of foot and covers the origin of the plantar vessels and nerves. Its tendon fuses with the medial portion of the tendon of the flexor hallucis brevis.
- **Abductor digiti minimi** lies along the lateral border of foot (Fig. 10.4b). Its tendon fuses with the tendon of the flexor digiti minimi brevis.

Plate 10.3: Muscles of first and second layers of sole of foot

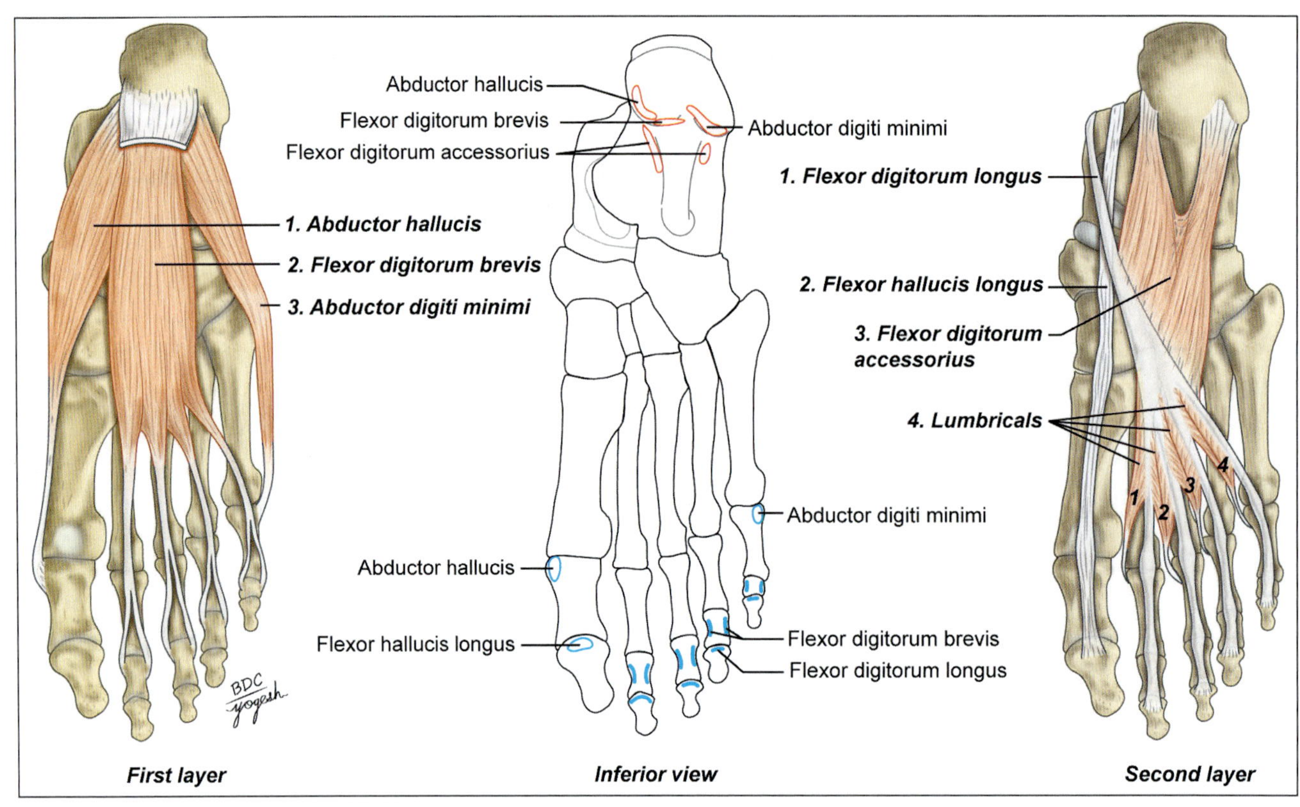

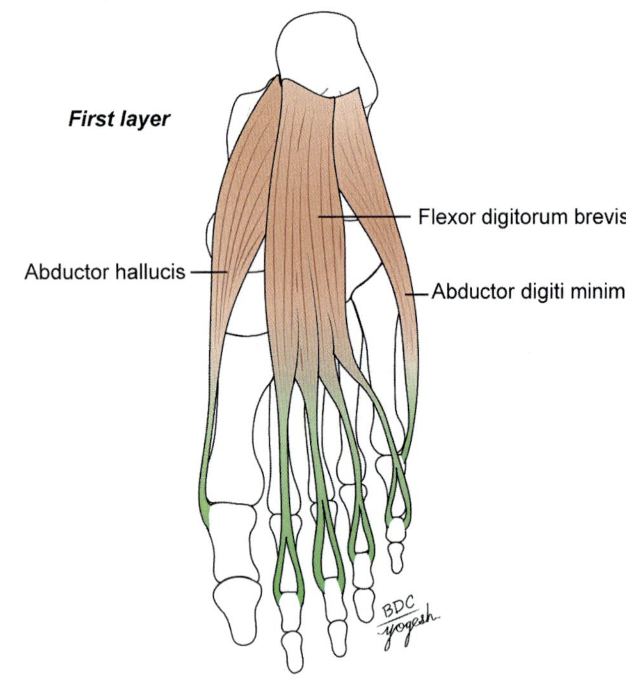

Fig. 10.5: Muscles of first layer of sole

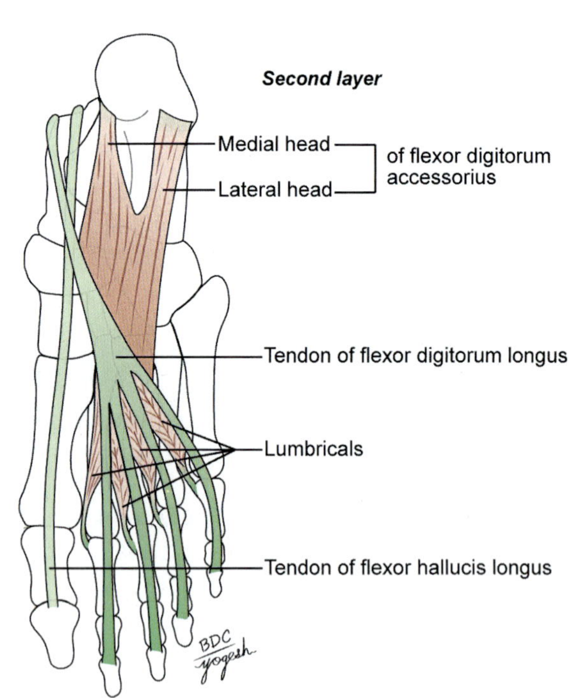

Fig. 10.6: Muscles and tendons of second layer of sole

Muscles of Second Layer

- The contents of second layer are the tendons of the flexor digitorum longus, and of the flexor hallucis longus; and the flexor digitorum accessorius and lumbrical muscles (Plate 10.3, Fig. 10.6, Table 10.2).
- *Flexor digitorum longus* is a muscle of calf.
- *Flexor digitorum accessorius* are so-called because it is accessory to the flexor digitorum longus.
- *Lumbricals* are four of them, numbered from medial to lateral side. They arise from the tendons of the flexor digitorum longus. The first lumbrical is unipennate, and the others are bipennate.

TABLE 10.1: Muscles of first layer of sole

Muscle	Origin	Insertion	Nerve supply	Actions
Flexor digitorum brevis	Medial tubercle of calcaneum Plantar aponeurosis Medial and lateral intermuscular septa	It ends in 4 tendons for the lateral 4 toes. Opposite the base of the proximal phalanx, each tendon divides into 2 slips that are inserted into the margins of the *middle phalanges of 2nd to 5th toe*	Medial plantar nerve	Flexion of the toes at the proximal interphalangeal joints and metatarsophalangeal joints of 2nd to 5th toe
Abductor hallucis	Medial tubercle of calcaneum Flexor retinaculum	It is inserted into the medial side of the base of the *proximal phalanx of the great toe*	Medial plantar nerve	Abduction of the great toe
Abductor digiti minimi	Medial and lateral tubercles of calcaneum	It is inserted into the lateral side of the base of the proximal phalanx of the little toe	Main trunk of lateral plantar nerve	Abduction of the little toe

TABLE 10.2: Muscles and tendons of second layer of sole

Muscle	Origin	Insertion	Nerve supply	Actions
Flexor digitorum longus (FDL) (muscle of calf)	Upper 2/3rd of the medial part of the posterior surface of tibia below the soleal line	The muscle divides into four tendons. Each is inserted to the plantar surface of *distal phalanx of 2nd to 5th toe*	Tibial nerve	Plantar flexion of lateral 4 toes Plantar flexion of ankle Maintains medial longitudinal arch
Flexor digitorum accessorius	***Medial head*** (large and fleshy): from the medial concave surface of the calcaneum ***Lateral head*** (smaller and tendinous): from the calcaneum in front of the lateral tubercle. The two heads unite at an acute angle	Lateral side of the tendon of the flexor digitorum longus	Main trunk of lateral plantar nerve	Straightens the pull of the long flexor tendons Flexes the toes through the long tendons
Lumbricals (4 in number, numbered from medial to lateral side. The 1st lumbrical is unipennate, and the others are bipennate)	Arise from the tendons of the flexor digitorum longus (FDL) ***1st lumbrical***: from medial side of 1st tendon of FDL ***2nd to 4th lumbricals***: from adjacent sides of corresponding tendons of FDL	Their tendons pass forwards on the medial sides of the metatarsophalangeal joints of the lateral 4 toes, and then dorsally for insertion into the extensor expansion and bases of proximal phalanges	1st by the medial plantar nerve 2nd–4th by the deep branch of lateral plantar nerve	Maintain extension of the digits at the interphalangeal joints so that in walking and running the toes do not buckle under
Flexor hallucis longus (muscle of calf)	Lower 3/4th of the posterior surface of fibula except lowest 2.5 cm and adjoining interosseous membrane	Plantar surface of the base of the distal phalanx of the great toe	Tibial nerve	Plantar flexor of the big toe Plantar flexor of ankle joint Maintains medial longitudinal arch

Muscles of Third Layer

- The third layer of the sole contains three muscles. These are the *flexor hallucis brevis*, the *flexor digiti minimi brevis*, and the *adductor hallucis* (Plate 10.4, Fig. 10.7, Table 10.3).
- *Flexor hallucis brevis* covers the plantar surface of the 1st metatarsal bone.
- *Flexor digiti minimi brevis* lies along the fifth metatarsal bone.

Plate 10.4: Muscles of third layer of sole of foot

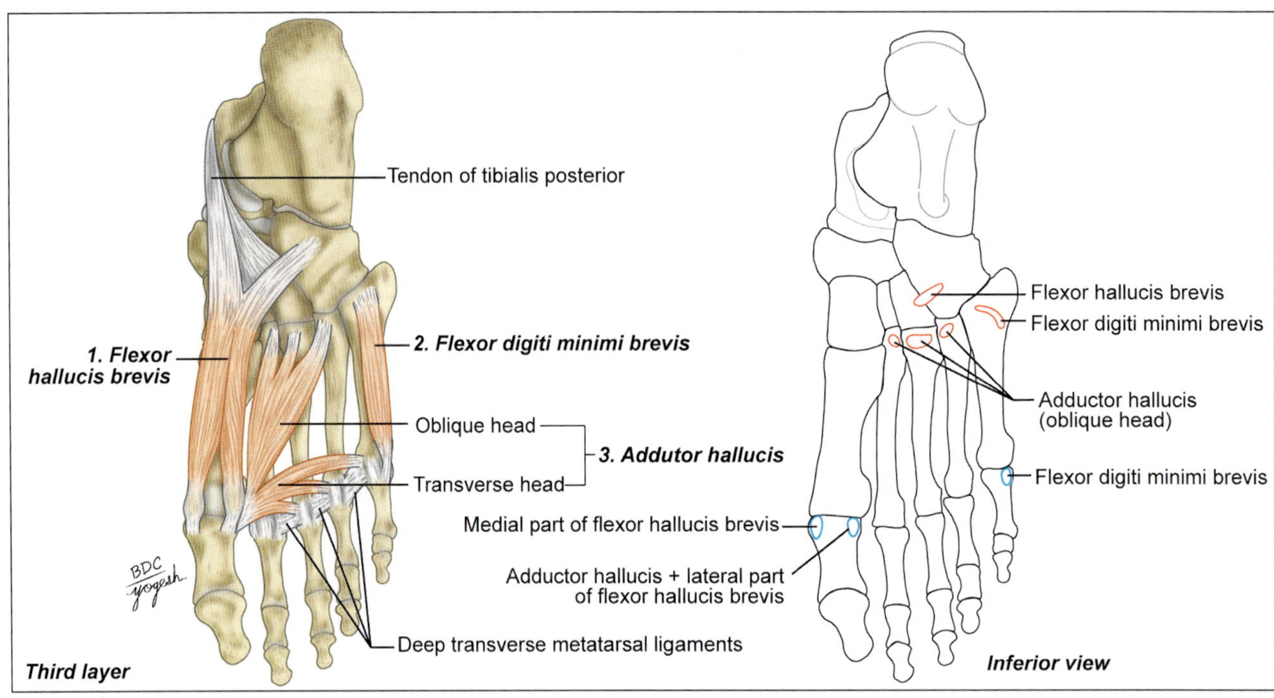

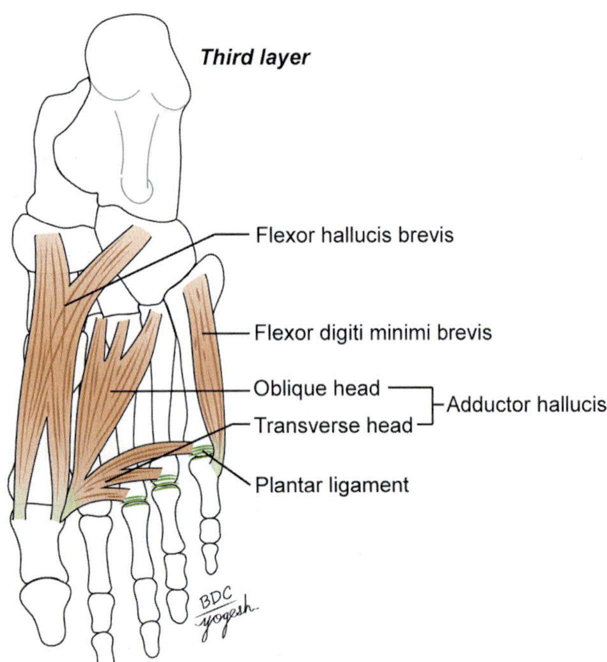

Fig. 10.7: Muscles of third layer of sole

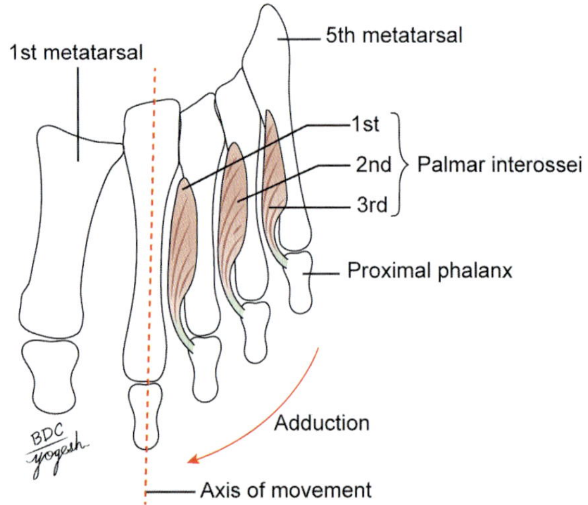

Fig 10.8: The plantar interossei

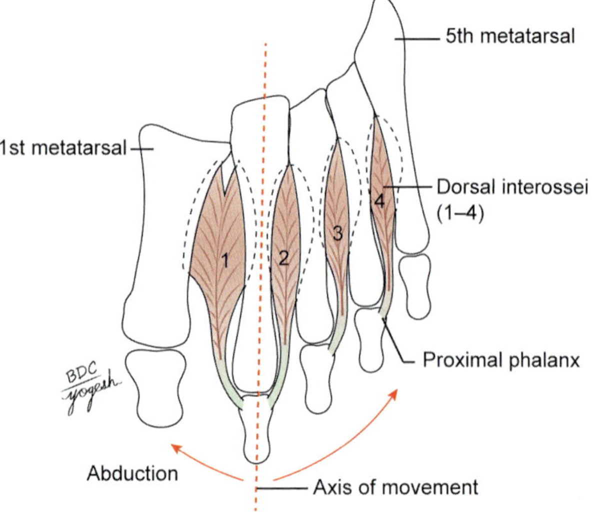

Fig 10.9: The dorsal interossei

Muscles of Fourth Layer

The structures present in the fourth layer of the sole are the *interosseous muscles*, and the *tendons* of the *tibialis posterior* and of the *peroneus longus* (Figs 10.8 to 10.10, Plate 10.5, Table 10.4).

Interosseous Muscles of the Foot

These are small muscles placed between the metatarsal bones. There are three plantar and four dorsal interossei.

TABLE 10.3: Muscles of third layer of sole

Muscle	Origin	Insertion	Nerve supply	Actions
Flexor hallucis brevis	Arises by a Y-shaped tendon: ***Lateral limb:*** from the medial part of the plantar surface of the cuboid bone ***Medial limb*** is a direct continuation of the tendon of tibialis posterior into the foot	The muscle splits into medial and lateral parts, each of which ends in a tendon. Each tendon is inserted into the corresponding side of the base of the *proximal phalanx of the great toe*	Medial plantar nerve	Flexes the proximal phalanx at the metatarsophalangeal joint of the great toe
Adductor hallucis	It arises by two heads: Large ***oblique head:*** from the bases of the 2nd, 3rd, and 4th metatarsals Small ***transverse head:*** from deep transverse metatarsal ligaments and plantar metatarsophalangeal ligaments of 3rd, 4th, and 5th toes	On the lateral side of the base of the *proximal phalanx of the big toe*, in common with the lateral tendon of the flexor hallucis brevis	Lateral plantar nerve (deep branch)	Adductor of great toe towards the 2nd toe Maintains transverse arches of the foot
Flexor digiti minimi brevis	Base of the 5th metatarsal bone Sheath of the tendon of the peroneus longus	Into the lateral side of the base of the proximal phalanx of the little toe	Lateral plantar nerve (superficial branch)	Flexes the proximal phalanx at the metatarsophalangeal joint of the little toe

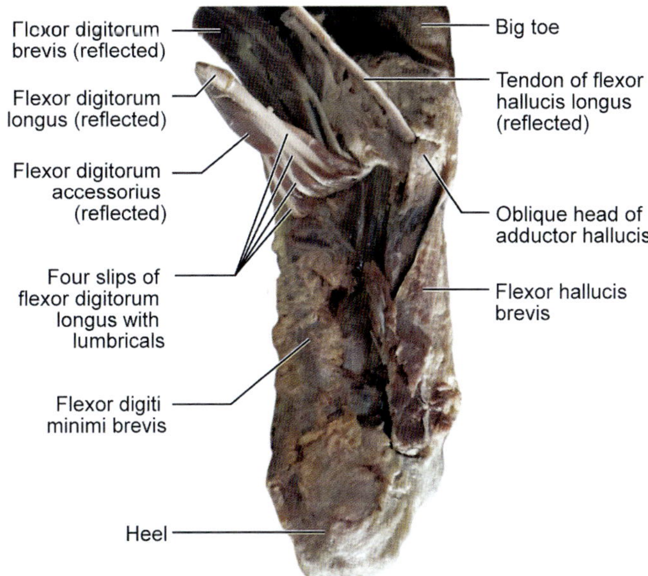

Fig. 10.10: Some muscles of 1st–3rd layers of sole

DISSECTION

Cut through the flexor digitorum brevis near its middle taking care to preserve the underlying lateral plantar nerve and vessels. Reflect the distal part distally till the toes.

Cut through abductor hallucis lying along medial border of foot. Identify plantar vessels and nerves deep to this muscle.

Identify and detach the abductor digiti minimi and identify the lateral head of the flexor digitorum accessories till its insertion into the tendon of flexor digitorum longus.

Trace the long flexor tendons through the fibrous flexor sheath into the base of distal phalanges of toes.

Follow the lumbricals to their insertion into the base of the proximal phalanx and into the extensor expansion of the dorsum of toes. Study the muscles of second layer comprising the long flexor tendons and associated muscles.

Cut through both the long flexor tendons (flexor hallucis longus and flexor digitorum longus) and flexor digitorum accessorius, where all three are united to each other. Reflect the ends proximally and distally to reveal the muscles of third layer of sole

Separate flexor hallucis brevis and oblique head of adductor hallucis from their origin and reflect them distally.

Preserve the plantar arch and deep plantar nerve. Look for sesamoid bones at the insertion of flexor hallucis brevis.

Reflect the transverse head of adductor hallucis medially. On cutting the deep transverse metatarsal ligament on both sides of second toe, tendons of interossei muscles are recognised.

Detach the flexor digiti minimi brevis from its origin and reflect it forwards. This will show the laterally situated interossei muscles.

Identify and examine the attachment of tendon of tibialis posterior on the medial side of foot.

Trace the course of tendon of peroneus longus through the groove in the cuboid bone across the sole to its insertions into lateral sides of base of first metatarsal and medial cuneiform bone.

After studying the muscles of the third layer, detach them from their origins towards their insertions. The muscles of the fourth layer are visualised.

Plate 10.5: Interossei muscles

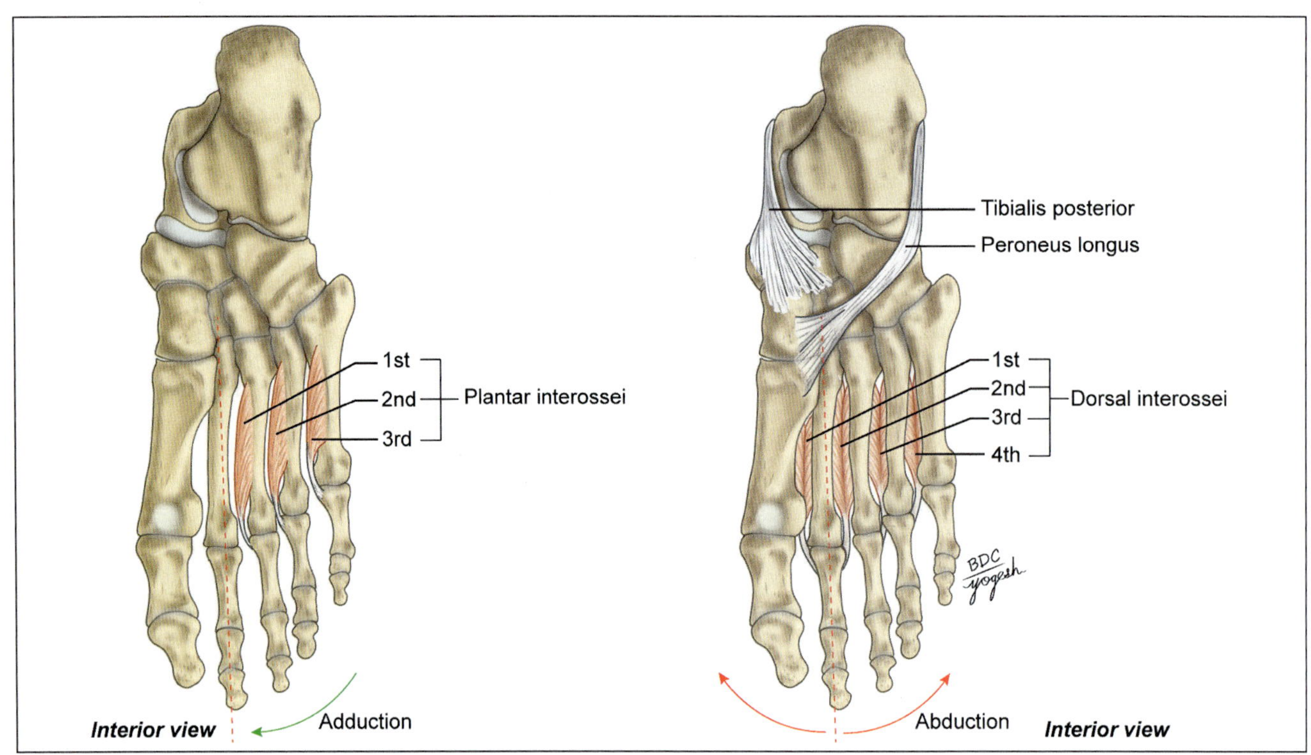

TABLE 10.4: Muscles of the fourth layer of sole

Muscle	*Origin*	*Insertion*	*Nerve supply*	*Actions*
Plantar interossei Three, small, unipennate muscles. Tendons pass on medial sides of 3rd, 4th and 5th toes	Bases and medial sides of 3rd, 4th and 5th metatarsals	Medial sides of bases of proximal phalanges and dorsal digital/extensor expansions of 3rd, 4th and 5th toes	Lateral plantar nerve	Adductors of 3rd, 4th and 5th toes Flexor of metatarso-phalangeal and extensor of inter-phalangeal joints of 3rd, 4th and 5th toes
Dorsal interossei Four bipennate, muscles. Fills up gaps between metatarsals	Adjacent sides of metatarsal bones	Bases of proximal phalanges and dorsal digital expansion of toes 1st on medial side of 2nd toe 2nd on lateral side of 2nd toe 3rd on lateral side of 3rd toe 4th on lateral side of 4th toe	Lateral plantar nerve	Abductors of 2nd to 5th toes
Tibialis posterior	Posterior surfaces of tibia and fibula	Tuberosity of navicular and all tarsal bones (except talus)	Tibial nerve	Plantar flexor of ankle
Peroneus longus	Upper part of lateral surface of fibula	Base of 1st metatarsal	Superficial peroneal nerve	Evertor of foot

PLANTAR VESSELS AND NERVES

1. The chief arteries of the sole are the medial and lateral plantar arteries. They are terminal branches of the posterior tibial artery (Plate 10.6).
2. The chief nerves of the sole are the medial and lateral plantar nerves. They are terminal branches of the tibial nerve (Plate 10.6).
3. These arteries and nerves begin deep into the flexor retinaculum. The posterior tibial artery divides into the medial and lateral plantar arteries, a little higher than the division of tibial nerve. As a result, the arteries are closer to the margins of the sole than the corresponding nerves.
4. The medial plantar vessels and nerve lie between the abductor hallucis and the flexor digitorum brevis.

Plate 10.6: Nerve and arteries of sole of foot

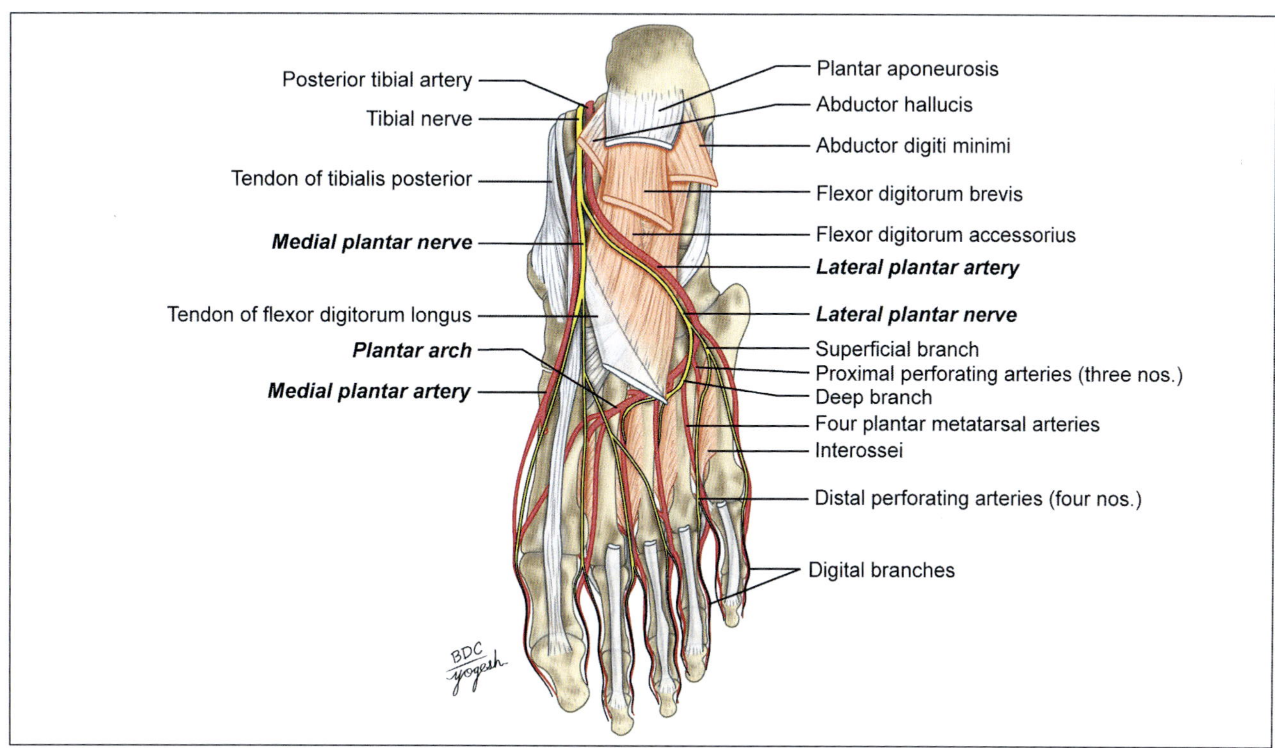

5. The lateral plantar vessels and nerve run obliquely towards the base of the 5th metatarsal bone, between the 1st and 2nd layers of the sole. Here, the artery turns medially and becomes continuous with the plantar arch. This arch lies between the 3rd and 4th layers of the sole. The plantar arch is accompanied by the deep branch of the lateral plantar nerve.

MEDIAL PLANTAR NERVE

Medial plantar nerve is the larger terminal branch of the tibial nerve (Plate 10.6, Fig. 10.11, Table 10.5, Flowchart 10.2). It passes forwards between *abductor hallucis* and *flexor digitorum brevis* and divides into its branches.

Root value: L4, 5, S1.

TABLE 10.5: Motor innervation of medial and lateral plantar nerves

Medial plantar nerve	*Lateral plantar nerve*
Abductor hallucis Flexor digitorum brevis Flexor hallucis brevis	*Main trunk* • Flexor digitorum accessories • Abductor digiti minimi
First lumbrical	*Superficial branch* • Flexor digiti minimi brevis • 3rd plantar interosseous • 4th dorsal interosseous *Deep branch* • 2nd, 3rd and 4th lumbricals • 1st, 2nd plantar interossei • 1st, 2nd and 3rd dorsal interossei • Adductor hallucis

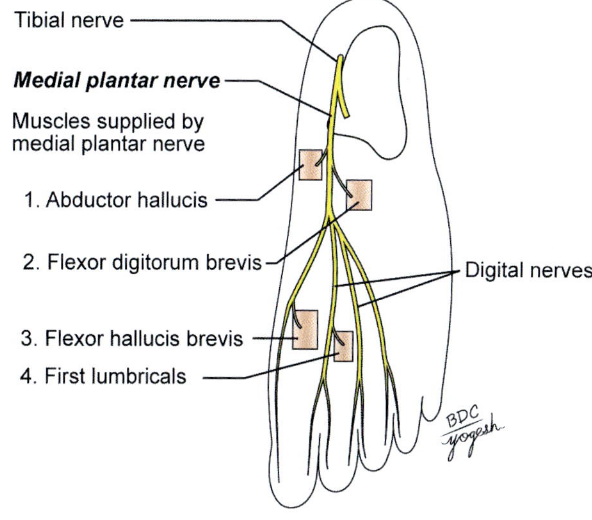

Fig. 10.11: Medial plantar nerve

Flowchart 10.2: Medial plantar nerve

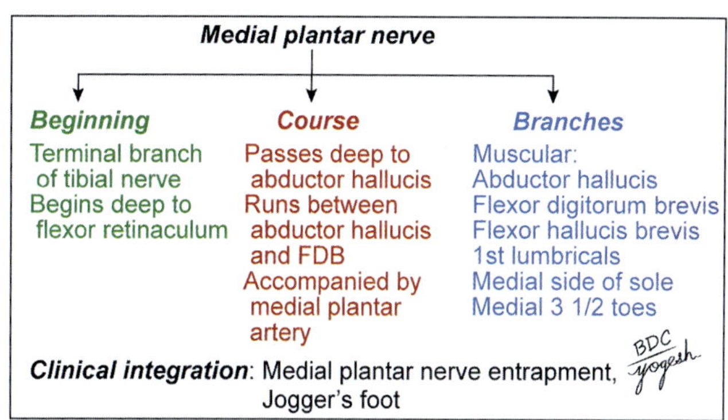

(FDB: Flexor digitorum accessorius)

Branches

Muscular branches supply four muscles:

1. Abductor hallucis
2. Flexor digitorum brevis.
3. Flexor hallucis brevis receives a branch from the 1st digital nerve.
4. The 1st lumbrical muscle receives a branch from the 2nd digital nerve.

Cutaneous branches (four digital nerves) supply the skin of the medial part of the sole, and of the medial 3½ toes. Each digital nerve gives off a dorsal branch, which supplies structures around the nail of the digit concerned.

Articular branches supply joints of the tarsus and metatarsus.

CLINICAL ANATOMY

- A neuroma may be formed on the branch of medial plantar nerve between 3rd and 4th metatarsal bones. It is called ***Morton's neuroma***. This causes pain between 3rd and 4th metatarsals. It may be also due to pressure on digital nerve between 3rd and 4th metatarsals.
- Any of the digital nerves, especially the one in the 3rd interdigital cleft may develop neuroma. This is a painful condition.
- ***Jogger's foot***: If medial plantar nerve gets pressed deep to flexor retinaculum, there is burning, numbness and tingling on the medial side of the sole in the region of tuberosity of navicular.

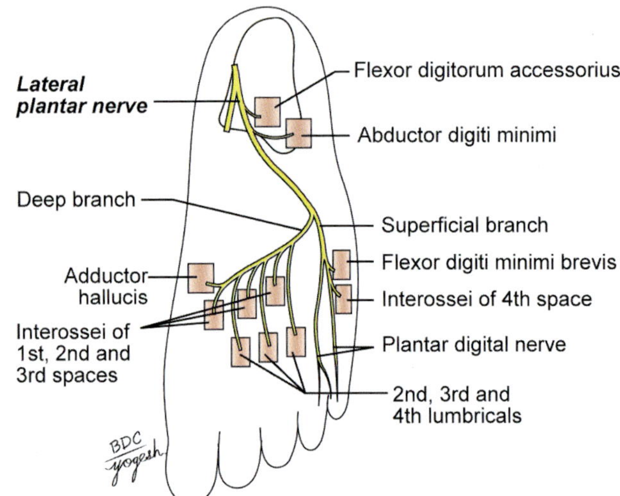

Fig. 10.12: Lateral plantar nerve

Flowchart 10.3: Lateral plantar nerve

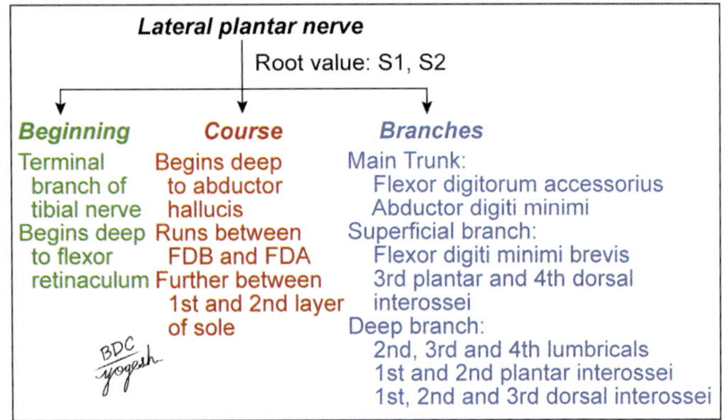

LATERAL PLANTAR NERVE

Lateral plantar nerve is the smaller terminal branch of the tibial nerve (Plate 10.6, Fig. 10.12, Flowchart 10.3, Table 10.5). It passes laterally and forwards till base of 5th metatarsal, where it divides into superficial and deep branches. It supplies 14 muscles of the sole.

Root value: S2, S3.

Branches

Main trunk

1. *Muscular branches* supply flexor *digitorum accessorius* and the *abductor digiti minimi*.
2. *Cutaneous branches supply* the skin of the sole.

Superficial branch: It divides into two branches—lateral and medial.

1. The *lateral branch* supplies three muscles—*flexor digiti minimi brevis*, the *3rd plantar* and *4th dorsal interossei*, and the skin on the lateral side of the little toe.
2. The *medial branch* communicates with the medial plantar nerve, and supplies the skin lining the 4th interdigital cleft.

Deep branch: It supplies *nine* muscles, including the 2nd, 3rd and 4th lumbricals; 1st, 2nd and 3rd dorsal interossei; 1st and 2nd plantar interossei and adductor hallucis.

DISSECTION

Dissect the medial plantar nerve and vessels on the medial side of sole. Lateral plantar nerve and vessels also enter the sole from the medial side. These cross the sole to reach the lateral side. Here lateral plantar artery forms a plantar arch across the sole which gives numerous branches. The lateral plantar nerve divides into a superficial and a deep branch. The latter runs in the concavity of the plantar arch. The course of branches of nerves and vessels are given in the text.

MEDIAL PLANTAR ARTERY

Medial plantar artery is a smaller terminal branch of the posterior tibial artery. It lies along the medial border of foot and divides into branches (Plate 10.6, Fig 10.13).

Branches

It gives off cutaneous, muscular branches to the overlying skin and to the adjoining muscles.

Its three small ***superficial digital branches*** that end by joining the 1st, 2nd and 3rd plantar metatarsal arteries which are branches of the plantar arch.

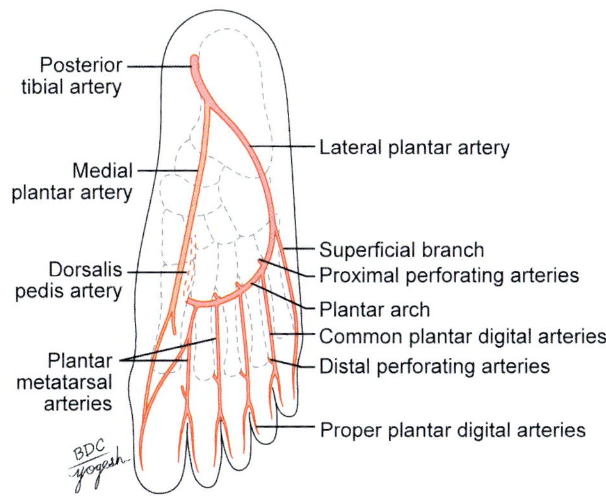

Fig. 10.13: Medial and lateral plantar arteries

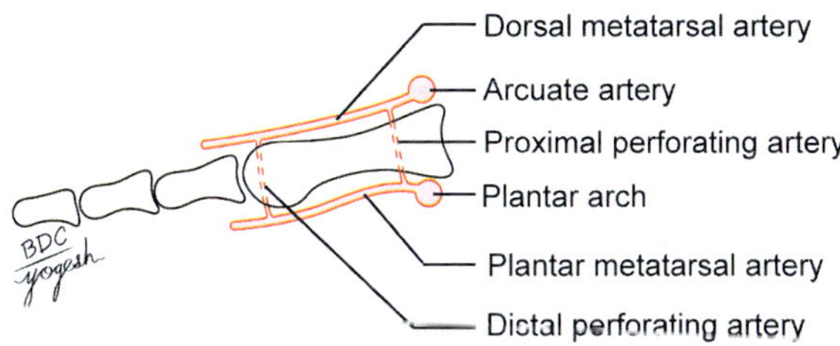

Fig. 10.14: Proximal and distal perforating arteries

LATERAL PLANTAR ARTERY

Lateral plantar artery is the larger terminal branch of the posterior tibial artery. At the base of the fifth metatarsal bone, it gives a superficial branch and then continues as the plantar arch (Plate 10.6, Fig. 10.13).

Branches

1. *Muscular branches* supply the adjoining muscles.
2. *Cutaneous branches* supply the skin and fasciae of the lateral part of the sole.
3. *Anastomotic branches* reach the lateral border of the foot and anastomose with arteries on the dorsum of the foot.
4. A *calcaneal branch* is occasionally given off to the skin of the heel.

PLANTAR ARCH

Plantar arch is the arterial arch located between the 3rd and 4th layers of the sole of foot.

Beginning, Course and Termination

Plantar arch is formed by the direct ***continuation of the lateral plantar artery*** after it has given off the superficial branch and is completed medially by the *dorsalis pedis artery*.

It extends from the base of the 5th metatarsal bone to the proximal part of the 1st intermetatarsal space, and lies between the 3rd and 4th layers of the sole. It is accompanied by venae comitantes. The deep branch of the lateral plantar nerve lies in the concavity of the plantar arch (Plate 10.6, Figs 10.13 to 10.15).

Branches

1. ***Four plantar metatarsal arteries*** run distally, one in each intermetatarsal space. Each artery ends by dividing into two *plantar digital branches* for adjacent sides of two digits. The 1st artery also gives off a branch to the medial side of the great toe. The lateral side of the little toe gets a direct branch from the lateral plantar artery.
2. The plantar arch gives off ***three proximal perforating arteries*** that pass through the 2nd, 3rd and 4th intermetatarsal spaces and communicate with the dorsal metatarsal arteries which are the branches of the arcuate artery.

The distal end of each plantar metatarsal artery gives off a ***distal perforating artery*** which joins the distal part of the corresponding dorsal metatarsal artery (Fig. 10.15).

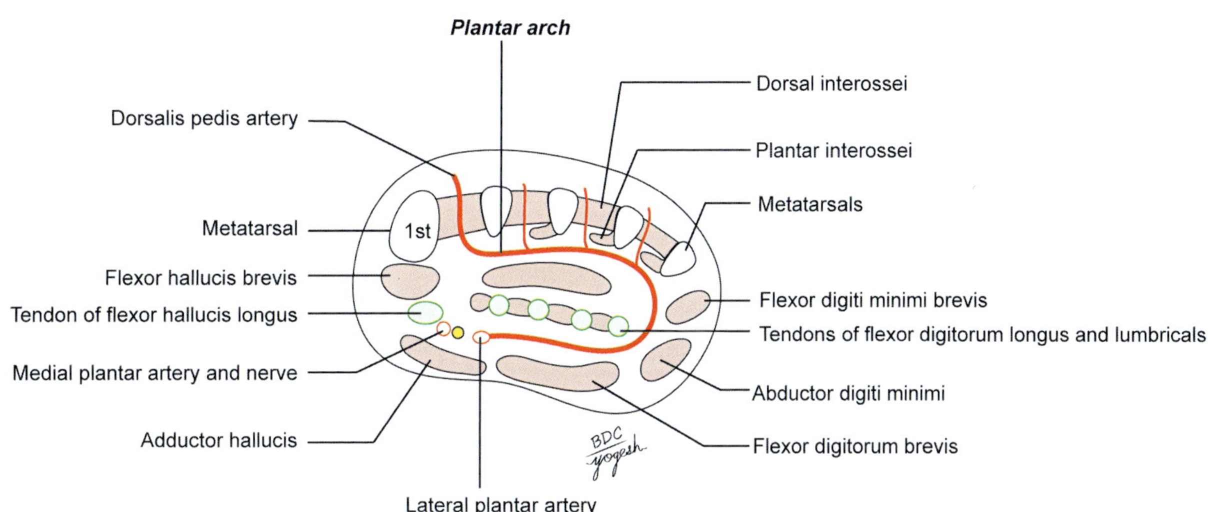

Fig. 10.15: Plantar arch

Video 2.10 Foot/Sole: Sole of the foot, nerve supply.

Facts to Remember

- Muscles of the sole are disposed in four layers.
- Medial plantar nerve supplies four intrinsic muscles—abductor hallucis, flexor digitorum brevis, flexor hallucis brevis and 1st lumbrical.
- Lateral plantar nerve supplies 14 intrinsic muscles—abductor digiti minimi, flexor digitorum accessorius, 2nd–4th lumbricals, flexor digiti minimi brevis, adductor hallucis, 1–3 plantar and 1–4 dorsal interossei.
- Foot has only one arterial arch – the plantar arch.
- The muscles of the sole maintain the arches of the foot.
- Plantar fasciitis – also called Policeman's heel, the most common hindfoot clinical problem.
- Morphologically, the plantar aponeurosis is a detached part of the tendon of plantaris.

BDC's Anatomy *e*-book

Baxter's nerve
Further reading
Viva voce questions

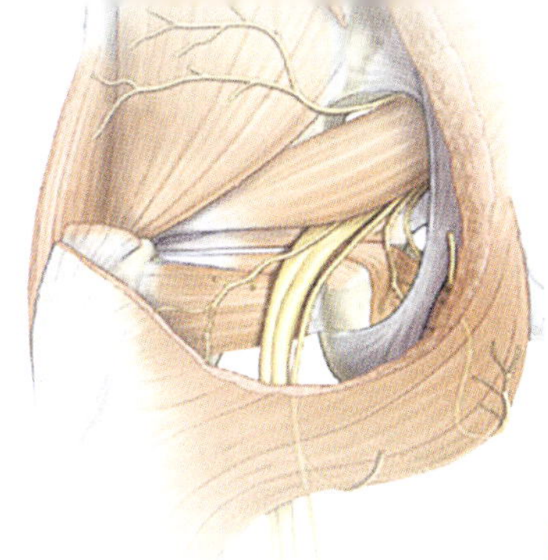

Chapter

11

Venous and Lymphatic Drainage; Segmental and Sympathetic Innervation

Competency:

AN20.3 Describe and demonstrate, venous drainage, lymphatic drainage and dermatomes of lower limb.

VENOUS DRAINAGE

Consideration of the venous drainage is of great importance because in the lower limb venous blood has to ascend against gravity. This is aided by a number of local factors, the failure of which gives rise to varicose veins.

Factors Helping Venous Return

1. *Negative intrathoracic pressure*, which is made more negative during inspiration.
2. Arterial pressure and overflow from the capillary bed.
3. Compression of veins accompanying arteries by arterial pulsation.
4. The presence of *valves*, which maintain a unidirectional flow.
5. The veins of the lower limb are *more muscular* than the veins of any other part of the body. They have greater number of valves. Superficial veins are connected to deep veins by *perforators*.
6. When the limb is active, *muscular contraction* compresses the deep veins and drives the blood in them upwards. It is helped by the suction action of the diaphragm.
7. The tight *sleeve of deep fascia* makes muscular compression of the veins much more effective by limiting outward bulging of the muscles.

VEINS OF LOWER LIMB

The veins may be classified into three groups: Superficial, deep and perforating (Figs 11.1 to 11.3).

Superficial Veins

They include the great and small saphenous veins, and their tributaries. They lie in the superficial fascia, on the surface of deep fascia. They are *thick-walled* because of the presence of smooth muscle and some fibrous and elastic tissues in their walls. *Valves are more numerous* in the distal parts of these veins than in their proximal parts. A large proportion of their blood is drained into the deep veins through the perforating veins.

Deep Veins

These are the medial plantar, lateral plantar, dorsalis pedis, anterior and posterior tibial, peroneal, popliteal and femoral veins and their tributaries. They accompany the arteries, and are supported by powerful surrounding muscles. The valves are more numerous in deep veins than in superficial veins. They are more efficient channels than the superficial veins because of the driving force of muscular contraction.

Perforating Veins

They connect the superficial with the deep veins. Their valves permit only *one way flow* of blood, from the superficial to the deep veins. There are about five perforators along the great saphenous vein, and one perforator along the small saphenous vein. The relevant details of these veins are given below.

DORSAL VENOUS ARCH

The ***dorsal venous arch*** lies on the dorsum of the foot over the proximal parts of the metatarsal bones. It receives ***four dorsal metatarsal veins*** each of which is formed by the union of ***two dorsal digital veins*** (Fig. 11.1).

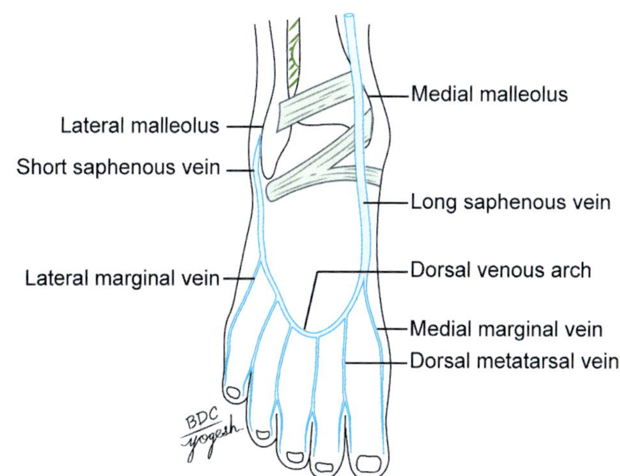

Fig. 11.1: Superficial veins of the front of the leg and dorsum of the foot

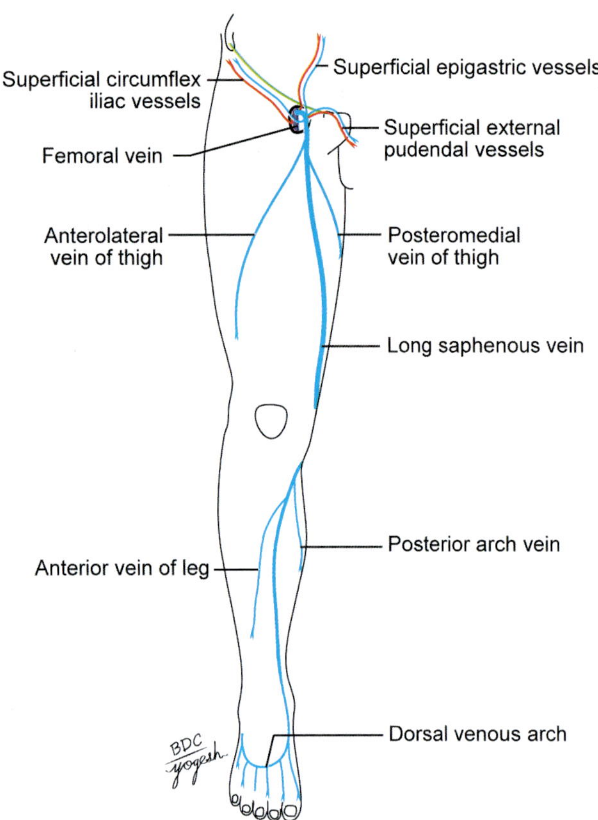

Fig. 11.2: Scheme to show the arrangement of the veins of lower limb (anterior view). Popliteal, short saphenous and venae comitantes of posterior tibial artery are on posterior aspect

LONG SAPHENOUS VEIN

1. The great or long saphenous vein lies in the superficial fascia of the lower limb (saphenous = easily seen, in Greek) (Figs 11.1 to 11.3). It is the longest vein of the body. It represents the pre-axial vein of the lower limb.
2. ***Formation*:** The long saphenous vein is formed by the union of the medial end of *dorsal venous arch* with the ***medial marginal vein***, which drains the medial side of great toe.
3. ***Course*:** It passes upwards in front of the medial malleolus, crosses the lower 1/3rd of the medial surface of tibia obliquely, and runs along its medial border to reach the back of the knee. The saphenous nerve runs in front of the great saphenous vein.
4. ***Termination*:** In the thigh, it inclines forwards to reach the saphenous opening where it pierces the cribriform fascia and opens into the femoral vein. Before piercing the cribriform fascia, it receives three named tributaries corresponding to the three cutaneous arteries, and also many unnamed tributaries (Fig. 11.2).
5. The vein is also connected to the deep veins of the limb by ***five perforating veins***. There are three medial perforators just above the ankle, one perforator just below the knee, and another one in the region of the adductor canal (Fig. 11.2). The perforating veins are also provided with valves, which permit flow of blood only from the superficial to the deep veins. Failure of the valves also gives rise to varicose veins.

Valves in the Long Saphenous Vein

There are 10–20 valves in the long saphenous vein at multiple locations. Two important locations are as follows:

1. Just before the long saphenous vein pierces the cribriform fascia.
2. At the junction of long saphenous vein with the femoral vein; this is called saphenofemoral valve. The valve located in the external iliac vein (continuation

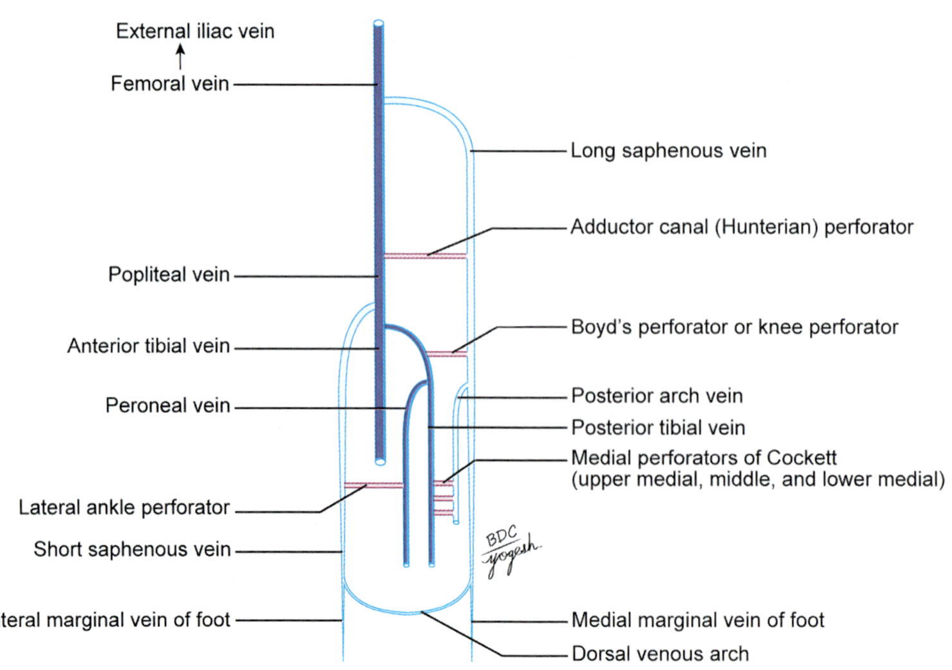

Fig. 11.3: Scheme of the veins of lower limb

of femoral vein) prevents the back pressure of blood on saphenofemoral vein. But in 20% individuals, the valve in the external iliac vein is absent and this makes them prone for varicose vein.

Tributaries

Formative tributaries: Medial end of dorsal venous arch of foot and medial marginal vein of foot.

In the leg: It communicates freely with the small saphenous vein and with deep veins through communicating veins.

Just below the knee:

1. Anterior vein of the leg runs upwards, forwards and medially, from the lateral side of the ankle.
2. Posterior arch vein is large and constant. It begins from a series of small venous arches, which connect the medial ankle perforators, and runs upwards to join the great saphenous vein just below the knee.
3. A vein from the calf: This vein also communicates with the small saphenous vein.

In the thigh:

- The accessory saphenous vein drains the posteromedial side of the thigh.
- The anterior cutaneous vein of the thigh drains the lower part of the front of the thigh.

Just before piercing the cribriform fascia:

1. Superficial epigastric
2. Superficial circumflex iliac
3. Superficial external pudendal.

Just before termination: Deep external pudendal vein.

Note: The ***thoracoepigastric vein*** runs along the anterolateral wall of the trunk. It connects the superficial epigastric vein with the lateral thoracic vein. Thus it is an important connection between the veins of the upper and lower limbs.

SMALL OR SHORT SAPHENOUS VEIN

Formation: The short saphenous vein is formed on the dorsum of the foot by the union of the lateral end of the dorsal venous arch with the lateral marginal vein (Fig. 11.3).

Course and termination: It enters the back of the leg by passing behind the lateral malleolus. In the leg, it ascends lateral to the tendo calcaneus, and then along the middle line of the calf, to the lower part of the popliteal fossa. Here, it pierces the deep fascia and opens into the popliteal vein.

It drains the lateral border of the foot, the heel, and the back of the leg. It is connected with the great saphenous and with the deep veins, and is accompanied by the sural nerve.

Comparison between long saphenous and short saphenous veins is given in Table 11.1.

PERFORATING VEINS

As already mentioned, they connect the superficial with the deep veins (Fig. 11.3). These are classified as follows.

TABLE 11.1: Comparison between long and short saphenous veins

Features	*Long saphenous vein*	*Short saphenous vein*
Beginning	Medial end of dorsal venous plexus	Lateral end of dorsal venous plexus
Position	Anterior to medial malleolus	Posterior to lateral malleolus
Number of valves	15–20 valves	8–10 valves
Relation of a sensory nerve	Saphenous nerve	Sural nerve
Termination	Femoral vein	Popliteal vein

Indirect Perforating Veins

Indirect perforating veins connect the superficial veins with the deep veins through the muscular veins (Figs 11.3 and 11.4).

Direct Perforating Veins

Direct perforating veins (Figs 11.4a and b) connect the superficial veins directly with the deep veins. The great and small saphenous veins are the large direct perforators. The small direct perforating veins (Fig. 11.3) are follows:

In the thigh: The *adductor canal perforator* connects the great saphenous vein with the femoral vein in the lower part of the adductor canal.

Below the knee: One perforator connects the great saphenous vein or the posterior arch vein with the posterior tibial vein.

In the leg: A *lateral perforator* is present at the junction of the middle and lower thirds of the leg. It connects the small saphenous vein, or one of its tributaries with the peroneal vein.

Medially, there are three perforators which connect the posterior arch vein with the posterior tibial vein.

1. The *upper medial perforator* lies at the junction of the middle and lower thirds of the leg.
2. The *middle medial perforator* lies above the medial malleolus.
3. The *lower medial perforator* lies posteroinferior to the medial malleolus.

Competency:

AN20.5 Explain anatomical basis of varicose veins and deep vein thrombosis.

CLINICAL ANATOMY

- ***Calf pump*** and ***peripheral heart:*** In the upright position of the body, the venous return from the lower limb depends largely on the contraction of calf muscles. These muscles are, therefore, known as the 'calf pump'. For the same reason the soleus is called the *peripheral heart* (Fig. 11.4). When this muscle contracts, blood contained in large sinuses within it is

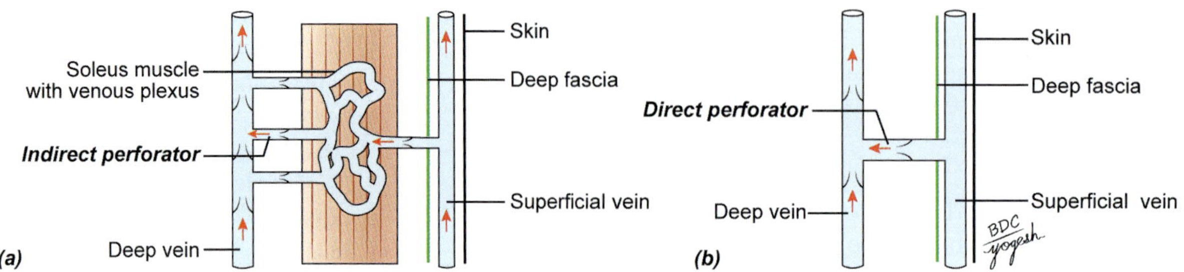

Figs 11.4a and b: Direct and indirect perforating veins

pumped into the deep veins (which ascend towards heart). When the muscle relaxes, blood flows into the sinuses from the superficial veins (Fig. 11.5).

- 'Cut open procedure'/***venesection*** is done on the great saphenous vein as it lies in front of medial malleolus. This vein is used for transfusion of blood/ fluids in case of non-availability or collapse of other veins. Saphenous nerve is identified and not injured as it lies anterior to the great saphenous vein (Fig. 11.6).
- ***Use in coronary artery bypass grafting*:** Great saphenous vein is used for bypassing the blocked coronary arteries. The vein is reversed so that valves do not block the passage of blood.

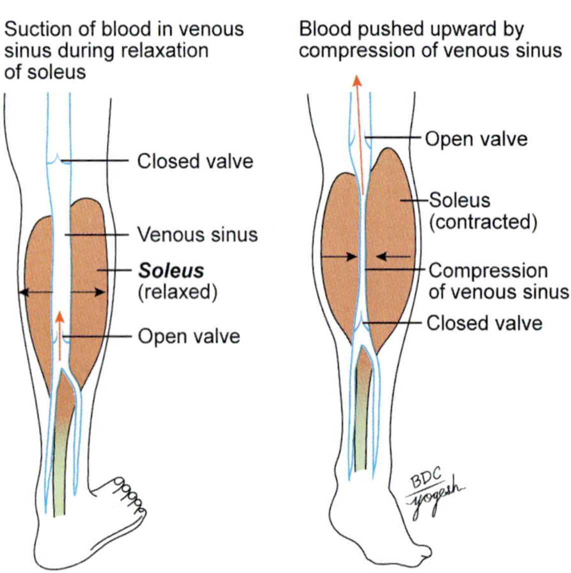

Fig. 11.5: Venous valves for unidirectional flow of blood

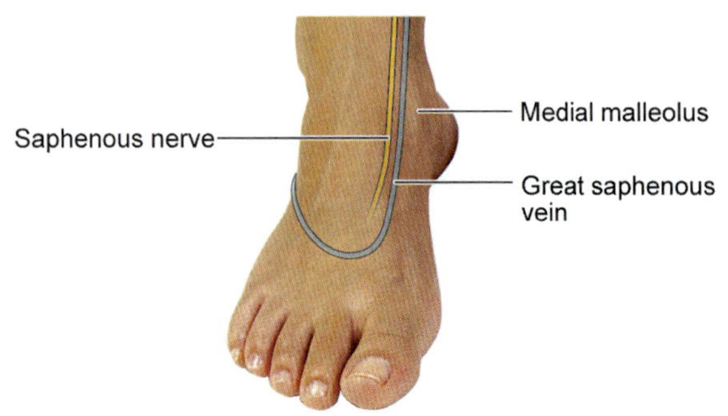

Fig. 11.6: Cut open (venesection) procedure is done on great saphenous vein

VARICOSE VEINS AND ULCERS

- **Varicose veins** are enlarged, swollen, and tortuous veins. These are referred as chronic venous insufficiency (Fig. 11.7).
- Superficial veins of the limbs commonly get varicosed, mostly in individuals with prolonged standing job such as bus conductors, traffic police, doctors and teachers. Varicose veins are more common in women than in men. Varicose veins often occur during third trimester of pregnancy, as the iliac vein get pressed due to enlarged uterus. These mostly subside after delivery.
- The main ***anatomical basis*** behind the varicose veins is the incompetencies of the venous valves. These incompetencies are grouped as follows:
  1. Incompetency of valves of perforators: It results in ***high pressure leaks***; that is, the blood reflux into superficial veins from deeper veins during muscle contraction (Fig. 11.8).
  2. Incompetency of saphenofemoral valve: It makes the long saphenous vein dilated and tortuous progressively.

Diagnosis of Incompetent Valve

Clinical examination with the following tests are useful to locate the site of incompetency of the valve.

1. ***Trendelenburg test*** [Friedrich Trendelenburg, German Surgeon, 1844–1924]
   - *Purpose*: To find out the leak or defective venous valve in a patient with varicose veins.
   - *Procedure*: Ask the patient to lie down and raise the lower limb to empty the superficial veins. It can be assisted with gently stroking the varicose veins in a proximal direction. Apply pressure with thumb at saphenofemoral junction and ask the patient to stand quickly.
   - *For superficial veins*: Release the applied pressure from saphenofemoral junction. Rapid filling of the varicose veins from above downward indicates incompetency of the superficial veins and test is called positive. If the veins are not filled rapidly, test is called negative.
   - *For perforating veins*: The pressure at the saphenofemoral junction is maintained for about 1 minute. Gradual filling of the varicose veins occurs below upward as perforating veins allow to pass the blood from the deep to superficial veins and the test is called positive.

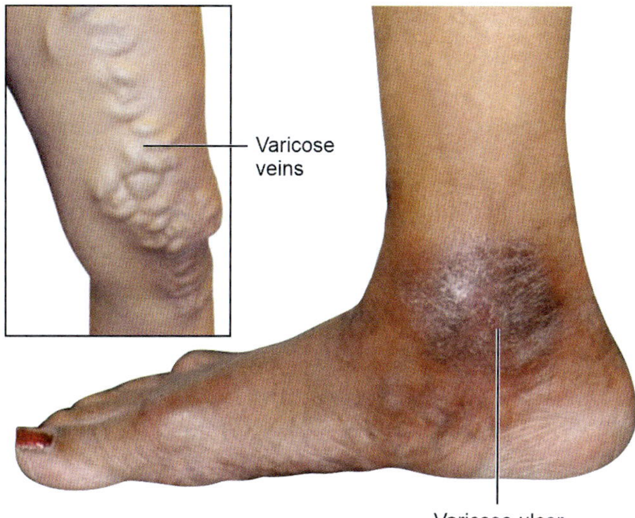

Fig. 11.7: Varicose veins and varicose ulcer

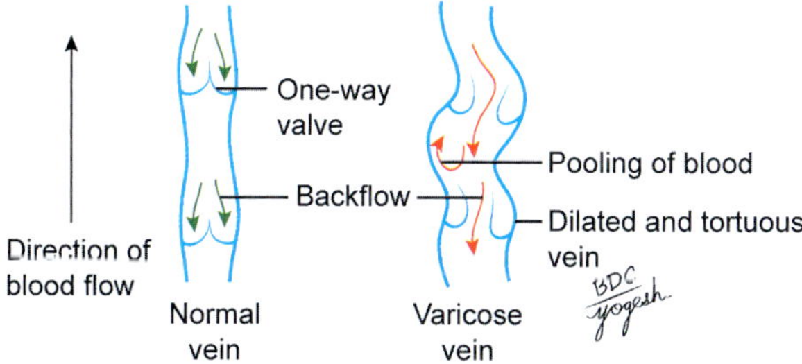

Fig. 11.8: Valve insufficiency in varicose veins

2. ***Perthe's test*** (tourniquet test) [George Clemens Perthes, German Surgeon, 1869–1927]
   - It is used to test the incompetence of deep veins.
   - *Procedure*: Tie the tourniquet around the upper part of thigh to occlude the long saphenous vein and not the femoral vein. Ask the patient to do gentle exercise (walk quickly for a while).
   - *Positive test*: If the perforating and deep veins are blocked, varicose veins will become more distended.
   - *Negative test*: If the perforating and deep veins are normal, varicose veins will shrink.

Note: Varicose veins are treated with sclerosing injections or laser treatment.

LYMPHATIC DRAINAGE

Most of the lymph from the lower limb drains into the inguinal lymph nodes, either mostly directly or partly indirectly through the popliteal and anterior tibial nodes.

LYMPH NODES

The lymph nodes of the lower limb are divided into two types: Superficial and deep.

a. Superficial lymph nodes include the superficial inguinal nodes.
b. Deep lymph nodes include the deep inguinal, popliteal and anterior tibial nodes.

Superficial Inguinal Lymph Nodes

They are divided into three sets (Figs 11.9 and 11.10):

1. The ***lower vertical group*** is placed along both sides of the terminal part of the great saphenous vein, and contains about four or five nodes. They drain the skin and fasciae of the lower limb (great saphenous territory), except the buttock and the short saphenous territory.
2. The ***upper lateral group*** is placed below the lateral part of the inguinal ligament, and contains about two or three nodes. They drain the skin and fasciae of the lateral part of infraumbilical part of anterior abdominal wall, the buttock, the flank and the back below the umbilical plane.
3. The ***upper medial group*** is placed below the medial end of the inguinal ligament. One or two nodes may lie above the inguinal ligament along the course of the superficial epigastric vessels. The group contains two to three nodes. They drain:
   a. The medial part of anterior abdominal wall below the level of the umbilicus.
   b. The perineum, including external genitalia (except the glans), the anal canal below the pectinate line, the vagina below hymen and the penile part of the male urethra.
   c. The superolateral angle of the uterus, via the round ligament.

Note: Efferents from all superficial inguinal nodes pierce the cribriform fascia, and terminate in the deep inguinal nodes. A few may pass directly to the external iliac nodes.

Deep Inguinal Lymph Nodes

These are about four to five in number, and lie medial to the upper part of the femoral vein.

The most proximal node of this group; ***gland of Cloquet*** or ***Rosenmüller***, lies in the femoral canal. These nodes receive afferents from:

1. The superficial inguinal nodes
2. The popliteal nodes
3. Glans penis or clitoris
4. The deep lymphatics of the lower limb accompanying the femoral vessels.

Their efferents pass to the external iliac nodes.

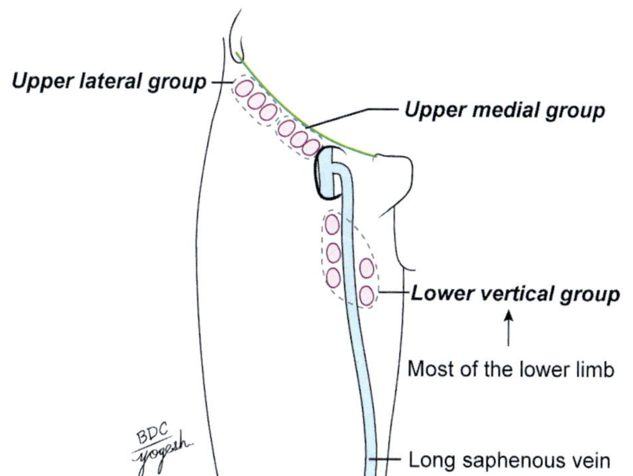

Fig. 11.9: Superficial inguinal lymph nodes

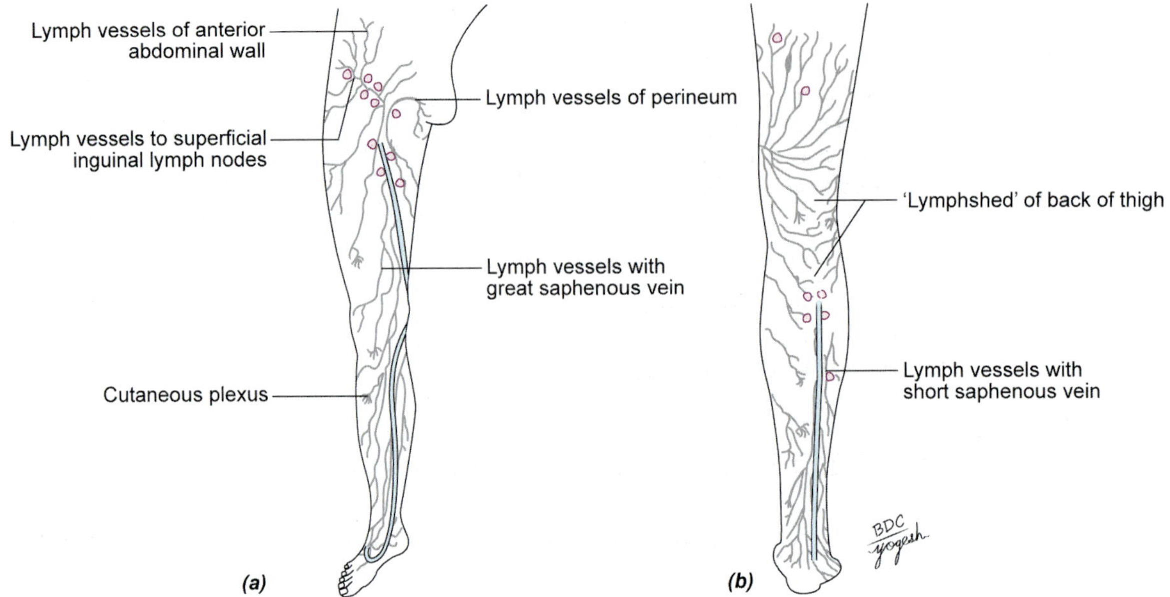

Figs 11.10a and b: Superficial lymphatics of the lower limb: (a) Anterior aspect and (b) posterior aspect

Popliteal Lymph Nodes

These nodes lie near the termination of the small saphenous vein, deep to the deep fascia. One node lies between the popliteal artery and the oblique popliteal ligament. They receive afferents from:

1. The territory of the small saphenous vein.
2. The deep parts of the leg (through vessels running along the anterior and posterior tibial vessels)
3. The knee joint.

Their efferents run along the popliteal and femoral vessels, and terminate in the deep inguinal nodes.

Anterior Tibial Lymph Node

One inconstant node may lie along the upper part of the anterior tibial artery. When present, it collects lymph from the anterior compartment of the leg, and passes it onto the popliteal nodes.

LYMPHATICS

The lymph vessels of lower limb are classified into two groups: superficial and deep (Fig. 11.10).

Superficial Lymphatics

These lymph vessels are larger and are more numerous than the deep lymphatics. They run in the superficial fascia and ultimately form two streams. The *main stream* follows the great saphenous vein, and ends in the lower vertical group of superficial inguinal lymph nodes. The *accessory stream* follows the small saphenous vein and ends in the popliteal lymph nodes.

Deep Lymphatics

These are smaller and fewer than the superficial lymphatics, although they drain all structures lying deep to the deep fascia. They run along the principal blood vessels, and terminate mostly into the deep inguinal nodes, either directly or indirectly through the popliteal nodes.

Note: The deep lymphatics from the gluteal region and from the upper part of the back of the thigh accompany the gluteal vessels and end in the internal iliac nodes.

Competency:

AN20.4 Explain anatomical basis of enlarged inguinal lymph nodes.

CLINICAL ANATOMY

- ***Elephantiasis***: Lymphatic obstruction caused by the parasite filaria is very common in the lower limb. This results in great hypertrophy of the skin and of subcutaneous tissue (elephantiasis) (Fig. 11.11).
- ***Inguinal lymphadenopathy*** is an enlargement of inguinal lymph nodes. The commonest cause of a swelling in the inguinal area is enlargement of the inguinal lymph nodes. This can be caused by infection, or carcinoma, anywhere in the area drained by these nodes (Fig. 11.10).

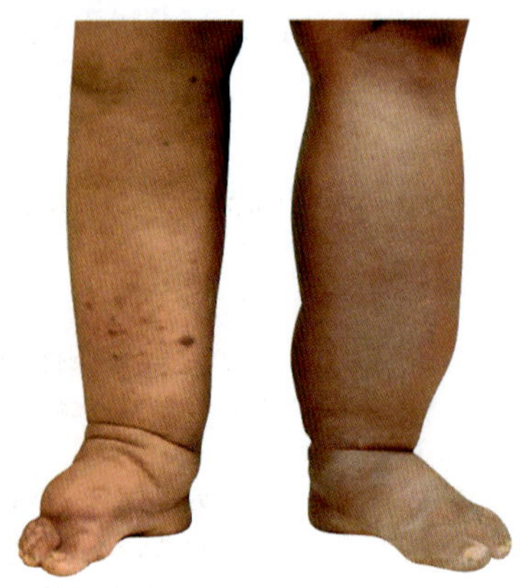

Fig. 11.11: Elephantiasis due to filariasis

SEGMENTAL INNERVATION

Dermatomes

The area of skin supplied by one spinal segment is called a dermatome.

Peculiarities of Cutaneous Nerves of Lower limb

1. The cutaneous innervation of the lower limb is derived from various nerves contributed by (Figs 11.12 and 11.13):
   a. Mainly from segments L1 to L5 and S1 to S3 of the spinal cord; and
   b. Partly from segments T12 and S4.
2. As a rule, the limb is supplied only by anterior primary rami. The exception to this rule is that the skin of the superomedial quadrant of the gluteal region is supplied by the posterior primary rami of nerves L1 to L3 and S1 to S3 (Figs 11.14 a and b).
3. There is varying degree of overlap of adjoining dermatomes, so that the area of sensory loss following damage to the spinal cord or nerve roots is always less than the actual area of the dermatome.
4. Initially, each limb bud has a cephalic border, and a caudal border. These are known as the *preaxial* and the *postaxial* borders, respectively. In the embryo, the great toe and tibia lie along the pre-axial border, and the little toe and fibula along the postaxial border. Later, the limb bud rotates medially through 90°, so that the great toe and tibia are carried medially, and the little toe and fibula laterally. Thus, tibial border is the original preaxial border, and fibular border is the postaxial border of the lower limb.
5. The dermatomes of the lower limb are distributed in an orderly numerical sequence (Figs 11.14 and 11.15).

   Along the pre-axial border from above downwards, the dermatomes are T12, L1–4.

   The middle three toes, the adjoining area of the dorsum of the foot and the lateral side of the leg are supplied by segment L5.

   Along the postaxial border from below upwards, there are dermatomes S1, 2, 3.
6. As the limb elongates, the central dermatomes (L4, 5, S1) get pulled in such a way that these are represented only in the distal part of the limb, and are buried proximally. The line along which the central dermatomes are buried is known as the *axial line*. In fact, an axial line is defined as a line along which certain dermatomes are buried (missing) so that distant dermatomes adjoin each other. Overlapping of the dermatomes is minimal across the axial line. There are *two axial lines*, one ventral and one dorsal, both of which extend largely on the back of the limb. On the posterior surface of the limb, the ***ventral axial line*** extends up to the heel, whereas the ***dorsal axial line*** ends at a higher level, at the junction of the upper 2/3rd and lower 1/3rd of the leg. On the anterior surface of the limb, the ventral axial line crosses the scrotum, and the dorsal axial line encroaches on the lateral side of the knee.
7. Area of dermatome distribution is shown in Figs 11.14 to 11.16 and Table 11.2.

CLINICAL ANATOMY

Like dermatomes, the myotomes are also helpful in determination of the level of a lesion in the spinal cord.

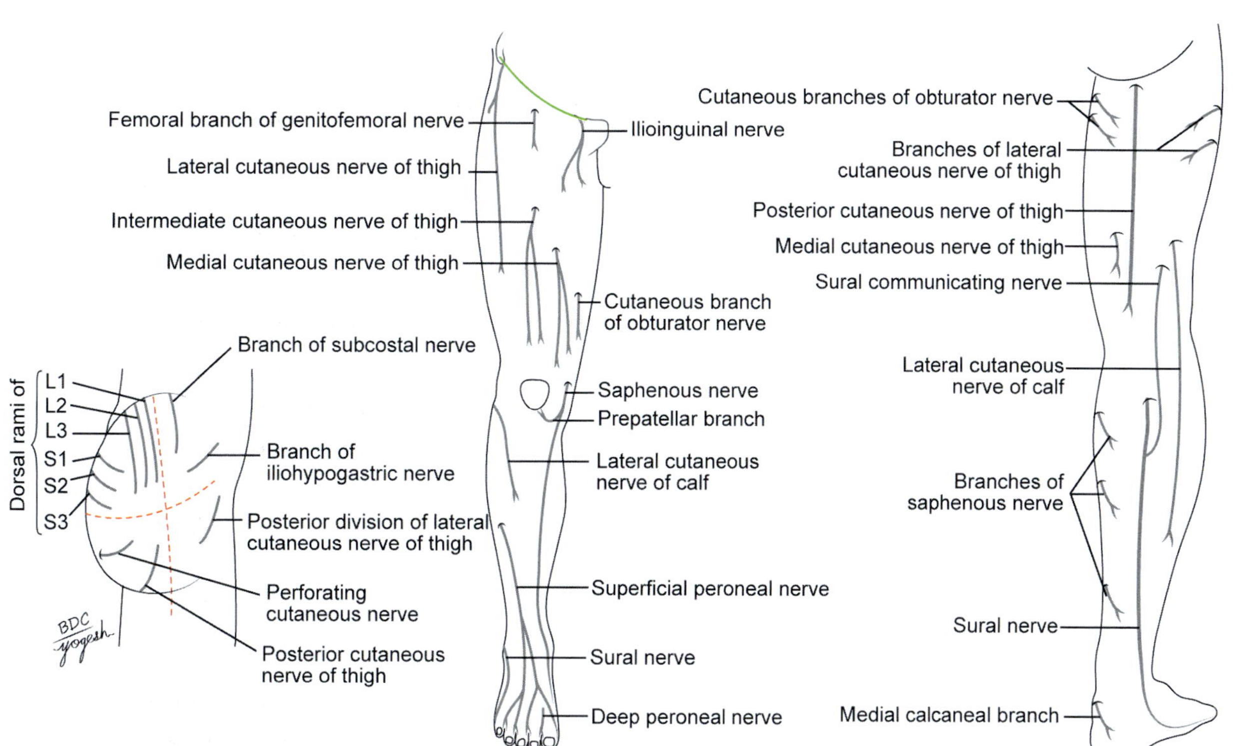

Fig. 11.12: Cutaneous innervation of the lower limb

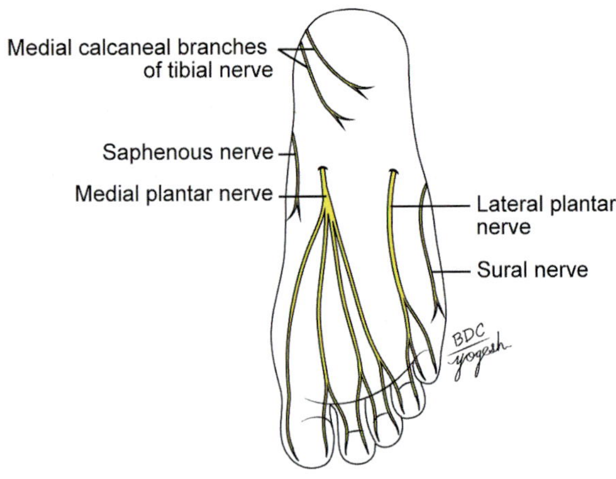

Fig. 11.13: Cutaneous innervation of the sole of foot

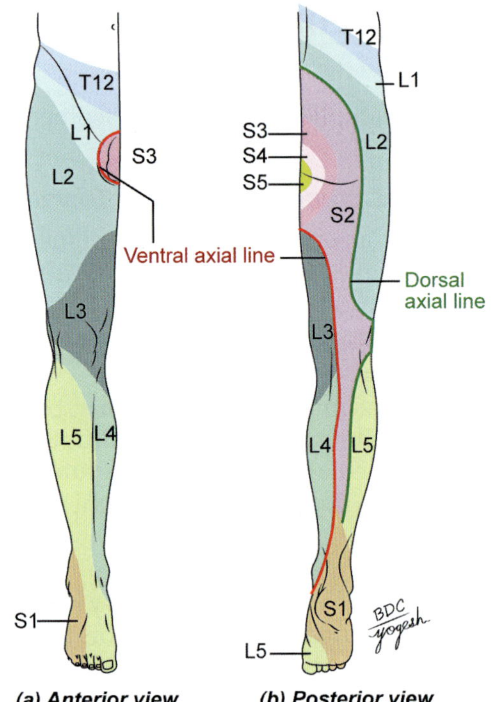

Figs 11.14a and b: Dermatomes of the lower limb: (a) Anterior view and (b) posterior view

SYMPATHETIC INNERVATION

1. Sympathetic innervation of the lower limb is derived from the lower three thoracic and upper two lumbar (***T10 to L2***) segments of the spinal cord. The fibres arise from the lateral horn cells, and pass out with the ventral roots as ***preganglionic*** (*white rami*) ***fibres***. These pass down the sympathetic chain to relay in the lumbar and upper two or three sacral ganglia.
2. The ***postganglionic fibres*** emerge from the lumbar sympathetic ganglia and pass through *grey rami* to reach the lumbar nerves. From these nerves, they pass into the femoral nerve. They supply the femoral artery and its branches in the thigh. Some postganglionic sympathetic fibres emerge from the upper two or three sacral ganglia. They travel through the tibial nerve to supply the popliteal artery and its branches in the leg and foot.
3. The blood vessels to skeletal muscles are dilated by sympathetic activity.
4. Sympathetic nerves are vasomotor, sudomotor and pilomotor to the skin.

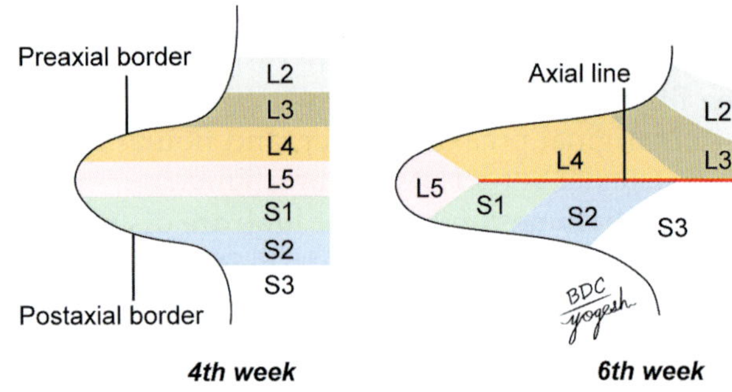

Fig. 11.15: Arrangements of dermatomes in the developing lower limb (at 4th week and 6th week of intrauterine life)

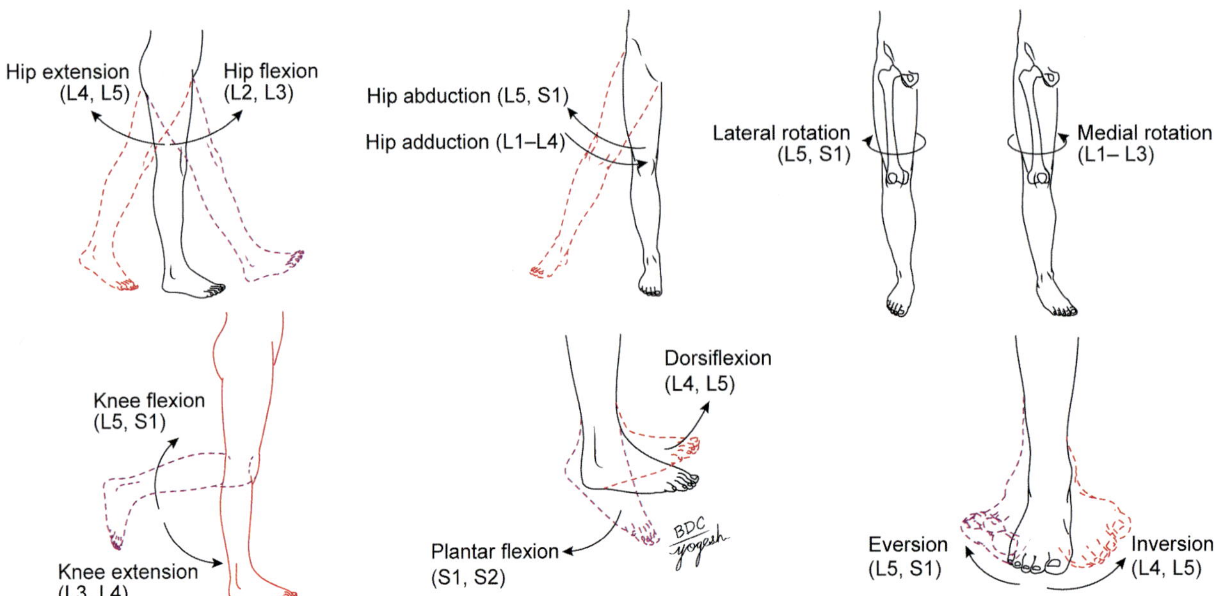

Fig. 11.16: Segmental innervation of the joints

TABLE 11.2: Segmental innervation of joints of the lower limb

Joint	*Movement*	*Segment*
Hip joint	Flexion	L2, L3
	Extension	L4, L5
	Adduction	L1–L4
	Abduction	L5, S1
	Medial rotation	L1–L3
	Lateral rotation	L5, S1
Knee joint	Extension	L3, L4
	Flexion	L5, S1
Ankle joint	Dorsiflexion	L4, L5
	Plantar flexion	S1, S2
Joints of foot	Inversion	L4, L5
	Eversion	L5, S1

CLINICAL ANATOMY

- ***Sympathetic denervation*** of the lower limb can be produced by removing the 2nd, 3rd and 4th lumbar ganglia with the intermediate chain. This divides all preganglionic fibres to the lower limb. The first lumbar ganglion is preserved because it controls the proximal urethral sphincter mechanism. Its removal is followed by dry coitus. Bilateral lumbar sympathectomy is done in patients with ***Buerger's disease***.

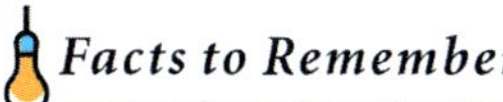

Facts to Remember

- Long saphenous vein (longest vein of the body) with saphenous nerve lies anterior to medial malleolus.
- Most preferred site of venesection is the great saphenous vein in front of medial malleolus.
- Short saphenous vein with sural nerve lies behind lateral malleolus.
- Vein of Leonardo da Vinci is a posterior arch vein, a tributary of great saphenous vein.
- Varicose veins are due to tortuosity of the long saphenous vein and occur mostly due to prolonged standing.
- Long saphenous vein is used to bypass the coronary artery after inverting the vein.
- Lymph node of Cloquet or Rosenmüller are deep inguinal lymph node which are present in the femoral canal.
- Elephantiasis is a massive oedema (lymph oedema) of lower limb due to blockage of its lymphatics by microfilarial parasites.

BDC's Anatomy *e*-book

1. Comparison of lower and upper limbs
2. Myotomes of lower limb
3. Further reading
4. Viva voce questions

Chapter 12

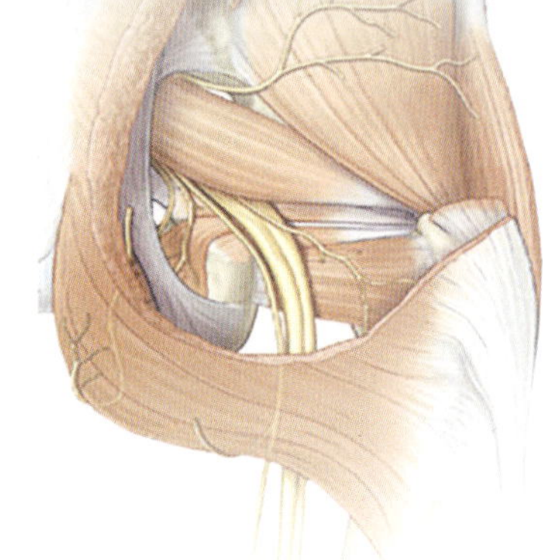

Joints of Lower Limb

The weight-bearing joints of the lower limb are more stable.

Peculiarities

1. *Hip joint* allows the same movement as the mobile shoulder joint, but the range of movement is restricted.
2. *Knee joint* allows similar movements as the elbow besides the very important locking of the joint for long time standing. The leg bones do not permit the movements of supination and pronation for reasons of stability.
3. *Ankle joint* also allows limited movements for the same reason.
4. The additional movements of inversion and eversion provided at the *subtalar joints* are to adjust the foot to the uneven ground.

Competency:

AN17.1 Describe and demonstrate the type, articular surfaces, capsule, synovial membrane, ligaments, relations, movements and muscles involved, blood and nerve supply and bursae around the hip joint.

HIP JOINT

The hip joint is a synovial joint between the head of femur and acetabular cavity of the hip bone. Hip joint transmits the weight of the upper part of the body to neck of the femur and supports the body weight in standing position. It is the largest ball-and-socket joint of the body (Fig. 12.1, Flowchart 12.1).

Type

Ball and socket variety of synovial joint (multiaxial).

Articular Surfaces

The head of the femur articulates with the acetabulum of the hip bone to form the hip joint.

1. The ***head of the femur*** forms more than half a sphere, and is covered with hyaline cartilage except at the *fovea capitis*.
2. The ***acetabulum*** presents a horseshoe-shaped, lunate articular surface, an acetabular notch and an acetabular fossa (Fig. 12.1). The lunate surface is covered with cartilage.

Though the articular surfaces on the head of the femur and on the acetabulum are reciprocally curved, they are not co-extensive.

Ligaments

The ligaments include:

1. Fibrous capsule or capsular ligament
2. Iliofemoral ligament
3. Pubofemoral ligament
4. Ischiofemoral ligament
5. Ligament of the head of the femur
6. Acetabular labrum
7. Transverse acetabular ligament.

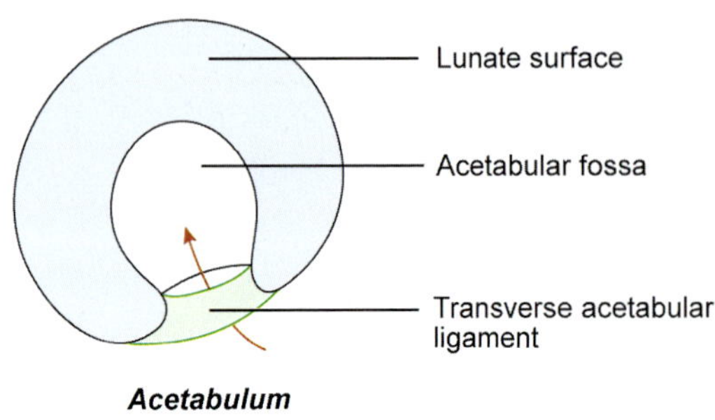

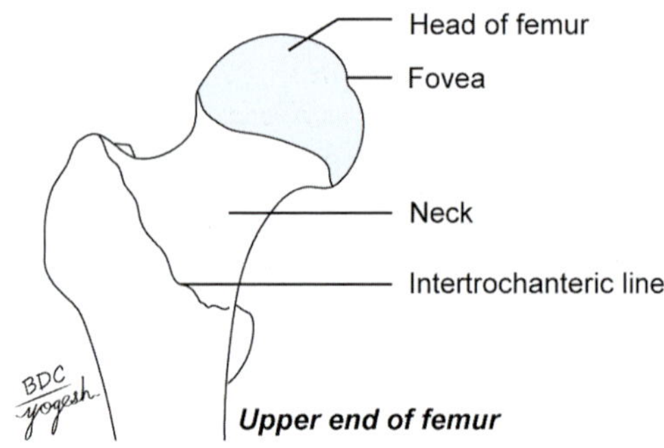

Fig. 12.1: Articular surfaces of the hip joint

Flowchart 12.1: Hip joint

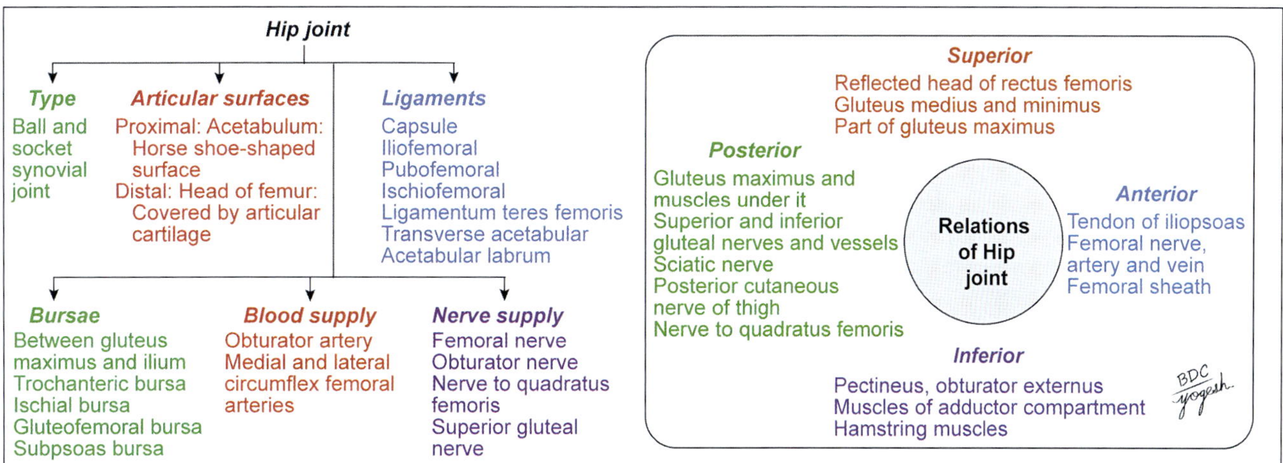

Capsular Ligament

- The capsular ligament is attached *on the hip bone* to the acetabular labrum including the transverse acetabular ligament, and to bone above and behind the acetabulum.
- *On the femur*, it is attached to the intertrochanteric line in front, and 1 cm medial to the intertrochanteric crest behind (Figs 12.2 and 12.3).
- The ***synovial membrane*** lines the fibrous capsule, the intracapsular portion of the neck of the femur, both surfaces of the acetabular labrum, the transverse ligament, and fat in the acetabular fossa. It also invests the round ligament of the head of the femur (Figs 12.2 and 12.3).

Note: ***Structure of the capsule***

1. Anterosuperiorly, the capsule is thick and firmly attached. This part is subjected to maximum tension in the standing posture. Posteroinferiorly, the capsule is thin and loosely attached to bone.
2. The capsule is made up of two types of fibres. The outer fibres are longitudinal and the inner circular ones are called ***zona orbicularis***. The longitudinal fibres are best developed anterosuperiorly, where many of them are reflected along the neck of the femur to form the ***retinacula***. Blood vessels supplying the head and neck of the femur, travel along these retinacula.

Iliofemoral Ligament *(Ligament of Bigelow)* (Plate 12.1 and Fig. 12.4)

The *iliofemoral ligament*, or inverted Y-shaped ligament, lies anteriorly. The ligament is triangular in shape. Its ***apex*** is attached to the lower half of the anterior inferior iliac spine; and the ***base*** to the intertrochanteric line. The upper oblique and lower vertical fibres form thick and strong bands, while the middle fibres are thin and weak.

Note: It is ***one of the strongest ligaments*** in the body. It prevents the trunk from falling backwards in the standing posture.

Pubofemoral Ligament (Plate 12.1 and Fig. 12.4)

The *pubofemoral ligament* supports the joint inferomedially. It is also *triangular* in shape. Superiorly, it is attached to the iliopubic eminence, the obturator crest and the obturator membrane. Inferiorly, it merges with the anteroinferior part of the capsule and with the lower band of the iliofemoral ligament.

Ischiofemoral Ligament

The *ischiofemoral ligament* is comparatively weak. It covers the joint posteriorly. Its fibres are twisted and extend from the ischium to the acetabulum. The fibres of the ligament form the zona orbicularis. Some of them are attached to the greater trochanter (Fig. 12.5).

Round Ligament of Head of Femur

The *round ligament of the head of the femur* or ligamentum teres, is a flat and *triangular* ligament. The ***apex*** is attached to the fovea capitis, and the ***base*** to the transverse ligament and the margins of the acetabular notch. It may be very thin, or even absent.

Note: The round ligament of head of femur transmits arteries to the head of the femur, from the acetabular branches of the obturator and medial circumflex femoral arteries. Morphologically this ligament is derived from the part of capsule that has been included within the joint.

Acetabular Labrum

The *acetabular labrum* is a fibrocartilaginous rim attached to the margins of the acetabulum. It narrows the mouth of the acetabulum. This helps in holding the head of the femur in position (Fig. 12.5).

Transverse Ligament of the Acetabulum

The *transverse ligament of the acetabulum* is a part of the acetabular labrum which bridges the acetabular notch. The notch is thus converted into a foramen which transmits acetabular vessels and nerves to the joint (Plate 12.2, Fig. 12.3).

Stability of the Hip Joint

The hip joint is unique in having a high degree of stability as well as mobility. A fairly wide range of mobility is possible because of the fact that the femur has a long neck which is narrower than the equatorial diameter of the head.

Plate 12.1: Iliofemoral, pubofemoral, and ischiofemoral ligaments

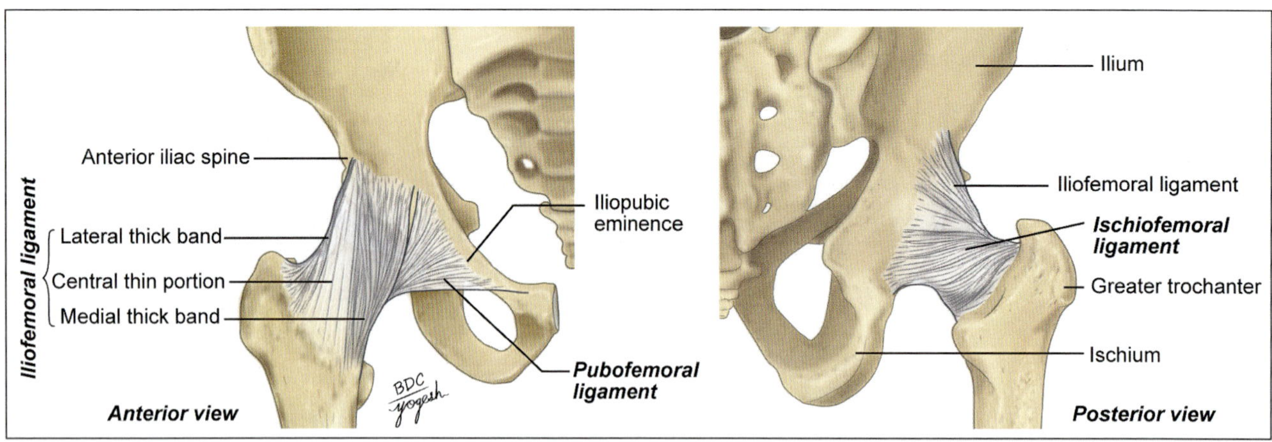

Plate 12.2: Acetabular labrum, transverse acetabular ligament and ligamentum teres femoris

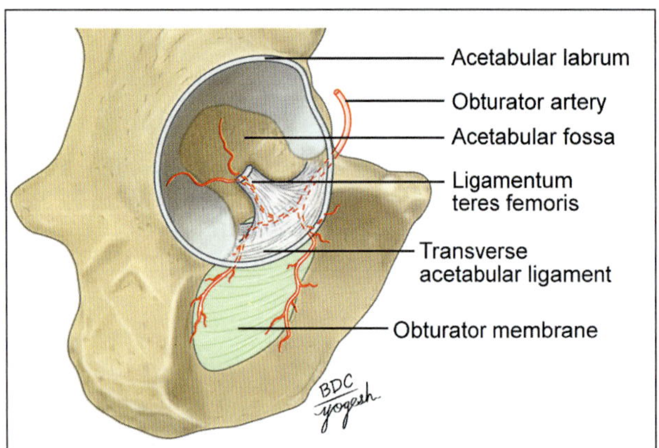

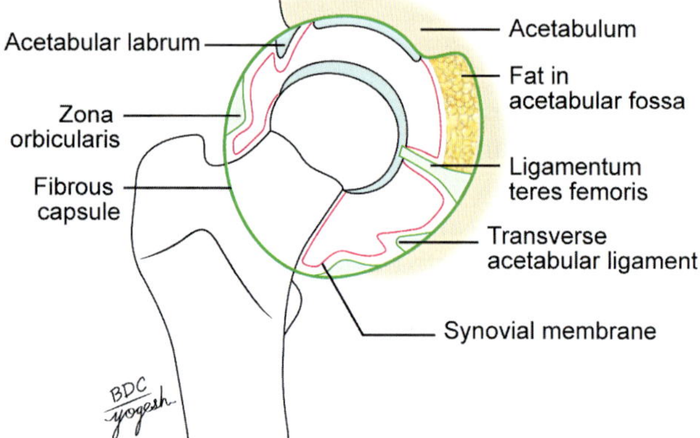

Fig. 12.3: Fibrous capsule with synovial membrane

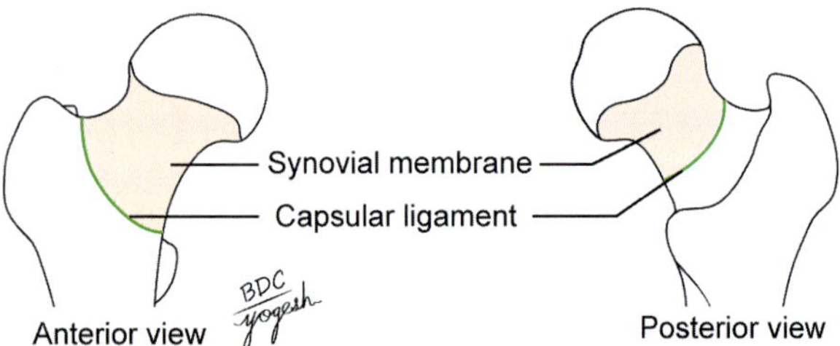

Fig. 12.2: Fibrous capsule of the hip joint

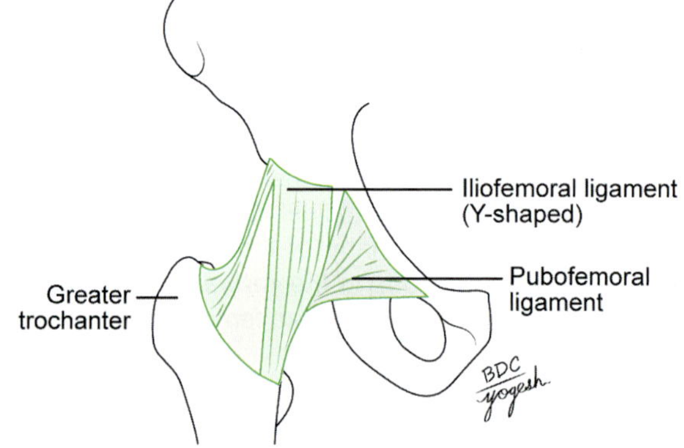

Fig. 12.4: The iliofemoral and pubofemoral ligaments

The stability or strength of the hip joint depends upon:

1. Depth of the acetabulum and the narrowing of its mouth by the acetabular labrum.
2. Tension and strength of ligaments.
3. Strength of the surrounding muscles.
4. Length and obliquity of the neck of the femur.
5. Atmospheric pressure.

Relations of the Hip Joint (Fig. 12.6)

Anterior

1. Tendon of the iliopsoas separated from the joint by a bursa
2. Femoral vein
3. Femoral artery
4. Femoral nerve.

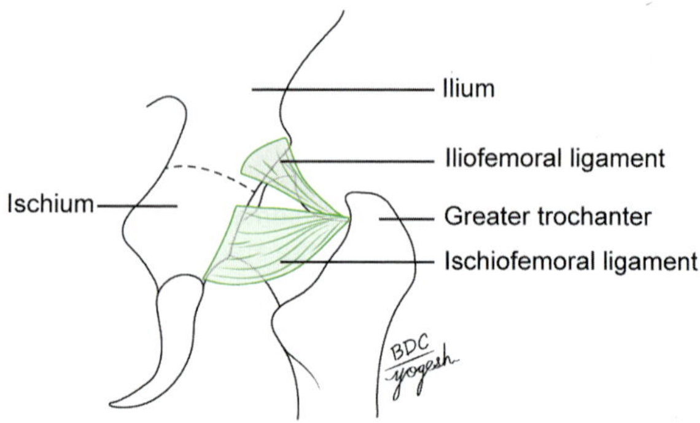

Fig. 12.5: Iliofemoral and ischiofemoral ligaments

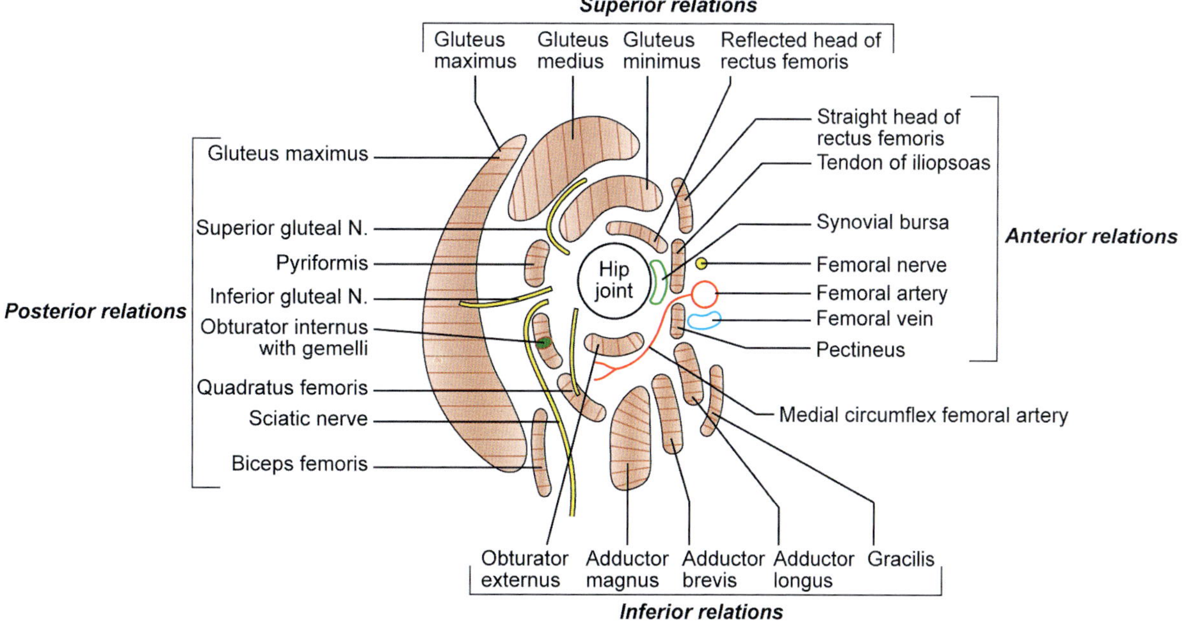

Fig 12.6: Relations of the hip joint

Posterior

1. Gluteus maximus
2. Piriformis
3. Sciatic nerve, and nerve to quadratus femoris
4. Obturator internus with two gemelli
5. Quadratus femoris.

Superior

1. Reflected head of the rectus femoris
2. Gluteus minimus
3. Gluteus medius
4. Part of the gluteus maximus.

Inferior

1. Lateral fibres of the pectineus
2. Obturator externus
3. Muscles of adductor compartment of thigh
4. Hamstring muscles.

Bursae Around the Hip Joint (Plate 12.3)

The hip joint is related to the following bursae:

1. *Trochanteric bursa*: Bursa between gluteus maximus and greater trochanter.
2. *Ischial bursa*: It lies between gluteus maximus and ischial tuberosity.
3. *Gluteofemoral bursa*: It lies between the tendon of gluteus maximus and vastus lateralis.
4. *Subpsoas bursa*: It lies between iliopubic eminence and psoas major tendon. It may communicate with the synovial cavity of the hip joint through a gap within the capsule between the iliofemoral and pubofemoral ligaments.
5. Bursa between gluteus medius and greater trochanter.
6. Bursa between gluteus minimus and greater trochanter.

Blood Supply

The hip joint is supplied by the branches of the following arteries (Fig. 12.7):

1. Obturator artery
2. Medial and lateral circumflex femoral arteries
3. Superior and inferior gluteal arteries.

Note: The medial and lateral circumflex femoral arteries form an ***arterial circle*** around the capsular attachment on the neck of the femur. ***Retinacular arteries*** (main source) arise from this circle and supply the intracapsular part of the neck and the greater part of the head of the femur. A small part of the head, near the fovea capitis, is supplied by the *acetabular branches of the obturator* and *medial circumflex femoral arteries* (*see* Fig. 4.7).

Nerve Supply

The hip joint is supplied by the branches of:

1. Femoral nerve, through the nerve to the rectus femoris
2. Anterior division of the obturator nerve
3. Nerve to the quadratus femoris
4. Superior gluteal nerve.

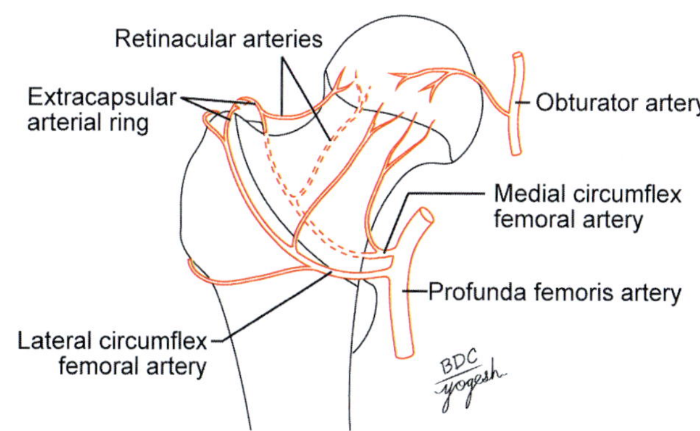

Fig. 12.7: Blood supply of hip joint

Plate 12.3: Bursae around the hip joint

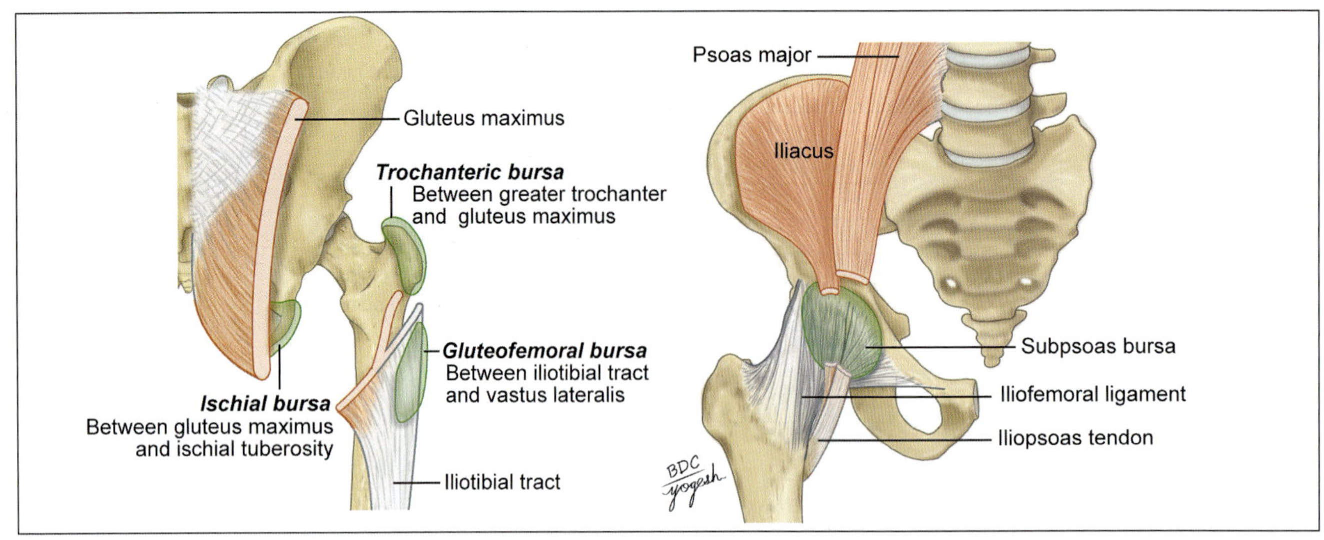

Movements (Fig. 12.8)

1. Flexion and extension occur around a transverse axis.
2. Adduction and abduction occur around an antero-posterior axis.
3. Medial and lateral rotations occur around a vertical axis.
4. Circumduction is a combination of the foregoing movements.

The muscles producing these movements are given in Table 12.1.

Range of Movements

The movements of the hip are limited by the ligaments, muscles and acetabulum. The range of the hip movements are as follows:

Flexion: 110°–120°
Extension: 15°
Abduction: 50°
Medial rotation: 25°
Lateral rotation: 60°

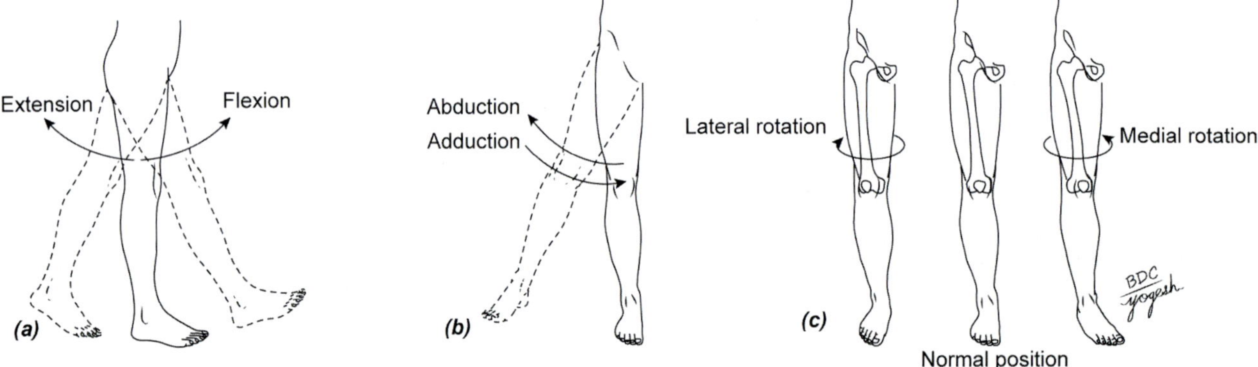

Figs 12.8a to c: Movements of hip joint: (a) Flexion and extension, (b) adduction and abduction, and (c) medial and lateral rotations

TABLE 12.1: Muscles producing movements at the hip joint

Movement	*Chief muscles*	*Accessory muscles*
1. Flexion	Psoas major and iliacus	Pectineus, rectus femoris and sartorius; adductors (mainly adductor longus) participate in early stages
2. Extension	Gluteus maximus and hamstrings	—
3. Adduction	Adductor: Longus, brevis and magnus	Pectineus and gracilis
4. Abduction	Glutei medius and minimus	Tensor fasciae latae and sartorius
5. Medial rotation	Tensor fasciae latae and the anterior fibres of the glutei medius and minimus	—
6. Lateral rotation	Two obturators, two gemelli and the quadratus femoris	Piriformis, gluteus maximus and sartorius

Competencies:

AN17.2 Describe anatomical basis of complications of fracture neck of femur.

AN17.3 Describe dislocation of hip joint and surgical hip replacement.

CLINICAL ANATOMY

- ***Congenital dislocation*** is more common in the hip than in any other joint of the body. The head of the femur slips upwards onto the gluteal surface of the ilium because the upper margin of the acetabulum is developmentally deficient (Fig. 12.9). This causes lurching gait, and Trendelenburg's test is positive.
- *Dislocation of the hip* may be posterior (more common), anterior (less common), or central (rare). The sciatic nerve may be injured in posterior dislocations.
- ***Coxa vara*** is a condition in which the neck-shaft angle is reduced from the normal angle of about 150° in a child, and 127° in an adult (Fig. 12.10). In ***coxa valga***, the neck-shaft angle is increased.
- Disease of the hip, like tuberculosis, may cause ***referred pain*** in the knee because of the common nerve supply of the two joints.
- ***Aspiration of the hip joint*** can be done by passing a needle from a point 5 cm below the anterior superior iliac spine, upwards, backwards and medially. It can also be done from the side by passing the needle from the posterior edge of the greater trochanter, upwards and medially, parallel with the neck of the femur.
- Hip diseases show an interesting ***age pattern***:
  a. Below 5 years: Congenital dislocation (Fig. 12.6) and tuberculosis
  b. 5 to 10 years: Perthes' disease
  c. 10 to 20 years: Coxa vara (Fig. 12.7)
  d. Above 40 years: Osteoarthritis.
- ***Osteoarthritis*** is a degenerative disease of the old age that results in wearing of articular cartilages. Bones show growth of osteophytes at articular ends that restrict the movements and cause pain on movements.
- ***Fracture of the neck of the femur*** may be subcapital, near the head (Fig. 12.11), cervical in the middle, or basal near the trochanters. Damage to retinacular arteries causes ***avascular necrosis of the head***. Such a damage is maximal in subcapital fractures and least in basal fractures (Fig. 12.11). These fractures are common in old age, between the age of 40 and 60 years.
- ***Intertrochanteric fractures*** have a bimodal age distribution. In young patients, they are a result of high energy trauma, while in elderly they occur due to trivial trauma. *Subtrochanteric fractures* occur in young adults and are a result of high energy trauma (Fig. 12.11).
- ***Shenton's line***, in an X-ray picture, is a continuous curve formed by the upper border of the obturator foramen and the lower border of the neck of the femur. In fracture neck femur, line becomes abnormal (Fig. 12.12).
- ***Shoemaker's line*** is a line projected from the tip of the greater trochanter to the anterior superior iliac spine, and it passes above or through the umbilicus. In case of fracture of the neck of the femur with elevation of the greater trochanter, the Shoemaker's line passes below the umbilicus.
- ***Perthes' disease*** or ***pseudocoxalgia*** is characterised by destruction and flattening of the head of the femur, with an increased joint space in X-ray (Fig. 12.13).
- ***Aspiration of the hip joint:*** For hip joint aspiration, the needle is passed with the following two approaches (Fig. 12.14):

  Anterior: At the point of intersection between a vertical line below ASIS and horizontal line from greater trochanter, in upward and slightly medial direction.

  Lateral: At the point superior and medial to greater trochanter until it hits the bone.
- ***Close packed position of hip joint***: In this position, the capsule of the hip joint is the most taut. It occurs at the hip joint extension with slight abduction and medial rotation.
- ***Hip replacement surgery*** or arthroplasty is a surgery for the replacement of a worn-out (by osteoarthritis) or damaged hip joint with an artificial joint (prosthesis) (Fig. 12.15). It may be partial or complete hip replacement surgery.
- ***Dynamic hip screw (DHS) fixation*** is an orthopaedic implant that is designed for fixation of fractures of neck of femur (Fig. 12.15).

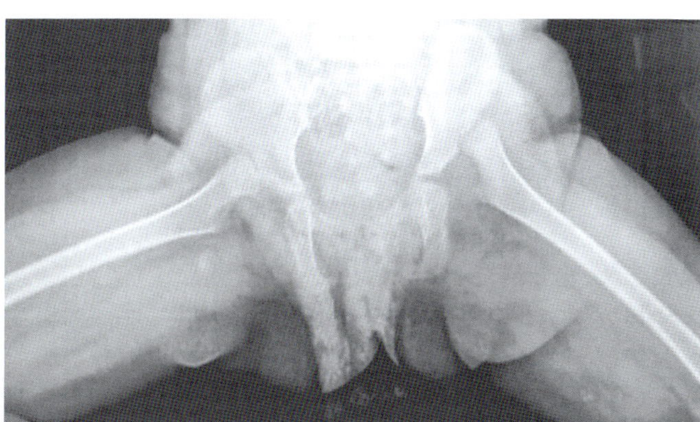

Fig. 12.9: Congenital dislocation of hip joint

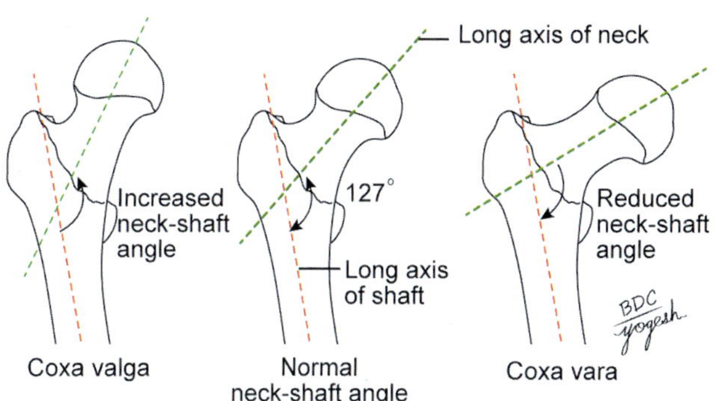

Fig. 12.10: Coxa vara and coxa valga

Joints of Lower Limb

12

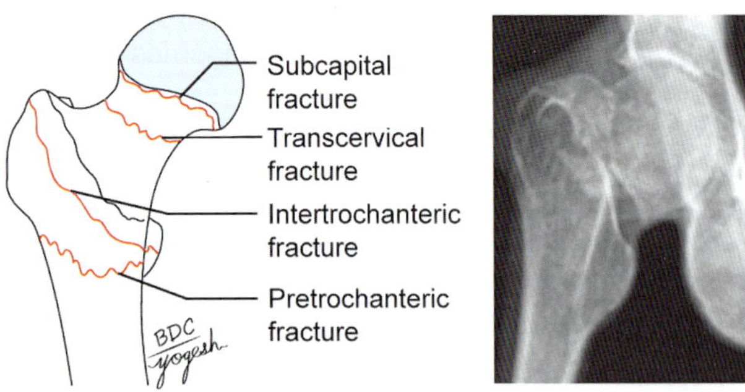

Fig. 12.11: Fracture of neck and trochanteric fractures and avascular necrosis of head of femur

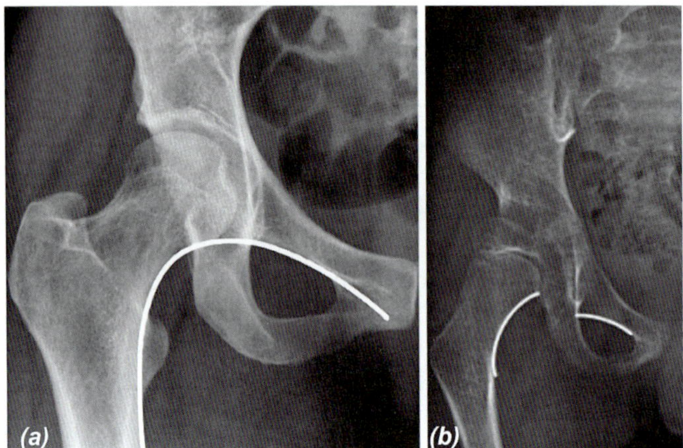

Figs 12.12a and b: Shenton's line: (a) Normal and (b) in fracture neck femur

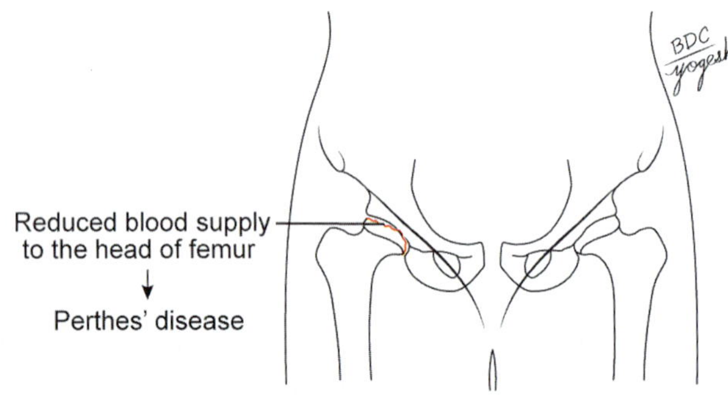

Fig. 12.13: Perthes' disease or pseudocoxalgia

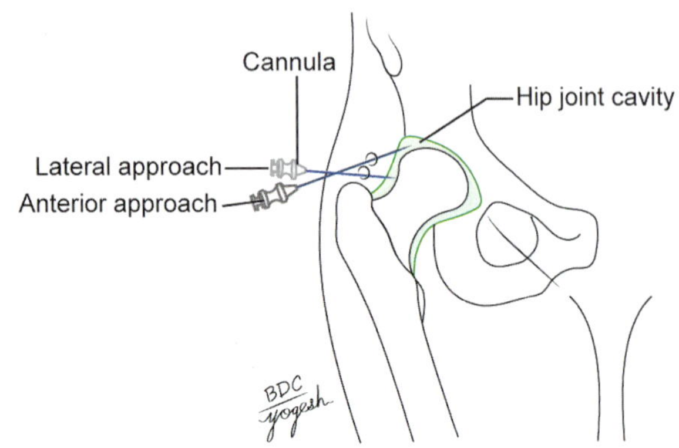

Fig. 12.14: Aspiration of the hip joint

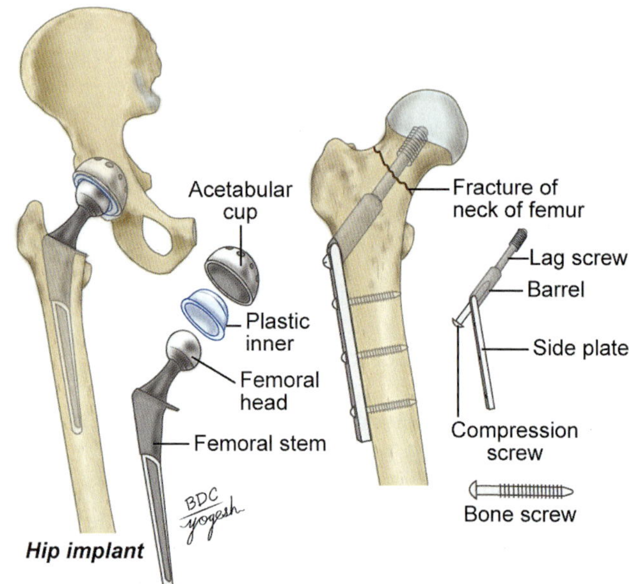

Fig. 12.15: Total hip replacement or arthroplasty and dynamic hip screw

DISSECTION

Ligate the femoral vessels and nerve with thick thread 2 cm below the inguinal ligament. Cut them above the ligature.

Cut sartorius muscle 5 cm below its origin and rectus femoris 3 cm below its origin and reflect these downwards. Detach the iliopsoas muscle from its insertion into lesser trochanter and separate the two parts.

The capsule of the joint and the thickened iliofemoral ligament are now exposed. Supplement the study of the ligaments and movements on the dried bones.

Competency:

AN18.4 Describe and demonstrate the type, articular surfaces, capsule, synovial membrane, ligaments, relations, movements and muscles involved, blood and nerve supply and bursae around the knee joint.

KNEE JOINT

The knee is the largest and most complex joint of the body. It is formed by fusion of the lateral femorotibial, medial femorotibial and femoropatellar joints (Plate 12.4, Fig. 12.16, Flowchart 12.2) .

Type

It is ***condylar synovial joint***, incorporating two condylar joints between the condyles of the femur and tibia, and one ***saddle joint*** between the femur and the patella. It is also a ***complex joint*** as the cavity is divided by the menisci.

Articular Surfaces

The knee joint is formed by condyles of the femur, patella and condyles of the tibia (Plate 12.4, Figs 12.17a and b).

Plate 12.4: Articular surfaces of knee joint

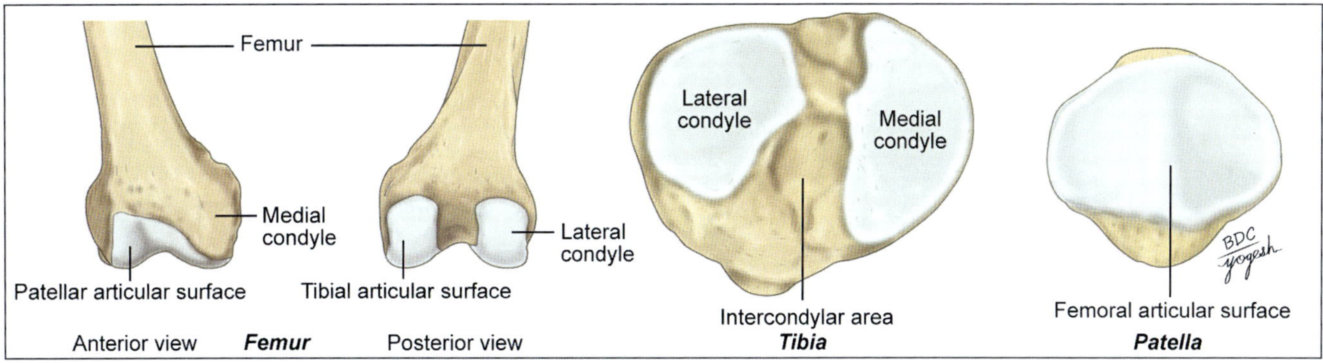

Flowchart 12.2: Knee joint: Classification of articular surfaces, movements, cruciate ligaments and menisci

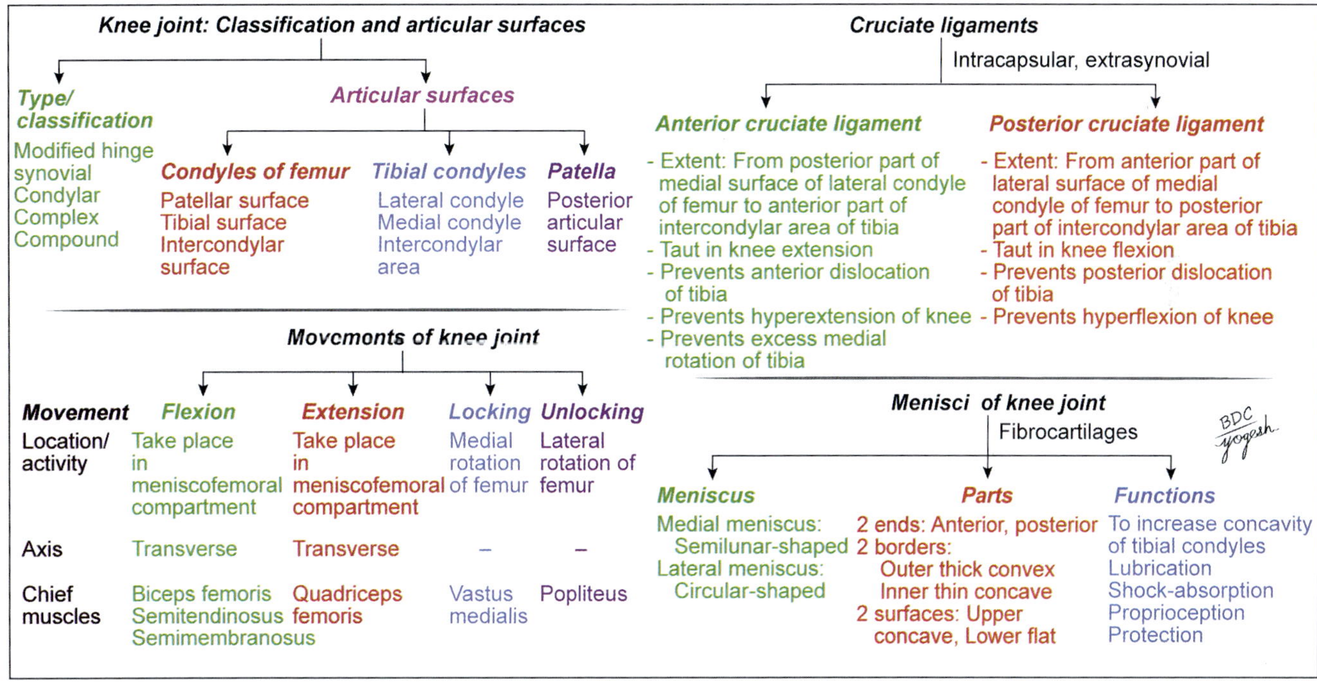

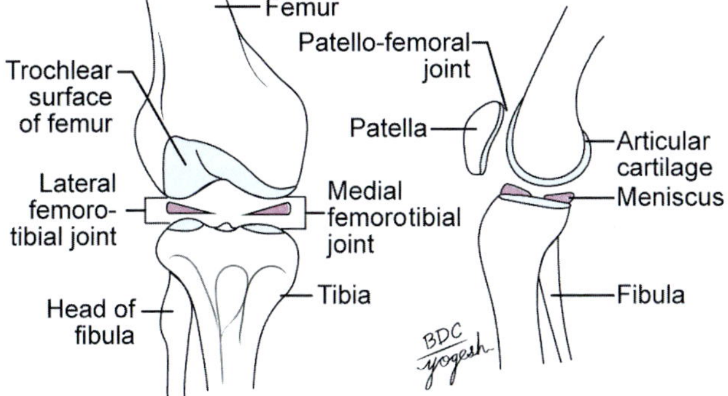

Fig. 12.16: Three primitive joints included in the knee joint: condylar type of medial and lateral femorotibial joints; saddle type of patellofemoral joint.

Condyles of Femur

The medial and lateral condylar articular surfaces of femur participate in knee joint. It has patellar and tibial articular surfaces. *Patellar articular surface* covers the anterior surface of the both condyles and is separated from tibial articular surface by a faint groove. *Tibial articular surface* covers the inferior and posterior surfaces of both femoral condyles and is separated from each other by *intercondylar notch.*

Tibial Condyles

Tibia has two condyles – lateral and medial. The superior surface of medial condyle has smooth oval facet, whereas the superior surface of lateral condyle has circular articular facet.

Patellar Articular Surface

The upper 3/4th of the posterior surface of the patella is articular, that is, divisible by a vertical ridge into larger lateral and smaller medial areas. This medial area is further subdivided into narrow medial strip and larger lateral part.

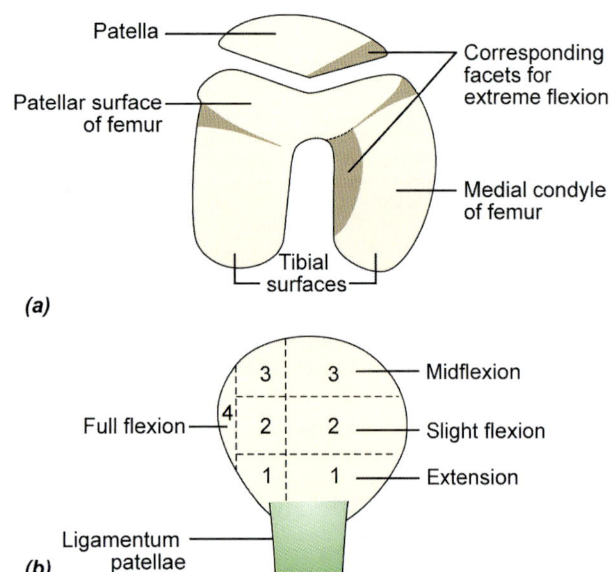

Figs 12.17a and b: (a) Lower end of the femur and patella and (b) posterior view of patella

CLINICAL ANATOMY

- Structurally, the knee is a weak joint because the articular surfaces are not congruent. The tibial condyles are too small and shallow to hold the large, convex, femoral condyles in place. The femoropatellar articulation is also quite insecure because of the shallow articular surfaces, and because of the outward angulation between the long axis of the thigh and of the leg.
- ***Factors maintaining the stability of the knee joint***: The stability of the joint is maintained by a number of factors:
  a. Cruciate ligaments maintain anteroposterior stability.
  b. Collateral ligaments maintain side-to-side stability.
  c. Various ligaments strengthen the capsule.
  d. Iliotibial tract plays an important role in stabilising the knee.

Ligaments (Plate 12.5, Fig. 12.18)

The knee joint is supported by the following ligaments:

1. Fibrous capsule
2. Ligamentum patellae
3. Tibial collateral or medial ligament
4. Fibular collateral or lateral ligament
5. Oblique popliteal ligament
6. Arcuate popliteal ligament
7. Anterior and posterior cruciate ligaments
8. Medial and lateral menisci
9. Transverse ligament.

Fibrous (Articular) Capsule

The fibrous capsule is very thin, and is deficient anteriorly, where it is replaced by the quadriceps femoris, the patella and the ligamentum patellae (Plate 12.5, Fig. 12.18).

Femoral attachment: It is attached about half to one centimetre beyond the articular margins. The attachment has three special features.

1. Anteriorly, it is deficient.
2. Posteriorly, it is attached to the intercondylar line.
3. Laterally, it encloses the origin of the popliteus.

Tibial attachment: It is attached about ½–1 cm beyond the articular margins. The attachment has three special features.

1. Anteriorly, it descends along the margins of the condyles to the tibial tuberosity, where it is deficient.
2. Posteriorly, it is attached to the intercondylar ridge which limits the attachment of the posterior cruciate ligament.
3. Posterolaterally, there is a gap behind the lateral condyle for passage of the tendon of the popliteus.

Synovial membrane lines the inner aspect of the fibrous capsule. It gives extensions to cover cruciate ligaments and infrapatellar pad of fat.

Ligamentum Patellae (Plate 12.5)

It is a strong thick fibrous band, which is a continuation of the tendon of quadriceps femoris. It extends from apex of patella to the tibial tuberosity. It stabilizes and prevents displacement of patella.

Tibial Collateral or Medial Ligament (Plate 12.5, Fig. 12.18)

This is a long band of great strength. Superiorly, it is attached to the medial epicondyle of the femur just below the adductor tubercle. Inferiorly, it divides into anterior/superficial and posterior/deep parts.

The ***superficial part*** extends from medial epicondyle of femur to the upper part of medial border and adjoining posterior part of medial surface of the tibia.

The ***deep part*** of the ligament is short and blends with the capsule and with the medial meniscus. It is attached to the medial condyle of the tibia above the groove for the semimembranosus.

Note: *Morphologically*, the tibial collateral ligament represents the degenerated tendon of the adductor magnus muscle. The knee joint gaps more on the medial side. Hence, the knee joint is supported medially for more stabilization with much thicker medial collateral ligament than the lateral collateral ligament.

Fibular Collateral or Lateral Ligament (Plate 12.5, Fig. 12.18)

This ligament is strong and cord-like. *Superiorly*, it is attached to the lateral epicondyle of the femur just above the popliteal groove. *Inferiorly*, it is attached to the head of the fibula in front of its apex.

Note: The fibular collateral ligament is separated from the lateral meniscus by the tendon of the popliteus. It is free from the capsule. The inferior lateral genicular vessels and nerve separate it from the capsule. *Morphologically*, it represents the femoral attachment of the peroneus longus.

Plate 12.5: Ligaments of knee joint

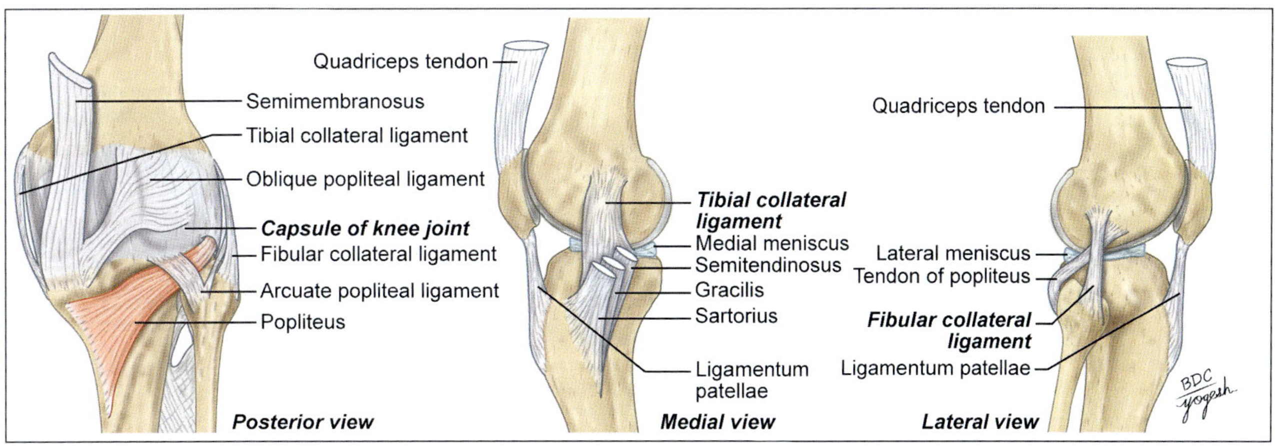

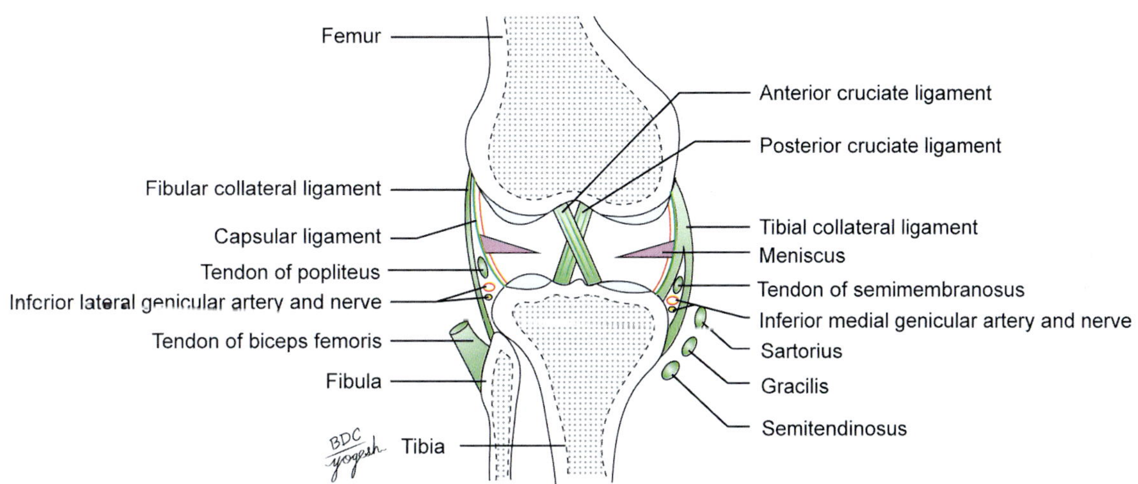

Fig. 12.18: Coronal section of knee joint

Oblique Popliteal Ligament (Plate 12.5)

This is an expansion from the tendon of the semimembranosus. It runs upwards and laterally, blends with the posterior surface of the capsule, and is attached to the intercondylar line and lateral condyle of the femur.

It is closely related to the popliteal artery and is pierced by: a. the middle genicular vessels, b. middle genicular nerve and c. the terminal part of the posterior division of the obturator nerve.

Arcuate Popliteal Ligament (Plate 12.5)

This is a posterior expansion from the short lateral ligament. It extends backwards from the head of the fibula, arches over the tendon of the popliteus, and is attached to the posterior border of the intercondylar area of the tibia.

Cruciate Ligaments
(Plate 12.6, Figs 12.18 and 12.19)

These are very thick and strong fibrous bands, which act as direct bonds of union between tibia and femur, to maintain anteroposterior stability of knee joint. They are that are arranged like a letter *X*, and named according to the attachment on tibia.

Anterior cruciate ligament: It begins from anterior part of intercondylar area of tibia, runs upwards, backwards and laterally and is attached to the posterior part of medial surface of lateral condyle of femur.

Posterior cruciate ligament: It begins from the posterior part of intercondylar area of tibia, runs upwards, forwards and medially and is attached to the anterior part of the lateral surface of medial condyle of femur. It is taut during flexion of the knee.

These are supplied by middle genicular vessels and nerves.

Functions

ACL is taut during extension of knee and prevents the hypertension of knee joint. It prevents the anterior dislocation of tibia, and posterior dislocation of femur. It also prevents excess medial rotation of the tibia. They perform these functions with the help of mechanoreceptors that are located within these ligaments.

PCL is taut during flexion of knee. PCL prevents anterior dislocation of femur on tibia, and posterior dislocation of tibia on femur. It prevents hyperflexion of the knee joint.

Plate 12.6: Cruciate ligaments and menisci of knee joint

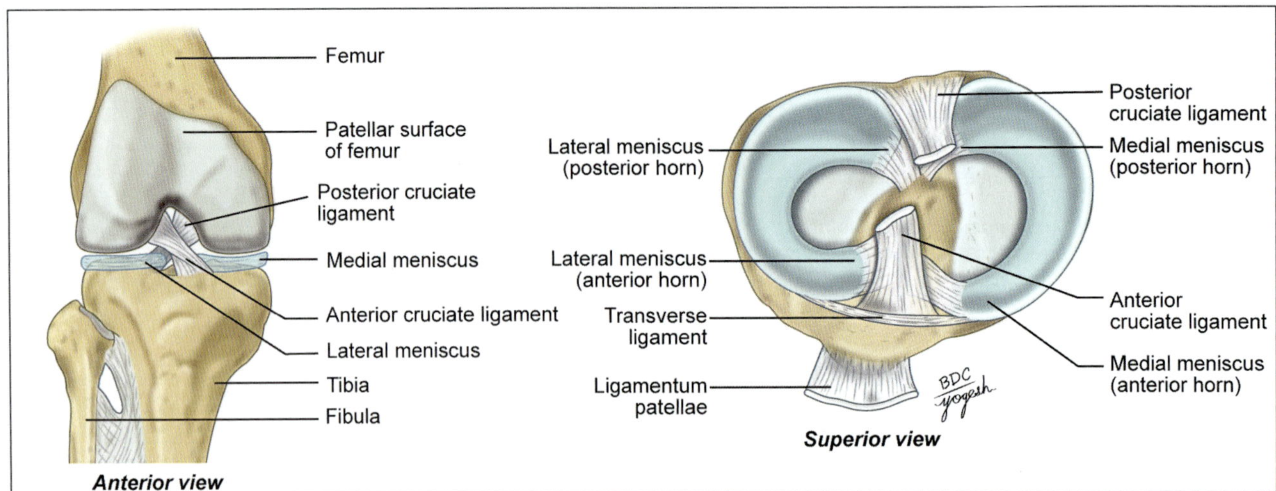

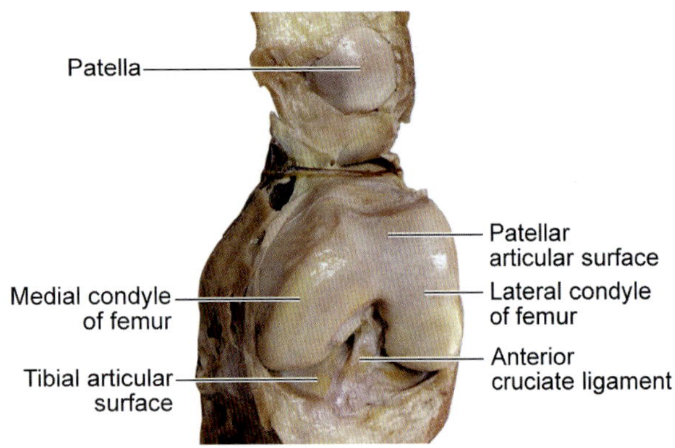

Fig. 12.19: Dissection of knee joint

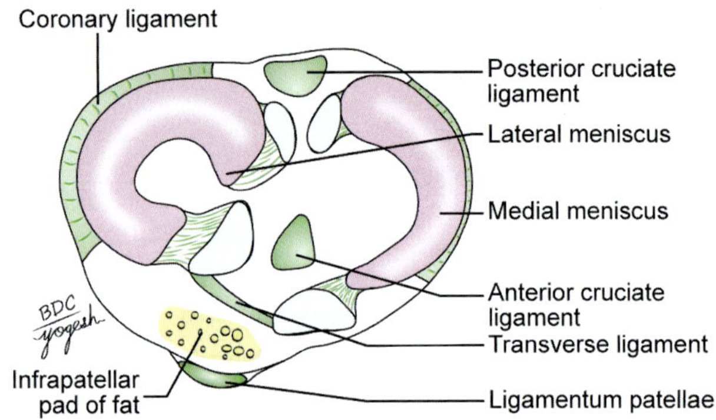

Fig. 12.20: Superior view of upper end of the right tibia

Menisci or Semilunar Cartilages

The menisci are two fibrocartilaginous discs (Plate 12.6, Figs 12.18 and 12.20, Table 12.2). They are shaped like crescents. They deepen the articular surfaces of the condyles of the tibia, and partially divide the joint cavity into upper and lower compartments. Flexion and extension of the knee take place in the *upper* compartment, whereas rotation takes place in the *lower* compartment (Fig. 12.18).

Each meniscus has the following:

a. *Two ends:* The anterior and posterior ends of menisci are attached to the tibia and are referred to as anterior and posterior horns.
b. *Two borders:* The 'outer' border is thick, convex and close to the fibrous capsule; while the 'inner' border is thin, concave and free.
c. *Two surfaces:* The upper surface is concave for articulation with the femur. The lower surface is flat and rests on the peripheral 2/3rd of the tibial condyle. The peripheral thick part is vascular. The inner part is avascular and is nourished by synovial fluid.

The ***medial meniscus*** is nearly *semicircular*, being wider behind than in front. The posterior fibres of the anterior end are continuous with the transverse

TABLE 12.2: Differences between the medial and lateral menisci

Medial meniscus	*Lateral meniscus*
Shape: C-shaped/semilunar	*Shape*: O-shaped or circular
Attachment: Attached to the medial collateral ligament	*Attachment*: Attached to the tendon popliteus muscle
Mobility: Less mobile	*Mobility*: More mobile
Blood supply: Poor	*Blood supply*: Better
Injury: More prone to injury	*Injury*: Less prone to injury

ligament. Its peripheral margin is adherent to the deep part of the tibial collateral ligament.

The ***lateral meniscus*** is nearly *circular*. The posterior end of the meniscus is attached to the medial condyle of femur through two meniscofemoral ligaments. The tendon of the popliteus and the capsule separate this meniscus from the fibular collateral ligament. The more medial part of the tendon of the popliteus is attached to the lateral meniscus. The mobility of the posterior end of this meniscus is controlled by the popliteus and by the two meniscofemoral ligaments.

Note:
Because of the attachments of the menisci to multiple structures, the motion of the menisci is limited to a great extent. Out of the two menisci, the medial meniscus has more firm attachments to the tibia.

Functions of menisci

1. They help in making the articular surfaces more congruent. Because of their flexibility, they can adapt their contour to the varying curvature of the different parts of the femoral condyles, as the latter glide over the tibia.
2. The menisci serve as shock absorbers.
3. They help in lubricating the joint cavity.
4. Because of their nerve supply, they also have a sensory function. They give rise to proprioceptive impulses.

Transverse Ligament

It connects the anterior ends of the medial and lateral menisci (Fig. 12.20). It is present only in 58% of individuals.

DISSECTION

Strip the extra structures around the knee joint, leaving behind the fibrous capsule, ligaments and parts of muscles/tendons attached to the bones/ligaments.

Study the articular surfaces, articular capsule, medial and lateral collateral ligaments, oblique popliteal ligament and arcuate popliteal ligament.

Bursae Around the Knee

As many as 12 bursae have been described around the knee—four anterior, four lateral, and four medial. These bursae are as follows (Fig. 12.21):

Anterior Bursae

1. ***Subcutaneous prepatellar bursa***: It lies deep to the skin in front of lower half of patella and upper half of ligamentum patellae.
2. ***Subcutaneous infrapatellar bursa***: It lies between the skin and ligamentum patellae.
3. ***Suprapatellar bursa***: It lies between anterior surface of lower part of femur and deep surface of quadriceps femoris.
4. ***Deep infrapatellar bursa***: It lies between ligamentum patellae and tibial tuberosity.

Lateral Bursae

1. ***Lateral gastrocnemius bursa***: It lies between the lateral head of gastrocnemius and the joint capsule.
2. ***Fibular bursa***: It lies between fibular collateral ligament and tendon of biceps femoris.
3. ***Fibulopopliteal bursa***: It lies between fibular collateral and tendon of the popliteus.
4. ***Subpopliteal bursa***: It lies between popliteus and lateral condyle of femur.

Medial Bursae

1. ***Medial gastrocnemius (Bordie's bursa)***: It lies between the medial head of gastrocnemius and joint capsule.
2. ***Anserine bursa***: It lies between tibial collateral ligament and pes anserinus (conjoined insertion of sartorius, semitendinosus and gracilis).
3. ***Bursa semimembranosus***: It lies between semimembranosus and tibial collateral ligament.
4. Bursa between semimembranosus and medial condyle of tibia.

CLINICAL ANATOMY

- ***Housemaids knee*** or ***Carpenter's knee*** is prepatellar bursitis. It occurs due to friction and infection of prepatellar bursa against the floor and patella. It is commonly observed in housemaid, hence, name housemaids knee. It is marked by swelling at knee that may be painful, tender and restrict the movements of knee joint (Fig. 12.22).
- ***Clergyman's knee*** is an inflammation of subcutaneous infrapatellar bursa (Fig. 12.23). It occurs due to friction of this bursa against the tibial tuberosity during kneeling or crawling. It occurs commonly in kneeling by Christian Priest or Clergyman during prayers. It presents with a swelling below the patella, just anterior to ligamentum patellae.
- ***Baker's cyst*** is popliteal (Baker's) cyst that occurs due to inflammation of bursa lying deep to semimembranosus. It presents a painful, fluid-filled sac in the medial popliteal fossa that restricts the knee movements.

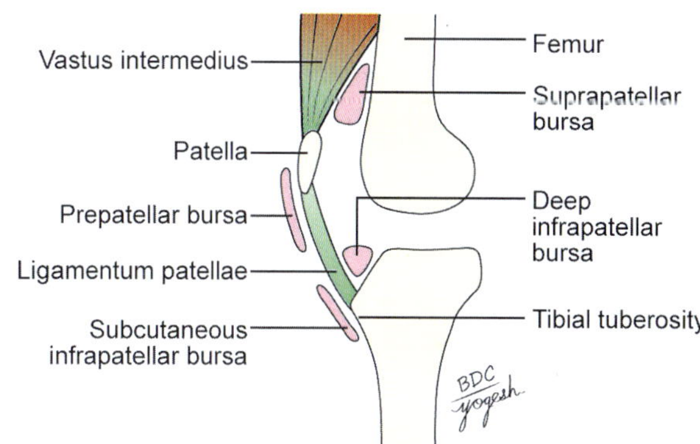

Fig. 12.21: The patellar bursae

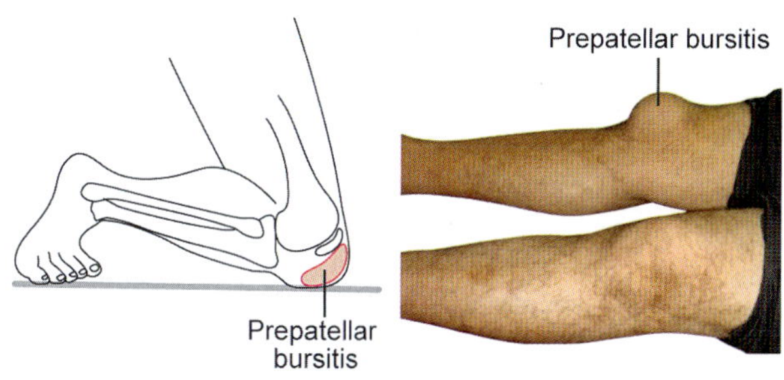

Fig. 12.22: Housemaid knee

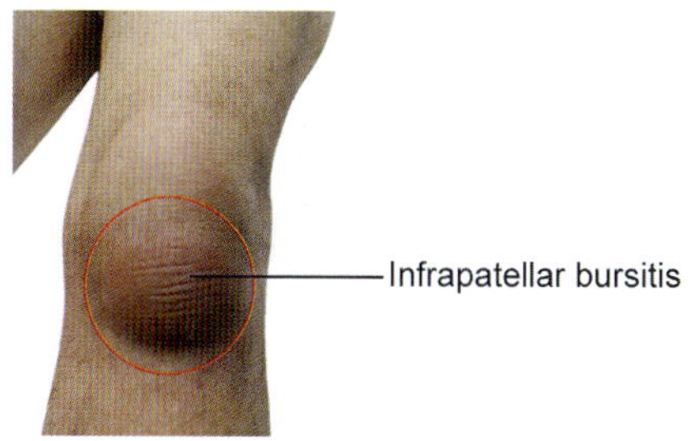

Fig. 12.23: Infrapatellar bursitis

Relations of Knee Joint (Fig. 12.24)

Anteriorly

Anterior bursae, ligamentum patellae and patellar plexus of nerves.

Posteriorly

1. *At the middle:* Popliteal vessels, tibial nerve.
2. *Posterolaterally:* Lateral head of gastrocnemius, plantaris and common peroneal nerve.
3. *Posteromedially:* Medial head of gastrocnemius, semitendinosus, semimembranosus, gracilis, and popliteus at its insertion.

Medially

1. Sartorius, gracilis and semitendinosus.
2. Great saphenous vein with saphenous nerve.
3. Semimembranosus.

Laterally

Biceps femoris, and tendon of origin of popliteus.

Blood Supply

The knee joint is supplied by the anastomoses around it. The chief sources of blood supply are:

1. Five genicular branches of the popliteal artery.
2. Descending genicular branch of the femoral artery.
3. Descending branch of the lateral circumflex femoral artery.
4. Two recurrent branches of the anterior tibial artery.
5. The circumflex fibular branch of the posterior tibial artery (*see* Fig. 6.14).

Nerve Supply

1. Femoral nerve, through its branches to the vasti, especially the vastus medialis.
2. Genicular branches of the tibial and common peroneal nerves.
3. Obturator nerve, through its posterior division.

Note: ***Morphology of Knee Joint***

1. The tibial collateral ligament is the degenerated tendon of the adductor magnus.
2. The fibular collateral ligament is the degenerated tendon of the peroneus longus.
3. Cruciate ligaments represent the collateral ligaments of the originally separate femorotibial joints.
4. Infrapatellar synovial fold indicates the lower limit of the femoropatellar joint.

Competency:
AN18.5 Explain the anatomical basis of locking and unlocking of the knee joint.

MOVEMENTS AT THE KNEE JOINT

Active movements at the knee are flexion, extension, medial rotation and lateral rotation (Table 12.3).

Flexion and extension

These are the chief/main movements of the knee joints. They take place in the meniscofemoral or upper compartment of the joint.

In the *flexion*, the posterior angle between the thigh and leg decreases, whereas in *extension* the posterior angle between the thigh and leg increases. The flexion and extension take place at the transverse axis. This axis moves forward and upward in extension and in the reverse direction during flexion.

Medial and lateral rotation

The medial and lateral rotation of knee joint occurs in meniscotibial or lower compartment of the joint. These rotatory movements take place at a small range. They

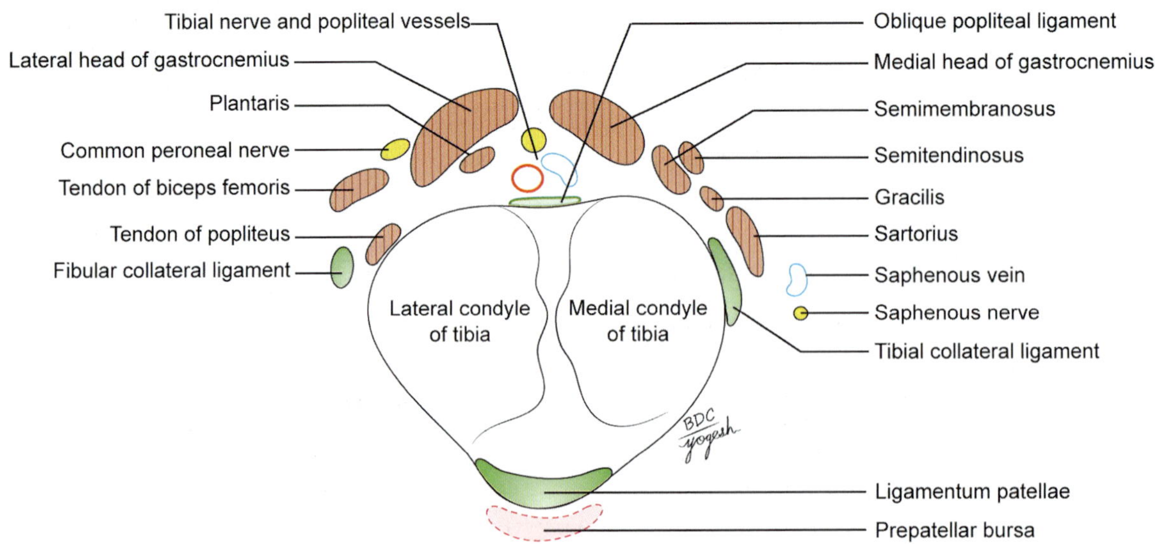

Fig. 12.24: Transverse section through the right knee joint showing the relations

TABLE 12.3: Muscles producing movements at the knee joint

Movement	*Principal muscles*	*Accessory muscles*
Flexion	1. Biceps femoris 2. Semitendinosus 3. Semimembranosus	Popliteus (initiates flexion) Sartorius Gracilis Gastrocnemius Plantaris
Extension (from sitting on a chair to standing)	Quadriceps femoris (four heads)	Tensor fasciae latae
Medial rotation of flexed leg	1. Popliteus 2. Semimembranosus 3. Semitendinosus	Sartorius Gracilis
Lateral rotation of flexed leg	Biceps femoris	Gluteus maximus Tensor fasciae latae
Locking (standing in 'attention')	Vastus medialis	—
Unlocking (standing 'at ease')	Popliteus	—

take place around the vertical axis. These rotatory movements can take place in isolation but mostly they take place in conjugation with flexion and extension at knee joint.

Locking and Unlocking of the Knee Joint

(Fig. 12.25, Table 12.4)

Locking of the knee joint

- It is defined as the positioning of the femur on the tibia to stabilise the leg and to minimise the muscular efforts during standing. When foot is on the ground, the medial rotation of femur in last phase of extension (in last 30°) locks the knee joint.
- *Muscle responsible*: Quadriceps femoris muscles, mainly vastus medialis.
- *Utility*: To reduce the muscle efforts in standing.
- *Anatomical basis*: The anteroposterior diameter of the lateral femoral condyle is less than the medial condyle. As a result, during extension, when lateral articular surface is fully used up, a part of medial condyle remains unused for further extension, lateral condyle rotates around its vertical axis and medial condyle rotates backward. It results in medial rotation of femur around the vertical axis passing through the lateral condyle of femur, till the remaining part of medial condylar surface is also taken up. This movement locks the knee joint.
- *Ligaments*: In the locking position, all knee ligaments are taut and knee becomes absolutely rigid.

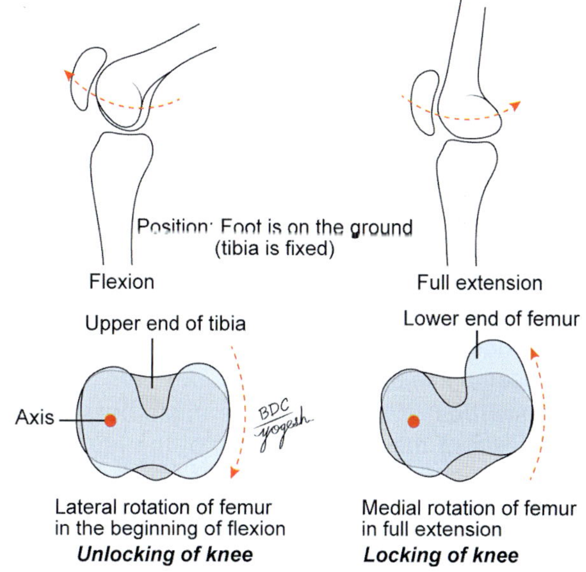

Fig. 12.25: Mechanism of locking and unlocking of knee

Unlocking of knee

- Unlocking of knee joint is defined as the lateral rotation of femur on the tibia during the initial phases of flexion. When the foot is on the ground, the lateral rotation of femur in the beginning of flexion unlocks the knee joint.
- *Muscle responsible*: Popliteus.
- *Ligaments*: In unlocking, the knee ligaments get relaxed and the joint losses its rigidity.

TABLE 12.4: Differences between locking and unlocking of knee

Feature	*Locking of knee joint*	*Unlocking of knee joint*
Occurrence	In the last phase of extension	In the beginning of flexion
Movement with foot on the ground	Medial rotation of femur	Lateral rotation of femur
Movement when foot is off the ground	Lateral rotation of tibia	Medial rotation of tibia
Muscle responsible for knee	Vastus medialis	Popliteus
Ligaments	Taut	Relaxed
Joint rigidity	Joint becomes rigid	Joint can be flexed

DISSECTION

Cut through the tendon of quadriceps femoris muscle just above the knee joint. Extend this incision on either side of patella and ligamentum patellae anchored to the tibial tuberosity. Reflect patella downwards to peep into the cavity of knee joint.

Note the huge infrapatellar synovial fold and pad of fat in it. Remove the fat and posterior part of fibrous capsule so that the cruciate ligaments and menisci are visualised.

Clean the articular surfaces of femur, tibia and patella on the soft specimen and on dried bones. Analyse the movements on them. Try all these movements on yourself and on your friends as well.

Competencies:

AN18.6 Describe knee joint injuries with its applied anatomy.

AN18.7 Explain anatomical basis of osteoarthritis.

CLINICAL ANATOMY

- ***Osteoarthritis*** is an age-related cartilage degeneration that causes progressive loss of articular cartilages. It occurs in elderly people. It causes knee pain of gradual onset and worsens with activity, stiffness and swelling of knee, and pain after prolonged sitting. Radiographs may show reduction in joint space, damage to articular surfaces, and osteophytes. Treatment involves conservative methods (exercises, weight loss, knee bracing) and surgical methods (knee replacement in severe cases).
- ***Deformities of the knee***: The angle between the long axis of the thigh and that of the leg may be abnormal and the leg may be abnormally abducted (***genu valgum*** or knock knee) or abnormally adducted (***genu varum*** or bow knee). This may occur due to rickets, and posture, or as a congenital abnormality (Fig. 12.26).
- ***Aspiration of knee joint***: Infections may be associated with collections of the fluid in the joint cavity. Aspiration of fluid can be done by passing a needle into the joint from lateral side at the midpoint of the triangle formed by the tibial tuberosity, lateral epicondyle of femur, and apex of patella (Fig. 12.27).
- ***Injuries to menisci***: Injuries of the menisci occur due to twisting strains in slightly flexed knee. It occurs commonly in football and soccer players during kicking a ball (Fig. 12.28). Medial meniscus is more commonly injured as it is more fixed, whereas popliteus muscle preserves the lateral meniscus from crushing. Clinical symptoms include pain on the medial rotation of tibia occurs in the injury of medial meniscus, whereas pain on the lateral rotation of tibia occurs in the injury of lateral meniscus. The injury involves detachment from capsule or tears of the meniscus (longitudinal or ***transverse tears***). The longitudinal tears are called ***bucket-handle tear*** of meniscus.
- ***Injuries to cruciate ligaments*** are also common. The ACL is more commonly damaged than the PCL. It may be injured in violent hyperextension of the knee or in anterior dislocation of the tibia. The PCL is injured in posterior dislocation of the tibia. The injury may vary from simple sprain to complete tear.
- ***Drawer sign:*** If the tibia gets pulled forward or backward more than normal, the test is considered positive. In ACL injury, tibia can be pulled excessively forward on the femur. This is called ***anterior drawer sign***. In posterior cruciate ligament injury, tibia can be pushed excessively backward over the femur. This is called ***posterior drawer sign*** (Fig. 12.29).
- ***Injuries to collateral ligaments*** are less common, and may be produced by severe abduction and adduction strains.
- ***Malalignment of patella***: Ideally, the patella is resting in the centre of the width of the femur in a relaxed standing position. However, the patellar position may be altered congenitally or due to tightness of surrounding structures, which may lead to painful conditions of the patellofemoral joint.
- ***Arthroscopy of knee joint*** is an endoscopic visualisation of the interior of knee joint. It may be useful for repair of damaged cruciate ligaments.
- ***Knee replacement***: In severe damaged cases, knee requires treatment with knee replacement. It consists of fixation of artificial joint with plastic tibial and metal femoral components that to be connected to tibia and femur after removal of damaged zone of the bone (Fig. 12.30).

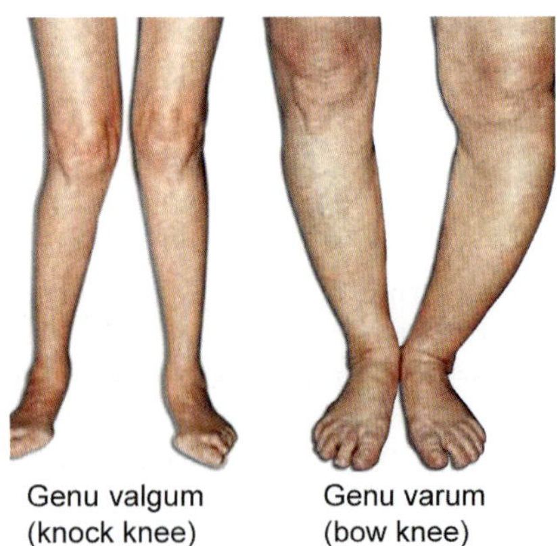

Fig. 12.26: Deformities of the knee

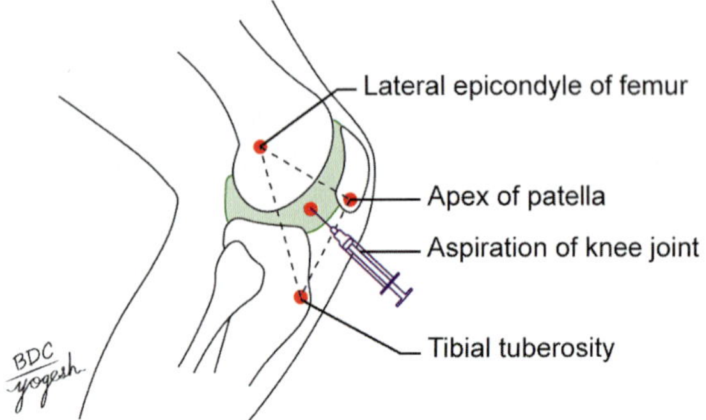

Fig. 12.27: Aspiration of knee

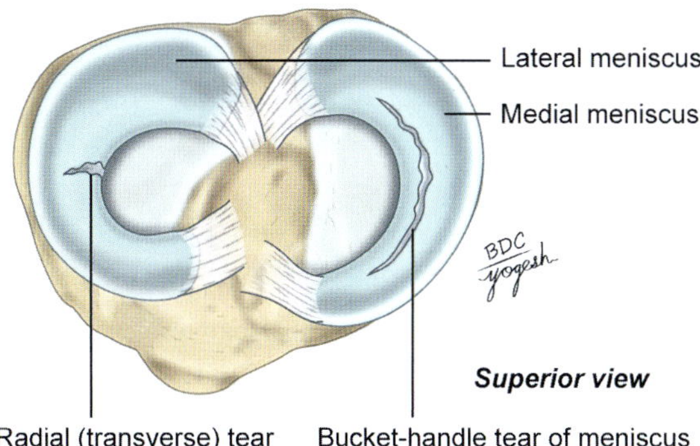

Fig. 12.28: Tears of knee menisci

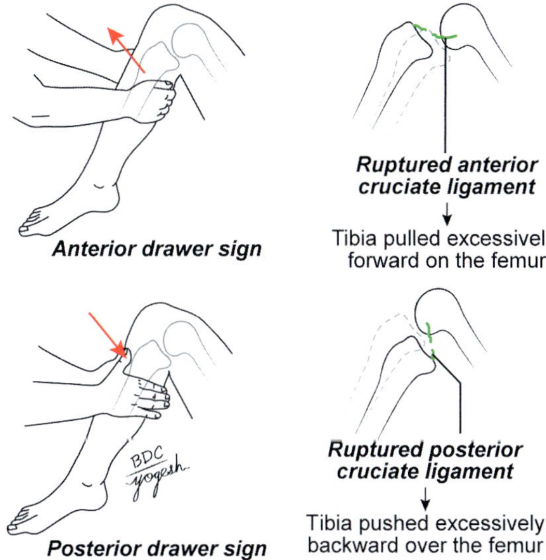

Fig. 12.29: Anterior and posterior drawer signs

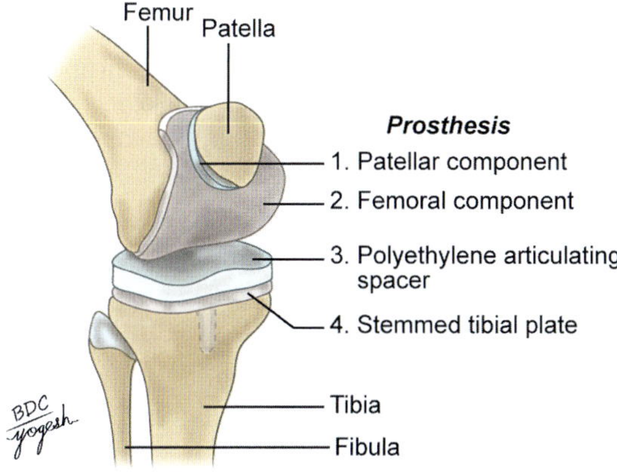

Fig. 12.30: Total knee replacement

Competency:

AN20.1 Describe and demonstrate the type, articular surfaces, capsule, synovial membrane, ligaments, relations, movements and muscles involved, blood and nerve supply of tibiofibular and ankle joint.

ANKLE JOINT

The ankle joint or talocrural joint is a strong weight-bearing joint placed between lower ends of tibia, and fibula and talus (Plate 12.7, Figs 12.31 and 12.32).

Type

This is a ***hinge*** variety of uniaxial synovial joint.

Articular Surfaces

Proximal articular surface is formed by:

1. Lower end of the tibia including the medial malleolus.
2. Lateral malleolus of the fibula.
3. Inferior transverse tibiofibular ligament.

These structures form a deep tibiofibular socket or ***tibiofibular mortise*** (Fig. 12.31).

Distal articular surface is formed by articular areas on the upper, medial and lateral aspects of the talus. Structurally, the joint is very strong.

Stability of Ankle Joint

The stability of the joint is ensured by:

a. Close interlocking of the articular surfaces.
b. Strong collateral ligaments on the sides.
c. The tendons that cross the joint, four in front and three on posteromedial side and two on posterolateral side.

Note: There are two factors, however, that tend to displace the tibia and fibula forwards over the talus. These factors are:

1. The forward pull of tendons, which pass from the leg to the foot.
2. The pull of gravity when the heel is raised.

Displacement is prevented by the following factors.

1. The talus is wedge-shaped, being wider anteriorly. The malleoli are oriented to fit this wedge.
2. The posterior border of the lower end of the tibia is prolonged downwards.
3. The presence of the inferior transverse tibiofibular ligament.
4. The tibiocalcanean, posterior tibiotalar (parts of deltoid ligament), calcaneofibular and posterior talofibular ligaments pass backwards and resist forward movement of the tibia and fibula.

Ligaments

The joint is supported by (Figs 12.31 and 12.32):

a. Fibrous capsule
b. Deltoid or medial collateral ligament
c. Lateral collateral ligament.

Fibrous Capsule

Fibrous capsule surrounds the joint but is weak anteriorly and posteriorly. It is attached all around the articular margins with two exceptions.

1. *Posterosuperiorly*, it is attached to the inferior transverse tibiofibular ligament.
2. *Anteroinferiorly*, it is attached to the dorsum of the neck of the talus at some distance from the trochlear surface.

The ***synovial membrane*** lines the capsule. The joint cavity ascends for some distance between the tibia and the fibula.

Note: The anterior and posterior parts of the capsule are loose and thin to allow hinge movements. On each side, however, it is supported by strong collateral ligaments.

Plate 12.7: Articular surfaces of ankle joint

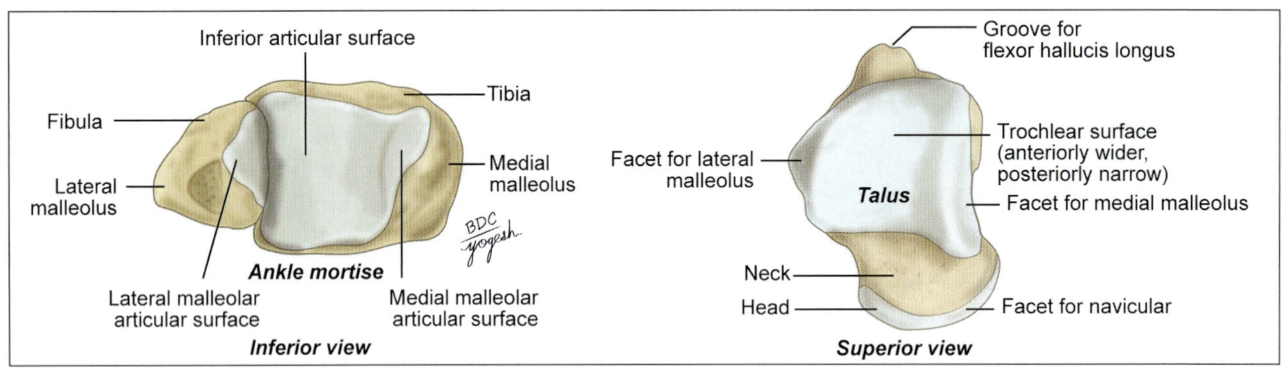

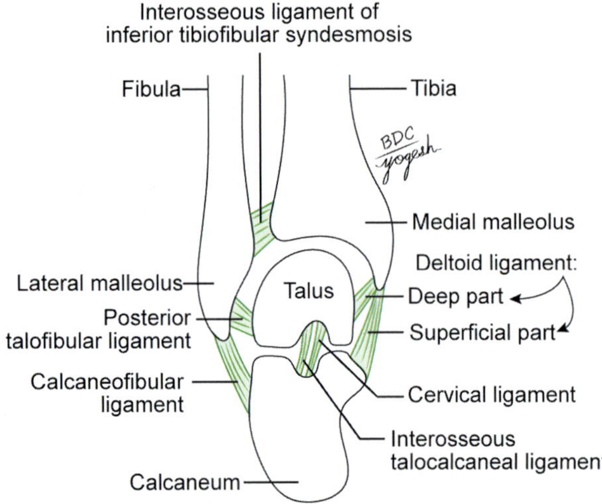

Fig. 12.31: Articular surfaces of ankle joint (coronal section passing through the ankle joint, right, anterior view)

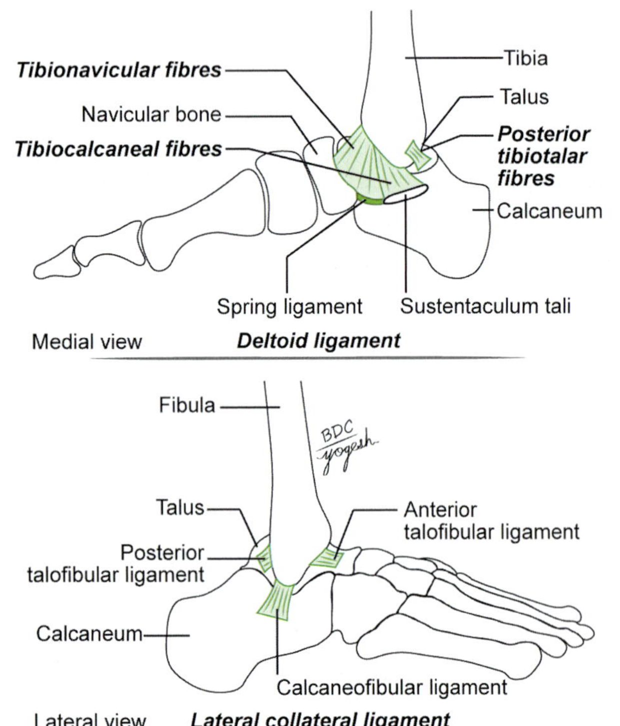

Fig. 12.32: Deltoid ligament and lateral collateral ligament of ankle joint

Deltoid or Medial Collateral Ligament

This is a very strong triangular ligament present on the medial side of the ankle. The ligament is divided into a superficial and a deep part. Both parts have a common attachment above to the apex and margins of the medial malleolus. The lower attachment is indicated by the name of the fibres (Fig. 12.32).

Superficial part has three components as follows:

1. Anterior fibres ***(tibionavicular fibres)*** are attached to the tuberosity of the navicular bone and to the medial margin of the spring ligament.
2. Middle fibres ***(tibiocalcanean fibres)*** are attached to the whole length of the sustentaculum tali.
3. Posterior fibres ***(posterior tibiotalar fibres)*** are attached to the medial tubercle of posterior process of the talus.

Deep or anterior tibiotalar part is attached to the anterior part of the medial surface of the talus.

Note: The deltoid ligament is a very strong ligament and excessive tensile forces on the ligament result in an avulsion fracture rather than a tear of the ligament. The ligament is prone to injuries in eversion.

Lateral Collateral Ligament

This ligament consists of three bands as follows:

1. ***Anterior talofibular ligament*** is a flat band which passes from the anterior margin of the lateral malleolus to the neck of the talus, just in front of the fibular facet (Fig. 12.32).
2. ***Posterior talofibular ligament*** passes from the lower part of the malleolar fossa of the fibula to the lateral tubercle of the talus.
3. ***Calcaneofibular ligament*** is a long rounded cord which passes from the notch on the lower border of the lateral malleolus to the tubercle on the lateral surface of the calcaneum.

Relations of the Ankle Joint (Fig. 12.33)

Anterior: The ankle joint is related anteriorly from medial to lateral to the following structures:

1. **T**ibialis anterior
2. Extensor **h**allucis longus
3. Anterior tibial **art**ery

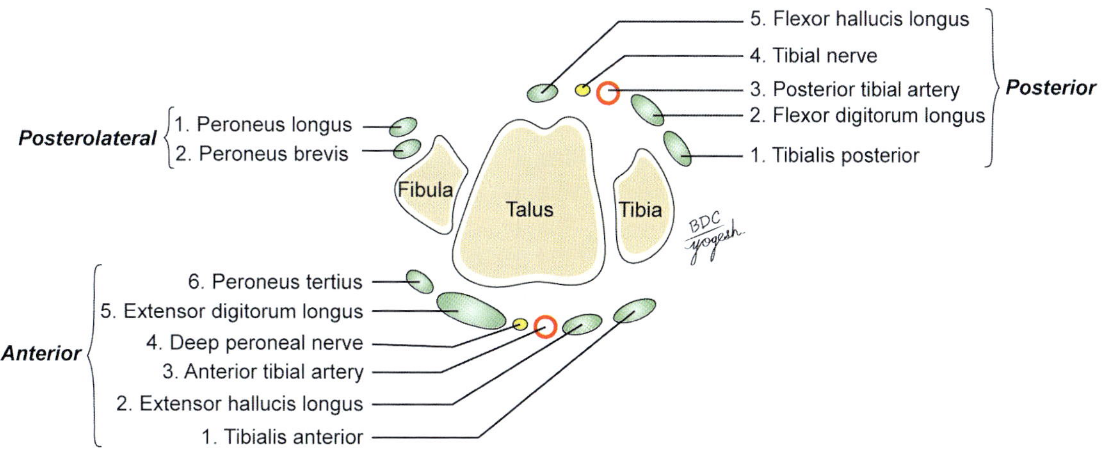

Fig. 12.33: Relations of ankle joint (transverse section passing through talus)

4. Deep peroneal **n**erve
5. Extensor **d**igitorum longus
6. **P**eroneus tertius.

[*Mnemonic*: **T**he **H**imalayas **A**re **N**ever **D**ry **P**laces.]

Posterior: The ankle joint is related posteriorly from medial to lateral side to the following structures:

1. **T**ibialis posterior
2. Flexor **d**igitorum longus
3. Posterior tibial **a**rtery
4. Tibial **n**erve
5. Flexor **h**allucis longus.

[*Mnemonic*: **T**alented **D**octors **A**re **N**ever **H**ungry.]

Posterolateral: The ankle joint is crossed posterolaterally by the tendons of peroneus longus and peroneus brevis.

Blood Supply

From the malleolar branches of anterior tibial, posterior tibial, and peroneal arteries.

Nerve Supply

From deep peroneal and tibial nerves.

TABLE 12.5: Movements of ankle joint

Movements	*Main muscles*	*Accessory muscles*
Dorsiflexion (forefoot is raised)	Tibialis anterior	Extensor digitorum longus Extensor hallucis longus
Plantar flexion (Forefoot is depressed)	Gastrocnemius Soleus	Plantaris Tibialis posterior Flexor hallucis longus Flexor digitorum longus

Note: Dorsiflexed position is a ***closed-packed position*** of the ankle joint. In dorsiflexion, there is maximum congruence of articular surfaces and tension in the ligament that stabilizes the joint and prevents dislocation. Plantar flexed position is a ***loose-packed position*** of the ankle joint. In plantar flexion, the narrow posterior part of trochlear surface of talus loosely fits into the tibiofibular mortise that makes the joint unstable and prone for dislocation.

The range of movement of dorsiflexion at ankle joint is 20° and the plantar flexion is 45°.

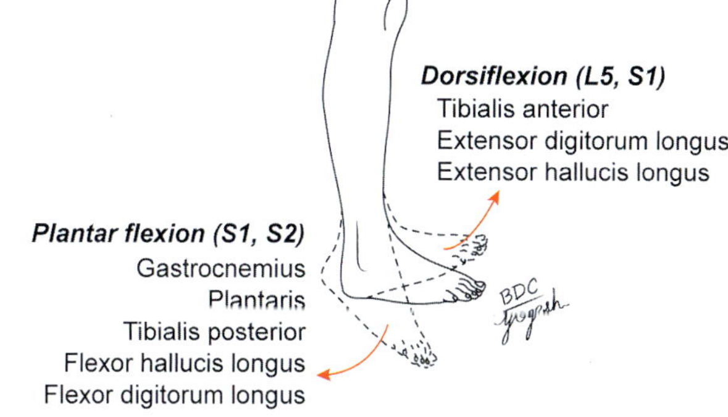

Fig. 12.34: Movements of ankle joint

Movements

The following two main movements take place at the ankle joint (Fig. 12.34):

1. ***Dorsiflexion*:** In dorsiflexion, the forefoot is raised and the angle between the front of the leg and dorsum of foot is decreased.
2. ***Plantar flexion*:** In plantar flexion, the forefoot is depressed and the angle between the front of the leg and dorsum of foot is increased.

The muscles producing the movements of ankle joints are listed in Table 12.5.

CLINICAL ANATOMY

- The ***sprains of the ankle*** are almost always abduction sprains of the subtalar joints, although a few fibres of the deltoid ligament are also torn. True sprains of the ankle joint are caused by forced plantar flexion, which leads to tearing of the anterior fibres of the capsule. The joint is unstable during plantar flexion (Fig. 12.35).
- ***Dislocations of the ankle*** are rare because joint is very stable due to the presence of deep tibiofibular socket. Whenever dislocation occurs, it is accompanied by fracture of one of the malleoli. Dislocation of ankle joint occurs mostly in plantar flexion as the joint becomes unstable in this position.

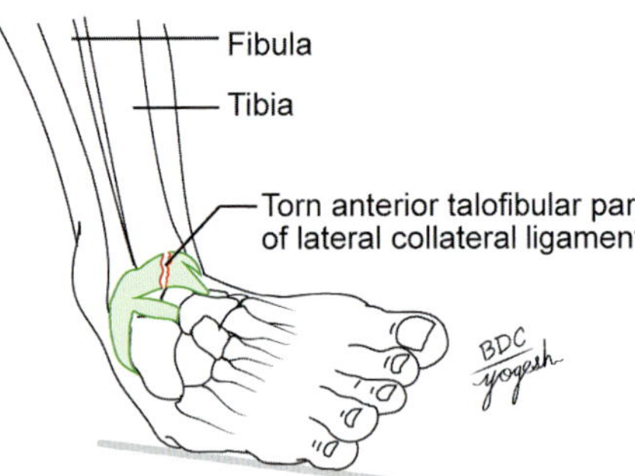

Fig. 12.35: Ankle sprain: Torn anterior talofibular part of lateral collateral ligament

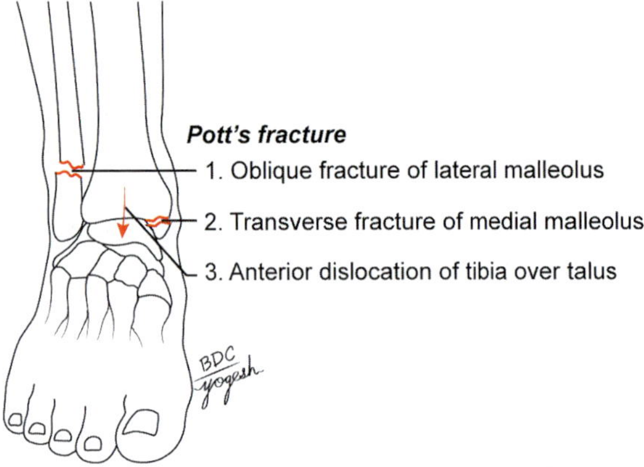

Fig. 12.36: Pott's fracture

- The ***optimal position*** of the ankle is one of slight plantar flexion. It prevents to avoid ankylosis (joint stiffness) on application of plater cast.
- ***Pott's fracture*** is a fracture dislocation of the ankle that involves the following features (Fig. 12.36):
  1. Oblique fracture of lateral malleolus
  2. Transverse fracture of medial malleolus
  3. Anterior dislocation of the tibia over talus
  4. Sometimes fracture of the posterior margin of lower end of tibia called third malleolus may also occur.

DISSECTION

Define the margins of both extensor retinacula, one flexor retinaculum and both peroneal retinacula. Identify the tendons enclosed in synovial sheaths, nerves and blood vessels passing under them. Displace these structures without removing them.

Clean and define the strong medial and lateral ligaments of ankle joint. Also demarcate the thin anterior and posterior parts of the capsule of the joint.

TIBIOFIBULAR JOINTS

The tibia and fibula articulate at three joints—the superior, middle and inferior tibiofibular joints (Plate 12.8).

Plate 12.8: Superior, middle and inferior tibiofibular joints

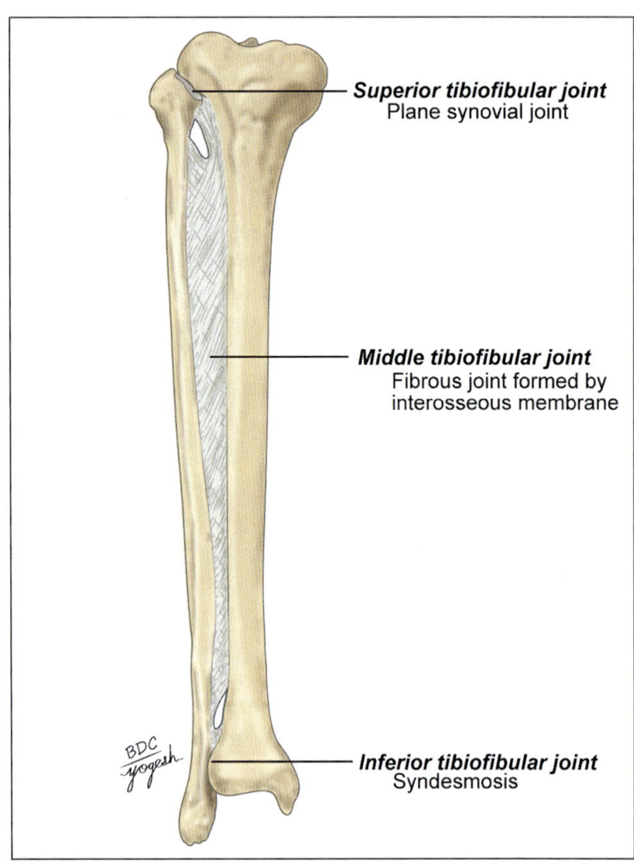

Superior Tibiofibular Joint

This is a small ***plane synovial joint***. It is formed by articulation of small, rounded, flat facets present on the head of the fibula, and on the lateral condyle of the tibia (Plate 12.8). The joint permits slight gliding or rotatory movements that help in adjustment of the lateral malleolus during movements at the ankle joint.

The bones are united by a fibrous capsule which is strengthened by anterior and posterior ligaments.

The cavity of the joint may communicate with the knee joint through the popliteal bursa.

Middle Tibiofibular Joint

This is a ***fibrous joint*** formed by the *interosseous membrane* connecting the shafts of the tibia and the fibula (Plate 12.8). The interosseous membrane is attached to the interosseous borders of the two bones. Its fibres are directed downwards and laterally. It is wide above and narrow below where it is continuous with the interosseous ligament of the inferior tibiofibular joint. It presents a large opening at the upper end for the passage of the anterior tibial vessels, and a much smaller opening near its lower end for the passage of the perforating branch of the peroneal artery.

Functions of Interosseous Membrane

1. The membrane provides additional surface for attachment of muscles.
2. Binds the tibia and the fibula.

3. Resists the downward pull exerted on the fibula by the powerful muscles attached to the bone. *Note* that the biceps femoris is the only muscle that pulls the fibula upwards.

Inferior Tibiofibular Joint

This is a ***syndesmosis*** uniting the lower ends of the tibia and the fibula (Plate 12.8). The bony surfaces are connected by a very strong ***interosseous ligament***, which forms the chief bond of union between the lower ends of these bones.

The interosseous ligament is concealed both in front and behind by the *anterior* and *posterior tibiofibular ligaments*, whose fibres are directed downwards and laterally. The posterior tibiofibular ligament is stronger than the anterior. Its lower and deep portion forms the *inferior transverse tibiofibular ligament*, which is a strong thick band of yellowish fibres passing transversely from the upper part of the malleolar fossa of the fibula to the posterior border of the articular surface of the tibia, reaching up to the medial malleolus.

The joint permits slight movements, so that the lateral malleolus can rotate laterally during dorsiflexion of the ankle.

Nerve Supply

1. Superior tibiofibular joint: Nerve to popliteus, recurrent genicular nerve
2. Middle tibiofibular joint: Nerve to popliteus
3. Inferior tibiofibular joint: Deep peroneal, tibial and saphenous nerves.

DISSECTION

Superior tibiofibular joint: Remove the muscles around the superior tibiofibular joint. Define the tendon of popliteus muscle on its posterior surface. Open the joint.

Middle tibiofibular joint: Remove the muscles from anterior and posterior surfaces of the interosseous membrane and define its surfaces.

Inferior tibiofibular joint: Define the attachments of anterior and posterior tibiofibular ligaments including inferior transverse tibiofibular ligament. Divide these to expose the strong interosseous tibiofibular ligament. Use dry bones and articulated foot to understand the attachments of the ligaments.

JOINTS OF THE FOOT

Classification

The joints of the foot are numerous. They can be classified as (Plate 12.9):

1. Intertarsal
2. Tarsometatarsal, are plane synovial joints.
3. Intermetatarsal, are plane synovial joints.
4. Metatarsophalangeal
5. Interphalangeal.

Plate 12.9: Joints of foot

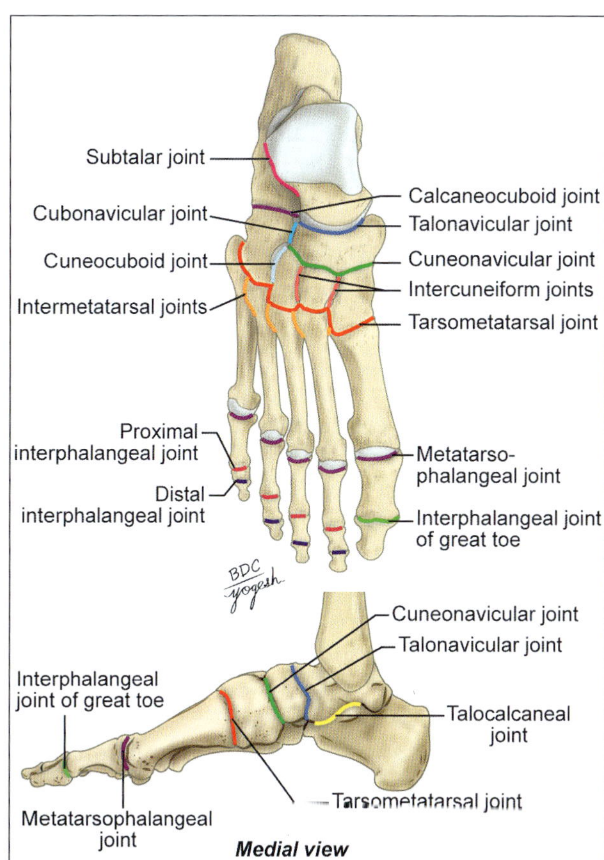

The movements permitted at these joints are as follows.

a. The intertarsal, tarsometatarsal and intermetatarsal joints permit gliding and rotatory movements, which jointly bring about inversion, eversion, of the foot. Pronation is a component of eversion, while supination is a component of inversion.
b. The metatarsophalangeal joints permit flexion, extension, adduction and abduction of the toes.

The interphalangeal joints of hinge variety permit flexion and extension of the distal phalanges.

Competency:
AN20.2 Describe the subtalar and transverse tarsal joints.

Intertarsal Joints

The intertarsal joints are the joints of the tarsal bones. These include the following joints:

1. Subtalar joint
2. Talocalcaneonavicular joints
3. Calcaneocuboid joint
4. Cuneonavicular joint
5. Intercuneiform joints.

Subtalar (Talocalcaneal) Joint

It is the articulation of talus with calcaneum (Fig. 12.37). It has two articular components.

1. ***Anterior talocalcaneal articulation***: It involves the articulation of a convex area of the talus that fits on a concave facet at superior surface of calcaneum.

2. ***Posterior talocalcaneal articulation*:** It involves articulation of concave surface of talus and convex surface of calcaneum.

The fibrous capsule, lateral and medial talocalcaneal ligaments, interosseous ligament and cervical ligament support the subtalar joint. Talocalcaneal joint is a plane synovial joint. It permits the inversion and eversion of the foot.

Talocalcaneonavicular Joint

It is a ball-and-socket variety of synovial joint (Fig. 12.37). It is a compound joint as three bones, talus, calcaneum, and navicular, form this joint. Head of talus fits into the socket formed by the calcaneum, navicular, and spring ligament. It permits the inversion and eversion movements.

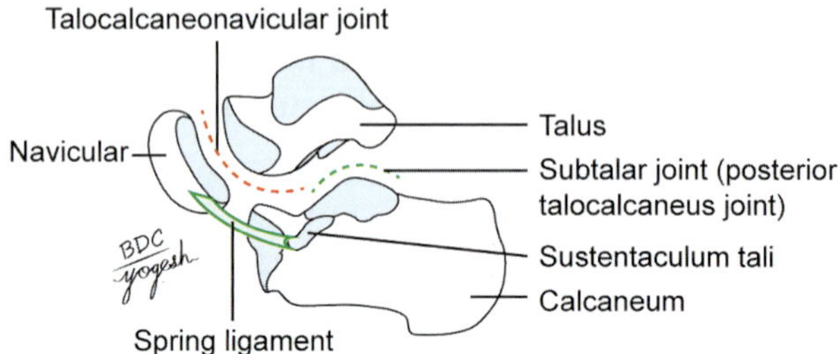

Fig. 12.37: Subtalar and talocalcaneonavicular joints

Calcaneocuboid Joint

It is a saddle type of synovial joint (Fig. 12.38). It is an articulation between calcaneum and cuboid. It is supported by fibrous capsule, calcaneocuboid ligament, bifurcated ligament and long plantar ligament.

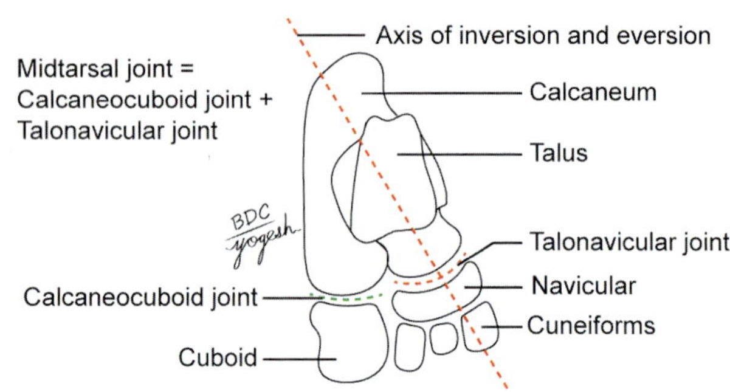

Fig. 12.38: Midtarsal joint

Transverse Tarsal or Midtarsal Joint *(Chopart's Joint)*

It is a compound synovial joint. It includes talonavicular and calcaneocuboid joints as they lie in the same plane but functionally they have different axes of movements (Fig. 12.38). It helps in eversion and inversion and adduction and abduction of foot.

Tarsometatarsal Joints

These are five plane synovial joints. They are supported by dorsal, plantar and interosseous tarsometatarsal ligaments. They permit limited gliding movements.

Intermetatarsal Joints

The intermetatarsal joints are plane synovial joints between the adjacent metatarsal bones and are stabilised by dorsal and plantar intermetatarsal ligaments.

Metatarsophalangeal Joints

These are five ellipsoid joints. These are supported by capsular, collateral plantar, and deep transverse metatarsal ligaments. They permit the following movements:

- Plantar flexion (30°–40°) and dorsiflexion (50°–60°)
- Adduction and abduction: The axis of adduction and abduction pass through the second metatarsal bone.

Interphalangeal Joints

These are nine hinge variety of synovial joints. They permit dorsiflexion and plantar flexion of distal phalanges.

Ligaments of Foot

The foot is supported by a number of ligaments. Some of the major ligaments are as follows (Plate 12.10):

1. ***Dorsal talonavicular ligament*** extends from the neck of talus to the dorsal surface of navicular bone.
2. ***Spring ligament*** (plantar calcaneonavicular ligament) connects the calcaneum with navicular bone.
3. ***Bifurcated*** (*internal calcaneocuboid*) ***ligament*** is a Y-shaped ligament that extends from sulcus calcanei to dorsal surface of navicular and cuboid bones.
4. ***Dorsal calcaneocuboid*** (*superior calcaneocuboid*) ***ligament*** extends from lateral surface of calcaneum to cuboid.
5. ***Long plantar*** (*long calcaneocuboid*) *ligament*: It extends from plantar surface of calcaneum to the groove on the cuboid and bases of middle three metatarsals.
6. ***Short plantar*** (*calcaneocuboid*) *ligament* lies deep to the long plantar ligament. It extends from anterior tubercle of calcaneum to the plantar surface of cuboid, behind the ridge.
7. ***Plantar calcaneonavicular ligament*** extends from plantar surface of navicular to the plantar surface of three cuneiforms.
8. ***Dorsal cuneonavicular ligament*** connects the dorsal surface of navicular bone to the dorsal surface of three cuneiforms.
9. ***Plantar cuboideonavicular ligament*** connect the plantar surfaces of cuboid and navicular bones.
10. ***Dorsal cuboideonavicular ligament*** connects the dorsal surfaces of cuboid and navicular bones.
11. ***Transverse metatarsal ligament*** connects the heads of all metatarsal bones.
12. ***Anterior talocalcaneal ligament*** extends from the front and lateral surface of neck of talus to the sinus tarsi of calcaneum.
13. ***Posterior talocalcaneal ligament*** extends from lateral tubercle of talus to the upper and medial part of calcaneum.

Plate 12.10: Ligaments of foot

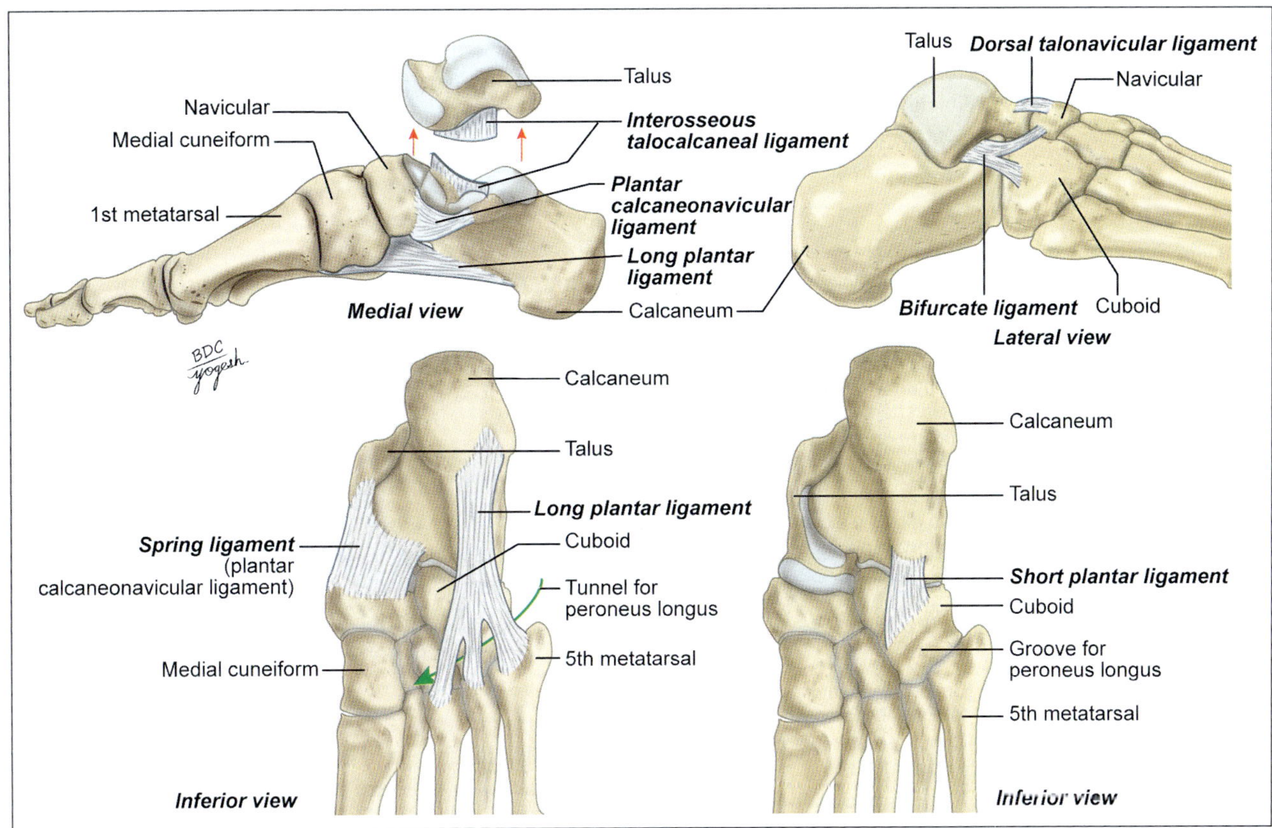

14. ***Lateral talocalcaneal ligament*** extends from lateral surface of talus to lateral surface of calcaneum.
15. ***Medial talocalcaneal ligament*** extends from medial tubercle of the talus to the sustentaculum tali.

INVERSION AND EVERSION OF THE FOOT

Inversion is a movement in which the medial border of the foot is elevated, so that the sole faces medially (Figs 12.40 and 12.41, Table 12.6).

Eversion is a movement in which the lateral border of the foot is elevated, so that the sole faces laterally.

These movements can be performed voluntarily only when the foot is off the ground. When the foot is on the ground these movements help to adjust the foot to uneven ground.

In inversion and eversion, the entire part of the foot below the talus moves together. The movement takes place mainly at the subtalar and talocalcaneonavicular joints and partly at the transverse tarsal joint. The calcaneum and the navicular bone, move medially or laterally round the talus carrying the forefoot with them. Inversion is accompanied by plantar flexion of the foot and adduction of the forefoot. Eversion is accompanied by dorsiflexion of the foot and abduction of the forefoot.

Joints Taking Part

Main

1. Subtalar (talocalcanean)
2. Talocalcaneonavicular

Accessory: Transverse tarsal which includes calcaneocuboid and talonavicular joints.

Axis of Movements

Inversion and eversion take place around an oblique axis which runs forwards, upwards and medially, passing from the back of the calcaneum, through the sinus tarsi, to emerge at the superomedial aspect of the neck of the talus. The obliquity of the axis partly accounts for adduction, abduction, plantar flexion and dorsiflexion which are associated with these movements (Fig. 12.39).

Range of Movements

1. Inversion is much more free than eversion.
2. The range of movements is appreciably increased in plantar flexion of the foot because, in this position, the narrow posterior part of the trochlear surface of the talus occupies the larger anterior part of lower end of tibia, permitting slight movements.

Muscles Producing Movements

Inversion is produced by the actions of the tibialis anterior and the tibialis posterior, helped by the flexor hallucis longus and the flexor digitorum longus (Table 12.6).

Mechanism: During inversion, the forepart of foot is adducted at midtarsal joint followed by lateral rotation of foot at subtalar joint. During eversion, the reverse of this occurs.

TABLE 12.6: Muscles producing movements of inversion and eversion

Movement	*Principal muscles*
A. Inversion	Tibialis anterior Tibialis posterior
B. Eversion	Peroneus longus Peroneus brevis

Note:

Pronation and Supination of the Foot: These are really components of the movements of inversion and eversion. In pronation and supination, the forefoot (i.e. the distal part of the tarsus and metatarsus) moves on the calcaneum and talus. The medial border or the forefoot is elevated in supination (which is thus a part of inversion), while the reverse occurs in pronation (and the eversion). These movements take place chiefly at the transverse tarsal joint and partly at smaller intertarsal, tarsometatarsal and intermetatarsal joints. Supination is adduction + inversion + plantar flexion.

There are differences when supination and pronation occur in weight-bearing and non-weight-bearing situations. In weight-bearing supination and pronation, the calcaneum is not free to move in all directions and the motions are thus completed by compensatory movements of the talus.

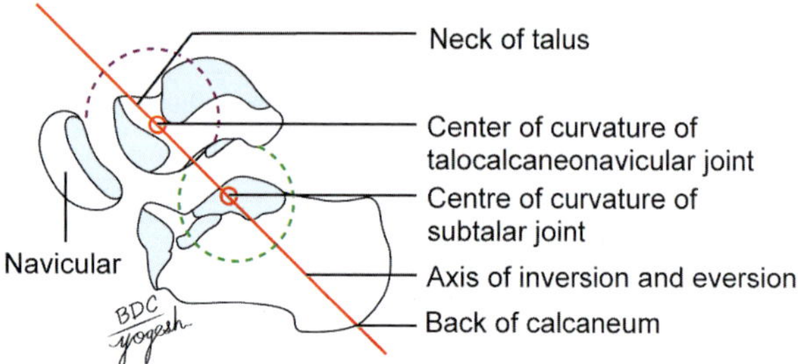

Fig. 12.39: Axis of inversion and eversion

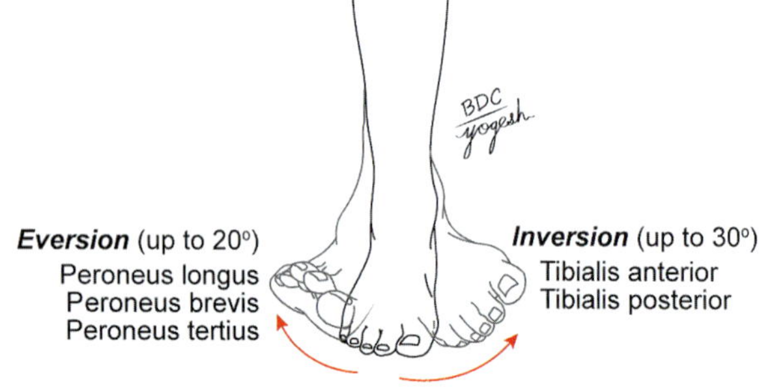

Fig. 12.40: Inversion and eversion of foot

Limiting Factors

Inversion is limited by:

1. Tension of peronei
2. Tension of cervical ligament.

Eversion is limited by:

1. Tension of tibialis anterior
2. Tension of tibialis posterior
3. Tension of deltoid ligament.

Functional Significance

Inversion and eversion greatly help the foot in adjusting to uneven and slippery ground. When feet are supporting the body weight, these movements occur in a modified form called supination and pronation, which are forced on the foot by the body weight.

DISSECTION

Remove all the tendons, muscles from both dorsal and plantar aspects of the tarsal, metatarsal and phalanges. Define, identify the ligaments joining the various bones. Ligaments are stronger on the plantar aspect than the dorsal aspect.

***Subtalar joint*:** Divide the ligaments which unite the talus and calcaneus together at the talocalcanean, talocalcaneonavicular joints. Study these joints carefully to understand the movements of inversion and eversion. On the lateral side of foot, define the attachments of long plantar ligament. Reflect this ligament from its proximal attachment to see the deeper plantar calcaneocuboid ligament.

Cut across the cuneocuboid, cuneonavicular and intercuneiform joints to expose the articulating surfaces. With a strong knife cut through tarsometatarsal and intermetatarsal joints. Try to separate the bones to see interosseous ligaments.

Detach abductor hallucis, flexor hallucis brevis, adductor hallucis from the sesamoid bones of the big toe.

Cut the deep transverse metatarsal ligaments on each side of the third toe. Now the tendons of dorsal and plantar interossei can be seen till their insertion. Identify the distal attachments of the lumbrical muscles as well.

Identify the extensor expansion on the dorsum of digits and see its continuity with the collateral ligaments. Study these joints from the text provided.

CLINICAL ANATOMY

- Females wearing high heels (more than 5 cm), put stress on their back and lower limbs. The spine is pushed forwards, knees are excessively bent, resulting in too much pull on some muscles and ligaments. High heels result in shift in position of centre of gravity. The problems caused by high heels are ***'fashionable diseases'***. The sprains of the medial and lateral ligaments of ankle joint are almost always due to high heels.
- Joints of the foot lead to various deformities like mallet toe, hammer toe and claw toe.
- ***Arthroscopy***: One can look into the joints by special instruments called the arthroscopes.

  For hip joint, the instrument is introduced 4 cm lateral to the femoral pulse and 4 cm below inguinal ligament.

  For knee joint, the arthroscope is introduced from the front of the semiflexed knee joint.

  For ankle joint, the instrument is introduced medial to the tendon of tibialis anterior muscle. One needs to be careful of the great saphenous vein.
- Fractured toe is bandaged with the adjacent toe, this is called ***buddy splint*** (Fig. 12.41).

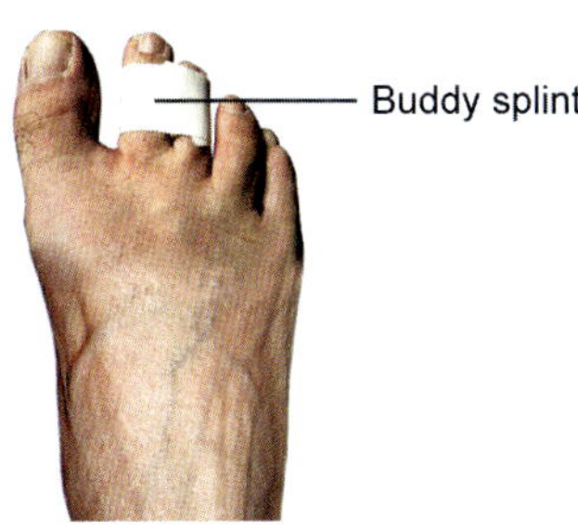

Fig. 12.41: Buddy splint

Video 2.12 **Joints of lower limb**

Facts to Remember

- Iliofemoral ligament is the most strongest ligament of hip joint.
- Hip joint dislocates commonly on posterior.
- Retinacular arteries are the main source of blood supply to the head of femur.
- Knee joint is the most complicated joint.
- Flexion and extension are allowed in the upper compartment of knee joint while rotation is permitted in the lower or meniscotibial compartment.
- Locking muscle is vastus medialis part of quadriceps femoris.
- Unlocking muscle is popliteus (key muscle of knee joint).
- Medial meniscus is commonly damaged than lateral meniscus.
- Unhappy triad of knee joint includes injury of tibial collateral ligament, medial meniscus and anterior cruciate ligament.
- Inversion and eversion occur at talocalcaneonavicular joint, assisted by movements at transverse tarsal joints, i.e. talonavicular and calcaneocuboid joints.
- Inferior tibiofibular joint is a syndesmosis type of joint, i.e. joint formed by ligaments only.
- Fibula does not take part in knee joint, but participates in the formation of ankle joint.
- Talus has no muscular attachment.
- The big toe carries double the weight to the ground than any of other four toes.

BDC's Anatomy *e*-book

1. Avascular necrosis of head of femur
2. Details of capsule of knee joint
3. Cruciate ligaments of knee joint
4. Menisci of knee joint
5. Synovial membrane of knee joint
6. Details of movements of knee joint
7. Details of ligaments of foot
8. Further reading
9. Viva voce questions

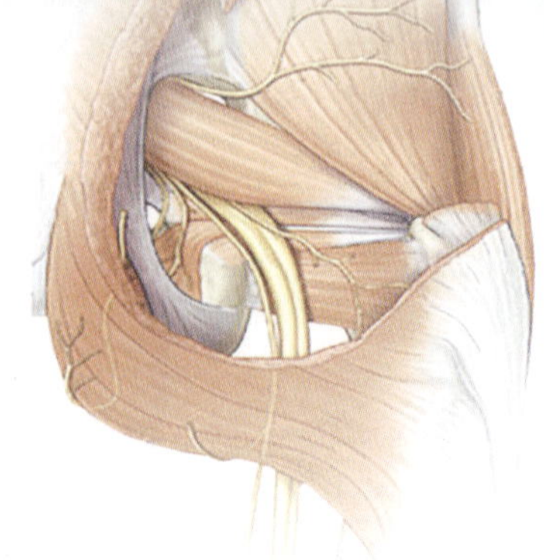

Chapter

13

Arches of Foot

Competency:

AN19.5 Describe factors maintaining important arches of the foot with its importance.

The foot is really unique to human beings. Arches of the foot helps in fast walking, running and jumping. In addition, these help in weight-bearing and in providing upright posture. Footprints are not complete due to the arches.

The foot has to act:

1. As a ***pliable platform*** to support the body weight in the upright posture, and
2. As a ***lever*** to propel the body forward in walking, running or jumping.

To meet these requirements, the human foot is designed in the form of elastic arches or springs. These arches are segmented, so that they can best sustain the stress of weight and of thrusts. The presence of the arches makes the sole *concave*. This is best appreciated by examining footprints which show the weight-bearing parts of the sole (Fig. 13.1).

Heel (posteroinferior tuberosity of calcaneum)

Lateral border of foot

Ball of little toe (head of 5th metatarsal)

Ball of great toe (head of 1st metatarsal)

Fig. 13.1: Footprint showing the weight-bearing points of the sole

***Definition*:** The skeletal architecture of the foot is arranged in an arched manner, both longitudinally and transversely. The concavity of these arches is directed towards the plantar surface. These arched bony arrangements in the foot bones are called arches of foot.

Note: The arches are present right from birth, although they are masked in infants by the excessive amount of fat in their soles.

CLASSIFICATION OF ARCHES

1. Longitudinal (Flowchart 13.1)
   - Medial
   - Lateral
2. Transverse
   - Anterior
   - Posterior

LONGITUDINAL ARCHES

Medial Longitudinal Arch

This arch is considerably higher, more mobile and resilient than the lateral. It is considered as a big arc of a small circle with more bones and more joints (Figs 13.2 and 13.3).

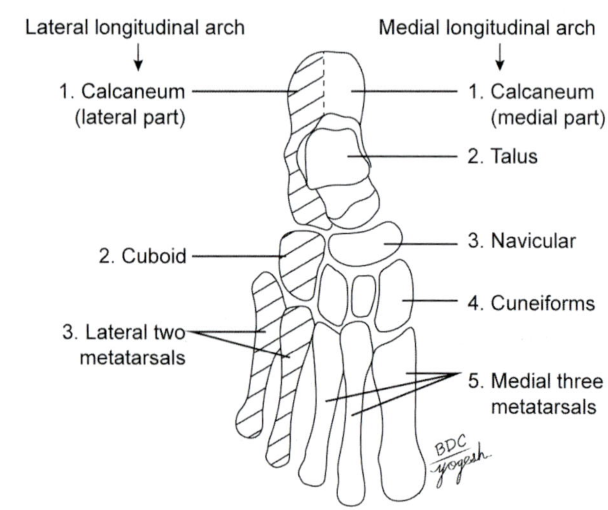

Fig. 13.2: Bones forming the longitudinal arch of foot: Superior view

Flowchart 13.1: Arches of foot

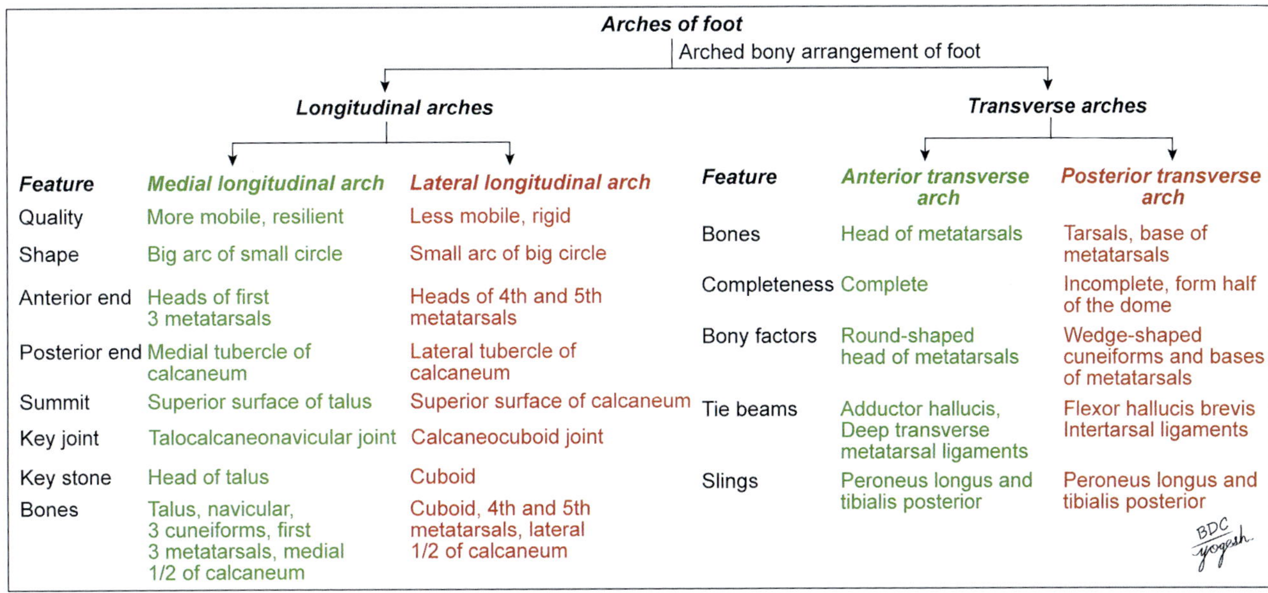

Arches of foot

Arched bony arrangement of foot

Longitudinal arches

Feature	Medial longitudinal arch	Lateral longitudinal arch
Quality	More mobile, resilient	Less mobile, rigid
Shape	Big arc of small circle	Small arc of big circle
Anterior end	Heads of first 3 metatarsals	Heads of 4th and 5th metatarsals
Posterior end	Medial tubercle of calcaneum	Lateral tubercle of calcaneum
Summit	Superior surface of talus	Superior surface of calcaneum
Key joint	Talocalcaneonavicular joint	Calcaneocuboid joint
Key stone	Head of talus	Cuboid
Bones	Talus, navicular, 3 cuneiforms, first 3 metatarsals, medial 1/2 of calcaneum	Cuboid, 4th and 5th metatarsals, lateral 1/2 of calcaneum

Transverse arches

Feature	Anterior transverse arch	Posterior transverse arch
Bones	Head of metatarsals	Tarsals, base of metatarsals
Completeness	Complete	Incomplete, form half of the dome
Bony factors	Round-shaped head of metatarsals	Wedge-shaped cuneiforms and bases of metatarsals
Tie beams	Adductor hallucis, Deep transverse metatarsal ligaments	Flexor hallucis brevis Intertarsal ligaments
Slings	Peroneus longus and tibialis posterior	Peroneus longus and tibialis posterior

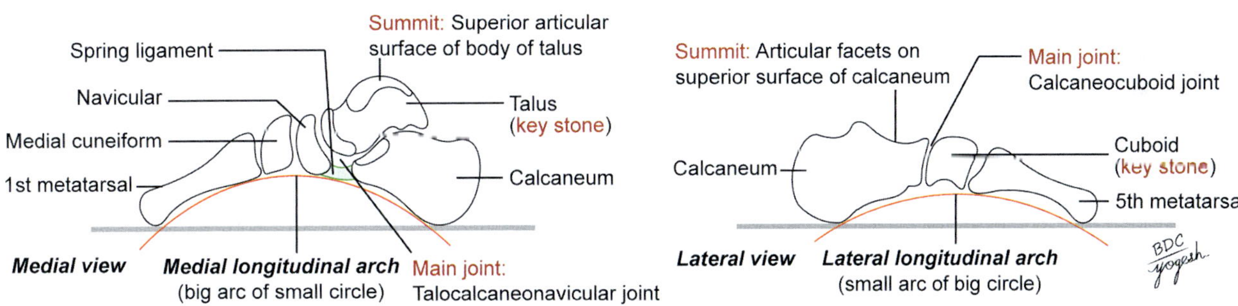

Fig. 13.3: Bones forming the longitudinal arch of foot

Bones are part of calcaneus, talus, navicular, all three cuneiform bones and 1st–3rd metatarsals.

Ends

1. The ***anterior end*** is formed by the heads of the first, second and third metatarsals. The phalanges do not take part in forming the arches.
2. The ***posterior end*** of this arch is formed by the medial tubercle of the calcaneum.
3. ***Keystone*** is the talus.

Summit

The summit of the arch is formed by the superior articular surface of the body of the talus.

Pillars

1. The ***anterior pillar*** is long and weak. It is formed by the talus, the navicular, the three cuneiform bones and the first three metatarsal bones.
2. The ***posterior pillar*** is short and strong. It is formed by the medial part of the calcaneum.

Main Joint

The *main joint* of the arch is the talocalcaneonavicular joint.

Lateral Longitudinal Arch

This arch is characteristically low, with less bones and joints, has limited mobility and is built to transmit weight and thrust to the ground. It is considered as a small arc of a big circle (Figs 13.2 and 13.3). This is in contrast to the medial longitudinal arch which acts as a shock absorber.

Bones forming this arch are part of calcaneus, cuboid and 4th, 5th metatarsals. The constitution of the lateral longitudinal arch is as follows:

Ends

1. The ***anterior end*** of the arch is formed by the heads of the 4th and 5th metatarsal bones.
2. The ***posterior end*** is formed by the lateral tubercle of the calcaneum. The keystone is the cuboid.

Summit

The *summit* lies at the level of the articular facets on the superior surface of the calcaneum at the level of the subtalar joint.

Pillars

1. The ***anterior pillar*** is long and weak. It is formed by the cuboid bone and by the 4th and 5th metatarsals.

2. The ***posterior pillar*** is short and strong. It is formed by the lateral half of the calcaneum.

Main Joint

The *main joint* of the arch is the calcaneocuboid joint.

Factors Responsible for Maintenance of Longitudinal Arches

For maintenance of longitudinal arch involves the proper maintenance of the shape of arch with its elastic behaviour to get altered during the weight transmission. The factors maintaining the longitudinal arches are as follows (Figs 13.4 to 13.6 and Table 21.2):

1. Shape of the bones concerned.
2. *Intersegmental ties/staples* or ligaments (and muscles) that hold the different segments of the arch together.
3. *Tie beams* or *bowstrings* that connect the two ends of the arch.
4. *Slings* that keep the summit of the arch pulled up.

The factors that maintain the arches of the foot can be understood by the example of the stone bridge.

Factors Maintaining Medial Longitudinal Arch

(Figs 13.4 and 13.5)

1. *Bones*: The sustentaculum tali partly supports the heads of talus.
2. *Ligaments*: The following ligaments act as intersegmental ties that maintain the medial longitudinal arch:
   Spring ligament that supports the head of talus.
   Interosseous ligaments that connect adjacent bones.
   Interosseous talocalcaneal ligament that connects talus and calcaneum.
3. *Muscles, tendons and aponeurosis*
   a. *Sling action*: The sling pulls the summit of the arches upward. These include tibialis posterior, flexor hallucis longus and flexor digitorum longus (the muscles of posterior compartment of leg).
   b. *Tie beams*: The tie beams prevent separation of pillars. The tie beams of the medial longitudinal arch include:
      - Plantar aponeurosis
      - Abductor hallucis
      - Flexor hallucis brevis.

Factors Maintaining Lateral Longitudinal Arch

(Figs 13.4 and 13.5)

1. *Bones*: Shape of cuboid (keystone of lateral longitudinal arch) helps to maintain lateral longitudinal arch.
2. *Ligaments*: The lateral longitudinal arch is supported by short and long plantar ligaments.
3. Muscles, tendons and aponeurosis.
   a. *Sling action*: The slings pull the summit of the arch upward. The slings of lateral longitudinal arch include tendon of peroneus brevis, peroneus tertius and peroneus longus.
   b. *Tie beams*: The tie beams prevent separation of pillars. The tie beams of lateral longitudinal arch include plantar aponeurosis, intrinsic muscles of little toe (lateral part of flexor digitorum brevis, abductor digiti minimi and flexor digiti minimi).

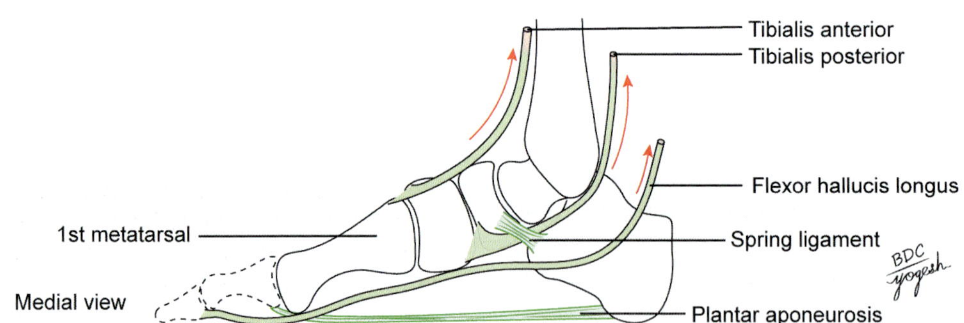

Fig. 13.4: Factors maintaining the medial longitudinal arch

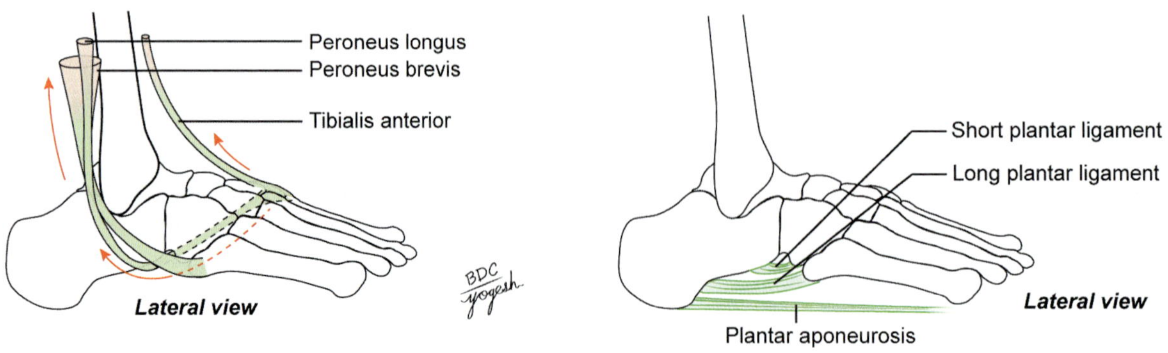

Fig. 13.5: Factors maintaining lateral longitudinal arches

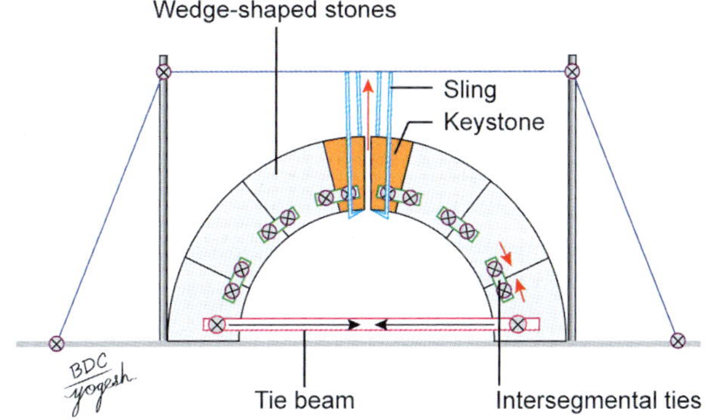

Fig. 13.6: Concept of arches of foot and supports of stone bridge

TRANSVERSE ARCHES

Anterior Transverse Arch

The *anterior transverse arch* is formed by the heads of the five metatarsal bones. It is complete because the heads of the 1st and 5th metatarsals come in contact with the ground and form the two ends of the arch (Figs 13.7 and 13.8).

Posterior Transverse Arch

The *posterior transverse arch* is formed by the greater parts of the tarsus and bases of metatarsus. It is incomplete because only the lateral end comes in contact with the ground, the arch forming a 'half dome' which is completed by a similar half dome of the opposite foot.

Factors Maintaining Transverse Arches

1. *Bones*: Most of the tarsals and metatarsals are wedge-shaped and have broader dorsal (superior) aspect and narrower plantar (inferior) aspect. It helps in formation of concavity towards the plantar aspect.
2. *Ligaments*: The superficial and deep transverse metatarsal ligaments maintain the anterior transverse arch. The ligaments and interossei muscles hold the adjacent tarsals and metatarsals together.
3. *Muscles and tendons*
   a. *Tie beams*: Tendons of peroneus longus and tibialis posterior support the transverse arch.
   b. *Sling action*: The tendon of peroneus tertius and peroneus brevis on the lateral side and tendon of tibialis anterior on the medial side form a sling that supports the transverse arches.
   c. *Intersegmental ties*: The dorsal interossei hold the adjacent metatarsals together and support transverse arches.

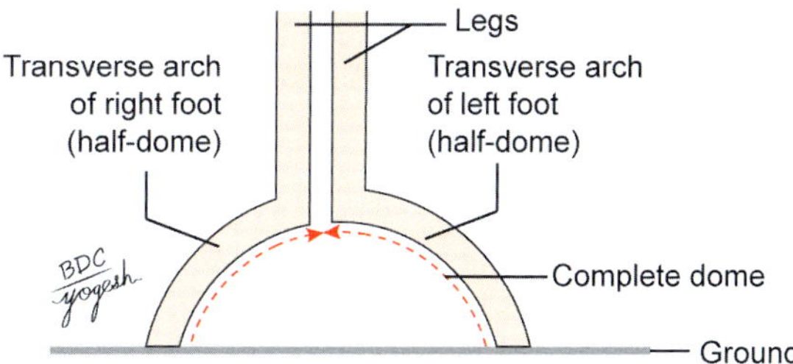

Fig. 13.7: Transverse arches of right and left feet together form complete dome

FUNCTIONS OF ARCHES

1. The arches of the foot ***distribute body weight*** to the weight-bearing areas of the sole, mainly the heel and the toes. The lateral border of the foot bears some weight, but this is reduced due to the presence of the lateral longitudinal arch.
2. The arches act as ***springs*** (chiefly the medial longitudinal arch) which are of great help in walking and running.
3. They also act as ***shock absorbers*** in stepping and particularly in jumping.
4. The concavity of the arches ***protects*** the soft tissues of the sole against pressure.
5. The character of medial longitudinal arch is ***resiliency*** and that of lateral longitudinal arch is ***rigidity***.

For the comparison of medial and lateral longitudinal arches and comparison of anterior transverse arch and posterior transverse arch in Tables 13.1 and 13.2.

Competency:

AN19.6 Explain the anatomical basis of flat foot and club foot.

CLINICAL ANATOMY

- ***Flat foot***: Absence or collapse of the longitudinal arches leads to flat foot (pes planus), which may be congenital or acquired (Fig. 13.9). The effects of a flat foot are as follows:
  a. Loss of spring in the foot leads to a clumsy, shuffling gait.
  b. Loss of shock absorbing function makes the foot more liable to trauma and osteoarthritis.
  c. Loss of the concavity of the sole leads to compression of the nerves and vessels of the sole.

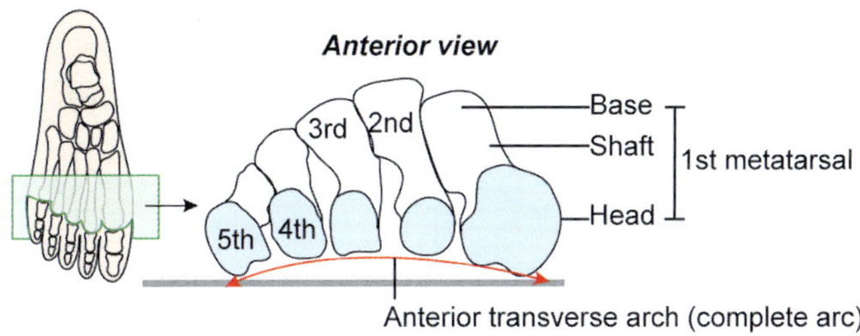

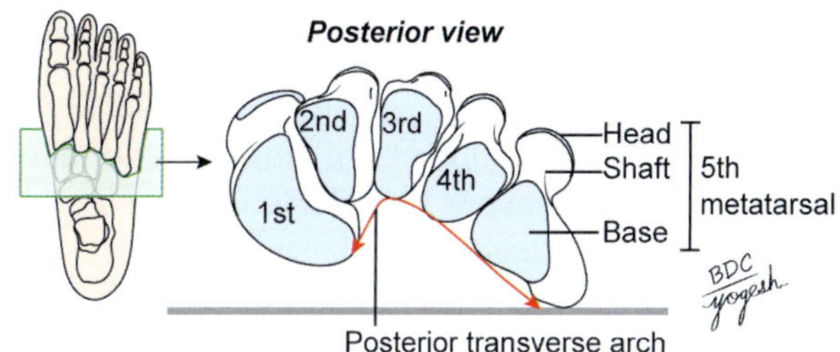

Fig. 13.8: Transverse arches

TABLE 13.1: Comparison of medial and lateral longitudinal arches

	Medial longitudinal arch	*Lateral longitudinal arch*
Features	Higher, more mobile, ***resilient*** and shock absorber	Lower, limited mobility transmits weight, ***rigid***
Anterior end	Heads of 1st, 2nd, 3rd metatarsal bones	Heads of 4th, 5th metatarsals
Posterior end	Medial tubercle of calcaneum	Lateral tubercle of calcaneum
Summit	Superior articular surface of talus	Articular facet on superior surface of calcaneum at level of subtalar joint
Anterior pillar	Talus, navicular, 3 cuneiforms and 1–3 metatarsals	Cuboid and 4th, 5th metatarsals
Posterior pillar	Medial half of calcaneum	Lateral half of calcaneum
Main joint	Talocalcaneonavicular joint	Calcaneocuboid joint
Bony factor	Head of talus is keystone	Cuboid is keystone
Intersegmental ties	Spring ligament	Long plantar ligament Short plantar ligament
Tie beams	Plantar aponeurosis (medial part) Abductor hallucis Medial part of flexor digitorum brevis	Plantar aponeurosis (lateral part) Abductor digiti minimi Lateral part of flexor digitorum brevis
Slings	Tibialis posterior Flexor hallucis longus Flexor digitorum longus	Peroneus longus Peroneus brevis
Suspension	Sling formed by tibialis anterior and peroneus longus	Sling formed by tibialis anterior and peroneus longus

TABLE 13.2: Comparison of anterior transverse arch and posterior transverse arch

	Anterior transverse arch	*Posterior transverse arch*
Formation	Heads of 1st to 5th metatarsals	Navicular, 3 cuneiforms, bases and shafts of metatarsals
Features	Complete arch	Incomplete. Arch is half dome raised medially
Bony factor	Round-shaped	Wedge-shaped
Intersegmental ties	Dorsal interosseous muscles	Dorsal interosseous muscles
Tie beams	Deep transverse metatarsal ligaments Adductor hallucis	Flexor hallucis brevis Intertarsal and tarsometatarsal ligaments
Slings	Peroneus longus + tibialis posterior	Peroneus longus + tibialis posterior

Compression of the communication between the lateral and medial plantar nerves causes neuralgic pain in the forefoot (***metatarsalgia***).

Compression of blood vessels may cause vascular disturbances in the toes.

- ***High arched foot (pes cavus)*** (= hallow foot in Latin): Exaggeration of the longitudinal arches of the foot is known as *pes cavus*. This is usually a result of contracture (plantar flexion) at the transverse tarsal joint (Fig. 13.9). When dorsiflexion of the metatarsophalangeal joints and plantar flexion of the interphalangeal joints (due to atrophy of lumbricals and interossei) are superadded, the condition is known as ***clawfoot***. The common causes of pes cavus and clawfoot (Fig. 13.9) are spina bifida and poliomyelitis.
- ***Clubfoot (talipes)***: Clubfoot is a birth defect or may be an acquired defect that is characterised by rotation of foot (*talipes* = clubfoot, Latin).

Types of clubfoot (Fig. 13.10)

a. ***Talipes equinus*** in which the patient walks on toes, with the heel raised.

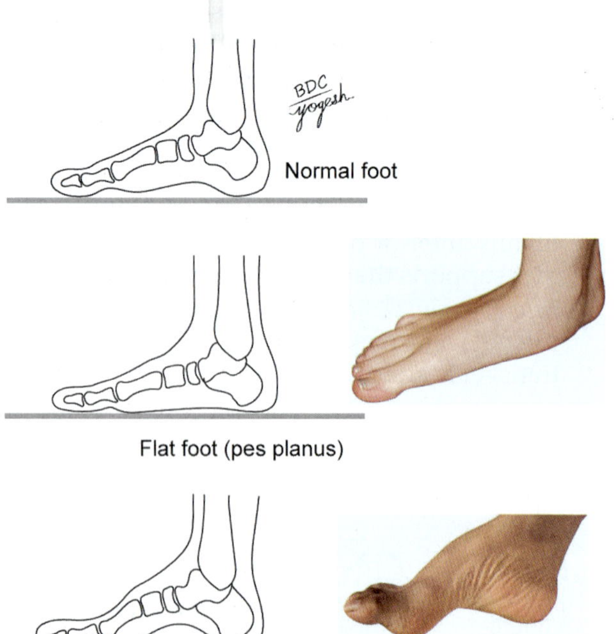

Fig 13.9: Normal foot, flat foot and high-arched foot

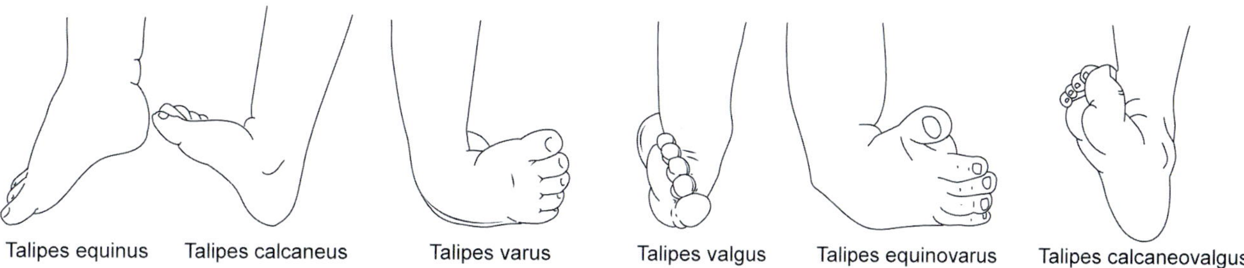

Fig. 13.10: Club foot/talipes equinovarus

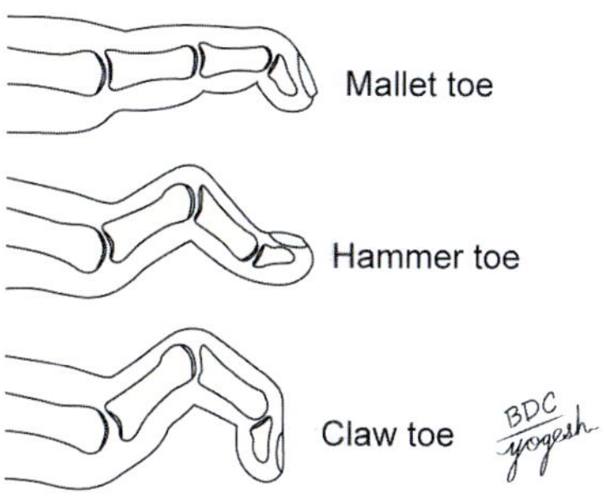

Fig. 13.11: Deformities of toes

b. ***Talipes calcaneus*** in which the patient walks on heel, with the forefoot raised.

c. ***Talipes varus*** in which the patient walks on the outer border of foot which is inverted and adducted.

d. ***Talipes valgus*** in which the patient walks on inner border of foot which is everted and abducted.

e. ***Talipes equinovarus***: It is the commonest deformity of the foot. In this condition, the foot is inverted, adducted and plantar flexed. The condition may be associated with spina bifida.

f. ***Talipes calcaneovalgus*** – foot is dorsiflexed at ankle joint, everted at midtarsal joints.

- ***Hallux valgus (bunion)***: In this condition, the tip of the big toe is deviated laterally. It involves metatarsophalangeal joint of the great toe. In most of the cases, the cause is unknown. Constant wearing of pointed shoe with high heel may cause hallux valgus. Bunion is adventitious bursa that covers and protects the heads of the first metatarsal.
- ***Hammer toe (contracted toe)***: In this condition, the toe resembles hammer. There is hyper extension of metatarsophalangeal and distal interphalangeal joints and acute flexion at proximal interphalangeal joints. It usually affects 2nd and 3rd toes (Fig. 13.11).
- ***Hallux varus***: In this condition, the great toe is deviated medially away from first metatarsal bone. Hallux rigidus (shift big toe). It occurs due to degenerative arthritis and stiffness due to bone spur that affect metatarsophalangeal joint of the great toe (Fig. 13.11).

Facts to Remember

- Talus is the summit and keystone of the medial longitudinal arch of the foot.
- Important joint of medial longitudinal arch is talocalcaneonavicular joint.
- Main supports of this arch are tibialis posterior, tibialis anterior and peroneus longus muscles.
- Arches distribute the weight evenly to the ground.
- Important joint of lateral longitudinal arch is calcaneocuboid joint and its keystone is cuboid.
- Posterior transverse arch is supported by tendon of peroneus longus muscle.
- Anterior transverse arch is supported by deep metatarsal ligaments and dorsal interossei muscles.
- Talipes equinovarus is the commonest deformity of the foot.

BDC's Anatomy *e*-book

1. Summary of arches of foot
2. Further reading
3. Viva voce questions

Chapter

14

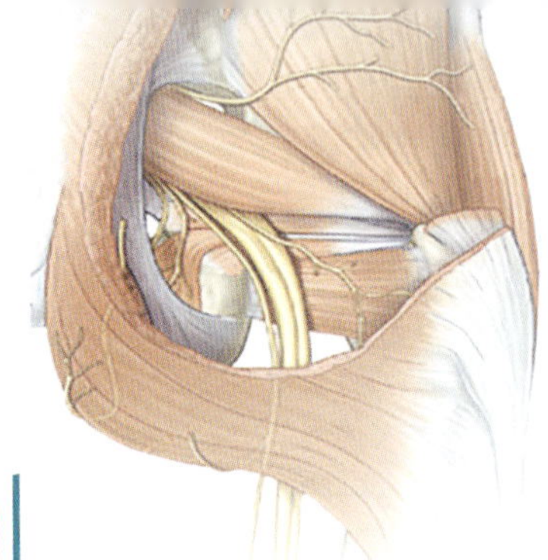

Surface and Radiological Anatomy of Lower Limb

Competencies:

AN20.7 Identify and demonstrate important bony landmarks of lower limb: Vertebral levels of highest point of iliac crest, posterior superior iliac spines, iliac tubercle, pubic tubercle, ischial tuberosity, adductor tubercle, tibial tuberosity, head of fibula, medial and lateral malleoli, condyles of femur and tibia, sustentaculum tali, tuberosity of fifth metatarsal, tuberosity of the navicular.

AN 20.8 Identify and demonstrate palpation of femoral, popliteal, posterior tibial, anterior tibial and dorsalis pedis blood vessels in a simulated environment.

PALPABLE PARTS OF THE BONES

The palpable parts of the bones are shown coloured both on the (a) anterior and (b) posterior aspects of lower limb (Figs 14.1a and b).

SURFACE MARKING

ARTERIES OF LOWER LIMB

Femoral Artery

It corresponds to the upper 2/3rd of a line joining the following two points (Fig. 14.2):

- *Point A: Midinguinal point* – A point midway between the anterior superior iliac spine and the pubic symphysis.
- *Point B: Adductor tubercle* – It lies at the lower end of the cordlike tendon of the adductor magnus. The tendon can be felt in a shallow groove just behind the prominence of the vastus medialis *when the thigh is semiflexed, abducted and laterally rotated.*

The upper 1/3rd of the line represents the upper half of the artery lying in the femoral triangle. The middle 1/3rd of the line represents the lower half of the artery lying in the adductor canal. The lower 1/3rd of the line represents the descending genicular and saphenous branches of the artery.

Clinical utility: Femoral artery can be felt at midinguinal point and can be compressed to stop bleeding from distal part of the limb. Femoral artery cannulation especially in angiography can be performed.

Popliteal Artery

It is marked by joining the following points (Fig. 14.3):

- *Point 1:* At the junction of the middle and lower thirds of the thigh, 2.5 cm medial to the midline on the back of the limb.
- *Point 2:* On the midline of the back of the knee.
- *Point 3:* On the midline of the back of the leg at the level of the tibial tuberosity.

Clinical utility: Popliteal artery pulse can be felt. This artery may be compressed to stop bleeding in leg injuries. This artery may show aneurysm.

Posterior Tibial Artery

It is marked by joining the following points (Fig. 14.3):

- *Point 3:* On the midline of the back of the leg at the level of the tibial tuberosity.
- *Point 4:* Midway between the medial malleolus and the tendo calcaneus.

Clinical utility: Posterior tibial pulse can be felt at the midpoint between medial malleolus and tendo calcaneus.

Anterior Tibial Artery

It is marked by joining points 1 and 2:

- *Point A:* 2.5 cm below the medial side of the head of the fibula (Fig. 14.4).
- *Point B:* Midway between the two malleoli.

The artery passes downwards and slightly medially.

Dorsalis Pedis Artery

It is marked by joining the following two points (Fig. 14.4):

- *Point B:* Midway between the two malleoli.
- *Point C:* At the proximal end of the first intermetatarsal space.

Clinical utility: Dorsalis pedis pulse is assessed during peripheral vascular examination and may be absent normally (in 14% people) or in peripheral vascular diseases.

Medial Plantar Artery

It is marked by joining the following two points (Fig. 14.5):

- *Point 1:* Midway between the medial malleolus and the prominence of the heel.

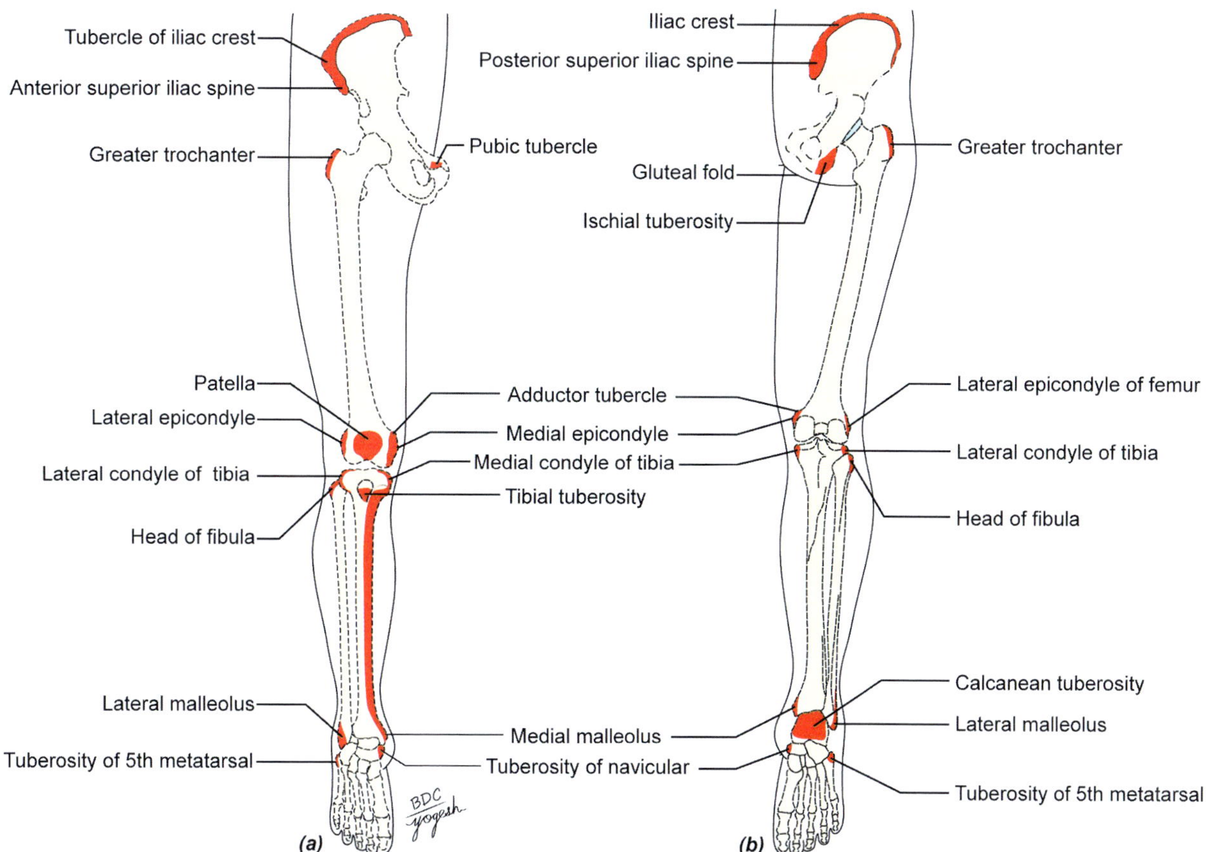

Figs 14.1a and b: Palpable parts of the bones are coloured: (a) Anterior aspect and (b) posterior aspect

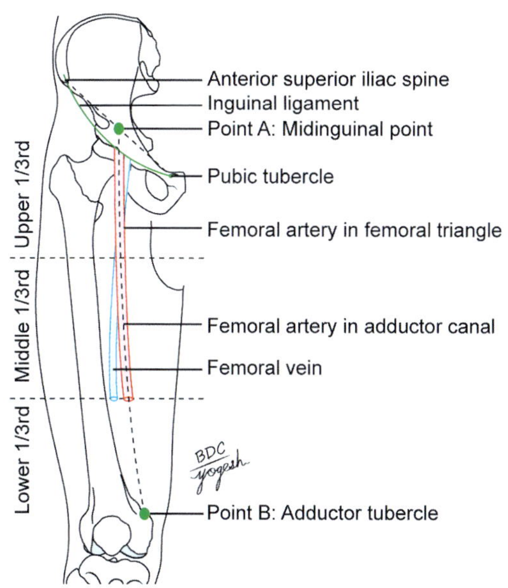

Fig. 14.2: Surface marking of femoral artery and femoral vein

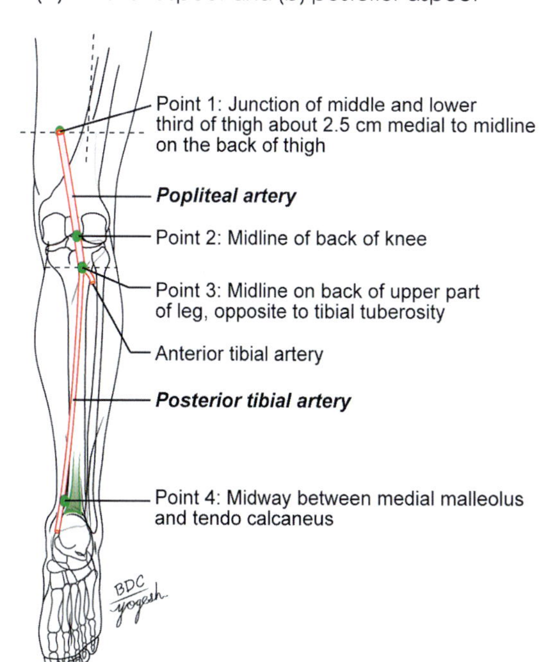

Fig. 14.3: Surface marking of popliteal artery and posterior tibial artery

- *Point 2:* On the navicular bone which lies midway between the back of the heel and the root of the big toe. The artery runs in the direction of the 1st interdigital cleft.

Lateral Plantar Artery

It is marked by joining the following two points (Fig. 14.5):

- *Point 1:* Midway between the medial malleolus and the prominence of the heel.
- *Point 3:* 2.5 cm medial to the tuberosity of the 5th metatarsal bone.

Plantar Arch

It is marked by joining the following two points (Fig. 14.5):

- *Point 3:* 2.5 cm medial to the tuberosity of the 5th metatarsal bone.
- *Point 4:* At the proximal end of the 1st intermetatarsal space, 2.5 cm distal to the tuberosity of the navicular bone.

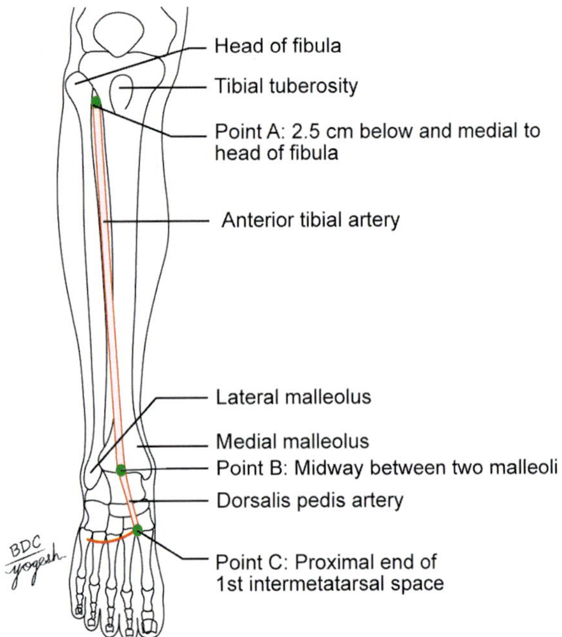

Fig. 14.4: Surface marking of anterior tibial and dorsalis pedis arteries

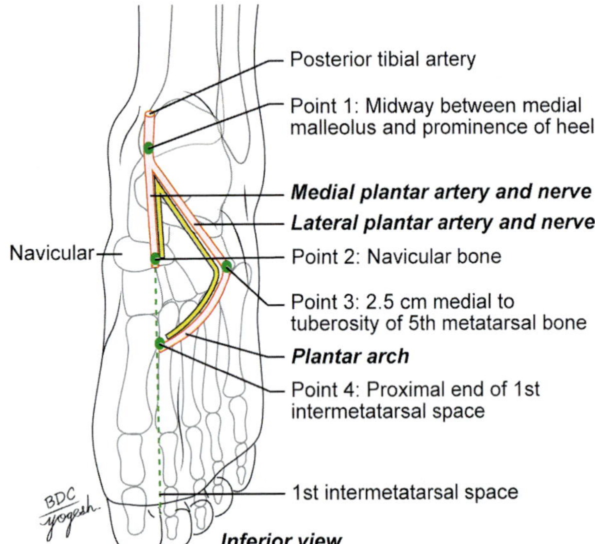

Fig. 14.5: Surface marking of medial and lateral plantar arteries and plantar arch

The arch is slightly curved with its convexity directed forward.

VEINS OF LOWER LIMB

Femoral Vein

Its marking is same as that of the femoral artery, except that the upper point is taken 1 cm medial to the midinguinal point, and the lower point 1 cm lateral to the adductor tubercle. The vein is medial to the artery at the upper end, posterior to it in the middle and lateral to it at the lower end (Fig. 14.2).

Clinical utility: Femoral vein is useful for intravenous infusion, right heart catheterisation.

Great Saphenous Vein

It can be marked by joining the following points, although it is easily visible in living subjects (Fig. 14.6):

- *Point 1*: On the dorsum of the foot at the medial end of the dorsal venous arch.
- *Point 2*: On the anterior surface of the medial malleolus and on lower 1/3rd of anterior border of tibia.
- *Point 3*: On the medial border of the tibia at the junction of the upper 2/3rd and lower 1/3rd of the leg.
- *Point 4*: At the adductor tubercle.
- *Point 5*: Just below the centre of the saphenous opening.

Clinical utility: Long saphenous vein is commonly used for venesection mostly in front of the medial malleolus; also useful for coronary bypass grafting. Failure of venous valves may result in varicose veins.

Small Saphenous Vein

It can be marked by joining the following points, although this vein is also easily visible in its lower part (Fig. 14.7):

- *Point A*: On the dorsum of the foot at the lateral end of the dorsal venous arch.
- *Point B*: Behind the lateral malleolus.
- *Point C*: Just lateral to the tendo calcaneus above the lateral malleolus.
- *Point D*: At the centre of the popliteal fossa.

Competency:
AN20.9 Identify and demonstrate palpation of vessels (femoral, popliteal, dorsalis pedis, post-tibial), mid-inguinal point, surface projection of: Femoral nerve, saphenous opening, sciatic, tibial, common peroneal and deep peroneal nerves, great and small saphenous veins.

NERVES OF LOWER LIMB

Femoral Nerve

It is marked by joining the following two points (Fig. 14.8):

- *Point 1*: 1.2 cm lateral to the midinguinal point.
- *Point 2*: 2.5 cm vertically below the first point.

Clinical utility: Femoral nerve is the chief nerve of the anterior compartment of thigh. Femoral nerve block may be useful for knee arthroplasty and other thigh operations.

Sciatic Nerve

It is marked by joining the following points (Fig. 14.9):

- *Point A*: 2.5 cm lateral to the midpoint between the posterior superior iliac spine and the ischial tuberosity.
- *Point B*: Just medial to the midpoint between the ischial tuberosity and the greater trochanter.
- *Point C*: In the midline of the back of the thigh at the junction of its upper 2/3rd and lower 1/3rd, i.e. at the apex of the popliteal fossa.

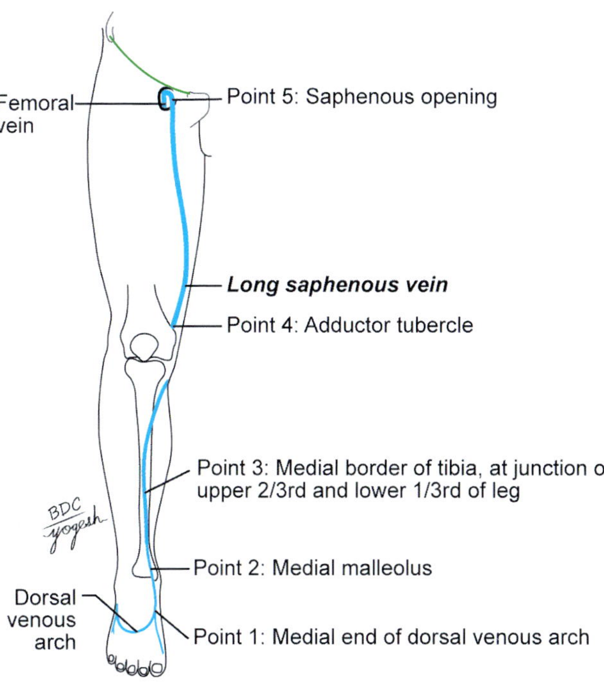

Fig. 14.6: Surface marking of great saphenous vein

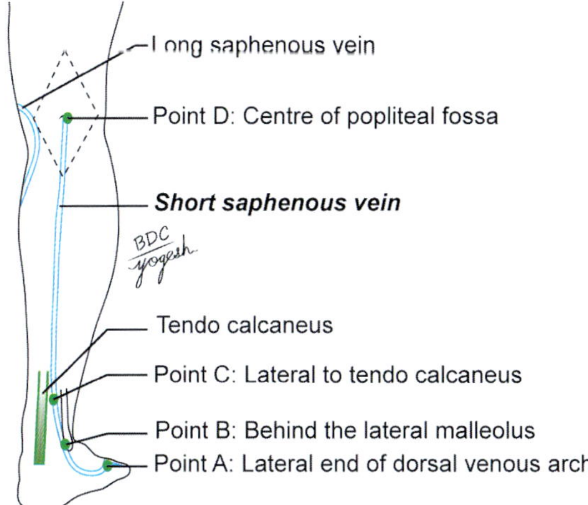

Fig. 14.7: Surface marking of small saphenous vein

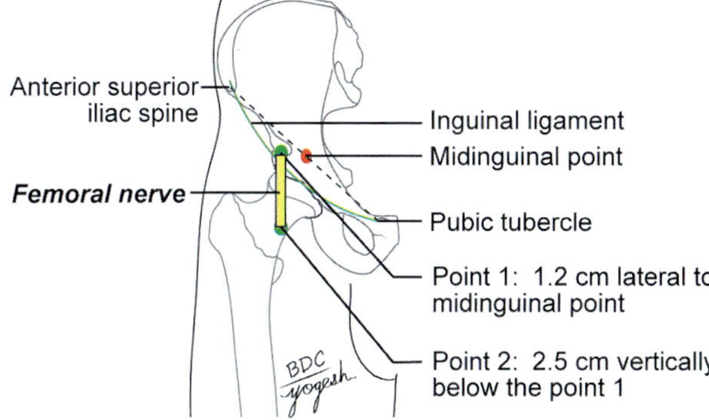

Fig. 14.8: Surface marking of femoral nerve

Clinical utility: Surface marking of sciatic nerve is essential to avoid the sciatic nerve during intramuscular injections and for sciatic nerve block.

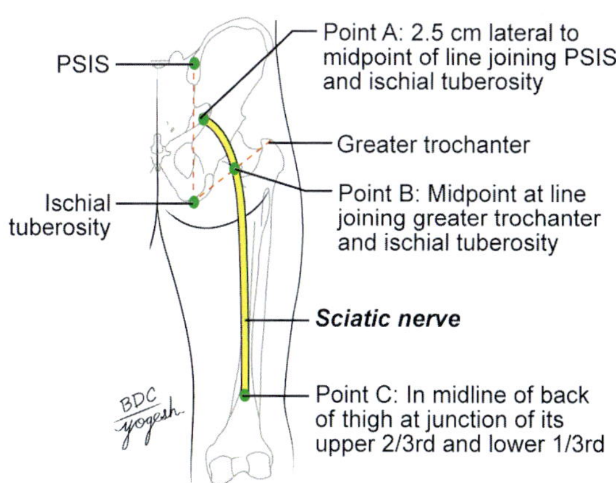

Fig. 14.9: Surface marking of sciatic nerve

Tibial Nerve

Mark the following points (Fig. 14.10):

- *Point 1:* In the midline of back of the thigh at the junction of its upper two-thirds and lower one-third, i.e. at the apex of the popliteal fossa.
- *Point 2:* In the midline of back of the leg at the level of tibial tuberosity.
- *Point 3:* Midway between the medial malleolus and tendo calcaneus.

The line joining (1) and (2) represents the tibial nerve in the popliteal fossa, and the line joining (2) and (3) represents it in the back of the leg.

Clinical utility: Tibial nerve is the main nerve of back of leg and sole of foot.

Common Peroneal Nerve

It is marked by joining the following points (Fig. 14.10):

- *Point 1*: At the apex of popliteal fossa
- *Point 4*: At the back of head of fibula
- *Point 5*: On the lateral aspect of neck of fibula.

Clinical utility: Common peroneal nerve can be palpated by rolling it against the neck of fibula.

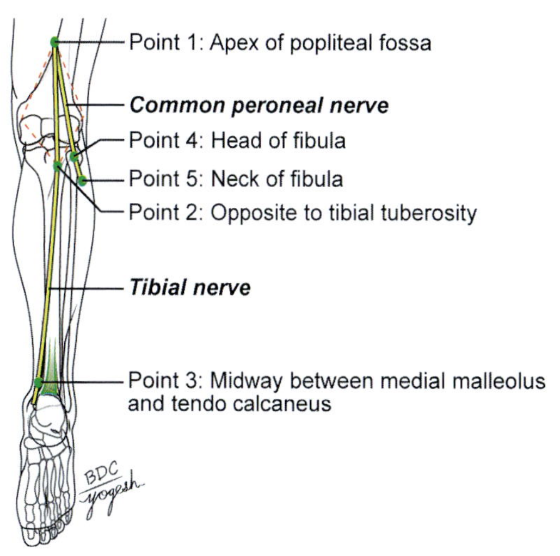

Fig. 14.10: Surface marking of tibial and common peroneal nerves

Deep Peroneal Nerve

It is marked by joining the following two points (Fig. 14.11):

- *Point 1:* On the lateral aspect of the neck of the fibula.
- *Point 2:* In front of the ankle, midway between the two malleoli where it divides into two branches. Medial branch runs till 1st interosseous space.

The nerve lies lateral to the anterior tibial artery in its upper and lower thirds, but anterior to the artery in its middle third.

Clinical utility: Injury to the deep peroneal nerve results in foot drop and sensory loss at the first interdigital cleft.

Superficial Peroneal Nerve

It is marked by joining the following two points (Fig. 14.11):

- *Point 1:* On the lateral aspect of the neck of the fibula.
- *Point 4:* On the anterior border of the peroneus longus at the junction of the upper 2/3rd and lower 1/3rd of the leg.

At the lower point, the nerve pierces the deep fascia and divides into medial and lateral branches.

Clinical utility: Injury to the superficial peroneal nerve results in loss of eversion of foot and loss of sensation over lower 1/3rd of leg and most of the dorsum of foot except the 1st web space.

Medial Plantar Nerve

It is marked in a manner similar to the medial plantar artery (*see* Fig. 14.5) and lies lateral to the artery.

Lateral Plantar Nerve

It is marked in a manner similar to that for the lateral plantar artery (*see* Fig. 14.5). Lies medial to the artery.

MISCELLANEOUS STRUCTURES

Superior Extensor Retinaculum

The retinaculum is about 3 cm broad vertically (Fig. 14.12). It is drawn from:

1. The anterior border of the triangular subcutaneous area of the fibula.
2. The lower part of the anterior border of the tibia, running medially and slightly upwards.

Inferior Extensor Retinaculum

1. The *stem* is about 1.5 cm broad. It extends from the anterior part of the upper surface of the calcaneum to a point medial to the tendon of the extensor digitorum longus on the dorsum of the foot (Fig. 14.12).
2. The *upper band* is about 1 cm wide and extends from the medial end of the stem to the anterior border of the medial malleolus.
3. The *lower band* is also about 1 cm wide. It extends from the medial end of the stem to the medial side of the foot, extending into the sole.

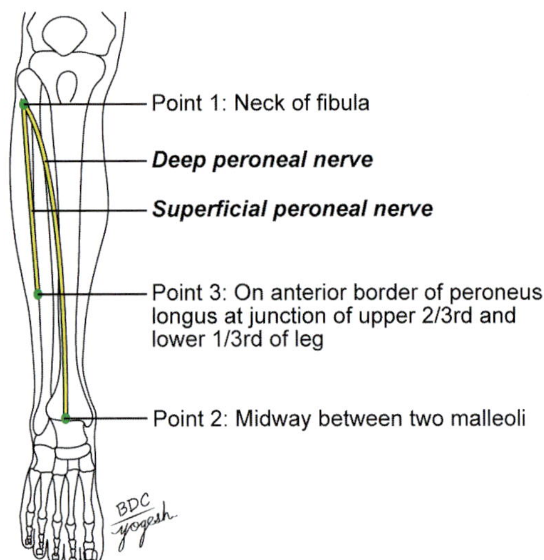

Fig. 14.11: Surface marking of deep and superficial peroneal nerves

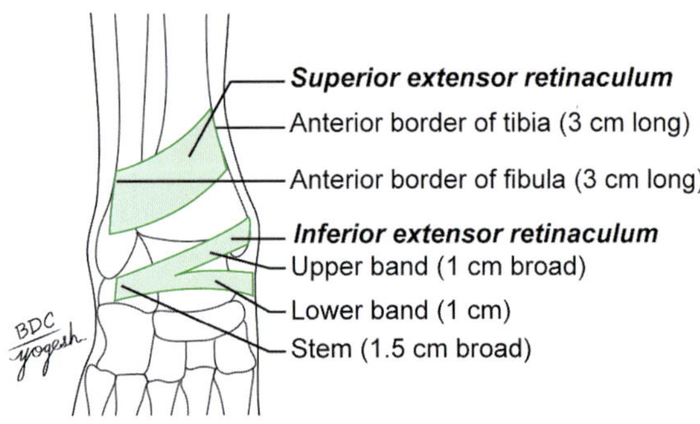

Fig. 14.12: Superior and inferior extensor retinacula of the ankle

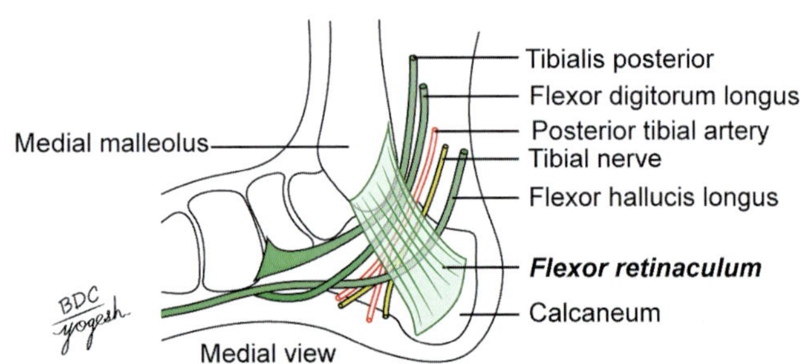

Fig. 14.13: Flexor retinaculum of the ankle and the structures passing deep to it

Flexor Retinaculum

It is about 2.5 cm broad and extends from the following:

- The medial malleolus
- The medial side of the heel, running downwards and backwards (Fig.14.13).

RADIOLOGICAL ANATOMY

In the study of plain skiagrams of the limbs, the following points should be noted:

1. View of the radiograph.
2. Identification of all bones visible.
3. Normal relations of the bones forming joints and the radiological 'joint space'.
4. The presence of epiphyses in the young bones.

Briefly, such skiagrams are helpful in the diagnosis of the following:

1. Fractures
2. Dislocations
3. Diseases:
    a. Infective (osteomyelitis)
    b. Degenerative (osteoarthritis)
    c. Neoplastic (benign and malignant)
    d. Deficiency (rickets and scurvy)
4. Developmental defects
5. The age below 25 years.

RADIOGRAPH OF HIP

Competency:
AN20.6 Identify the bones and joints of lower limb seen in anteroposterior and lateral view radiographs of various regions of lower limb.

Identify the Following Bones in AP View

Anteroposterior (AP) view of the hip shows the following structures (Fig. 14.14):

1. *Hip bone,* including ilium, pubis, ischium and acetabulum.
2. *Upper end of femur,* including the head, neck, greater trochanter, lesser trochanter and upper part of shaft.
3. The *lumbosacral spine* may have been included.
4. *Hip joint:* Normal relation of the head of femur with the acetabulum is indicated by the *Shenton's line,* which is a continuous curve formed by the upper border of obturator foramen and the lower border of the neck of femur.
5. *Pubic symphysis*
6. *Sacroiliac joint*

Note: The **neck-shaft angle** is about 125° in adults, being more in children (140°) and less in females.

In the head, a dense wedge or triangle of cancellous bone is known as ***Ward's triangle***. It represents the epiphyseal scar.

Calcar femorale is a dense plate of compact bone forming a buttress to strengthen the concavity of the neck-shaft angle in front of the lesser trochanter. It transmits weight from the head of femur to the linea aspera.

Cervical torus is a thickened band or ridge of compact bone on the upper part of the neck between the head and the greater trochanter.

The epiphyses and other incomplete ossifications, if any, and determine the age. The ischiopubic rami fuse by 7–8 years, and the acetabulum is ossified by 17 years.

KNEE

Identify the Following Bones

Plain radiographs of AP and lateral views of the knee show the following:

1. *Lower end of femur,* including the two condyles (Fig. 14.15).
2. *Patella* is clearly seen only in the lateral views; in AP views, it overlaps the lower end of femur. It lies about 1 cm above the knee joint.
3. *Upper end of tibia,* including the two condyles, intercondylar eminence and tibial tuberosity.
4. *Upper end of fibula,* including the head, neck and upper part of shaft.
5. *Knee joint*: The joint space varies inversely with the age. In young adults, it is about 5 mm. It is entirely due to articular cartilage and not due to menisci.
6. *Superior tibiofibular joint.* Note the epiphyses, if any, and determine the age with the help of ossification studied.

Note: Bilateral separation of the superolateral angles of the patellae is known as *bipartite patella*. The small fragment may be further subdivided to form the multipartite patella. This is due to failure of the ossification centres to fuse.

In *emargination of patella*, its outer margin is concave. The concavity is bounded by a tubercle above and a spine below. This reflects the mode of attachment of the vastus lateralis.

Fabella is a small, rounded sesamoid bone in the lateral head of gastrocnemius. It articulates with the posterior surface of the lateral condyle of femur. It measures 1–1.5 cm in diameter and is present in about 15% of individuals. As a rule, it is bilateral and appears at 12–15 years of age.

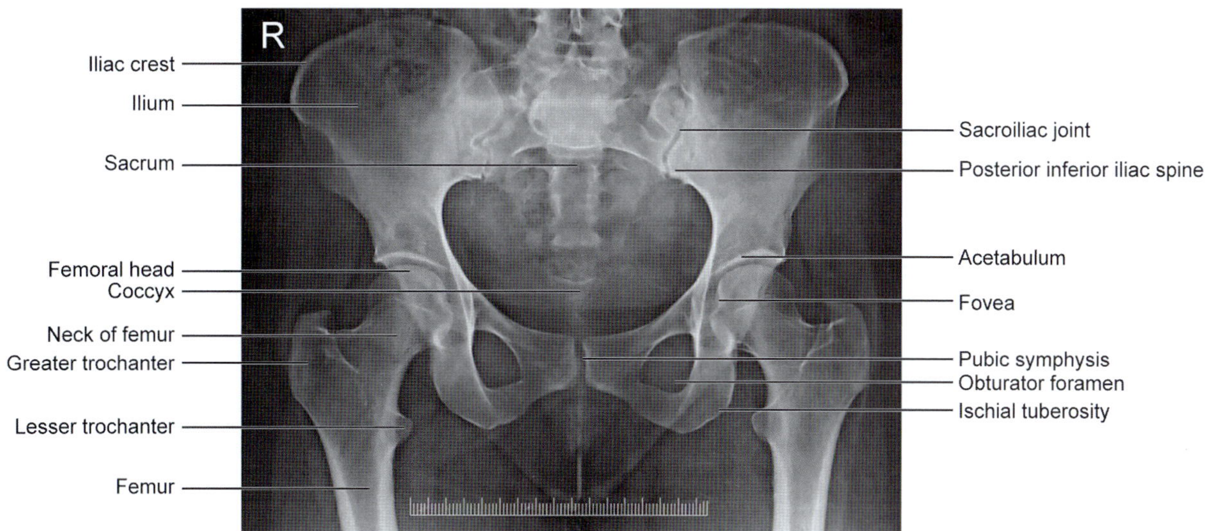

Fig. 14.14: Anteroposterior view of the pelvis (*Courtesy*: Dr Satya Jha, AIIMS, Jodhpur)

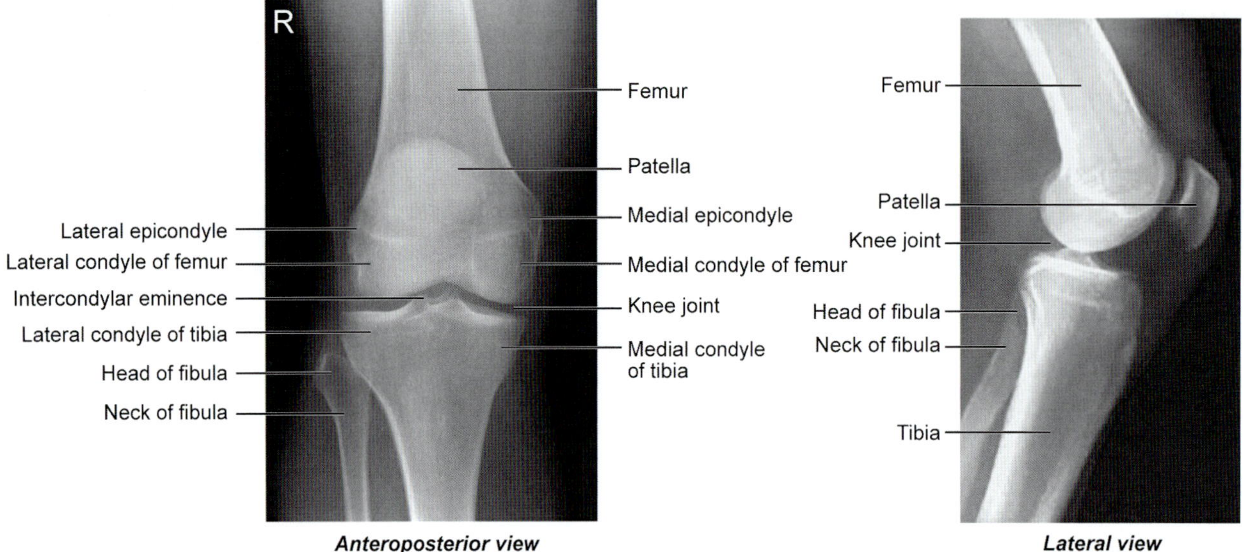

Fig. 14.15: Radiograph of the knee joint

FOOT

Identify the Following Bones

Plain radiograph of foot shows (Fig. 14.16):

1. *Talus* and *calcaneum* are better seen in lateral view.
2. *Navicular* and *cuboid* are seen clearly in almost all the views.
3. *Cuneiform bones* are seen separately in dorsoplantar views; they overlap each other in a lateral view.
4. *Metatarsals* and *phalanges* are seen separately in dorsoplantar views, but overlap each other in lateral views.
5. Sesamoid and accessory bones should be distinguished from fractures.
6. Ankle joint
7. Subtalar, talocalcaneonavicular and transverse tarsal joints
8. Tarsometatarsal, intermetatarsal, metatarsophalangeal and interphalangeal joints.

Note: The common *sesamoids* are found on the plantar surface of the head of 1st metatarsal bone. They may also be present in the tendons of tibialis anterior, tibialis posterior and peroneus longus. *Accessory bones* are separate small pieces of bone which have not fused with the main bone. For example, os trigonum (lateral tubercle of talus) and os vesalianum (tuberosity of fifth metatarsal bone).

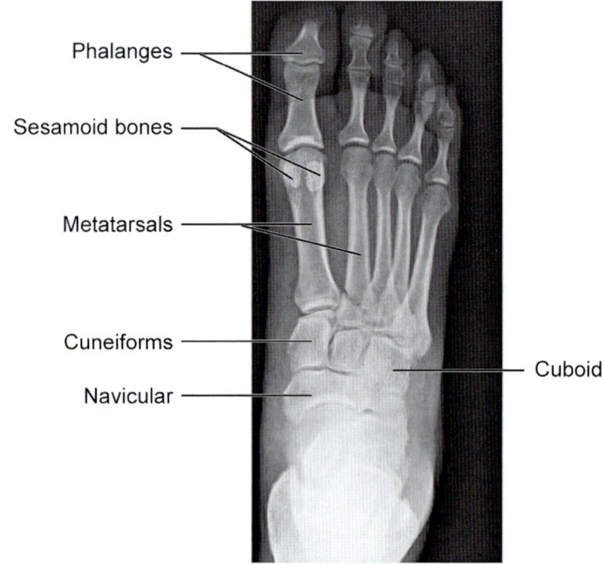

Fig. 14.16: Dorsoplantar view of the ankle and foot

BDC's Anatomy *e*-book

1. Surface marking of some structures of lower limb
2. Further reading
3. Viva voce questions

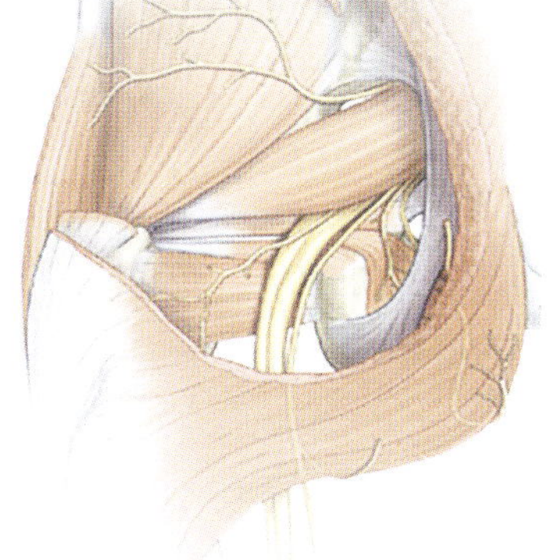

Appendix

1

Major Nerves and Arteries of Lower Limb

MAJOR NERVES OF LOWER LIMB

FEMORAL NERVE

Femoral nerve is the nerve of anterior compartment of thigh. Its cutaneous branch, the saphenous nerve, extends to the medial side of leg and medial border of foot till the ball of the big toe (Fig. A1.1).

Root value: Dorsal division of ventral rami of L2, 3, 4 segments of spinal cord.

Beginning and course: It emerges at the lateral border of psoas major muscle in the abdomen. It passes downwards between psoas major and iliacus muscles. The nerve enters the thigh behind the inguinal ligament, lateral to femoral sheath. It is not a content of femoral sheath as its formation is behind fascia iliaca.

Termination: It ends by dividing into two divisions 2.5 cm below the inguinal ligament. Both these divisions end in a number of branches. In between the two divisions, lateral circumflex femoral artery is present.

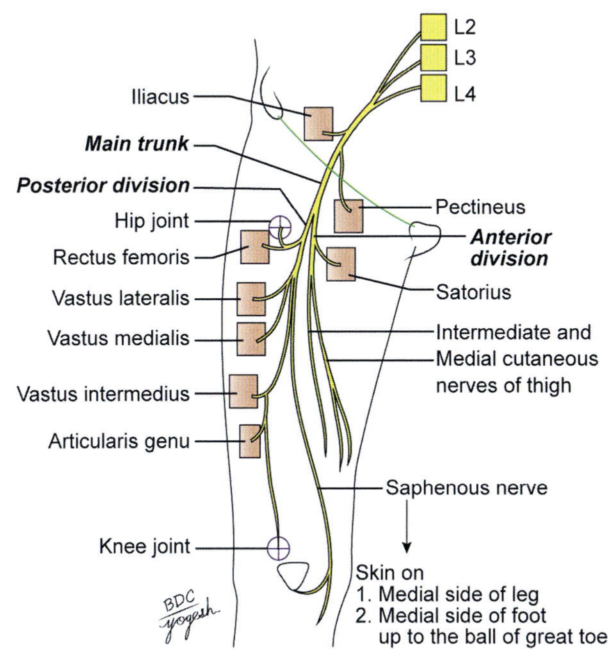

Fig. A1.1: Formation and branches of femoral nerve

Branches

In the abdomen

Main trunk: Muscular branches from main trunk for iliacus, and pectineus.

In thigh

Anterior division

- Muscular branch for sartorius
- Cutaneous branches: Medial and intermediate cutaneous nerves of thigh.

Posterior division

- Muscular branches for rectus femoris, vastus medialis, vastus lateralis, vastus intermedius, and articularis genu through branch to vastus intermedius.
- Cutaneous branch: Saphenous nerve (largest cutaneous branch of femoral nerve).
- Articular branches to hip and knee joints.

OBTURATOR NERVE

Root value: Obturator nerve is a branch of lumbar plexus. It arises from ventral division of ventral rami of L2, 3, 4 segments of spinal cord (Fig. A1.2).

Beginning and course: It emerges on the medial border of psoas major muscle within the abdomen. It crosses the pelvic brim to run downwards and forwards on the lateral wall of pelvis to reach the upper part of obturator foramen.

Termination: It ends by dividing into anterior and posterior divisions. In between the divisions, adductor brevis is seen.

Branches

Anterior division: It passes downwards in front of the obturator externus being separated from the posterior division by a few fibres of this muscle. It then descends behind the pectineus and the adductor longus, and in front of the adductor brevis. The anterior division supplies the following structures:

a. *Muscles*: Pectineus, adductor longus, gracilis, adductor brevis (if not supplied by the posterior division)
b. Hip joint
c. Subsartorial plexus and femoral artery.

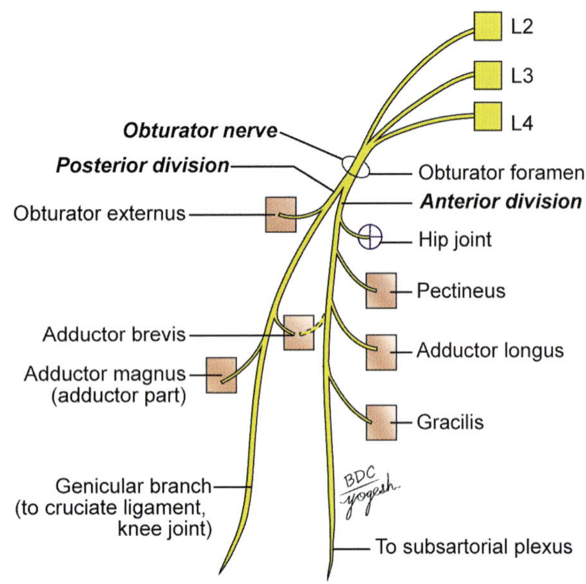

Fig. A1.2: Formation and distribution of obturator nerve

Posterior division: It enters the thigh by piercing the upper border of the obturator externus muscle. It descends behind the adductor brevis and in front of the adductor magnus. It gives branches to the following structures:

a. *Muscles*: Obturator externus, adductor magnus, adductor brevis (if not supplied by the anterior division)
b. Genicular branch to supply the capsule and the cruciate ligaments of the knee joint and the popliteal artery.

Note: ***Accessory obturator nerve*** is present in 30% subjects, which arises from the ventral division of ventral rami of L3, 4 nerves. It runs along medial border of psoas major, crosses superior ramus of pubis behind pectineus muscle. It supplies pectineus, hip joint and gives a communicating branch to anterior division of obturator nerve.

SCIATIC NERVE

Sciatic nerve is the thickest nerve of the body. It is the terminal branch of the lumbosacral plexus (Fig. A1.3).

Root value: Ventral rami of L4, 5, S1, 2, 3. It consists of two parts.

- *Tibial part:* Its root value is ventral division of ventral rami of L4, 5, S1, 2, 3, segments of spinal cord.
- *Common peroneal part:* Its root value is dorsal division of ventral rami of L4, 5, S1, 2 segments of spinal cord.

Course: Sciatic nerve arises in the pelvis. Leaves the pelvis by passing through greater sciatic foramen below the piriformis to enter the gluteal region.

In the gluteal region, it lies deep to the gluteus maximus muscle, and crosses superior gemellus, obturator internus, inferior gemellus, quadratus femoris to enter the back of thigh. During its short course, it lies between ischial tuberosity and greater trochanter with a convexity to the lateral side. It gives no branches in the gluteal region.

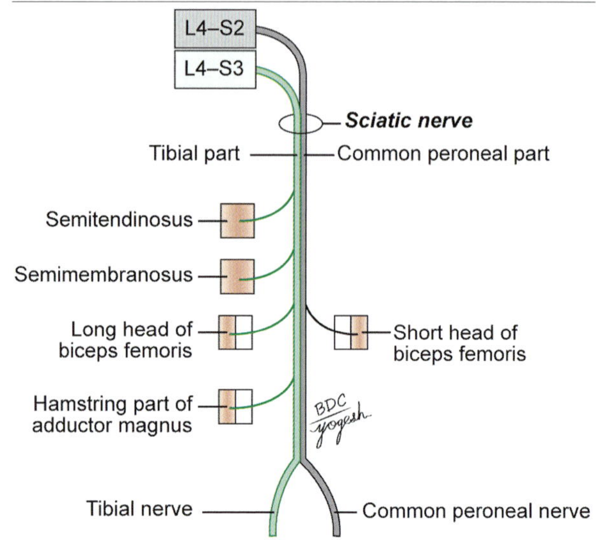

Fig. A1.3: Branches of sciatic nerve

In the back of thigh, it lies deep to long head of biceps femoris and superficial to adductor magnus.

Termination: It ends by dividing into its two terminal branches in the back of thigh.

Branches

1. *Tibial part:* Semitendinosus, semimembranosus, long head of the biceps femoris, and ischial head of the adductor magnus from its medial side, and hip joint.
2. *Common peroneal part* supplies only the short head of the biceps femoris.
3. *Terminal branches*: Tibial nerve, and common peroneal nerve.

TIBIAL NERVE

Root value: Ventral division of ventral rami of L4, 5, S1, 2, 3 segments of spinal cord (Fig. A1.4).

Beginning: It begins as the larger subdivision of sciatic nerve in the back of thigh.

Course: It has a long course first in the popliteal fossa and then in the back of leg.

Popliteal fossa: The nerve descends vertically in the popliteal fossa from its upper angle to the lower angle. It lies superficial to the popliteal vessels. It continues in the back of leg beyond the distal border of popliteus muscle.

In back of leg: The nerve descends as the neurovascular bundle with posterior tibial vessels. It lies superficial to tibialis posterior and deep to flexor digitorum longus. Lastly, it passes deep to the flexor retinaculum of ankle.

Termination: The tibial nerve terminates by dividing into medial plantar and lateral plantar nerves as it lies deep to the flexor retinaculum.

Branches

1. *Muscular branches* to tibialis posterior, flexor digitorum longus, flexor hallucis longus, and deep part of soleus.

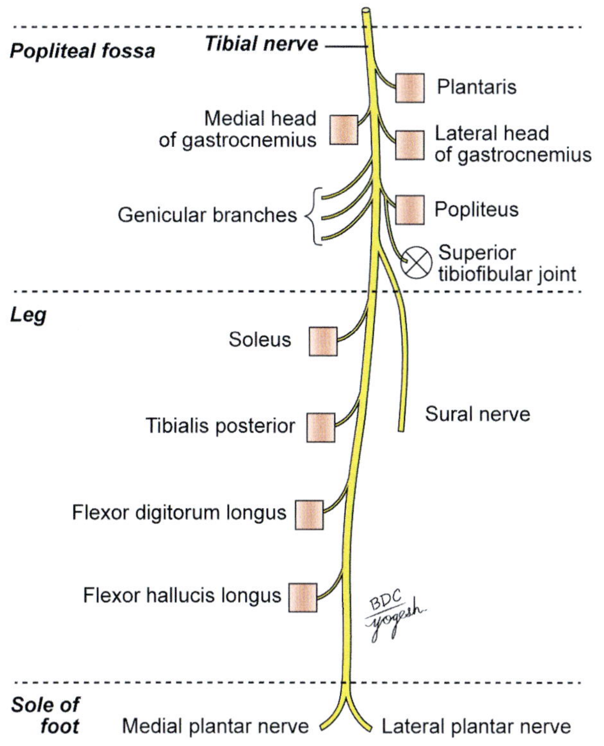

Fig. A1.4: Branches of tibial nerve

2. *Cutaneous branches*: Medial calcaneal nerve pierces the flexor retinaculum and supplies the skin over the heel.
3. *Articular branches* to ankle joint.
4. *Terminal branches*: Medial and lateral plantar nerves.

MEDIAL PLANTAR NERVE

It is the larger terminal branch of tibial nerve (Fig. A1.5). Its distribution is similar to median nerve of the hand. It lies between abductor hallucis and flexor digitorum brevis and ends by giving muscular, cutaneous and articular branches.

Branches

Muscular branches supply four muscles:
1. Abductor hallucis
2. Flexor digitorum brevis
3. Flexor hallucis brevis receives a branch from the 1st digital nerve.
4. The 1st lumbrical muscle receives a branch from the 2nd digital nerve.

Cutaneous branches (four digital nerves) supply the skin of the medial part of the sole, and of the medial 3½ toes. Each digital nerve gives off a dorsal branch which supplies structures around the nail of the digit concerned.

Articular branches supply joints of the tarsus and metatarsus.

LATERAL PLANTAR NERVE

It is the smaller terminal branch of tibial nerve, resembling the ulnar nerve of the hand in its distribution.

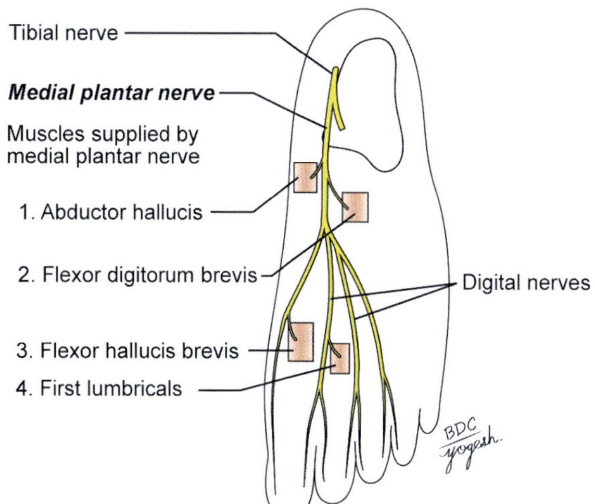

Fig. A1.5: Medial plantar nerve

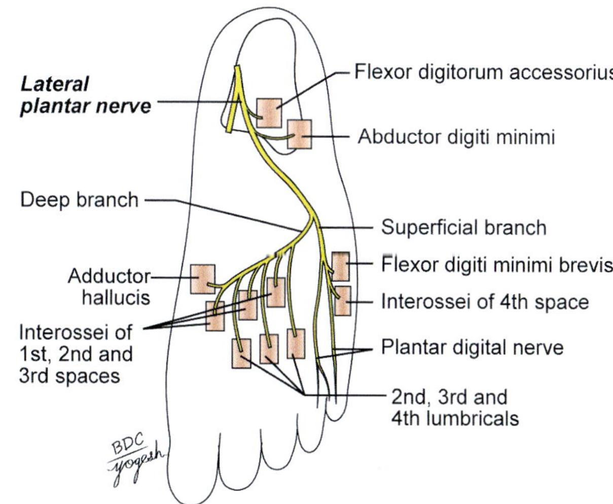

Fig. A1.6: Lateral plantar nerve

It runs obliquely between the 1st and 2nd layers of sole till the tuberosity of 5th metatarsal bone, where it divides into its superficial and deep branches (Fig. A1.6).

Branches

Main trunk

a. *Muscular branches* supply flexor *digitorum accessorius* and the *abductor digiti minimi*.
b. *Cutaneous branches supply* the skin of the sole.

Superficial branch: It divides into two branches—lateral and medial.

a. The *lateral branch* supplies three muscles—*flexor digiti minimi brevis*, the *3rd plantar* and *4th dorsal interossei*, and the skin on the lateral side of the little toe.
b. The *medial branch* communicates with the medial plantar nerve, and supplies the skin lining the 4th interdigital cleft.

Deep branch: It supplies *nine* muscles, including the 2nd, 3rd and 4th lumbricals; 1st, 2nd and 3rd dorsal interossei; 1st and 2nd plantar interossei and adductor hallucis.

COMMON PERONEAL NERVE

This is the smaller terminal branch of sciatic nerve. Its root value is dorsal division of ventral rami of L4, 5, S1, 2 segments of spinal cord (Fig. A1.7).

Beginning: It begins in the back of thigh as a smaller subdivision of the sciatic nerve.

Course: It lies in the upper lateral part of popliteal fossa, along the medial border of biceps femoris muscle. It turns around the lateral surface of fibula and lies in the substance of peroneus longus muscle.

Termination: Ends by dividing into two terminal branches, i.e. superficial peroneal and deep peroneal nerves.

Branches

1. *Cutaneous branches* are two:
   a. *Lateral cutaneous nerve of the calf* descends to supply the skin of the upper 2/3rd of the lateral side of the leg.
   b. *Sural communicating nerve* arises in the upper part of the fossa. It runs on the posterolateral aspect of calf and joins the sural nerve.
2. *Articular branches*:
   a. *Superior lateral genicular nerve* accompanies the artery of the same name and lies above the lateral femoral condyle.
   b. *Inferior lateral genicular nerve* also runs with the artery of the same name to the lateral aspect of knee joint above the head of fibula.
   c. *Recurrent genicular nerve* arises where common peroneal nerve divides into superficial and deep peroneal nerves. It ascends anterior to the knee joint and supplies tibialis anterior muscle in addition to the knee joint.

Note: The common peroneal nerve does not give muscular branches in the popliteal fossa. However, it may give a branch to the short head of biceps femoris.

DEEP PERONEAL NERVE

The deep peroneal nerve is the nerve of the anterior compartment of the leg and the dorsum of the foot (Fig. A1.7). It corresponds to the posterior interosseous nerve of the forearm. This is one of the two terminal branches of the common peroneal nerve given off between the neck of the fibula and the peroneus longus muscle.

Course and relations: The deep peroneal nerve begins on the lateral side of the neck of fibula under cover of the upper fibres of peroneus longus. It enters the anterior compartment of leg by piercing the anterior intermuscular septum. It then pierces the extensor digitorum longus and comes to lie next to the anterior tibial vessels.

In the leg, it accompanies the anterior tibial artery and has similar relations. The nerve lies lateral to the artery in the upper and lower third of the leg, and anterior to the artery in the middle one-third.

The nerve ends on the dorsum of the foot, close to the ankle joint, by dividing into the lateral and medial terminal branches.

The lateral terminal branch turns laterally and ends in a pseudoganglion deep to the extensor digitorum brevis. Branches arise from the pseudoganglion and supply the extensor digitorum brevis and the tarsal joints.

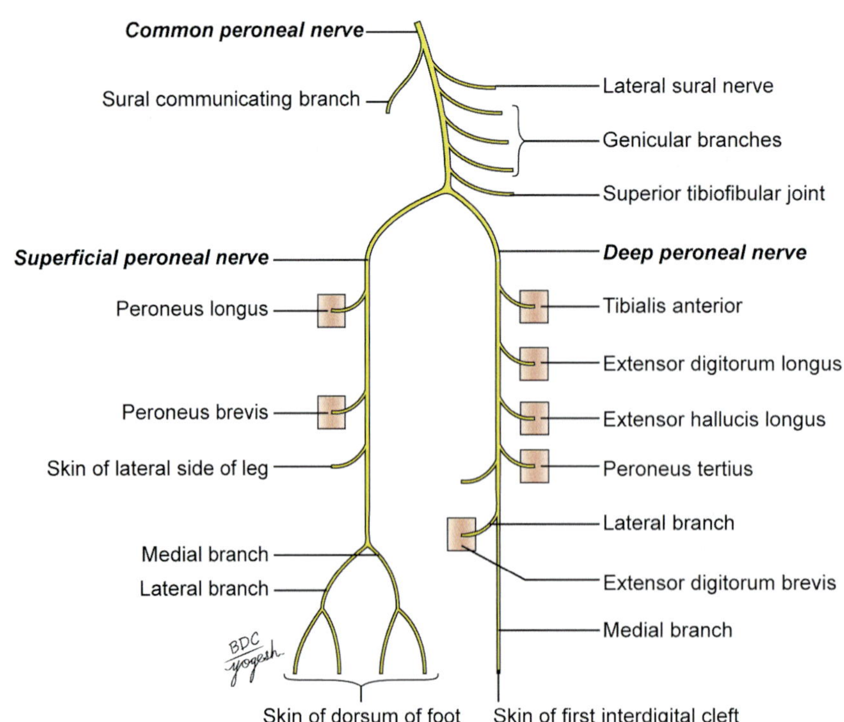

Fig. A1.7: Common, superficial and deep peroneal nerves

The medial terminal branch ends by supplying the skin adjoining the first interdigital cleft and the proximal joints of the big toe.

Branches

1. *Muscular branches* supply tibialis anterior, extensor digitorum longus, extensor hallucis longus and peroneus tertius, extensor digitorum brevis.
2. *Cutaneous branch* supplies adjacent sides of the 1st and 2nd toes.
3. *Articular branches* supply ankle joint, tarsal joints, tarsometatarsal and metatarsophalangeal joints.

SUPERFICIAL PERONEAL NERVE

It is the smaller terminal branch of the common peroneal nerve (Fig. A1.8).

Origin: It arises in the substance of peroneus longus muscle, lateral to the neck of fibula.

Course: It descends in the lateral compartment of leg deep to peroneus longus and lies between peroneus longus and peroneus brevis muscles and lastly between the peronei and extensor digitorum longus.

It pierces the deep fascia in distal one-third of leg and descends to the dorsum of foot.

Branches

1. *Muscular branches:* Peroneus longus and the peroneus brevis.
2. *Cutaneous branches:* Through its terminal branches, the superficial peroneal nerve supplies the lower 1/3rd of the lateral side of the leg and the greater part of the dorsum of the foot, except for the territories supplied by the saphenous, sural, deep peroneal and plantar nerves.
3. *Medial branch:* It crosses the ankle and divides into two dorsal digital nerves—one for the medial side of the big toe and the other for the adjoining sides of the 2nd and 3rd toes.
4. *Lateral branch:* It divides into two dorsal digital nerves for the adjoining sides of the 3rd and 4th and 4th and 5th toes.
5. *Communicating branches:* The medial branch communicates with the saphenous and deep peroneal nerves, and the lateral branch with the sural nerve.

CLINICAL ANATOMY

- The motor and sensory loss in case of injury to the various nerves is shown in Table A1.1.
- Femoral nerve supplying the quadriceps femoris through L2, 3, 4 segments of spinal cord is tested by doing the ***'patellar jerk'***. The ligamentum patellae is hit by the hammer and the contraction of the quadriceps is felt with extension of knee.
- Since obturator nerve supplies both the hip and knee joints, pain of one joint may be referred to the other joint.
- The paralysis of left superior gluteal nerve leads to paralysis of left gluteus medius and minimus muscle. During walking when the body is supported on left foot, the right unsupported side of the pelvis droops, causing inability to walk with right foot. This is called *positive Trendelenburg's gait*.

TABLE A1.1: Injuries to nerves and their effects

	Motor loss	*Sensory loss*
Femoral	Quadriceps femoris: Inability to extend the knee Iliacus and sartorius: Weak flexion of the thigh	Anterior side of thigh, medial side of leg till ball of big toe
Obturator	Adductors of thigh except hamstring part of adductor magnus: Loss of adduction of the thigh	Small area on the medial side of thigh
Sciatic	Hamstring muscles; dorsiflexors and plantar flexors of ankle joint and evertors of foot ***Foot drop*** occurs	Back of leg, anterolateral side of leg, most of dorsum of foot, sole of foot
Tibial	Paralysis of the muscles of posterior compartment of the leg: Loss of plantar flexion of foot Intrinsic muscles of sole	Skin of sole. Later trophic ulcers develop
Common peroneal	Extensor digitorum longus and extensor hallucis longus: Loss of dorsiflexion of ankle (***foot drop***) Peroneus longus and peroneus brevis: Loss of eversion of foot	Lateral and anterior sides of leg, most of dorsum of foot, most of digits
Deep peroneal	Muscles of anterior compartment of leg ***Foot drop*** occurs	1st interdigital cleft
Superficial peroneal	Peroneus longus and peroneus brevis, loss of eversion of foot	Lateral aspect of leg, most of dorsum of foot except at the 1st web space
Medial plantar	Four intrinsic muscles of sole	Medial 2/3rd of sole and digital nerves to medial 3½ toes, including nail beds
Lateral plantar	Most of intrinsic muscles of sole	Lateral one-third of sole and digital nerves to lateral 1½ toes, including nail beds

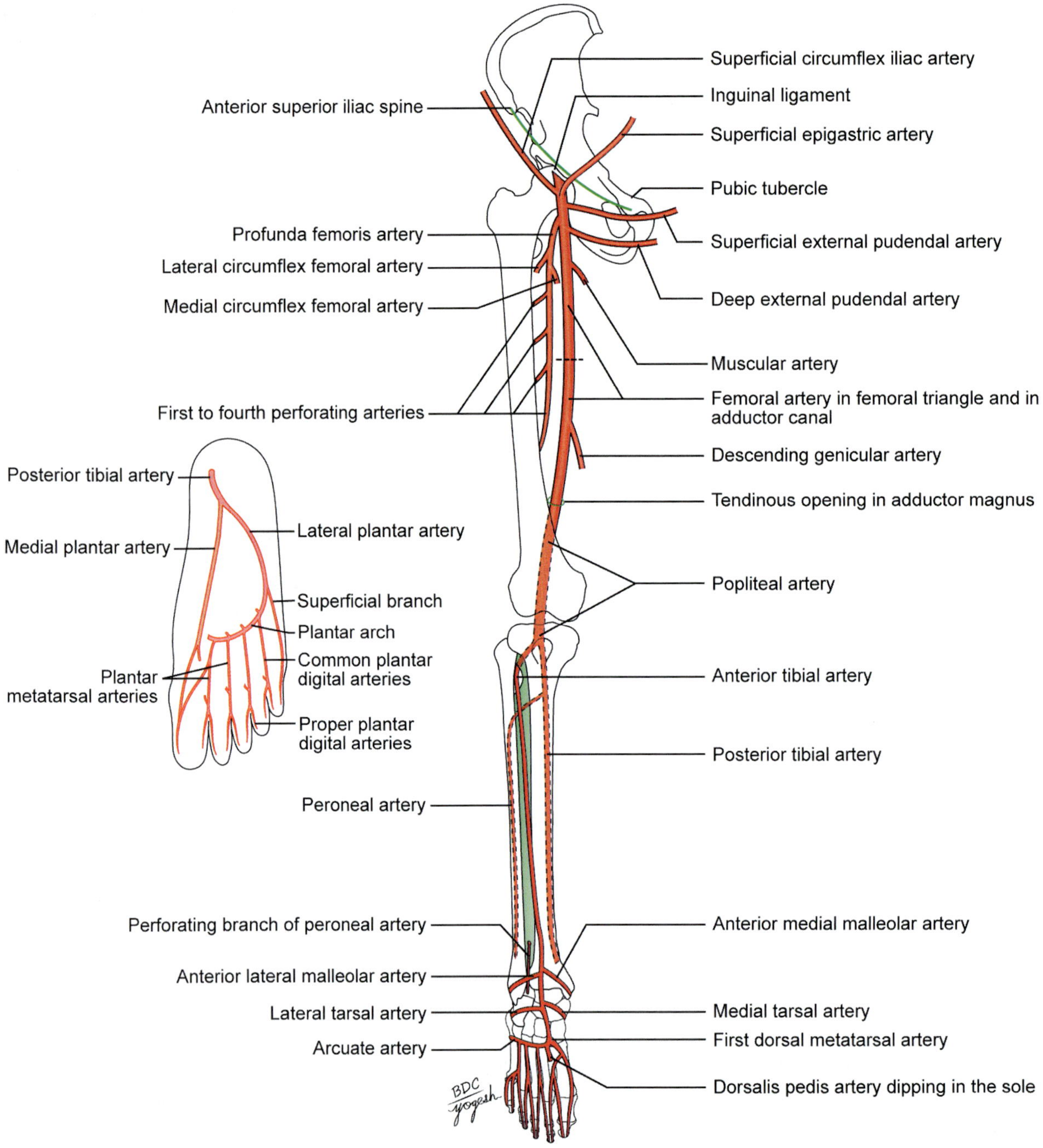

Fig. A1.8: Arterial supply of lower limb

- ***Sleeping foot***: Sometimes it happens that one is awake but the foot sleeps. Sciatic nerve lies on quadratus femoris and adductor magnus. Between the two muscles, the nerve lies on the hard femur. So the nerve gets pressed between the femur and the hard edge of table, chair or bed. There is numbness of the lower limb till the foot is hit against the ground a few times. The sensations come back.
- ***Injury to sciatic nerve***: Injury to sciatic nerve leads to paralysis of hamstrings and all plantar flexors of ankle, dorsiflexors of ankle and evertors of foot along with sensory loss over back of leg, anterolateral aspect of leg, most of dorsum and sole of foot skin supplied by saphenous nerve (medial aspect of leg and medial border of foot till ball of great toe) is spared leading to ***'foot drop'***.
- ***Sciatica*** is the name given when there is radiating pain in the back of lower limb. It may be due to slip disc.
- Common peroneal nerve is the commonest nerve to be paralysed. This is injured due to fracture of neck of fibula, 'lathi injury' on the lateral side of knee joint or due to plaster on the leg. In the last case, the nerve gets compressed between hard plaster and neck of fibula. To prevent this, cotton must be placed on the upper lateral side of the leg. The effects of injury are:
  - *Motor loss* to dorsiflexors and evertors of foot. The typical position of the foot is 'foot drop'; sensory loss

is to the back of leg; lateral side of leg and most of dorsum of foot.
- *Articular loss* to the lateral side of knee joint.

- Paralysis of muscles of the anterior compartment of the leg results in loss of the power of dorsiflexion of the foot. As a result, the foot is plantar flexed. The condition is called '***foot drop***'.
- Thus most of the muscles of the lower limb are supplied by sciatic nerve except the adductors of thigh, extensors of knee joint.

MAJOR ARTERIES OF LOWER LIMB

The arterial supply of lower limb is shown in Fig. A1.8 and Table A1.2.

TABLE A1.2: Arteries of lower limb

Artery	*Beginning, course and termination*	*Branches*
Femoral artery	It is the continuation of external iliac artery, begins behind the inguinal ligament at the midinguinal point. Femoral artery courses through femoral triangle and adductor canal. Then it passes through opening in adductor magnus to continue as the popliteal artery	3 superficial branches: 1. Superficial external pudendal 2. Superficial epigastric 3. Superficial circumflex iliac 3 deep branches are: 1. Profunda femoris 2. Deep external pudendal 3. Muscular branches. *In the adductor canal:* Descending genicular artery. Muscular branches.
Profunda femoris	Largest branch of femoral artery which descends posterior to femoral vessels, and ends as the fourth perforating artery	Medial circumflex femoral artery Lateral circumflex femoral artery Four perforating arteries Muscular branches
Popliteal artery	It is the continuation of femoral artery and lies in the popliteal fossa. Popliteal artery ends by dividing into anterior tibial artery and posterior tibial artery at the distal border of popliteus muscle	Cutaneous branches Muscular branches Five genicular or articular branches: Superior medial, superior lateral, inferior medial, inferior lateral, and middle genicular arteries
Anterior tibial artery	Smaller terminal branch of popliteal artery reaches the front of leg through an opening in the interosseous membrane. Runs amongst muscles of front of leg till midway between medial and lateral malleoli, where it ends by changing its name to dorsalis pedis artery	Anterior and posterior tibial recurrent branches Anterior medial malleolar and anterior lateral malleolar branches Muscular branches to adjacent muscles
Dorsalis pedis artery	Continuation of anterior tibial artery. Runs along medial side of dorsum of foot to reach proximal end of 1st intermetatarsal space where it enters the sole. In the sole, it completes the plantar arch	Lateral tarsal artery Medial tarsal branches Arcuate artery 1st dorsal metatarsal artery
Posterior tibial artery	It begins as the larger terminal branch of popliteal artery at the distal border of popliteus muscle. It descends down medially between the long flexor muscles to reach midway between medial malleolus and medial tubercle of calcaneus where it ends by dividing into medial plantar and lateral plantar arteries	Peroneal artery Muscular branches Nutrient artery to tibia Circumflex fibular branch Communicating branch Malleolar branch Calcaneal branches Medial plantar and lateral plantar arteries
Medial plantar artery	The smaller terminal branch of posterior tibial artery given off under flexor retinaculum. Runs along the medial border of foot and ends by giving digital arteries	Three superficial digital branches Muscular and cutaneous branches
Lateral plantar artery	The large terminal branch of posterior tibial artery given off under the flexor retinaculum. It runs laterally between muscles of 1st and 2nd layers of sole till the base of 5th metatarsal bone by becoming continuous with the plantar arch	Anastomotic branches Calcanean branch Muscular and cutaneous branches
Plantar arch	It is the direct continuation of lateral plantar artery and is completed medially by dorsalis pedis artery. The arch lies between 3rd and 4th layers of muscles of sole. The deep branch of lateral plantar nerve lies in its concavity	Four plantar metatarsal arteries Three proximal perforating arteries

CLINICAL ANATOMY

- ***Arterial occlusive disease of the lower limb***: Occlusive disease causes ischaemia of the muscles of lower limb leading to cramp-like pain. The pain disappears with rest but comes back with activity. The condition is called 'intermittent claudication'.
- ***Palpation*** of dorsalis pedis artery and posterior tibial artery gives information about peripheral arterial diseases.
- Sympathetic innervation of the arteries: T10–T12 and L1–L3 segments provide sympathetic innervation to arteries of lower limb. Preganglionic fibres relay in the ganglia associated with these segments. Postganglionic fibres reach blood vessels via branches of lumbar and sacral plexuses.
- Femoral artery receives postganglionic fibres from femoral and obturator nerves.
- Arteries of the leg receive postganglionic fibres via the tibial and common peroneal nerves.
- Lumbar sympathectomy for occlusive arterial disease: Sympathectomy, i.e. removal of L2 and L3 ganglia with intervening sympathetic trunk is advised for this condition. This increases the collateral circulation. L1 ganglion is not removed as it is responsible for ejaculation.
- Excessive fluid from knee joint can be aspirated by putting in a needle in the joint cavity from its lateral side.

BDC's Anatomy *e*-book

1. Clinical Terms

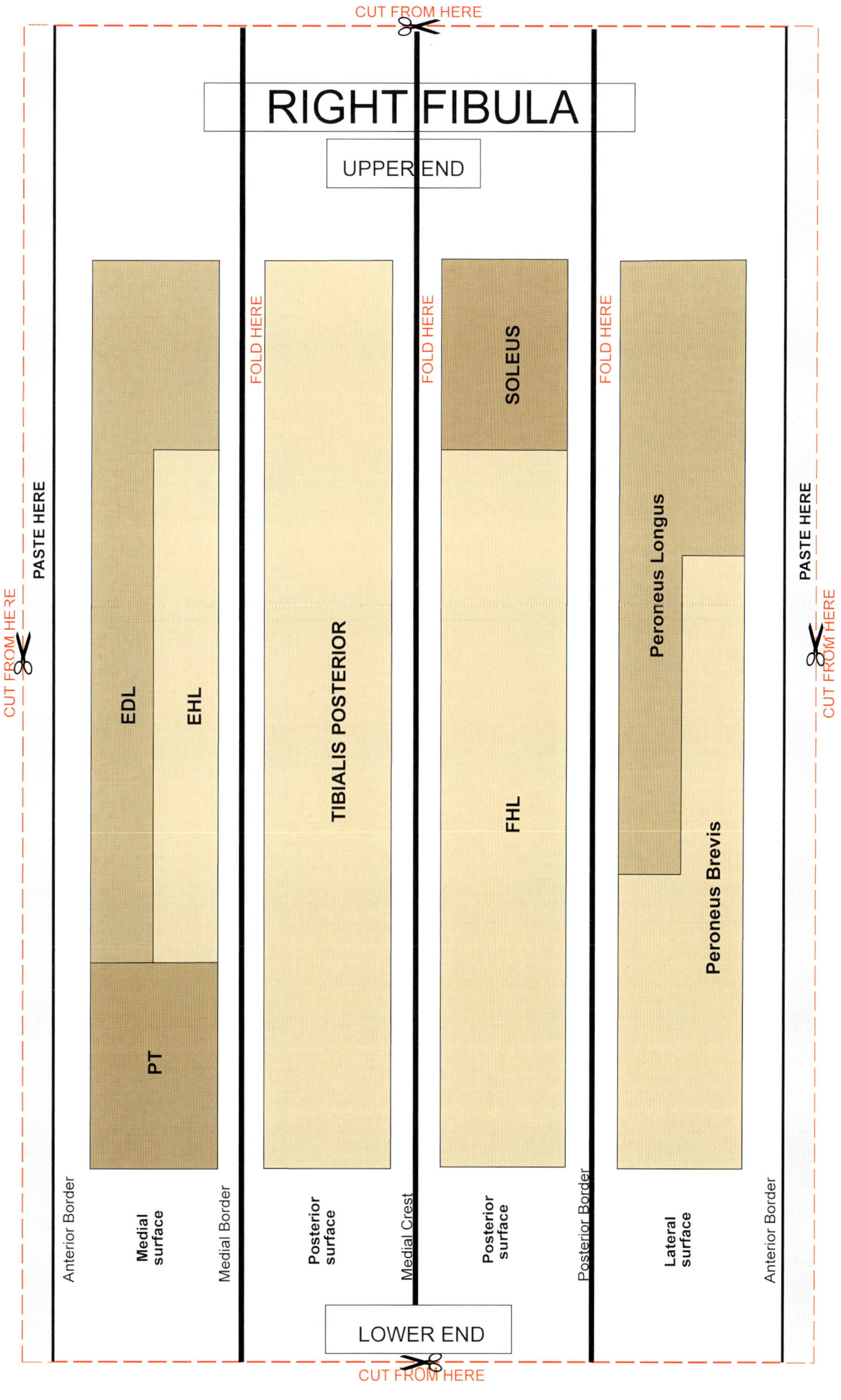

CUT FROM HERE

RIGHT FIBULA

UPPER END

PASTE HERE

CUT FROM HERE

FOLD HERE

FOLD HERE

FOLD HERE

EDL

EHL

PT

TIBIALIS POSTERIOR

SOLEUS

FHL

Peroneus Longus

Peroneus Brevis

PASTE HERE

CUT FROM HERE

Anterior Border

Medial surface

Medial Border

Posterior surface

Medial Crest

Posterior surface

Posterior Border

Lateral surface

Anterior Border

LOWER END

CUT FROM HERE

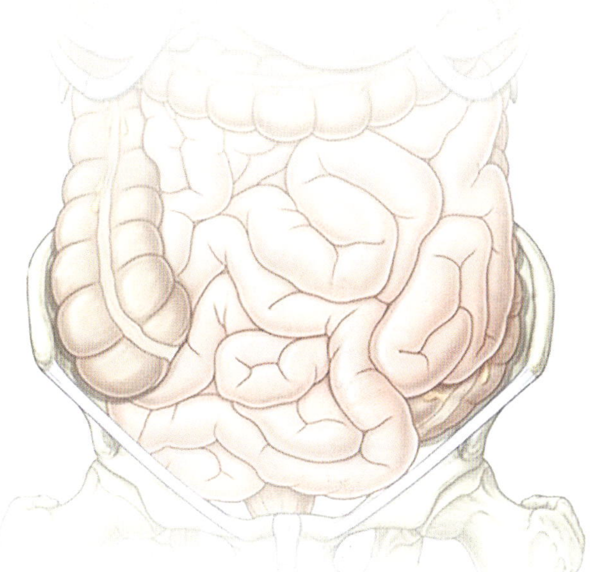

Section 2

Abdomen and Pelvis

Chapter

15

Introduction and Osteology of Abdomen

INTRODUCTION OF ABDOMEN

Trunk or torso is the central part of the human body that extends from the neck and limbs. The trunk includes the thorax and abdomen. For descriptive purposes, the lower part of the trunk is divided into abdomen, pelvis and perineum.

The ***abdomen*** is the lower part of the trunk that lies between the diaphragm and the pelvis. The cavity of the abdomen is the *abdominal cavity* (Fig. 15.1). The ***pelvis*** (basin in Latin) is a part of the trunk that is posteroinferior to the abdomen and above the lower limbs. The cavity of pelvis is the *pelvic cavity*. Abdominal and pelvic cavities are continuous with each other.

ABDOMINAL CAVITY

The abdominal cavity is bounded by dynamic, multilayered, musculoaponeurotic abdominal walls with anterolateral and posterior walls.

Boundaries

The abdominal cavity is bounded as follows (Fig. 15.1):

Anterolaterally: Anterolateral wall – formed by muscles and lower ribs.

Posteriorly: Posterior wall – formed by lumbar vertebrae and muscles.

Superiorly: Diaphragm, which separates abdominal cavity from thoracic cavity.

Inferiorly: It continues with the pelvic cavity at the pelvic inlet.

Contents

The abdominal cavity contains the following:

1. Abdominal viscera:
   - Stomach, small intestine and most of the large intestine
   - Liver, gallbladder, pancreas and spleen.
   - Kidneys, ureters and suprarenal glands.
2. Major blood vessels:
   - Abdominal aorta and its branches
   - Inferior vena cava and its tributaries.
3. Lymph nodes and lumbar nerve plexus.

PELVIC CAVITY

The pelvic cavity is funnel-shaped. It is bounded as follows (Fig. 15.1):

Superiorly: Continuous above with the abdominal cavity at the pelvic inlet

Inferiorly: Muscular pelvic diaphragm

Anteriorly: Pubic symphysis and pubic bones

Posteriorly: Sacrum and coccyx

Laterally: Hip bones

Contents

The contents of the pelvic cavity are as follows:

- Sigmoid colon and rectum
- Urinary bladder and ureters
- In males: Prostate, ductus deferens and seminal vesicles
- In females: Uterus, uterine tubes, round ligament of uterus, ligament of ovary, ovaries and vagina
- Nerves, vessels, peritoneum and pelvic fascia.

PERINEUM

The perineum is the lowest region of the trunk that lies in between two thighs (Fig. 15.1). It lies between pelvic diaphragm and pelvic outlet.

External Features

- In males, the perineum has two openings: Anal canal and urethra.
- In females, the perineum has three openings: Anal canal, urethra and vagina.
- In males, it shows penis, scrotum and anal orifice, whereas in females, it shows vulva and anal orifice.

Note:

The abdominal examination is an integral part of the clinical examination. To an obstetrician and gynaecologist, the importance of the abdomen is obvious. The surgeon considers the abdomen as an enigma because in a good proportion of his/her cases, the cause of abdominal pain, or the nature of an abdominal lump, may not be decided in spite of all possible investigations. *Laparotomy*, i.e. opening up of the abdomen by a surgeon.

The peritoneal cavity is a closed sac in the male. In the female, it communicates to the exterior through the openings of the uterine tubes.

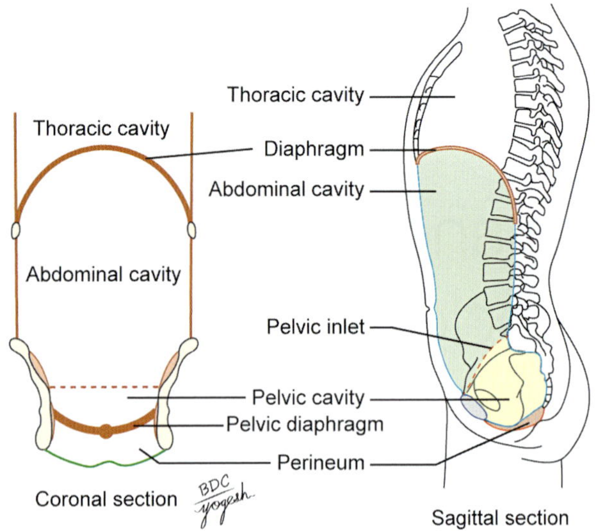

Fig. 15.1: Orientation of pelvic and abdominal cavities

Plate 15.1: Supporting bony framework of abdomen and pelvis

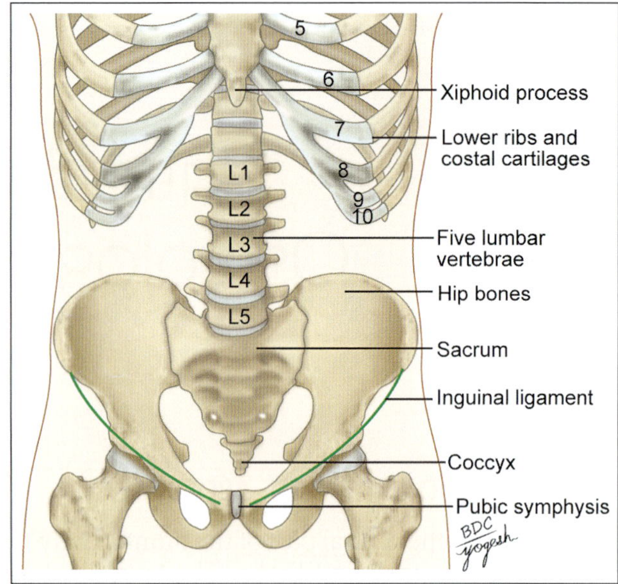

OSTEOLOGY

The abdominal and pelvic cavities are supported by a bony framework (Plate 15.1) that includes:

1. Lower ribs and costal cartilages
2. Five lumbar vertebrae
3. Sacrum
4. Coccyx
5. Bony pelvis or hip bones.

The bony architecture of ribs and costal cartilages are described in detail in *Thorax (Section 2) in Volume 1*. This chapter includes the description of lumbar vertebrae, sacrum, coccyx and the bony pelvis.

LUMBAR VERTEBRAE

The posterior abdominal wall is supported by lumbar vertebrae (*lumbar* = loin in Latin). There are five lumbar vertebrae (numbered 1st to 5th above downward). The lumbar vertebrae are grouped as follows:

A. Typical lumbar vertebrae: 1st to 4th
B. Atypical lumbar vertebra: 5th.

Identification of Lumbar Vertebrae

The identifying features of the lumbar vertebrae are as follows:

1. Large reniform (kidney-shaped) bodies.
2. Absence of foramen transversarium in the transverse process (*Note*: Foramen transversarium is a feature of typical cervical vertebrae).
3. Absence of costal facets on the body (*Note*: Costal facets are the feature of thoracic vertebrae).
4. The body of lumbar vertebrae is longer transversely than anteroposteriorly.
5. The spinous process is thick and quadrilateral.

Typical Lumbar Vertebra (L1–L4)

The typical lumbar vertebra has body, vertebral foramen and vertebral arch. The vertebral arch consists of pedicles, laminae, spine, transverse processes and superior and inferior articular processes (Plate 15.2, Fig. 15.2, Flowchart 15.1).

1. ***Body:*** It is large, kidney-shaped and is wider from side-to-side than from before backwards. The height of the body is slightly greater anteriorly than posteriorly; this difference contributes to the forward convexity of the lumbar spine (Fig. 15.2).
2. The ***vertebral foramen*** is triangular in shape and is larger than in the thoracic region, but is smaller than in the cervical region.
3. The ***pedicles*** are short and strong. They project backwards from the upper part of the body, so that the inferior vertebral notches are much deeper than the superior.

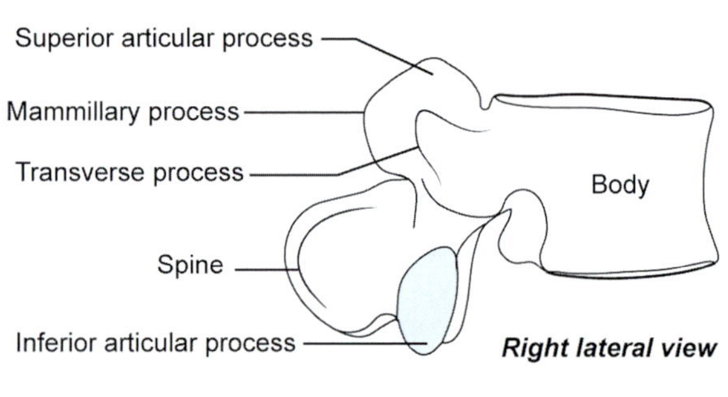

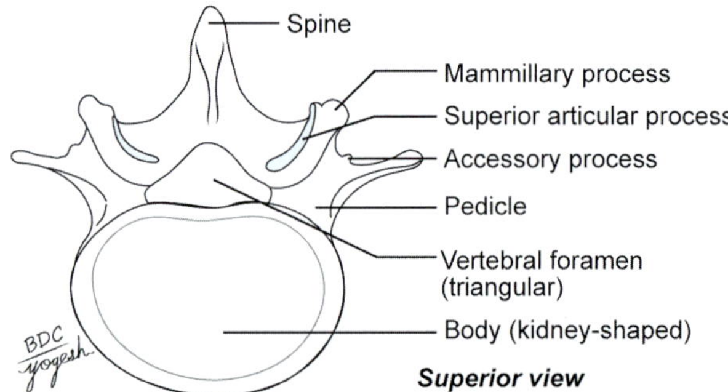

Fig. 15.2: Typical lumbar vertebra

Plate 15.2: Typical lumbar vertebra

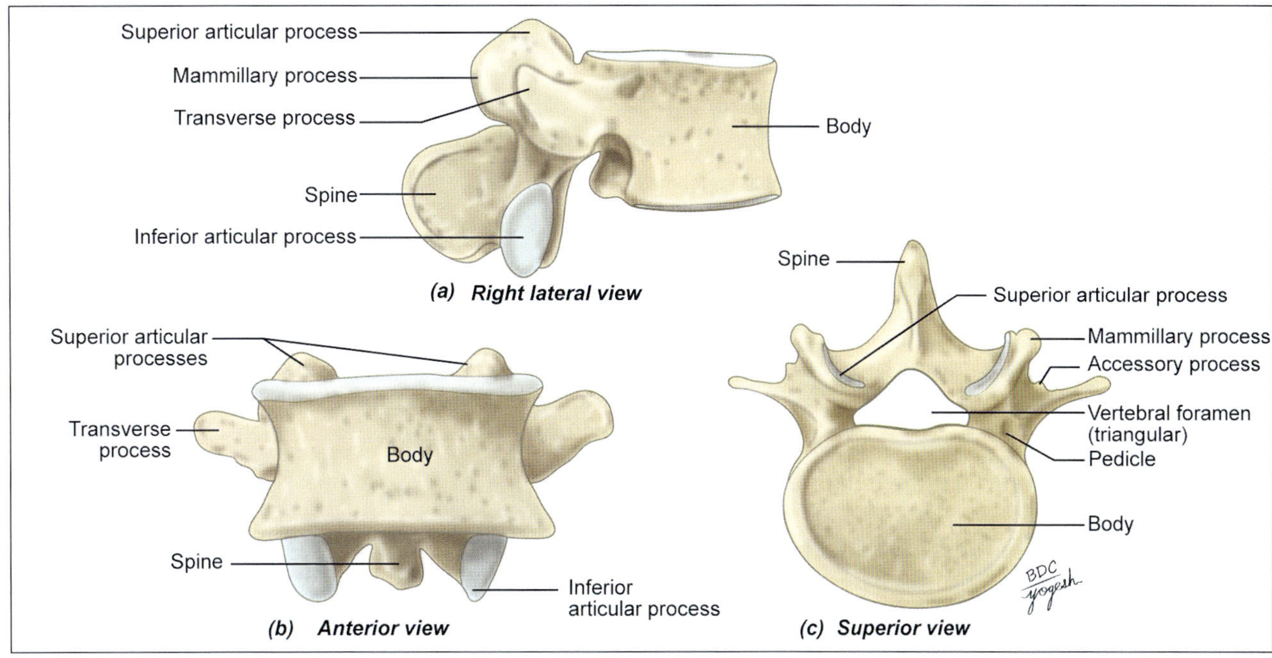

Flowchart 15.1: Typical lumbar vertebra

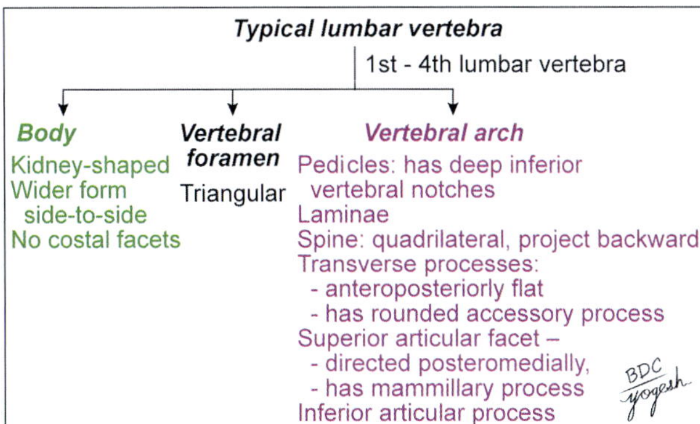

4. The ***laminae*** are short, thick and broad. They are directed backwards and medially to complete the vertebral foramen posteriorly. The overlapping between the laminae of the adjoining vertebrae is minimal.
5. The ***spine*** forms a vertical quadrilateral plate, directed almost backwards and only slightly downwards. It is thickened along its posterior and inferior borders.
6. The ***transverse processes*** are thin and tapering and are directed laterally and slightly backwards. The posteroinferior aspect of the root of each transverse process is marked by a small, rough elevation, the ***accessory process***, which represents the true transverse process of the vertebra as it develops from the transverse element of vertebra. The length of the transverse processes increases from vertebrae L1 to L3 and, thereafter, it decreases.
7. The ***superior articular processes*** lie farther apart than the inferior. Each process bears a concave facet facing medially and backwards. The posterior border is marked by a rough elevation, the mammillary process.
8. The ***inferior articular processes*** lie nearer to each other than the superior. Each process bears a convex facet facing laterally and forwards.

Fifth (Atypical) Lumbar Vertebra

1. The most important distinguishing features are as follows (Fig. 15.3, Flowchart 15.2):
   a. The ***transverse processes*** are thick, short and pyramidal in shape. Their base is attached to the whole thickness of the pedicle and encroaches on the side of the body.
   b. The ***spine*** is small, short and rounded at the tip.
   c. The distance between the ***inferior articular processes*** is equal to or more than the distance between the superior articular processes.
2. Other features of the fifth lumbar vertebra are as follows:
   a. The ***body*** is the largest of all lumbar vertebrae. Its anterior surface is much extensive than the posterior surface. This difference is responsible for the creation of the sharp lumbosacral angle or sacrovertebral angle and is 120° in an adult.
   b. The ***pedicles*** are directed backwards and laterally.
   c. The ***superior articular facets*** look more backwards than medially, and the ***inferior articular facets*** look more forwards than laterally, as compared to other lumbar vertebrae.

Flowchart 15.2: Features of the 5th lumbar vertebra

5th lumbar vertebra
↓
1. Atypical lumbar vertebra
2. Bulky, stout, pyramidal transverse process
3. Short spine
4. Large body
5. Equal distances between superior articular processes and inferior articular processes.

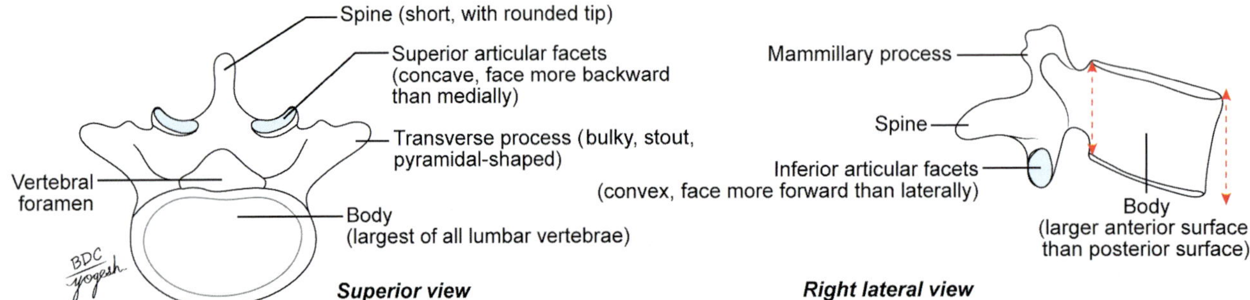

Fig. 15.3: Fifth lumbar vertebra

Attachments and Some Relations of Lumbar Vertebrae (Figs 15.4a to d)

Body

1. The upper and lower surfaces lie in contact with the *intervertebral discs*.
2. The upper and lower borders give attachment to the anterior and posterior longitudinal ligaments in front and behind, respectively.
3. Lateral to the anterior longitudinal ligament, the right crus of the diaphragm is attached to the upper three vertebrae and the left crus of the diaphragm to the upper two vertebrae.
4. Behind the line of the crura, the upper and lower borders of all the lumbar vertebrae give origin to the psoas major.
5. Across the constricted part of the body on either side, tendinous arches of psoas major are attached.

Vertebral Canal

The part of vertebral canal formed by the 1st lumbar vertebra contains the ***conus medullaris***. The part formed by lower four vertebrae contains the ***cauda equina***. The canal of all the lumbar vertebrae contains the *spinal meninges*.

Vertebral Arch

The ***pedicles*** are related above and below to spinal nerves.

The ***laminae*** provide attachment to the ligamentum flava.

The ***spine*** provides attachment to:

- The posterior layer of the lumbar fascia.
- The interspinous and supraspinous ligaments.
- The erector spinae, the multifidus and the interspinous muscles (EMI).

Transverse Processes

1. The tips of the transverse processes of all lumbar vertebrae give attachment to the middle layer of the lumbar fascia. In addition, the tip of the 1st process gives attachment to the medial and lateral arcuate ligaments and the tip of the 5th process to the iliolumbar ligament.

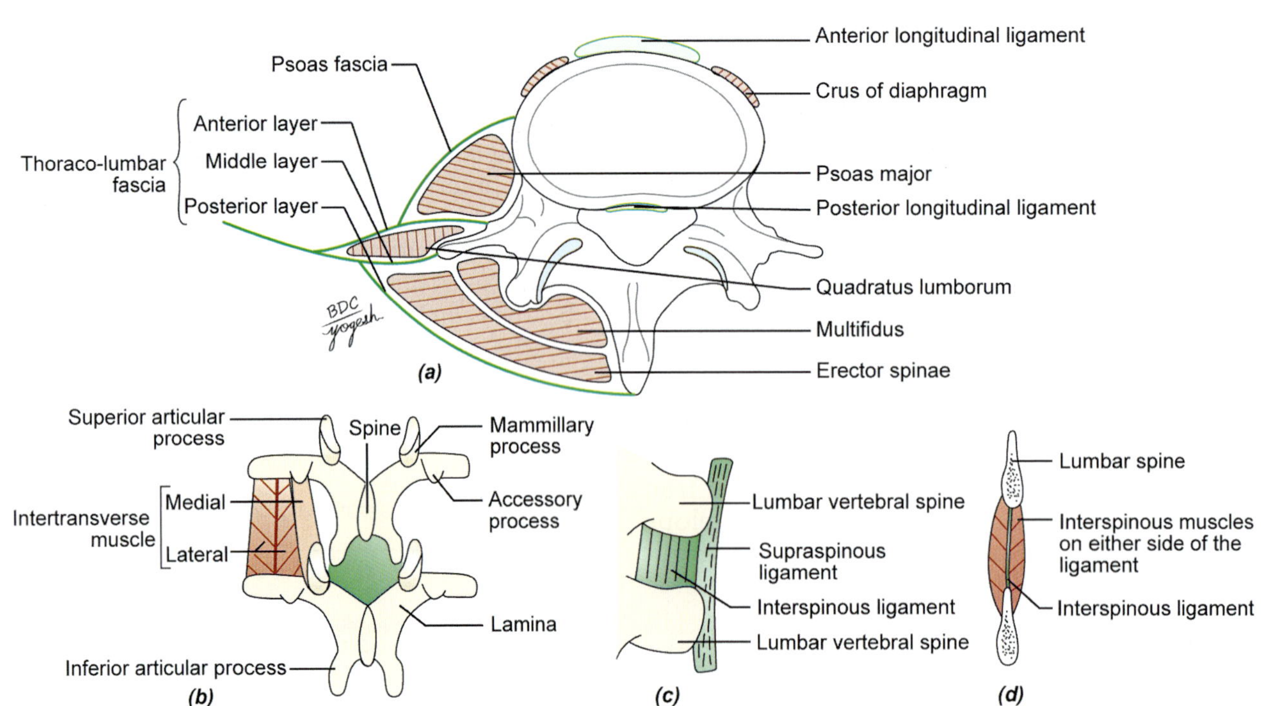

Figs 15.4a to d: Attachments of the lumbar vertebra

2. The faint vertical ridge on the anterior surface of each transverse process gives attachment to the anterior layer of the lumbar fascia. Medial to the ridge, the anterior surface gives origin to the psoas major, and lateral to the ridge to the quadratus lumborum.
3. The posterior surface is covered by deep muscles of the back and gives origin to the fibres of the longissimus thoracis (part of erector spinae). The *accessory process* gives attachment to the medial intertransverse muscles.
4. The upper and lower borders provide attachment to the lateral intertransverse muscles.

Spinous Processes

Between adjacent spines are interspinous ligaments with interspinous muscles on either side of the ligament. Supraspinous ligaments cover 2–3 spines.

Articular Processes

The *mammillary process* gives attachment to the multifidus and to the medial intertransverse muscles.

OSSIFICATION

The lumbar vertebra ossifies from three primary and seven secondary centres as follows:

Three primary centres

- One centre for centrum
- Two centres for two halves of vertebral arches

The primary centres appear during 8th–9th week of intrauterine life. Two halves of vertebral arches fuse during the 1st year and vertebral arches fuse with the body during 6th year.

Seven secondary centres

- One for upper surface of the body
- One for lower surface of the body
- One for tip of spinous process
- Two for the tips of two transverse processes
- Two for two mammillary processes

All the secondary centres appear at puberty and fuse with primary centres by 25th year of age.

Competencies:

AN50.4 Explain the anatomical basis of scoliosis, lordosis, prolapsed disc, spondylolisthesis and spina bifida.

AN53.4 Explain and demonstrate clinical importance of bones of abdominopelvic region (sacralization of lumbar vertebra, lumbarization of 1st sacral vertebra and types of bony pelvis and coccyx).

CLINICAL ANATOMY

Sacralisation of the 5th lumbar vertebra is the fusion of *5th lumbar vertebra* with the sacrum (Fig. 15.5). This may press on the 5th lumbar nerve. Sometimes the body ossifies from two primary centres, and if one centre fails to develop, it results in a '***hemivertebra***'.

Spina bifida: The two halves of the neural arch may fail to fuse leaving a gap in the midline. This is called *spina bifida* (Fig. 15.6). Meninges and spinal cord may herniate out through the gap. Protrusion of meninges alone results in the formation of a cystic swelling filled with cerebrospinal fluid. This swelling is called ***meningocele***. When the spinal cord is also present in the swelling the condition is called ***myelomeningocele***. Sometimes a spina bifida is present, but there is no protrusion through it so that there is no swelling on the surface. This is referred to as ***spina bifida occulta***.

Spondylolysis: In this condition, there is a separation of body of 5th lumbar vertebra from vertebral arch (Fig. 15.7).

Spondylolisthesis: Sometimes the greater part of the 5th lumbar vertebra slips forwards over the sacrum (Fig. 15.7). Normally, the tendency to forward slipping is prevented by the fact that the inferior articular processes of the 5th lumbar vertebra lie behind the superior articular processes of the 1st sacral vertebra. Spondylolisthesis may be the cause of backache and pain radiating along the course of the sciatic nerve known as ***sciatica***.

Fracture-dislocation of lumbar vertebrae results in the ***cauda equina syndrome*** (Fig. 15.8). It is characterised by:

a. Flaccid paraplegia
b. Saddle-shaped area of anaesthesia and analgesia
c. Sphincter disturbances in the form of incontinence of urine and faeces
d. Impotence
e. Absence of knee and ankle jerks.

- ***Disc prolapse*** is usually posterolateral (Fig. 15.9). This presses upon the adjacent nerve roots and gives rise to referred pain, such as sciatica. Disc prolapse occurs most commonly in lower lumbar region and is also common in lower cervical region (C5–C7). In sciatica, the pain is increased with rise of pressure in canal (as in sneezing); straight leg raising tests are positive; and the motor effects, with loss of power and reflexes, may follow.
- The spine of thoracic vertebrae may point to one side. The condition is ***scoliosis*** (Fig. 15.10). There may be projection of the spines posteriorly due to osteoporosis of the bodies of vertebrae leading to ***kyphosis*** Fig. 15.10). Anterior convexity of lumbar vertebrae may get exaggerated, leading to '***lumbar lordosis***' (Fig. 15.10).

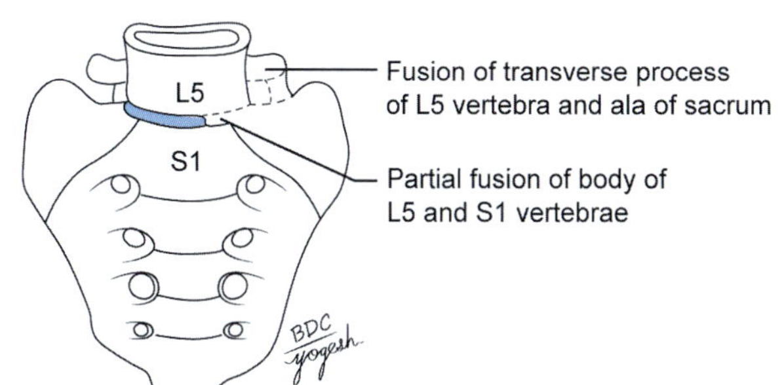

Fig. 15.5: Sacralisation of 5th lumbar vertebra (dotted lines indicate normal anatomy, anterior view)

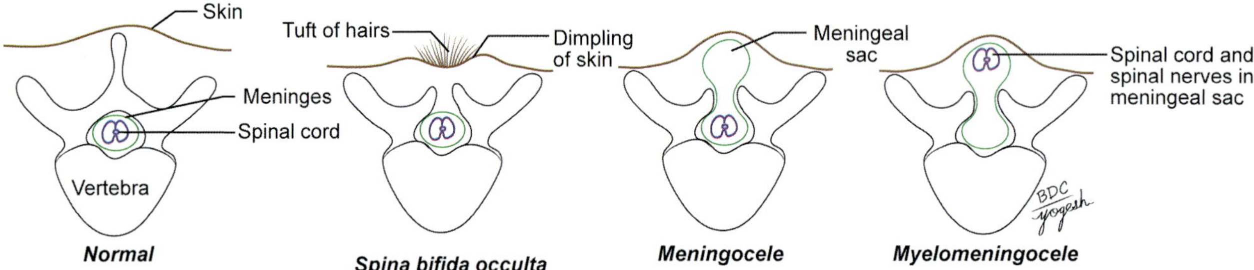

Fig. 15.6: Spina bifida

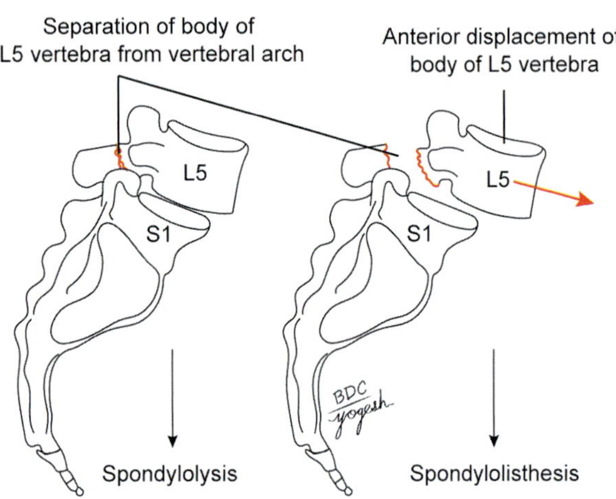

Fig. 15.7: Spondylolysis and spondylolisthesis

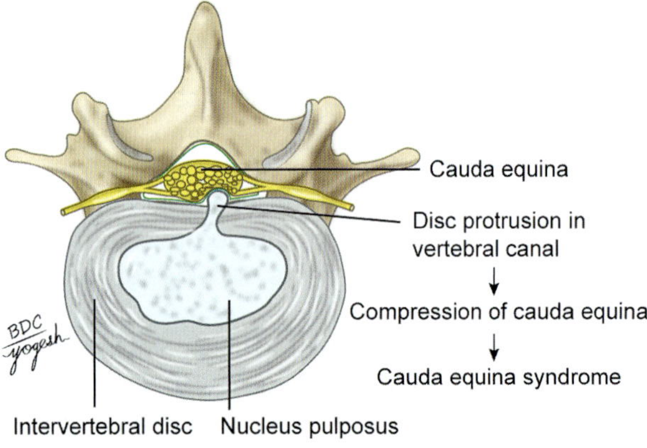

Fig. 15.8: Cauda equina syndrome

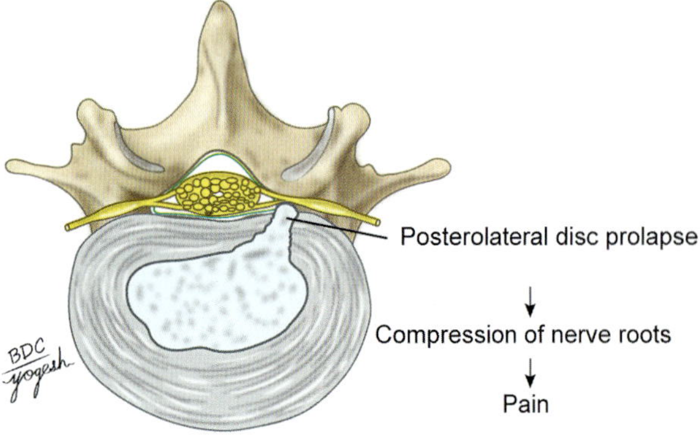

Fig. 15.9: Posterolateral disc prolapse

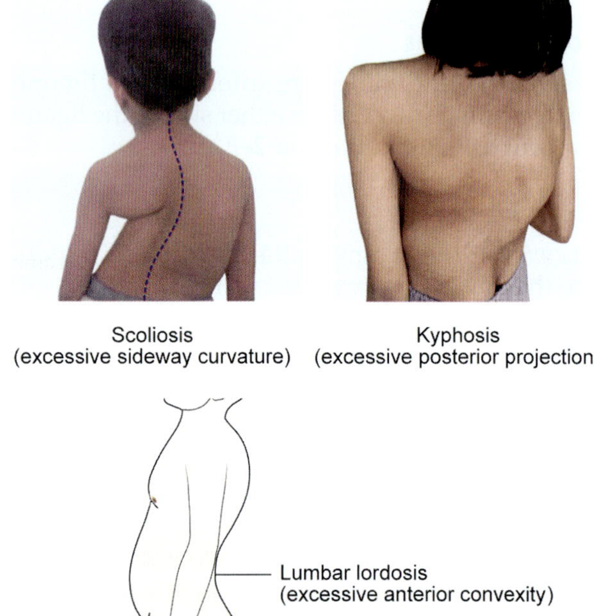

Fig. 15.10: Scoliosis, kyphosis and lumbar lordosis

SACRUM/VERTEBRA MAGNUM

The sacrum (Latin *sacred*) is a large, flattened, triangular bone formed by the fusion of five sacral vertebrae (Plate 15.3, Fig. 15.11, Flowchart 15.3).

Being triangular, the sacrum has the following parts:

1. *Base*: It is broad, has central articular part formed by upper surface of body of S1 vertebra and lateral nonarticular parts called *ala of sacrum*.
2. *Apex*: It is a narrow, rounded inferior part of sacrum.
3. *Surfaces*: It has four surfaces—pelvic (concave), dorsal (rough and convex) and two lateral surfaces.
4. *Sacral canal*: It is formed by fused superimposed vertebral foramina. It opens at *sacral hiatus*.

Anatomical position:

Hold the sacrum in such a way that:

1. Its concave pelvic surface faces downward and forward and rough, convex dorsal surface faces upward and backward.
2. Upper surface of the body of S1 vertebra slopes forward at an angle of about 30° with horizontal plane.

Plate 15.3: Sacrum

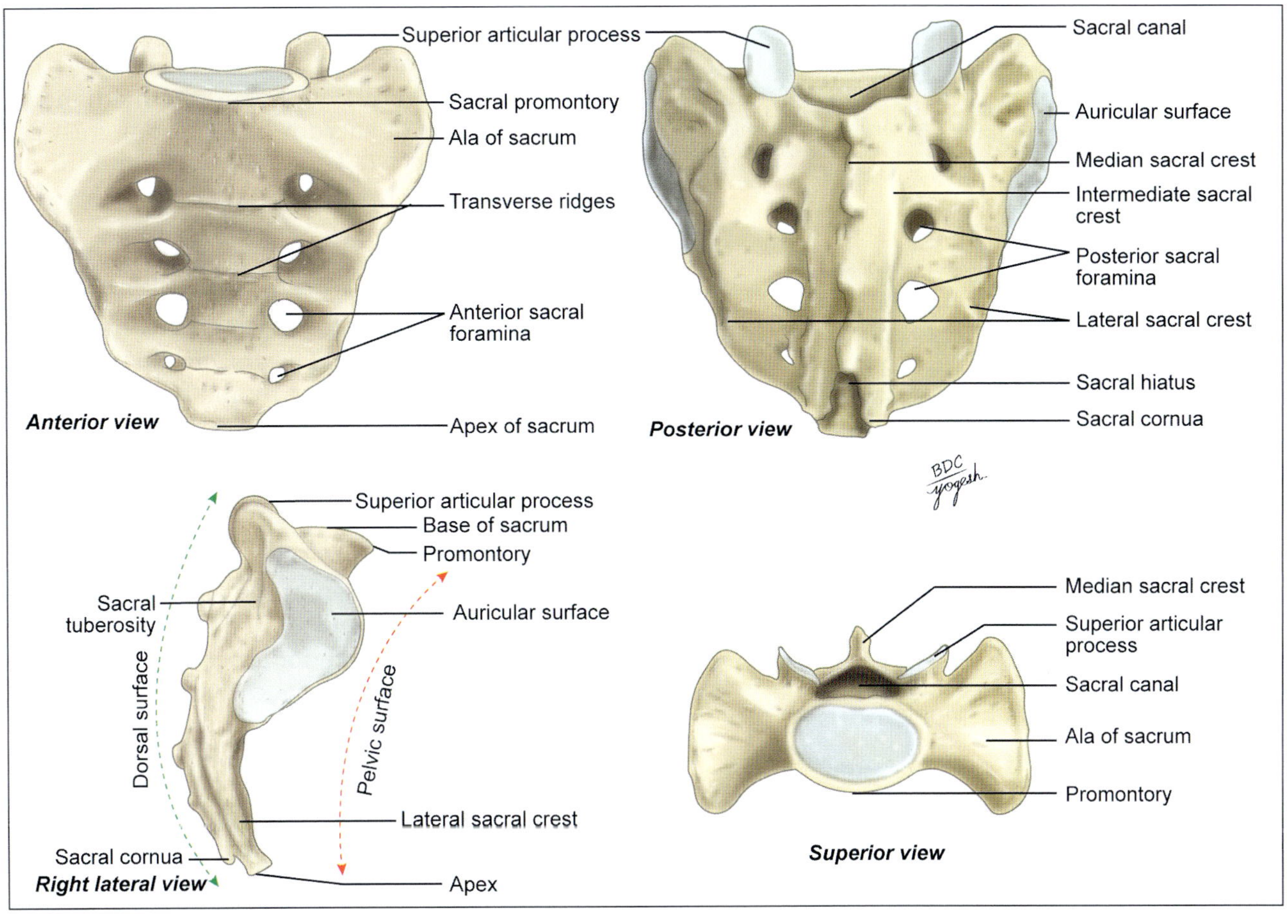

Superior articular process
Sacral promontory
Ala of sacrum
Transverse ridges
Anterior sacral foramina
Apex of sacrum
Anterior view

Sacral canal
Auricular surface
Median sacral crest
Intermediate sacral crest
Posterior sacral foramina
Lateral sacral crest
Sacral hiatus
Sacral cornua
Posterior view

Superior articular process
Base of sacrum
Promontory
Sacral tuberosity
Auricular surface
Dorsal surface
Pelvic surface
Lateral sacral crest
Sacral cornua
Apex
Right lateral view

Median sacral crest
Superior articular process
Sacral canal
Ala of sacrum
Promontory
Superior view

Flowchart 15.3: Sacrum

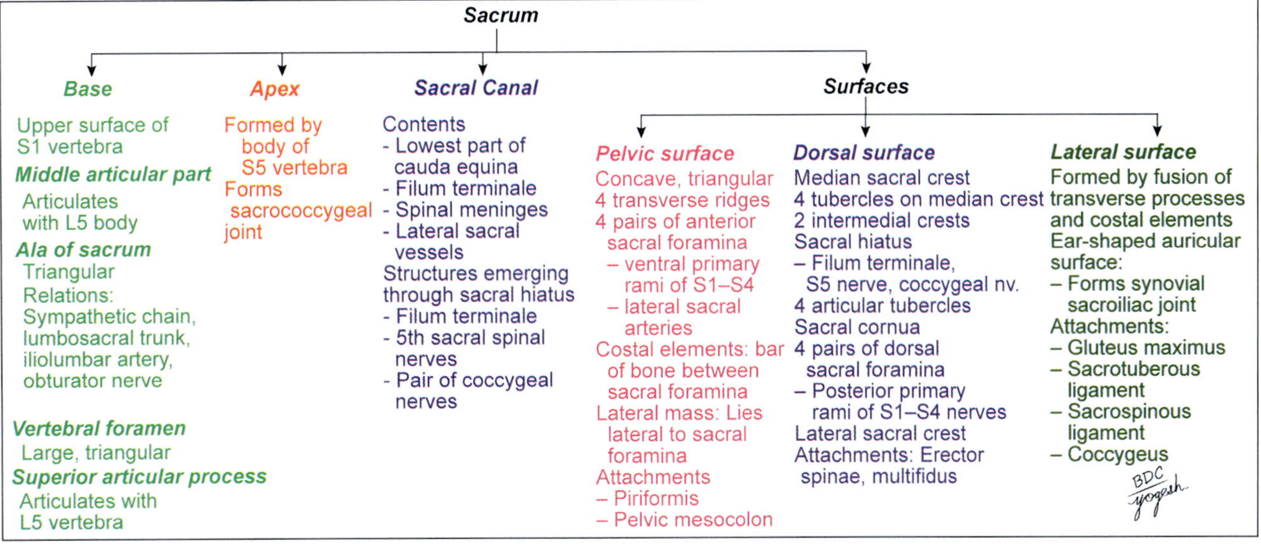

Features

Base

The base is directed upwards and forwards. It is formed by the upper surface of the S1 vertebra and presents features of a typical vertebra in a modified form.

1. The body is lumbar in type. It articulates with vertebra L5 at the ***lumbosacral joint***. The projecting anterior margin is called the ***sacral promontory***. The surface slopes forwards at an angle of 30°.
2. The *vertebral foramen* lies behind the body and leads into the ***sacral canal***. It is triangular in shape.
3. The *pedicles* are short and are directed backwards and laterally.
4. The *laminae* are oblique.

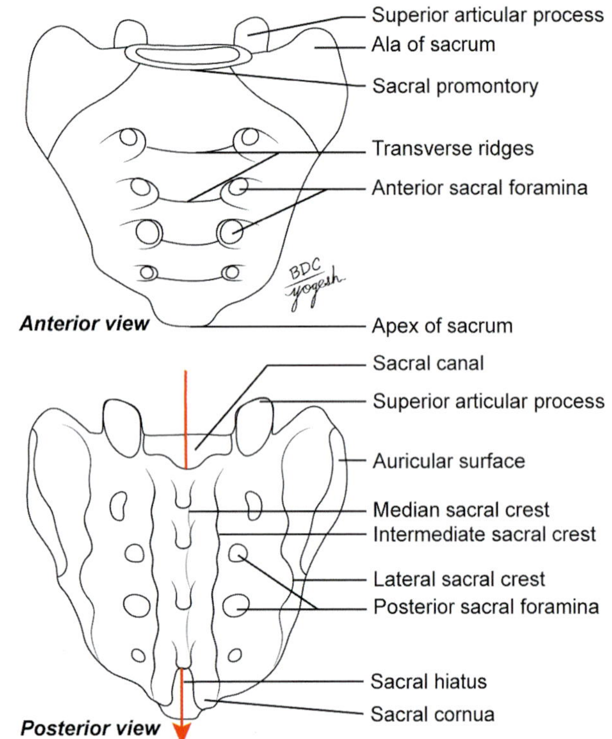

Fig. 15.11: Sacrum

5. The *spine* forms the 1st spinous tubercle.
6. The *superior articular processes* project upwards. The facets on them are directed backwards and medially.
7. The *transverse processes* are highly modified. Each process is massive and fused with the corresponding costal element to form the upper part of the lateral mass of the sacrum.

The base of the ***lateral mass*** forms a broad sloping surface spreading fan-wise from the side of the body. It is called the ***ala*** of the sacrum. The ala is subdivided into a smooth medial part and a rough lateral part.

Apex

The apex of the sacrum is formed by the inferior surface of the body of the S5 vertebra. It bears an oval facet for articulation with the coccyx at ***sacrococcygeal joint***.

Pelvic Surface

This is concave and directed downwards and forwards. It has the following features:

1. *Four transverse* ridges in the median plane that indicate fusion of five sacral vertebrae.
2. *Four pairs of anterior or* ***pelvic sacral foramina*** at the lateral ends of transverse ridges. They transmit the ventral primary rami of upper four sacral nerves and lateral sacral artery. They communicate with sacral canal.
3. *Costal elements* are represented by the bar of bone intervening between two sacral foramina of the same side.
4. *Lateral mass*: Lateral to the anterior sacral foramina, the costal elements fuse to form lateral mass.

Dorsal Surface

The dorsal surface of the sacrum is rough, irregular and convex and is directed backwards and upwards. It shows the following features:

1. ***Median sacral crest***: Opposite the median plane, dorsal surface of sacrum has raised a crest called *median sacral crest*. The crest presents four small tubercles that represent the spinous processes of fused sacral vertebrae.
2. ***Fused laminae***: Lateral to the median crest, the irregular convex area is formed by fusion of the laminae of the upper four sacral vertebrae.
3. *Two* ***intermediate sacral crests***, one on either side of median crest, are formed by the fusion of articular processes of sacral vertebrae.
4. ***Sacral hiatus***: The lamina of the 5th sacral vertebra fails to meet behind causing a U-shaped gap called sacral hiatus.
5. *Four articular tubercles*: They lie lateral to the fused laminae. They represent fused articular processes of adjacent sacral vertebrae.
6. ***Sacral cornua***: The inferior articular processes of 5th sacral vertebra are free and form horn-like sacral cornua that project downward at sides of sacral hiatus.
7. *Four posterior or* ***dorsal sacral foramina***: Dorsal surface shows four posterior sacral foramina that communicate with the sacral canal through intervertebral foramen.
8. ***Lateral sacral crest***: Lateral to the posterior sacral foramina, there is the lateral sacral crest with transverse tubercles. It represents fused transverse processes.

Lateral Surface

It is formed by the fused transverse processes and the costal elements of the sacral vertebrae. It is wide above and narrow below. The upper wider part bears an ***L-shaped auricular surface*** anteriorly, and a rough, deeply pitted area posteriorly. The auricular surface is formed by the costal elements. It articulates with the auricular surface of the hip bone at the ***sacroiliac joint***.

The posterior, roughened and pitted area is formed by the transverse processes.

The abrupt medial bend at the lower end of the lateral surface is called the ***inferior lateral angle*** of the sacrum.

Sacral Canal

It is formed by the sacral vertebral foramina and is *triangular* on cross-section. The upper end of the canal appears oblique, but actually it is directed upwards in the anatomical position. Inferiorly, the canal opens at the ***sacral hiatus***, and laterally, it communicates through the intervertebral foramina with the pelvic and dorsal sacral foramina.

Contents of sacral canal

1. Lowest part of cauda equina
2. Filum terminale
3. Spinal meninges
4. Lateral sacral vessels

Structures emerging through sacral hiatus

1. Filum terminale
2. Fifth sacral spinal nerves
3. Pair of coccygeal nerves.

Note: The *filum terminale internum internum*, the *subdural* and *subarachnoid spaces* end at the level of the second sacral vertebra. Therefore, the lower sacral nerves and filum terminale pierce the dura and arachnoid at this (S2) level.

Attachments on the Sacrum (Fig. 15.12)

1. The rough part of the ***ala*** gives origin to the iliacus anteriorly and attachment to the lumbosacral ligament posteriorly. The upper part of the ventral sacroiliac ligament is attached to its margin.
2. The part of the pelvic surface lateral to the bodies of the middle three pieces of the sacrum gives origin to the piriformis. The area extends into the intervals between the pelvic sacral foramina and is E-shaped.
3. The dorsal surface gives origin to the erector spinae along a U-shaped line passing over the spinous and transverse tubercles. The area in the concavity of the 'U' gives origin to the multifidus.
4. The lower narrow part of the lateral surface, below the auricular surface, gives origin to the gluteus maximus; attachment to the sacrotuberous and sacrospinous ligaments; and origin to the coccygeus, in that order from behind forwards.

Relations of the Sacrum

Relations of smooth part of ***ala of sacrum*** (medial to lateral) are as follows (Fig. 15.13):

1. **S**ympathetic chain
2. **L**umbosacral trunk
3. **I**liolumbar artery
4. **O**bturator nerve [*mnemonics*: **SLIO**]

All these structures are overlapped by the psoas major muscle. These structures form contents of ***triangle of Marcille***. The boundaries of triangle are:

Medial: Body of L5 vertebra
Lateral: Medial border of psoas major
Apex: Origin of psoas from L5 vertebra
Base: Ala of sacrum

The ***pelvic surface*** is related to:

1. The *median sacral vessels* in the median plane.
2. The *sympathetic trunks* along the medial margin of the pelvic foramina.
3. The *peritoneum* in front of the bodies of the upper 2½ pieces, interrupted obliquely by the attachment of medial limb of the *pelvic or sigmoid mesocolon*.
4. The *rectum* in front of the bodies of the lower 2½ pieces. The bifurcation of the superior rectal artery lies between the rectum and the third sacral vertebra.

Structures Transmitted through Foramina

1. The ***pelvic sacral foramina*** transmit:
   a. *Ventral rami of upper four sacral nerves.*
   b. Lateral sacral arteries.
2. The ***dorsal sacral foramina*** transmits the *dorsal rami of the upper four sacral nerves.*

Sacral Index

Sacral index is the ratio between the length and breadth of the sacrum.

Sacral index = (Breadth across the base × 100)/Length of sacrum from promontory to apex.

The sacral index is lower in males than in females as the male sacrum is longer. The sacral index is 105% in males and 115% in females (*Reference*: *Gray's Anatomy*, 42nd edn.).

Sex Differences

Distinguishing features of male and female sacrum are listed in Table 15.1 (Flowchart 15.4).

Flowchart 15.4: Differences between male and female sacrum

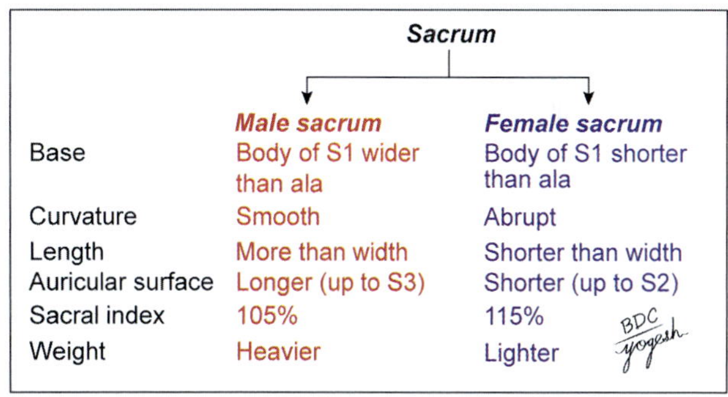

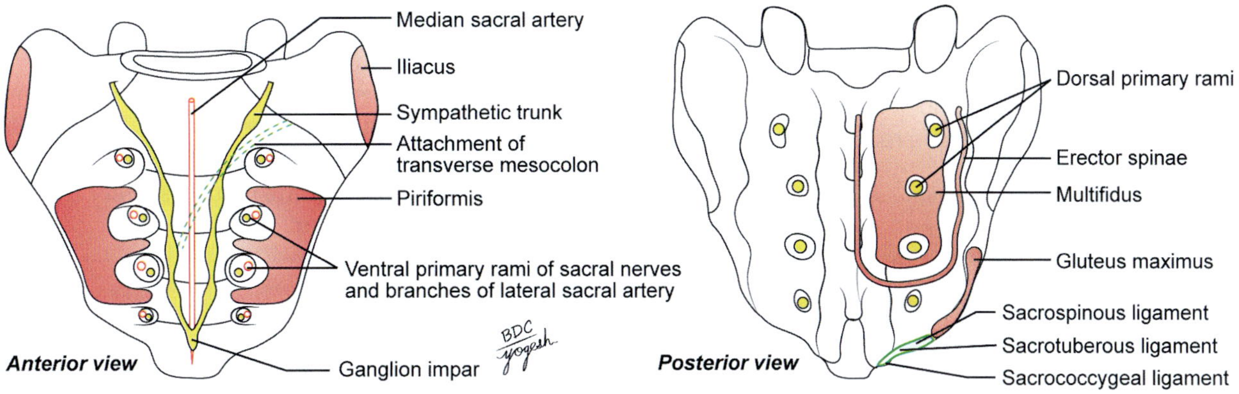

Fig. 15.12: Attachments and relations of sacrum

TABLE 15.1: Differences between the male and female sacrum

Features	*Male sacrum*	*Female sacrum*
Base of sacrum	Transverse diameter of the superior surface of body of S1 vertebra is longer than the ala of one side	Transverse diameter of the superior surface of body of S1 vertebra is shorter than the ala of one side
Curvature	Smoothly curved anterior surface (C-shaped) from above downward	Abruptly curved lower part of anterior surface (S-shaped)
Length	Length is more than the maximum width	Length and width are usually equal
Auricular surface	Auricular surface extends up to the upper two-and-half sacral vertebrae	Auricular surface extends up to the upper two sacral vertebrae
Sacral index	Lesser (105%)	Greater (115%)
Weight	Heavier	Lighter
Muscular impression	More marked	Less marked

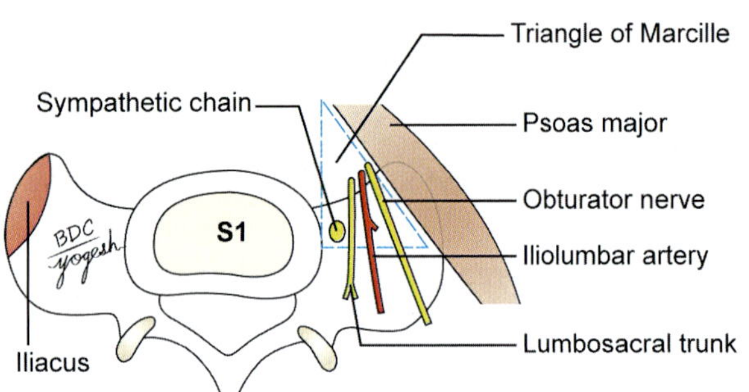

Fig. 15.13: Structure related to the smooth medial part of the ala of sacrum with triangle of Marcille

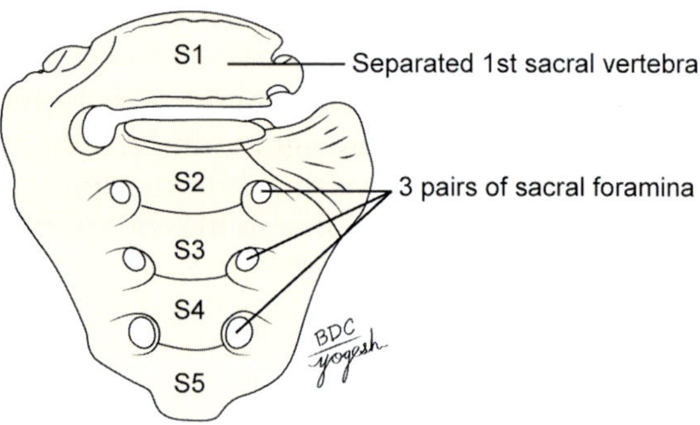

Fig. 15.14: Lumbarization of sacral vertebra (anterior view)

OSSIFICATION

- The sacrum ossifies from fusion of five separate vertebrae. The ossification of sacrum corresponds to the ossification of typical vertebrae.
- The primary centre for the centrum and each half of vertebral arch appears between 10th and 12th weeks. The primary centres for costal elements of the upper three vertebrae appears in 6th–8th month of intrauterine life and fuse with each other by 8th–9th year of life.
- There are two secondary centres for epiphysis or body (in total 10 centres for S1 to S5 vertebrae), two for auricular surfaces and two for inferolateral margins. All secondary centres appear by puberty and fuse by 25th year.

CLINICAL ANATOMY

Lumbarization of sacral vertebra: In this condition, the 1st sacral vertebra is separated from the sacrum and may be fused with the 5th lumbar vertebra. As a result, the number of sacral foramina is reduced to three pairs (Fig. 15.14).

COCCYX

The coccyx or ***tail bone*** (Greek *cuckoo's beak*) is a small triangular bone formed by fusion of four rudimentary coccygeal vertebrae, which progressively diminish in size from above downwards (Plate 15.4, Figs 15.15a and b). The bone is directed downwards and forwards, making a continuous curve with the sacrum. The first coccygeal piece is the largest. It is commonly found as a separate vertebra.

Features

Coccyx has the following parts:
1. Base
2. Apex (tip)
3. Two surfaces: Pelvic and dorsal
4. Lateral margins.

The upper surface of its body forms the ***base*** of the coccyx, which articulates with the apex of the sacrum. Projecting upwards from the posterolateral side of the base are the ***coccygeal cornua***, which represent the pedicles and superior articular processes. They articulate with the sacral cornua and are connected to them by ***intercornual ligaments***.

Rudimentary transverse processes project laterally and slightly upwards from the side of the base. They may articulate or fuse with the inferior lateral angle of the sacrum, creating a 5th pair of sacral foramina.

The 2nd, 3rd and 4th coccygeal vertebrae are mere bony nodules which diminish successively in size and are usually fused together.

Attachments

The ***dorsal surface*** of the coccyx gives:
1. Origin to the gluteus maximus on either side.
2. Origin to the sphincter ani externus at the tip.
3. Attachment to the *filum terminale* at the first piece.

Plate 15.4: Coccyx

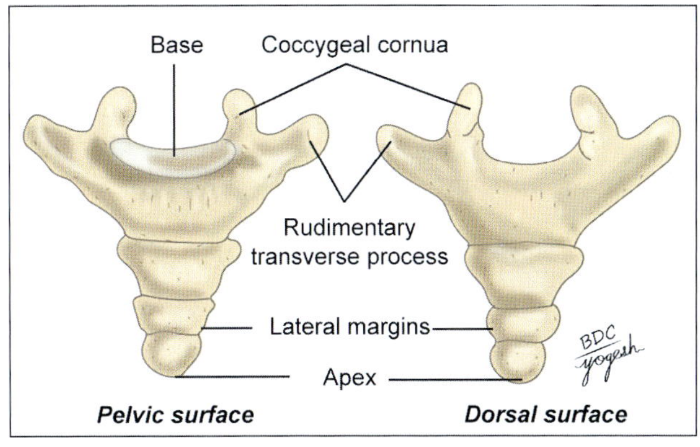

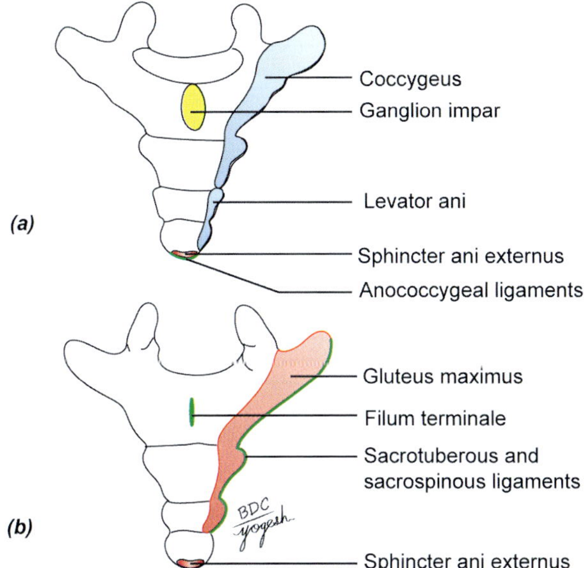

Figs 15.15a and b: Attachments of coccyx: (a) Pelvic surface and (b) dorsal surface

The *pelvic surface* of the coccyx:

1. Provides insertion to the coccygeus and to the levator ani on either side.
2. It is related to the ***ganglion impar*** and the ***glomus coccygeum***. The lateral margins provide attachment to sacrotuberous and sacrospinous ligaments.

OSSIFICATION

The coccyx ossifies from 4 primary centres one for each segment, which appears between 1st and 20th years, and fuses with each other between 20th and 30th years. The coccyx is slightly mobile at the sacrococcygeal joint, but fuses with it late in life.

BONY PELVIS

The pelvis is a lower division of the abdominal cavity that resembles a basin (Latin basin) (Fig. 15.16). The pelvis is formed by the articulation of two hip bones, sacrum and coccyx. This bony framework is called *pelvis* or *bony pelvis* or *pelvic girdle*.

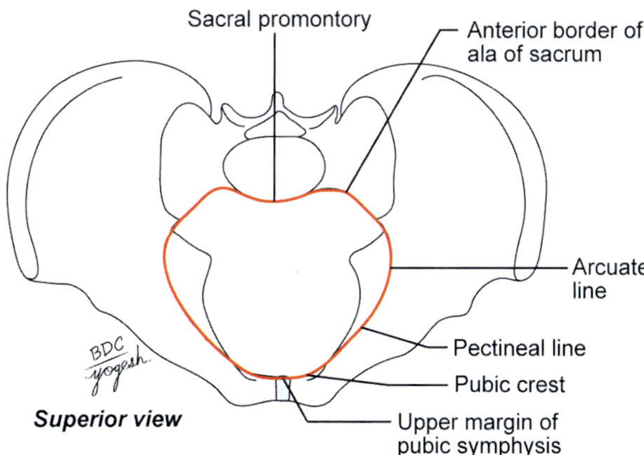

Fig. 15.16: Pelvic inlet or pelvic brim

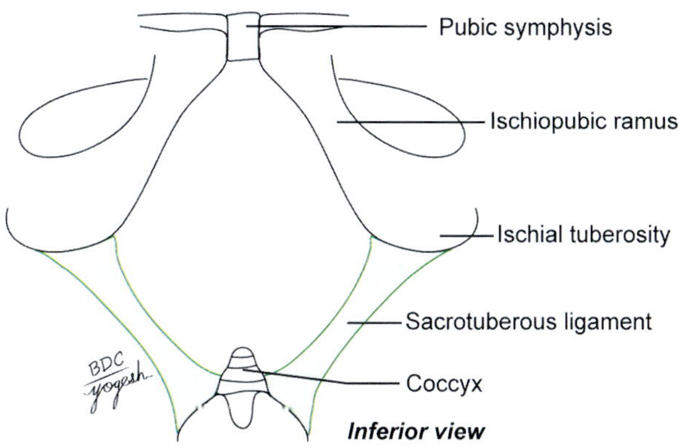

Fig. 15.17: Boundaries of pelvic outlet

The pelvis is subdivided into two parts: Greater pelvis and lesser pelvis by the ***pelvic inlet*** or ***pelvic brim*** (Fig. 15.17). The brim of the pelvis is formed by anterior by upper margin of pubic symphysis, on either side by anterior border of ala of sacrum, arcuate line, pectineal line (pecten pubis) and pubic crest, and posteriorly by the sacral promontory.

Anatomical Position of the Pelvis

Hold the bony pelvis with forward tilt in such a way that:

1. Anterior superior iliac spines and pubic tubercles are in the same coronal plane.
2. Upper border of pubic symphysis lies in a same level with tip of the coccyx.
3. Dorsal wall of the bony pelvis looks mostly upward while its ventral wall faces downward.

Pelvimetry

The importance of the measurements of the pelvis is mainly obstetric, but also forensic and anthropological.

Pelvimetry can be done in the following ways.

- Pelvimetry on the skeletonised pelvis prepared from cadavers.
- Clinical and internal pelvimetry on living subjects.
- Radiological pelvimetry.

Pelvimetry on Skeletonised Pelvis

The relevant diameters are summarised in Table 15.2.

Plate 15.5: Diameters of pelvic inlet and outlet

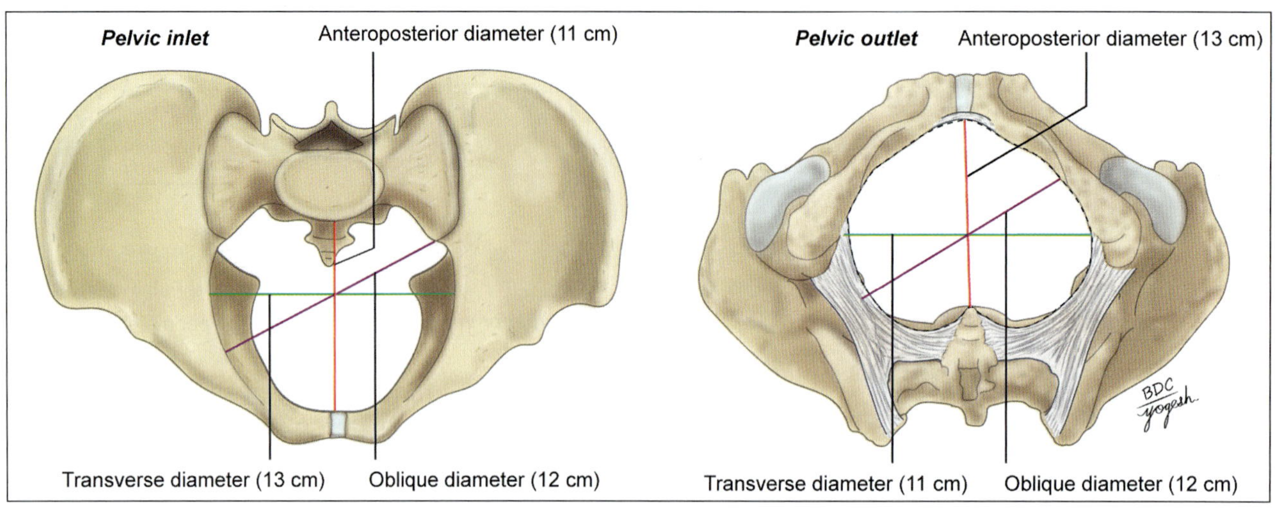

TABLE 15.2: Dimensions of the pelvis in female (Plate 15.5, Fig. 15.18)

	Region	*Diameter*	*Average measurements in cm*
I.	Pelvic inlet (Fig. 15.14a)	1. *Anteroposterior diameter* (true conjugate), from the midpoint of the sacral promontory to the upper border of the pubic symphysis	11
		2. *Transverse diameter* (maximum)	13
		3. *Oblique diameter*, from one iliopubic eminence to the opposite sacroiliac joint	12
II.	Pelvic cavity	1. *Anteroposterior diameter*, from midpoint of vertebra S3 to the middle of the posterior surface of the pubic symphysis	12
		2. *Transverse diameter*	12
		3. *Oblique diameter*, from the lowest point of one sacroiliac joint to the midpoint of the opposite obturator membrane	12
III.	Pelvic outlet	1. *Anteroposterior diameter*, from the tip of the coccyx to the inferior margin of the pubic symphysis (maximum)	13
		2. *Transverse diameter* (bituberous diameter), between ischial tuberosities	11
		3. *Oblique diameter*, from the midpoint of the sacrotuberous ligament on one side to the junction of the ischiopubic rami on the other side	12

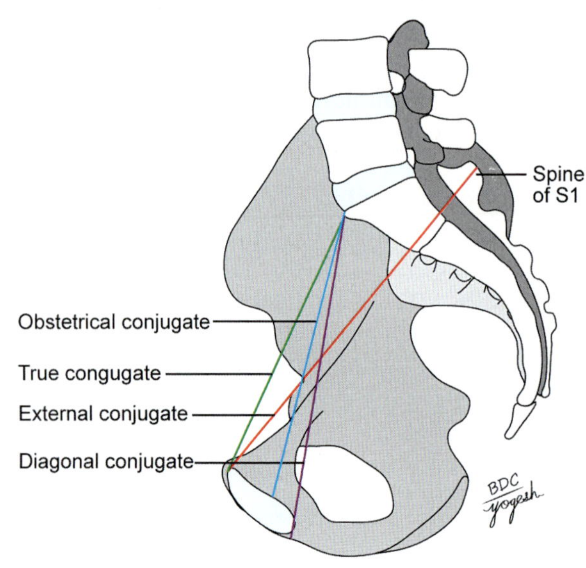

Fig. 15.18: Conjugate diameters

Clinical Pelvimetry

Pelvic measurements in obstetric cases can be done both externally and internally. External pelvimetry has been mostly given up because of its limited value. It is helpful in diagnosis of gross pelvic contraction.

1. ***External conjugate*** or ***Baudelocque's diameter:*** It is the distance between the upper margin of pubic symphysis to the tip of the spine of S1 vertebra, measures not less than 19 cm.
2. ***True conjugate***: It is the anteroposterior diameter of the pelvic inlet. It extends from the midpoint of the sacral promontory to the upper border of pubic symphysis.
3. ***Diagonal conjugate***: It extends between midpoint of promontory to the lower border of anterior surface of pubic symphysis. It can be determined by digital examination per vaginum (P/V examination). Usually, it is 12.5 cm. True conjugate can be roughly

calculated by deducting 1.5 to 2 cm from diagonal conjugate.

4. ***Obstetrical conjugate*:** It is the distance between the sacral promontory and the inner aspect of pubic symphysis. It is 2 cm less than diagonal conjugate.

Note: ***Internal pelvimetry***: It is a digital examination per vaginum (P/V examination) to determine various diameters of the pelvis, to palpate bony pelvic prominences including curvature of sacrum, mobility of coccyx and length of sacrospinous ligaments. It is useful to determine diagonal conjugate, interischial spinous diameter and guide for calculating obstetrical conjugate.

Morphological Classification of Pelvis

(Fig. 15.19, Flowchart 15.5)

1. ***Gynaecoid*** *type* (41.4%): This is normal female pelvis, the average diameters of which have already been mentioned. The inlet is round or slightly ovoid with transverse diameter placed well forward from the sacrum. The side walls are more vertical than in the android pelvis.
2. ***Android*** *type* (32.5%) resembles a male pelvis.

   The inlet is triangular with the greatest transverse diameter placed much nearer the promontory than in the gynaecoid pelvis. The subpubic angle and greater sciatic notches are narrower so that the cavity is funnel-shaped and the outlet is reduced in all diameters.
3. ***Anthropoid*** *type* (23.5%) shows resemblance to the pelvis of anthropoid apes.
4. ***Platypelloid*** *type* (2.6%) is somewhat opposite to the anthropoid pelvis.

Out of the various types mentioned, only a gynaecoid pelvis permits a normal delivery of the child. The other three represent different types of *contracted pelvis*.

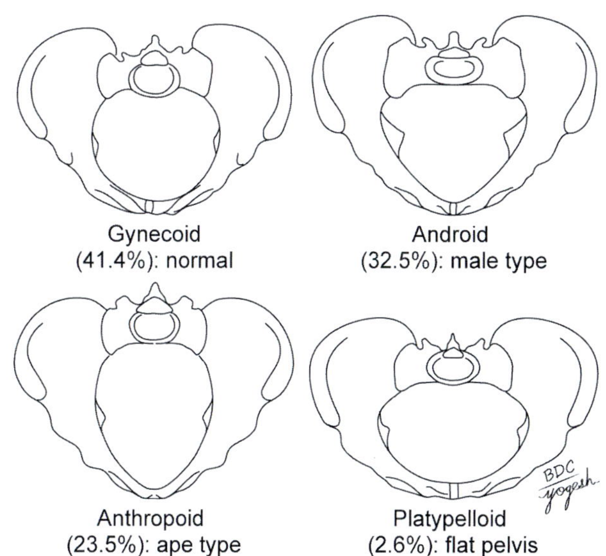

Fig. 15.19: Types of female pelvis

Competency:

AN53.3 Define true pelvis and false pelvis and demonstrate sex determination in male and female bony pelvis.

Sex Differences in the Pelvis

The most marked of these differences are due to adaptation of female pelvis for child-bearing. The sex differences between the male pelvis and female pelvis are listed in Table 15.3 (Fig. 15.20).

INTERVERTEBRAL JOINTS

These joints include:

1. The joints between vertebral bodies
2. The joints between vertebral arches

TABLE 15.3: Differences between male and female pelvis

Feature	*Male pelvis*	*Female pelvis*
Bony feature	Heavier and thicker	Lighter and thinner
Muscle attachments	Well-marked	Less marked
Subpubic angle	<90° (50°–60°)	90° or more
Pelvic inlet	Heart-shaped	Oval
Pelvic cavity	Funnel-shaped (long segment of small cone)	Tubular (small segment of large cone)
Acetabulum	Large Acetabular diameter *equals* the distance between acetabulum and symphysis pubis	Small Acetabular diameter is *smaller* than the distance between acetabulum and symphysis pubis
Obturator foramen	Large, oval	Small, triangular
Greater sciatic notch	~70° (narrower)	90° (wider)
Preauricular sulcus	Less marked	Well-marked, prominent
Ischial tuberosity	Inverted	Everted
Base of sacrum	Transverse diameter of the anterior surface of body of S1 vertebra is longer than the ala of one side	Transverse diameter of the superior surface of body of S1 vertebra is shorter than the ala of one side
Curvature of sacrum	Smoothly curved anterior surface (C-shaped) from above downward	Abruptly curved lower part of anterior surface (S-shaped)
Length of sacrum	Length is more than the maximum width	Length and width are usually equal

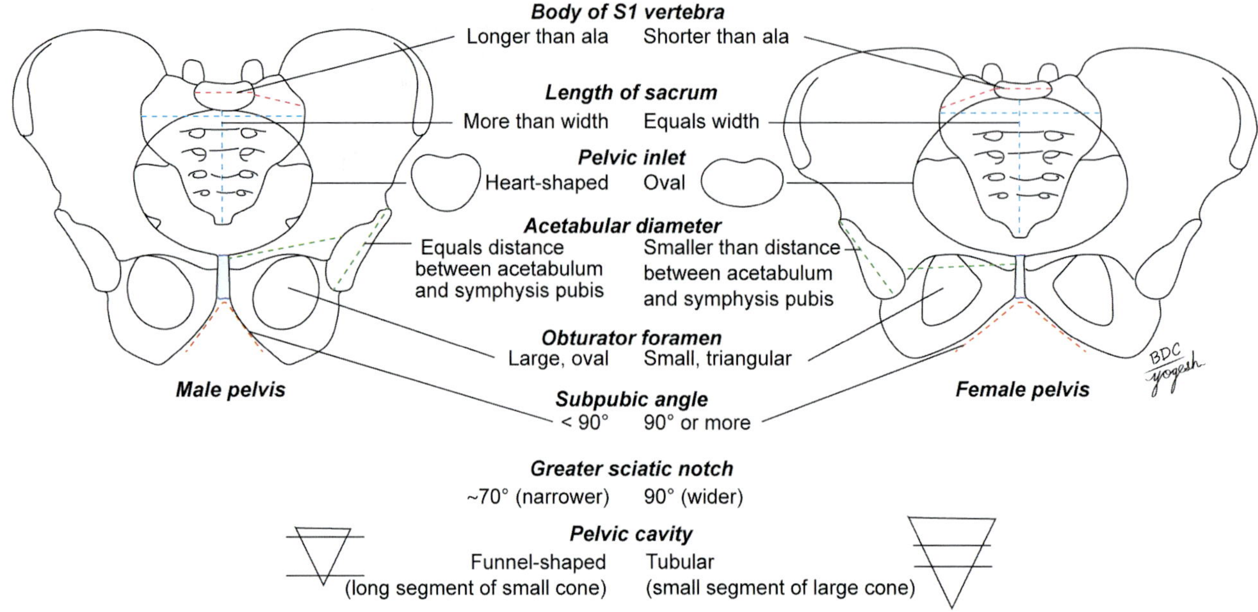

Fig. 15.20: Differences between the male pelvis and female pelvis

Flowchart 15.5: Types of female pelvis

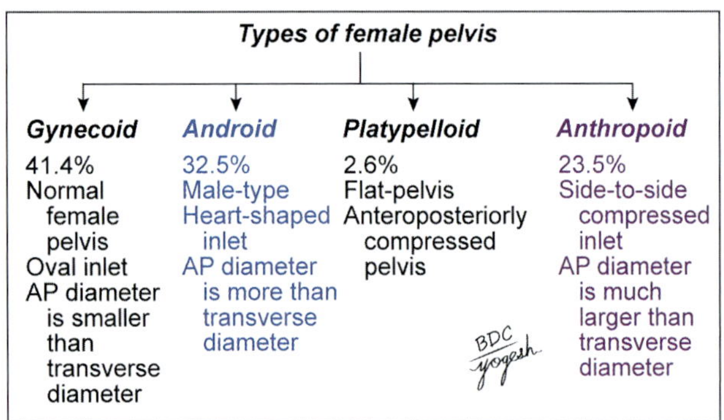

The joints between vertebral bodies are *secondary cartilaginous* joints held by the intervertebral disc.

Joints of the vertebral arches are formed by the articular processes of the adjacent vertebrae. These are plane synovial joints, permitting gliding movements.

The lumbar spine permits maximum extension, considerable amount of flexion and lateral flexion and least rotation.

Note: The thickness of the intervertebral disc varies in different regions of the column and in different parts of the same disc. In *cervical* and *lumbar* regions, the *discs* are *thicker in front* than behind, while in the *thoracic* region, they are of uniform thickness. The discs are thinnest in the upper thoracic and thickest in the lumbar regions.

VIDEO

- Video 2.15.1 **Lumbar Vertebrae**
- Video 2.15.2 **Sacrum and Coccyx**
- Video 2.15.3 **Bony Pelvis**
- Video 2.15.4 **Pelvic Cavity**

Facts to Remember

- Transverse diameter is the biggest at inlet of true pelvis. All the three diameters, anteroposterior, transverse and oblique, are equal in mid cavity.
- Anteroposterior diameter is the biggest at the outlet of true pelvis.
- Fifth lumbar vertebra is the largest and is atypical.
- Sacrum on its dorsal surface shows 5 crests—one median, two medial and two lateral. Median is formed by fusion of sacral spines. Medial ones are formed by fusion of articular processes and lateral ones by fusion of transverse processes.
- Abdominal cavity continues in downward and backward direction with the pelvic cavity.
- Herniation of nucleus pulposus of the intervertebral disc is common in lumbar region. It presses upon the nerve roots causing severe pain in the area of cutaneous supply.
- Coccyx is a tail bone.

BDC's Anatomy *e*-book

1. Lumbosacral (sacrovertebral) angle
2. Sacral index
3. Further reading
4. Viva voce questions

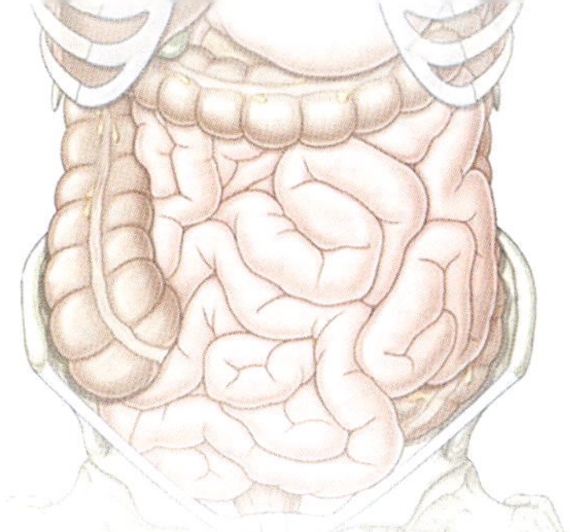

Chapter

16

Anterior Abdominal Wall

The heading 'anterior abdominal wall' usually includes both the front as well as the side walls of the abdomen and needs to be called ***anterolateral abdominal wall***.

SURFACE LANDMARKS

The surface landmarks of abdominal region are useful guide for clinical examination and surgical approaches (Plate 16.1, Figs 16.1 and 16.2).

1. In the anterior median plane, the abdominal wall extends from the ***xiphoid process*** which lies at the level of the 9th thoracic vertebra to the pubic symphysis, which lies at the level of the coccyx.
2. The superolateral margins of the anterior abdominal wall are formed by the right and left ***costal margins***. Each margin is formed by the 7th to 10th costal cartilages. The costal margin reaches its lowest level in the *midaxillary line*. Here the margin is formed by the tenth costal cartilage.
3. The ***infrasternal*** or ***subcostal angle*** is formed between the right and left costal margins.
4. The ***iliac crest*** forms the lower limit of the abdominal wall at the side. The highest point of the iliac crest lies at the level of the 4th lumbar vertebra.
5. The ***anterior superior iliac spine*** lies at the level of the *sacral promontory*. ***Posterior superior iliac spine*** lies about 4 cm lateral to the median plane.
6. The ***tubercle of the iliac crest*** is situated on the outer lip of iliac crest about 5 cm behind the anterior superior iliac spine. The ***intertubercular*** *or* ***transtubercular plane*** passes through the tubercles. It passes through the 5th lumbar vertebra.
7. The ***inguinal ligament*** or ***Poupart's ligament*** extends from the anterior superior iliac spine to the pubic tubercle. It is convex downwards. It is placed at the junction of the anterior abdominal wall with the front of the thigh (Fig. 16.1).
8. The ***spermatic cord*** is a soft rounded cord present in the male. It can be felt through the skin as it passes downwards near the medial end of the inguinal ligament to enter the scrotum. It can be picked up between the finger and the thumb. When palpated in this way a firm cord-like structure can be felt within the posterior part of the spermatic cord. This is the ***ductus deferens***.
9. The anterior abdominal wall is divided into right and left halves by a vertical groove. It marks the position of the underlying ***linea alba*** (Latin *white line*).
10. A little below the middle of the median furrow, there is an irregular depressed or elevated area called the ***umbilicus*** (Latin *navel*). It lies at the level of the junction between 3rd and 4th lumbar vertebrae. The level may vary from L2 vertebra to upper border of S1 vertebra. It is lower in children, obese persons and persons with pendulous abdomen (*Gray's Anatomy*, 42nd edition).
11. A few centimetres lateral to the median furrow, the abdominal wall shows a curved vertical groove. Its upper end reaches the costal margin at the tip of the 9th costal cartilage. Inferiorly, it reaches the pubic tubercle. This line is called the ***linea semilunaris***. It corresponds to the lateral margin of a muscle called the *rectus abdominis*.

PLANES OF ABDOMEN

The planes of abdomen are helpful in abdominal examination of the patient in clinics. These planes are also useful as guides for many surgical and medical procedures (Plate 16.1).

Transpyloric plane (Addison's plane): It is an imaginary, transverse plane that passes through the midpoint of the line joining the jugular or suprasternal notch to the pubic symphysis. It passes anteriorly through the tip of 9th costal cartilage and posteriorly through the lower border of the body of L1 vertebra. This plane lies roughly a hand's breadth below the xiphisternal joint.

Clinical significance: Structures present at transpyloric plane are as follows:

1. Pylorus of stomach
2. Hilum of both the kidneys
3. Fundus of gallbladder
4. Origin of superior mesenteric artery
5. Lower end of spinal cord.

Plate 16.1: Bony landmarks and planes of abdomen

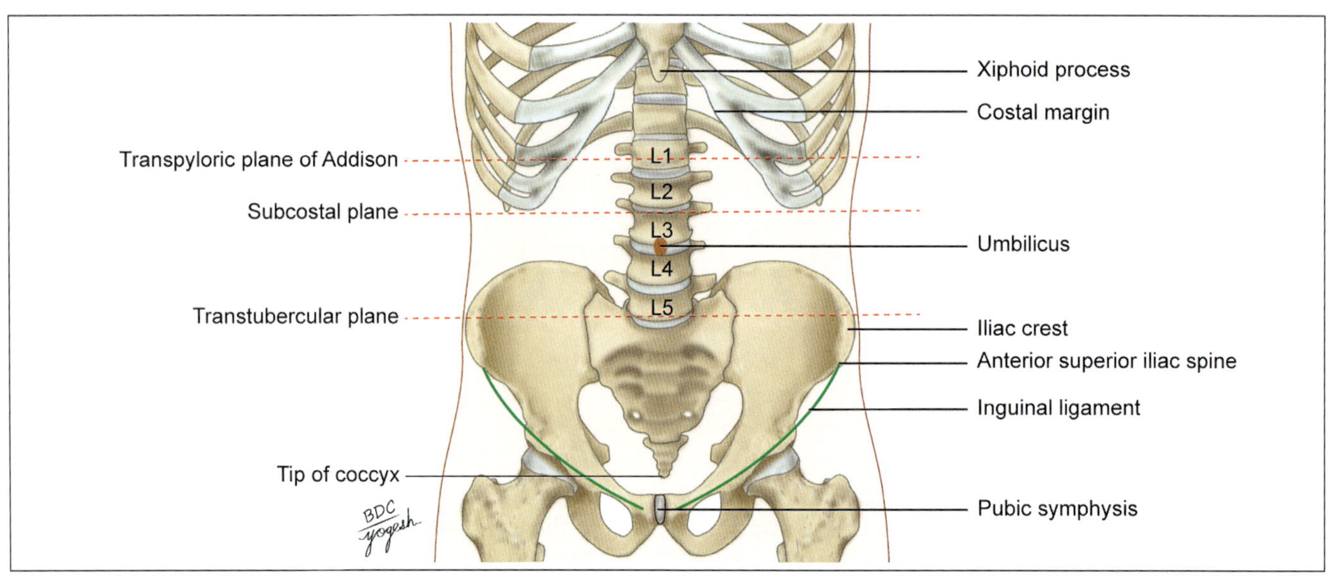

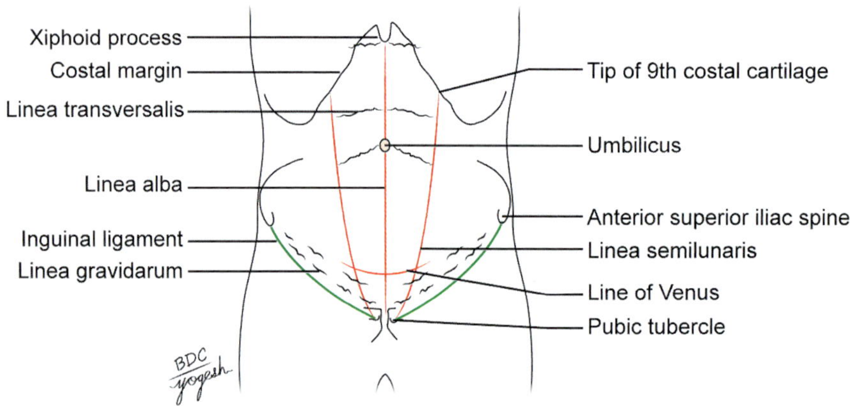

Fig. 16.1: Landmarks of the abdomen

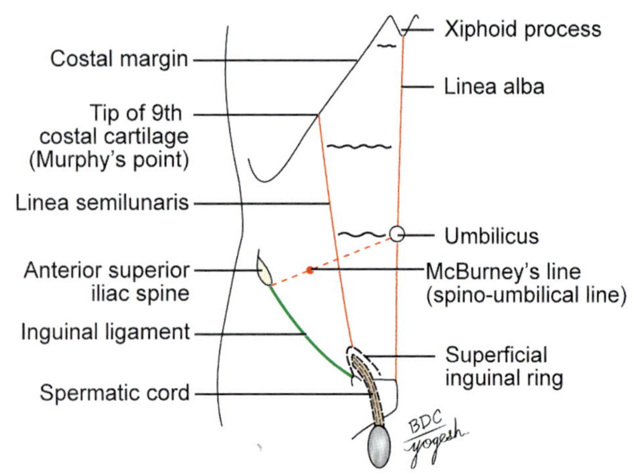

Fig. 16.2: Some superficial features in relation to the anterior abdominal wall

Subcostal plane: It is an imaginary transverse plane that passes immediately below the costal margins. It passes anteriorly through the lowest part of the 10th rib and posteriorly through the body of L3 vertebra.

Trans-umbilical plane: It is an imaginary transverse plane that passes through umbilicus or navel. It passes through intervertebral disc between L3 and L4 vertebrae.

Transtubercular plane: It is an imaginary transverse plane which is drawn by joining the tubercles of iliac crests. It passes posteriorly through the body of L5 vertebra.

Vertical (midclavicular) planes: There are right and left vertical or *midclavicular planes*. They can be drawn by a vertical line joining the midpoint of the clavicle superiorly and midinguinal point inferiorly. The *midinguinal point* is the midpoint of the line joining anterior superior iliac spine and pubic symphysis. These horizontal and vertical planes divide the abdomen or abdominal cavity into nine quadrants. These planes include transpyloric plane, intertubercular plane and right and left vertical or midclavicular planes. The nine quadrants are as follows:

Right hypochondrium	Epigastric	Left hypochondrium
Right lumbar	Umbilical	Left lumbar
Right iliac	Hypogastric	Left iliac

LAYERS OF ANTERIOR ABDOMINAL WALL

The anterior abdominal wall is firm but elastic. It consists of eight layers from superficial to deep as follows (Fig. 5.4):

1. Skin
2. Superficial fascia
3. External oblique muscle and its aponeurosis
4. Internal oblique muscle and its aponeurosis
5. Transverse abdominis muscle and its aponeurosis
6. Fascia transversalis
7. Extra peritoneal connective tissue
8. Parietal layer of peritoneum.

Note: The deep fascia is absent in the anterior abdominal wall that permits the distention of abdomen during inspiration, after meals, in pregnancy and so on. The deep fascia is also absent in penis, scrotum, perineum and face.

DISSECTION

Give an incision from xiphoid process till the umbilicus. Make a small circular incision around the umbilicus and extend it till the pubic symphysis. Carry the incision laterally from the umbilicus to the lateral abdominal wall on both sides. Give curved incisions 3 cm below from anterior superior iliac spine to pubic symphysis on either side (Fig. 16.3).

Finally, give an oblique incision from the xiphoid process along the costal margin to the lateral abdominal wall on either side.

Carefully reflect the skin in four flaps leaving both the layers of superficial fascia on the anterior abdominal wall. Make a transverse incision through the entire thickness of the superficial fascia from the anterior superior iliac spine to the median plane. Raise the lower margin of the cut fascia and identify its fatty and membranous layers. Note that the fatty layer is continuous with the fascia of adjoining parts of the body.

The membranous layer of anterior abdominal wall is continuous with the similar fascia (Colles' fascia) of the perineum. Note its attachment to pubic arch and posterior margin of *perineal membrane* (inferior fascia of urogenital diaphragm).

Locate the *superficial inguinal ring* immediately superolateral to the pubic tubercle.

Note the anterior cutaneous branch of the *iliohypogastric nerve* piercing the aponeurosis of the external oblique muscle a short distance superior to the ring. The spermatic cord/round ligament of uterus along with *ilioinguinal nerve* leaves the abdomen through the superficial inguinal ring. Identify the external spermatic fascia attaching the spermatic cord to the margins of the ring.

Divide the superficial fascia vertically in the median plane and in the line of the posterior axillary fold as far as the iliac crest.

Reflect the fascia by blunt dissection from these two cuts and find the anterior and lateral cutaneous branches of the lower intercostal nerves along with respective blood vessels coming out from the anterior and lateral regions of the abdominal wall.

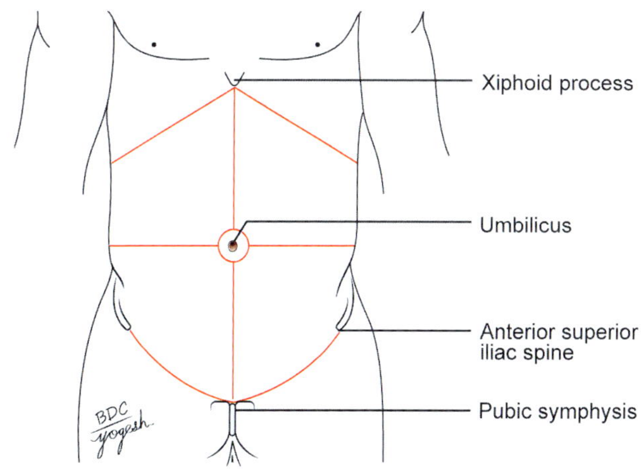

Fig. 16.3: Lines for dissection

SKIN AND SUPERFICIAL FASCIA

SKIN

The skin of the anterior abdominal wall is capable of undergoing enormous stretching.

Features of Skin of Anterior Abdominal Wall

The skin of the anterior abdominal wall shows the following features:

1. Umbilicus
2. Midline groove or furrow
3. Linea semilunaris corresponds to the lateral margin of a muscle called the *rectus abdominis*.
4. ***Transverse furrows (linea transversalis)*:** These are two to three transverse grooves that correspond to the tendinous intersections of the rectus abdominis muscle.
5. ***Line of Venus*** is a semilunar line with upward convexity. It lies between umbilicus and pubic symphysis, mostly in females.
6. ***Linea gravidarum*:** Several irregularly branched white lines on the skin of lower abdominal part of parous female are called linea gravidarum. They appear on undue stretching of the anterior abdominal wall by gravid uterus in pregnancy.
7. ***Cleavage lines of Langer*** are horizontal cleavage lines produced by arrangement of bundles of collagen fibres of the dermis. An incision given along these lines heal with invisible linear scars. Hence, in the abdominal surgeries, horizontal incisions are more preferred by surgeons.
8. Undue stretching may result in the formation of whitish streaks in the skin of the lower part of the anterior abdominal wall; these are known as ***lineae albicantes***.

Umbilicus

The umbilicus is the normal scar in the anterior abdominal wall formed by the remnants of the root of the *umbilical cord* (Fig. 16.4).

The position of the umbilicus is variable. In healthy adults, it lies in the anterior median line, at the level of the disc between the 3rd and 4th lumbar vertebrae. It is lower in infants and in persons with a pendulous abdomen.

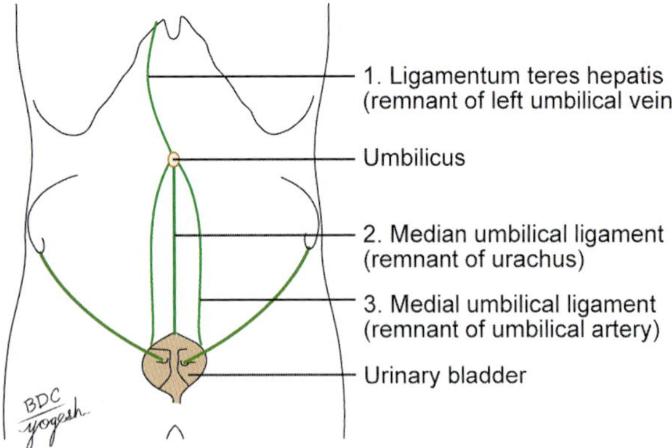

Fig. 16.4: Embryological remnants at the umbilicus

Anatomical Importance

- With reference to the lymphatic and venous drainage, the level of the umbilicus is a *watershed*. Lymph and venous blood flow upwards above the plane of the umbilicus; and downwards below this plane. These do not normally cross umbilical plane.
- The skin around the umbilicus is supplied by segment *T10* of the spinal cord.
- The umbilicus is one of the important sites at which tributaries of the portal vein anastomose with systemic veins (*portocaval anastomoses*). In portal hypertension, these anastomoses open up to form dilated veins radiating from the umbilicus called the *caput medusae*. However, the blood flow in the dilated veins is normal and does not break the barrier of the watershed line.

Embryological Importance

Umbilicus is the site of meeting of all folds (head fold, tail fold and two lateral folds) of the embryo.

During embryonic life, the gap at the umbilicus called umbilical ring gives passage to the following structures:

a. Midgut loop up to 12th week of intrauterine life. It produces *physiological umbilical hernia* up to 12th week, later the midgut communicates with umbilical vesicle through vitellointestinal duct.
b. ***Allantois*:** It is a diverticulum of endodermal cloaca. Its proximal part of allantois forms urinary bladder, whereas distal part obliterates to form urachus.
c. ***Umbilical vessels*:** Two umbilical arteries and one umbilical vein pass through the umbilicus to connect placenta with fetus. Obliterated umbilical arteries (remnant) form medial umbilical ligaments and obliterated umbilical vein forms ligamentum teres hepatis after birth.

CLINICAL ANATOMY

- ***Referred pain around umbilicus*:** The skin of umbilicus is supplied by T10 spinal segment. Therefore, pain of appendix is referred (felt) at the umbilicus.
- In portal vein obstruction, the radiating dilated superficial veins around the umbilicus are called ***caput medusae*** as they resemble serpents on the head of Medusa (a mythical lady in Greek mythology) (Fig. 16.5).
- ***Congenital anomalies*:** The following congenital anomalies may be observed at umbilicus:
  1. ***Faecal fistula*:** The persistent vitellointestinal duct results in faecal fistula at the umbilicus (Fig. 16.6).
  2. ***Urinary fistula*:** The persistent allantois or urachus results in urinary fistula at the umbilicus (Fig. 16.7).
  3. ***Exomphalos* or *omphalocele*:** Usually physiological hernia reduces by the 12th week of intrauterine life. After birth, persistent gut loop at the closed umbilicus produces rounded mass called exomphalos (Fig. 16.8).
  4. ***Congenital umbilical hernia*** is the protrusion of the coils of intestine at umbilicus (Fig. 16.9).
  5. ***Raspberry tumour at umbilicus*:** Persistent distal part of the vitellointestinal duct, at the umbilicus) produces raspberry red tumour.
  6. ***Enterocystoma* (*Vitelline cyst*)** is the cyst of the vitellointestinal duct that occurs due to small persistent middle part of the duct.

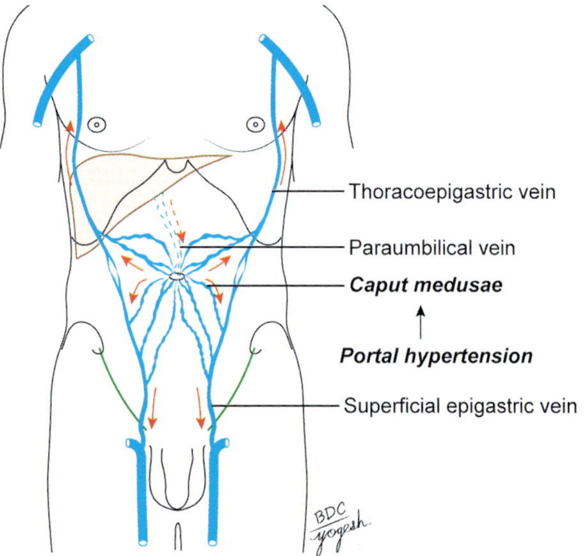

Fig. 16.5: Caput medusae (red arrows indicate normal flow of blood)

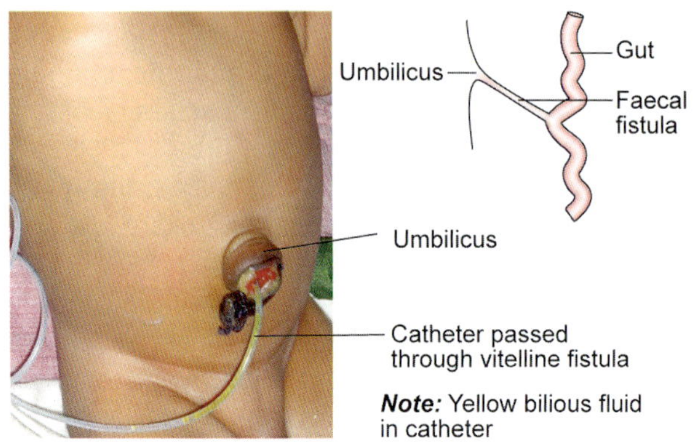

Fig. 16.6: Faecal fistula

Section 2: Abdomen and Pelvis

16

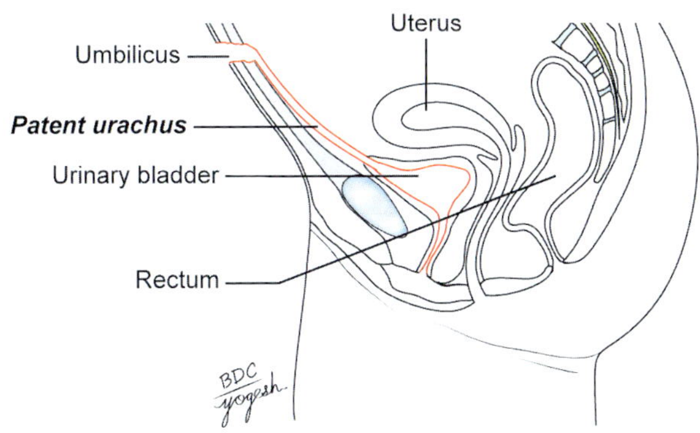

Fig. 16.7: Patent urachus

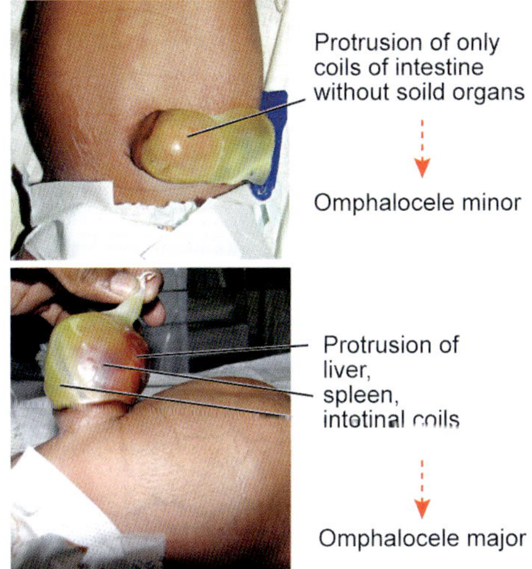

Fig. 16.8: Omphalocele minor and major

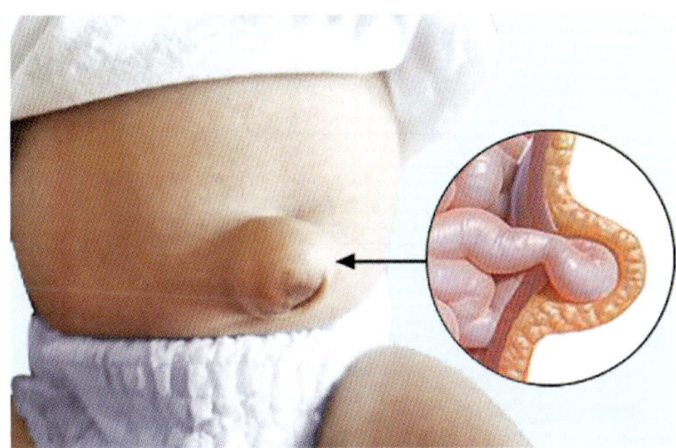

Fig. 16.9: Infantile umbilical hernia

Competency:

AN44.2 Describe and identify the fascia, nerves and blood vessels of anterior abdominal wall.

SUPERFICIAL FASCIA

Below the level of the umbilicus, the superficial fascia of the anterior abdominal wall is divided into a superficial fatty layer (***fascia of Camper***) and a deep membranous layer (***fascia of Scarpa***). The various contents of the superficial fascia run between these two layers.

Fascia of Camper (Superficial Fatty Layer)

The *fatty layer* is continuous with the superficial fascia of the adjoining part of the body. In the penis, it is devoid of fat, and in the scrotum, it is replaced by the *dartos muscle*.

Scarpa's Fascia (Deep Membranous Layer)

The *membranous* layer is continuous below with a similar membranous layer of superficial fascia of the perineum known as *Colles' fascia*. Above the umbilicus, the membranous layer merges with the fatty layer.

In the median plane, the membranous layer is thickened to form the ***suspensory ligament*** and ***fundiform ligament of the penis*** or ***clitoris***.

Note: The attachments of Scarpa's fascia of the abdomen and of Colles' fascia of the perineum are such that they prevent the passage of extravasated urine due to rupture of urethra backwards into the ischiorectal fossa and downwards into the thigh (Figs 16.10a and b). The line of attachment passes over the following:

a. Holden's line (it begins little lateral to pubic tubercle and extends laterally for 8 cm)
b. Pubic tubercle
c. Body of the pubis and the deep fascia on the adductor longus and the gracilis near their origin
d. Margins of the pubic arch
e. The posterior border of the perineal membrane.

Contents of Superficial Fascia

1. An extremely variable quantity of fat, which tends to accumulate in the lower part of the abdomen after puberty
2. Cutaneous nerves
3. Cutaneous vessels
4. Superficial lymphatics.

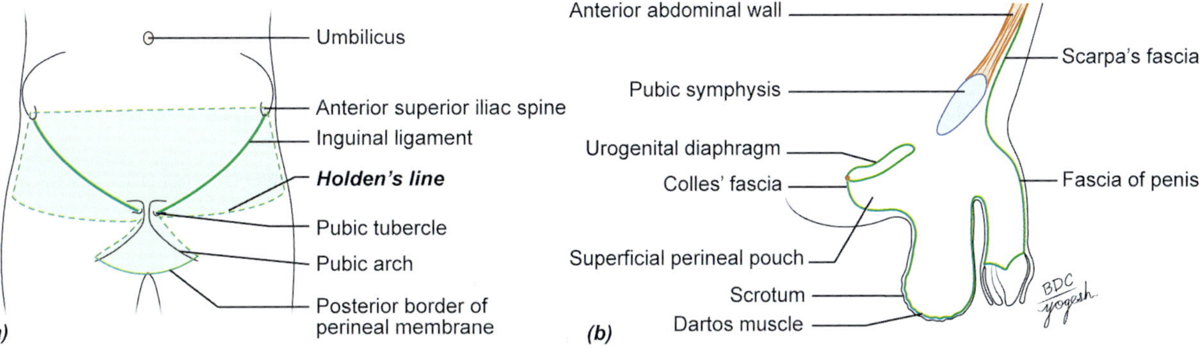

Figs 16.10a and b: The extent and attachments of the membranous layer of superficial fascia of the abdomen and perineum in a male: (a) Anterior view and (b) sagittal section

CLINICAL ANATOMY

Membranous layer of superficial fascia of abdomen is continuous with the superficial perineal pouch via scrotum and penis. At times, the urethra may rupture and urine extravasates into this space.

Cutaneous Nerves

The skin of the anterior abdominal wall is supplied by the lower six thoracic nerves (lower five intercostal and subcostal) and by the 1st lumbar nerve through (Figs 16.11 and 16.12):

1. ***Anterior cutaneous nerves*** (seven in number) derived from the lower five intercostal nerves, the subcostal nerve and the iliohypogastric nerve (L1).
2. ***Lateral cutaneous nerves*** are two in number and are derived from the lower two intercostal nerves (T10, T11).

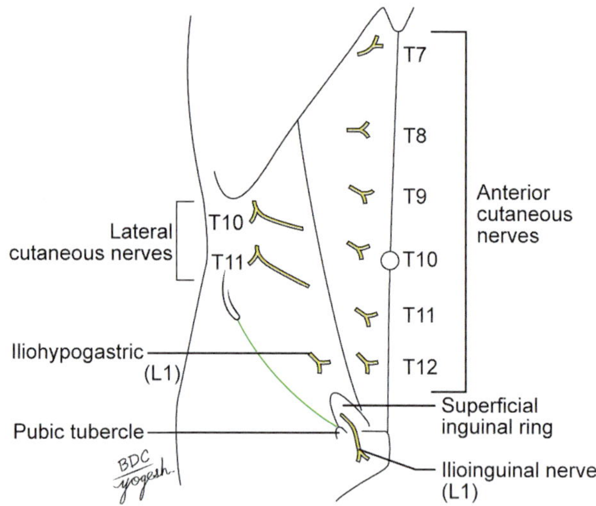

Fig. 16.11: Cutaneous nerves of the anterior abdominal wall

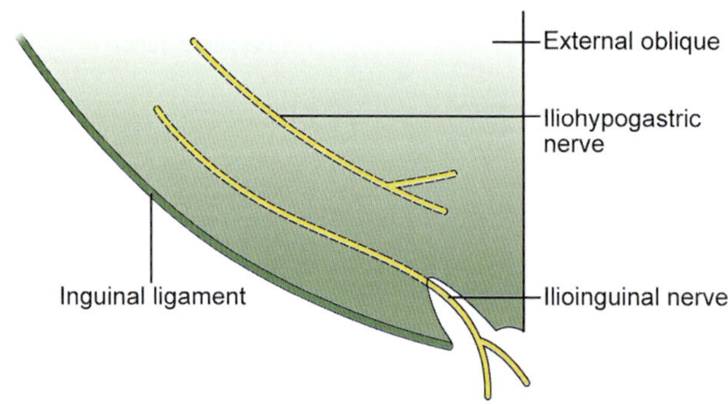

Fig. 16.12: Course of the iliohypogastric and ilioinguinal nerves

Cutaneous Arteries (Fig. 16.13)

1. Anterior cutaneous branches of superior and inferior epigastric arteries.
2. Lateral cutaneous branches of posterior intercostal arteries.
3. Three superficial branches of femoral artery:
   a. Superficial external pudendal artery
   b. Superficial epigastric artery
   c. Superficial circumflex iliac artery.
4. Deep circumflex iliac artery (branch of external iliac artery).

Cutaneous Veins

The veins accompany the arteries as follows (Fig. 16.14):

1. ***Above the umbilicus***, these veins run towards the axilla and drain into the axillary vein and finally to the superior vena cava.
2. ***Below the umbilicus***, the cutaneous veins run towards the groin and drain into great saphenous vein and finally to the inferior vena cava.
3. Small veins (***paraumbilical veins***) from the umbilicus run along the ligamentum teres and drain into portal vein.

Note: When the portal vein, or the superior vena cava, or the inferior vena cava is obstructed, the superficial abdominal veins are dilated and provide a collateral circulation. The dilated veins that radiate from the umbilicus are given the name ***caput medusae***. They are seen typically in portal obstruction in which blood flow is upwards above the umbilicus and downwards below the umbilicus.

CLINICAL ANATOMY

- Superior vena cava blockage → backflow in descending order → brachiocephalic → subclavian vein → axillary vein → lateral thoracic vein → thoracoepigastric vein → superficial epigastric vein → great saphenous vein → femoral vein → inferior vena cava → heart.
- Inferior vena cava blockage → back flow in common iliac → external iliac → femoral → great saphenous → superficial epigastric vein → thoracoepigastric vein → lateral thoracic vein → axillary vein → subclavian vein → brachiocephalic vein → superior vena cava → heart.

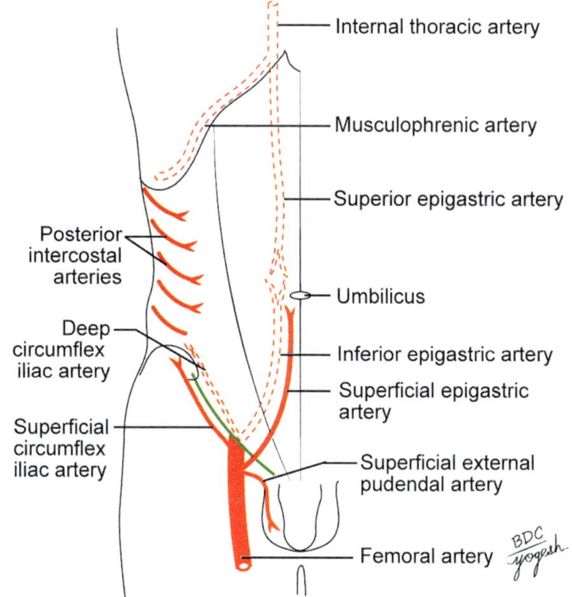

Fig. 16.13: Arteries of the anterior abdominal wall

Superficial Lymphatics

Lymphatics also pay due respect to the watershed line. Above the level of the umbilicus, the lymphatics run upwards to drain into the *axillary lymph nodes*. Below the level of the umbilicus, the lymphatics run downwards to drain into the *superficial inguinal lymph nodes* (Fig. 16.14).

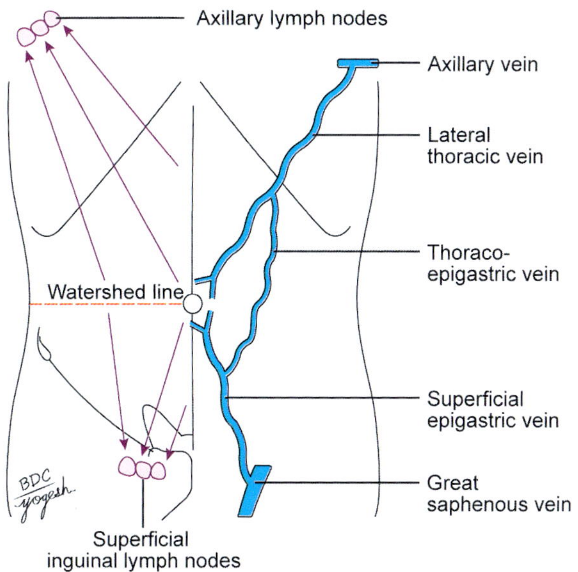

Fig. 16.14: Superficial lymphatics and veins of the anterior abdominal wall

Competency:
AN44.6 Describe and demonstrate attachments of muscles of anterior abdominal wall.

MUSCLES OF THE ANTEROLATERAL ABDOMINAL WALL

The anterolateral abdominal wall is supported by five pairs of muscles as follows:

1. External oblique
2. Internal oblique
3. Transverse abdominis
4. Rectus abdominis
5. Pyramidalis

The external oblique, the internal oblique and the transversus abdominis are large, flat muscles placed in the anterolateral part of the abdominal wall. Each of them ends in an extensive ***aponeurosis*** that reaches the midline. Here, the aponeuroses of the right and left sides decussate to form a median band called the ***linea alba***. The rectus abdominis runs vertically on either side of the linea alba. It is enclosed in a *sheath* formed by the aponeuroses of the flat muscles named above.

EXTERNAL OBLIQUE MUSCLE

Origin

The muscle arises by eight fleshy slips from the outer surfaces of middle of the shaft of the ***lower eight ribs***. The fibres run downwards, forwards and medially (Plate 16.2, Fig. 16.15, Flowchart 16.1).

Insertion

1. The posterior most fibres of the muscle are inserted directly into the anterior 2/3rd of the outer lip of the ***iliac crest***.
2. The remaining fibres of the muscle end in a broad ***aponeurosis*** through which they are inserted from above downwards into the xiphoid process, linea alba, pubic symphysis, pubic crest and the pectineal line of the pubis (Fig. 16.12).

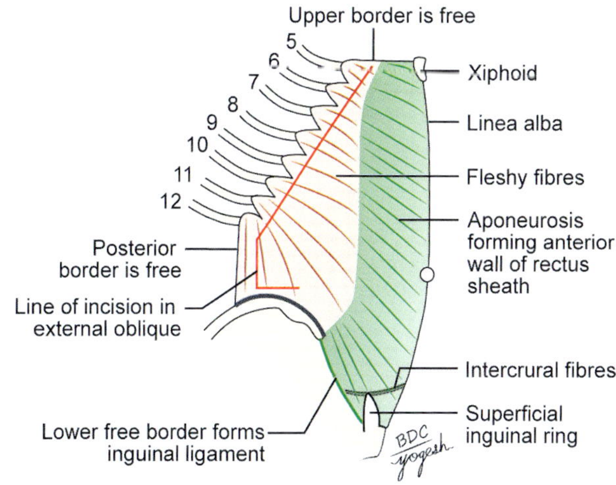

Fig. 16.15: External oblique muscle of the abdomen

Flowchart 16.1: Muscles of anterolateral abdominal wall

Muscles of anterolateral abdominal wall

	Origin	*Insertion*	*Nerve supply*	*Actions*
External oblique	8 slips from outer surface of lower 8 ribs	Outer lip of anterior 2/3rd of iliac crest, Linea alba	Lower six thoracic nerves (T7–T12)	Bilateral contraction: Flexion of trunk, increases intra-abdominal pressure Unilateral contraction: Rotation of trunk to opposite side, Lateral flexion of trunk
Internal oblique	Lateral 2/3rd of inguinal ligament Anterior 2/3rd of iliac crest, Thoracolumbar fascia	7th–9th costal cartilages Xiphoid process, Linea alba, Pubic crest, Pectineal line	Lower six thoracic (T7–T12) and L1 spinal nerves	Bilateral contraction: Flexion of trunk, increases intra-abdominal pressure Unilateral contraction: Lateral flexion of trunk, Rotation of trunk to same side
Transverse abdominis	Lateral 1/3rd of inguinal ligament Anterior 2/3rd of iliac crest Thoracolumbar fascia Lower six ribs	Linea alba Pubic crest Pecten pubis	Ventral primary rami of T7–T12 nerves and L1 nerve	Bilateral contraction: Increases intra-abdominal pressure, Expiration Unilateral contraction: Rotation of trunk to same side
Rectus abdominis	Medial head: Pubic symphysis Lateral head: Pubic crest	Xiphoid process 5th, 6th, 7th costal cartilages	T7–T12 spinal nerves	Increases intra-abdominal pressure Flexion of trunk, expiration

Plate 16.2: External oblique, internal oblique, transverse abdominis and rectus abdominis muscles

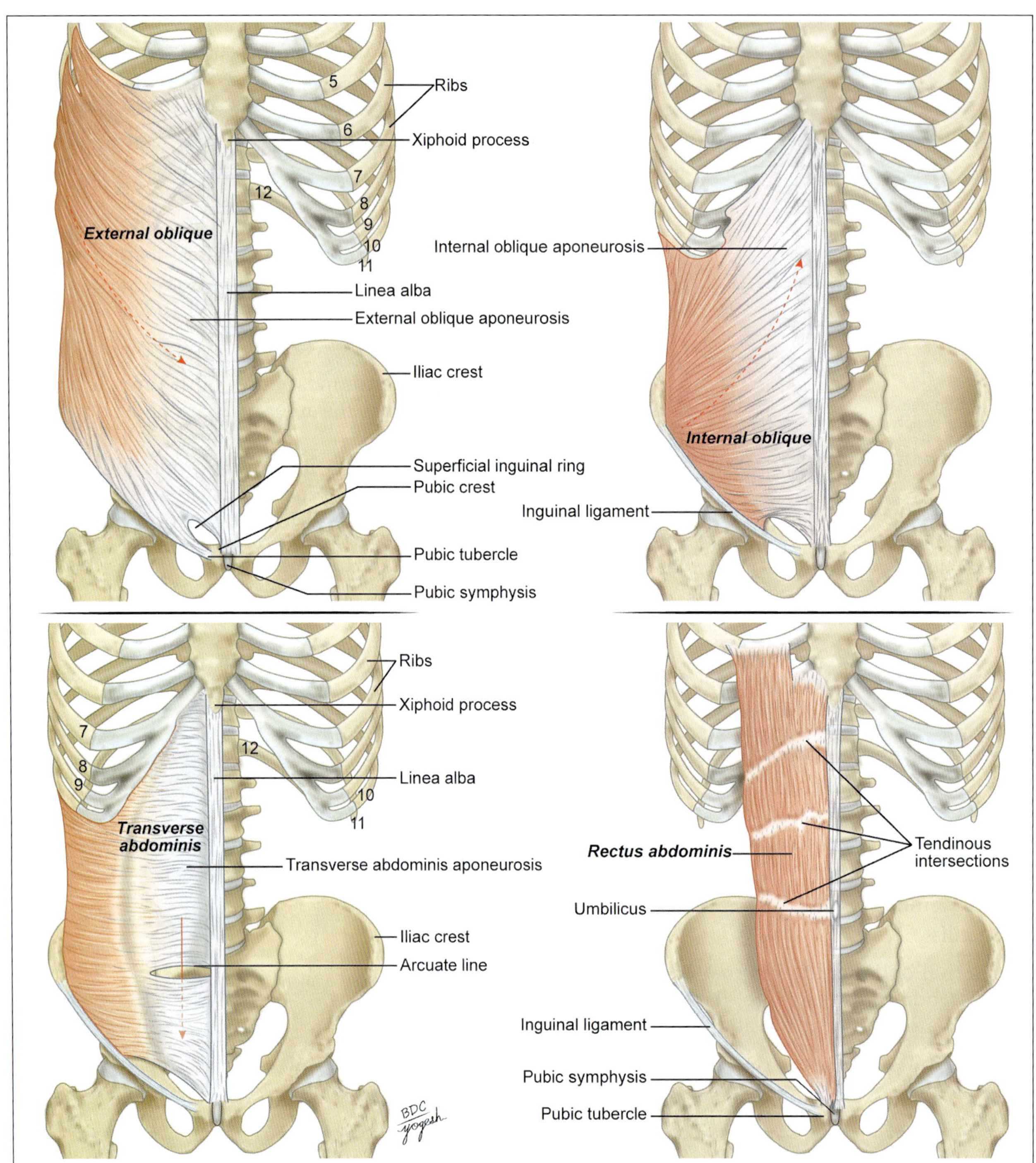

Nerve Supply

Lower six thoracic nerves (T7–T12) (Fig. 16.12).

Note: Interesting fact:

1. Between the anterior superior iliac spine and the pubic tubercle, the aponeurosis has a free inferior border that is folded on itself to form the ***inguinal ligament***. The ligament is described in detail later.
2. Between the linea semilunaris and the linea alba, the aponeurosis helps to form the anterior wall of rectus sheath.
3. Just above the pubic crest, the aponeurosis of the external oblique muscle presents a triangular aperture called the ***superficial inguinal ring*** (Figs 16.12 and 16.16).
4. The muscle has free posterior and upper borders.

INTERNAL OBLIQUE MUSCLE

Origin

The muscle arises from (Plate 16.2, Fig. 16.16, Flowchart 16.1):

a. Lateral 2/3rd of the ***inguinal ligament***
b. Anterior 2/3rd of the intermediate area of the ***iliac crest***
c. Thoracolumbar fascia.

From this origin, the fibres run upwards, forwards and medially crossing the fibres of the external oblique muscle at right angles.

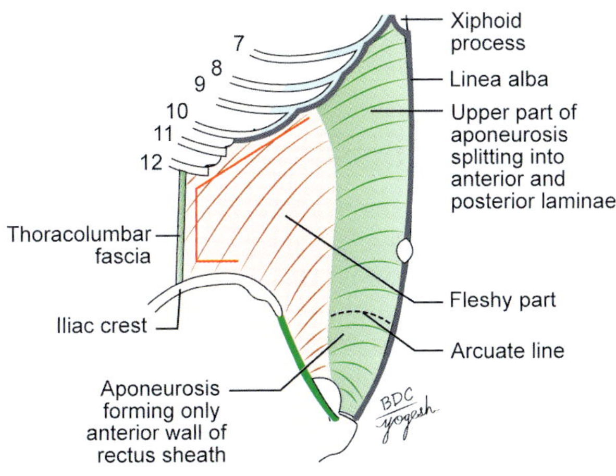

Fig. 16.16: Internal oblique muscle of the abdomen

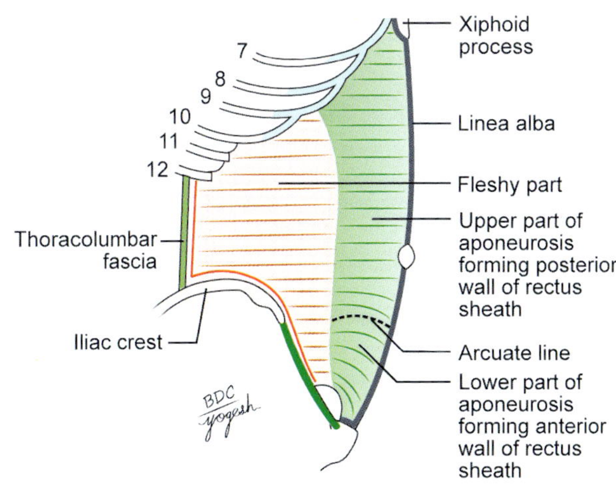

Fig. 16.17: Transversus abdominis muscle

Insertion

1. The ***uppermost fibres*** are inserted directly into the lower three or four ribs and their cartilages.
2. The remaining fibres of the muscle end in an ***aponeurosis*** through which it is inserted into the 7th, 8th and 9th costal cartilages, the xiphoid process, linea alba, pubic crest and the pectineal line of the pubis. *It does not extend beyond the costal margin.*

Nerve Supply

Lower six thoracic nerves (T7–T12) and the first lumbar nerve (L1).

Note: Interesting fact:

1. The aponeurosis of external oblique muscle takes part in the formation of *rectus sheath* as follows. Up to the lateral margin of rectus abdominis, the aponeurosis has only one layer. Thereafter, the arrangement of aponeurosis differs in its upper and lower parts.
   a. In the upper 3/4th of the wall, the aponeurosis splits into an anterior lamina that passes medially in front of the rectus abdominis and a posterior lamina that lies behind the rectus. The posterior lamina ends below, at the level midway between the umbilicus and the pubic symphysis, in a free curved margin called the ***arcuate line*** or ***linea semicircularis***, or ***fold of Douglas***. The line is concave downwards.
   b. Below a level midway between the umbilicus and the pubic symphysis (lower 1/4th of the wall), the aponeurosis remains a single layer. It passes in front of rectus abdominis to reach linea alba. It, thus, takes part in forming the anterior wall of rectus sheath.
2. The ***conjoint tendon*** is formed partly by this muscle.
3. The *cremaster* muscle is formed by fibres of this muscle.

TRANSVERSUS ABDOMINIS MUSCLE

Origin

The muscle has a fleshy origin from (Plate 16.2, Fig. 16.17, Flowchart 16.1):

1. Lateral 1/3rd of the inguinal ligament
2. Anterior 2/3rd of the inner lip of the iliac crest
3. Thoracolumbar fascia
4. Inner surfaces of the lower six costal cartilages.

The fibres are directed horizontally forward.

Insertion

The fibres end in a broad aponeurosis which is inserted into the xiphoid process, the linea alba, the pubic crest and the pectineal line of the pubis.

The lowest fibres of the muscle fuse with the lowest fibres of the internal oblique to form the ***conjoint tendon***.

Nerve Supply

Lower six thoracic nerves (T7–T12) and the first lumbar nerve (L1).

Note: Interesting fact:

1. The aponeurosis of the transversus abdominis takes part in forming the rectus sheath. In the uppermost part, some fleshy fibres of the transversus abdominis may lie behind the rectus abdominis.
2. The *neurovascular plane* of the abdominal wall lies between the *internal oblique* and *transversus muscles*. This plane is continuous with the neurovascular plane otf the thoracic wall.
3. The aponeuroses of three flat muscles seem to end in the fibrous raphe—the *linea alba*. Each aponeurosis is made up of the two laminae—the superficial and deep laminae. The laminae of the two sides interdigitate in a manner that the superficial lamina of one gets continuous with deep lamina of the opposite side and vice versa. This provides enough strength to the anterior abdominal wall.

RECTUS ABDOMINIS MUSCLE

Origin

The muscle arises by two tendinous heads as follows (Plate 16.2, Fig. 16.18, Flowchart 16.1):

1. ***Lateral head*** from the lateral part of the pubic crest (Fig. 16.15).
2. ***Medial head*** from the medial part of pubic crest and anterior pubic ligament. The fibres run vertically upwards.

Insertion

On the front of the wall of the thorax, along a horizontal line passing laterally from the xiphoid process, and cutting in that order, the 7th, 6th and 5th costal cartilages.

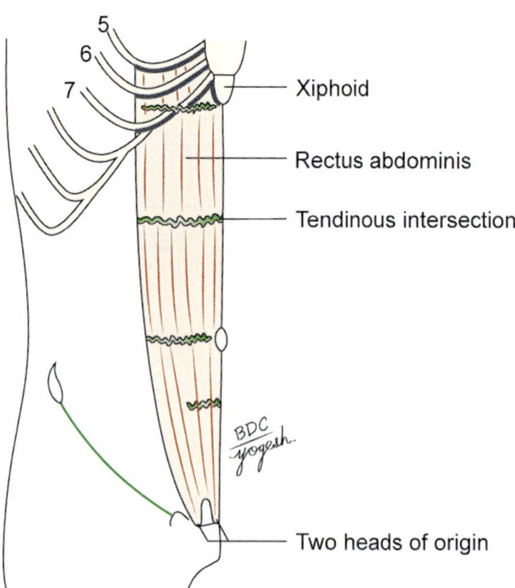

Fig. 16.18: Rectus abdominis muscle

Nerve Supply

Lower six or seven thoracic nerves.

Note: Interesting fact:

1. The muscle is enclosed in a ***rectus sheath*** formed mainly by the aponeuroses of the three flat muscles of the abdominal wall. The sheath is described later.
2. ***Tendinous intersections*:** These are three transverse fibrous bands that divide the muscle into smaller parts. One lies opposite the umbilicus, the second opposite the free end of the xiphoid process and the third in between the two. One or two incomplete intersections may be present below the umbilicus.

   The intersections are actually zigzag in course, traverse only the anterior half of the muscle and are adherent to the anterior wall of rectus sheath.

   Embryologically, they may represent the segmental origin of muscle, but functionally they make the muscle more powerful by increasing the number of muscle fibres.

ACTIONS OF THE MAIN MUSCLES OF THE ANTERIOR ABDOMINAL WALL

1. ***Support for abdominal viscera:*** The abdominal muscles provide a firm but elastic support for the abdominal viscera against gravity. This is chiefly due to the tone of the oblique muscles, especially the internal oblique.
2. ***Expulsive acts:*** The oblique muscles, assisted by the transversus, can compress the abdominal viscera and thus help in all expulsive acts, like micturition, defaecation, parturition, vomiting, etc. This is one of the most important actions of the abdominal muscles.
3. ***Forceful expiratory acts:*** The external oblique can markedly depress and compress the lower part of the thorax producing forceful expiration, as in coughing, sneezing, blowing, shouting, etc. This is also an important action of the abdominal muscles.
4. ***Movements of the trunk:***
   a. Flexion of the trunk or lumbar spine is brought about mainly by the rectus abdominis.
   b. Lateral flexion of the trunk is done by one-sided contraction of the oblique muscles.
   c. Rotation of the trunk is produced by a combined action of the external oblique with the opposite internal oblique.

DISSECTION

Identify the origin of the external oblique from the lower eight ribs and its interdigitations with serratus anterior in the upper part and with latissimus dorsi in the lower part of its origin. Separate 1–6 digitations from the ribs.

Cut vertically, through the muscle to the iliac crest posterior to the sixth digitation. Separate the external oblique from the iliac crest in front of this. Try to avoid injury to the lateral cutaneous branches of the subcostal and iliohypogastric nerves which pierce it close to the iliac crest.

Reflect the upper part of the external oblique forwards and expose the deeper internal oblique and its aponeurosis to the line of its fusion with the aponeurosis of the external oblique anterior to rectus abdominis. Just lateral to this line of fusion, divide the external oblique aponeurosis vertically till the pubic symphysis. Turn the muscle and aponeurosis inferiorly. This exposes the inferior part of the internal oblique and the lowest portion of aponeurosis of external oblique, i.e. the *inguinal ligament*.

Identify the deep fibres of the inguinal ligament passing posteriorly to the *pecten pubis*. This is the *lacunar ligament* or pectineal part of the inguinal ligament.

Lift the internal oblique and cut carefully through its attachments to the inguinal ligament, iliac crest and costal margin.

Carefully preserve the nerves of the anterior abdominal wall which lie between internal oblique and transversus abdominis. Cut vertically through the internal oblique from the twelfth costal cartilage to the iliac crest and reflect the muscle forwards from the transversus and the nerves.

Identify internal oblique deep to external oblique muscle. Remove the fascia from the surface of the internal oblique and its aponeurosis.

Identify the part of the internal oblique which passes around the spermatic cord. This is the *cremaster muscle*.

Trace the fibres of internal oblique into the conjoint tendon.

Dissect the *triple* relation of internal oblique to the inguinal canal.

Intercrural fibres of inguinal ligament pass towards the apex of the superficial inguinal ring. These try to approximate the two crura.

INGUINAL LIGAMENT

The inguinal or Poupart's ligament is formed by the lower border of the ***external oblique aponeurosis*** which is thickened and folded backwards on itself.

It is about 12–14 cm long. It extends from the anterior superior iliac spine to the pubic tubercle and lies beneath the fold of the groin. Its lateral half is rounded and oblique. Its medial half is grooved upwards and is more horizontal (Fig. 16.19, Flowchart 16.2).

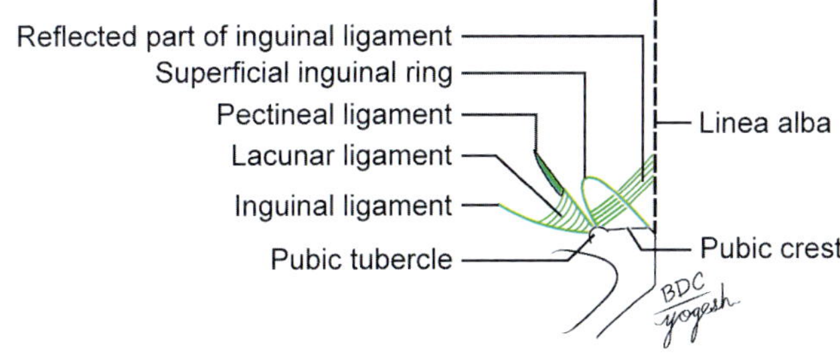

Fig. 16.19: Extensions of the inguinal ligament

Flowchart 16.2: Inguinal ligament

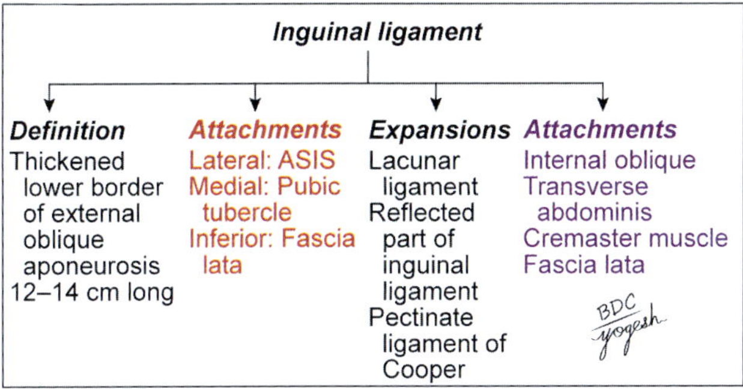

(ASIS: Anterior superior iliac spine)

Attachments

a. The ***fascia lata*** is attached to the lower border. Traction of this fascia makes the ligament convex downwards.

b. The upper surface of the ligament gives origin to the internal oblique from its lateral 2/3rd, to the transversus abdominis from its lateral 1/3rd and to the cremaster muscle from its middle part.

Relations: The upper grooved surface of the medial half of the inguinal ligament forms the *floor of the inguinal canal* and lodges the ***spermatic cord*** or round ligament of the uterus.

Extensions

1. The ***pectineal part of the inguinal ligament*** or ***lacunar ligament*** is triangular. Anteriorly, it is attached to the medial end of the inguinal ligament. Posteriorly, it is attached to the pecten pubis. The apex is attached to the pubic tubercle. The base is directed laterally (Fig. 16.16). It forms the medial boundary of the femoral ring. It is horizontal in position and supports the spermatic cord.
2. The ***pectineal ligament*** or ***ligament of Cooper*** is an extension from the posterior part of the base of the lacunar ligament. It is attached to the pecten pubis.
3. The ***reflected part of the inguinal ligament*** consists of fibres that pass upwards and medially from the lateral crus of the superficial inguinal ring. It lies behind the superficial inguinal ring and in front of the conjoint tendon. Its fibres interlace with those of the opposite side at the linea alba.
4. Intercrural fibres arise from middle of inguinal ligament, arch over the superficial inguinal ring to keep its crura together (Fig. 16.19).

CONJOINT TENDON/APONEUROSIS OR FALX INGUINALIS

Formation: The conjoint tendon/aponeurosis is formed by fusion of the lowest aponeurotic fibres of the internal oblique and of the transversus muscles, attached to the pubic crest and to the medial part of the pecten pubis. Medially, it is continuous with the anterior wall of the rectus sheath. Laterally, it is usually free (Fig. 16.20).

Sometimes it may be continuous with an inconstant ligamentous band, named the ***interfoveolar ligament***, which connects the lower border of the transversus abdominis to the superior ramus of the pubis.

The conjoint aponeurosis strengthens the abdominal wall at the site where it is weakened by the superficial inguinal ring. Weakness of conjoint tendon in old age predisposes the occurrence of direct inguinal hernia.

CREMASTER MUSCLE

The cremaster muscle consists of muscle fasciculi embedded in the *cremasteric fascia*. The fasciculi form superficial loops from middle 1/3rd of upper surface of inguinal ligament and deep loops from pubic tubercle, pubic crest and conjoint tendon. Here some fibres may be continuous with the internal oblique or transversus muscles. The medial ends of the loops are attached to the pubic tubercle, the pubic crest or the conjoint tendon (Plate 16.3).

The muscle is fully developed only in the male. In the female, it is represented by a few fibres only. Along with the intervening connective tissue, the muscle loops to form a sac-like *cremasteric fascia* around the spermatic cord and testis. It lies deep in the *external spermatic fascia*.

Nerve Supply

Genital branch of the genitofemoral nerve (L1).

Action

The cremaster helps to suspend the testis and can elevate it. The muscle also tends to close the superficial inguinal ring when the intra-abdominal pressure is raised.

Cremasteric Reflex

Upon stroking the skin of the upper part of the medial side of the thigh, there is reflex contraction of the cremaster muscle, as evidenced by elevation and retraction of the testis. The reflex is more brisk in children. In upper motor neuron lesions above segment L1, the reflex is lost (Plate 16.3, Fig. 16.21).

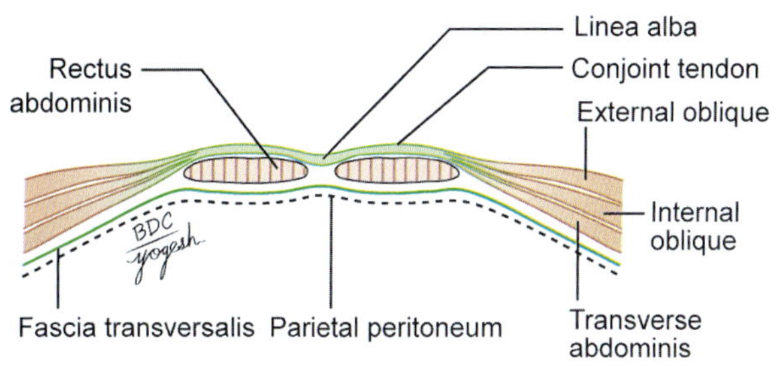

Fig. 16.20: Conjoint tendon (section of the anterior abdominal wall passing below the umbilicus)

Plate 16.3: Pyramidalis and cremaster muscles

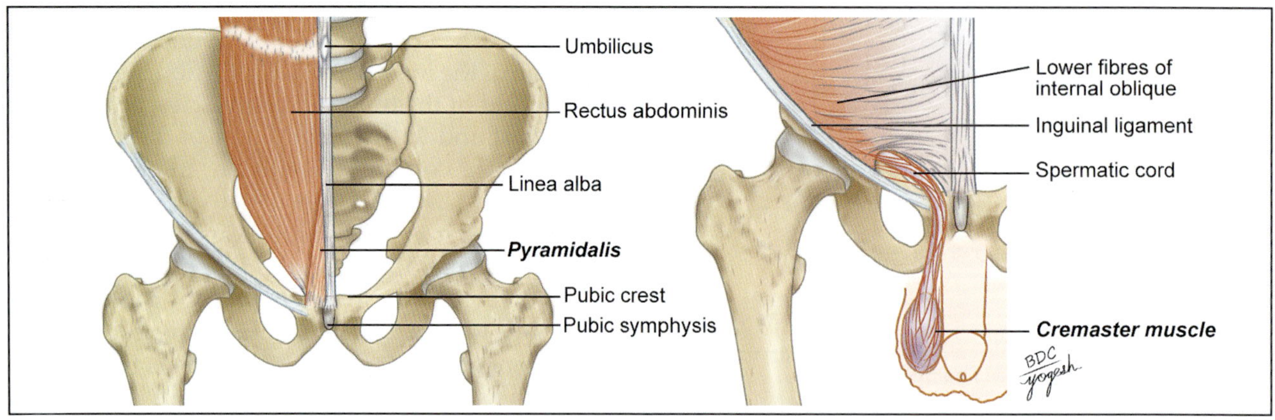

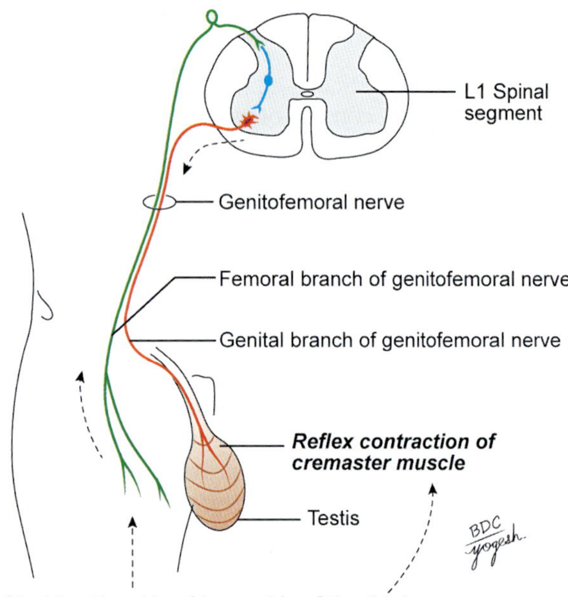

Fig. 16.21: Cremasteric reflex

PYRAMIDALIS

This is a small triangular muscle. It is rudimentary in human beings (Plate 16.3).

Origin: Front pubic crest and anterior pubic ligament. Its fibres run upward and medially.

Insertion: It inserts into the linea alba, midway between the umbilicus and the pubic symphysis.

Innervation: Subcostal nerve (T12).

Action: It tenses the linea alba.

Competency:
AN44.7 Enumerate common abdominal incisions.

CLINICAL ANATOMY

- Due to lack of exercise, the tone of muscles of the anterior abdominal wall decreases leading to protrusion of the wall. This is called ***visceroptosis***.

Abdominal incisions: The anterior abdominal wall is punctured for various procedures, like surgeries of gallbladder, vermiform appendix, etc. (Fig. 16.22).

1. ***Supraumbilical median incisions*** through the linea alba have several advantages as being bloodless; safety to muscles and nerves but tend to leave a postoperative weakness through which a ventral hernia may develop.
2. ***Infraumbilical median incisions*** are safer because the close approximation of recti prevents formation of any ventral hernia.
3. ***Paramedian incisions*** through the rectus sheath are more sound than median incisions. The rectus muscle is *retracted laterally* to protect the nerves supplying it from any injury. In these cases, the subsequent risk of weakness and of incisional or ventral hernia are minimal.
4. ***Kocher subcostal incision*** (oblique incision) or subcostal incision is useful to access the gallbladder and the biliary tree. It is given parallel to the costal margin, starting below the xiphoid and extending laterally.
5. ***Gridiron incision*** (McBurney incision) is useful for appendectomy. It is given obliquely at the McBurney point, in the right iliac fossa.
6. ***Pfannenstiel incision*** is an useful incision for gynaecological surgery, caesarean section, retropubic approach to the prostate and the bladder neck. This incision is placed in the curving interspinous skin crease, immediately inferior to the pubic hair line in the female.
7. ***Transverse incision*** in the lower part of the abdomen with slight concavity upward is given about 2 cm below the umbilicus. It is used to explore the pelvic organs, such as surgeries related to the uterus and ovaries.

DEEP NERVES

The anterior abdominal wall is supplied by the lower six thoracic nerves or lower five intercostal, and subcostal; and by the first lumbar nerve through its iliohypogastric and ilioinguinal branches. These are the nerves which emerge as cutaneous nerves.

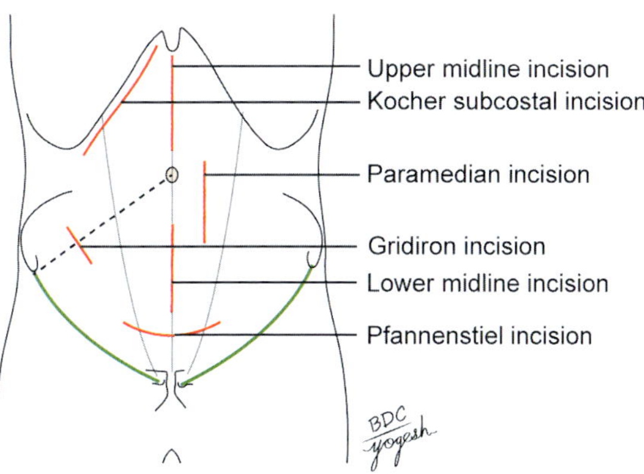

Fig. 16.22: Incisions in the anterior abdominal wall

DEEP ARTERIES

The anterior abdominal wall is supplied by:

1. Two large arteries from above—the *superior epigastric* and *musculophrenic*.
2. Two large arteries from below—the *inferior epigastric* and the *deep circumflex iliac*.
3. Small branches of the intercostal, subcostal and lumbar arteries, which accompany the corresponding nerves (Fig. 16.21).

Superior epigastric artery: It is one of the two terminal branches of the internal thoracic artery. It begins in the 6th intercostal space and enters the abdomen by passing behind the 7th costal cartilage between the costal and xiphoid origins of the diaphragm. It enters the rectus sheath and runs vertically downwards, supplies the rectus muscle and ends by anastomosing with the inferior epigastric artery.

Musculophrenic artery: It is the other terminal branch of the internal thoracic artery. It runs downwards and laterally behind the 7th costal cartilage and enters the abdomen by piercing the diaphragm between the 7th and 8th cartilages. It continues downwards and laterally along the deep surface of the diaphragm as far as the tenth intercostal space. It gives branches to the diaphragm, the anterior abdominal wall and the 7th, 8th and 9th intercostal spaces as the ***anterior intercostal arteries***.

Inferior epigastric artery: It arises from the external iliac artery near its lower end just above the inguinal ligament. It runs upwards and medially, pierces the fascia transversalis and enters the rectus sheath by passing in front of the arcuate line. Within the sheath, it supplies the rectus muscle and ends by anastomosing with the superior epigastric artery. Its pubic branch may replace the obturator artery and is then known as the ***abnormal obturator artery***.

Deep circumflex iliac artery: The deep circumflex iliac artery is the other branch of the external iliac artery, given off from its lateral side opposite the origin of the inferior epigastric artery. It runs laterally and upwards behind the inguinal ligament, pierces the fascia transversalis and the transversus abdominis to enter the interval between the transversus and the internal oblique muscles.

FASCIA TRANSVERSALIS

The inner surface of the abdominal muscles is lined by fascia which is separated from peritoneum by extraperitoneal connective tissue. That part of the fascia which lines the inner surface of the transversus abdominis muscle is called the fascia transversalis (Figs 16.23a and b).

Extent

Superiorly: It is continuous with the diaphragmatic fascia.

Inferiorly: It is continuous with the fascia iliaca.

Anteriorly: It is adherent to the linea alba above the umbilicus.

Posteriorly: It merges with the anterior layer of the thoracolumbar fascia and is continuous with the renal fascia.

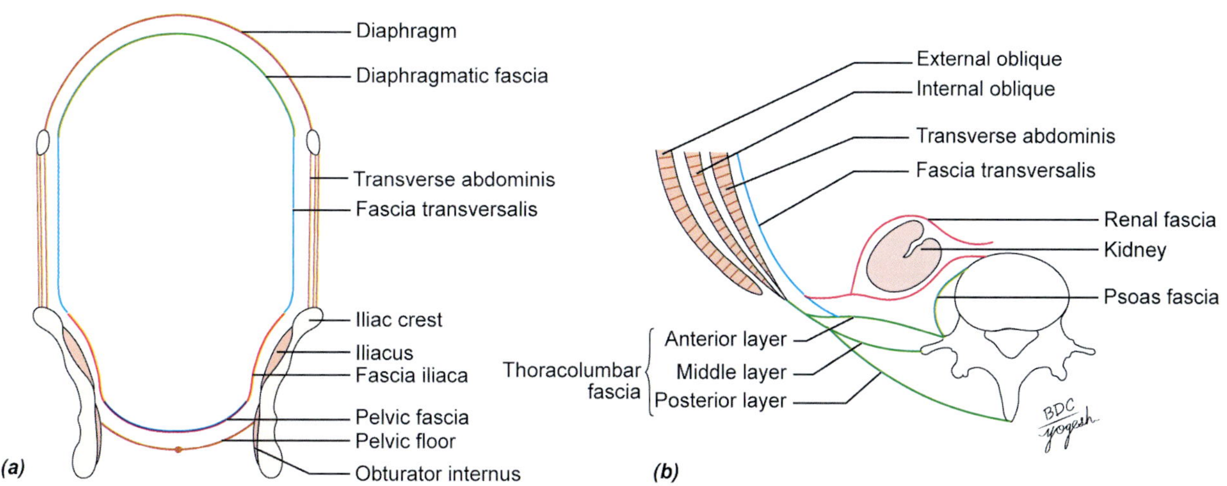

Figs 16.23a and b: Continuation of the fascia transversalis: (a) Coronal section and (b) transverse section

Features

1. **Deep inguinal ring:** About 1.2 cm above the mid-inguinal point, there is an oval opening in the fascia transversalis. This opening is the *deep inguinal ring*. The ring lies immediately lateral to the inferior epigastric artery. It transmits the spermatic cord in males and the round ligament of the uterus in females.
2. **Prolongations**
   a. A tubular prolongation of the fascia transversalis surrounds the spermatic cord forming the ***internal spermatic fascia***.
   b. Over the femoral vessels, the fascia transversalis is prolonged into the thigh as the *anterior wall of femoral sheath*.
3. The main arteries of the abdominal wall and pelvis lie inside the fascia transversalis, while the main nerves are outside. That is why the femoral vessels are inside the femoral sheath, while the femoral nerve is outside the sheath.
4. ***Ilio-pubic tract*** or ***Thomson's ligament*** is a thickened lower part of fascia transversalis that extends from the anterior superior iliac spine to pubic tubercle and pubic crest.

Plate 16.4: Rectus sheath (arrow)

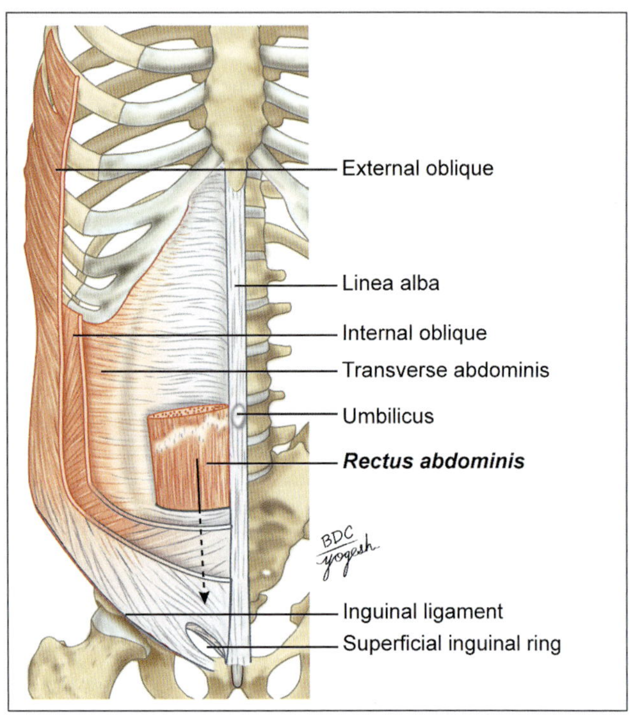

Competency:
AN44.3 Describe the formation of rectus sheath and its contents.

RECTUS SHEATH

Definition: Rectus sheath is an aponeurotic sheath covering the rectus abdominis (Plate 16.4, Figs 16.24 to 16.26, Flowchart 16.3).

Features

It has two walls—anterior and posterior.

1. ***Anterior wall***: It is complete, covering the muscle from end to end. It is firmly adherent to the tendinous intersections of the rectus muscle (Fig. 16.22).
2. ***Posterior wall:*** It is incomplete, being deficient below the arcuate line. It is free from the rectus muscle.

Fusion of all the aponeuroses in the midline is called *linea alba*.

Laterally, the anterior and posterior walls extend till *linea semilunaris*, which extends from tip of 9th costal cartilage to pubic tubercle.

Midway between the umbilicus and the pubic symphysis, the posterior wall of the rectus sheath ends in the arcuate line or *linea semicircularis* or *fold of Douglas*.

(a) Above the costal margin

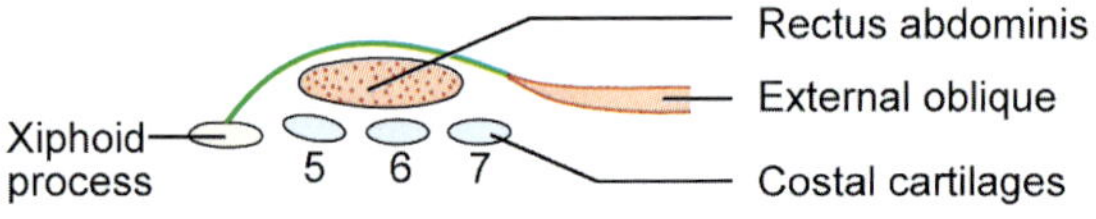

(b) Between costal margin and arcuate line

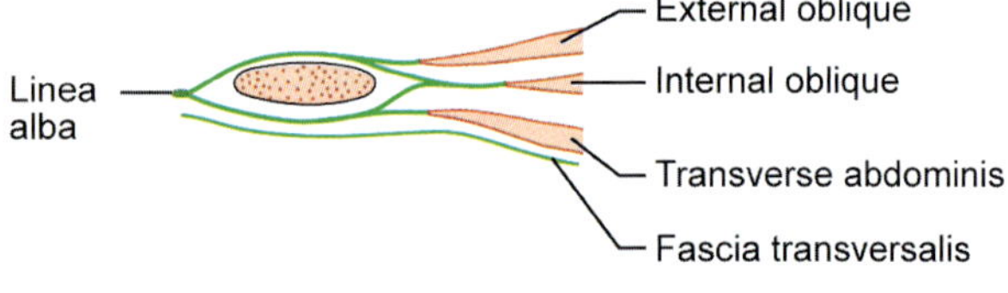

(c) Below the arcuate line

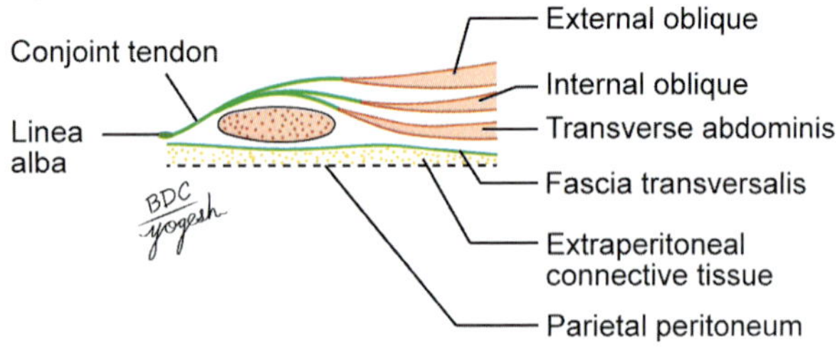

Figs 16.24a to c: Transverse sections through the rectus abdominis and its sheath

Formation of Rectus Sheath

The formation of rectus sheath from above downward is as follows:

1. ***Above the costal margin***
   - *Anterior wall*: External oblique aponeurosis
   - *Posterior wall*: It is deficient. It is formed by the 5th, 6th and 7th costal cartilages.
2. ***Between costal margin and arcuate line***
   - *Anterior wall*: It is formed by fusion of external oblique aponeurosis and anterior lamina of aponeurosis of internal oblique.
   - *Posterior wall*: It is formed by fusion of posterior lamina of aponeurosis of internal oblique and aponeurosis of transverse abdominis.

Section 2: Abdomen and Pelvis

16

Flowchart 16.3: Rectus sheath

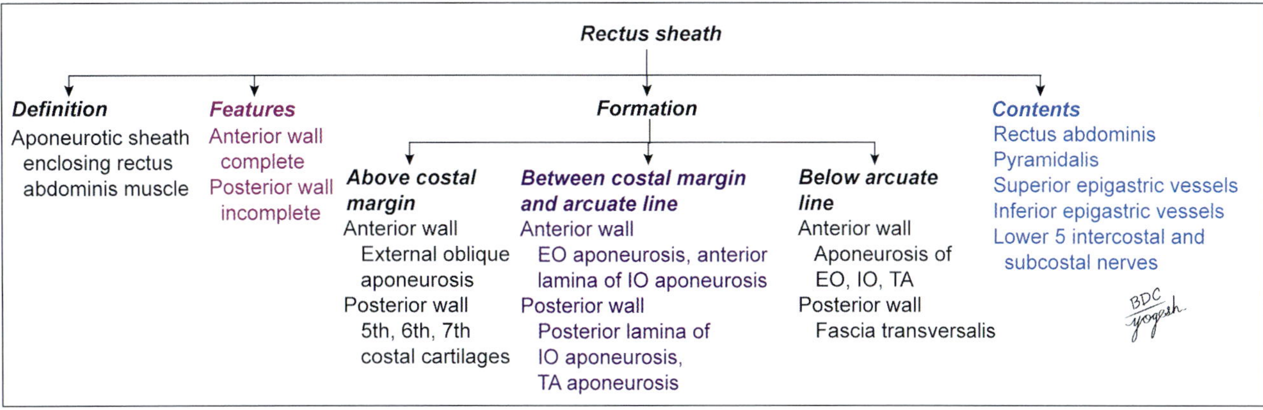

(EO: External oblique, IO: Internal oblique, TA: Transverse abdominis)

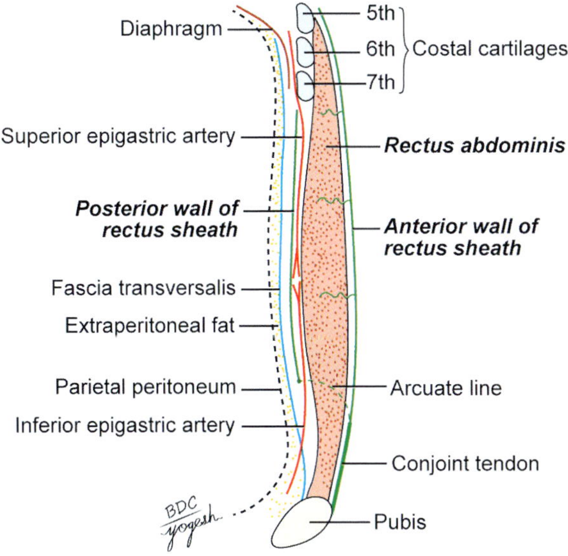

Fig. 16.25: Anterior and posterior walls of rectus sheath

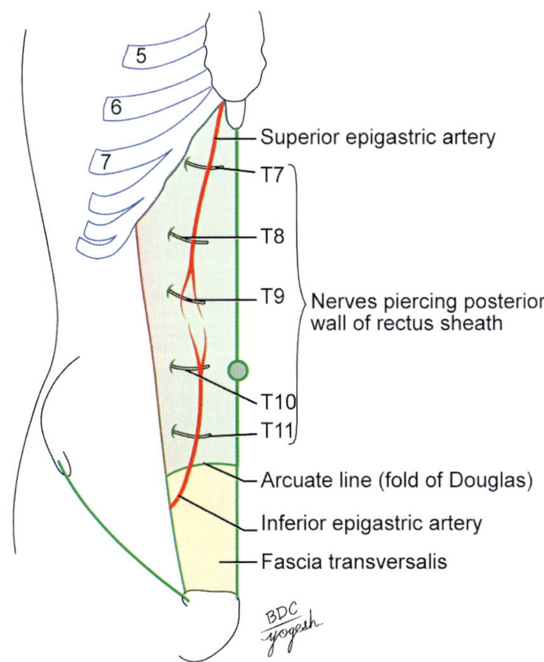

Fig. 16.26: Contents and posterior wall of rectus sheath

3. ***Below the arcuate line***
   - *Anterior wall*: It is formed by the aponeurosis of all three flat muscles of anterolateral abdominal wall. Here, aponeurosis of external oblique remains separated, and aponeurosis of internal oblique and transverse abdominis fuse to form conjoint tendon.
   - *Posterior wall*: It is deficient. It is formed by fascia transversalis.

Contents

A. *Two muscles*
   1. Rectus abdominis
   2. Pyramidalis (if present)

B. *Two arteries*
   1. Superior epigastric
   2. Inferior epigastric

C. *Two veins*
   1. Superior epigastric
   2. Inferior epigastric

D. *Six nerves*: Lower five intercostal and subcostal nerves (T7 to T12 thoracic nerves).

Functions

1. It checks bowing of rectus muscle during its contraction and thus increases the efficiency of the muscle.
2. It maintains the strength of the anterior abdominal wall.

CLINICAL ANATOMY

1. ***Flap of rectus abdominis*:** A flap of rectus abdominis muscle with superior epigastric vessels is commonly used in reconstructive surgery of breast following the mastectomy.
2. ***Divarication*** or ***separation of rectus abdominis muscles*:** In elderly multiparous woman, the separation of two rectus abdominis muscles occurs due to weakness and stretching of rectus abdominis muscle and rectus sheath (Fig. 16.27).
3. ***Epigastric hernia*** (midline hernia)**:** It occurs through weak linea alba. It mostly occurs in umbilical region, commonly in adults and obese multiparous females. It may involve herniation of extraperitoneal fat or a portion of greater omentum.

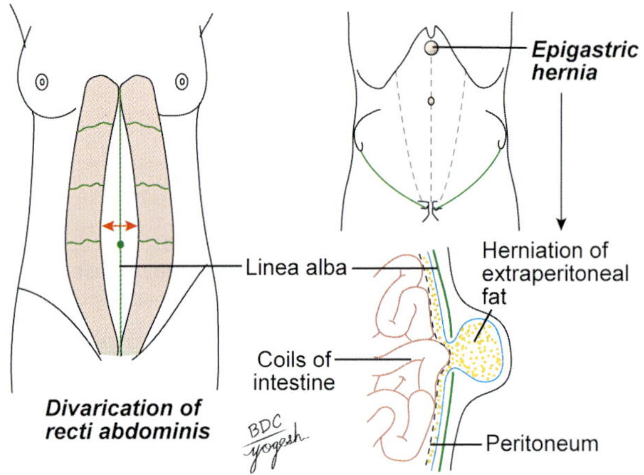

Fig. 16.27: Divarication of the recti abdominis and epigastric hernia

DISSECTION

Identify the rectus abdominis muscle. At the lateral edge of the rectus abdominis, the aponeurosis of the internal oblique splits to pass partly posterior and partly anterior to the rectus abdominis; the anterior layer fusing with the aponeurosis of external oblique and the posterior layer with that of the transversus abdominis. Identify the arcuate line midway between umbilicus and pubic symphysis.

Define the origins of the transversus and follow its aponeurosis to fuse with that of the internal oblique, posterior to the rectus abdominis above the arcuate line and anteriorly to the unsplit aponeurosis of internal oblique below the line.

Open the rectus sheath by a vertical incision along the middle of the muscle. Reflect the anterior layer of the sheath sideways, cutting its attachments to the tendinous intersections in the anterior part of the rectus muscle.

Lift the rectus muscle and identify the 7–11 intercostal and subcostal nerves entering the sheath through its posterior lamina, piercing the muscle and leaving through its anterior wall.

Divide the rectus abdominis transversely at its middle. Identify its attachments and expose the posterior wall of the rectus sheath by reflecting its parts superiorly and inferiorly. Identify and trace the superior and inferior epigastric arteries.

Define the arcuate line on the posterior wall of the rectus sheath.

Competency:

AN44.4 Describe and demonstrate extent, boundaries, contents of inguinal canal including Hesselbach's triangle.

INGUINAL CANAL

Definition: Inguinal canal is an oblique musculoaponeurotic passage in the lower part of the anterior abdominal wall, situated just above the medial half of the inguinal ligament (Plate 16.5, Figs 16.28 to 16.30, Flowchart 16.4).

Length: About 4 cm (1.5 inches) long.

Note: The inguinal canal is larger in males than in females.

Direction: It is directed downwards, forwards and medially.

Extent: The inguinal canal extends from the deep inguinal ring to the superficial inguinal ring.

Inguinal Rings (Flowchart 16.5)

1. ***Deep inguinal ring***

   It is an *oval* opening in the *fascia transversalis*, situated 1.2 cm above the midinguinal point, and immediately lateral to the stem of the inferior epigastric artery.
2. ***Superficial inguinal ring***

   It is a *triangular* gap in the external oblique aponeurosis. It is 2.5 cm long and 1.2 cm broad at the base.

   It is shaped like an obtuse-angled triangle.

   The *base* of the triangle is formed by the pubic crest.

   The two sides of the triangle form the lateral or lower and the medial or upper margins of the opening.

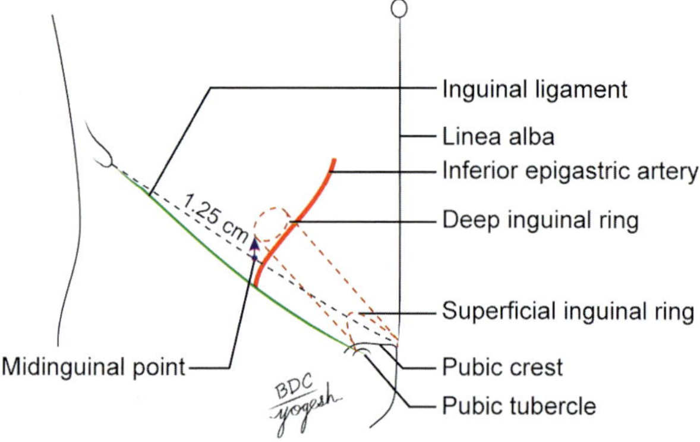

Fig. 16.28: Locations of superficial and deep inguinal rings

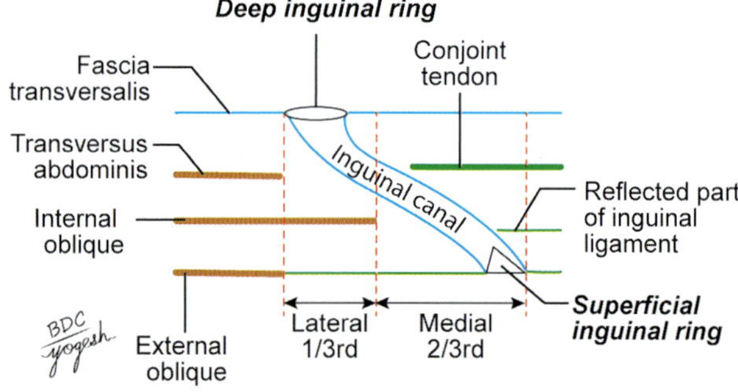

Fig. 16.29: Anterior and posterior walls of inguinal canal

Flowchart 16.4: Inguinal canal: Boundaries

Inguinal ligament

Anterior wall	***Posterior wall***	***Roof***	***Floor***	***Structures passing***
Skin Superficial fascia EO aponeurosis	In its whole length: - Fascia transversalis - Extraperitoneal fat - Parietal peritoneum In medial 2/3rd: - Conjoint tendon Reflected part of inguinal ligament	Arched fibres of IO and TA muscles	Inguinal ligament Lacunar ligament	In male: - Spermatic cord - Ilioinguinal nerve In female: - Round ligament of uterus - Ilioinguinal nerve

(EO: External oblique, IO: Internal oblique, TA: Transverse abdominis)

Plate 16.5: Formation of inguinal canal

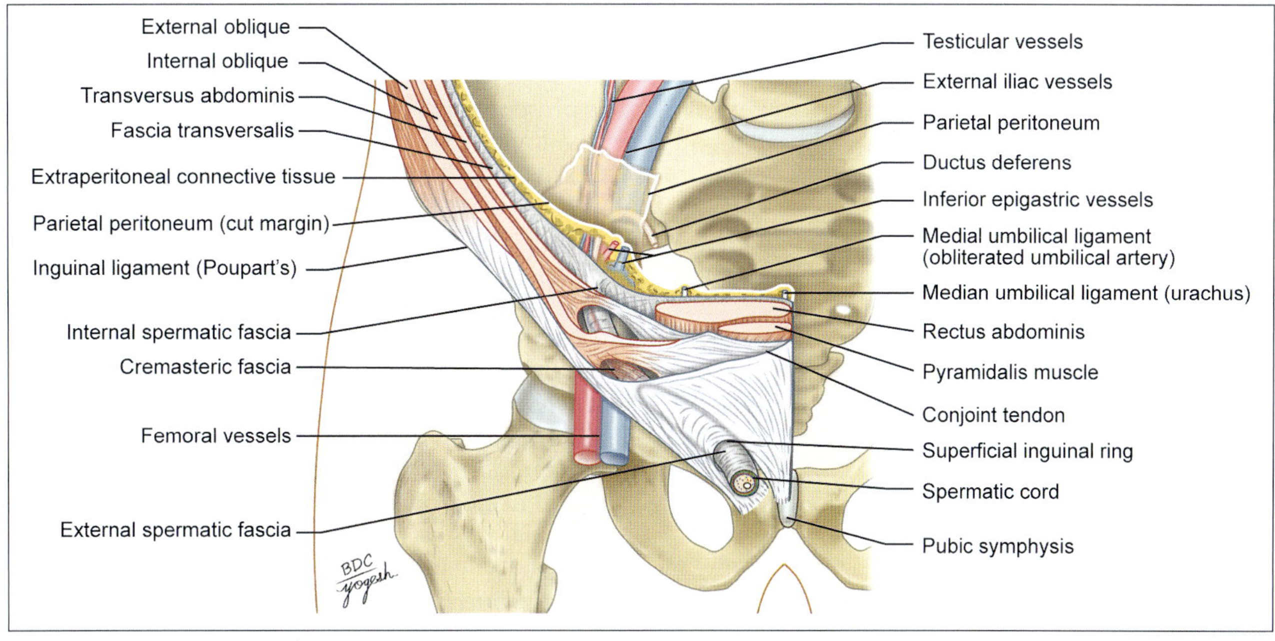

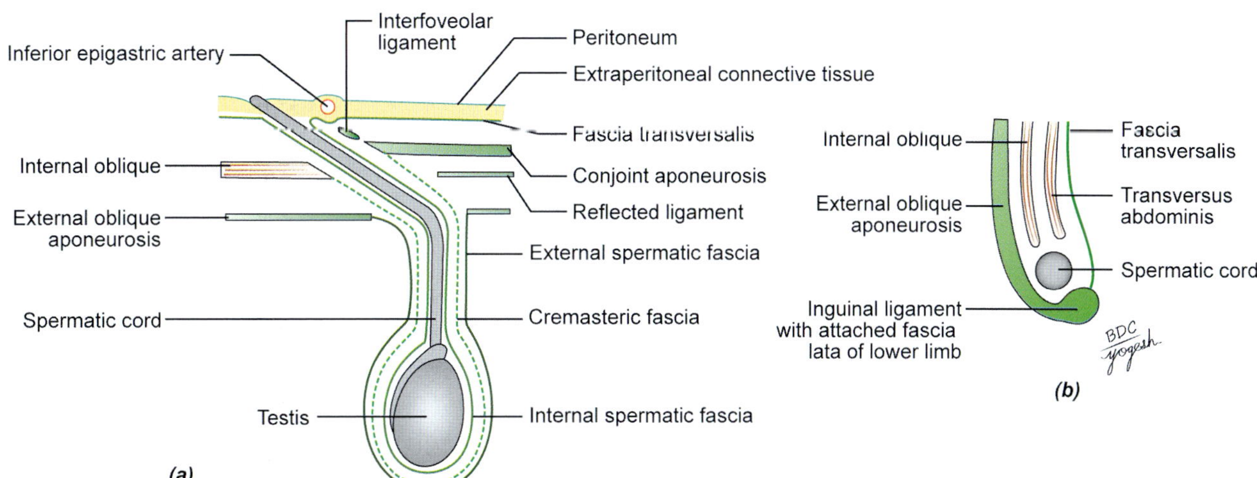

Figs 16.30a and b: Boundaries of the inguinal canal: (a) Anterior and posterior walls in a horizontal section and (b) the roof and floor in a sagittal section

Flowchart 16.5: Inguinal rings

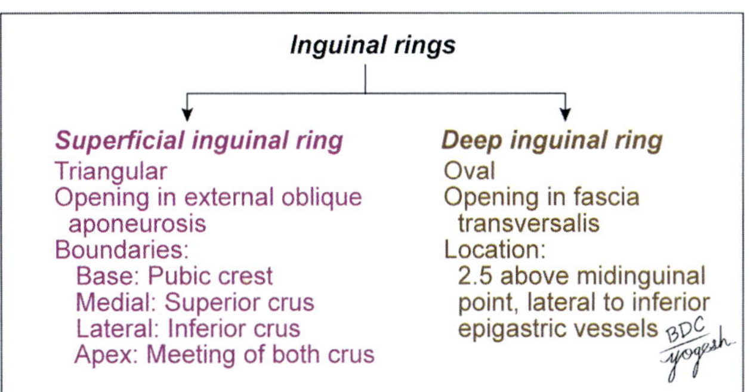

These margins are referred to as ***crura***. At and beyond the apex of the triangle, the two crura are united by intercrural fibres.

Boundaries

Anterior Wall

1. *In its whole extent:*
   a. Skin
   b. Superficial fascia
   c. External oblique aponeurosis.
2. *In its lateral 1/3rd:* The fleshy fibres of the internal oblique muscle (Figs 16.25c and 16.26a).

Posterior Wall

1. *In its whole extent:*
   a. Fascia transversalis
   b. Extraperitoneal tissue
   c. Parietal peritoneum.

2. *In its medial 2/3rd:*
   a. Conjoint aponeurosis
   b. At its medial end by the reflected part of the inguinal ligament.

Roof

It is formed by the arched fibres of the internal oblique and transversus abdominis muscles.

Floor

It is formed by the grooved upper surface of the inguinal ligament; and at the medial end by the lacunar ligament.

Structures Passing Through Inguinal Canal

The following structures traverse the inguinal canal:

In male: Spermatic cord, ilioinguinal nerve

In female: Round ligament of uterus and ilioinguinal nerve.

Note: The ilioinguinal nerve enters the canal through the interval between the external and internal oblique muscles and passes out through the superficial inguinal ring.

SPERMATIC CORD

The spermatic cord is the cord-like structure that is present in the male formed by the vas deferens and its covering. It extends from deep inguinal ring to each testis. Spermatic cord is about 16 mm thick (Fig. 16.31).

Constituents of the Spermatic Cord

1. Ductus deferens.
2. Testicular and cremasteric arteries and the artery of the ductus deferens.
3. Pampiniform plexus of veins.
4. Lymph vessels from the testis.
5. Genital branch of the genitofemoral nerve and the plexus of sympathetic nerves around the artery to the ductus deferens and visceral afferent nerve fibres.
6. Remains of the processus vaginalis.

Coverings of Spermatic Cord

From within outwards, these are as follows:

1. External spermatic fascia
2. Cremasteric fascia with Cremaster muscle (skeletal and smooth muscle)
3. Internal spermatic fascia
4. Vestigium.

MECHANISM OF INGUINAL CANAL

The presence of the inguinal canal is a cause of weakness in the lower part of the anterior abdominal wall. This weakness is compensated by the following factors (Table 16.1):

1. ***Obliquity of the inguinal canal:*** The two inguinal rings do not lie opposite each other. Therefore, when the intra-abdominal pressure rises the anterior and posterior walls of the canal are approximated, thus obliterating the passage. This is known as the flap valve mechanism.
2. ***Guards of inguinal ring:*** The *superficial inguinal ring is guarded* from behind by the conjoint tendon and by the reflected part of the inguinal ligament. The *deep inguinal ring is guarded* from the front by the fleshy fibres of the internal oblique.
3. ***Shutter mechanism of the internal oblique:*** Internal oblique muscle has a *triple relation* to the inguinal canal. It forms the anterior wall, the roof, and the posterior wall of the canal. When it contracts the roof is approximated to the floor, like a shutter. The arching fibres of the transversus also take part in the shutter mechanism.
4. ***Ball valve mechanism:*** Contraction of the cremaster muscle helps the spermatic cord to plug the superficial inguinal ring.
5. ***Slit valve mechanism:*** Contraction of the external oblique results in approximation of the two crura of the superficial inguinal ring. The integrity of the

TABLE 16.1: Mechanism of integrity of inguinal canal

Mechanism	*Factor responsible*
Flap valve mechanism	Obliquity of inguinal canal
Guarding of inguinal ring • Superficial inguinal ring • Deep inguinal ring	 • Posteriorly guarded by conjoint tendon • Fleshy fibres of internal oblique
Shutter mechanism	Triple relation of internal oblique
Slit valve mechanism	Contraction of external oblique
Ball valve mechanism	Plug action of cremaster muscle

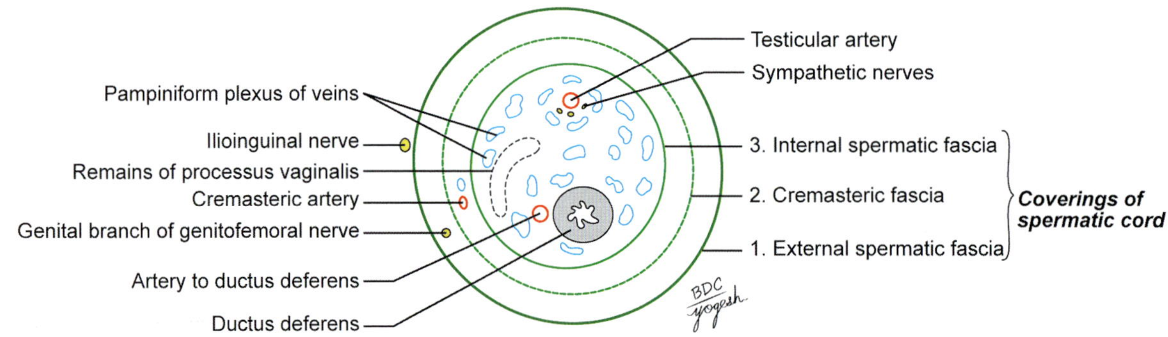

Fig. 16.31: Transverse section through the spermatic cord showing coverings and contents

superficial inguinal ring is greatly increased by the intercrural fibres.

6. ***Hormones*** may play a role in maintaining the tone of the inguinal musculature.

Note: Whenever there is a rise in intra-abdominal pressure as in coughing, sneezing, lifting heavy weights, all these mechanisms come into play, so that the inguinal canal is obliterated, its openings are closed and herniation of abdominal viscera is prevented.

HESSELBACH'S TRIANGLE (INGUINAL TRIANGLE)

Definition: Hesselbach's triangle is situated deep to the posterior wall of inguinal canal. It can be seen from inner aspect to the lower part of the anterior abdominal wall (Fig. 16.32, Flowchart 16.6).

Boundaries: The boundaries of the Hesselbach's triangle are as follows:

Medial: Lateral border of rectus abdominis muscle

Lateral: Inferior epigastric artery

Inferior: Medial half of inguinal ligament

Floor: It is covered by peritoneum, extraperitoneal connective tissue and fascia transversalis.

Divisions

The medial umbilical ligament (obliterated umbilical artery) divided the triangle into:

Medial part: The floor of the triangle in the medial part is supported by conjoint tendon.

Lateral part: The floor of the triangle in the lateral part is weak. Hence, direct inguinal hernia occurs through lateral part.

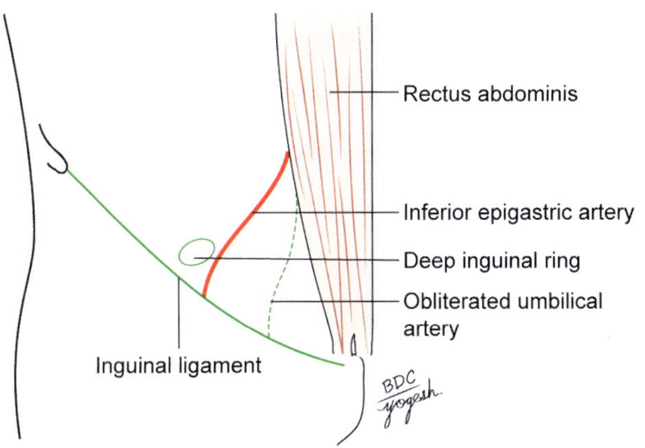

Fig. 16.32: Hesselbach's triangle

Flowchart 16.6: Hesselbach's triangle

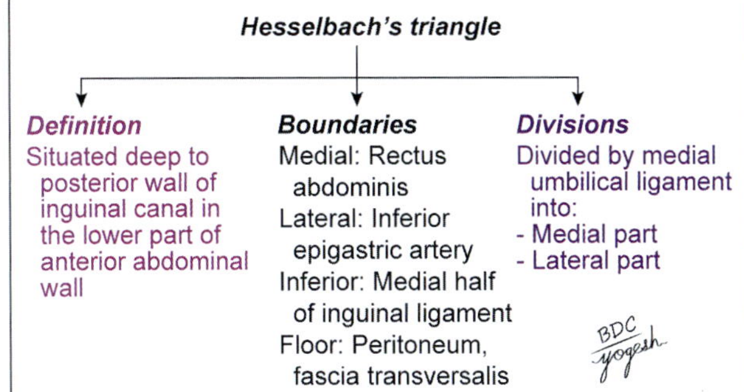

DISSECTION

Identify again the superficial inguinal ring above the pubic tubercle. It lies in the aponeurosis of external oblique muscle and provides the external spermatic fascia to the spermatic cord/round ligament of uterus.

Identify internal oblique muscle deep to external oblique. Note that its fibres lie anterior to deep inguinal ring, then arch over the inguinal canal and finally fuse with the fibres of transversus abdominis to form the conjoint tendon attached to pubic crest and pecten pubis.

Lastly, identify the deep inguinal ring in the fascia transversalis situated 1.2 cm above the midinguinal point. This fascia provides the internal spermatic fascia to the spermatic cord/round ligament of uterus.

Competency:

AN44.5 Explain the anatomical basis of inguinal hernia.

CLINICAL ANATOMY

Hernia

Definition: Hernias is an abnormal protrusion of the abdominal content through the abdominal walls. Hernia may be of two types:

External hernia: Protrusion of contents of abdomen outside the abdominal cavity.

Internal hernia: Protrusion of abdominal content into a space within the abdominal cavity. Internal hernia mostly occurs in epiploic foramen or opening into the lesser sac or foramen of Winslow.

Composition of Hernia

Hernia consists of the following parts (Fig. 16.33):

1. *Sac*: It is protrusion of peritoneum. The sac has narrow *neck* and expanded *body*.
2. *Contents*: It may consist of coils of intestine, omentum, or other abdominal viscera.
3. *Coverings*: They consist of layers of abdominal wall.

Types of External Abdominal Hernias

External abdominal hernias are of the following types:

1. *Congenital umbilical hernia* occurs due to failure of midgut loop to return to the abdominal cavity.
2. *Acquired infantile umbilical hernia* occurs due to weak umbilical scar. It may disappear as the infant grows.
3. *Paraumbilical hernia* (belly button hernia) occurs due to the protrusion of intestinal coils through the linea alba surrounding the umbilicus.
4. *Femoral hernia* is the protrusion of abdominal contents through femoral canal. It is more common in females due to wider pelvis (Fig. 34).
5. *Inguinal hernia* is the protrusion of abdominal content in the inguinal canal (Fig. 16.34).
6. *Epigastric hernia* occurs through the anterior abdominal wall in the epigastric region.
7. *Petit's hernia* occurs in the Petit's lumbar triangle on the posterolateral abdominal wall.

8. *Spiegel's hernia* occurs at the junction of linea semilunaris and the arcuate line (Adriaan van den Spiegel, Flemish anatomist, 1578–1625).
9. *Incisional hernia* occurs through the incompletely healed surgical wound of the abdominal wall.

Inguinal Hernia

Definition: Protrusion of the abdominal content in the inguinal canal is called *inguinal hernia*.

There are two types of inguinal hernia: Indirect and direct (Figs 16.35 and 16.36, Flowchart 16.7).

Indirect inguinal hernia

If the abdominal contents enter through the deep inguinal ring in the inguinal canal, it is called indirect inguinal hernia (Flowchart 16.7). Indirect inguinal hernia may be:

a. *Congenital indirect inguinal hernia*: It occurs due to persistent processus vaginalis that connect the peritoneal cavity with tunica vaginalis (abdomen to scrotum).
b. *Acquired indirect inguinal hernia*: It occurs due to increased intra-abdominal pressure as in weightlifting

Features of indirect inguinal hernia

1. Common in children and young adults.
2. Entry of hernial sac lies lateral to the inferior epigastric artery.
3. More common than direct inguinal hernia.
4. More common in males.

Coverings of indirect inguinal hernia

The coverings of indirect inguinal hernia within and outside are as follows:

1. Parietal peritoneum and extraperitoneal connective tissue
2. Internal spermatic fascia
3. Cremasteric fascia
4. External spermatic fascia
5. Skin

Direct inguinal hernia

If the abdominal contents enter the inguinal canal through its posterior wall, it is called direct inguinal hernia.

Features

1. More common in elderly due to weak abdominal wall.
2. Entry of hernial sac lies medial to the inferior epigastric artery through Hesselbach's triangle.
3. Direct inguinal hernia is more common in females.

Types of direct inguinal hernia

a. *Lateral direct inguinal hernia* that occurs through the lateral part of Hesselbach's triangle (lateral to medial umbilical ligament or obliterated umbilical artery).

   Coverings of lateral direct inguinal hernia

   1. Parietal peritoneum and extraperitoneal connective tissue
   2. Fascia transversalis
   3. Cremasteric fascia
   4. External spermatic fascia
   5. Skin

b. *Medial direct inguinal hernia* that occurs through the medial part of Hesselbach's triangle (medial to the medial umbilical ligament).

   Coverings of medial direct inguinal hernia

   1. Parietal peritoneum and extraperitoneal connective tissue
   2. Fascia transversalis
   3. Conjoint tendon
   4. External spermatic fascia
   5. Skin

Complications

1. ***Irreducibility:*** In the beginning, the loop of intestine herniates out but comes back to the abdomen. At times, the loop goes out but does not return, leading to irreducible hernia.
2. ***Obstruction:*** The loop may get narrowed in part, so that contents of the loop cannot move forwards, leading to obstruction.
3. ***Strangulation:*** When the arterial supply is blocked, the loop gets necrosed.

Treatment of Hernia

- Treatment of the hernia depends on the cause, signs, symptoms and the complications.
- ***Herniorrhaphy*** is the surgical repair of the hernia or weaken abdominal wall. Ilioinguinal and iliohypogastric nerves may get damaged in herniorrhaphy.

The differences between indirect and direct inguinal hernia are listed in Table 16.2.

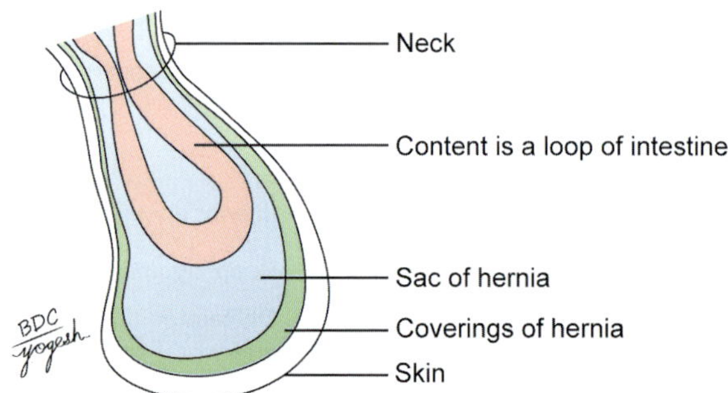

Fig. 16.33: Parts of a hernia

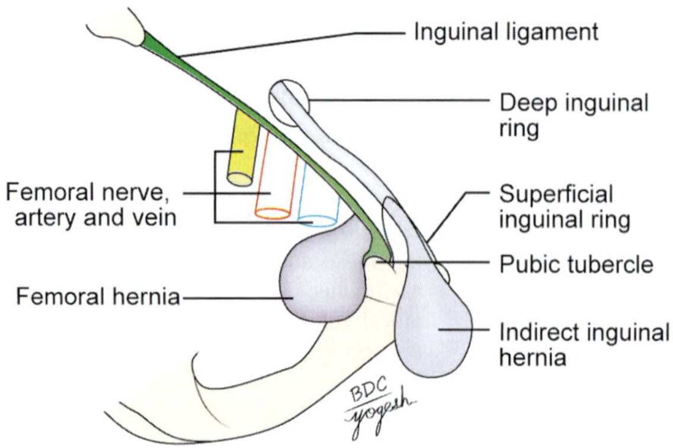

Fig. 16.34: Femoral and inguinal hernia

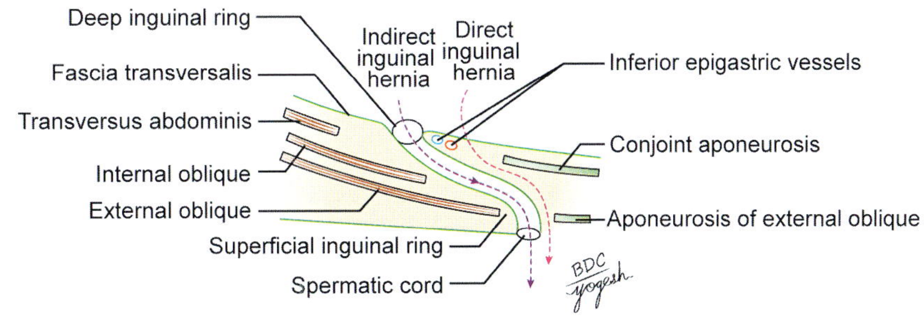

Fig. 16.35: Indirect and direct inguinal hernia

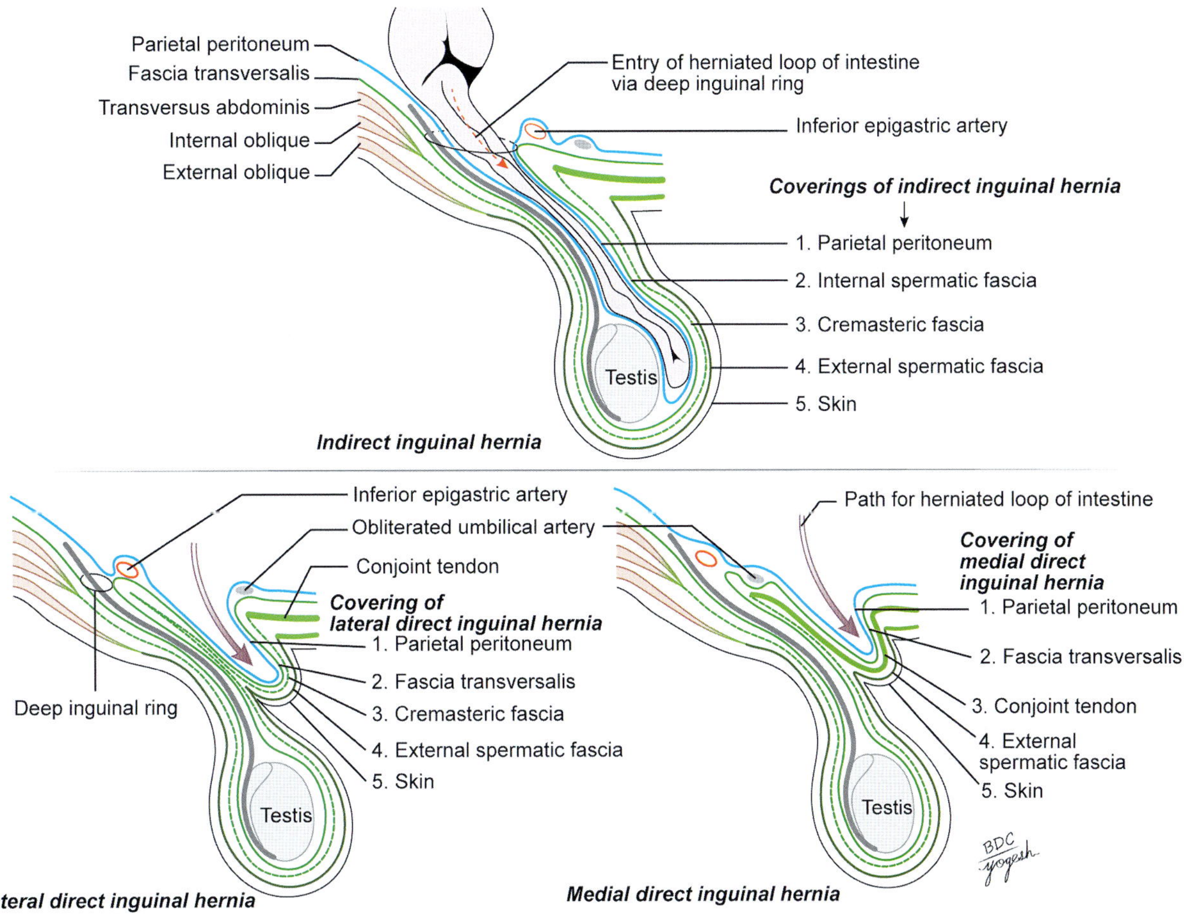

Fig. 16.36: Types of inguinal hernia

Flowchart 16.7: Inguinal hernia

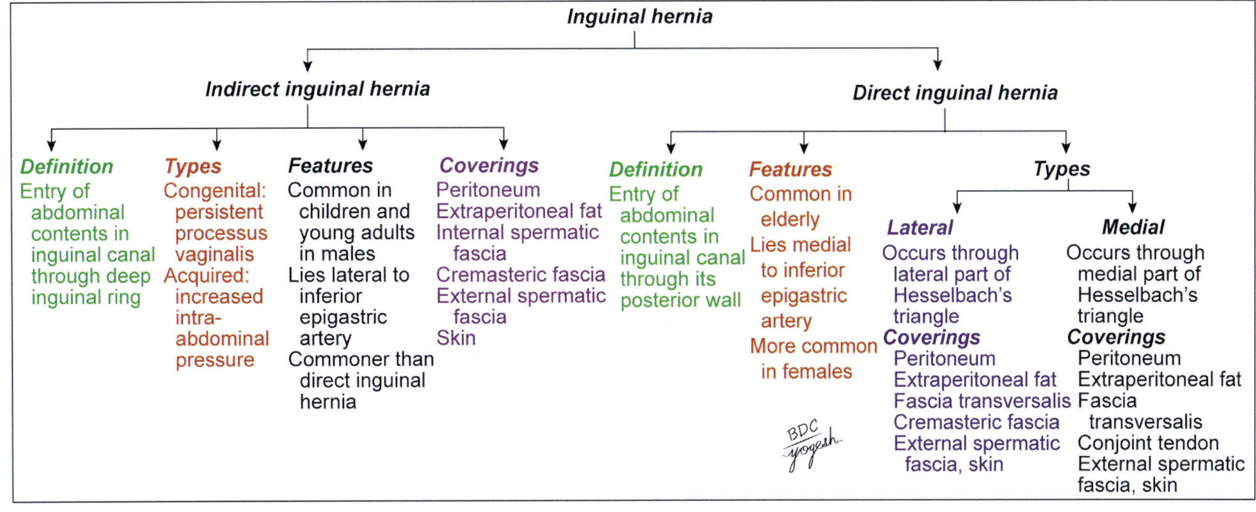

TABLE 16.2: Differences between indirect and direct inguinal hernia

Feature	*Indirect inguinal hernia*	*Direct inguinal hernia*
Site of entry of hernia	Through deep inguinal ring	Through posterior wall of inguinal canal
Aetiology	Preformed sac	Weakness of posterior wall of inguinal canal
Shape of hernial sac	Pear shaped	Globular
Extent	Extends usually up to scrotum	Remains confined to inguinal canal
Direction of sac	Oblique (downward, forward and medially)	Straightforward
On standing	Does not come out	Comes out
Neck of hernial sac	Narrow	Wide
Reducibility	Sometimes irreducible	Always reducible
Internal ring occlusion test	Positive	Negative
Obstruction	Common, as neck is narrow	Not common because neck is wide

Video 2.16 Anterior Abdominal Wall: Boundaries, muscles of the abdominal wall, inguinal canal.

Facts to Remember

- Transpyloric plane is an important landmark in the abdominal cavity.
- Umbilicus is normally a region of 'watershed' for the lymphatic and venous drainage. It is an important landmark. Umbilical region is supplied by. T10 spinal segment.
- At umbilicus, three systems meet: Digestive (vitello-intestinal duct), excretory (urachus) and vascular (umbilical vessels).
- External oblique is the largest and most superficial muscle of anterior abdominal wall.
- Rectus abdominis is the largest content of rectus sheath.
- Transversus abdominis interdigitates with the fibres of thoracoabdominal diaphragm.
- Inguinal ligament forms the boundary between abdomen and lower limb.
- Cremasteric reflex indicates that L1 segment of spinal cord is intact.
- Inguinal hernia lies above and medial to pubic tubercle. Femoral hernia lies below and lateral to pubic tubercle.
- Femoral hernia is never congenital. Femoral hernia is common in females because of the larger pelvis, bigger femoral canal and smaller femoral artery.
- Indirect inguinal hernia is more liable to obstruction as the neck of such a hernia is narrow.
- Paramedian incision in the anterior abdominal wall is mostly preferred.

BDC's Anatomy *e*-book

1. Cutaneous nerves of anterior abdominal wall
2. Structures at umbilicus during foetal life
3. Further reading
4. Viva voce questions

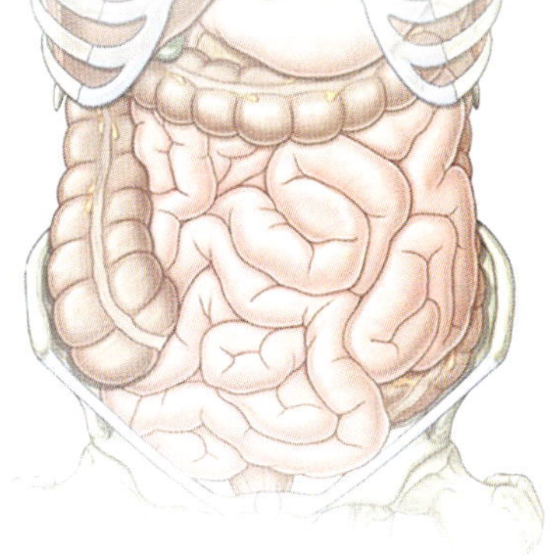

Chapter

17

Male External Genital Organs

The male genital organs are grouped as external and internal organs.

The external organs include penis and scrotum containing testis, epididymis and part of vas deferens.

The internal organs include (Fig. 17.1):

1. Part of vas deferens
2. Ejaculatory ducts
3. Prostate
4. Seminal vesicles
5. Bulbourethral glands.

DISSECTION

From the superficial inguinal ring, make a longitudinal incision downwards through the skin of the anterolateral aspects of the scrotum till its lower part. Reflect the skin alone, if possible, otherwise reflect skin, *dartos* and the other layers together till the testis enveloped in its *tunica vaginalis* is visualised.

Lift the testis and spermatic cord from the scrotum. Cut through the spermatic cord at the superficial inguinal ring, remove it together with the testis and put it in a tray of water.

Incise and reflect the coverings, if any, e.g. remains of external spermatic fascia, cremaster muscle, cremasteric fascia and internal spermatic fascia. Separate the various structures of spermatic cord. Feel ductus deferens as the important constituent of spermatic cord. Make a transverse section through the testis to visualise its interior.

Identify the *epididymis* capping the superior pole and lateral surface of the testis. The slit-like *sinus of epididymis* formed by tucking-in of the visceral layer of peritoneum between the testis and the epididymis is seen on the posterolateral aspect of the testis.

Cut through and reflect the skin along the *dorsum of the penis* from the symphysis pubis to the end of the *prepuce*.

Find the extension of the membranous layer of the superficial fascia of the abdominal wall onto the penis (*fundiform ligament*). The *superficial dorsal vein* of the penis lies in the superficial fascia. Trace it proximally to drain into any of the superficial external pudendal veins of thigh.

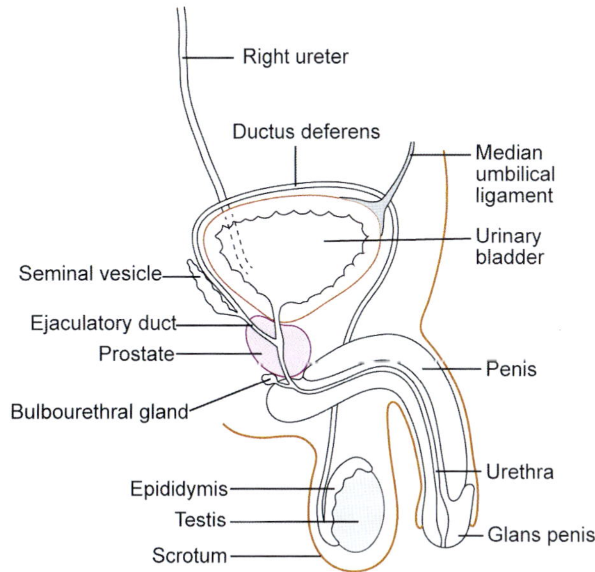

Fig. 17.1: Male genital organs

Deep to this vein is the deep fascia and *suspensory ligament* of the penis. Divide the deep fascia in the same line as the skin incision. Reflect it to see the *deep dorsal vein* with the *dorsal arteries* and *nerves* on each side.

Make a transverse section through the body of the penis, but leave the two parts connected by the skin of urethral surface or ventral surface. Identify two *corpora cavernosa* and single *corpus spongiosum* traversed by the urethra.

Competencies:

AN46.3 Describe penis under following headings: Parts, components, blood supply and lymphatic drainage.

AN52.2 Describe and identify the microanatomical features of penis (For detail, *see* page 424).

PENIS

The penis is the male organ of copulation. that is traversed by urethra. It gives a common passage to the semen and urine. It can erect due to the presence of erectile tissue (Plate 17.1, Flowchart 17.1).

Plate 17.1: Penis: Parts, muscles covering the parts of the root of penis and glans penis

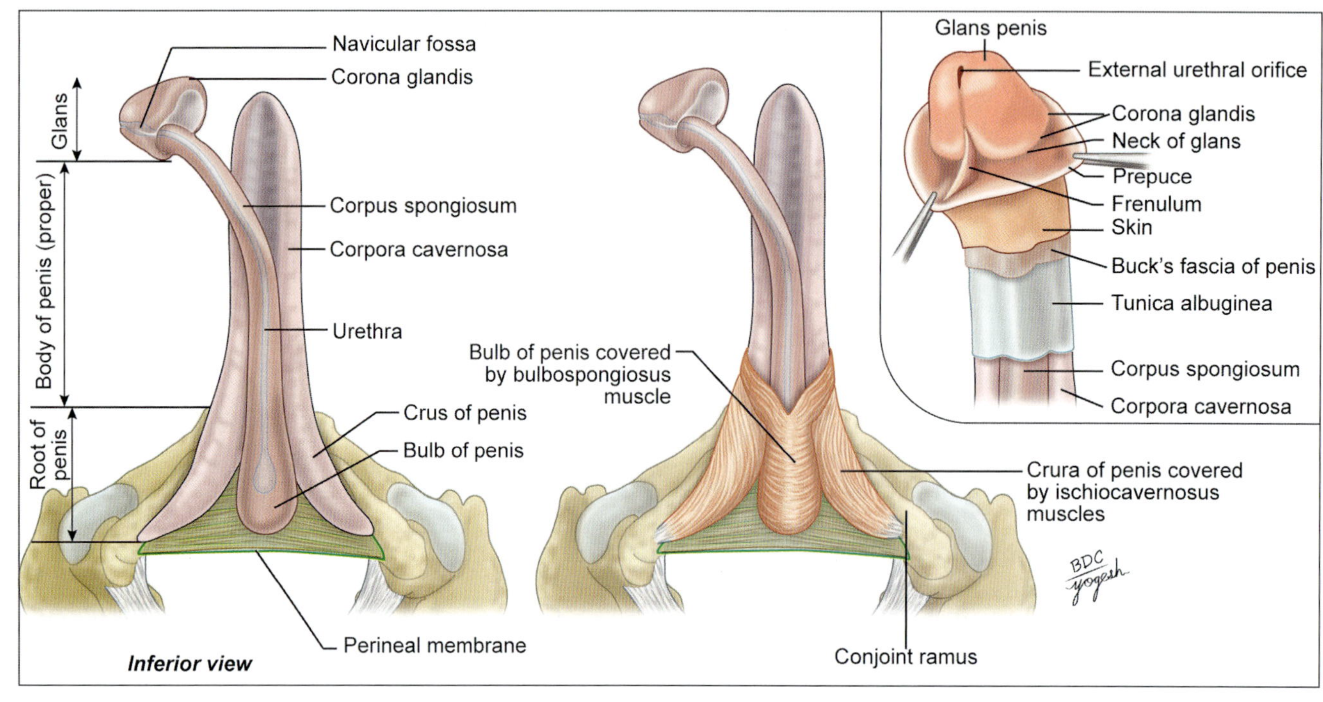

Flowchart 17.1: Penis

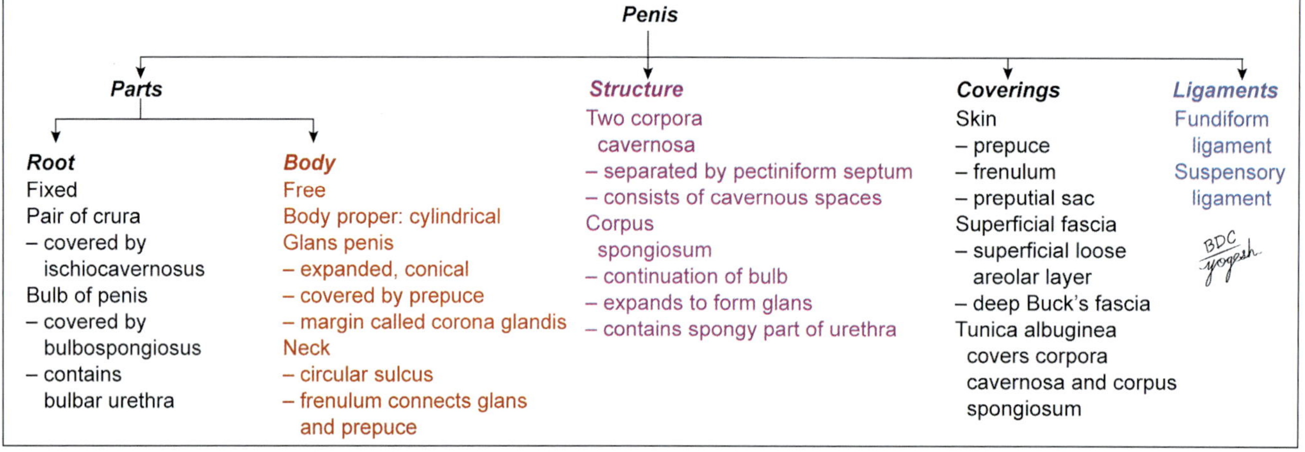

Parts of Penis

Penis has two parts (Plate 17.1, Figs 17.2 to 17.5):

1. Root — fixed part
2. Body of corpus — a free portion.

Root of Penis

The root of the penis is fixed and situated in the *superficial perineal pouch*. It is composed of three masses of erectile tissue, namely the two crura and one bulb (Fig. 17.4).

1. Each ***crus of penis*** (Latin *leg*) is firmly attached to the margins of the pubic arch and is covered by the ischiocavernosus.
2. The ***bulb of penis*** is attached to the perineal membrane in between the two crura. It is covered by the ***bulbospongiosus***. Its deep surface is pierced (above its centre) by the ***urethra***, which traverses its substance to reach the ***corpus spongiosum*** (located in the body). This part of the urethra within the bulb shows a dilatation in its floor, called the ***intrabulbar navicular fossa*** (Fig. 17.3).

Body or Corpus of Penis

The free portion of the penis is completely enveloped by skin. It is continuous with the root (Plate 17.1 and Figs 17.3 to 17.5).

The body of penis can be divided into three parts: Body proper, neck and glans penis.

Body proper: In flaccid state, it is cylindrical or pendulous and directed downwards and forwards. In erect state, it is directed upward and forward and has two surfaces: a. Ventral surface that faces backwards and downwards; and b. Dorsal surface that faces forwards and upwards.

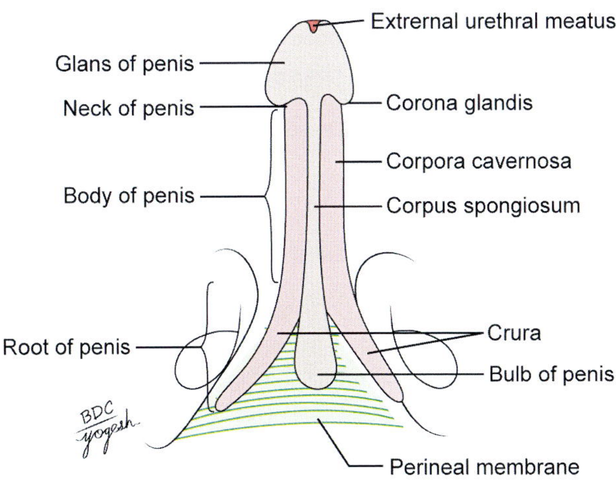

Fig. 17.2: Parts of penis (ventral aspect)

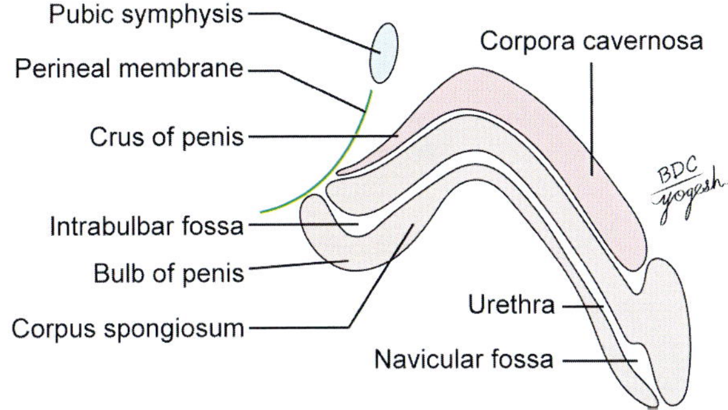

Fig. 17.3: Sagittal section showing parts of penis

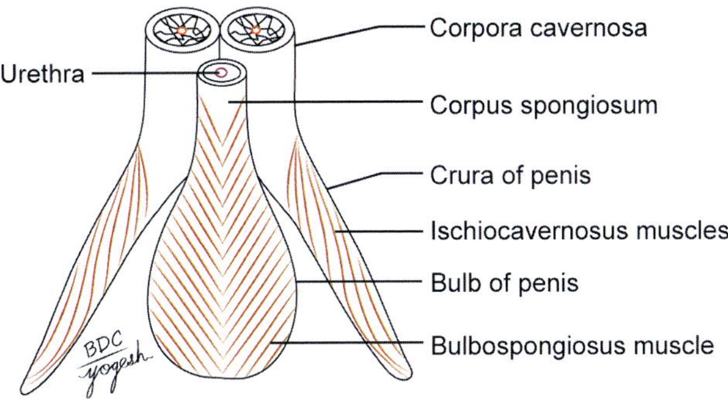

Fig. 17.4: Root of penis and muscles covering it

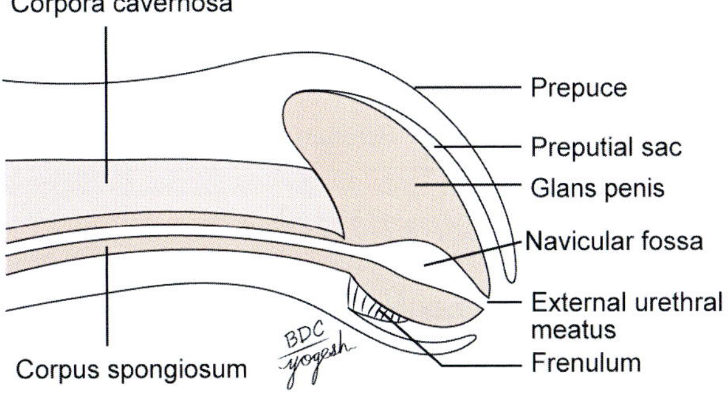

Fig. 17.5: Glans penis and prepuce

Glans penis (Latin *acorn*): The distal end of the penis has an expanded and conical mass called glans penis. It is covered with a fold of skin called ***prepuce*** of foreskin (Latin *before penis*). The **external urethral meatus** is the sagittal slit-like opening close to the tip of glans penis. The ***corona glandis*** (Latin *crown*) is the raised margin of the base of glans.

Neck of penis: It is a circular sulcus just behind the corona glandis or base of the glans.

Structure of Penis

The penis is composed of three elongated masses of erectile tissue – the right and left corpora cavernosa and a median corpus spongiosum (Fig. 17.6).

1. The two ***corpora cavernosa*** (Latin *hollow*) are the forward continuations of the crura. The corpora cavernosa terminate under cover of the *glans penis* in a blunt conical extremity. They are surrounded by a strong fibrous envelope called the ***tunica albuginea***. The tunica albuginea has superficial longitudinal fibres enclosing both the corpora and deep circular fibres that enclose each corpus separately and also form a ***median or pectiniform septum***.
2. The ***corpus spongiosum*** is the forward continuation of the bulb of the penis. Its terminal part is expanded to form a conical enlargement, called the ***glans penis***. Throughout its whole length, it is traversed by the urethra. Like the corpora, it is also surrounded by a fibrous sheath (Fig. 17.6).

Covering of the Penis

The body of the penis is covered by skin, superficial fascia and the fibrous envelope (Fig. 17.6)

1. ***Skin***: The *skin* covering the penis is very thin. It is loosely connected with the fascial sheath of the organ. At the neck, it is folded to form the ***prepuce* or *foreskin***. On the undersurface of the glans, there is a median fold of skin called the ***frenulum*** (Latin *bridle*). The potential space between the glans and the prepuce is known as the ***preputial sac***. On the corona glandis and on the neck of the penis, there are numerous small preputial or sebaceous glands which secrete a sebaceous material called the ***smegma***.
2. ***Superficial fascia of the penis***: It consists of very loosely arranged areolar tissue, completely devoid of fat. It contains the superficial dorsal vein of the penis (Fig. 17.6).
3. ***Deep fascia of penis***: The deep layer of superficial fascia is membranous and is called the *deep fascia of penis* or ***Buck's fascia***. It surrounds all three masses of erectile tissue, but does not extend into the glans. Deep to it, there are the deep dorsal vein, the dorsal arteries and dorsal nerves of the penis. Proximally, it is continuous with the dartos and with the fascia of the urogenital triangle.

Ligaments of Penis

The supports of the body of penis are the following (Fig. 17.7):

1. ***Fundiform ligament*** which extends downwards from the linea alba and splits to enclose the penis. It lies superficial to the suspensory ligament.

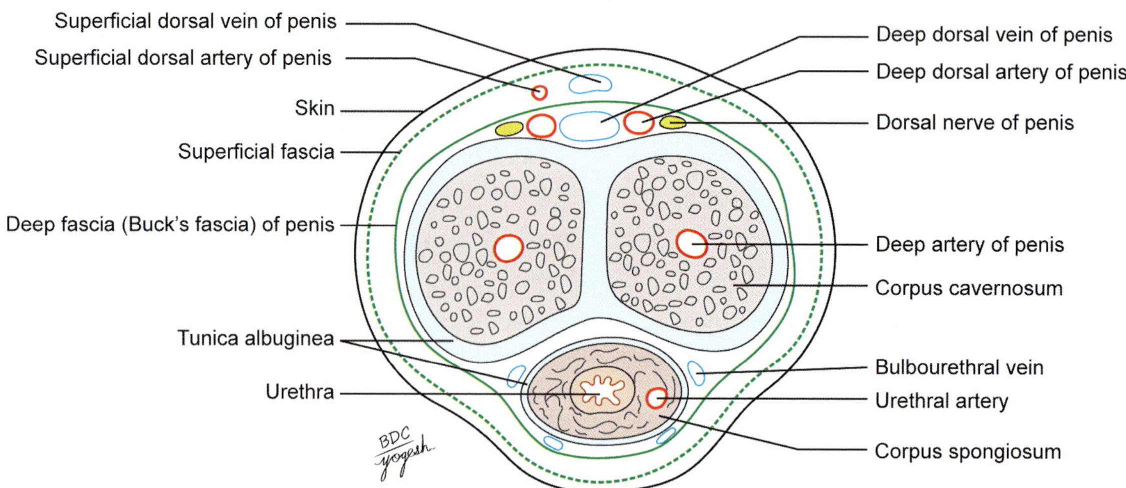

Fig. 17.6: Transverse section of penis through the body of the penis

2. ***Suspensory ligament*** lies deep to the fundiform ligament. It extends from the pubic symphysis and blends below with the fascia on each side of the penis.

Arteries of the Penis (Fig. 17.8)

1. Deep arteries of the penis
2. Dorsal arteries of the penis
3. Arteries of the bulb
4. Superficial dorsal arteries of the penis.

Note: The internal pudendal artery gives off three branches which supply the penis: Deep arteries of the penis, dorsal arteries of penis and arteries of the bulb. The superficial external pudendal artery is a branch of the femoral artery.

The *deep artery of the penis* runs in the corpus cavernosum. It breaks up into arteries that follow a spiral course and are, therefore, called ***helicine arteries***.

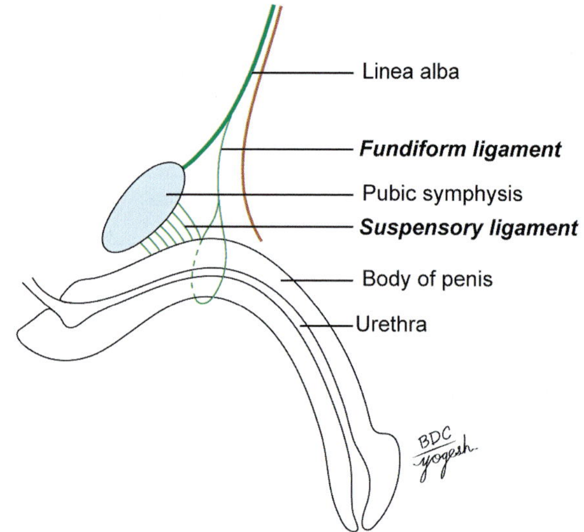

Fig. 17.7: Ligaments of the penis

Veins of the Penis

The penis is drained by two unpaired veins (Fig. 17.8):

1. Superficial dorsal vein of the penis
2. Deep dorsal vein of the penis.

Note: ***Superficial dorsal vein*** drains the prepuce and penile skin. It runs back in subcutaneous tissue and inclines to right or left before it opens into one of the external pudendal veins.

Deep dorsal vein lies deep to Buck's fascia. It receives blood from the glans penis and corpora cavernosa penis and courses back in midline between paired dorsal arteries. It passes deep to the suspensory ligament and through a gap between the arcuate pubic ligament and anterior margin of perineal membrane, it divides into right and left branches and ultimately enters the prostatic plexus.

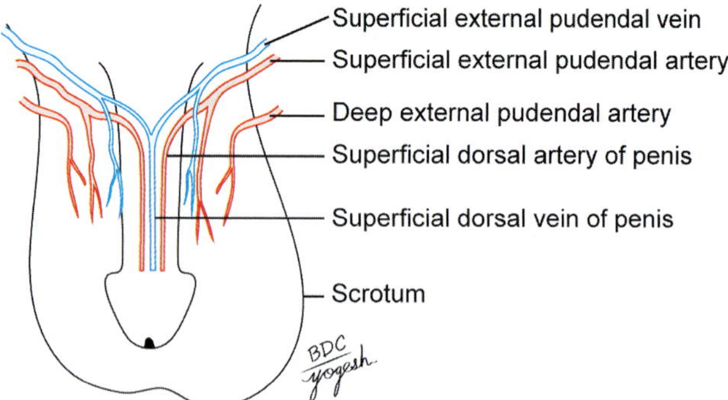

Fig. 17.8: Blood supply of penis: Superficial vessels

Nerve Supply of the Penis

1. ***Sensory innervation***: The sensory nerve supply to the penis is derived from:
   - Dorsal nerve of the penis
   - Ilioinguinal nerve.
2. ***Motor innervation***: The muscles of the root of the penis are supplied by the *perineal branch of the pudendal nerve.*
3. ***Autonomic innervation***: The autonomic nerves are derived from the pelvic plexus via the *prostatic plexus.* The autonomic fibres are distributed through the branches of the *pudendal nerve.*
   - The *sympathetic nerves* are *vasoconstrictor*.
   - The *parasympathetic* nerves (S2–4) are *vasodilator*.

Lymphatic Drainage

Lymphatics from the glans drain into the deep inguinal nodes also called gland of Cloquet. Lymphatics from the rest of the penis drain into the superficial inguinal lymph nodes.

Mechanism of Erection and Ejaculation

Erection

It is a purely vascular phenomenon. Erection is controlled by parasympathetic nerves (nervi erigentes, S2–S4). The sexual arousal leads to the following sequence:

Sexual arousal → dilation of helicine arteries → increased blood supply to cavernous spaces of corpora cavernosa and corpus spongiosum → filling of cavernous spaces → enlargement of veins → block in venous outflow → erection of penis.

Ejaculation

It consists of two processes:

1. Emission is the transmission of seminal fluid from vas deferens, seminal vesicles and prostate into the prostatic urethra.
2. Ejaculation proper is the ejection of seminal fluid from prostatic urethra to the exterior.

The ejaculation involves sympathetic and somatic innervations which are as follows:

1. *Sympathetic nerves* (T11–L2) cause emission of semen by contraction of smooth muscles of vas deferens, seminal vesicles and prostate. These nerves enhance the tone of internal urethral sphincter and prevent retrograde flow of semen into the bladder.
2. *Somatic innervations* by perineal branch of pudendal nerve cause contraction of bulbospongiosus that compress the penile urethra and cause ejaculation properly.

Competency:
AN46.5 Explain the anatomical basis of phimosis and circumcision.

CLINICAL ANATOMY

- ***Smegma***: The preputial glands are modified sweat glands. They secrete sebaceous material at corona glandis called smegma that has characteristic odour. This smegma has medicolegal significance in the cases of rape.
- ***Phimosis*** is narrowing of distal end of prepuce that prevents its retraction over the glans penis. It may interfere with micturition.
- ***Paraphimosis*** is the narrowing of distal end of prepuce that stuck the retracted prepuce on glans during erection of the penis. Paraphimosis does not interfere with micturition.
- ***Circumcision*** is the surgical separation of foreskin or prepuce from the glans penis.
- ***Peyronie's disease*** or ***chordee*** occurs due to presence of strands of dense fibrous tissue in corpora cavernosa. It results in curvature of the penis on erection with concavity on the ventral surface. It may result in painful erection.
- ***Priapism*** is the persistent erection due to spasm of venous smooth muscles.
- ***Impotence*** is the failure of erection. It may be psychological, or due to damage to nervi erigentes, secondary to diabetes or may be due to decreased blood supply because of atherosclerosis.

SCROTUM

The scrotum (Latin *bag*) is a cutaneous bag located in the lower part of anterior abdominal wall, below and behind the penis (*scrotum* = bag in Latin) (Fig. 17.9):

Contents of Scrotum

1. Two testes
2. Two epididymis
3. Lower part of spermatic cords.

Features

1. Externally, the scrotum is divided into right and left parts by a ridge or ***raphe*** which is continued forwards onto the undersurface of the penis and backwards along the middle of the perineum to the anus (Fig. 17.3).
2. The left half of the scrotum hangs a little lower than the right, in correspondence with the greater length of the left spermatic cord.
3. Due to the presence of dartos muscle that lies subcutaneously, the skin of scrotum is corrugated or rough, especially on exposure to the cold.

Note: The dartos muscle helps in the regulation of temperature of the scrotum. Under the influence of cold and in young and robust persons, the scrotum is short, corrugated and closely applied to the testis. This is due to contraction of the *dartos.* However, under the influence of warmth and in old and debilitated persons, the scrotum is elongated and flaccid due to relaxation of dartos.

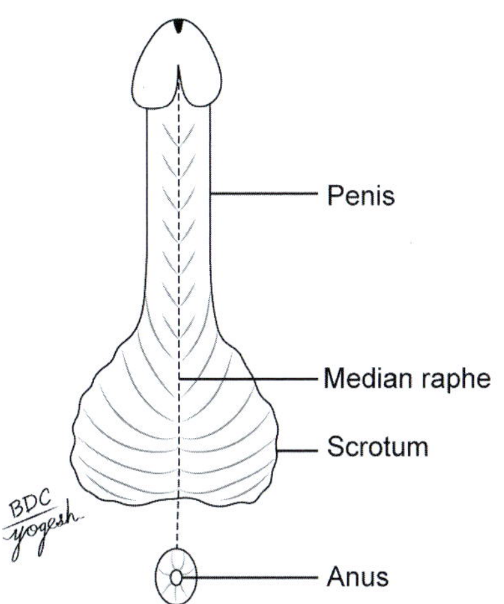

Fig. 17.9: Scrotum and penis viewed from below to show the median raphe

Layers of the Scrotum

The scrotum is made up of the following layers from outside inwards (Fig. 17.10, Table 17.1):

1. Skin
2. Dartos muscle (which replaces the superficial fascia) (Greek *skinny*)
3. External spermatic fascia (from external oblique muscle)
4. Cremasteric (Greek *to hang*) muscle and fascia (from internal oblique muscle)
5. Internal spermatic fascia (from fascia transversalis).

TABLE 17.1: Layers of scrotum and corresponding layers of the anterior abdominal wall

Layer of scrotum	*Layer of anterior abdominal wall*
Skin	Skin
Dartos muscle	Superficial fascia (fascia of Camper and fascia of Scarpa)
External spermatic fascia	External oblique muscle
Cremasteric muscle and fascia	Internal oblique muscle
Internal spermatic fascia	Fascia transversalis

Note: There is no derivative or continuity of transverse abdominis muscle in the scrotum.

Blood Supply

The scrotum is supplied by (*see* Fig. 17.8):

1. Superficial external pudendal artery
2. Deep external pudendal artery
3. Scrotal branches of internal pudendal artery
4. Cremasteric branch of inferior epigastric artery.

The venous blood from scrotum partly goes to the great saphenous vein and partly to the internal iliac vein.

Nerve Supply (Fig. 17.11)

1. ***Anterior 1/3rd of the scrotum:*** It is supplied by segment L1 of the spinal cord through:
   - Ilioinguinal nerve
   - Genital branch of the genitofemoral nerve.
2. ***Posterior 2/3rd of the scrotum:*** It is supplied by *segment S3* of the spinal cord through:
   - Posterior scrotal branches of the pudendal nerve
   - Perineal branch of the posterior cutaneous nerve of the thigh.
   - The areas supplied by segments L1 and S3 are separated by the *ventral axial line*.
3. The dartos muscle is supplied by the *genital branch of the genitofemoral nerve.*

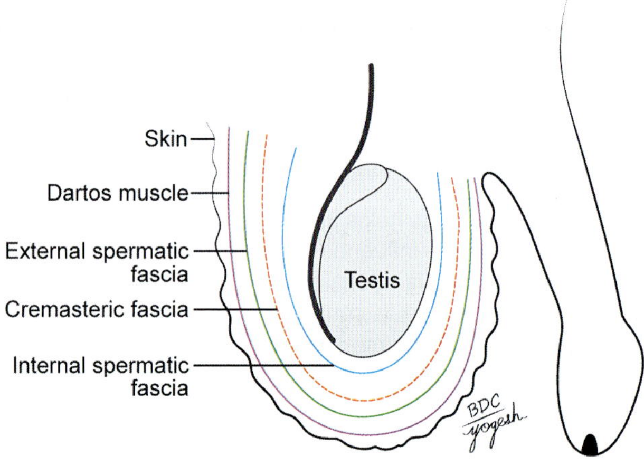

Fig. 17.10: Layers of the scrotum

Development of Scrotum

During the development male external genitalia, on fusion of the urethral folds, both the ***genital swellings*** enlarge to form *scrotal swellings* (labial swellings in female). These scrotal swellings enlarge and fuse in the midline to form scrotum. The line of fusion of scrotal swellings forms midline fibrous raphe on the scrotum.

CLINICAL ANATOMY

- ***Scrotal oedema***: Due to laxity of skin and its dependent position, the scrotum is a *common site for oedema*.
- ***Sebaceous cyst***: Abundance of hair and of sebaceous glands also makes it a *site of sebaceous cysts* (Fig. 17.12).
- The scrotum is *bifid* in male—*pseudohermaphroditism.*
- ***Scrotal elephantiasis***: Infection of filarial parasite (*Wuchereria bancrofti*) causes blockage of lymphatic vessels. It may affect scrotum and produce scrotal enlargement called scrotal elephantiasis.

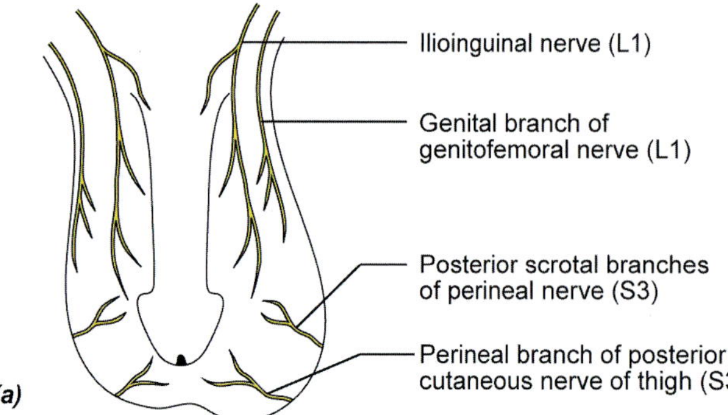

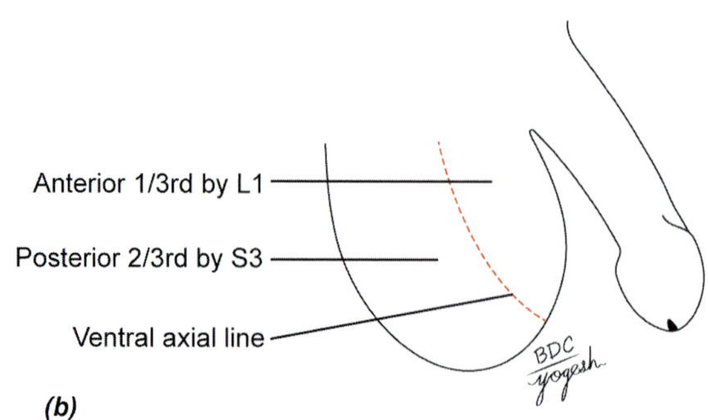

Figs 17.11a and b: Innervation of the scrotum: (a) Cutaneous nerves of the scrotum and (b) segmental innervation of the scrotum

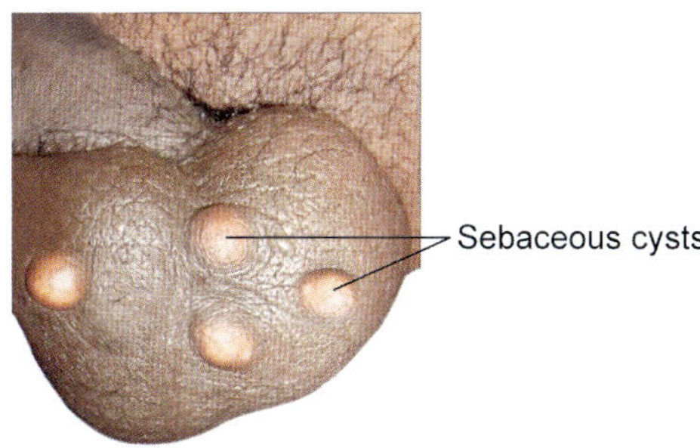

Fig. 17.12: Sebaceous cysts on the scrotum

Competencies:

AN46.1 Describe and demonstrate coverings, internal structure, side determination, blood supply, nerve supply, lymphatic drainage and descent of testis with its applied anatomy.

AN46.4 Explain the anatomical basis of varicocele.

AN52.2 Describe and identify the microanatomical features of testis/seminiferous tubule.

AN52.8 Describe the development of male and female reproductive system.

TESTIS

The testis is the male gonad. It is homologous with the ovary of the female (Plate 17.2, Figs 17.13 and 17.14, Flowchart 17.2).

Shape and Size

It is oval or ellipsoid in shape. It is compressed from side-to-side.

It measures as follows:

Length: 4 cm (4–5 cm)

Breadth: 2.5 cm (2–3 cm)

Anteroposterior diameter: 3 cm (3–4 cm)

Weight: 12–20 gm [*Reference*: *Gray's Anatomy*, 42nd edn.]

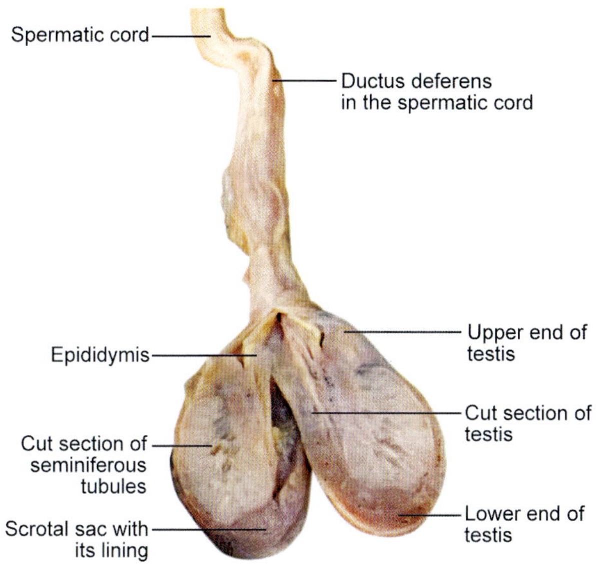

Fig. 17.13: Section of testis with spermatic cord—sagittal

Position in Scrotum

The testis is suspended in the scrotum by the spermatic cord. The testis lies obliquely so that its upper pole is tilted forward and laterally and lower pole backward and medially.

The left testis is slightly lower than the right due to longer left spermatic cord and early descent of left testis in embryonic life.

Anatomical Position of Testis

Hold the testis with the spermatic cord in such a way that:

1. Upper pole of testis gives attachment to the spermatic cord
2. Anterior border is smooth, convex and free
3. Posterior border provides attachment to the epididymis.

The lateral surface of testis is separated from epididymis by a cavity called *sinus of the epididymis*, and it looks in the direction to which the testis belongs.

External Features

The testis has (Plate 17.2, Figs 17.13 and 17.14, Flowchart 17.2):

1. *Two poles or ends*: Upper and lower.
2. *Two borders*: Anterior and posterior (Fig. 17.14).
3. *Two surfaces*: Medial and lateral (Fig. 17.14).

The *upper* and *lower* poles are convex and smooth. The upper pole provides attachment to the spermatic cord.

The *anterior border* is convex and smooth and is fully covered by the tunica vaginalis. The *posterior border* is straight and is only partially covered by the tunica vaginalis. The *epididymis* lies along the posterolateral aspect of testis. Lateral surface of testis is separated from epididymis by a semilunar extension of vaginal sac, called the ***sinus of epididymis*** (Plate 17.2, Figs 17.13 and 17.14).

The *medial* and *lateral surfaces* are convex and smooth.

Note: Attached to the upper pole of the testis, there is a small oval body called the ***appendix of the testis.*** It is a remnant of the *paramesonephric duct* (Fig. 17.14).

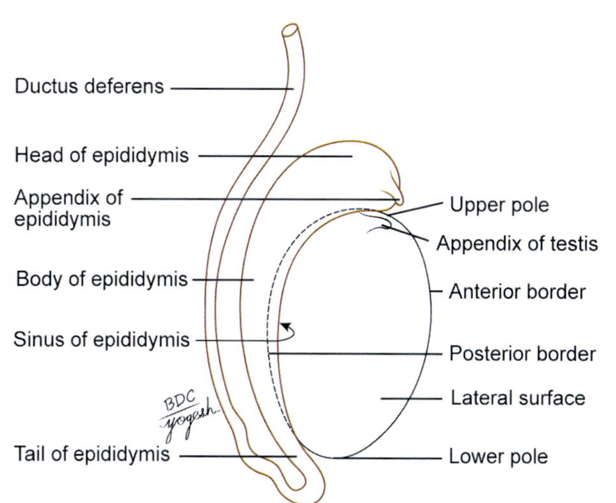

Fig. 17.14: Lateral view of the right testis and surrounding structures with the embryonic remnants present in the region

Plate 17.2: Right testis and epididymis

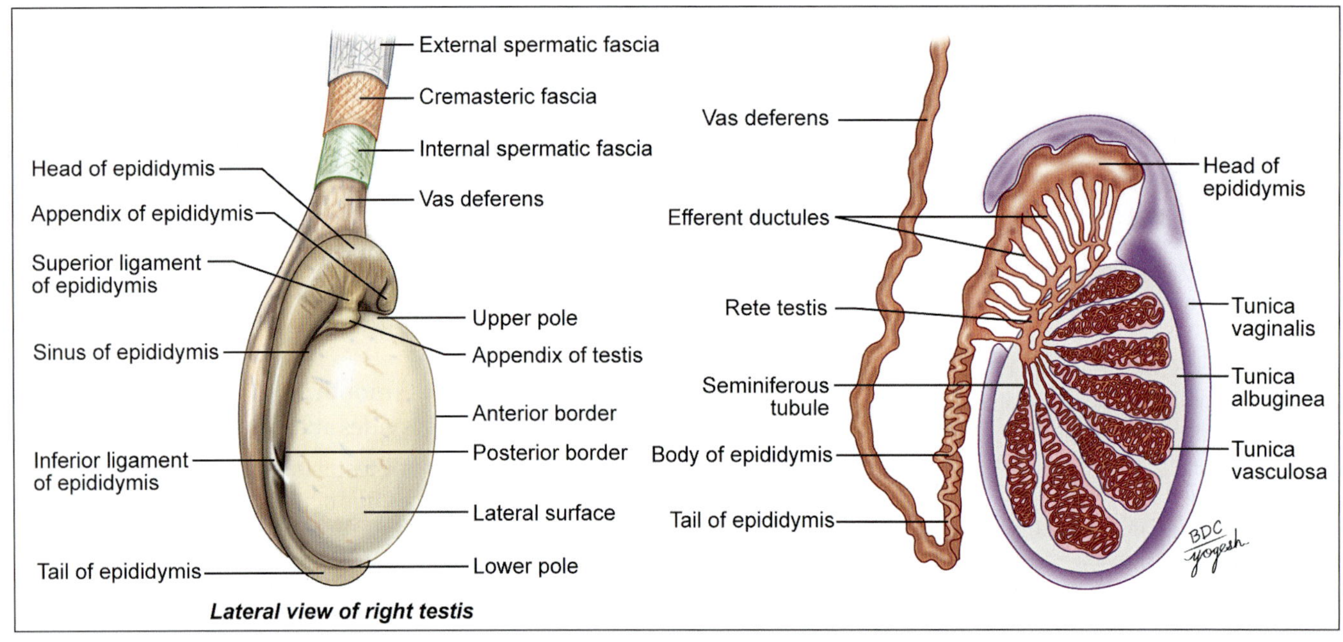

Flowchart 17.2: Testis

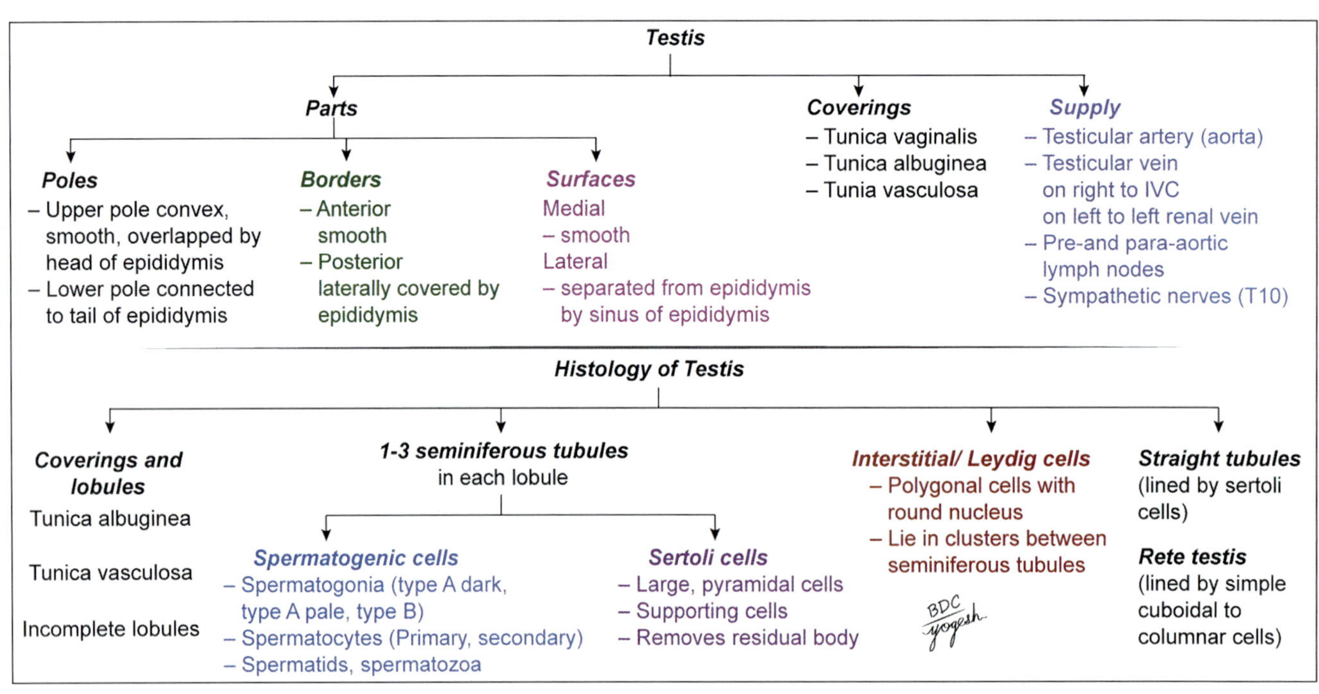

(IVC: Inferior vena cava)

Coverings of the Testis

The testis is covered by layers of the scrotum. In addition, it is also covered by three coats (from outside inwards) (Fig. 17.15):

1. Tunica vaginalis
2. Tunica albuginea
3. Tunica vasculosa.

The ***tunica vaginalis*** (Latin *sheath*) represents the lower persistent portion of the processus vaginalis. It is invaginated by the testis from behind and, therefore, has a parietal layer and a visceral layer. A ***vaginal sac*** is a cavity between two layers of tunica vaginalis. It covers the whole testis, except for its posterior border.

The ***tunica albuginea*** (Latin *white*) is a dense, white fibrous coat covering the testis all around. It is covered by the visceral layer of the tunica vaginalis, except posteriorly where the testicular vessels and nerves enter the gland. The posterior border of the tunica albuginea is thickened to form an incomplete vertical septum, called the ***mediastinum testis***, which is wider above than below. Numerous septa extend from the mediastinum to the inner surface of the tunica albuginea. They incompletely divide the testis into 200 to 300 lobules.

The ***tunica vasculosa*** is the innermost, vascular coat of the testis lining its lobules.

Structure and Histology of the Testis

The testis is covered by fibrous tunica albuginea and vascular tunica vasculosa. The septae divide the testis into approximately 250 incomplete lobules (Plate 17.3, Figs 17.15 and 17.16).

Each lobule contains 1–3 highly coiled ***seminiferous tubules*** (60 cm long and 0.2 mm diameter) that are surrounded by lamina propria, blood vessels, lymphatics and Leydig cells. The seminiferous tubules are lined by seminiferous epithelium with two types of cells: Spermatogenic cells (spermatogonia, spermatids and sperms) and Sertoli cells. The ***Sertoli cells*** are tall columnar cells that support development of spermatogenic cells. The ***Leydig (interstitial) cells*** are polyhedral eosinophilic cells that lie in clusters and produce testosterone. These cells are epithelioid cells.

The seminiferous tubules join together at the apices of the lobules to form 20 to 30 ***straight tubules*** (lined by Sertoli cells), which enter the mediastinum. Here, they anastomose with each other to form a network of tubules, called the ***rete testis*** (lined by simple cuboidal to columnar epithelium).

In its turn, the rete testis gives rise to 12 to 30 ***efferent ductules,*** which emerge near the upper pole of the testis and enter the epididymis. Here, each tubule becomes highly coiled and forms a lobe of the head of the epididymis. The tubules end in a single duct which is coiled on itself to form the body and tail of the epididymis. It is continuous with the ductus deferens.

Arterial Supply

The testis supplied by the following arteries (Fig. 17.17):

1. *Testicular artery* is a branch of abdominal aorta and it supplies most of the testis.
2. *Artery to vas deferens* is a branch of superior or inferior vesical artery.
3. *Cremasteric artery* is a branch of the inferior epigastric artery.

Note: The ***testicular artery*** is a branch of the abdominal aorta given off at the level of vertebra L2. It descends on the posterior abdominal wall to reach the deep inguinal ring, where it enters the spermatic cord. At the posterior border of the testis, it divides into branches.

Venous Drainage

The veins emerging from the testis form the ***pampiniform plexus*** (pampiniform = like a vine). The plexus condenses into four veins at the superficial inguinal ring and into two veins at the deep inguinal ring. Ultimately, one testicular vein is formed, which drains into the inferior vena cava on the right side and into the *left renal vein* on the *left side* (Fig. 17.17).

Note: The right testicular vein drains into inferior vena cava, whereas left testicular vein into the left renal vein. *Explanation*: The portion of the inferior vena cava, which receives the right testicular, vein is developed from the anastomosis between right supracardinal and right subcardinal veins. The anastomosis of corresponding veins on the left side forms a part of left renal vein that drains the left testicular vein. This explains the embryological basis for the dissimilar termination of the two testicular veins.

Countercurrent heat exchange: The testicular artery is surrounded by pampiniform plexus that absorbs the heat from the artery. Thus, it helps to maintain the temperature of scrotum and testis 3° to 4°C lower than the abdomen. This mechanism of heat transfer is called *countercurrent heat exchange*. Lower temperature is essential for spermatogenesis and not for testosterone production.

Lymphatic Drainage

The lymphatics from the testis ascend along the testicular vessels and drain into the *preaortic* and *paraaortic* groups of lymph nodes at the level of L2 vertebra.

Nerve Supply

The testis is supplied by sympathetic nerves arising from segment T10 of the spinal cord. They pass through the renal and aortic plexuses. The nerves are both afferent for testicular sensation and efferent to the blood vessels (vasomotor).

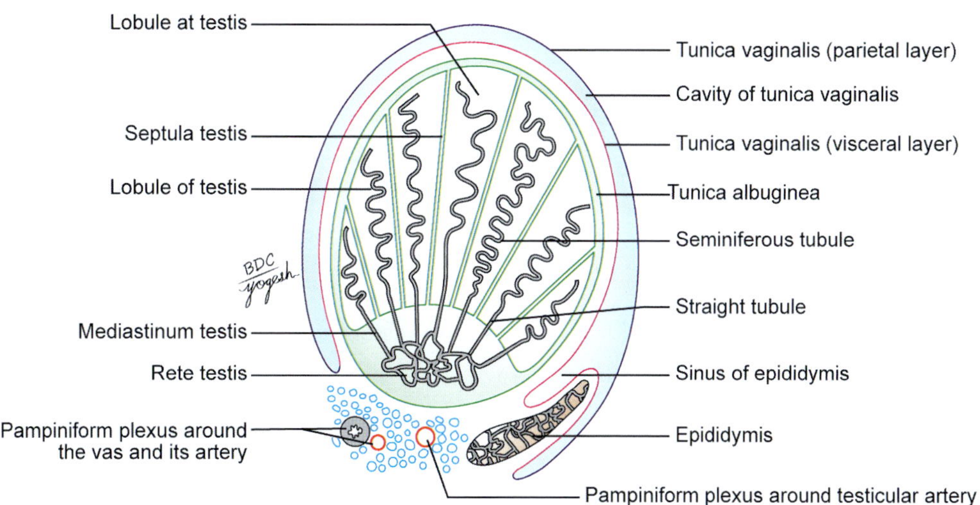

Fig. 17.15: Transverse section of the testis and epididymis

Plate 17.3: Histology of testis (low magnification) and seminiferous tubule (high magnification on left side)

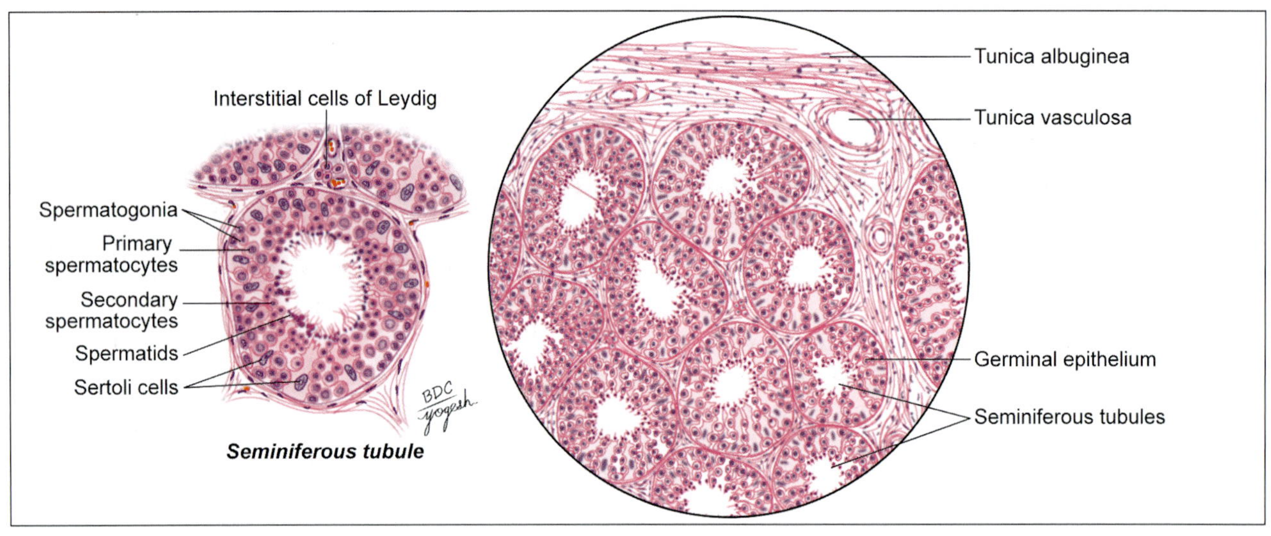

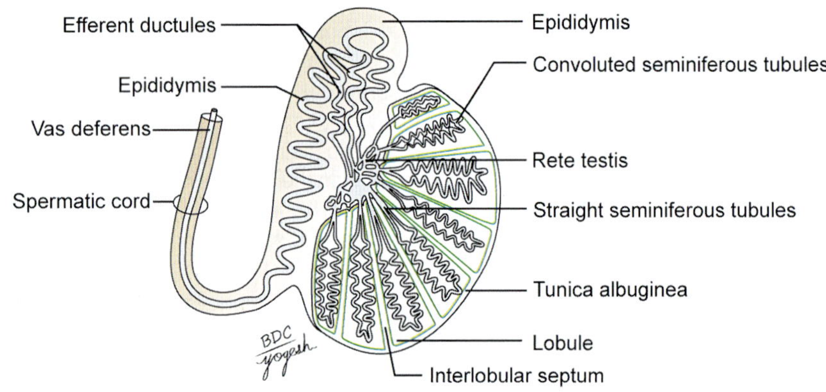

Fig. 17.16: Longitudinal section of testis and epididymis

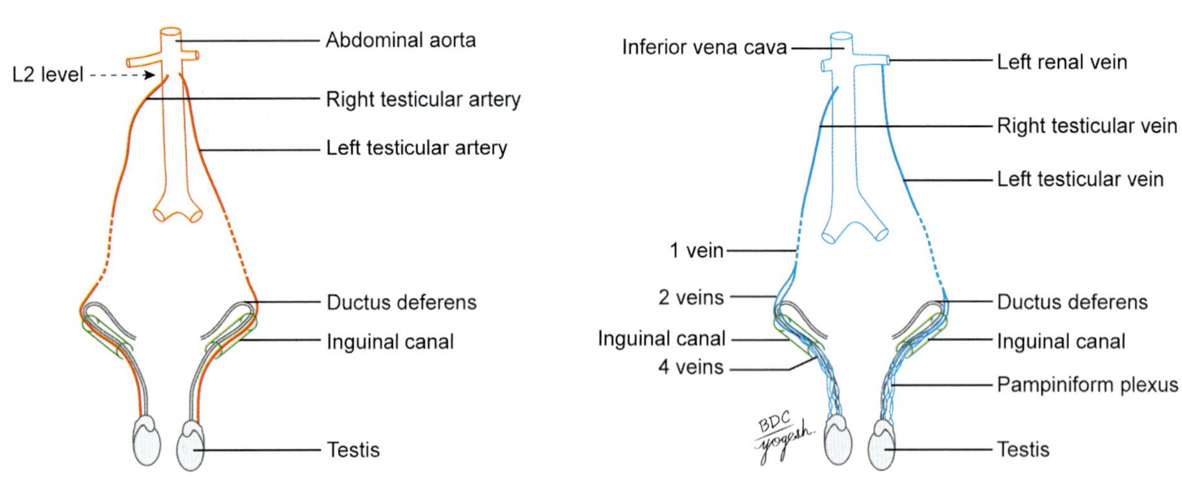

Fig. 17.17: Testicular vessels

Development of Testis

The development of the various components of the testis are as follows:

1. Seminiferous tubules and rete testis develop from medulla of genital ridge or sex cords.
2. Interstitial cells of Leydig, fibrous septa and coverings of testis are derived from mesenchymal condensation of genital ridge.
3. Efferent ductules develop from 12–15 mesonephric tubules.

4. Canal of epididymis and vas deferens are derived from mesonephric duct.

Descent of Testis

Testis develops in dorsal abdominal wall at the level of upper lumbar vertebrae (Figs 17.18a to e). During development, the testis descends slowly from lumbar region to the scrotum. After birth, testis lies outside the body (within the scrotal sac).

Note: Embryological remnants present in relation to the testis (Fig. 17.19)

1. *Appendix of the testis* or pedunculated hydatid of Morgagni.
2. *Appendix of the epididymis* is a small rounded pedunculated body attached to the head of the epididymis. It represents the cranial end of the mesonephric duct.
3. *Superior aberrant ductules* are attached to the testis cranial to the efferent ductules. They represent the upper mesonephric tubules.
4. *Inferior aberrant ductules*, one or two, are attached to the tail of the epididymis and represent the intermediate mesonephric tubules. One of them, which is more constant, may be as long as 25 cm.
5. *Paradidymis* or organ of Giraldes consists of free tubules lying in the spermatic cord above the head of the epididymis. They are neither connected to the testis nor to the epididymis and represent the caudal mesonephric tubules.

CLINICAL ANATOMY

- Unilateral absence of testis—***monorchism*** or bilateral absence of testis—***anorchism***.
- ***Undescended testis** or **cryptorchidism***: The organ may lie in the lumbar, iliac, inguinal, or upper scrotal region (Fig. 17.20). The important features of an undescended testis are as follows:
  a. The testis may complete its descent after birth.
  b. Spermatogenesis may fail to occur in it.
  c. A malignant tumour is more prone to develop in it.
  d. The condition can be surgically corrected.
- ***Ectopic testis***: The testis may occupy an abnormal position due to deviation from the normal route of descent. It may be under the skin of the lower part of the abdomen, under the skin of the front of the thigh, in the femoral canal, under the skin of the penis and in the perineum behind the scrotum (Fig. 17.20).
- ***Hermaphroditism*** or ***intersex*** is a condition in which an individual shows some features of a male and some of a female. In true hermaphroditism, both testis and ovary are present. In pseudohermaphroditism, the gonad is of one sex, while the external or internal genitalia are of the opposite sex.
- ***Varicocele*** is produced by dilatation of the pampiniform plexus of veins (Fig. 17.21). The varicocele of testis is ***common on the left***; possibly because the left testicular vein is:
  1. Longer than the right
  2. Enters the left renal vein at a right angle
  3. Crossed by the colon, which may compress it when loaded.

  On palpation, the veins of pampiniform plexus feel like '***bag of worms***'.
- ***Tumours of testis***: The testis may have:
  1. Seminoma – tumour cells of seminiferous tubules, and
  2. Teratoma – malignant tumour arising from totipotent cells.

  Most of the testicular cancers spread upward via the lymphatic vessels to the abdomen.
- ***Torsion of testis*** is the abnormal rotation of testis around the spermatic cord within the scrotum. It produces severe pain and mostly occurs in active young adults and children.
- ***Hydrocele:*** It is the accumulation of the fluid in the vaginal sac which lies between parietal and visceral layers of processus vaginalis. Hydrocele may be vaginal, infantile, congenital, or encysted (Figs 17.22a to d).
- ***Tapping a hydrocele*** is a procedure for removing the excess fluid from tunica vaginalis. The layers penetrated by the instrument are:
  1. Skin
  2. Dartos muscle and membranous layer of superficial fascia
  3. External spermatic fascia
  4. Cremasteric muscle and fascia
  5. Internal spermatic fascia
  6. Parietal layer of tunica vaginalis.

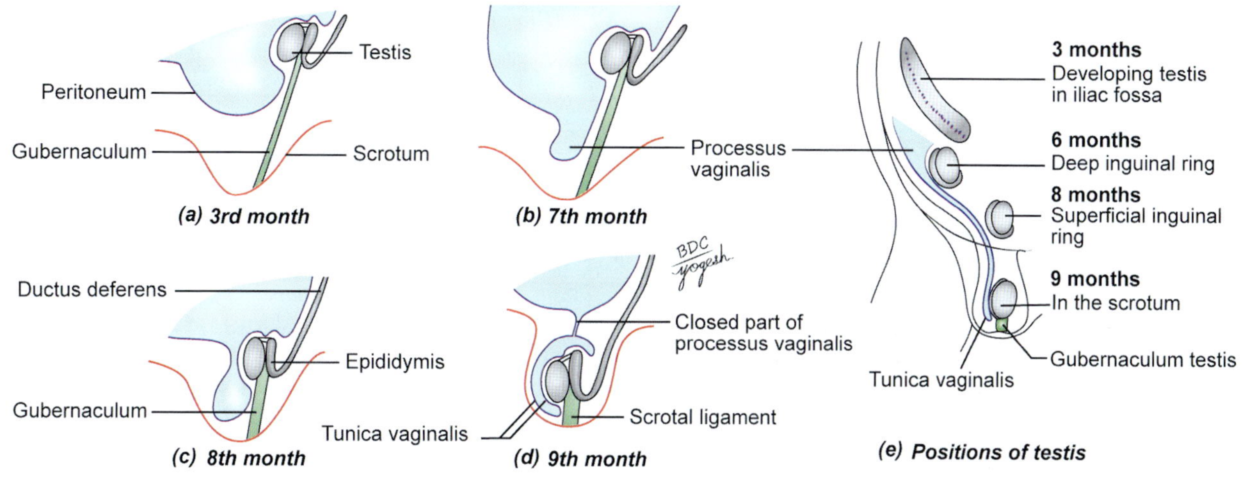

Figs 17.18a to e: Stages of descent of testis include formation of processus vaginalis

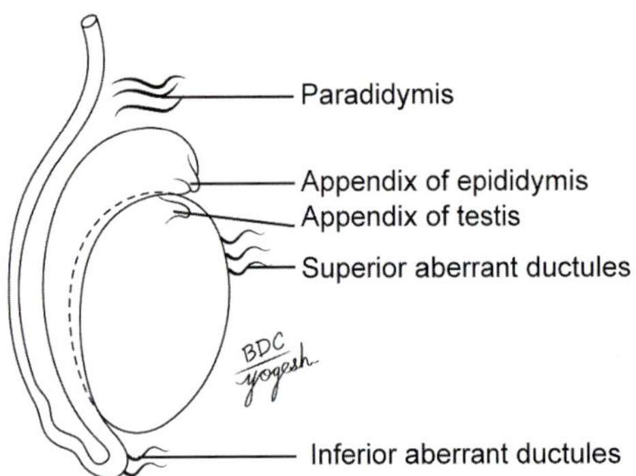

Fig. 17.19: Embryological remnants related to testis and epididymis

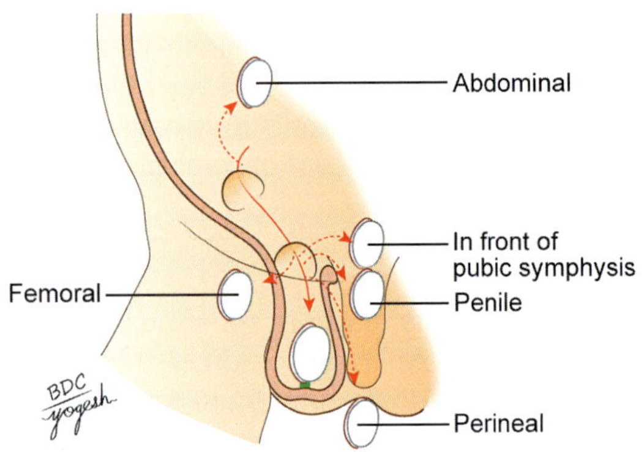

Fig. 17.20: Positions of ectopic testis

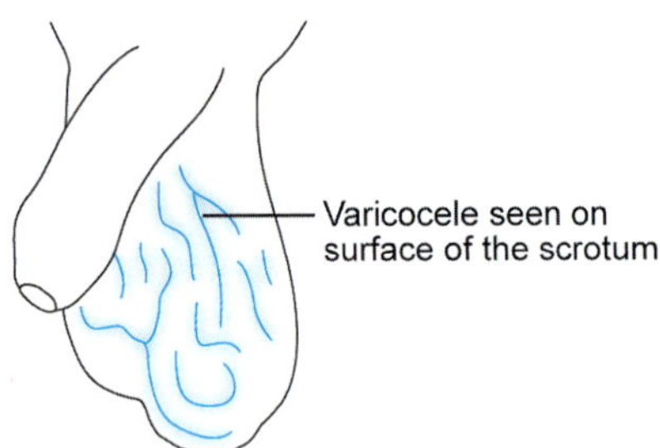

Fig. 17.21: Varicocele

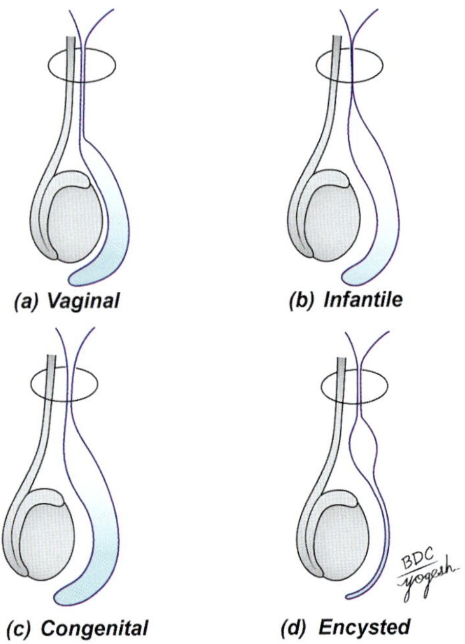

Figs 17.22a to d: Types of hydrocoele

Competencies:

AN46.2 Describe parts of epididymis.

AN52.2 Describe and identify the microanatomical features of epididymis.

EPIDIDYMIS

The epididymis is an organ made up of highly coiled tube that acts as reservoir of spermatozoa (Flowchart 17.3).

Functions

1. Storage and maturation of spermatozoa.
2. Absorption of excess fluid secreted by testis.
3. Phagocytosis of residual bodies and defective sperms.
4. Secretion of surface-associated decapacitation factor that coats the sperms. This factor is removed during capacitation of sperms.

Parts

It has head, body and tail.

1. *Head* is the enlarged upper part and connected to the upper pole of the testis by efferent ductules. It is made up of highly coiled efferent ductules.
2. *Body* is the middle part. It is made up of a single duct, *the duct of the epididymis* which is highly coiled on itself.
3. *Tail* is the lower narrow part. At the lower end of the testis, the tail continues as the *ductus deferens* (Latin *carrying away*).

Vessels and Nerves

The epididymis is supplied by the testicular artery through a branch that anastomoses with and reinforces the tiny artery to the ductus deferens. The venous and lymphatic drainages are similar to those of the testis. Like the testis, the epididymis is supplied by sympathetic nerves through the testicular plexus, the fibres of which are derived from segments T11 to L1 of the spinal cord.

Histology of Epididymis

The histology of epididymis is summarised in Flowchart 17.4 (Fig. 17.4).

Flowchart 17.3: Epididymis

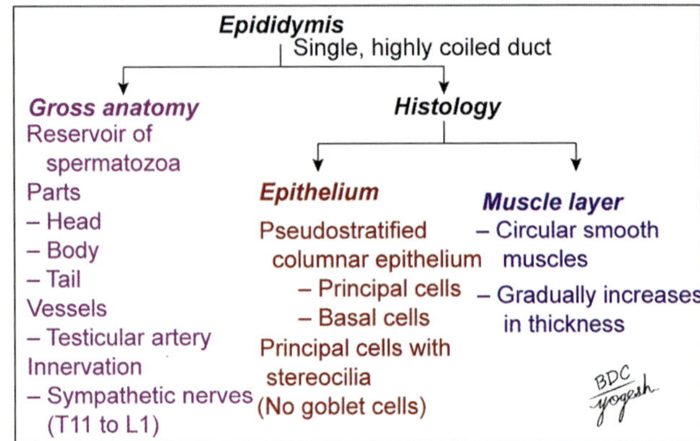

Plate 17.4: Histology of epididymis (low magnification on left and high magnification on right

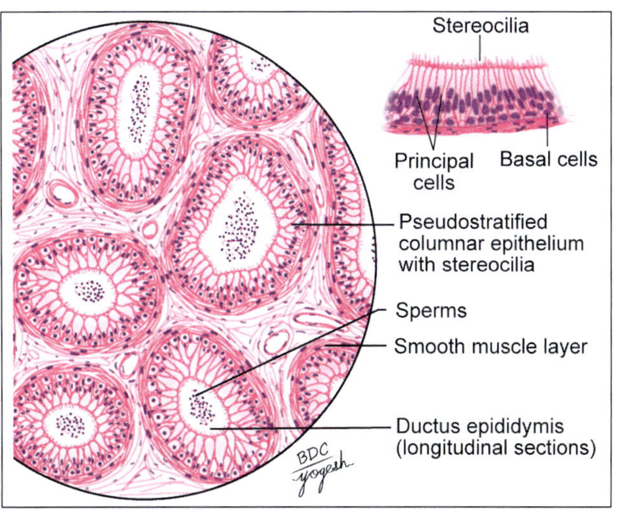

CLINICAL ANATOMY

The common causes of epididymitis and epididymo-orchitis are tuberculosis, filariasis, the gonococcal and other pyogenic infections.

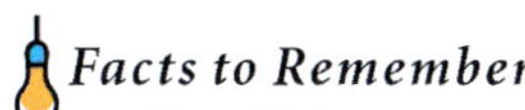

Facts to Remember

- The penis is composed of three masses of erectile tissue — the right and left corpora cavernosa and a median corpus spongiosum.
- The cavernous tissue is finer in corpus spongiosum as it contains urethra.
- Phimosis is narrowing of distal end of prepuce.
- Circumcision is the surgical separation of foreskin or prepuce.
- Tunica vaginalis is the lower persistent part of processus vaginalis, an extension of peritoneal cavity.
- Right testicular vein drains into inferior vena cava. Left testicular vein drains into left renal vein.
- Lymph node of Cloquet is involved in cancer of the penis. Varicocele is common on left side.
- Hydrocoele is the commonest cause of swelling of the scrotum.

BDC's Anatomy e-book

1. Factors responsible for descent of testis
2. Molecular regulation of development of testis
3. Further reading
4. Viva voce questions

Chapter

18

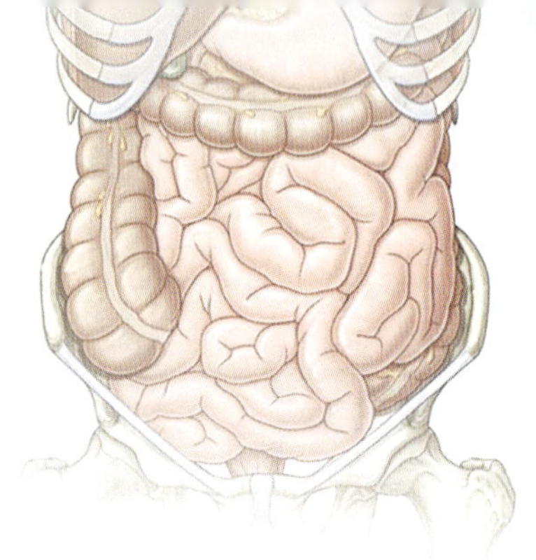

Abdominal Cavity and Peritoneum

ABDOMINAL CAVITY

The abdominal cavity is bounded by dynamic, multi-layered, musculoaponeurotic abdominal walls with anterolateral and posterior walls. It is the largest cavity. It encloses the peritoneal cavity between its parietal and visceral layers of peritoneum.

Boundaries

The abdominal cavity is bounded as follows:

Anterolaterally: Anterolateral wall – formed by muscles and lower ribs

Posteriorly: Posterior wall – formed by lumbar vertebrae and muscles

Superiorly: Diaphragm, which separates abdominal cavity from thoracic cavity

Inferiorly: It continues with the pelvic cavity at the pelvic inlet.

Competency:

AN44.1 Describe and demonstrate the planes (transpyloric, transtubercular, subcostal, lateral vertical, linea alba, linea semilunaris), regions and quadrants of abdomen.

NINE REGIONS OF ABDOMEN

For the purpose of describing the location of viscera, the abdomen is divided into nine regions by two horizontal and two vertical imaginary planes as follows (Figs 18.1a and b; Table 18.1):

- ***Transpyloric plane (Addison's plane):*** It is an imaginary, transverse plane that passes through the midpoint of the line joining the jugular or suprasternal notch to the pubic symphysis. It passes anteriorly through the tip of 9th costal cartilage and posteriorly through the lower border of the body of L1 vertebra. This plane lies roughly a hand's breadth below the xiphisternal joint.
- ***Transtubercular plane:*** It is an imaginary transverse plane which is drawn by joining the tubercles of iliac crests. It passes posteriorly through the body of L5 vertebra.
- ***Vertical (midclavicular) planes:*** There are right and left vertical or *midclavicular planes*. They can be drawn by a vertical line joining the midpoint of the clavicle superiorly and midinguinal point inferiorly.

These planes divide the abdomen or abdominal cavity into nine quadrants as follows:

On the right	*In the midline*	*On the left*
Right hypochondrium	Epigastric	Left hypochondrium
Right lumbar	Umbilical	Left lumbar
Right iliac	Hypogastric	Left iliac

The position of many organs is mentioned in Table 18.1.

TABLE 18.1: Abdominal regions and their main contents

Regions	*Contents*
Right hypochondrium	Liver Gallbladder
Left hypochondrium	Stomach Spleen Left colic flexure
Epigastric region	Stomach Duodenum and pancreas
Right lumbar	Right kidney and ureter Ascending colon
Left lumbar	Left kidney and ureter Descending colon
Umbilical region	Aorta and inferior vena cava Coils of small intestine
Right iliac fossa	Caecum and vermiform appendix
Left iliac fossa	Sigmoid colon
Hypogastric region	Urinary bladder Coils of small intestine

PERITONEUM

The peritoneum (Greek *stretched over*) is a large serous membrane lining the abdominal cavity (Fig. 18.2 and Flowchart 18.1).

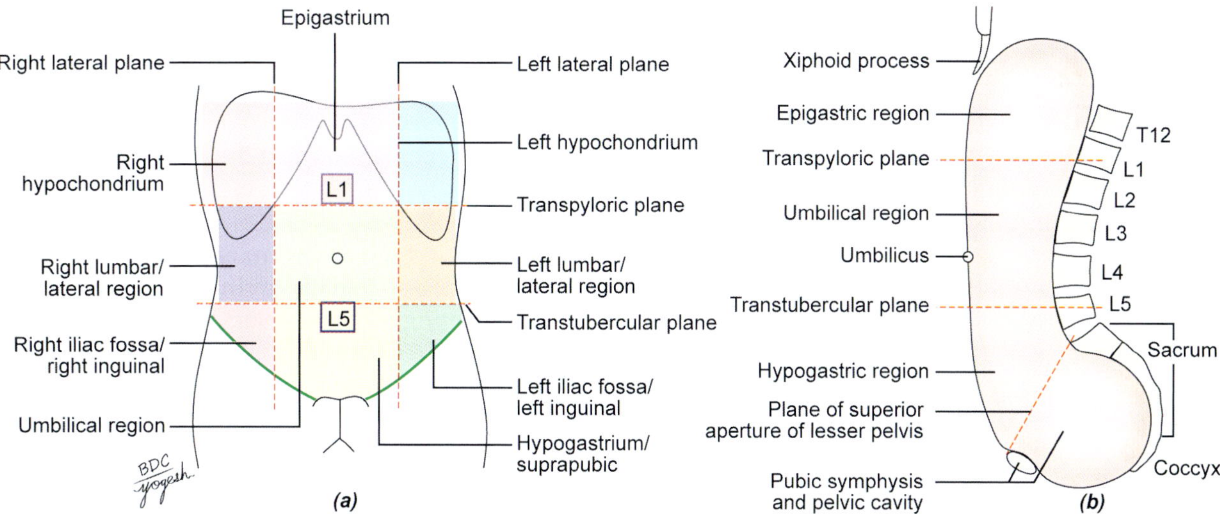

Figs 18.1a and b: (a) Regions of the abdomen and (b) sagittal section of regions of abdomen and pelvic cavity

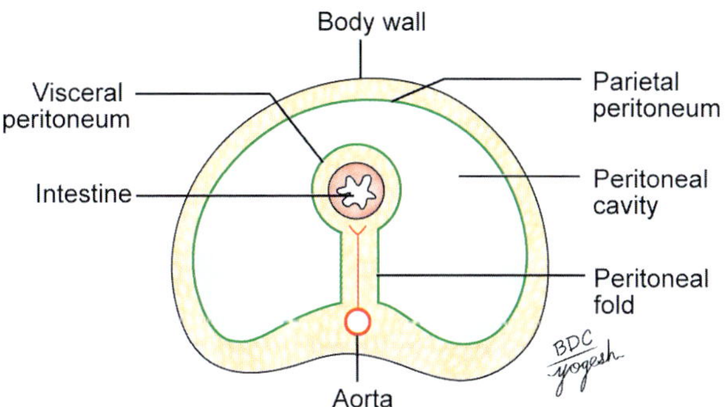

Fig. 18.2: Diagrammatic transverse section of the abdomen showing the arrangement of the peritoneum. The peritoneal cavity is actually a potential space and not as spacious as shown

Flowchart 18.1: Peritoneum

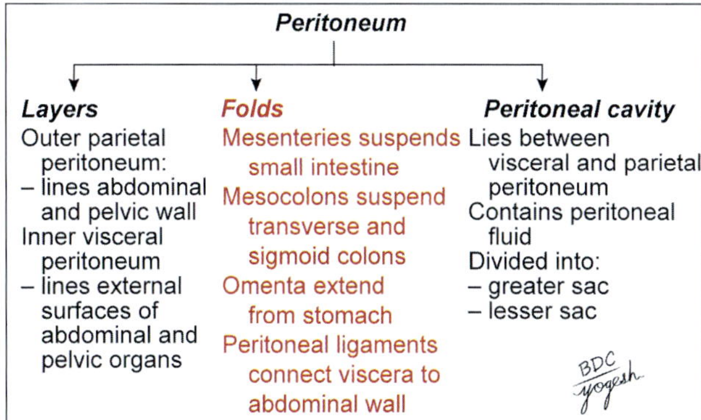

Structure

Histologically, it is composed of an outer ***layer of fibrous tissue***, which gives strength to the membrane and an inner layer of ***mesothelial cells*** which secrete a serous fluid which lubricates the surface, thus allowing free movements of viscera.

Note: The peritoneum covering the ovaries is lined by the cuboidal epithelium.

Layers of Peritoneum

The peritoneum is in the form of a closed sac which is invaginated by a number of viscera. As a result, the peritoneum is divided into (Fig. 18.2):

a. Outer or parietal layer
b. Inner or visceral layer
c. Folds of peritoneum (in which the viscera are suspended).

Parietal Peritoneum

It lines the inner surface of the abdominal and pelvic walls and the lower surface of the diaphragm. It is loosely attached to the walls by extraperitoneal connective tissue.

Visceral Peritoneum

It lines the outer surface of the viscera, to which it is firmly adherent.

The differences between the parietal and visceral peritoneum are listed in Table 18.2.

TABLE 18.2: Differences between the parietal and visceral peritoneum

Feature	*Parietal peritoneum*	*Visceral peritoneum*
Definition	Lines inner surface of abdominal and pelvic walls and diaphragm	Lines outer surface of viscera
Separation	As it is loosely attached to the walls by intraperitoneal connective tissue, it can be easily stripped off	As it is firmly adherent to viscera, it cannot be stripped off
Embryological source	Develops from somatopleuric layer of lateral plate mesoderm	Develops from splanchnopleuric layer of lateral plate mesoderm
Pain sensitivity	Pain sensitive	Pain insensitive
Blood and nerve supply	Same as body wall (somatic nerves)	Same as viscera (autonomic nerves)

Peritoneum and Abdominal Organs (Table 18.3)

1. ***Intraperitoneal organs*** are suspended by folds of peritoneum. Such organs are mobile.
2. ***Retroperitoneal organs*** are fixed and immobile. They rest directly on the posterior abdominal wall and may be covered by peritoneum on one side.
3. ***Subperitoneal organs*** lie below the peritoneum and they include the pelvic viscera such as urinary bladder, prostate, seminal vesicles, cervix of uterus and vagina.

Note: Some organs are suspended by peritoneal folds in early embryonic life, but later become retroperitoneal by the process of zygosis (Fig. 18.3). The ***zygosis*** is a process of absorption of fold of visceral peritoneum.

Folds of Visceral Peritoneum

The visceral peritoneum shows the following folds (Plate 18.1):

1. ***Mesenteries*** is a fold that suspends the small intestine.
2. ***Mesocolons*** are folds that suspend the transverse colon and sigmoid colon. For example, transverse mesocolon and sigmoid mesocolon.
3. ***Omenta*** are folds of peritoneum that extend from stomach. They include lesser omentum and greater omentum.
4. ***Peritoneal ligaments*** are double-layered folds of peritoneum that connect the viscera to the abdominal wall. These include gastrosplenic ligament (connects spleen to stomach), lienorenal ligament (connects kidney with spleen) and coronary ligaments (connects liver with diaphragm).

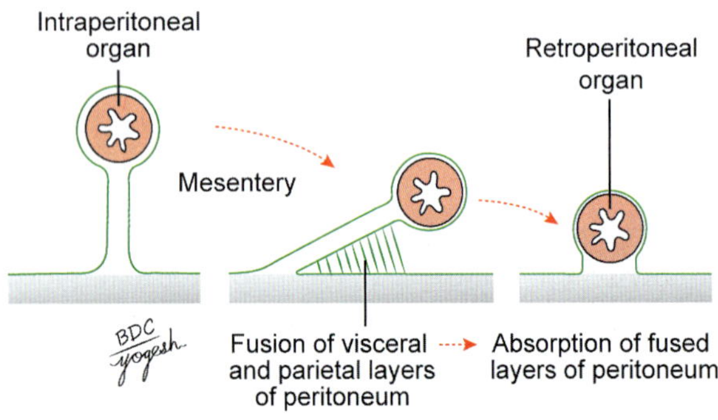

Fig. 18.3: Scheme to show how a loop of gut may lose its mesentery

TABLE 18.3: Relation of peritoneum to various viscera

Relation to peritoneum	*Organs*
Intraperitoneal	Stomach, jejunum, ileum, caecum, appendix, transverse colon and sigmoid colon
Partially covered	Ascending colon, descending colon and rectum
Retroperitoneal	Duodenum, pancreas, kidney, ureter and suprarenal
Subperitoneal	Urinary bladder, prostate, seminal vesicle, cervix uteri and vagina

Significance of Folds of Peritoneum

1. They provide mobility to the viscera.
2. They provide passage to nerves, vessels and lymphatics to the viscera.
3. They protect and support the viscera.

Peritoneal Cavity

The viscera which invaginate the peritoneal cavity completely fill it so that the cavity is reduced to a potential space separating adjacent layers of peritoneum. Between these layers, there is a thin film of serous fluid secreted by the mesothelial cells. This fluid performs a lubricating function and allows free movement of one peritoneal surface over another.

The folds of peritoneum divide the peritoneal cavity into the following:

1. ***Greater sac*** is the main larger part of the peritoneal cavity.
2. ***Lesser sac*** is the smaller part of the peritoneal cavity that lies behind the liver and stomach.

The ***epiploic foramen*** or *foramen of Winslow* is a communicating channel between greater and lesser sacs.

Sex Differences

In the male, the peritoneum is a closed sac lined by mesothelium or flattened epithelium. The female peritoneum has the following distinguishing features.

The peritoneal cavity communicates with the exterior through the uterine tubes.

The peritoneum covering the ovaries is lined by cubical epithelium.

The peritoneum covering the fimbria is lined by columnar ciliated epithelium.

Functions of Peritoneum

The functions of peritoneum are as follows:

1. *Free movements of viscera*: The peritoneum and peritoneal fluid provide a slippery surface for the free movements of the abdominal viscera.
2. *Protection*: Phagocytic cells of peritoneum protect the viscera from the infection.
3. *Absorption*: The mesothelium provides a large surface area for absorption. It can be utilized for *peritoneal dialysis*.
4. Storage of fat.
5. Prevents the spread of infection by the formation of adhesions.
6. Provides passage for nerves, vessels and lymphatics of viscera.

Competency:
AN47.3 Explain anatomical basis of ascites and peritonitis.

CLINICAL ANATOMY

- ***Peritonitis***: Parietal peritoneum of abdomen is supplied by T7–T12 and L1 nerves, while that of the

Plate 18.1: Peritoneal relationships of the abdominopelvic organs (midsagittal section through the male abdominopelvic cavity viewed from the left)

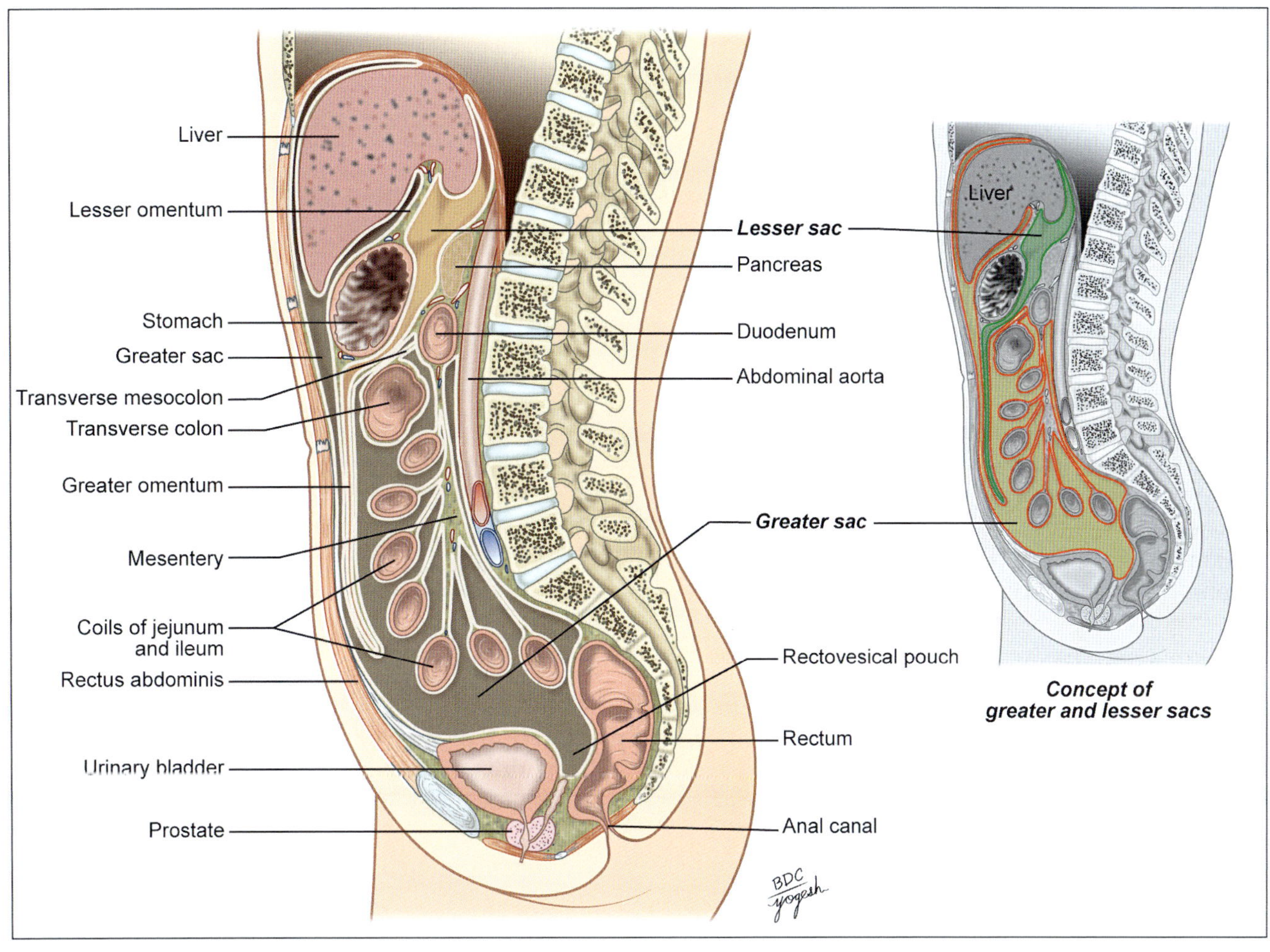

pelvis is supplied by the obturator nerve. Peritonitis may occur:

a. By an opening in the closed gastrointestinal tract in abdominal cavity, by ruptured appendix or gastric ulcer perforation or typhoid ulcer perforation.
b. Infection by any opening through anterior abdominal wall.
c. Infection through vagina, uterine cavity and fallopian tube to reach the peritoneal cavity.

- Collection of free fluid in the peritoneal cavity is known as ***ascites***. Common causes of ascites are cirrhosis of the liver, tubercular peritonitis, congestive heart failure and malignant infiltration of the peritoneum. Veins also get prominent in cirrhosis of liver.
- Fluid from the (peritoneal cavity) may be removed by puncturing the abdominal wall either in the median plane midway between the umbilicus and pubic symphysis, or at a point just above the anterior superior iliac spine. The procedure is called ***paracentesis***. Urinary bladder must be emptied before the procedure.
- Inflammation of the peritoneum is called ***peritonitis***. It may be localized when a subjacent organ is infected; or may be generalized. The latter is a very serious condition.
- The presence of air in the peritoneal cavity is called ***pneumoperitoneum***. It may occur after perforation of the stomach or intestines.
- *Laparoscopy* is the examination of the peritoneal cavity under direct vision using an instrument called ***laparoscope***.
- Opening up the abdominal cavity by a surgeon is called ***laparotomy***.
- Greater omentum limits the spread of infection by sealing off the site of ruptured vermiform appendix or gastric ulcer and tries to delay the onset of peritonitis. It is called 'abdominal policeman'.
- Inflammation of parietal peritoneum causes localized severe pain and rebound tenderness on removing the fingers.
- Peritoneal dialysis is done in case of renal failure. The procedure removes the urea, etc. as it diffuses through blood vessels into the peritoneal cavity.

PERITONEAL FOLDS

Embryological Basis of Peritoneal Folds

The folds can be best understood by recapitulating the embryology of the gut.

Plate 18.2: Dorsal and ventral mesenteries of the gut (Section of the embryo through the region of the stomach showing changes in the position of stomach, liver, spleen and mesogastrium)

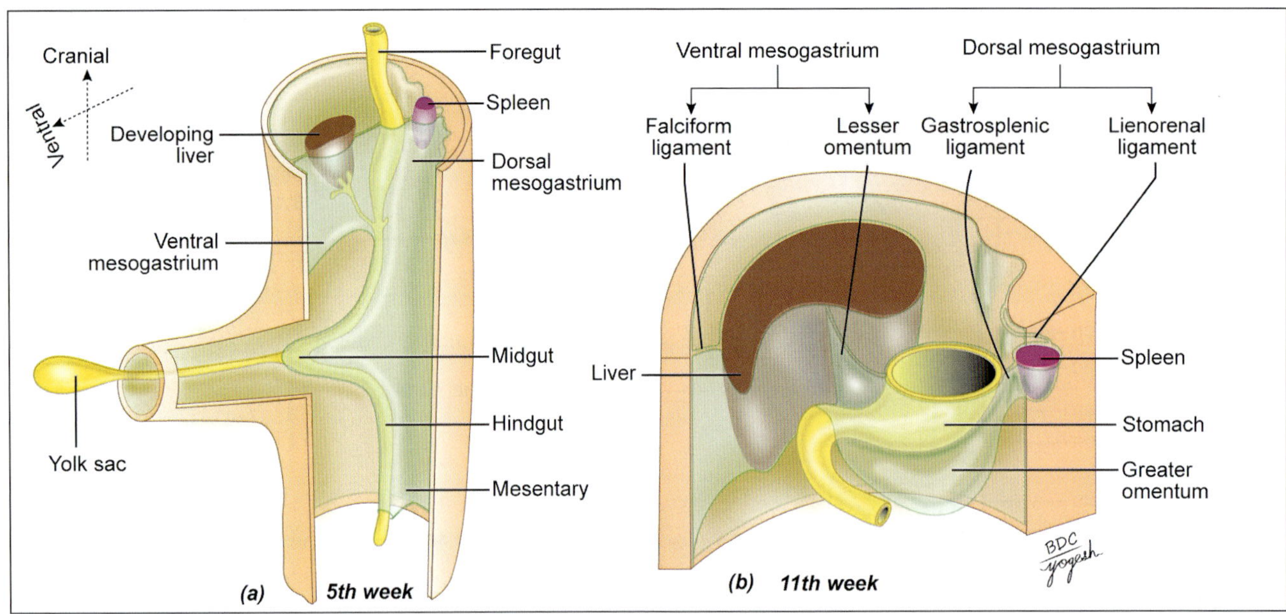

The developing gut is divisible into three parts—foregut, midgut and hindgut. Each part has its own artery which is a ventral branch of the abdominal aorta. The coeliac artery supplies the foregut; the superior mesenteric artery supplies the midgut; and the inferior mesenteric artery supplies the hindgut (Plate 18.2 and Fig. 18.4).

1. Apart from some other structures, the ***foregut*** forms the oesophagus, the stomach and the upper part of the duodenum up to the opening of the bile duct.
2. The ***midgut*** forms the rest of the duodenum, the jejunum, the ileum, the appendix, the caecum, the ascending colon and the right 2/3rd of the transverse colon.
3. The ***hindgut*** forms the left 1/3rd of the transverse colon, the descending colon, the sigmoid colon, proximal part of the rectum. The anorectal canal forms distal part of rectum and the upper part of the anal canal up to the pectinate line.

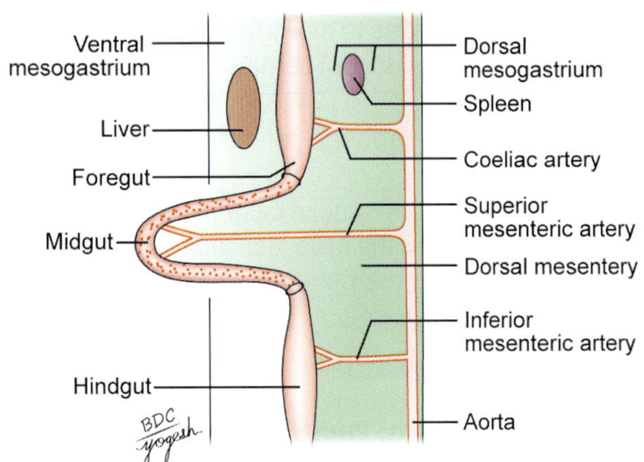

Fig. 18.4: Three parts of the primitive gut with their arteries

The abdominal part of the foregut is suspended by mesenteries both ventrally and dorsally. The ventral mesentery of the foregut is called the *ventral mesogastrium*, and the dorsal mesentery is called *dorsal mesogastrium* (*gastrium* means stomach) (Figs 18.5a and b).

1. The ***ventral mesogastrium*** becomes divided by the developing liver into a ventral part and a dorsal part.

   The ventral part forms the ligaments of the liver, namely:

   a. Falciform ligament
   b. Right and left triangular ligaments
   c. Superior and inferior layers of the coronary ligament.

   The dorsal part of the ventral mesogastrium forms the lesser omentum.

2. The fate of the ***dorsal mesogastrium*** is as follows:

   a. The greater or caudal part of the dorsal mesogastrium becomes greatly elongated and forms the *greater omentum*.
   b. The spleen develops in relation to the cranial part of the dorsal mesogastrium and divides it into dorsal and ventral parts. The ventral part forms the *gastrosplenic ligament* while the dorsal part forms the *lienorenal ligament*.
   c. The cranial most part of the dorsal mesogastrium forms the *gastrophrenic ligament*.

Note: The *midgut* and *hindgut* have only a dorsal mesentery, which forms (Fig. 18.6):

1. Mesentery of jejunum and ileum
2. Mesoappendix
3. Transverse and sigmoid mesocolons.

The mesenteries of the duodenum, the ascending colon, the descending colon and the rectum are lost during development.

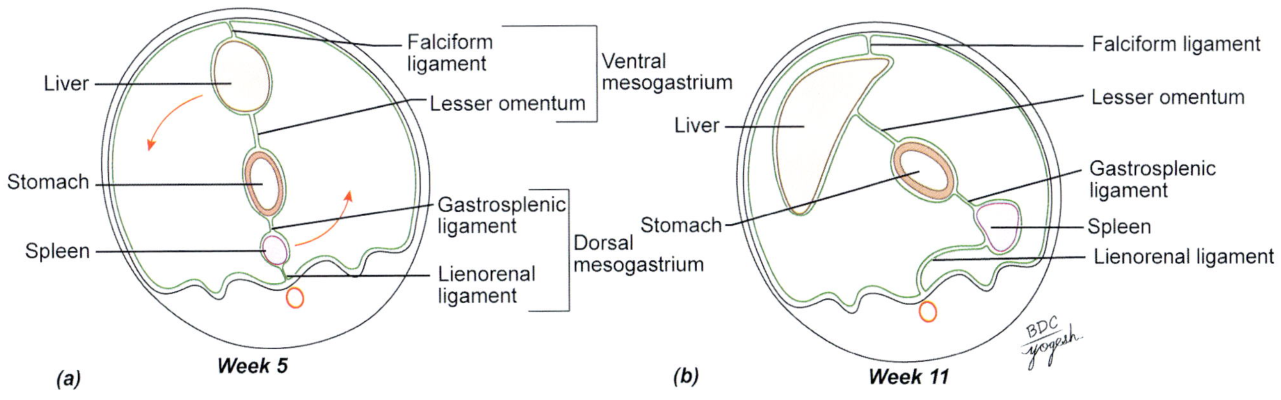

Figs 18.5a and b: Developing mesogastria and changes in the position of stomach, liver and spleen: (a) Positions at the end of the 5th week and (b) positions at the end of the 11th week

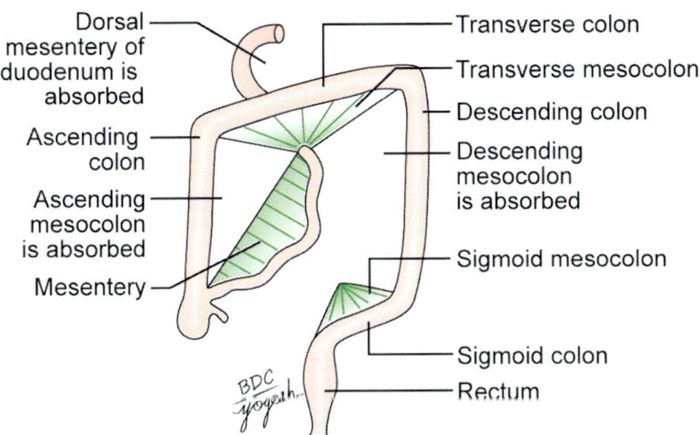

Fig. 18.6: Fate of dorsal mesentery of midgut and hindgut

Fig. 18.8: Dissected greater omentum

GREATER OMENTUM

The greater omentum (Latin *apron*) is a large fold of peritoneum which hangs down from the greater curvature of the stomach like an apron (Plate 18.3, Figs 18.7 to 18.9 and Flowchart 18.2).

It is made up of *four layers* of peritoneum all of which are fused together to form a thin fenestrated membrane containing variable quantities of fat.

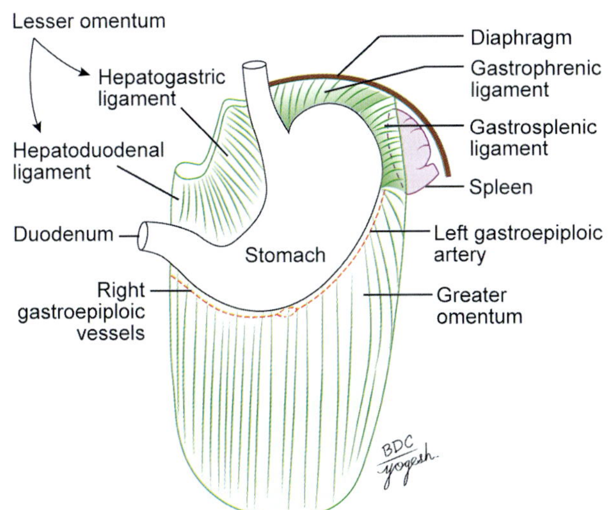

Fig. 18.7: Anterior view of the peritoneal folds attached to the greater and lesser curvatures of the stomach

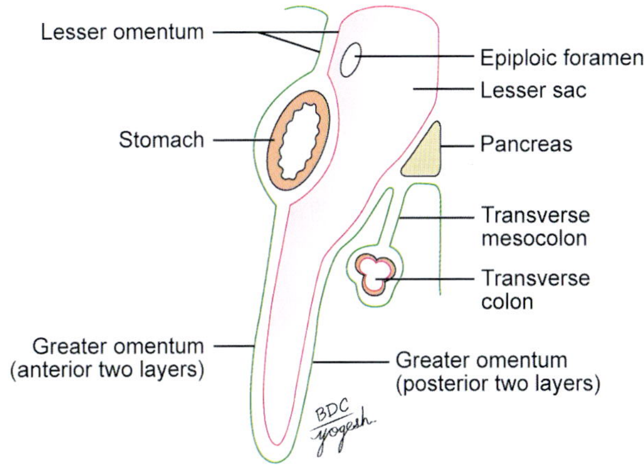

Fig. 18.9: Left view of a sagittal section of the abdomen showing the greater and lesser omenta and the transverse mesocolon

Attachments (Fig. 18.9)

- The *anterior two layers* descend from the greater curvature of the stomach to a variable extent and fold upon themselves to form the *posterior two layers* which ascend to the anterior surface of the head and the anterior border of the body of the pancreas.

Plate 18.3: Greater omentum

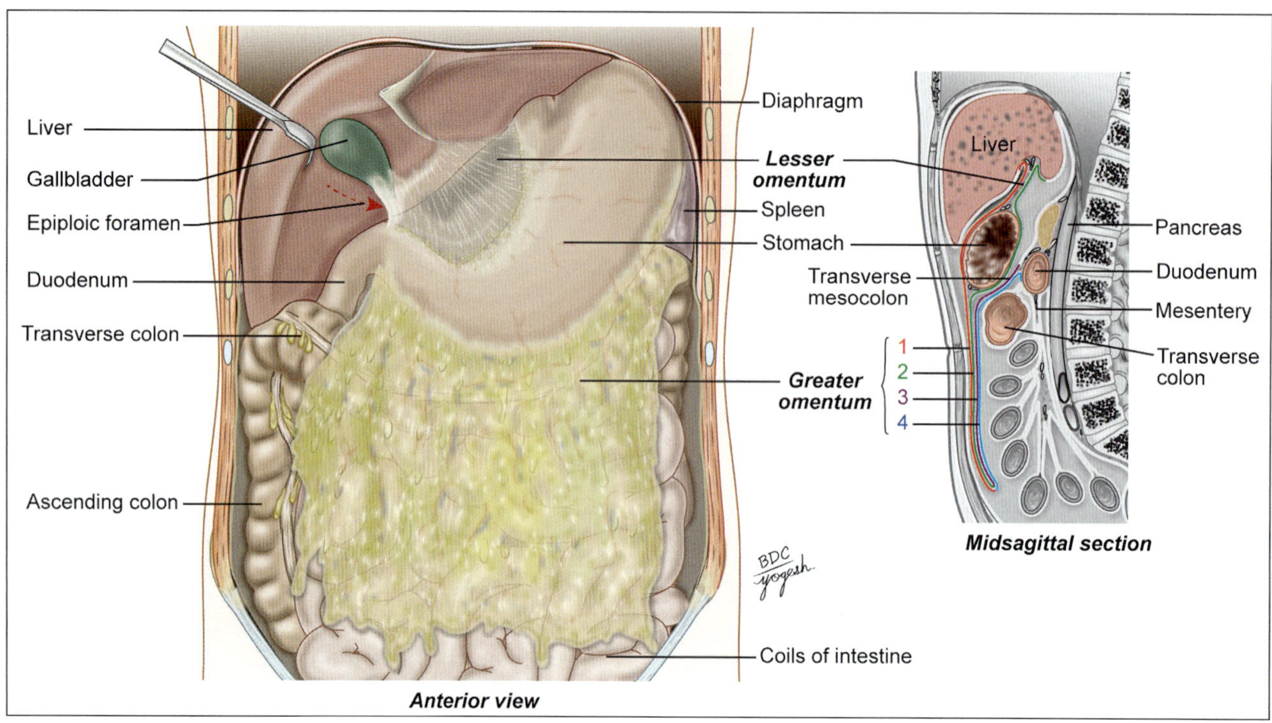

Flowchart 18.2: Greater omentum

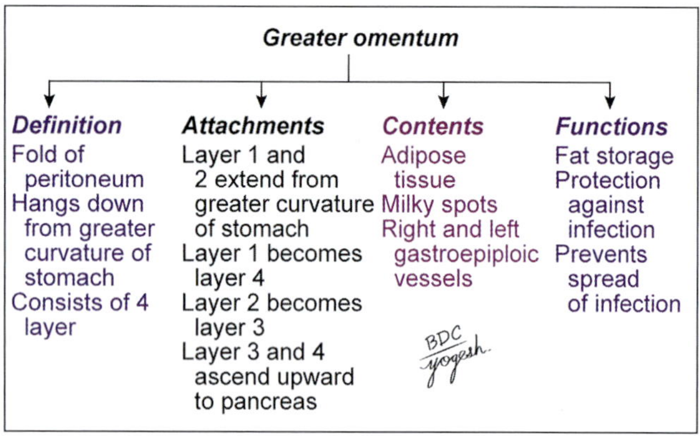

- The folding of the omentum is such that the 1st layer becomes the 4th layer and the 2nd layer becomes the 3rd layer.
- In its upper part, the 4th layer is partially fused to the anterior surface of the transverse colon and of the transverse mesocolon.
- The part of the peritoneal cavity called the ***lesser sac*** between the 2nd and third layers gets obliterated, except for about 2.5 cm below the greater curvature of the stomach.

Contents

1. The right and left gastroepiploic vessels anastomose with each other in the interval between the first two layers of the greater omentum a little below the greater curvature of the stomach.
2. It is often laden with fat.
3. *Milky spots* are the aggregation of macrophages.

Functions

1. It is a *storehouse of fat*.
2. It *protects* the peritoneal cavity against infection because of the presence of macrophages in it. Collections of macrophages form small, dense patches, known as ***milky spots***, which are visible to the naked eye.
3. It also *limits the spread of infection* by moving to the site of infection and sealing it off from the surrounding areas. On this account, the greater omentum is also known as the ***policeman of the abdomen***.
4. The greater omentum forms a partition between the supracolic and infracolic compartments of the greater sac.

DISSECTION

Expose the extensive abdominal cavity by reflecting anterior abdominal wall into four flaps—two (right and left) above and two below the umbilicus.

Identify the *peritoneum*. Divide and reflect it with the anterior abdominal wall. Cut the fold of peritoneum which passes from the median part of the supraumbilical part of the anterior abdominal wall to the liver known as the *falciform ligament*. This fold contains the *ligamentum teres* of the liver or the *obliterated left umbilical vein* in its free posterior border.

Examine the posterior surface of the reflected lower parts of anterior abdominal wall. Identify five ill-defined *peritoneal folds* which pass upwards towards the umbilicus. These are *two lateral*, *two medial* and *one median umbilical folds.*

Identify the parietal peritoneum, adherent to the parieties or walls of the abdominal cavity. Trace it from the walls to form various double-layered folds which spread out to enclose the viscera as the visceral peritoneum.

Identify and lift up the greater omentum. See its continuity with the stomach above and the transverse colon fused with its posterior surface a short distance inferior to the stomach.

Cut through the anterior layers of the greater omentum 2–3 cm inferior to the arteries to open the lower part of the omental bursa sufficiently to admit a hand. Explore the bursa.

Pull the liver superiorly and lift its inferior margin anteriorly to expose the lesser omentum. Examine the right free margin of lesser omentum, containing the bile duct, proper hepatic artery and portal vein. This free margin forms the anterior boundary of the opening into the lesser sac, i.e. epiploic foramen. The posterior boundary is the inferior vena cava. Superior to opening into the lesser sac is the caudate process of liver and inferiorly is the first part of duodenum.

Remove the anterior layer of peritoneum from the lesser omentum along the lesser curvature of the stomach. Find and trace the left gastric vessels along the lesser curvature of stomach. Trace the oesophageal branches to the oesophagus.

Trace the right gastric artery to the proper hepatic artery and the vein to the portal vein. Expose the proper hepatic artery and trace its branches to the porta hepatis.

Trace the cystic duct from the gallbladder. Follow the common hepatic duct to the porta hepatis and the bile duct till it passes posterior to the duodenum.

LESSER OMENTUM

This is a fold of peritoneum which extends from the lesser curvature of the stomach and the first 2 cm of the duodenum to the liver (Plate 18.3, Fig. 18.10 and Flowchart 18.3).

Flowchart 18.3: Lesser omentum

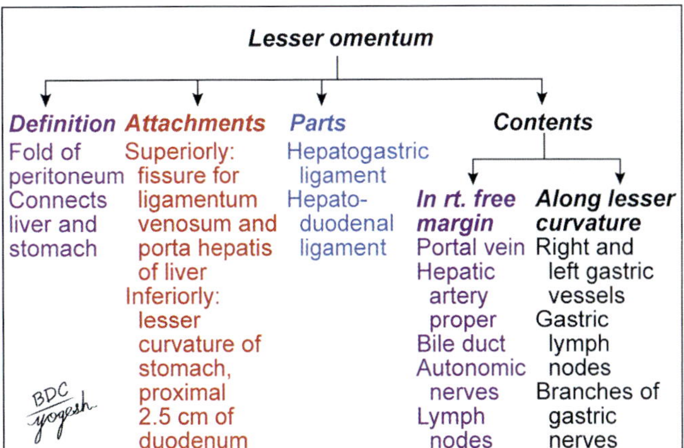

Parts

The portion of the lesser omentum between the stomach and the liver is called the ***hepatogastric ligament***, and the portion between the duodenum and the liver is called the ***hepatoduodenal ligament***.

Note:

Behind the lesser omentum, there lies a part of the *lesser sac*.

The lesser omentum has a free right margin behind which there is the ***epiploic foramen***. The greater and lesser sacs communicate through this foramen.

Attachments

Inferiorly, the lesser omentum is attached to the lesser curvature of the stomach and to the upper border of the first 2 cm of the duodenum.

Superiorly, it is attached to the liver, the line of attachment being in the form of an inverted 'L'. The vertical limb of the 'L' is attached to the bottom of the fissure for the ligamentum venosum and the horizontal limb to the margins of the porta hepatis.

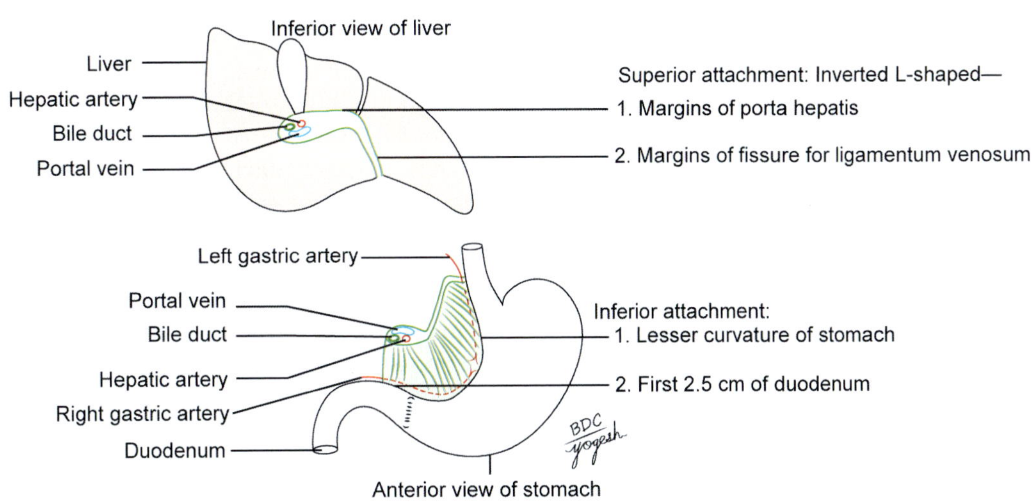

Fig. 18.10: The attachments and contents of the lesser omentum. The liver has been turned upwards so that its posteroinferior surface can be seen

Contents

A. The *right free margin* of the lesser omentum contains:
   1. Hepatic artery proper
   2. Portal vein
   3. Bile duct
   4. Lymph nodes and lymphatics, and
   5. Hepatic plexus of nerves, all enclosed in a perivascular fibrous sheath.

B. *Along the lesser curvature of the stomach*, it contains:
   1. Right gastric vessels
   2. Left gastric vessels
   3. Gastric group of lymph nodes and lymphatics
   4. Branches from the gastric nerves.

MESENTERY

The mesentery (Greek *fold of intestine*) of the small intestine or mesentery proper is a broad, ***fan-shaped fold of peritoneum*** which suspends the coils of jejunum and ileum from the posterior abdominal wall (Fig. 18.11 and Flowchart 18.4).

Border

The mesentery has two borders:
1. Attached border or root
2. Free or intestinal border.

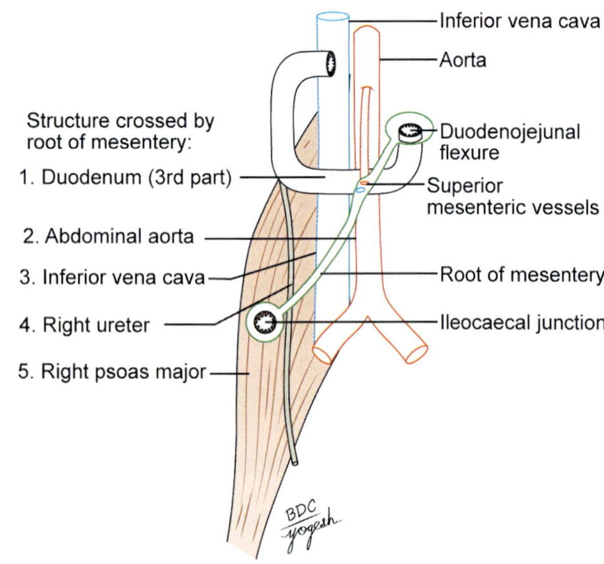

Fig. 18.11: Structures crossed by the root of mesentery

Flowchart 18.4: Mesentery

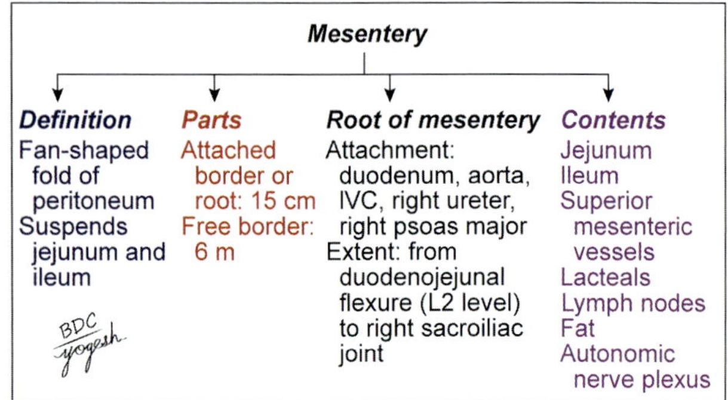

***Attached border (root of the mesentery)*:** It is 15 cm (6 inches) long. It extends from the duodenojejunal flexure on the left side of vertebra L2 to the upper part of right sacroiliac joint. It crosses the following structures:
1. Third part of the duodenum
2. Abdominal aorta
3. Inferior vena cava
4. Right ureter
5. Right psoas major.

***Free* or *intestinal border*:** It is 6 metres (20 feet) long, and is thrown into pleats. It encloses jejunum and ileum, forming their visceral peritoneum or serous coat.

Distribution of Fat

Fat is most abundant in the lower part of the mesentery, extending from the root to the intestinal border. The upper part of the mesentery contains less fat, which tends to accumulate near the root. Near the intestinal border, it leaves oval or circular fat free, translucent areas, or ***windows***.

Contents

The contents of the mesentery are:
1. Jejunum and ileum enclosed in the free border
2. Jejunal and ileal branches of the superior mesenteric artery and accompanying veins
3. Lymphatics or lacteals
4. 100–200 mesenteric lymph nodes
5. Connective tissue with fat
6. Autonomic nerve plexuses.

MESOAPPENDIX

It is a small, triangular fold of peritoneum which suspends the vermiform appendix from the posterior surface of the lower end of the mesentery close to the ileocaecal junction. Usually the fold extends up to the tip of the appendix, but sometimes it fails to reach the distal 1/3rd or so. It contains vessels, nerves, lymph nodes and lymphatics of the appendix (Plate 18.4).

DISSECTION

Remove the remains of the lesser omentum leaving the vessels and duct intact and examine the abdominal wall posterior to the omentum and the omental bursa.

Turn the small intestine to the left. Cut through the right layer of peritoneum of the mesentery along the line of its attachment to the posterior abdominal wall and strip it from the mesentery. Remove the fat from the mesentery to expose the superior mesenteric vessels in its root and their branches and tributaries in the mesentery.

Trace the superior mesenteric vessels proximally and distally. Dissect the branches to the jejunum, ileum, caecum, appendix, ascending colon, right 2/3rd of transverse colon, the distal part of duodenum and pancreas.

Plate 18.4: Mesoappendix

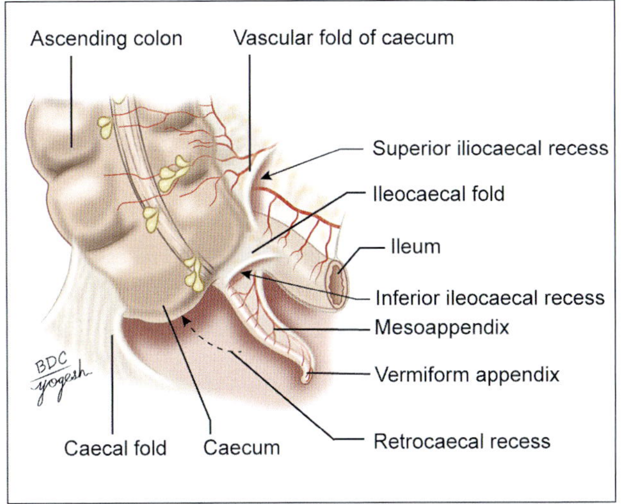

Turn the small intestine and its mesentery to the right. Remove the peritoneum and fat on the posterior abdominal wall between the mesentery and descending colon to expose the inferior mesenteric vessels and the autonomic nerves and lymph nodes associated with them.

Turn the caecum upwards and uncover the structures posterior to it. Trace the three taeniae on the external surface of the colon and cranial to the root of the vermiform appendix.

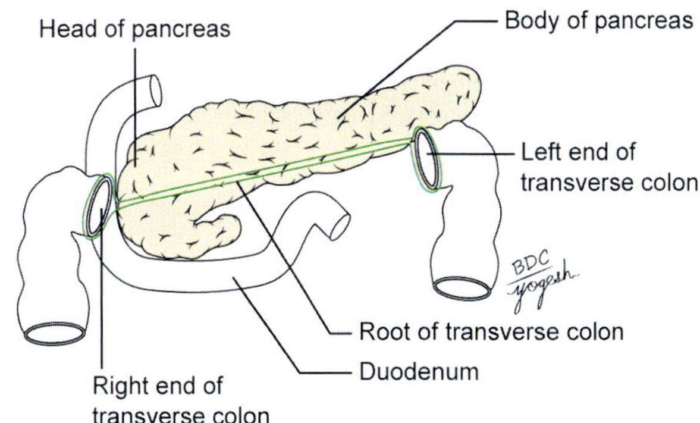

Fig. 18.12: Attachment of the root of the transverse mesocolon

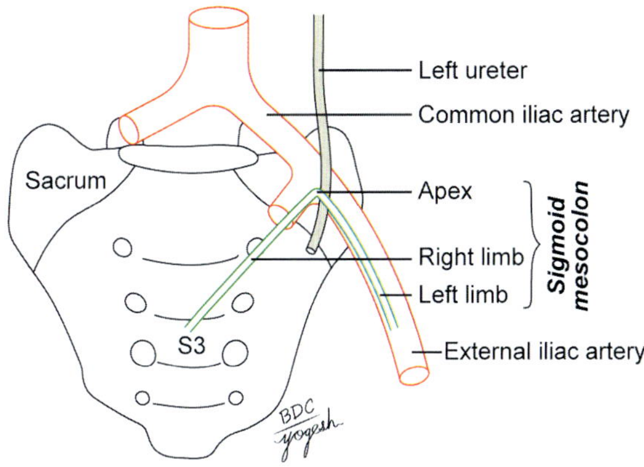

Fig. 18.13: Attachment of the root of the sigmoid mesocolon

TRANSVERSE MESOCOLON

This is a broad fold of peritoneum which suspends the transverse colon from the upper part of the posterior abdominal wall (Fig. 18.12).

Attachments

The root of the transverse mesocolon is attached to the anterior surface of the head and the anterior border of the body of the pancreas.

Contents

1. Transverse colon
2. Anastomosis between middle colic and ascending branch of left colic vessels
3. Autonomic nerves and lymphatics of transverse colon
4. Fat and connective tissue.

SIGMOID MESOCOLON

This is a triangular (Greek *'S' shape*) fold of peritoneum which suspends the sigmoid colon from the pelvic wall (Fig. 18.13).

Attachments

The root is shaped like an inverted 'V'. Its *apex* lies over the left ureter at the termination of the left common iliac artery. The *left limb* of 'V' is attached along the upper half of the left external iliac artery; and the *right limb* to the posterior pelvic wall extending downwards and medially from the apex to the median plane at the level of vertebra S3 (Fig. 18.13).

Contents

1. Sigmoid colon
2. Sigmoid branches of inferior mesenteric vessels
3. Branches of superior rectal vessels
4. Lymphatics and autonomic nerves of sigmoid colon
5. Lymph nodes, fat, connective tissue.

DISSECTION

Expose the anterior border of the pancreas and define the attachments of the transverse mesocolon. Trace the duodenum from the pylorus to the duodenojejunal flexure.

Trace the fold of peritoneum from the upper half of left external iliac artery to the termination of left common iliac artery and then downwards till the third piece of sacrum.

PERITONEAL LIGAMENTS

Falciform Ligament

The falciform ligament is a sickle-shaped double-layered fold of peritoneum that connects liver to the undersurface of diaphragm and the anterior abdominal wall up to the umbilicus (Fig. 18.14).

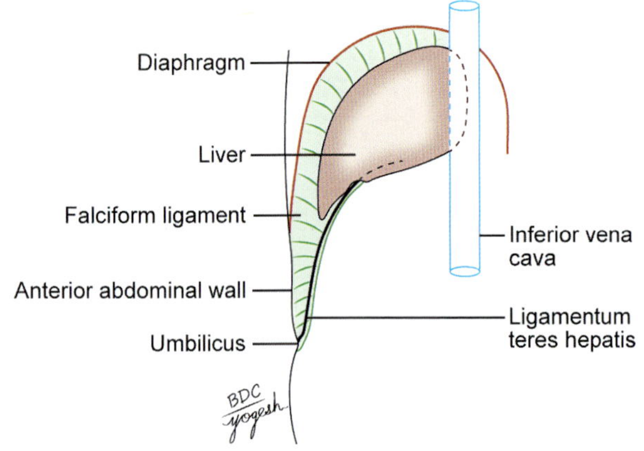

Fig. 18.14: Falciform ligament

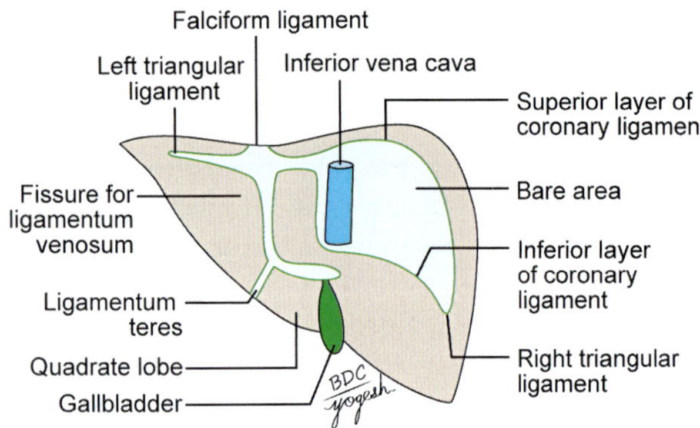

Fig. 18.15: Reflections of peritoneum on the liver—superior and posterior aspects

Attachments

The falciform ligament has free and attached margins.

1. *Free margin* extends from umbilicus to the inferior border of liver, and it contains ligamentum teres hepatis.
2. *Attached margin* connects anterior surface of liver to diaphragm and anterior abdominal wall.

Contents

1. Ligamentum teres hepatis (along the free margin)
2. Paraumbilical veins
3. Accessory portal system of Sappey that communicates paraumbilical veins with diaphragmatic veins.

Other Ligaments

Coronary Ligaments

These are layers of peritoneum that connect the liver with the diaphragm and kidney. It has two layers (Fig. 18.15):

1. Upper layer connects the liver with undersurface of diaphragm, and
2. Lower layer connects the liver with kidney (*hepatorenal ligament*).

Right Triangular Ligament

It connects the right surface of liver to the diaphragm.

Left Triangular Ligament

It connects the upper surface of left lobe of liver to the diaphragm.

For details about coronary and triangular ligaments, refer to Chapter 21.

Note: Ligamentum teres hepatis is a remnant of obliterated left umbilical vein.

Competency:

AN47.1 Describe and identify boundaries and recesses of lesser and greater sacs.

PERITONEAL CAVITY

Peritoneal cavity is enclosed within the parietal and visceral layers of the peritoneum. It is a potential space that permits the space for free mobility and expansion of the abdominal viscera.

The cavity of the peritoneum is closed in the males. In females, the peritoneal cavity communicates with the exterior through fallopian tube, uterus and vagina.

Subdivisions of Peritoneal Cavity

The peritoneal cavity is divided into (Figs 18.16a and b):

1. ***Greater sac***: Larger and the main compartment.
2. ***Lesser sac*** or ***omental bursa***: Smaller compartment that lies behind the liver, lesser omentum and stomach.

The ***epiploic foramen*** is the communication between the greater and lesser sacs. The ***peritoneal recesses*** or *fossae* are small pockets of peritoneal cavity that are created by folds of peritoneum.

The layout of the greater sac can be studied by tracing the peritoneum both vertically and horizontally.

TRACINGS OF PERITONEUM

Vertical Tracing or Sagittal Tracing (Fig. 18.16)

Peritoneum

- Lines the deep surface of anterior abdominal wall
- Covers the undersurface of diaphragm
- Covers the superior, anterior and inferior surface of liver
- Continues as anterior layer of lesser omentum
- Covers anterior surface of stomach
- Continues downward as the anterior-most layer (layer 1) of greater omentum
- Folds backwards to continue as the posterior-most layer (layer 4) of greater omentum
- Reach the pancreas located at the posterior abdominal wall
- Continue as anterosuperior layer of transverse mesocolon
- Covers the transverse colon and continues upward as posterior layer of transverse mesocolon
- Projects forward as mesentery that covers the jejunum and ileum
- Covers posterior abdominal wall and descends into pelvic cavity.

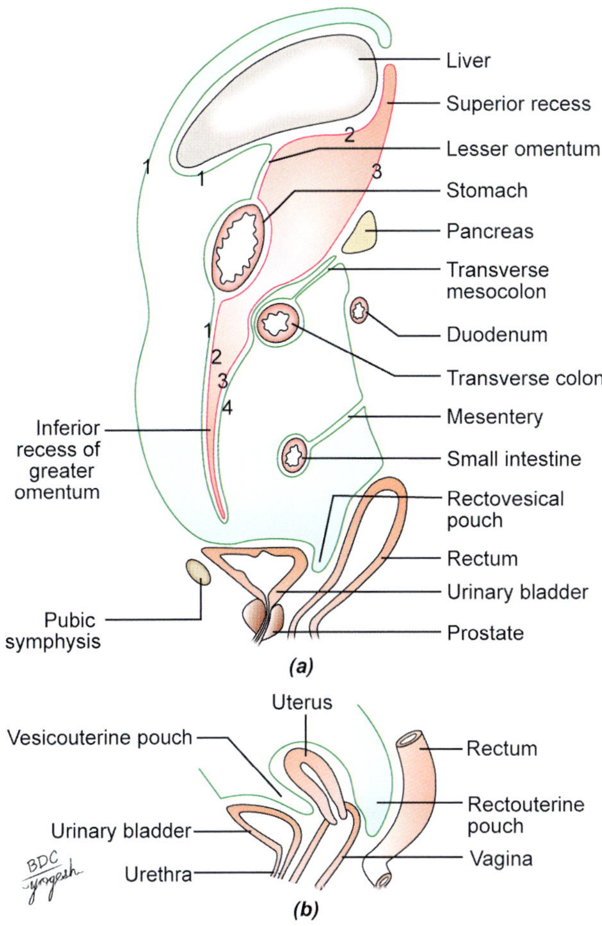

Figs 18.16a and b: (a) Sagittal section through the abdomen (male) to show the reflections of peritoneum, and 1–4 layers of greater omentum and (b) sagittal section through a female pelvis showing the peritoneal reflections

In males

Covers anterior surface of upper part rectum (Fig. 18.16a):

- Forms rectovesical pouch
- Covers superior surface of urinary bladder
- Runs upward on the inner surface of anterior abdominal wall.

In females

Covers anterior surface of upper part of rectum (Fig. 18.16b):

- Forms rectouterine pouch
- Covers uterus
- Forms vesicouterine pouch
- Covers superior surface of urinary bladder
- Runs upward on the inner surface of anterior abdominal wall.

Horizontal Tracing above Transverse Colon

(Fig. 18.17)

The two layers (right and left) get reflected as *falciform ligament* on the liver

- Encloses the liver
- At *porta hepatis,* it forms lesser omentum which encloses the stomach
- The two layers of lesser omentum pass to left towards spleen as *gastrosplenic* ligament
- At the hilum, the two layers of gastrosplenic ligament diverge
- The anterior layer encloses the spleen, forms one layer of *lienorenal ligament*, covers left kidney and continues to line the structures in the anterior abdominal wall
- The posterior layer forms the other layer of lienorenal ligament and lines the structures in the posterior abdominal wall
- The two layers (right and left) get reflected as *falciform ligament* on the liver.

Horizontal Tracing below the Level of the Transverse Colon

On the back of the anterior abdominal wall, we see a number of peritoneal folds and fossae (Fig. 18.18).

Starting from the median plane, these are:

1. *Median umbilical fold* raised by the median umbilical ligament (remnant of the urachus).
2. Supravesical fossa.
3. *Medial umbilical fold* raised by the obliterated umbilical artery.

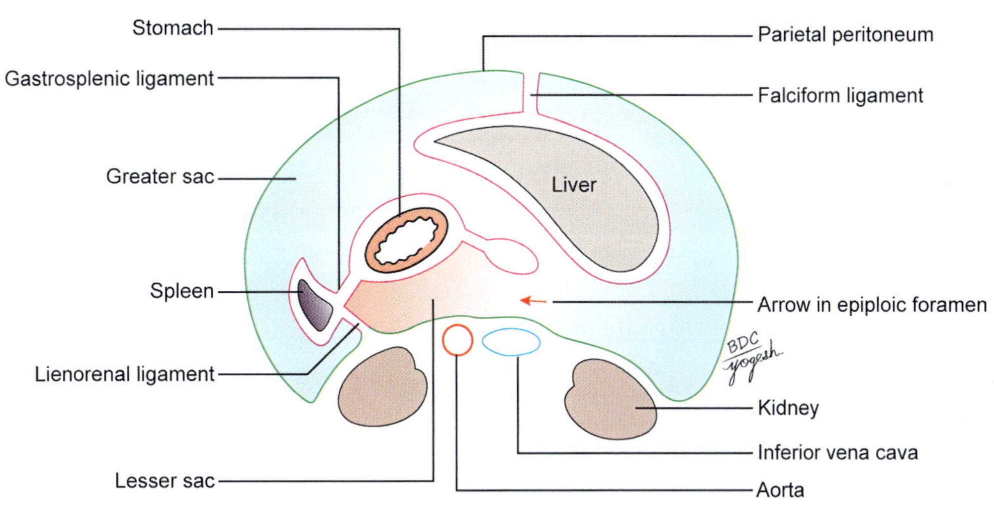

Fig. 18.17: Horizontal section through the supracolic compartment of the abdomen showing the horizontal disposition of the peritoneum

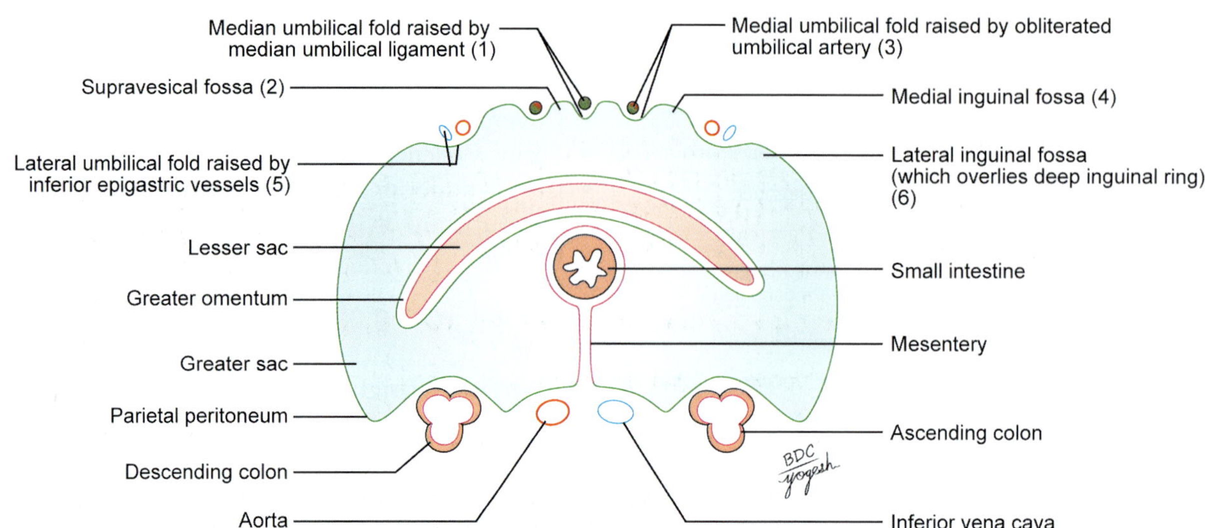

Fig. 18.18: Horizontal section through infracolic compartment of the abdomen showing the horizontal disposition of the peritoneum

4. Medial inguinal fossa.
5. *Lateral umbilical fold* raised by the inferior epigastric vessels.
6. *Lateral inguinal fossa* overlying the deep inguinal ring.

Further laterally, the peritoneum passes over the lateral part of abdominal wall to reach the posterior abdominal wall.

Near the middle, the peritoneum becomes continuous with the two layers of the mesentery and thus reaches the small intestine.

LESSER SAC OR OMENTAL BURSA

This is a large recess of the peritoneal cavity behind the stomach, the lesser omentum and the caudate lobe of the liver. It is closed all around, except in the upper part of its right border where it communicates with the greater sac through the epiploic foramen (Figs 18.16a, 18.19 and 18.20, Flowchart 18.5).

Boundaries of Lesser Sac

Anterior

1. Peritoneum covering caudate lobe and caudate process of liver
2. Posterior layer of lesser omentum
3. Peritoneum covering posterior surface of stomach
4. Second layer of greater omentum.

Posterior

1. Third layer of greater omentum
2. Peritoneum covering anterosuperior surface of transverse colon
3. Upper layer of transverse mesocolon
4. Peritoneum covering the anterior surface of body of pancreas, left suprarenal, left kidney, splenic vessels and diaphragm.

Upper

Reflection of peritoneum from diaphragm to liver.

Lower

Right margin of greater omentum. Reflection of peritoneum from neck of pancreas to 1st part of duodenum.

Right

- Epiploic foramen
- Peritoneal reflection from diaphragm to caudate lobe.

Left

- Left margin of greater omentum.
- Inner layers of gastrosplenic and lienorenal ligaments.

Subdivision of the Lesser Sac

The downward and forward course of the common hepatic artery raises a sickle-shaped fold of peritoneum from the posterior wall; this is known as the ***right gastropancreatic fold***. Similarly, the upwards course of the left gastric artery raises another similar fold, called the ***left gastropancreatic fold***. These folds divide the lesser sac into a superior and an inferior recess (Fig. 18.19).

1. The ***superior recess*** of the lesser sac lies behind the lesser omentum and the liver. The portion behind the lesser omentum is also known as the *vestibule* of the lesser sac.

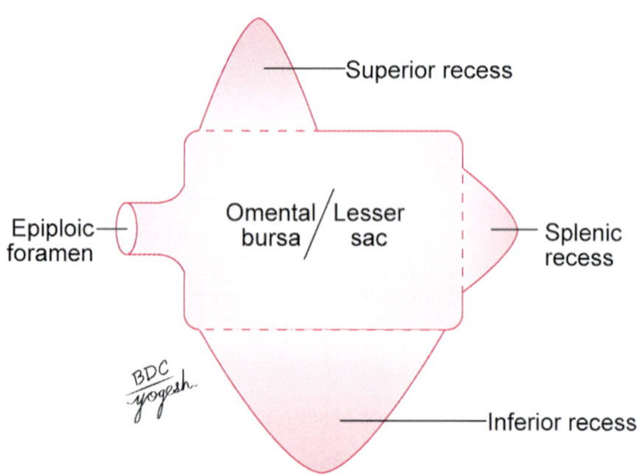

Fig. 18.19: Lesser sac with its opening and recesses

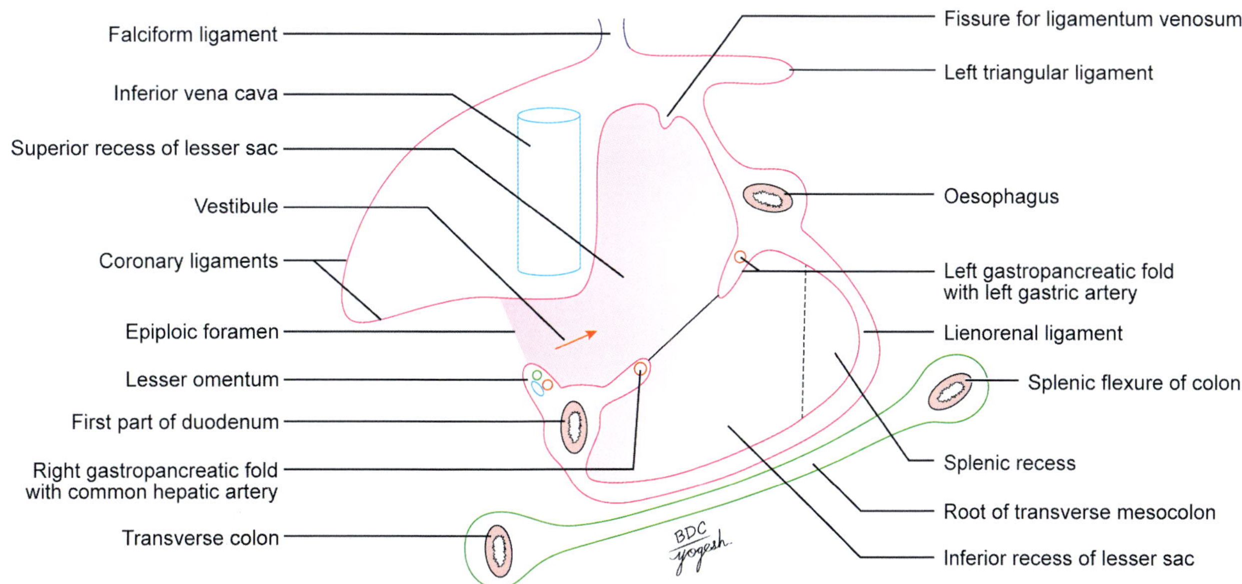

Fig. 18.20: Lesser sac seen after removal of its anterior wall

Flowchart 18.5: Lesser sac (omental bursa)

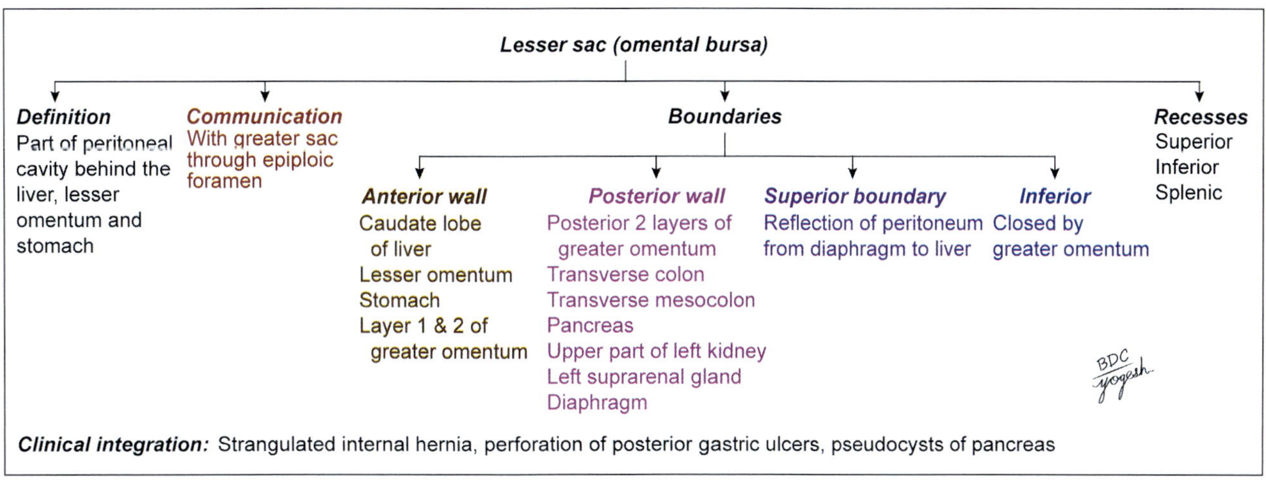

2. The ***inferior recess*** of the lesser sac lies behind the stomach and within the greater omentum.
3. The ***splenic recess*** of the lesser sac lies between the gastrosplenic and lienorenal ligaments.

EPIPLOIC FORAMEN/OMENTAL FORAMEN/FORAMEN OF WINSLOW

This is a vertical slit-like opening through which the lesser sac communicates with the greater sac (Figs 18.21 and 18.22, Flowchart 18.6).

Synonyms: Foramen of Winslow, aditus or opening to the lesser sac.

The foramen is situated behind the right free margin of the lesser omentum at the level of the 12th thoracic vertebra.

Boundaries

Anteriorly: Right free margin of the lesser omentum containing the portal vein, proper hepatic artery and the bile duct.

Posteriorly: Inferior vena cava, right suprarenal gland and T12 vertebra.

Superiorly: Caudate process of the liver.

Inferiorly: 1st part of the duodenum and the horizontal part of the hepatic artery.

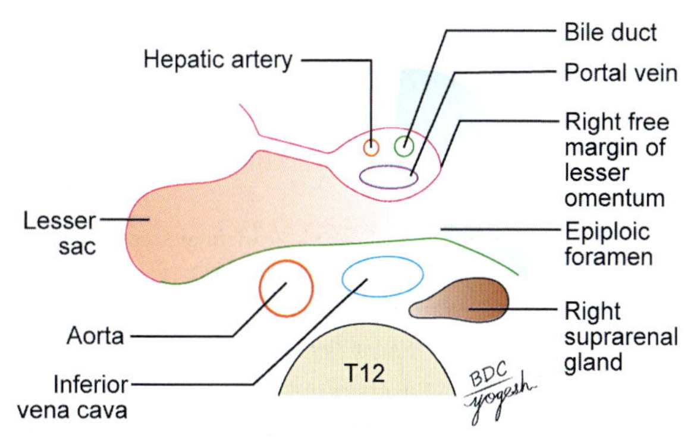

Fig. 18.21: Epiploic foramen as seen in a transverse section at the level of the 12th thoracic vertebra

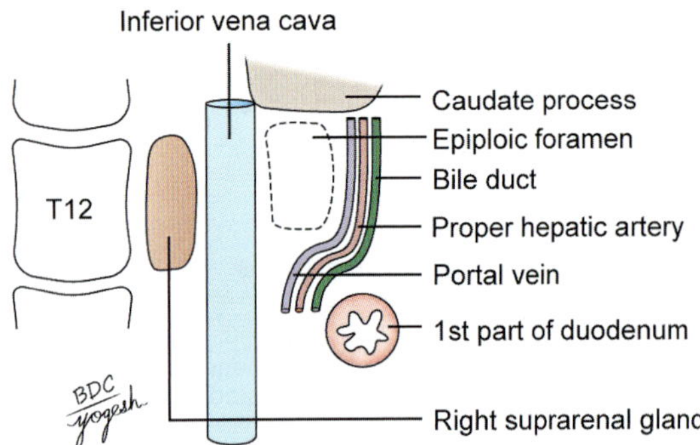

Fig. 18.22: Boundaries of epiploic foramen

Flowchart 18.6: Epiploic foramen of Winslow

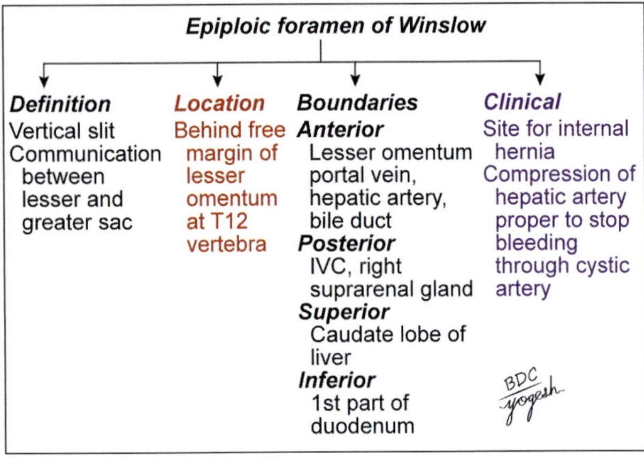

CLINICAL ANATOMY

- *Internal hernia*: Sometimes the coils of intestine may herniate to the lesser sac through the epiploic foramen. This herniation is called *internal hernia*.
- Strangulated ***internal hernia*** into the lesser sac through epiploic foramen is approached through the greater omentum because the epiploic foramen cannot be enlarged due to the presence of important structures all around it (Fig. 18.23).

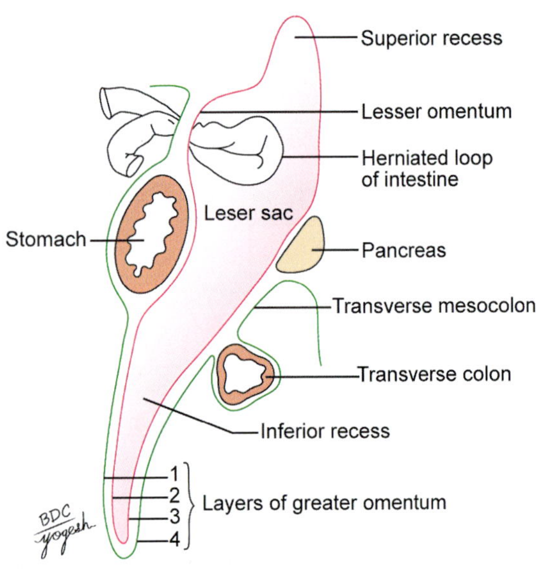

Fig. 18.23: Internal hernia into the lesser sac

- *Compression of hepatic artery proper*: In cholecystectomy surgery, the bleeding through torn cystic artery can be stopped by compressing the hepatic artery proper at the right free margin of lesser omentum (as cystic artery is a branch of right hepatic artery – branch of hepatic artery proper).
- A ***posterior gastric ulcer*** may perforate into the lesser sac. The leaking fluid passes out through epiploic foramen to reach the hepatorenal pouch. Sometimes in these cases, the epiploic foramen is closed by adhesions. Then the lesser sac becomes distended and can be drained by a tube passed through the lesser omentum.

Competency:

AN47.2 Name and identify various peritoneal folds and pouches with its explanation.

SPECIAL REGIONS OF THE PERITONEAL CAVITY

From a surgical point of view, the peritoneal cavity has two main parts—the abdomen proper and the pelvic cavity. The abdominal cavity is divided by the transverse colon and the transverse mesocolon into the *supracolic* and *infracolic compartments*.

The supracolic compartment is subdivided by the reflection of peritoneum around the liver into a number of *subphrenic spaces*.

The infracolic compartment is also subdivided, by the mesentery, into right and left parts. Further, the right *paracolic gutter* lies along the lateral side of the ascending colon, and the *left paracolic gutter* lies along the lateral side of the descending colon.

Hepatorenal Pouch (Morrison's Pouch)

Hepatorenal pouch is a subhepatic recess of a peritoneal cavity that lies between the liver and right kidney. It is the most dependent part of the peritoneal cavity in recumbent position (Figs 18.24 and 18.25 and Flowchart 18.7).

Boundaries

Anterior: 1. Inferior surface of the right lobe of liver
2. Gallbladder

Posterior: 1. Right suprarenal gland
2. Right kidney
3. Second part of duodenum
4. Hepatic flexure of colon

Superior: Inferior layer of coronary ligament

Inferior: Communicates with greater sac

On the right: Diaphragm

On the left: Epiploic foramen.

CLINICAL ANATOMY

1. Hepatorenal pouch is the most dependent (lowest) part of the peritoneal cavity in supine position (Fig. 18.25). This is the most common site of a subphrenic

abscess, which may be caused by spread of infection from the gallbladder, the appendix, or other organs in the region.

2. After cholecystectomy (surgical removal of gallbladder), bile or pus may accumulate in Morrison's pouch. Hence, after gallbladder surgeries, drainage tube is inserted in Morrison's pouch and kept for a few days till no fluid is aspirated.

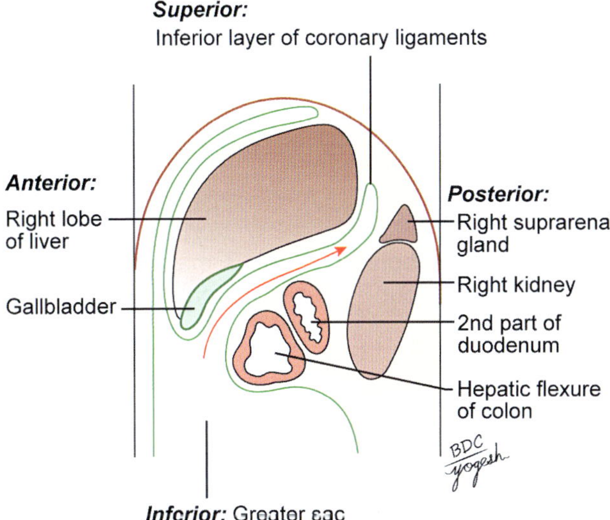

Fig. 18.24: Hepatorenal pouch

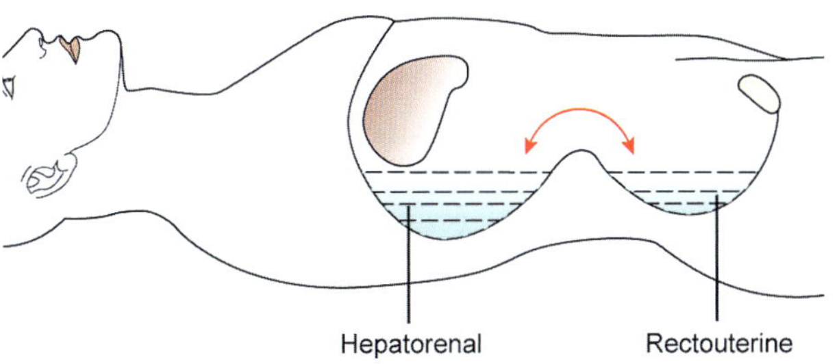

Fig. 18.25: Morrison's or hepatorenal pouch with rectouterine or Douglas pouch

Flowchart 18.7: Morrison's (hepatorenal) pouch

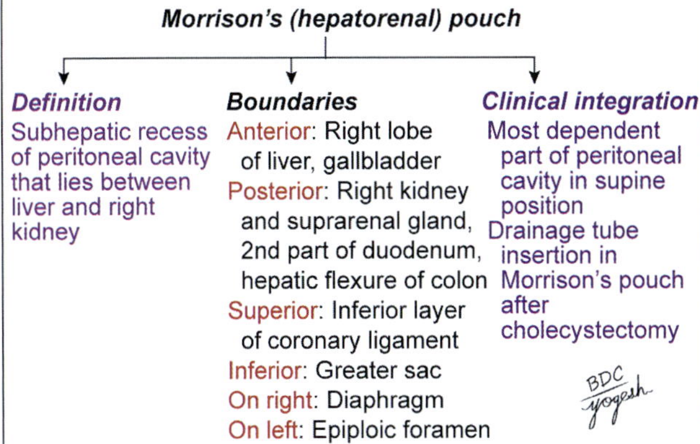

Rectouterine Pouch (Pouch of Douglas)

This is the most dependent part of the peritoneal cavity when the body is in the upright position. In the supine position, it is the most dependent part of the pelvic cavity (Fig. 18.26, Flowchart 18.8).

Boundaries

Anterior:	Uterus, posterior fornix of the vagina
Posterior:	Rectum
Inferior (floor):	Rectovaginal fold of the peritoneum
On each side:	Rectouterine folds of the peritoneum.

Contents

Coils of intestine.

CLINICAL ANATOMY

- The floor of the rectouterine pouch lies about 5.5 cm above the anus and 7.5 cm above the external opening of vagina.
- The contents of the rectouterine pouch can be palpated by finger on per rectal or per vaginal examination.
- In peritoneal infection, a pus tends to collect in rectouterine pouch due to its dependent position (Fig. 18.25). In such cases, the pus can be drained by an incision through posterior fornix of the vagina (posterior colpotomy).

Paracolic Gutters

Paracolic gutters are longitudinal peritoneal recesses that lie between the ascending and descending colons and the abdominal walls.

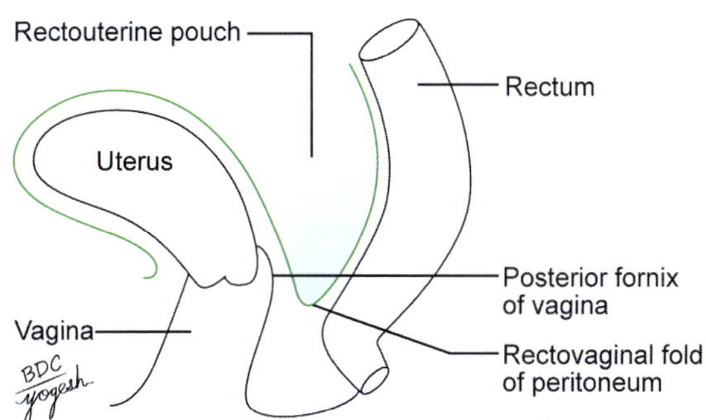

Fig. 18.26: Left view of a sagittal section through the rectouterine pouch

Flowchart 18.8: Rectouterine pouch of Douglas

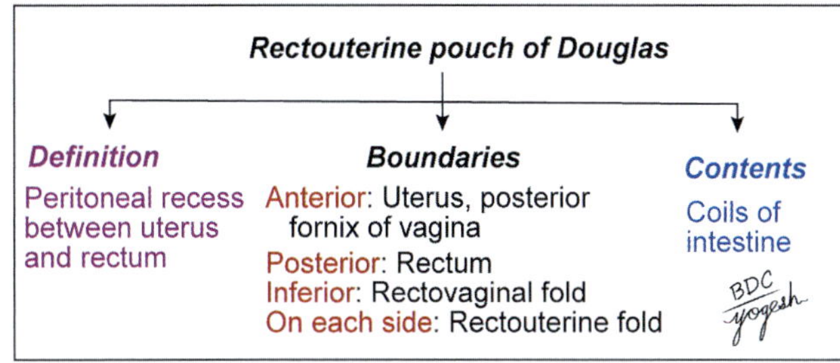

These are:

1. *Right lateral paracolic gutter*: It lies between ascending colon and the anterolateral body wall. It opens into hepatorenal pouch at its upper end. Infection from hepatorenal pouch, lesser sac, or from appendix may spread to right lateral paracolic gutter.
2. *Left lateral paracolic gutter*: It lies between descending colon and the anterolateral body wall. It opens into the pelvic cavity at its lower end.

Competency:
AN47.4 Explain anatomical basis of subphrenic abscess.

Subphrenic Spaces (Supracolic Compartment)

Subphrenic spaces are present just below the diaphragm in relation to the liver (Fig. 18.27).

Classification

The *intraperitoneal spaces* are:

The subphrenic spaces are classified as follows:

A. ***Intraperitoneal spaces*** (Fig. 18.27)
   1. Left anterior or *left subphrenic space* lies between the left lobe of the liver and diaphragm, in front of left triangular ligament.

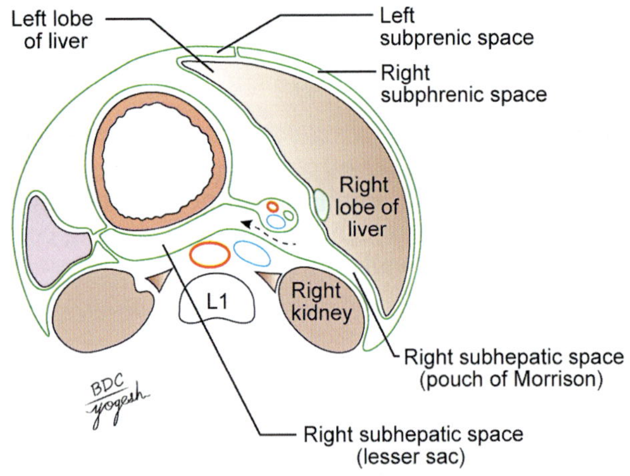

Fig. 18.27: Intraperitoneal subphrenic spaces (Transverse sections through the abdomen)

   2. Right anterior or *right subphrenic space* lies between the right lobe of liver and diaphragm, in front of superior layer of coronary ligament and right triangular ligament.
   3. Left posterior or *left subhepatic space* is a lesser sac or omental bursa.
   4. Right posterior or *right subhepatic space* is a hepatorenal pouch of Morrison.

B. ***Extraperitoneal spaces***
   1. Right extraperitoneal space lies around the upper pole of the right kidney.
   2. Left extraperitoneal space lies around the left suprarenal gland and upper pole of the left kidney.
   3. Midline extraperitoneal space lies between the bare area of liver and the diaphragm.

CLINICAL ANATOMY

Intraperitoneal subphrenic spaces may get distended by collection of pus. These are called subphrenic abscesses.

PERITONEAL FOSSAE (RECESSES)

These are small pockets of the peritoneal cavity enclosed by small, inconstant folds of peritoneum. They commonly occur at the transitional zones between the absorbed and unabsorbed parts of the mesentery. These are best observed in foetuses and are mostly obliterated in adults. Sometimes they persist to form potential sites for internal hernia and their strangulation.

These spaces are grouped as follows (Figs 18.28a to c):

1. Lesser sac (largest recess)
2. Duodenal recesses: These are inconsistent peritoneal fossae that lie surrounding the duodenum. These include superior, inferior, paraduodenal, retroduodenal recess, mesocolic recess and mesentericoparietal fossa of Waldeyer.
3. Caecal recess are spaces formed by the peritoneum around the caecum. These are superior, inferior ileocaecal recess and retrocaecal recess.

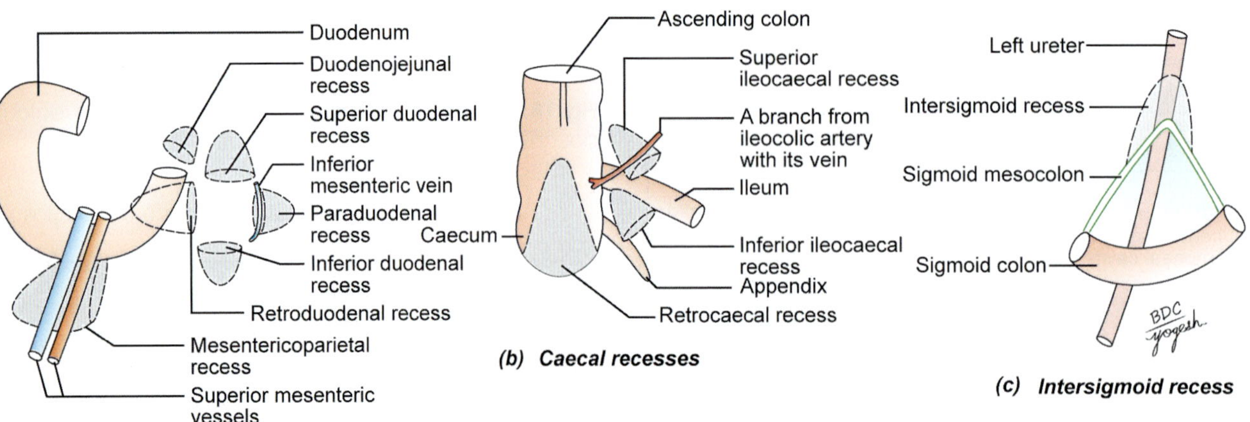

Figs. 18.28a to c: Peritoneal recesses: (a) Duodenal recesses of peritoneum, (b) Caecal recesses of peritoneum, and (c) Intersigmoid recess of peritoneum

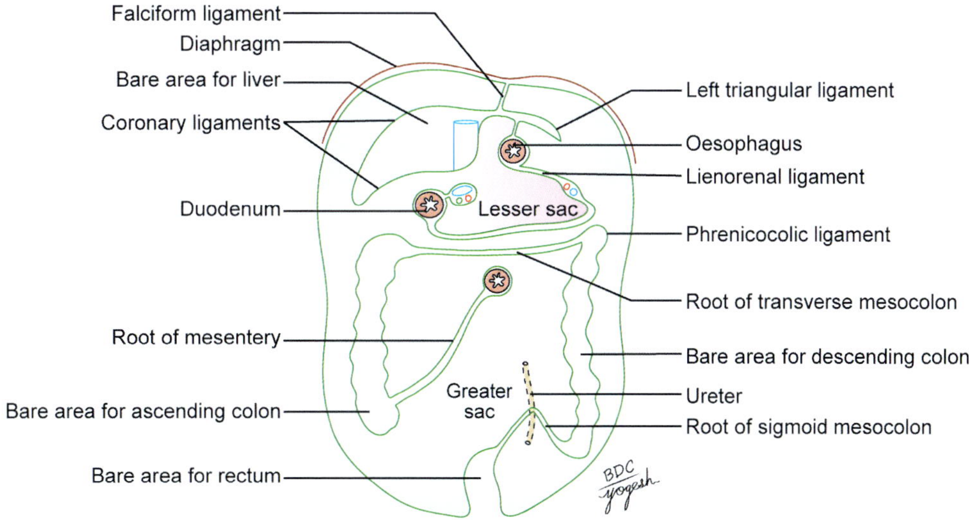

Fig. 18.29: Attachments of the peritoneum on the posterior abdominal wall and bare area of viscera

4. Intersigmoid recess is present in fetal life and childhood and disappears in later life. It lies posterior to the apex of V-shaped sigmoid mesocolon. This space is funnel shaped and opens downward.

The attachment of the peritoneum to the posterior abdominal wall and bare areas of abdominal viscera are shown in Fig. 18.29.

Video 2.18 **Peritoneal Cavity**

Facts to Remember

- There are 9 regions of the abdominal cavity. These are right and left hypochondrium and middle epigastrium in upper part. In middle part are right and left lumbar/ lateral and middle umbilical regions. In the lower part are right and left iliac fossae and middle hypogastrium.
- Abdominal part of foregut has a dorsal and ventral mesentery each.
- Midgut and hindgut have only the dorsal mesenteries each.
- Lesser sac with its fluid prevents compression of most of the posterior abdominal organs by the full stomach.
- Rectouterine pouch in female is 5.5 cm from surface of perineal skin.
- Rectovesical pouch in male is 7.5 cm away from the perineal skin.
- Peritoneal recesses are mostly present at the junction of intraperitoneal and retroperitoneal organs.
- Right posterior subphrenic space or Morrison's pouch is the deepest pouch in lying position.

BDC's Anatomy *e*-book

1. Details of functions of peritoneum
2. Development of gut and its folds
3. Horizontal tracing of peritoneum in the true pelvis
4. Further reading
5. Viva voce questions

Chapter

19

Abdominal Part of Oesophagus and Stomach

Competency:

AN47.5 Describe and demonstrate major viscera of abdomen under the following headings: Anatomical position, external and internal features, important peritoneal and other relations, blood supply, nerve supply, lymphatic drainage and applied aspects.

ABDOMINAL PART OF OESOPHAGUS

1. The abdominal part of the oesophagus is only about 1.25 cm long (Plate 19.1 and Flowchart 19.1).
2. ***Oesophageal opening of diaphragm***: The oesophagus enters the abdomen through the ***oesophageal opening*** of the diaphragm situated at the level of vertebra T10, slightly to the left of the median plane. It continues with the cardiac end of stomach.

   The oesophageal opening also transmits the anterior and posterior gastric nerves, the oesophageal branches of the left gastric artery and the accompanying veins.
3. The oesophagus runs downwards and to the left in front of the left crus of the diaphragm and of the inferior surface of the left lobe of the liver and ends by opening into the cardiac end of the stomach at the level of vertebra T11, about 2.5 cm to the left of the median plane. Its *right border* is continuous with the lesser curvature of the stomach, but the *left border* is separated from the fundus of the stomach by the ***cardiac notch***. Peritoneum covers the oesophagus only anteriorly and on the left side.
4. ***Phreno-oesophageal ligament*** anchors the oesophagus to crural fibres of thoracoabdominal diaphragm and stabilises it.
5. ***Arterial supply***: The oesophagus is supplied by numerous oesophageal branches of left gastric artery. It is also supplied by branches from short gastric arteries and terminal arteries from oesophageal branches of thoracic aorta.
6. ***Venous drainage***: The veins of oesophagus drain partly into portal and partly into systemic circulation. Veins accompanying left gastric vein drain into portal vein. Others drain into hemiazygos in thoracic cavity and continue into vena azygos and superior vena cava. So it is a ***site of portosystemic anastomoses*** (Fig. 19.1).

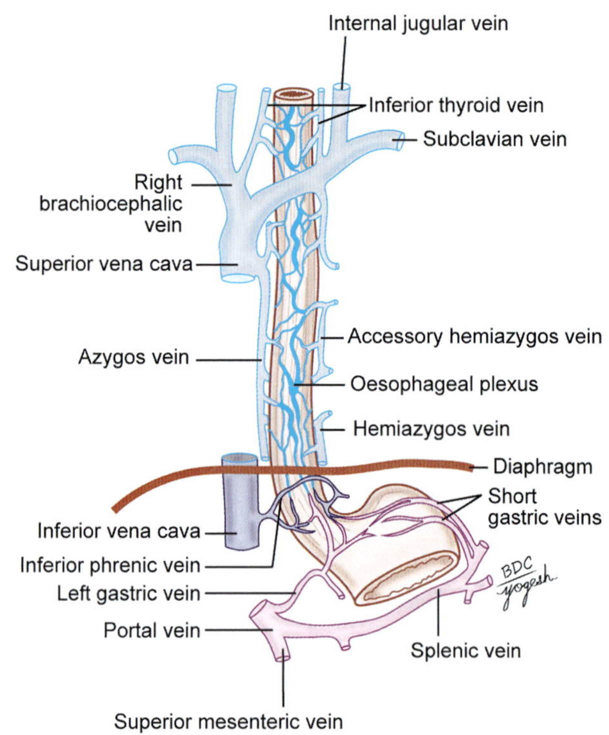

Fig. 19.1: Venous drainage of oesophagus

7. ***Innervation***: The abdominal part of oesophagus is supplied by the following fibres:

   Parasympathetic fibres from vagus nerves. They control coordinated contraction and relaxation of lower oesophageal sphincter (LES).

   Sympathetic fibres from T5 to T12 spinal segments through greater and lesser splanchnic nerves and coeliac plexus.
8. ***Lymphatic drainage***: Lymph from lower part of oesophagus drains into left gastric, right and left paracardial and ends in coeliac nodes.

HISTOLOGY OF OESOPHAGUS

Oesophagus has the following layers (Plate 19.2):

1. ***Mucosae***: It consists of stratified squamous epithelium (nonkeratinized), lamina propria and muscularis mucosa (thick, longitudinal smooth muscles).

Plate 19.1: Abdominal part of oesophagus and upper part of stomach

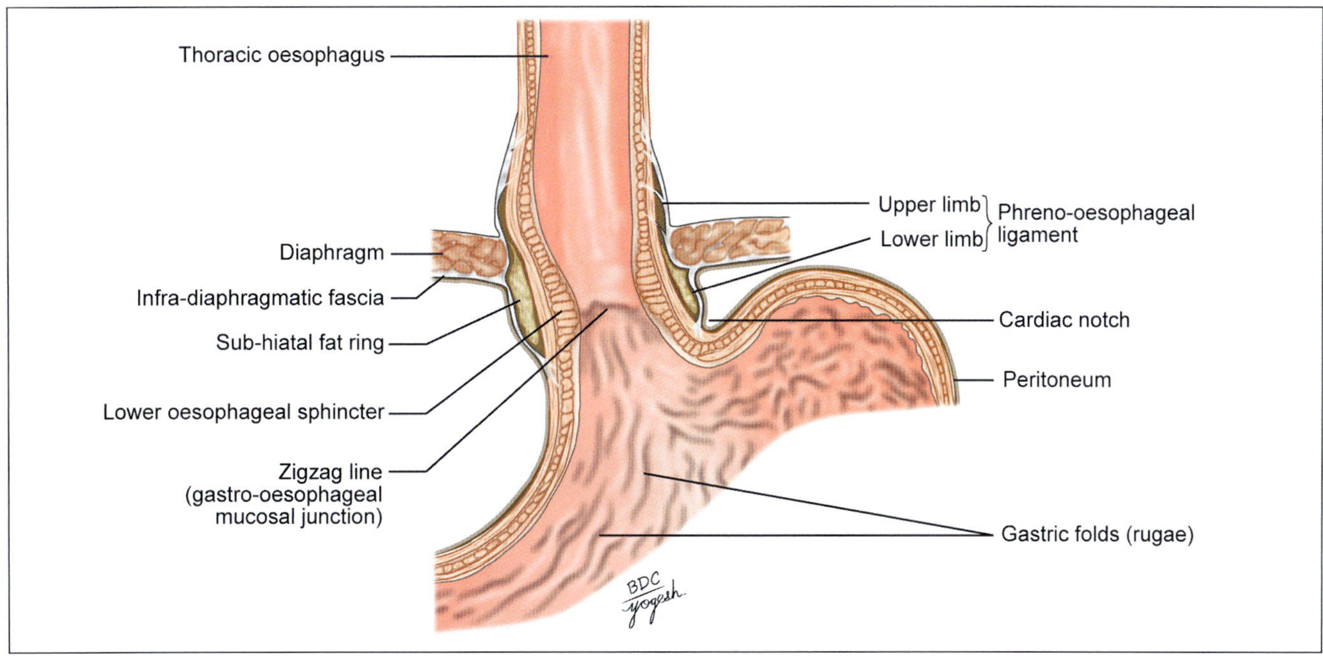

Plate 19.2: Histology of lower part of oesophagus

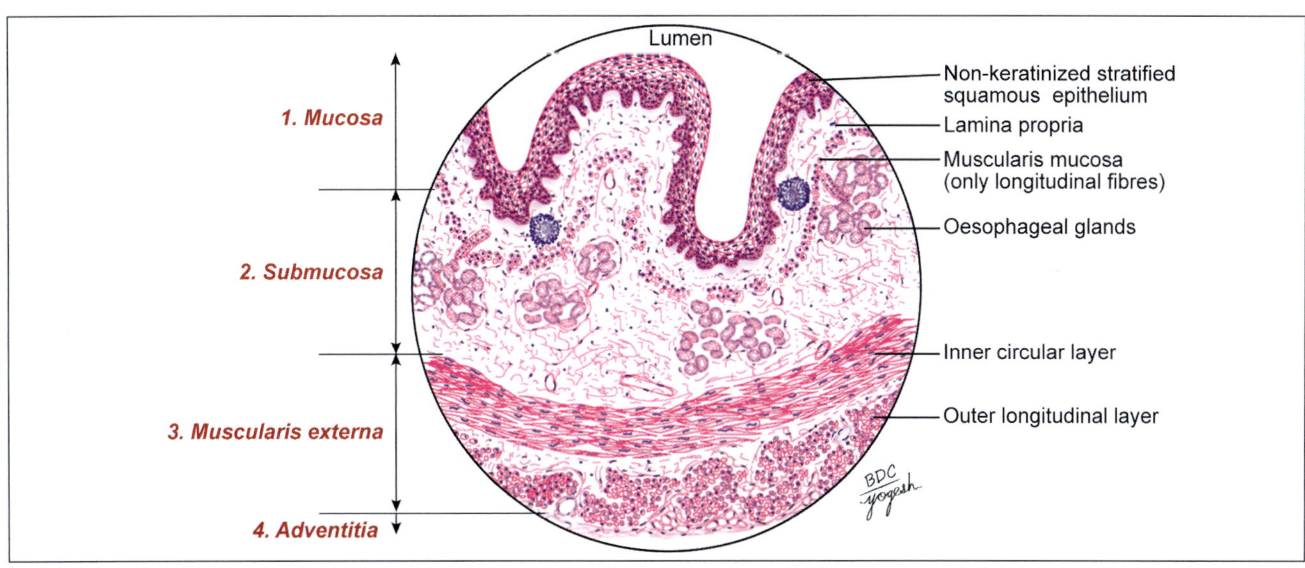

(*Source*: Textbook of Human Histology, Yogesh Sontakke)

Flowchart 19.1: Abdominal part of oesophagus

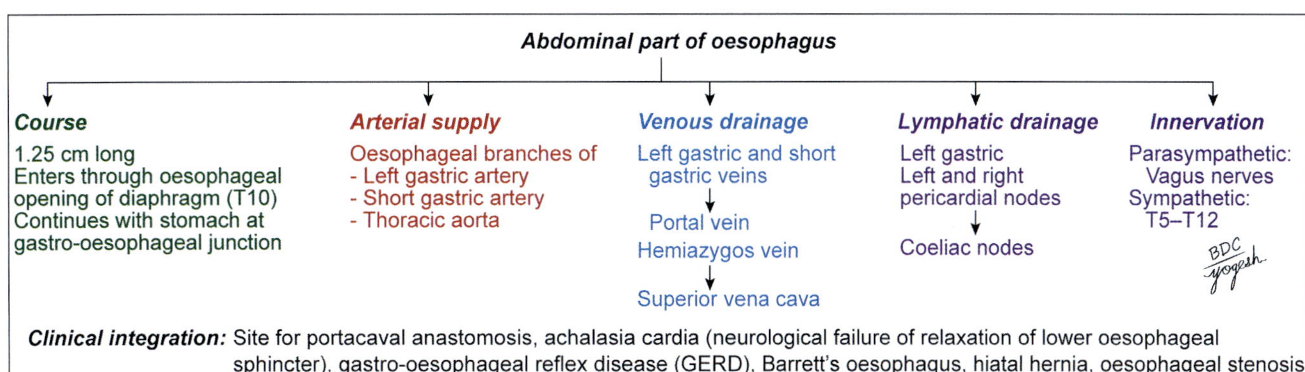

2. ***Submucosa*:** It consists of dense irregular connective tissue with elastic fibres and compound tubuloalveolar glands.
3. ***Muscularis externa*:** In upper third of oesophagus, it has skeletal muscle fibres; in middle third, both skeletal and smooth muscle fibres; whereas in lower third, only smooth muscle fibres.
4. ***Adventitia*:** Oesophagus is surrounded by connective tissue. Only the lowest 1 inch, it is surrounded by serosa (peritoneum).

Factors Preventing Gastroesophageal Reflux

The following factors prevent the gastroesophageal reflux:

1. *Flutter valve*: The abdominal part of oesophagus is directed obliquely (downward and to the left). On an increase in intra-abdominal pressure, it compresses the oesophagus as flutter valve.
2. *Flap valve*: The mucosal fold at the cardiac notch in the stomach wall acts as a flap valve during the contraction of stomach muscles.
3. *Phreno-oesophageal ligament*: It is derived from subdiaphragmatic fascia and anchors exophages to crural muscles of diaphragm. It has upper and lower limbs. It limits upward and downward mobility of oesophagus.
4. *Mucosal rosette* in the abdominal oesophagus acts as a water-tight plug.
5. *Pinch-cock action of oesophageal opening* of the diaphragm prevents the mobility of oesophagus.

CLINICAL ANATOMY

- ***Portacaval anastomosis*:** The lower end of oesophagus has portacaval anastomosis. In portal hypertension, veins of oesophagus dilate and may cause oesophageal varices and severe hematemesis (Fig. 19.2).
- ***Oesophageal varices*** are dilated veins at the lower end of oesophagus. It occurs in portal hypertension (pressure >10 mm Hg). It involves oesophageal tributaries of left gastric and inferior hemiazygos vein.
- ***Oesophagoscopy*** is the visualization of interior of the oesophagus using oesophagoscope.
- ***Achalasia cardia*:** It is also called *cardiospasm*. In achalasia cardia, because of neuromuscular dysfunctions, lower oesophageal sphincter (cardiac sphincter) fails to relax (Fig. 19.3). It results in mega-oesophagus (dilatation of oesophagus) and patient complaints of dysphagia (difficulty in swallowing), and in severe cases, there may be a regurgitation of undigested food in respiratory tract.
- ***Gastroesophageal reflux disease*** (*GERD*)**:** In GERD, because of failure of lower oesophageal sphincter mechanism, the acidic contents of stomach enter the lower part of oesophagus. It causes heartburn (chest pain) and inflammation of oesophagus.
- ***Barrett's oesophagus*:** In Barrett's oesophagus, lining epithelium of oesophagus changes from stratified squamous to simple columnar epithelium with goblet cells. The main cause of Barrett's oesophagus is GERD. This is a precancerous condition.
- ***Hiatal hernia*** is a herniation of oesophagus through the oesophageal opening. It may be sliding or rolling (paraesophageal) (Fig. 19.4).
- ***Oesophageal stenosis*** is abnormal narrowing of lumen of oesophagus.

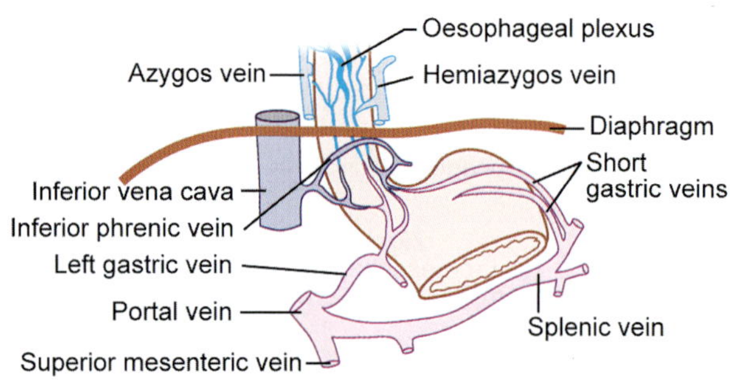

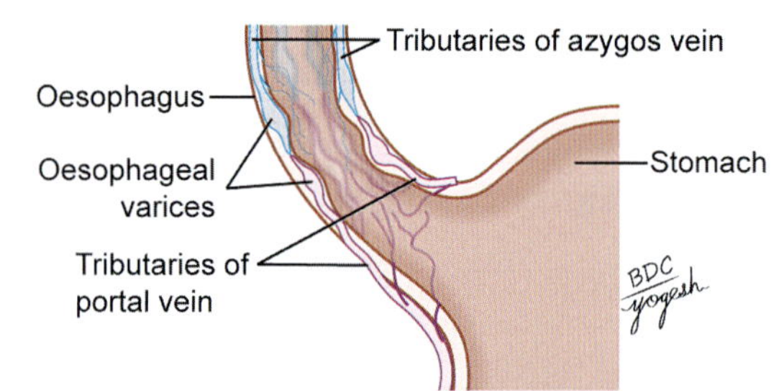

Fig. 19.2: Oesophageal varices

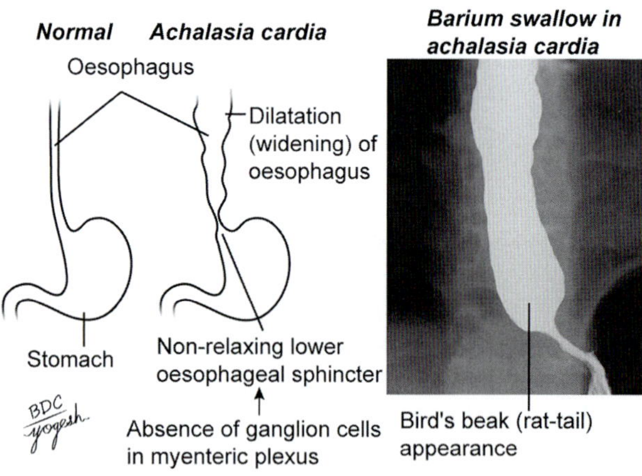

Fig. 19.3: Achalasia cardia

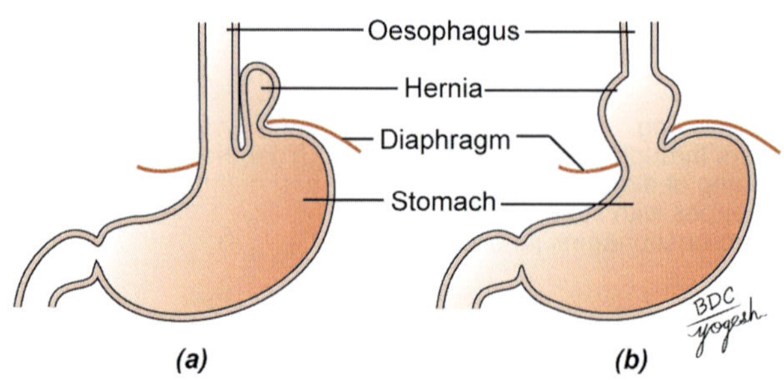

Figs 19.4a and b: Hiatal hernia: (a) Rolling and (b) sliding

DISSECTION

Identify the stomach and trace it towards the abdominal part of oesophagus. Clean this part of oesophagus. Note various parts of stomach, e.g. cardiac end, fundus, body and pyloric parts. Trace the right and left gastric arteries along the lesser curvature and right and left gastroepiploic arteries along the greater curvature.

Tie two ligatures each at the lowest part of oesophagus and the pylorus. Remove the stomach by cutting between two upper ligatures through the oesophagus, left gastric artery, gastrophrenic ligament; and by cutting the pylorus between the lower two ligatures. Free the stomach from the adherent peritoneum, if any, and put it in a tray for further dissection.

STOMACH

The stomach is also called the gaster (Greek *belly*) or venter from which we have the adjective gastric applied to structures related to the organ.

The stomach is a muscular bag forming the widest and most distensible part of the digestive tube. It is connected above to the lower end of the oesophagus and below to the duodenum. It acts as a reservoir of food and helps in digestion of carbohydrates, proteins and fats.

Functions of Stomach

The functions of stomach are as follows:

1. Acts primarily as a reservoir of food. It also acts as a mixer of food.
2. Softens and mixes the food with the gastric juice.
3. Produce gastric juice which contains enzymes that play an important role in digestion of food.
4. Produce hydrochloric acid which destroys many organisms present in food and drink.
5. Produce abundant mucus which protects the gastric mucosa against the corrosive action of hydrochloric acid.
6. Absorb alcohol, water, salt and a few drugs.
7. Produces the 'intrinsic factor' of Castle which helps in the absorption of vitamin B12.

Location

The stomach lies obliquely in the upper and left part of the abdomen, occupying the epigastric, umbilical and left hypochondriac regions. Most of it lies under cover of the left costal margin and the ribs (Fig. 19.5).

Shape and Position

The shape of the stomach depends upon the degree of tone of its muscles and tone of muscles of the body. In normal active persons (sthenic), its shape is somewhat J-shaped (Plate 19.3 and Fig. 19.6).

Size and Capacity

Length: about 25 cm

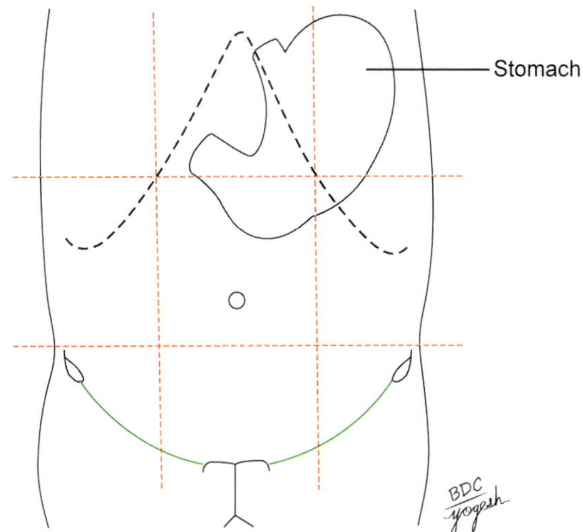

Fig. 19.5: Location of the stomach

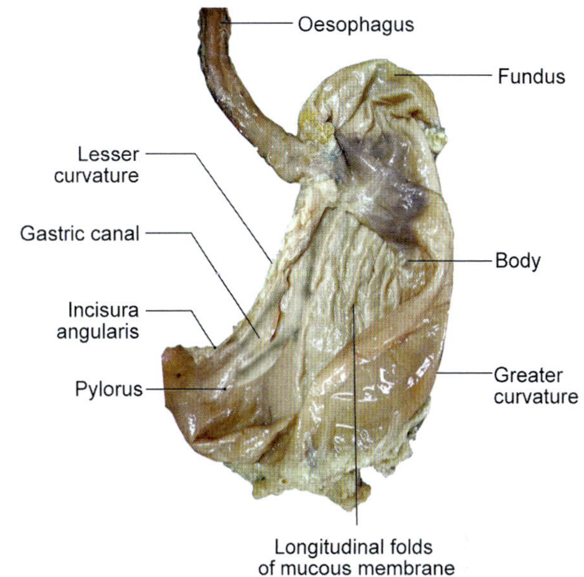

Fig. 19.6: Oesophagus and stomach

Capacity: The stomach is a very distensible organ. It capacity is as follows:

1. One ounce (30 ml) at birth
2. One litre (1000 ml) at puberty
3. One to one and half (1000–1500 ml) in adults.

Note: In thin, tall persons (hyposthenic), its shape is J-shaped, while in broad, strong and very active persons, its shape is horizontal.

25 cm long structures: Oesophagus, stomach, duodenum and ureter.

EXTERNAL FEATURES

The stomach has the following presenting features (Plate 19.3, Fig. 19.7 and Flowchart 19.2):

1. ***Two orifices***: Cardiac and pyloric
2. ***Two curvatures***: Lesser and greater
3. ***Two surfaces***: Anterior and posterior (in distended stomach) or superior and inferior (in empty stomach).

Plate 19.3: Stomach: External features and parts

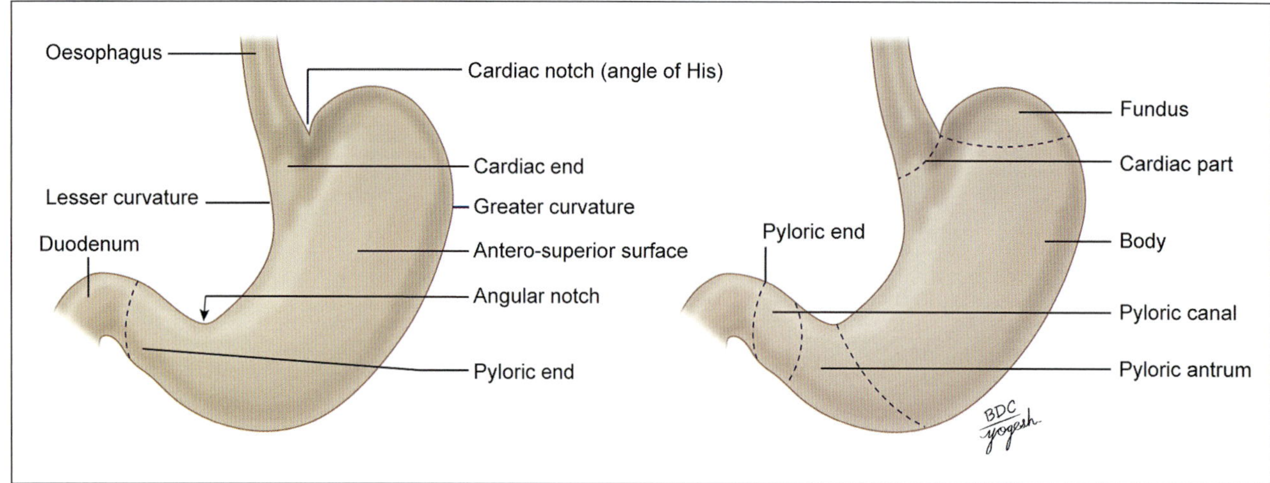

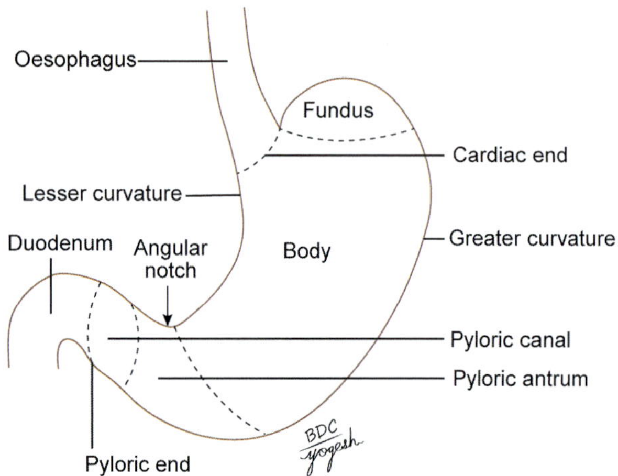

Fig. 19.7: External features of the stomach

Flowchart 19.2: External features of stomach

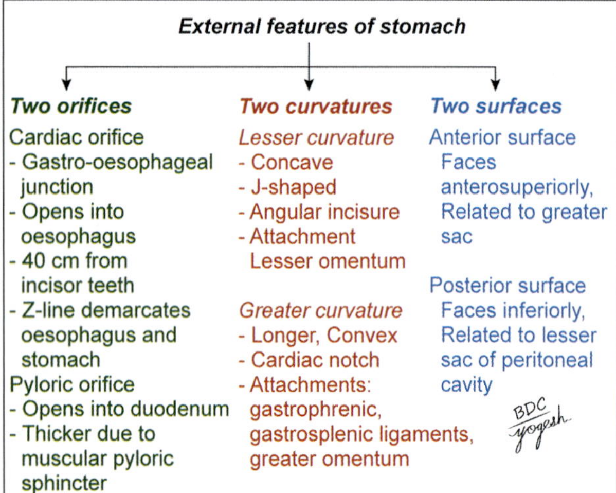

Anatomical Position

Hold the stomach in such a way that:

1. The stomach is flat anteroposteriorly.
2. Concave lesser curvature faces to the right and convex greater curvature faces to the left and inferiorly.
3. Thick pyloric end is directed downward and to the right.
4. The cardiac or upper end of the stomach lies at higher level and to the left than the pyloric end.

Two Orifices/Ends

1. ***Cardiac orifice:*** It is joined by the lower end of the oesophagus.

   Note: It lies behind the left 7th costal cartilage 2.5 cm from its junction with the sternum, at the level of vertebra T11. There is physiological evidence of sphincteric action at this site, but a sphincter cannot be demonstrated anatomically.

2. ***Pyloric orifice*** opens into the duodenum. Its position is indicated on the surface of the stomach:
   a. By a circular groove (*pyloric constriction* produced by the underlying pyloric sphincter or pylorus; *pylorus* = gate guard) which feels like a large firm nodule.
   b. By the *prepyloric vein* of Mayo which lies in front of the constriction.

   Note: In an empty stomach and in the supine position, it lies 1.2 cm to the right of median plane, at the level of lower border of vertebra L1 or transpyloric plane.

Two Curvatures

1. The ***lesser curvature*** is concave and forms the right border of the stomach. It provides attachment to the lesser omentum. The most dependent part of the curvature is marked by the *angular notch* or ***incisura angularis***.
2. The ***greater curvature*** is convex and forms the left border of the stomach. At its upper end, the greater curvature presents the ***cardiac notch*** which separates it from the oesophagus.

   It provides attachment to the greater omentum, the gastrosplenic ligament and the gastrophrenic ligament.

Two Surfaces

1. The *anterior* or *anterosuperior surface* faces forwards and upwards.
2. The *posterior* or *posteroinferior surface* faces backwards and downwards.

Parts of Stomach

The stomach is divided into four parts: Fundus, body, pyloric antrum and pyloric canal (*Reference:* Gray's Anatomy, 42nd edition).

Lines Dividing the Stomach

- Horizontal line at the level of cardiac notch extending to the greater curvature.
- Slightly oblique line extending from incisura angularis to a notch on the left side of pyloric antrum on the greater curvature (This notch may not be clearly visible.)
- *Sulcus intermedius* is an occasional sulcus that intervenes between the pyloric antrum and pyloric canal.

1. ***Fundus*:** It is the upper convex part of the stomach that lies above the horizontal line passing through the cardiac notch to the greater curvature.
2. ***Body*:** It lies between the fundus and pyloric antrum. It is separated from the pyloric antrum by a slightly oblique line extending to left from the incisura angularis to the greater curvature.
3. ***Pyloric antrum*:** It is separated from the pylorus by sulcus intermedius. It is 7.5 cm long.
4. ***Pylorus** or **pyloric canal*:** It is about 1–2 cm long, narrow, tubular part. It continues with duodenum at its right end.

Note: ***Traube's area*** is the area overlying the fundus of the stomach which is tympanic on percussion. It is bounded as follows:
Superiorly: Lower border of left lung
Inferiorly: Left costal margin
On the left: Spleen
On the right: Lower border of the left lobe of liver.
Traube's space shows dull note on percussion in case of pleural effusion and splenomegaly.

RELATIONS OF STOMACH

Peritoneal Relations

The stomach is lined by peritoneum on both surfaces except where the vessels run along its curvatures and at the bare area of the stomach (Figs 19.8, Plate 19.4 and Flowchart 19.3).

Bare area of the stomach is a small area that is devoid of peritoneum and comes in direct contact with the left crus of diaphragm. It is located near the cardiac end on the posterior surface.

The folds of peritoneum extending from stomach:

1. Lesser omentum extends from the lesser curvature to the liver.
2. Greater omentum extends downward from the greater curvature.
3. Gastrosplenic ligament extends from upper part of greater curvature to the spleen.
4. Gastrophrenic ligament extends from fundus of stomach to the diaphragm.

Thus, the greater curvature of the stomach gives attachment to gastrophrenic ligament, gastrosplenic ligament and greater omentum from above downward.

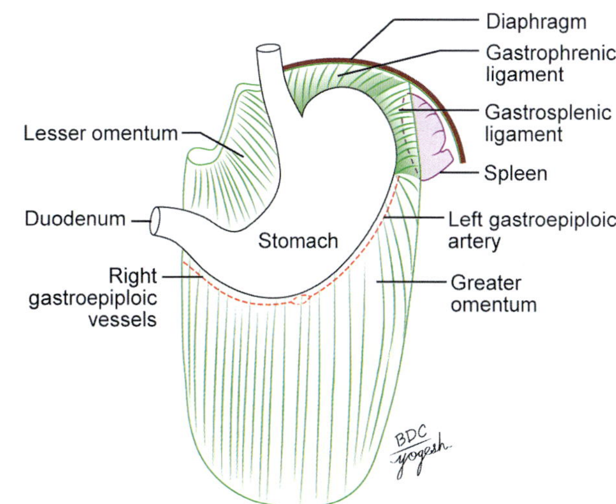

Fig. 19.8: Peritoneal relations of stomach

Flowchart 19.3: Relations of stomach

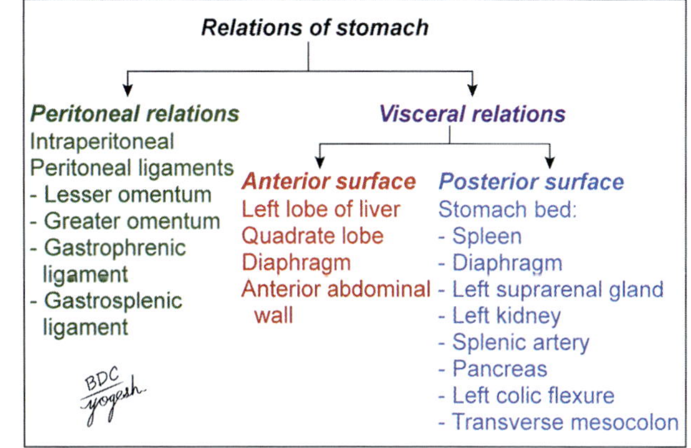

Visceral Relations

Relations of Anterior Surface

The anterior surface of the stomach is related to the liver, the diaphragm and the anterior abdominal wall (Fig. 19.9).

The diaphragm separates the stomach from the left pleura, the pericardium and the 6th to 9th ribs. The costal cartilages are separated from the stomach by

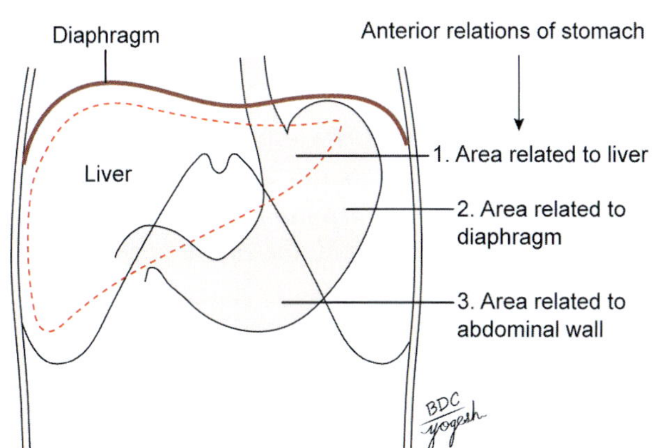

Fig. 19.9: Anterior relations of stomach. Area 1st is covered by the liver, area 2nd by the diaphragm and area 3rd by the anterior abdominal wall

Plate 19.4: Relations of stomach

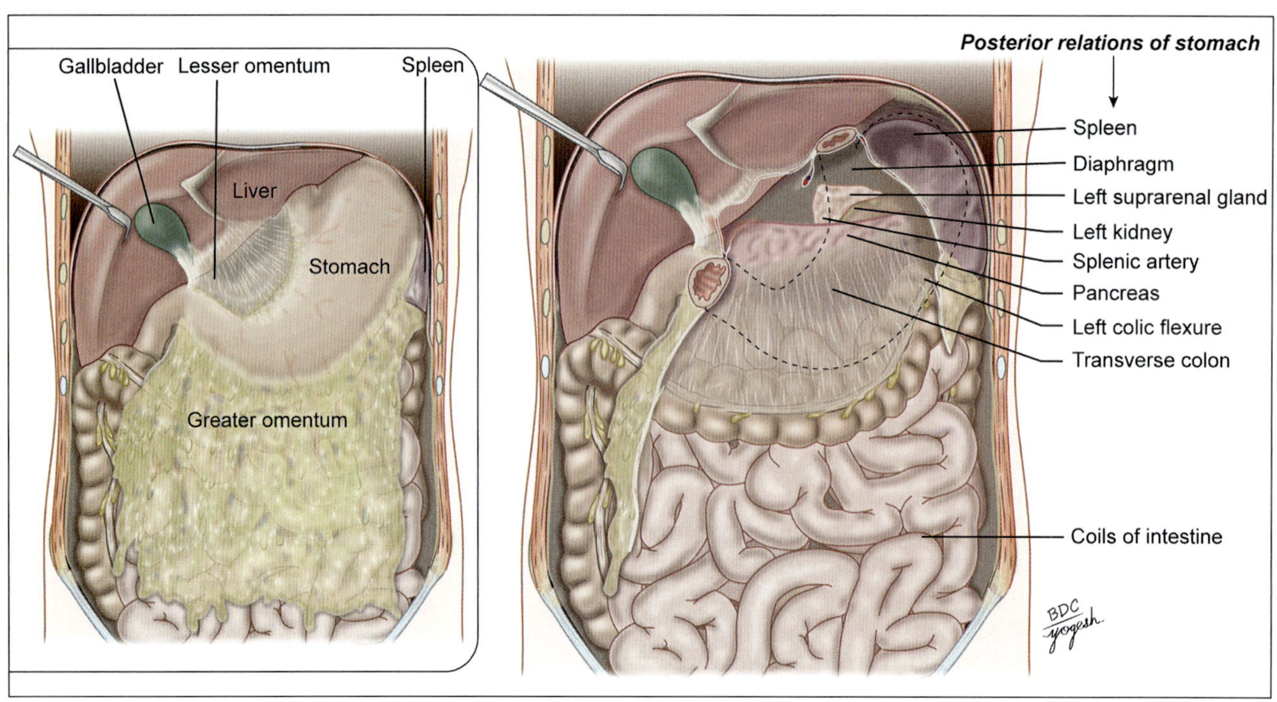

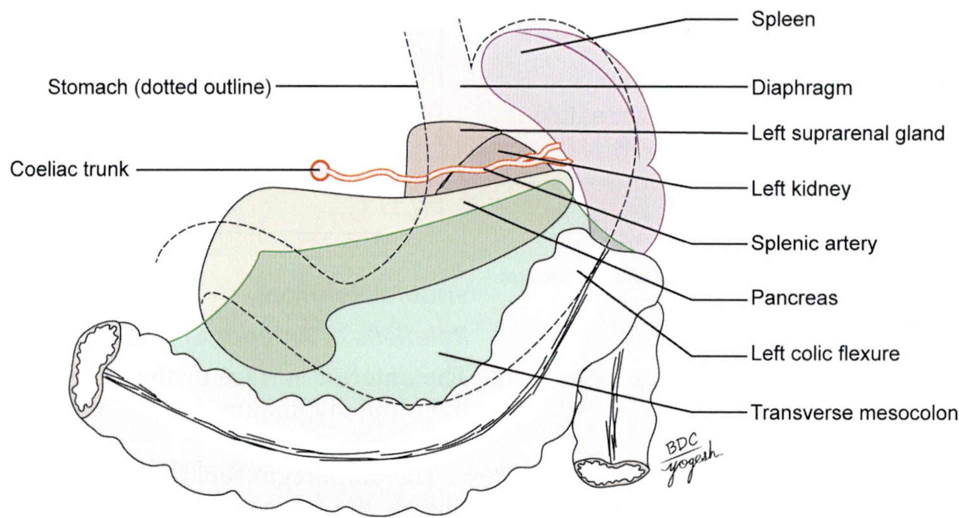

Fig. 19.10: The stomach bed

the transversus abdominis. Gastric nerves and vessels ramify deep to the peritoneum.

Relations of Posterior Surface (Stomach Bed)

The posterior surface of the stomach is related to structures forming the ***stomach bed***, *all of which are separated from the stomach by the cavity of the lesser sac* (Fig. 19.10).

These structures are:

1. Diaphragm
2. Spleen
3. Left kidney
4. Left suprarenal gland
5. Pancreas
6. Transverse mesocolon
7. Left colic flexure
8. Splenic artery
9. Spleen.

Note: All the structures of the stomach bed are separated from the stomach by the cavity of the lesser sac except the spleen which is separated from the stomach by the cavity of the greater sac.

BLOOD SUPPLY

Arterial Supply

The stomach is supplied by the following arteries (Fig. 19.11 and Flowchart 19.4):

1. Left gastric artery — branch of coeliac trunk.
2. Right gastric artery — branch of common hepatic artery.
3. Left gastroepiploic artery — branch of splenic artery.

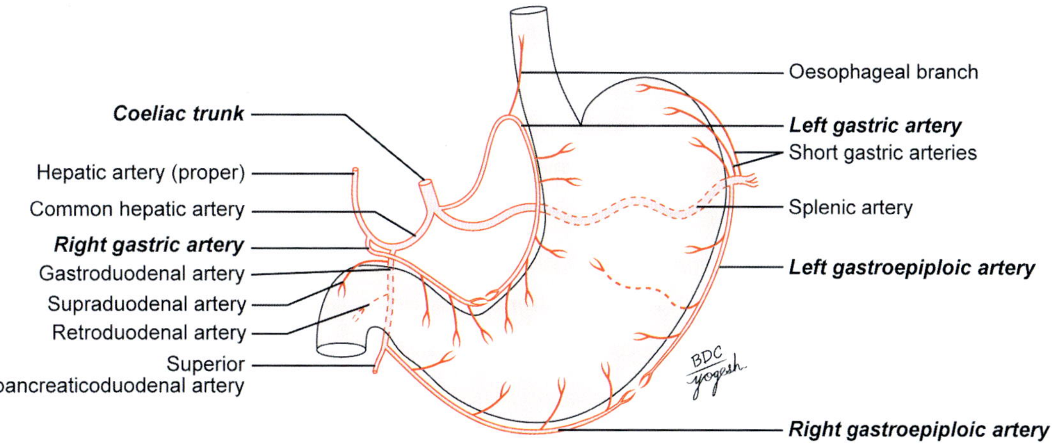

Fig. 19.11: Arteries supplying the stomach

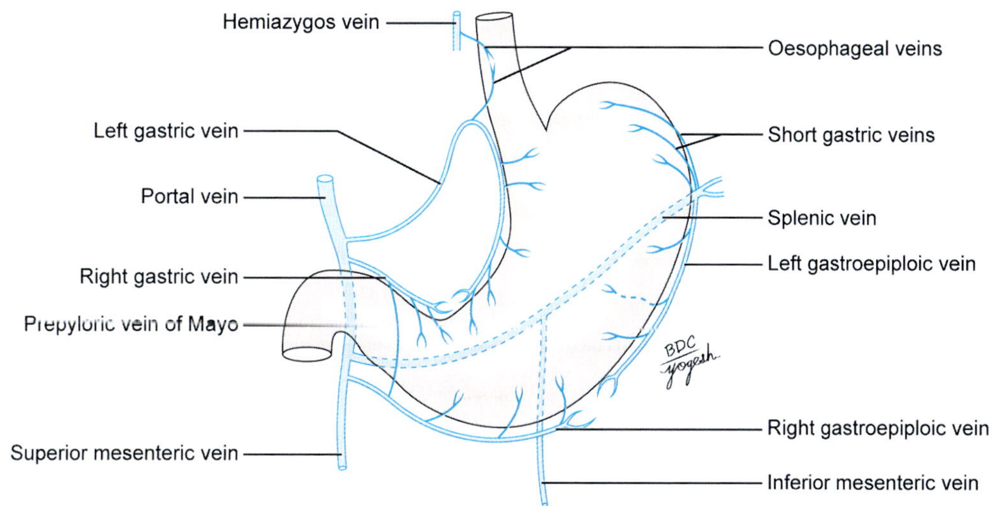

Fig. 19.12: Venous drainage of the stomach

4. Right gastroepiploic artery—branch of gastroduodenal artery.
5. Short gastric arteries (5–7 in number) — branch of splenic artery.
6. Posterior gastric artery — branch of splenic artery.

Venous Drainage

The venous blood from the stomach is drained by the following veins (Fig. 19.12, Flowchart 19.4):

1. Left gastric vein
2. Right gastric vein
3. Left gastroepiploic vein
4. Right gastroepiploic vein
5. Short gastric veins
6. Posterior gastric vein.

LYMPHATIC DRAINAGE

The lymphatics from the stomach follows the course of the arteries supplying the stomach. The following nodes drain the lymphatics from stomach (Fig. 19.13, Flowchart 19.4):

1. Left paracardial nodes, lesser curvature nodes, right paracardial nodes and left gastric nodes.

Flowchart 19.4: Stomach: Blood supply, innervation and lymphatic drainage

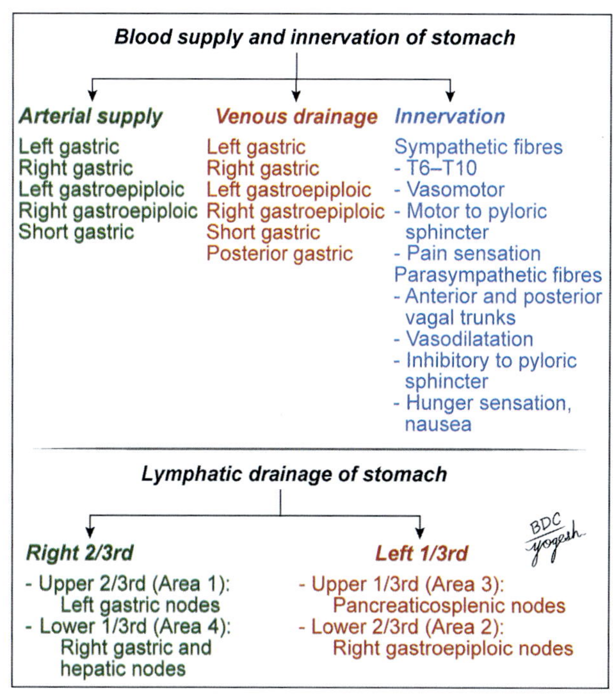

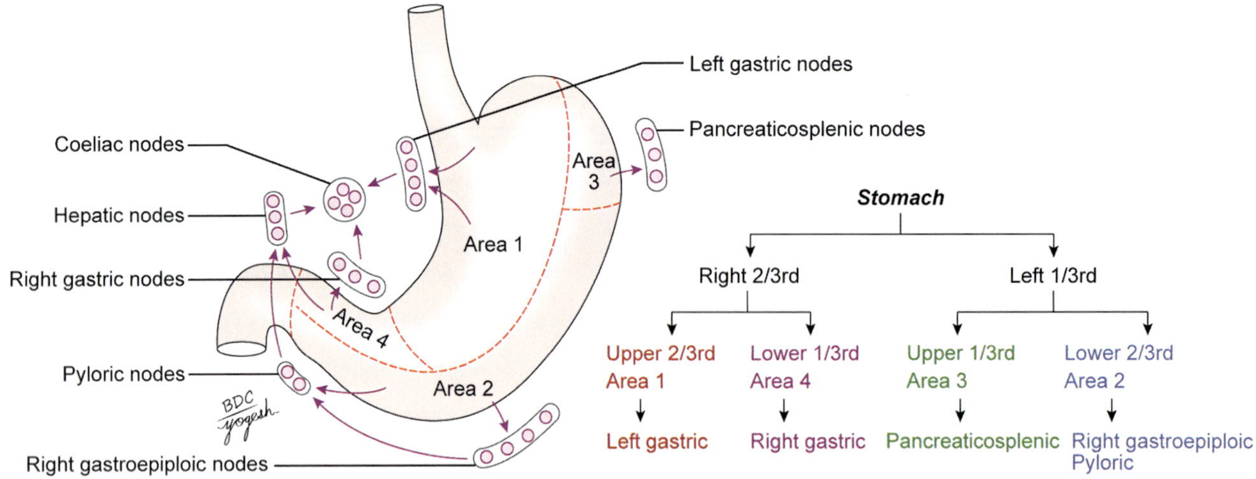

Fig. 19.13: Lymphatic drainage of the stomach

2. Short gastric nodes, left gastroepiploic nodes, splenic hilar nodes and splenic nodes.
3. Right gastroepiploic nodes, infrapyloric nodes, suprapyloric nodes and common hepatic nodes.

Four Lymphatic Territories of Stomach

The lymphatics from the stomach follow four territories. The stomach is divided into the right 2/3rd and left 1/3rd by its long axis. Each of these areas is divided into upper and lower areas.

1. ***Area 1*** is the upper 2/3rd part of right 2/3rd of the stomach. It is the largest area. It lies along the lesser curvature. It drains into ***left gastric nodes***.
2. ***Area 2*** is the lower 2/3rd part of left 1/3rd of the stomach. It lies along pyloric antrum and pyloric canal along the greater curvature of stomach. It drains into ***right gastroepiploic nodes*** and ***pyloric nodes***. It is the most common site for gastric carcinoma.
3. ***Area 3*** (pancreaticosplenic area) is the upper 1/3rd of left 1/3rd area of the stomach. It drains into ***pancreaticosplenic nodes***.
4. ***Area 4*** is the lower third of right 2/3rd of the stomach. It includes pyloric antrum and pyloric canal along the lesser curvature of stomach. It drains into ***right gastric*** and ***hepatic nodes***.

Note: The lymph from all areas of the stomach ultimately reaches the ***coeliac nodes***. From here, it passes through the *intestinal lymph trunk* to reach the *cisterna chyli*.

NERVE SUPPLY

The stomach is supplied by sympathetic and parasympathetic nerves.

Sympathetic Innervation

The *sympathetic nerves* are derived from T6–T10 of the spinal cord, via the greater splanchnic nerves, coeliac and hepatic plexuses. They travel along the arteries supplying the stomach.

These nerves are:

a. Vasomotor
b. Motor to the pyloric sphincter, but inhibitory to the rest of the gastric musculature
c. The chief pathway for pain sensations from the stomach.

Parasympathetic Innervation

The *parasympathetic nerves* (Figs 19.14a and b, Flowchart 19.4) are derived from the vagi, through the oesophageal plexus and gastric nerves.

The anterior gastric nerve (made up of one or two trunks) contains mainly the left vagal fibres, and the posterior gastric nerve (again made up of one to two trunks) contains mainly the right vagal fibres. The ***anterior gastric nerve*** or anterior nerve of Latarjet divides into:

a. A number of gastric branches for the anterior surface of the fundus and body of the stomach.
b. Two pyloric branches, one for the pyloric antrum and another for the pylorus.

The ***posterior gastric nerve*** or posterior nerve of Latarjet divides into:

a. Smaller, gastric branches for the posterior surface of the fundus, the body and the pyloric antrum.
b. Larger, coeliac branches for the coeliac plexus.

The parasympathetic fibres perform the following functions:

a. Vasodilation
b. Motor to gastric musculature, inhibitory to pyloric sphincter
c. Carry the sensation of hunger and nausea.

INTERIOR OF STOMACH

Interior of the stomach shows thick, soft and velvety mucosa. It shows the following features (Plate 19.5):

1. ***Gastric rugae*** or ***gastric folds*** are mucosal folds of an empty stomach. They are longitudinal along the lesser curvature and irregular elsewhere. The rugae disappear (flatten) on distention of stomach.
2. ***Gastric pits:*** The surface of mucosa show small depressions. These are openings of gastric glands.
3. ***Gastric canals*** or ***magenstrasse*** are longitudinal mucosal folds or rugae along the lesser curvature.

Plate 19.5: Stomach: Interior
Inset: Arrangements of the muscle layers in the wall of stomach

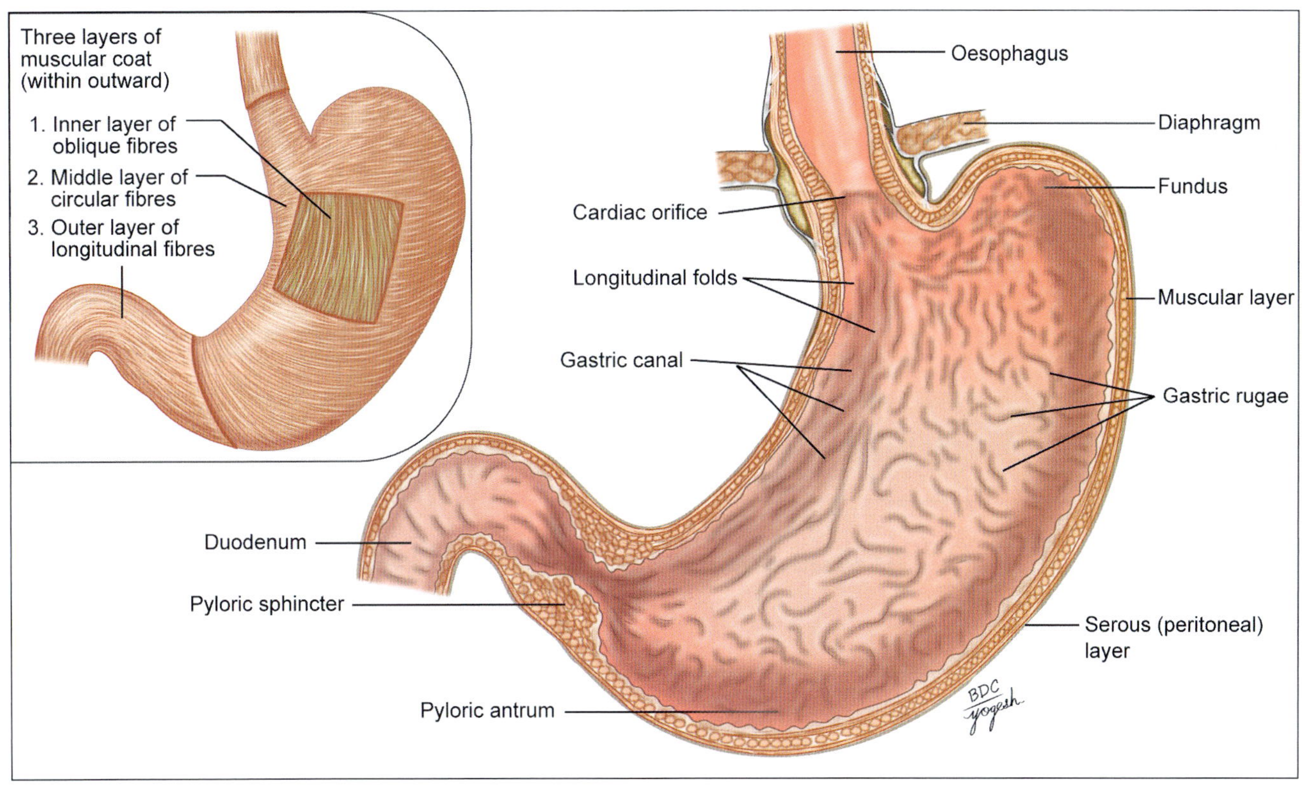

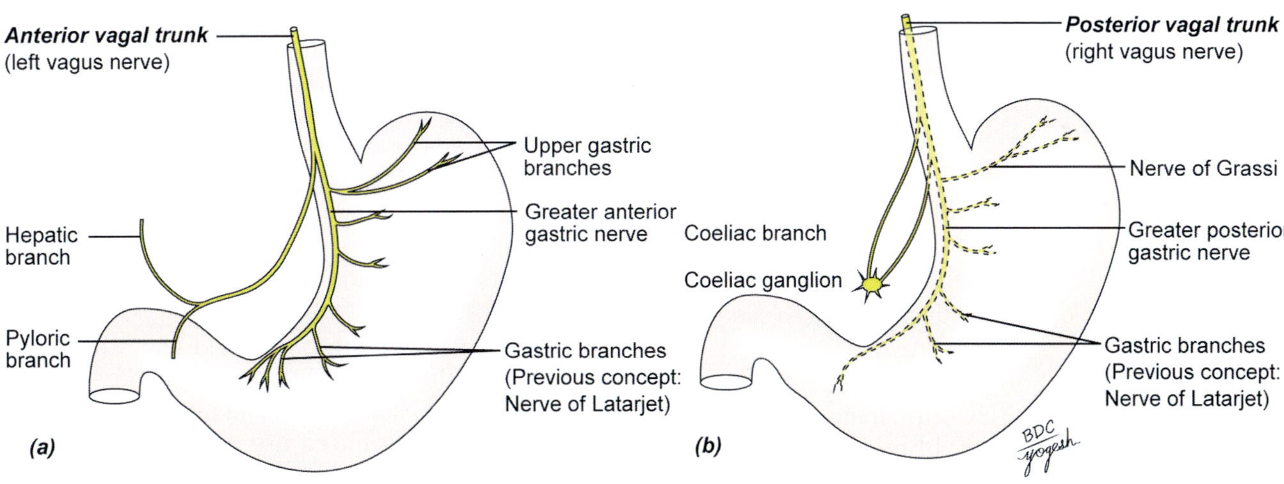

Figs 19.14a and b: Parasympathetic innervation of the stomach: (a) Distribution of the anterior vagal trunk and (b) distribution of the posterior vagal trunk

They extend from cardiac orifice to the pyloric antrum. They give passage to the fluid content of the food without encountering other parts of the stomach.

4. ***Z-line*** is a line of demarcation at gastroesophageal junction. It separates pale-coloured oesophageal mucosa (lined by stratified squamous epithelium) from pink-coloured gastric mucosa (lined by tall columnar epithelium). Z-line is a circumferential zigzag line.

Note: The lesser curvature gets maximum exposure to swallowed foods and drinks which makes it more vulnerable to peptic ulcers.

DISSECTION

Open the stomach along the greater curvature and examine the mucous membrane with a hand lens. Then strip the mucous membrane from one part and expose the internal muscle coat. Dissect the muscle coat, e.g. outer longitudinal, middle circular and inner oblique muscle fibres. Feel thickened pyloric sphincter. Incise the beginning of duodenum and examine the duodenal and pyloric aspects of the pyloric sphincter.

Plate 19.6: Histology of stomach: Body/fundus and pyloric parts

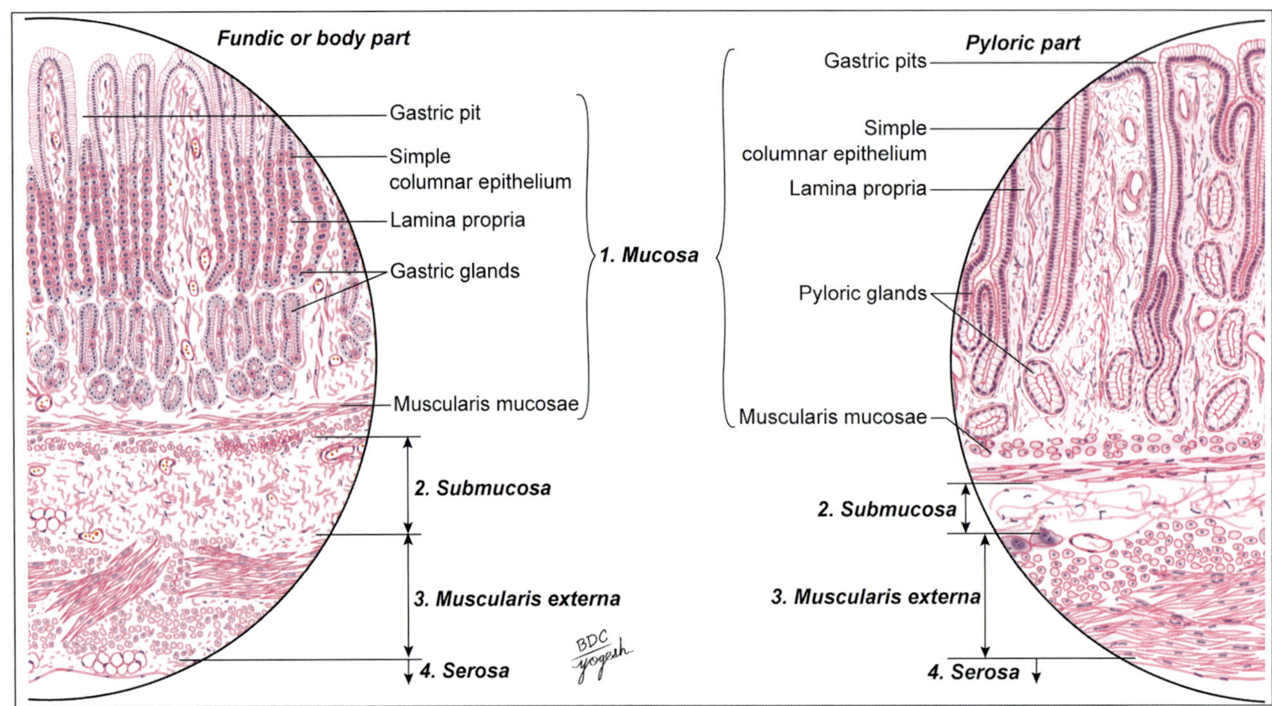

HISTOLOGY OF STOMACH

Histologically stomach shows three regions: Cardiac region, fundus or body and pyloric region. All regions show four layers: Mucosa, submucosa, muscularis externa and serosa as follows (Plate 19.6):

1. ***Mucosa*:** It is lined by surface mucous cells. These are *simple columnar cells* with basal oval nuclei and secrete visible mucus. Mucosa shows gastric pits (openings of glands).
   - Fundus/body: Short gastric pits
   - Pylorus: Long gastric pits

   ***Gastric glands*:** Branched tubular glands.
   - Cardiac end: Cardiac glands show mucus-secreting cells.
   - Fundus/body: Long gastric glands that show pink oxyntic cells (HCl, intrinsic factor), neck mucous cells (mucus), blue-coloured deeper chief cells (pepsinogen) and enteroendocrine cells (histamine, gastrin).
   - Pylorus: Pyloric glands are short and mostly lined by mucous-secreting cells.

   Muscularis mucosae show inner circular and outer longitudinal smooth muscles.
2. ***Submucosa*:** It consists of dense irregular connective tissue and has blood vessels, nerve fibres and Meissner's (submucosal) plexus.
3. ***Muscularis externa*:** Randomly oriented smooth muscle cells: Inner oblique, middle circular and outer longitudinal layers (Plate 19.5). In pylorus, thick circular fibres form pyloric sphincter.
4. ***Serosa*:** Stomach is covered by a connective tissue layer with mesothelial lining of visceral peritoneum.

CLINICAL ANATOMY

- ***Infantile hypertrophic pyloric stenosis*:** It is an idiopathic hypertrophy of circular muscles of pylorus that causes obstruction of gastric outlet. It is treated with *pyloromyotomy* (surgical division of thickened pyloric muscles).
- ***Gastrostomy*** is a surgical insertion of tube in stomach. It is performed through the gastric triangle to feed the patient in case of oesophageal obstruction.
- The nerve of Grassi may be missed during selective vagotomy (resection of vagus) – acid-reducing surgery for treatment of gastric ulcers. Hence, it is also called criminal nerve of Grassi.
- ***Crow-foot fibres*** are the lowest fibres of greater anterior gastric nerve (branch of anterior/left vagal trunk) that supplies antrum and pylorus. In selective vagotomy, these fibres are spared to retain the functions of pyloric sphincter.
- ***Gastric pain*** is referred to the epigastrium through the sympathetic fibres (T6–T9 spinal segments).
- ***Vagotomy*** is a surgical resection of the vagus nerve to reduce acid secretion of the stomach for treatment of peptic ulcers. Vagotomy is of three types (Fig. 19.15):
  1. *Truncal vagotomy* involves surgical resection of both the vagal trunks at the gastroesophageal junction.
  2. *Selective vagotomy* involves surgical resection of gastric branches of both the vagal trunks.
  3. *Highly selective vagotomy* involves surgical resection of the branches of both the vagal trunks that supply only body and fundus of the stomach (acid secreting area). As it denervates parietal cells (acid secreting

Plate 19.7: Development of stomach

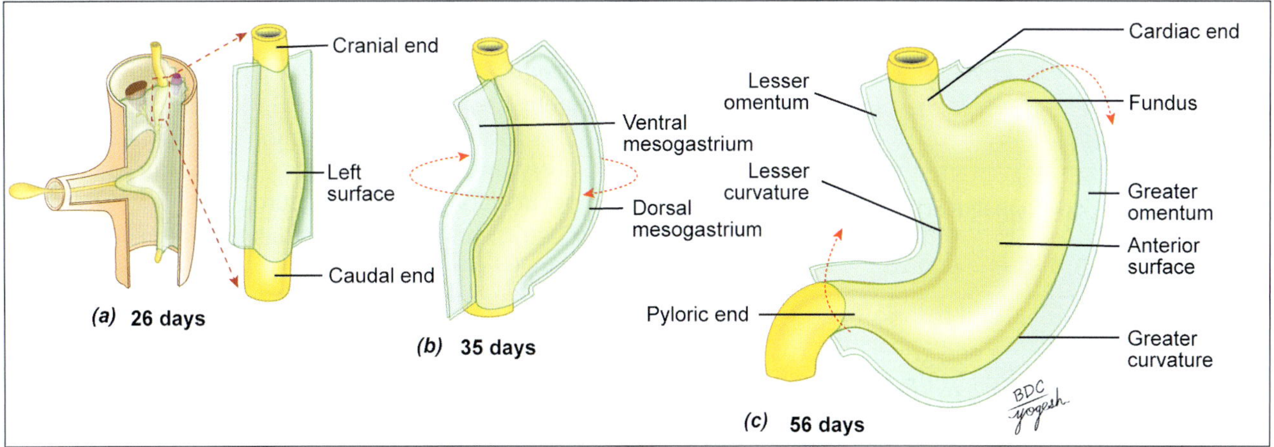

cells), it is also called *parietal cell vagotomy*. It preserves the innervations of the pylorus and prevents *postvagotomy retention syndrome*.

- Normal basal acid outflow is 1.2–2.0 mmol per hour.
- ***Peptic ulcers*** are the ulcers (discontinuity of the lining epithelium) due to acidic content of stomach. It may be *gastric ulcers* that occur in the stomach, *duodenal ulcers* that occur in the duodenum, or *oesophageal ulcers* at lower end of oesophagus. These are more common in individuals with blood group O. In the stomach, the gastric ulcers occur more commonly along the lesser curvature.
- The common causes include infection by *Helicobacter pylori* and long-term use of non-steroidal anti-inflammatory drugs (e.g. paracetamol and ibuprofen). Stress and spicy food worsen the symptoms.
- *Hyposthenic stomach* is more prone for gastric ulcers, whereas hypersthenic stomach is prone for duodenal ulcers.
- ***Gastric carcinoma*** commonly occurs in the region of gastric antrum along the greater curvature. It commonly spreads through lymphatics. Gastric carcinoma is common in individuals of blood group A. *Lymphatic spread of gastric carcinoma*.

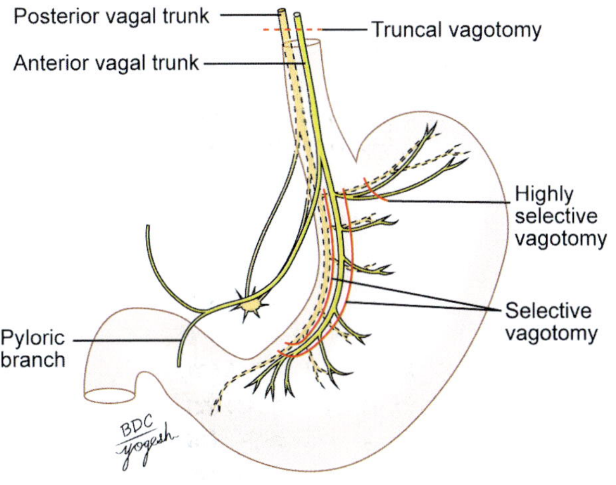

Fig. 19.15: Types of vagotomy

- ***Troisier sign*** is enlarged supraclavicular lymph nodes and it may be the first sign in gastric carcinoma. Hence, these nodes are called signal nodes.

Competencies:

AN52.1 Describe and identify the microanatomical features of fundus and pylorus of stomach.

AN52.6 Describe the development of foregut.

DEVELOPMENT OF STOMACH

The stomach develops from a fusiform dilatation of the foregut distal to the oesophagus. The developmental stages are shown in Plate19.7 and Flowchart 19.5.

Flowchart 19.5: Development of stomach

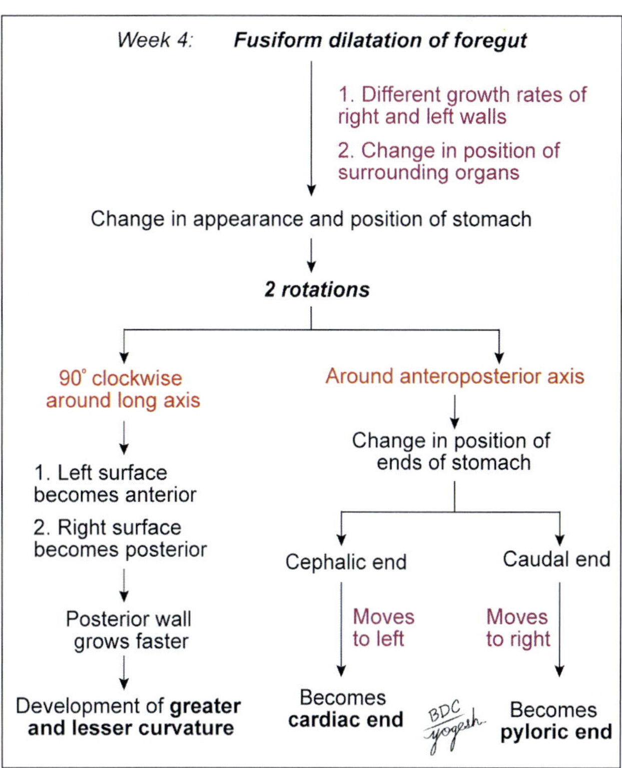

Video 2.19 **Stomach**

Facts to Remember

- Abdominal part of oesophagus is the site of portosystemic anastomoses.
- Stomach comprises:
  - *Two orifices*: Cardiac and pyloric
  - *Two curvatures*: Lesser and greater
  - *Four parts*: Fundus, body, pyloric antrum and pyloric canal.
- Cardiac notch is also called angle of His.
- Triangular non-peritoneal area on the posterior surface of the cardiac end is the bare area of the stomach.
- Anterior gastric nerve contains left vagal fibres and posterior gastric nerve contains right vagal fibres.
- Left and right gastric arteries run along lesser curvature; whereas the left and right gastroepiploic arteries lie along greater curvature.
- The gastric ulcer is common in people who 'worry, hurry and eat hot curries'. Gastric ulcer commonly occurs along lesser curvature.
- Gastric cancer mostly occurs along greater curvature. Lymph from cancer → thoracic duct → left supraclavicular node. It is called Virchow's node. This sign is called Troisier's sign.

BDC's Anatomy *e*-book

1. Molecular regulation of gut tube development
2. Further reading
3. Viva voce questions

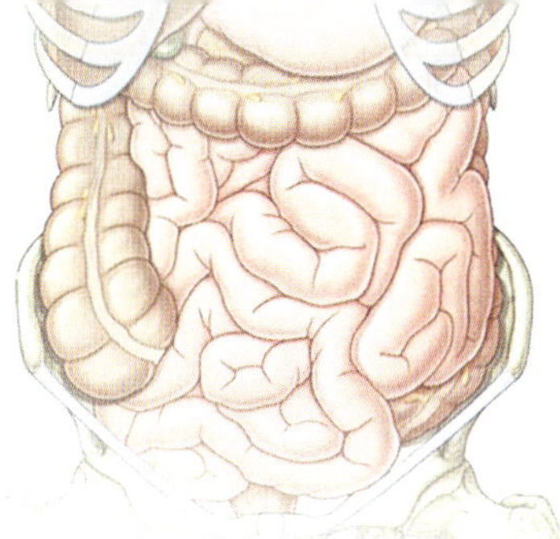

Chapter

20

Small and Large Intestines

The intestine, which is the longest part of the digestive tube, is divided into long, less distensible, small intestine, and shorter, more distensible large intestine. The small intestine is the longest part of the digestive tube. It extends from the pylorus of stomach to the ileocecal junction. The large intestine extends from ileocaecal junction to the anus.

Competency:

AN47.5 Describe and demonstrate major viscera of abdomen under following headings: Anatomical position, external and internal features, important peritoneal and other relations, blood supply, nerve supply, lymphatic drainage and applied aspects.

SMALL INTESTINE

The small intestine extends from the pylorus to the ileocaecal junction.

It is about 5 meters (3–8.5 m) long when measured in the living adult. The length is greater in males than in females, and greater in cadavers, due to loss of tone than in the living.

It is divided into (Fig. 20.1):

1. Proximal part — duodenum
2. Middle part — jejunum
3. Distal part — ileum.

The duodenum is 25 cm long and fixed part. The jejunum and ileum are mobile. The proximal 2/5th, and ileum forms distal 3/5th of the remaining small intestine.

Structure of Small Intestine

The small intestine is principally concerned with the digestion and absorption of food. The wall of small intestine consists of four layers (from inside outward):

1. *Mucosa* consists of lining epithelium, lamina propria and muscularis mucosae.
2. *Submucosa* consists of dense irregular connective tissue.
3. *Muscularis externa* has inner circular and outer longitudinal smooth muscle layer.
4. *Serosa* is a connective tissue layer covered by peritoneum. *Adventitia* is only a connective tissue layer.

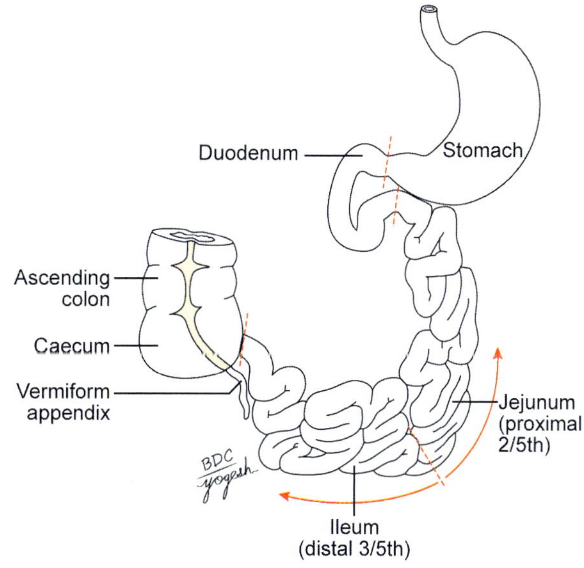

Fig. 20.1: Parts of small intestine

Modifications to Enhance Surface Area

To increase the surface area for the absorption, the small intestine shows the following modifications:

1. ***Plicae circulares*** (circular mucosal folds or valves of Kerckring) are circumferential, permanent submucosal folds. These folds are not obliterated by distension of the gut.
2. ***Intestinal villi*** are finger-like projections of mucosa. They make the surface of intestine velvety.
3. ***Microvilli*** are the cell-surface projections seen under microscope.
4. Other than these factors, *length* of the intestine and *crypts* (depressions of epithelium in the lamina propria) also increase the surface area of the intestine.

Note:

1. *Plicae circulares* are absent in proximal 5–6 cm of duodenum and terminal part of ileum. These folds decrease the speed of passage of intestinal contents.
2. *Crypts of Lieberkühn* or intestinal glands are simple tubular intestinal glands that extend in the lamina propria up to muscularis mucosa. These glands are lined by tall columnar epithelium that continues with epithelial lining of villi. These glands secrete the digestive enzymes and mucous.

3. *Lymphatic follicles*: The mucosa of the small intestine is associated with two types of lymphatic follicles:
   A. *Solitary lymph follicles* are 1–2 mm in diameter. These are distributed throughout the small and large intestines.
   B. *Aggregated lymph follicles* or ***Peyer's patches*** are circular or oval patches (2–10 cm long) and contain 10–200 lymphatic follicles. They are more numerous in terminal part of ileum. Peyer's patches are placed longitudinally along the long axis of the intestine, specifically along the antimesenteric border of the intestine.

Arterial Supply

1. The duodenum is supplied by branches of coeliac trunk and superior mesenteric artery.
2. The jejunum and ileum are supplied by jejunal and ileal branches of the superior mesenteric artery. These are 12–15 branches and arise from the left side of the superior mesenteric artery. These branches run in the mesentery to reach the intestine.
3. Branches of jejunal and ileal artery form series of anastomotic *arterial arcades* in the mesentery.
4. ***Vasa recta*** are the straight parallel branches arising from the terminal arterial arcade. Vasa recta passes to mesenteric border of the intestine and distributes alternatively to the opposite surfaces of small intestine. Anastomosis between the vasa recta is poorly developed.

Venous Drainage

The veins correspond to the branches of superior mesenteric artery. The veins from the intestine drain into the ***portal vein***.

Lymphatics

The ***lacteals*** are small lymphatic capillaries that are present in the intestinal villi. They absorb the dietary fat. Lacteals have circular course in the walls of intestine. Lymphatics from intestine pass through the mesenteric nodes (located around the beginning of superior mesenteric artery).

Nerve Supply

The small intestine is supplied by the following nerves:

A. *Parasympathetic fibres* from vagus nerve through coeliac and superior mesenteric plexuses. They stimulate the peristalsis and inhibit the sphincters. They enhance intestinal secretions.
B. *Sympathetic fibres* from T9 and T11 segments of spinal cord through splanchnic nerves join celiac and superior mesenteric plexus. They stimulate sphincters and inhibit peristalsis and intestinal secretions.

The nerve fibres entering the wall of the intestine form the following plexuses:

A. *Myenteric plexus of Auerbach* lies in between circular and longitudinal muscle coats.
B. *Submucous plexus of Meissner* lies in the submucosa.

Both plexuses contain the *parasympathetic ganglia*, and all together, they form *enteric nervous system*.

CLINICAL ANATOMY

- ***Typhoid or tubercular ulcers***: Peyer's patches in the terminal part of ileum are oriented longitudinally; that is, they are elongated and are along the long axis of the intestine. Hence, in typhoid or tubercular infection, they produce longitudinal oval ulcers. Typhoid ulcers do not heal with scar.
- ***Circular tubercular ulcers*** are observed in the small intestine due to infection of lymphatic vessels (as they have circular course).

Mesentery of Small Intestine

The peritoneal fold covering the small intestine is called *mesentery* (*mesentery* = fold of intestine in Greek). During the embryonic life, due to rotation of gut and the process of *zygosis* (fusion and absorption of folds of peritoneum), the duodenum becomes retroperitoneal organ (loses its mesentery). Thus, the mesentery hangs the jejunum and ileum only.

The *mesentery* is a broad fan-shaped double-layered fold of the peritoneum that suspends small intestine (jejunum and ileum) from the posterior abdominal wall (*mesentery* = fold of intestine in Greek).

The mesentery has two borders:

1. *Attached border* or *root* is fixed to the posterior abdominal wall. It is attached obliquely to the posterior abdominal wall along a 15 cm long line. It extends from duodenojejunal flexure on the left of L2 vertebra to the upper part of right sacroiliac joint.
2. *Free* or *intestinal border* encloses jejunum and ileum.

For details, *see* Chapter 18, page 244.

DUODENUM

The duodenum is the proximal (first) part of the small intestine. The term *duodenum* is a Latin corruption of the Greek word, *dudekadactulos*, meaning twelve fingers long (Plate 20.1, Fig. 20.3).

The duodenum is the shortest, widest and most fixed part of the small intestine. It extends from the pylorus to duodenojejunal flexure.

Location

It is curved around the head of pancreas in the form of letter 'C'. The duodenum lies above the level of umbilicus, opposite L1, L2 and L3 vertebrae (Fig. 20.2).

It lies on the posterior abdominal wall along with the pancreas. Due to its deep location, it is the least accessible for physical examination in clinics.

Length and Parts

Duodenum is 25 cm long and is divided into the following four parts (Fig. 20.3):

1. *1st or superior part*: 5 cm or 2 inches long.
2. *2nd or descending part*: 7.5 cm or 3 inches long.
3. *3rd or horizontal part*: 10 cm or 4 inches long.
4. *4th or ascending part*: 2.5 cm or 1 inch long.

Plate 20.1: Parts of the duodenum

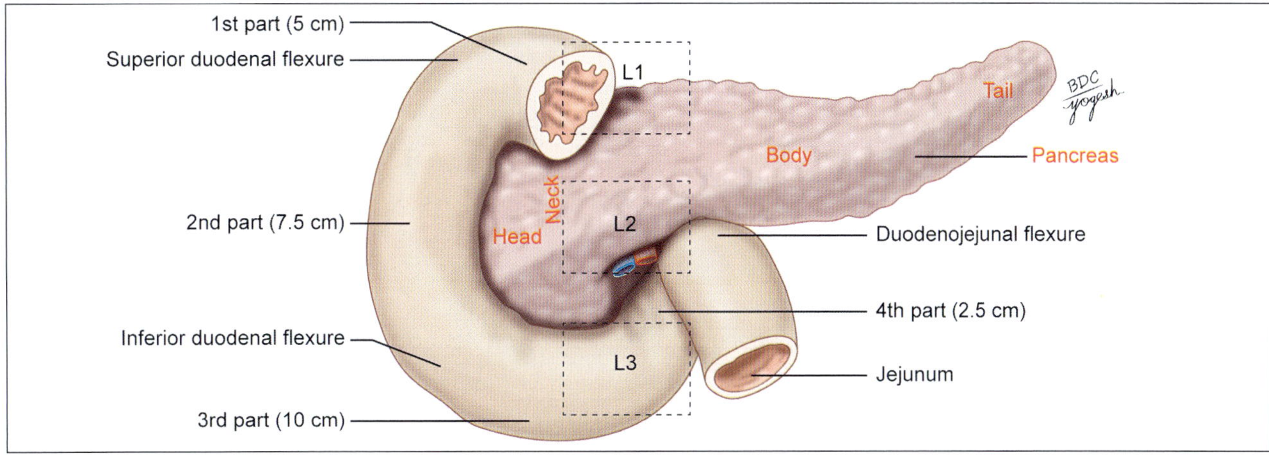

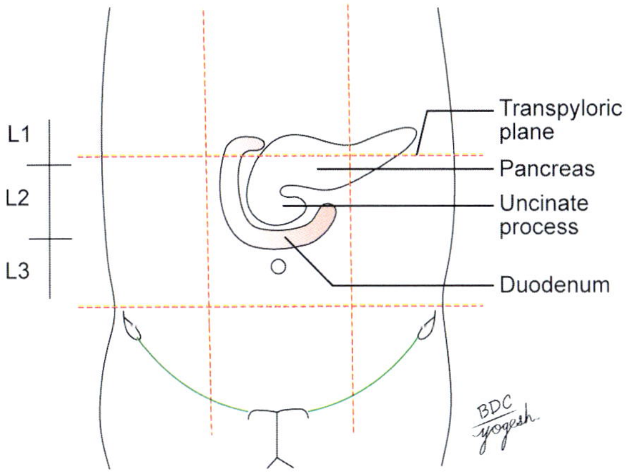

Fig. 20.2: Location of the duodenum

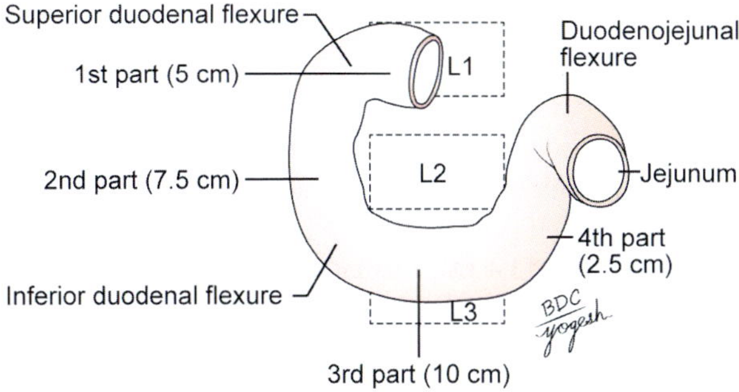

Fig. 20.3: Parts of the duodenum

Peritoneal Relations

The duodenum is mostly retroperitoneal and fixed, except at its two ends where it is suspended by folds of peritoneum, and is, therefore, mobile.

The proximal 2.5 cm of the 1st part is movable. It gives attachment to the lesser omentum above and to the greater omentum below. The remaining part of the duodenum is fixed and retroperitoneal, that is covered with peritoneum only on its anterior aspect.

Note: The anterior surface of the 2nd part is covered with peritoneum, except near the middle, where it is directly related to the colon. The anterior surface of the 3rd part is covered with peritoneum, except in the median plane, where it is crossed by the superior mesenteric vessels and by the root of the mesentery. The terminal part of the duodenum is suspended by the uppermost part of the mesentery and is mobile.

Duodenal Recesses (Fossae) are the small pockets of the peritoneal cavity that lie in relation to the duodenojejunal flexure. These include superior and inferior duodenal, paraduodenal, retroduodenal, mesocolic recesses and mesentericoparietal fossa of Waldeyer (for details, *see* Chapter 18, page 252).

First Part

Course

The 1st part begins at the pylorus and passes backwards, upwards and to the right to meet the 2nd part at the ***superior duodenal flexure*** (Plate 20.1, Figs 20.2, 20.4a and b, Flowchart 20.1).

Peculiarities of 1st Part

The 1st part of the duodenum shows the following features:

1. Its proximal 2.5 cm is intraperitoneal and remaining 2.5 cm is retroperitoneal.
2. It is mobile and distensible.
3. It has an absence of plicae circulares (it does not show circular mucosal folds).
4. It is the only part of duodenum that is supplied by end arteries.

Flowchart 20.1: The 1st part of duodenum

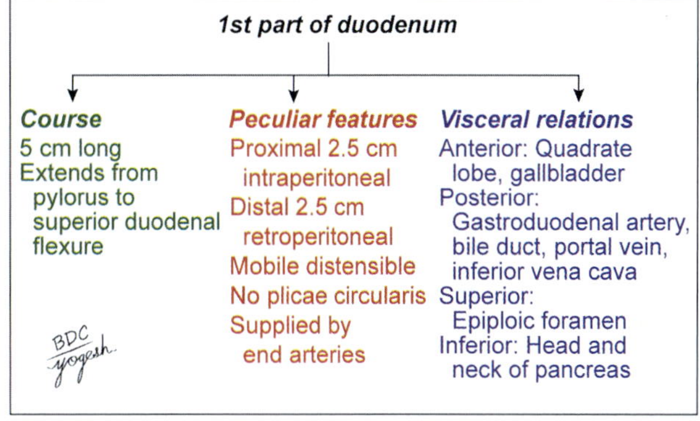

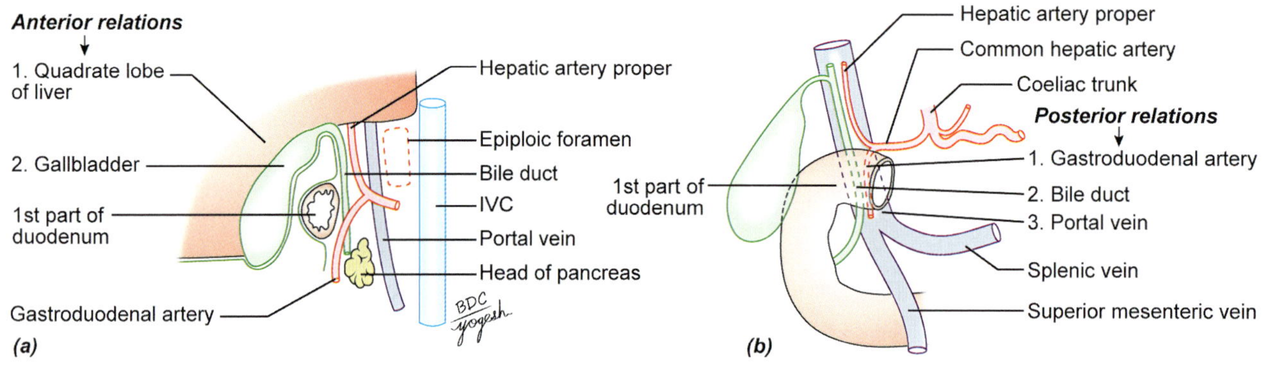

Figs 20.4a and b: Relations of the first part of the duodenum: (a) Sagittal section viewed from the left side and (b) posterior relations

5. It develops from the foregut; hence, supplied by branches of coeliac trunk.
6. ***Duodenal cap*** on barium meal: It is seen as duodenal cap in barium meal radiography.
7. It is a common site for duodenal ulcers.

Visceral Relations (Figs 20.4a and b)

Anteriorly: Quadrate lobe of liver and gallbladder

Posteriorly: Gastroduodenal artery, bile duct and portal vein

Superiorly: Epiploic foramen

Inferiorly: Head and neck of the pancreas.

Second Part

Course

This part is about 7.5 cm long. It begins at the superior duodenal flexure and passes downwards to reach the lower border of the L3 vertebra, where it curves towards the left at the ***inferior duodenal flexure***, to become continuous with the 3rd part (Plate 20.1, Figs 20.2, 20.5a and b, Flowchart 20.2).

Peculiarities of 2nd Part

1. The 2nd part of duodenum is retroperitoneal and fixed.
2. It gives opening to the main bile duct and accessory pancreatic duct.
3. *Development*: Its upper part is developed from foregut and lower part from midgut.
4. *Dual blood supply*: It is supplied by superior and inferior pancreaticoduodenal arteries. It is supplied by double rows of vasa recta.

Visceral Relations (Figs 20.5a and b)

Anteriorly: Right lobe of the liver, transverse colon, root of the transverse mesocolon, small intestine

Posteriorly: Anterior surface of the right kidney near the medial border, right renal vessels, right edge of the inferior vena cava, right psoas major

Medially: Head of the pancreas, bile duct

Laterally: Right colic flexure.

Interior of Second Part

The interior of the 2nd part of duodenum has the following features (Plate 20.2):

1. ***Plicae circulares*** are closely placed circular mucous folds.
2. ***Major duodenal papilla*** is a conical elevation on the posteromedial wall. It is located at about 8–10 cm distal to the pylorus. Through the major duodenal papilla, the hepatopancreatic ampulla of Vater opens in the 2nd part of duodenum.
3. ***Minor duodenal papilla*** is a small projection on the posteromedial wall of the 2nd part of duodenum. It is located about 2 cm proximal to the major duodenal papilla or 6–8 cm distal to the pylorus of stomach.
4. ***Plica semicirculares*** is a mucosal fold that arches above the major duodenal papilla and resembles monk's hood.
5. ***Plica longitudinalis*** is a vertical mucosal fold extending downwards from the major papilla.

Third Part

Course

This part is about 10 cm long. It begins at the inferior duodenal flexure, on the right side of the lower border of the L3 vertebra. It passes almost horizontally and slightly upwards in front of the inferior vena cava and ends by joining the 4th part in front of the abdominal aorta (Figs 20.6a and b, Flowchart 20.3).

Visceral Relations

Anteriorly: Superior mesenteric vessels, root of mesentery

Posteriorly: Right ureter, right psoas major, right testicular or ovarian vessels, inferior vena cava, abdominal aorta with origin of inferior mesenteric artery

Superiorly: Head of the pancreas with uncinate process

Inferiorly: Coils of jejunum.

Fourth Part

Course

This part is 2.5 cm long. It runs upwards on or immediately to the left of the aorta, up to the upper border of the second

Plate 20.2: Interior of the duodenum

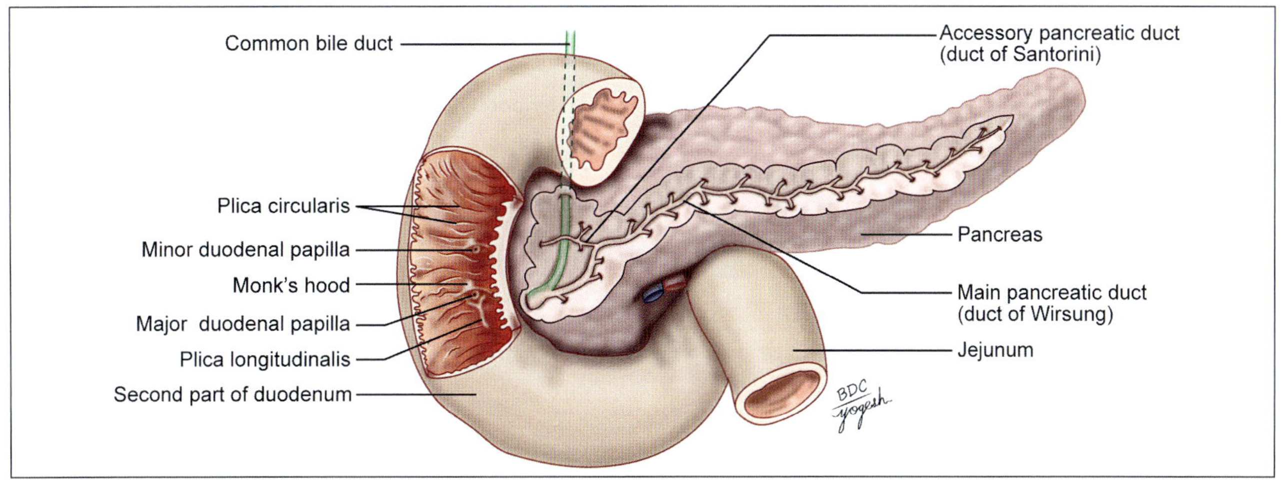

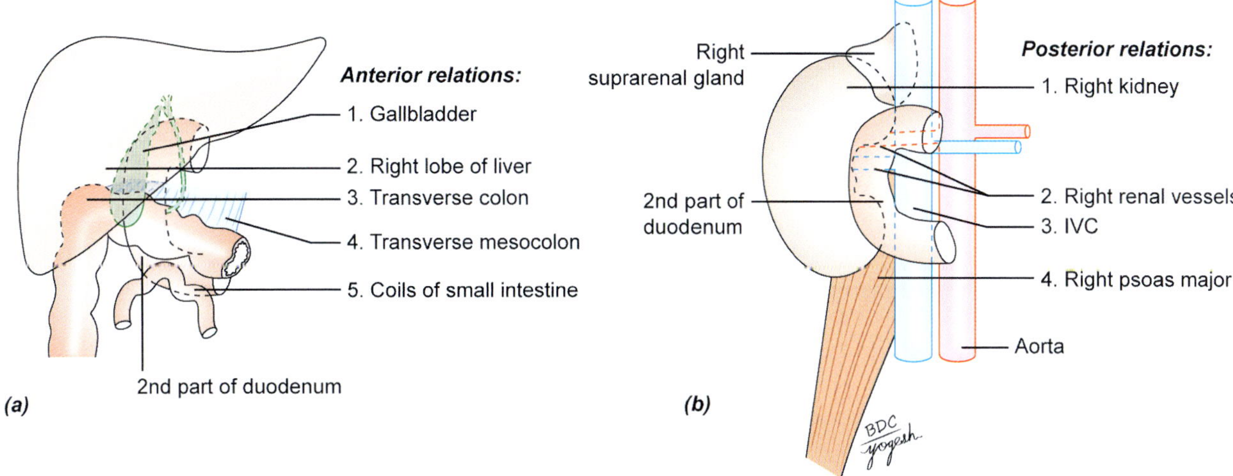

Figs 20.5a and b: Relations of the 2nd part of the duodenum: (a) Anterior relations and (b) posterior relations

Flowchart 20.2: The 2nd part of duodenum

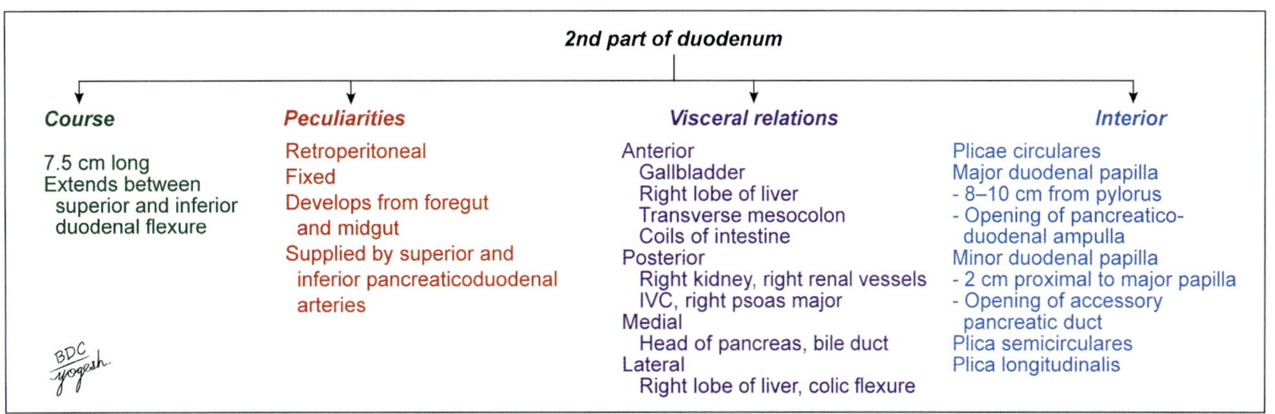

lumbar vertebra, where it turns forwards to become continuous with the jejunum at the duodenojejunal flexure (Figs 20.2, 20.7a and b).

Visceral Relations

Anteriorly: Transverse colon, transverse mesocolon, lesser sac, stomach.

Posteriorly: Left sympathetic chain, left renal artery, left gonadal artery, inferior mesenteric vein.

To the right: Attachment of the upper part of the root of the mesentery.

To the left: Left kidney and left ureter.

Superiorly: Body of pancreas.

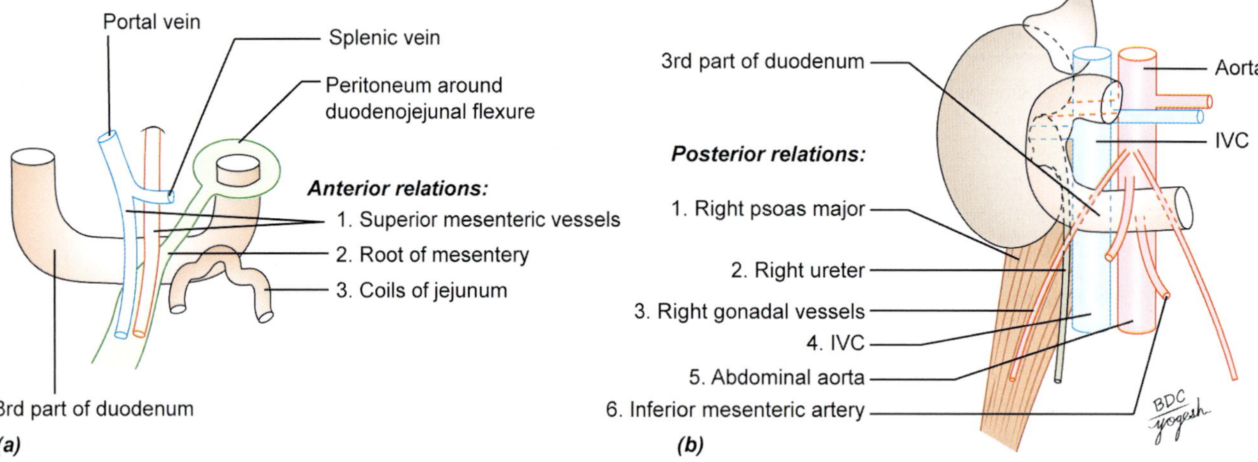

Figs 20.6a and b: Relations of the 3rd part of the duodenum: (a) Anterior relations and (b) posterior relations

Flowchart 20.3: The 3rd part of duodenum

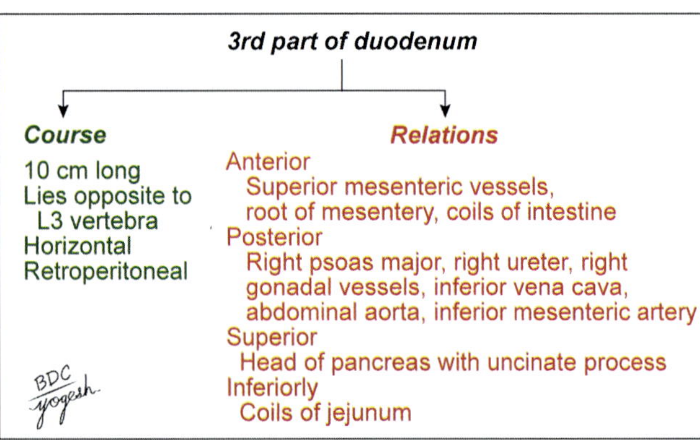

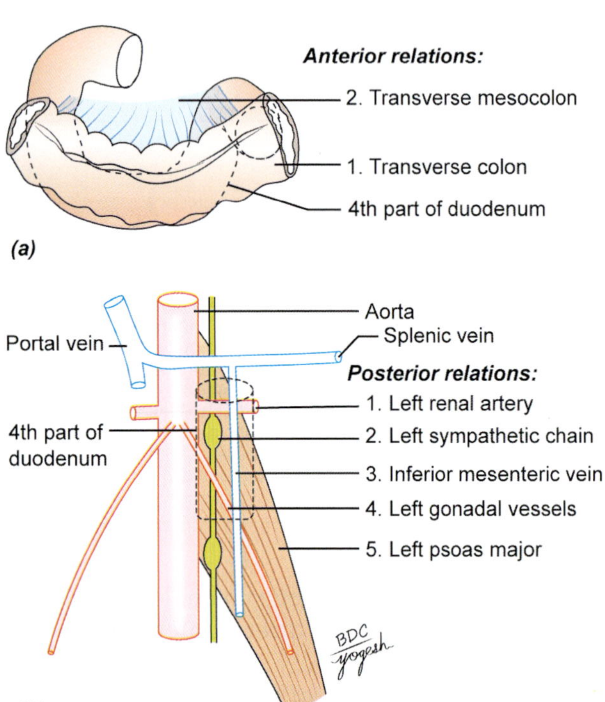

Figs 20.7a and b: Relations of the fourth part of the duodenum: (a) Anterior relations and (b) posterior relations

Suspensory Muscle of Duodenum or Ligament of Treitz

This is a fibromuscular band which suspends and supports the duodenojejunal flexure.

Attachments: It arises from the right crus of the diaphragm, close to the right side of the oesophagus, passes downwards behind the pancreas and is attached to the posterior surface of the duodenojejunal flexure and the third and fourth parts of the duodenum (Fig. 20.8).

Structure: It is made up of:

a. Striped muscle fibres in its upper part
b. Elastic fibres in its middle part
c. Smooth muscle fibres in its lower part.

Functions: Normally, its contraction increases the angle of the duodenojejunal flexure. Sometimes it is attached only to the flexure, and then its contraction may narrow the angle of the flexure, causing partial obstruction of the gut.

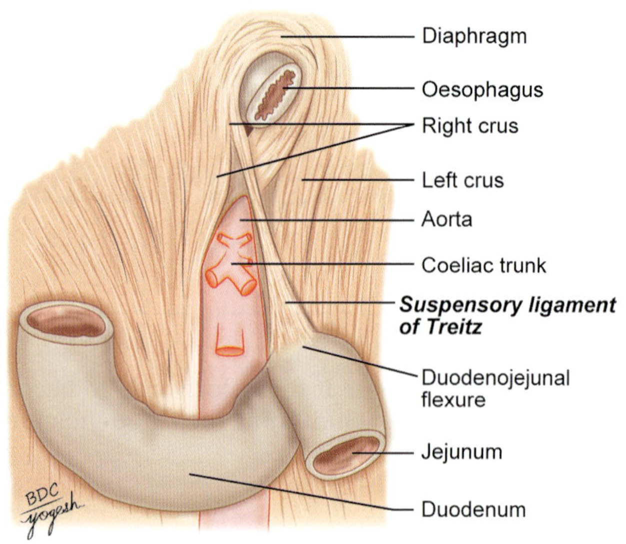

Fig. 20.8: Suspensory muscle of the duodenum

CLINICAL ANATOMY

1. *Partial intestinal obstruction* may occur due to kinking or narrowing of the duodenojejunal flexure because of contraction of suspensory ligament.
2. The suspensory muscle of duodenum is important landmark from duodenojejunal flexure that separates upper and lower gastrointestinal tracts.
3. Radiological location of ligament of Treitz is important indicator for rotation of gut. Its abnormal position indicates malrotation of gut.

Arterial Supply

The duodenum develops partly from the foregut and partly from the midgut. The opening of the bile duct into the 2nd part of the duodenum represents the junction of the foregut and the midgut.

Up to the level of the opening, the duodenum is supplied by the ***superior pancreaticoduodenal artery***, and below it by the ***inferior pancreaticoduodenal artery*** (Fig. 20.9).

The 1st part of the duodenum receives additional supply from:

a. Right gastric artery.
b. Supraduodenal artery of Wilkie, which is usually a branch of the common hepatic artery.
c. Retroduodenal branches of the gastroduodenal artery.
d. Some branches from the right gastroepiploic artery.

Venous Drainage

The veins of the duodenum drain into the splenic, superior mesenteric and portal veins.

Lymphatic Drainage

Lymphatics from the duodenum drain into ***pancreaticoduodenal nodes*** lying along the inner curve of duodenum. These nodes drain into:

1. Hepatic and coeliac nodes
2. Superior mesenteric nodes and finally to cisterna chili.

Nerve Supply

The duodenum is supplied by the following fibres:

A. *Sympathetic fibres* derived from T6 to T9 segment of spinal cord.
B. *Parasympathetic fibres* from both vagi through coeliac and superior mesenteric plexuses.

Competency:

AN52.1 Describe and identify the microanatomical features of duodenum.

Histology of Duodenum

- Duodenum has four layers: Mucosa, submucosa, muscularis externa and serosa/adventitia (Plate 20.3).
- Duodenum shows ***finger-like villi*** lined by simple columnar epithelium and a few goblet cells. Epithelial cells show striated border because of microvilli.
- *Crypts of Lieberkühn* (intestinal glands) are present in lamina propria above muscularis mucosa.
- ***Brunner's glands*** are highly branched, tubuloalveolar mucous glands that are located in the submucosa. Brunner's glands are present deep to muscularis mucosa.
- *Submucosal folds* are circular folds called plicae circulares.
- *Muscularis externa* has inner circular and outer longitudinal smooth muscle layers.
- Most of the duodenum is covered by adventitia except a small portion that is covered by peritoneum (serosa).

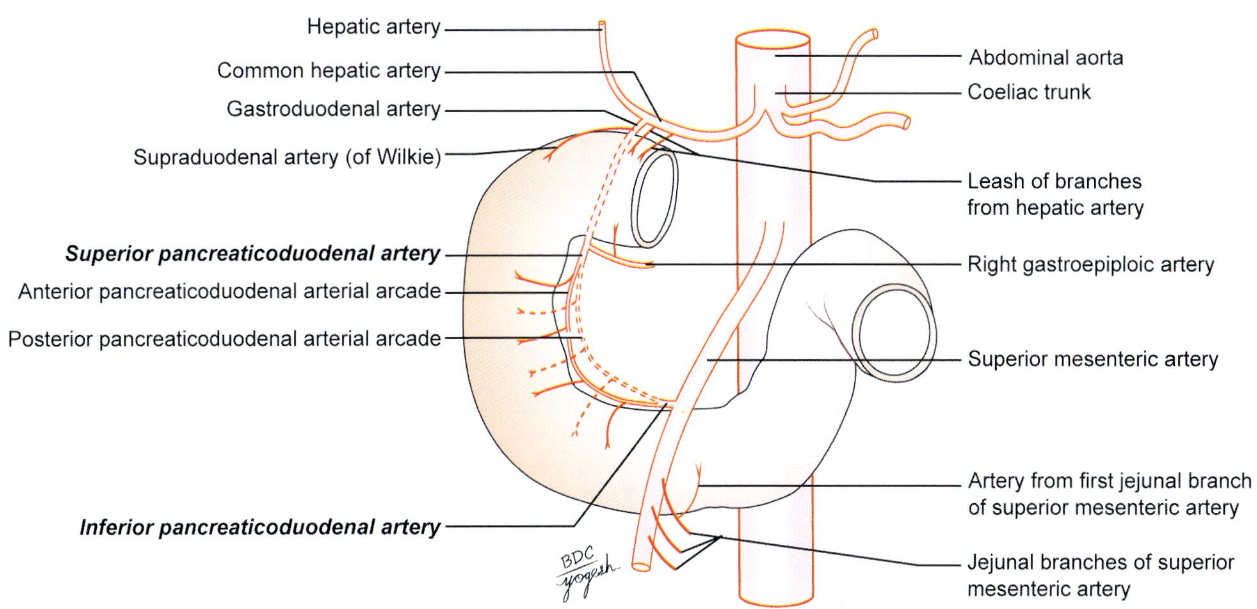

Fig. 20.9: Arterial supply of the duodenum

Plate 20.3: Histology of duodenum

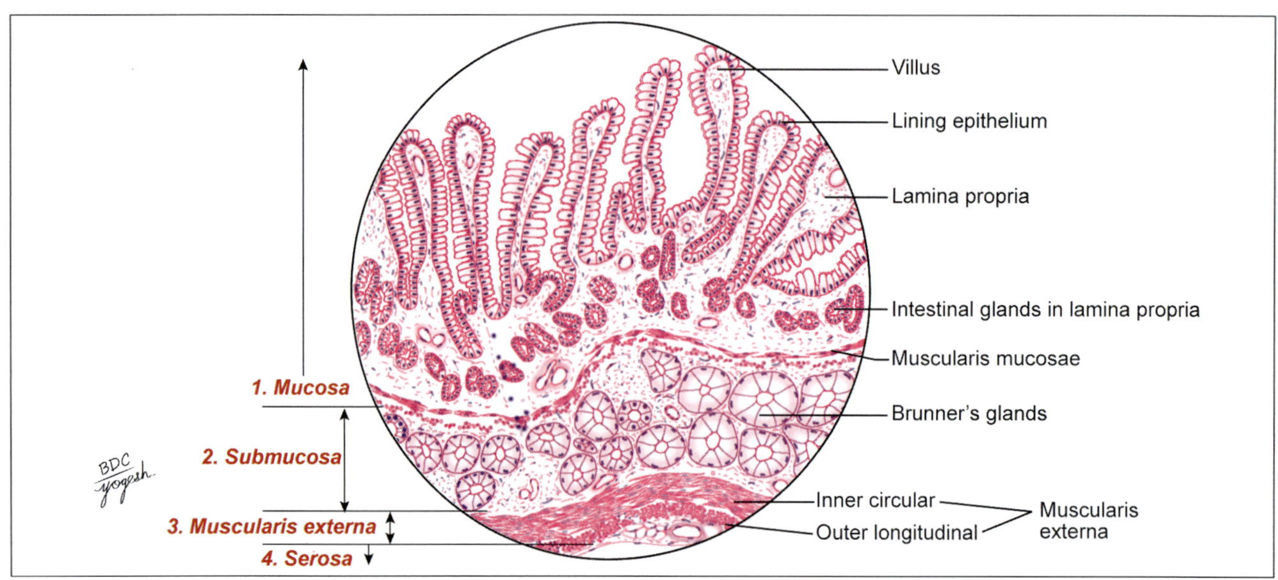

Development of Duodenum

The duodenum develops from two sources:

a. *Foregut* forms the part of duodenum proximal to the opening of common bile duct.

b. *Midgut* forms the part of duodenum distal to the opening of bile duct.

CLINICAL ANATOMY

1. ***Duodenal cap***: The 1st part of duodenum is seen as triangular shadow (white-coloured) called duodenal cap on the barium meal (Fig. 20.10). Pyloric sphincter separates duodenal cap from the pyloric antrum of stomach.
2. ***Peptic ulcers***: The 1st part of duodenum is one of the most common sites of peptic ulcers as it is directly exposed to the acidic contents coming from the stomach. The peptic ulcers are common in busy young persons. These ulcers present as pain in the right part of epigastrium. The pain is typically relieved by taking meals and reappears on fasting (empty stomach). Erosion by peptic ulcer may cause severe haemorrhage.
3. ***Duodenal diverticula*** are small outpouching of the duodenal wall, mostly found along the medial border of the 2nd part of duodenum. Diverticula occurs at the weakness of duodenal wall, specifically at the site of entry of arteries in the wall.
4. ***Duodenal injuries***: The 3rd part of duodenum is the most vulnerable to the external injuries, because it gets compressed between anterior abdominal wall and vertebral column following the violence. *Note*: Due to deeper location, the 2nd part of duodenum is protected from external injuries.
5. ***Duodenal obstruction*** may occur in the following conditions: Annular pancreas, pressure by superior mesenteric artery on the 3rd part of duodenum and contraction of the suspensory muscle of the duodenum, and duodenal carcinoma, congenital duodenal stenosis and atresia (Fig. 20.11).
6. ***Partwise common duodenal diseases***:

   First part – peptic ulcer

   Second part – duodenal diverticula

   Third part – prone to external injuries

   Fourth part – related to duodenal recesses and internal hernia.

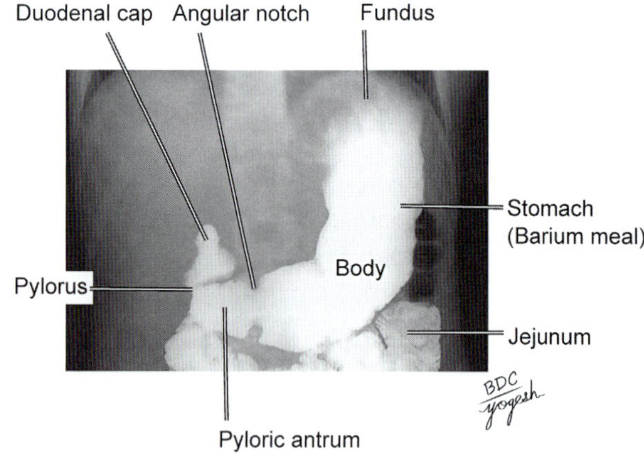

Fig. 20.10: Radiograph of the stomach after barium meal

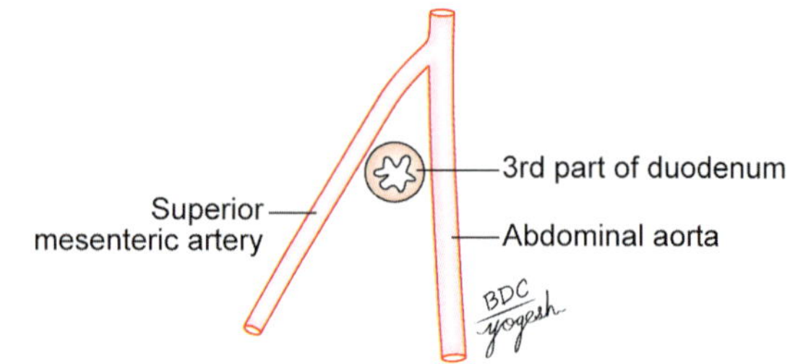

Fig. 20.11: Obstruction of third part of the duodenum between the two arteries

DISSECTION

Examine the C-shaped duodenum and head of pancreas lying in its concavity (Plate 20.2). Cut through the lower wall of the first part extending the cut on medial wall of second and upper wall of third part of duodenum to see its interior.

Carefully look for the longitudinal fold on the postero-medial wall below the middle of second part. The longitudinal fold is often covered by a circular fold containing orifice of the major duodenal papilla draining both the bile and pancreatic ducts.

Identify and dissect the structures related to all the four parts of the duodenum.

JEJUNUM AND ILEUM

Features

The jejunum and ileum are suspended from the posterior abdominal wall by the ***mesentery*** and, therefore, enjoy considerable mobility.

The jejunum constitutes the upper 2/5th of the mobile part of the small intestine, while the ileum constitutes the lower 3/5th. The jejunum begins at the ***duodenojejunal flexure***. The ileum terminates at the ***ileocaecal junction***. The differences between the jejunum and the ileum are given in Table 20.1.

Blood Supply

The jejunum and ileum are supplied by branches from the ***superior mesenteric artery*** and are drained by corresponding veins.

Lymphatic Drainage

Lymph from lacteals drains into plexuses in the wall of the gut. From there, it passes into lymphatic vessels in the mesentery. Passing through numerous lymph nodes present in the mesentery, and along the superior mesenteric artery, it ultimately drains into paraaortic and preaortic lymph nodes present in front of the aorta at the origin of the superior mesenteric artery.

Nerve Supply

Sympathetic nerves are from T9–T11 spinal segments, and parasympathetic nerve is from vagus.

Competency:

AN52.1 Describe and identify the microanatomical features of jejunum and ileum.

Histology of Jejunum and Ileum

Histologically, jejunum and ileum show four layers: Mucosa, submucosa, muscularis externa and serosa (Plate 20.5).

1. *Mucosa* is lined by *simple columnar epithelium with striated border of microvilli*. The mucosa shows tongue-shaped villi in jejunum and finger-like villi in ileum. Terminal part of ileum shows aggregation of lymphatic follicles as ***Peyer's patches*** in lamina propria. *M cells* (antigen-presenting cells) are present in ileum that overlie Peyer's patches.
2. *Submucosa*: Absence of submucosal Brunner's glands differentiates jejunum and ileum from duodenum.
3. *Muscularis externa* has inner circular and outer longitudinal smooth muscle layers.
4. Externally the jejunum and ileum are covered by peritoneum (*serosa*).

Development of Duodenum

The jejunum and ileum develop from the U-shaped ***midgut loop***. Its cephalic part gives rise to the jejunum and upper part of the ileum, and the caudal part gives rise to the lower part of the ileum.

In the embryonic life, the apex of the midgut loop communicates with the yolk sac through the vitello-intestinal duct. The vitelline duct is generally obliterated by the 6th week of intrauterine life.

The midgut undergoes 270° counterclockwise rotation to accommodate herniated midgut loop in the small abdominal cavity.

Meckel's Diverticulum (Diverticulum Ilei)

Meckel's diverticulum is the persistent proximal part of the vitellointestinal duct which is present in the embryo,

TABLE 20.1: Differences between jejunum and ileum (Plate 20.4)

Feature macroscopic	*Jejunum*	*Ileum*
Location	Occupies upper and left parts of the intestinal area	Occupies lower and right parts of the intestinal area
Walls	Thicker and more vascular	Thinner and less vascular
Lumen	Wider and often empty	Narrower and often loaded
Mesentery	a. Windows present b. Fat less abundant c. Arterial arcades, 1 or 2 d. Vasa recta longer and fewer	a. No windows b. Fat more abundant c. Arterial arcades, 3 or 6 d. Vasa recta shorter and more numerous
Circular mucosal folds	Larger and more closely set	Smaller and sparse
Microscopic		
Villi	Large, thick (leaf-like) and more abundant	Shorter, thinner (finger-like) and less abundant
Peyer's patches	Absent	Present
Solitary lymphatic follicles	Fewer	More numerous

Plate 20.4: Differences between the jejunum and ileum

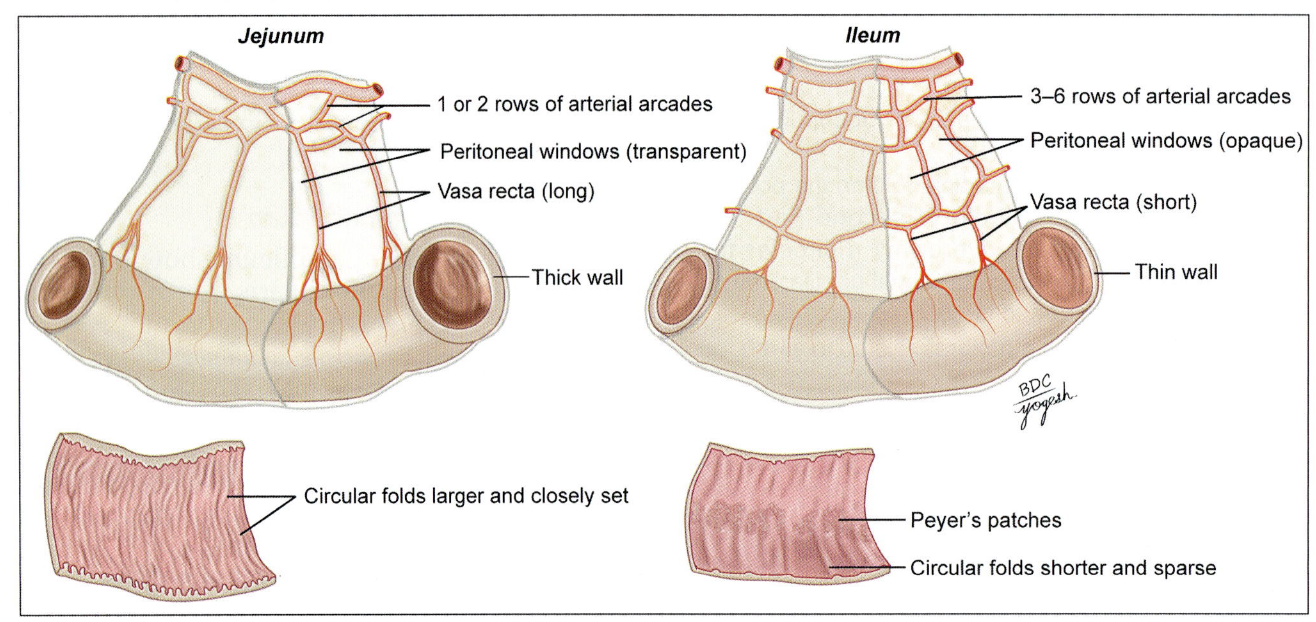

Plate 20.5: Histology of jejunum and ileum

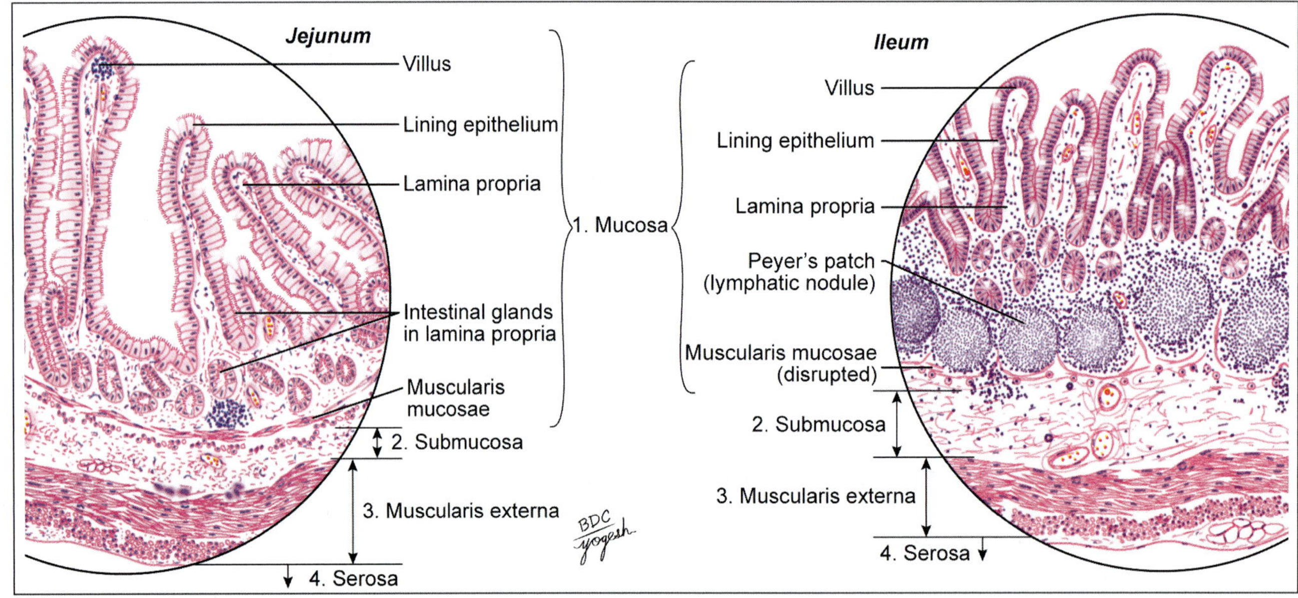

and which normally disappears during the 6th week of intrauterine life (Figs 20.12a and b, Flowchart 20.4).

Features

1. It occurs in 2% subjects.
2. Male: Female ratio is 2:1.
3. The most common age at clinical presentation is 2 years.
4. Usually, it is 2 inches or 5 cm long.
5. It is situated about 2 feet or 60 cm proximal to the ileocaecal valve, attached to antimesenteric border of the ileum.
6. It shows 2 types of common ectopic tissues (gastric and pancreatic).
7. Its calibre is equal to that of the ileum.
8. Its apex may be free or may be attached to the umbilicus, to the mesentery, or to any other abdominal structure by a fibrous band.

[**Mnemonics**: *Meckel's diverticulum details: "di-" means "two", so diverticulum is the thing with all the twos:* 2 inches long, 2 feet from end of ileum, 2 times more common in men, 2% occurrence in population, 2 types of tissue may be present]

Note:

***Umbilical faecal fistula* (*vitelline fistula*)** is caused by patent vitellointestinal duct. It involves communication of the small intestine with exterior and results in discharge of faecal matter.

Enterocystoma (*Vitelline cyst*) is the cyst of the vitellointestinal duct that occurs due to small persistent middle part of the duct.

Flowchart 20.4: Meckel's diverticulum (diverticulum ilei)

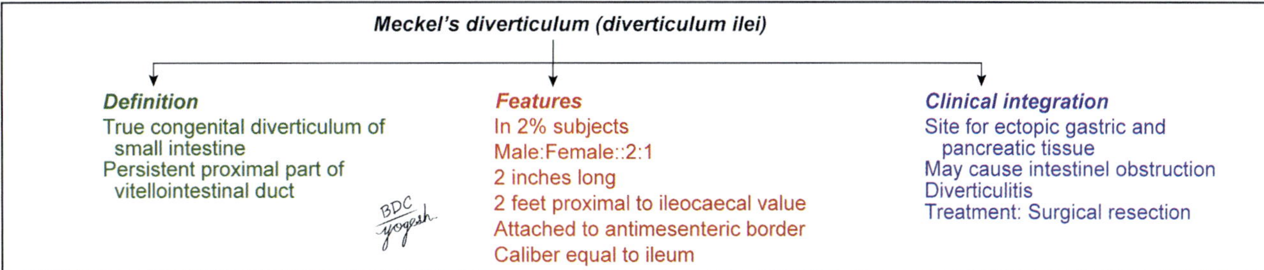

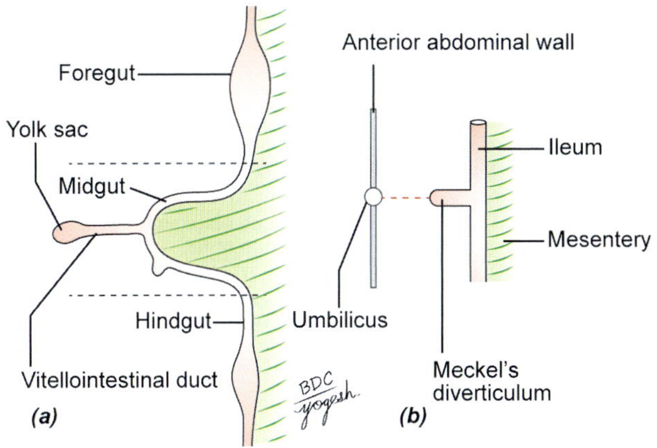

Figs 20.12a and b: Meckel's diverticulum: (a) Vitellointestinal duct in an early embryo and (b) the proximal persistent part of the vitellointestinal duct

CLINICAL ANATOMY

- Meckel's diverticulum may cause intestinal obstruction.
- Acute inflammation of the diverticulum may produce symptoms that resemble those of appendicitis.

DISSECTION

For examining the jejunum and ileum, tie a pair of ligatures around the jejunum close to the duodenojejunal flexure and a pair around the ileum close to the caecum. Cut through the small intestine between each pair of ligatures and remove it by dividing the mesentery close to the intestine. Wash intestine with running tap water. Remove 10 cm each of jejunum and ileum and open it longitudinally. Remove the peritoneal coat to expose the longitudinal muscle layer.

Identify villi with a hand lens. Remove only the mucous membrane and submucosa to see the underlying circular muscle coat. Examine the differences between jejunum and ileum.

LARGE INTESTINE

The large intestine extends from the *ileocaecal junction* to the *anus*. It is about 1.5 m long.

Functions of Large Intestine

The large intestine performs the following functions:

1. Absorption of water and minerals
2. Secretion of mucus to lubricate faeces
3. Storage and expulsion of faeces
4. Synthesis of vitamin B with the help of bacterial flora
5. Protection from microorganisms by secreting of IgA antibodies.

Parts of Large Intestine

Anatomically, the large intestine is divided into the following parts (Plate 20.6, Fig. 20.13):

1. Caecum
2. Appendix
3. Colon: Ascending colon, right or hepatic flexure, transverse colon, left or splenic flexure, descending colon, sigmoid colon
4. Rectum
5. Anal canal.

Cardinal Features of Large Intestine

Three cardinal features: The large intestine presents three cardinal features as follows (Plate 20.6, Fig. 20.13):

1. ***Taenia coli*:** These are three ribbon-like bands of the longitudinal muscle layer of muscularis externa of colon.
2. ***Appendices epiploicae*:** These are small bags of peritoneum filled with fat (meaning to float on in Greek). They are scattered all over the surface of large intestine, except at appendix, caecum and rectum.
3. ***Sacculations (haustrations)*:** These are series of dilations of the wall of caecum and colon. These are

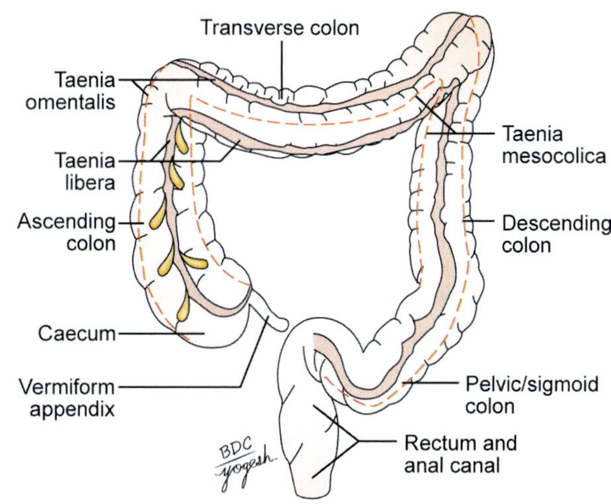

Fig. 20.13: Large intestine and the position of three taeniae

Plate 20.6: Large intestine

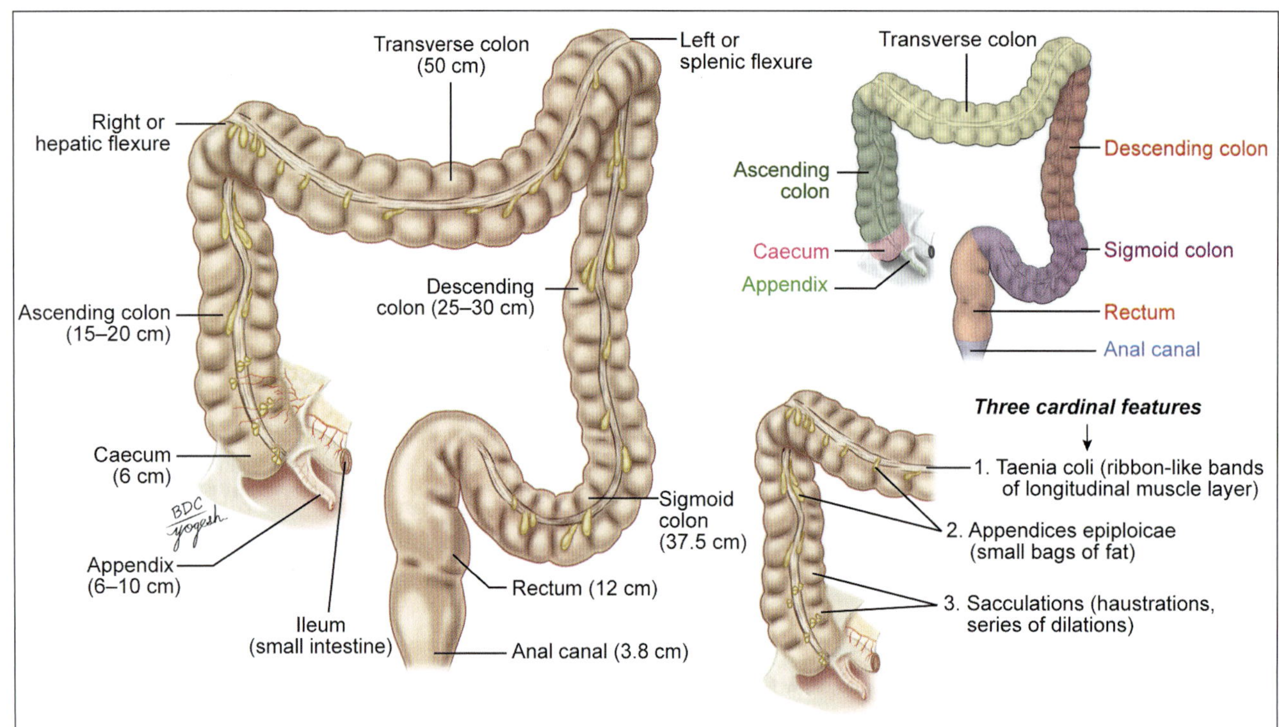

produced because of shorter length of taenia coli than the circular muscle coat. It gives puckered appearance to the large intestine.

Other Features of Large Intestine

1. *Wide caliber*: Large intestine is wider in caliber than small intestine.
2. *Peritoneal coverings*: The most of large intestine is retroperitoneal and fixed except for transverse and sigmoid colons.
3. Appendices epiploicae are most numerous on the sides of sigmoid colon and posterior surface of transverse colon.
4. *Microscopic features*: Large intestine does not show villi, transverse muscular folds and Peyer's patches. It contains a large number of goblet cells that secret mucus for lubrication of faeces.

The differences between the small intestine and large intestine are summarised in Table 20.2.

Note: ***Positions of taenia coli***

1. ***Taenia libera***: It lies anteriorly, but at transverse colon, it is placed inferiorly.
2. ***Taenia mesocolica***: It lies posteromedially, but at transverse colon, it is placed at the attachment site of transverse mesocolon.
3. ***Taenia omentalis***: It lies posterolaterally, but at transverse colon, it is placed anterosuperiorly.

This change in position is due to twist in transverse colon.

Arterial Supply

1. The *blood supply* to the colon is derived from the ***marginal artery of Drummond***. It is formed by ***colic branches of superior and inferior mesenteric arteries*** (Fig. 20.14).
2. Terminal branches from the marginal artery are distributed to the intestine as long and short vessels, ***vasa longa*** and ***vasa brevia***. The long arteries divide into anterior and posterior branches close to the mesocolic taenia to pass between the serous and muscular coats and reach the amesocolic taeniae. They gradually pierce the muscular coat and reach the submucosa. The anastomosis between the two amesocolic taeniae is extremely poor. So longitudinal incisions should be made along this line.

   Note: Short branches arise either from the marginal artery or from the long branches, and the majority of them at once sink into the bowel wall at the mesocolic border. The short and long branches together thus provide the mesocolic region of the wall with abundant blood supply. It is only the amesocolic region which has scanty blood supply.

   Bowel wall is weakened where it is pierced by the vessels and at the sites of attachment of appendices epiploicae. Mucosa may herniate in these situations causing diverticulosis, with associated dangers of diverticulitis, fibrosis and stricture.
3. Veins of the large intestine follow the corresponding branches of superior and inferior mesenteric arteries and drain into portal vein through superior and inferior mesenteric veins.

Lymphatic Drainage

Lymphatics from large intestine are drained by the following nodes (Fig. 20.15):

1. *Epiploic nodes* – lie on the wall of gut.
2. *Paracolic nodes* – lie on the medial sides of ascending and descending colons and mesocolic border of transverse and sigmoid colon.
3. *Intermediate nodes* – lie along the branches of main arteries.

TABLE 20.2: Differences between the small intestine and the large intestine

Feature	***Small intestine***	***Large intestine***
Macroscopic		
1. Appendices epiploicae	Absent	Present
2. Taeniae coli	Absent	Present
3. Sacculations	Absent	Present
4. Distensibility and diameter	Less distensibility and less diameter	More distensibility and more diameter
5. Fixity	Greater part is freely mobile	Greater part is fixed
Microscopic		
1. Villi	Present	Absent
2. Transverse mucosal folds	Permanent	Obliterated when longitudinal muscle coat relaxes
3. Peyer's patches	Present in ileum	Absent
Clinical		
1. Common site for	a. Intestinal worms b. Typhoid c. Tuberculosis	a. *Entamoeba histolytica* b. Dysentery organisms c. Carcinoma
2. Effects of infection and irritation	Diarrhoea	Dysentery (Greek *bad intestine*)

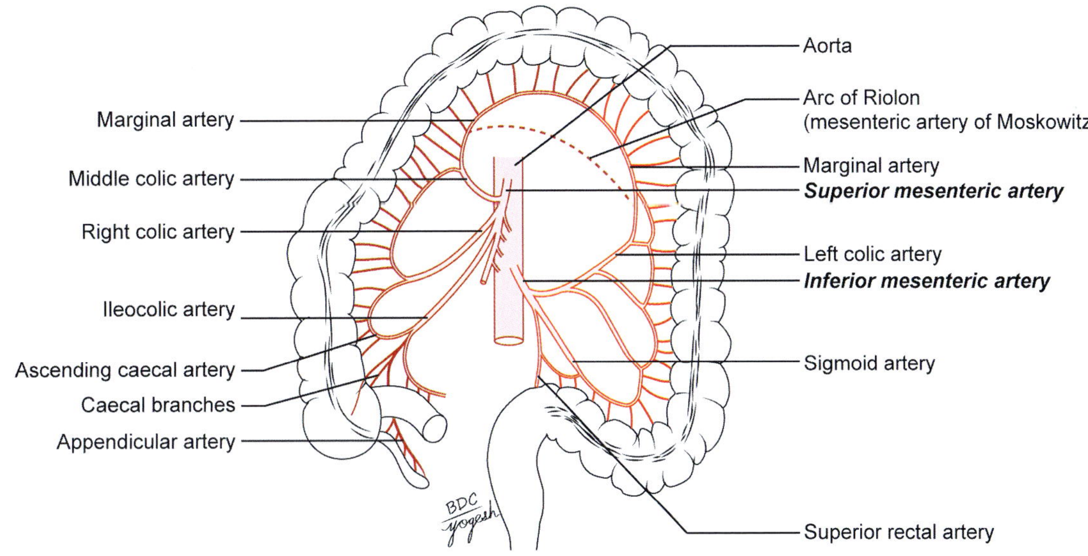

Fig. 20.14: Arterial supply of large intestine

4. *Terminal nodes* – include superior and inferior mesenteric nodes.

Note: In carcinoma of the colon, the related paracolic and intermediate lymph nodes have to be removed. Their removal is possible only after the ligature of the main branch of the superior or inferior mesenteric artery along which the involved lymph nodes lie. It is necessary, therefore, to remove a large segment of the bowel than is actually required by the extent of the disease, in order to avoid gangrene as a result of interference with the blood supply. It is always wise to remove the whole portion of the bowel supplied by the ligated vessel.

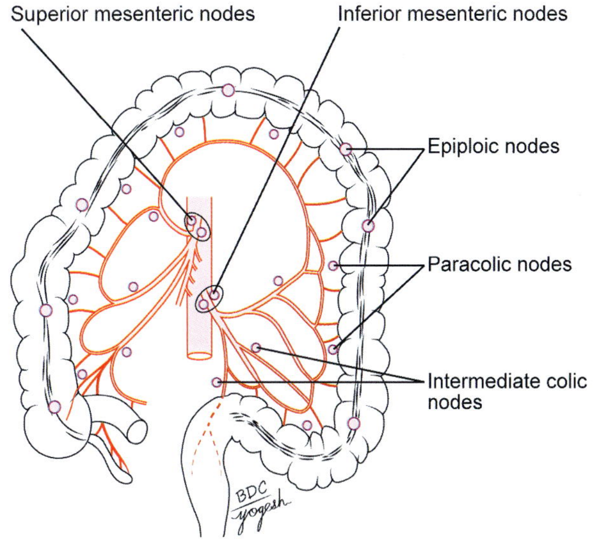

Fig. 20.15: Lymphatic drainage of the colon

Nerve Supply

Large intestine is supplied by the following fibres:

1. *Sympathetic fibres* from coeliac and superior mesenteric plexuses (T11 and L1 spinal segment). These are vasomotor, motor for internal anal sphincter and inhibitory for colon. They carry *pain sensations* from

large intestine up to the descending colon (*Note*: Pelvic splanchnic nerves carry sensations from sigmoid colon and rectum).

2. *Parasympathetic fibres* from pelvic splanchnic nerves (*nervi erigentes*) via superior and inferior mesenteric plexuses. These fibres are motor to large intestine and inhibitory to internal anal sphincter.

Competency:

AN52.6 Describe the development and congenital anomalies of foregut, midgut and hindgut.

Histology of Large Intestine (Colon)

The colon shows four layers: Mucosa, submucosa, muscularis externa and serosa (Plate 20.7).

1. ***Mucosa*** is lined by simple columnar absorptive cells with microvilli and ***goblet cells***. Lamina propria is filled with intestinal glands (crypts of Lieberkühn). These glands are lined by number of goblet cells. Lamina propria shows discrete lymphatic follicles.
2. ***Submucosa*** consists of dense irregular connective tissue.
3. ***Muscularis externa*** has inner circular and outer longitudinal fibres. Longitudinal fibres form three bands of taenia coli.
4. Externally, colon is covered by *serosa/adventitia*.

The colon does not have plicae circulares, villi and Paneth cells.

Plate 20.7: Histology of large intestine

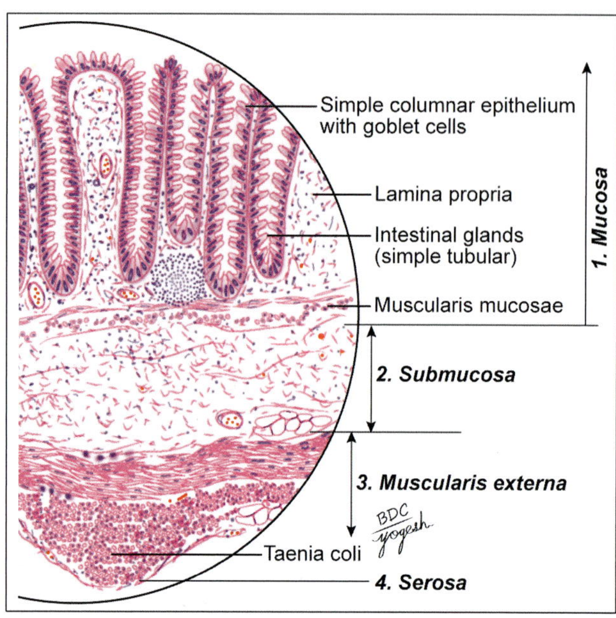

CLINICAL ANATOMY

- Large intestine can be directly viewed by a procedure called ***colonoscopy***.
- Diverticulum is a small evagination of mucous membrane of colon at the entry point of the arteries. Its inflammation is called diverticulitis (Fig. 20.16).
- ***Barium enema*** is given to visualize internal structure of the large intestine on radiographs.

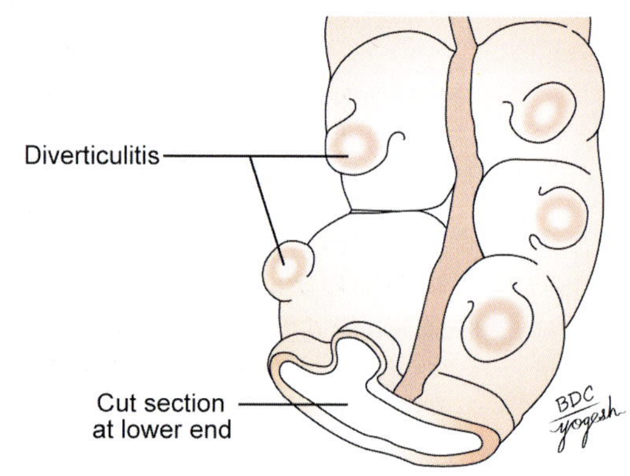

Fig. 20.16: Diverticulitis

DISSECTION

Locate the various parts of large intestine, beginning from caecum, vermiform appendix, ascending, transverse, descending and sigmoid colons and ending with the rectum and anal canal. Identify the taenia, haustration and appendices epiploicae. Trace the taenia from the root of the vermiform appendix through the ascending colon to the transverse colon and note the change in their respective positions.

CAECUM

Caecum is a large blind sac (Latin *blind*) forming the commencement of the large intestine (Plate 20.8, Fig. 20.17, Flowchart 20.5).

Location

It is situated in the right iliac fossa, above the lateral half of inguinal ligament. It lies anterior to iliacus and psoas major muscles.

Communications

Caecum communicates:

1. *Superiorly* with ascending colon
2. *Medially* with ileum through ileocaecal junction
3. *Posteromedially* with appendix.

Dimensions

Length: 6 cm

Width: 7.5 cm.

Note: The organs of the body that have greater width than the length are caecum, prostate, pons and pituitary.

Relations

Visceral Relations

Anterior: Coils of intestine and anterior abdominal wall.

Posterior:

1. *Muscles:* Right psoas and iliacus (Fig. 20.17).
2. *Nerves:* Genitofemoral, femoral and lateral cutaneous nerve of thigh (all of the right side).
3. *Vessels:* Testicular or ovarian.
4. Appendix in the retrocaecal recess.

Plate 20.8: Caecum, appendix and related structures

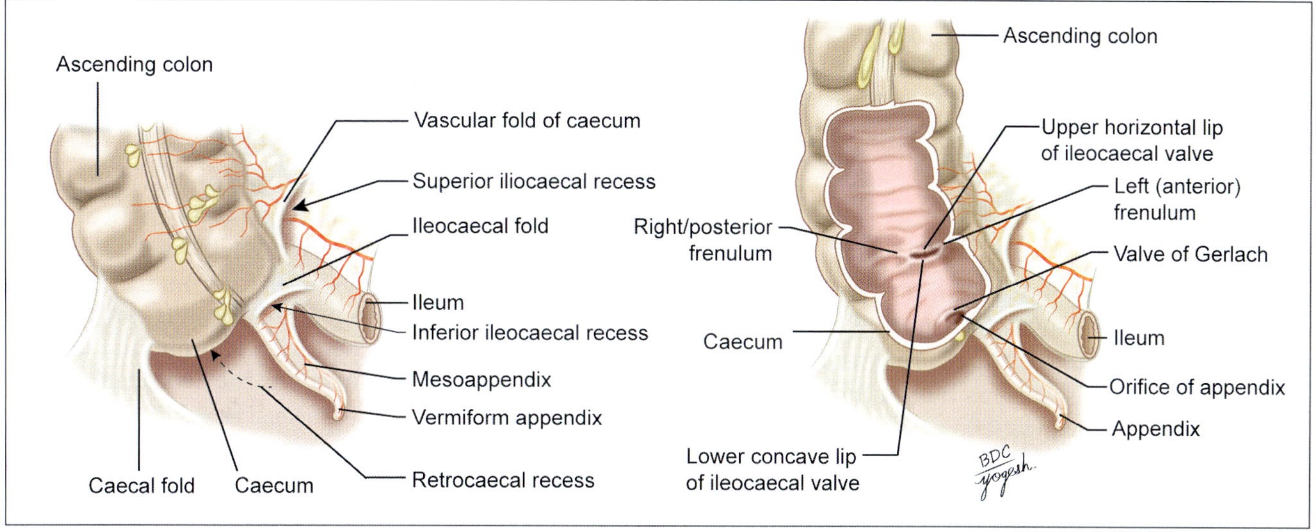

Flowchart 20.5: Caecum

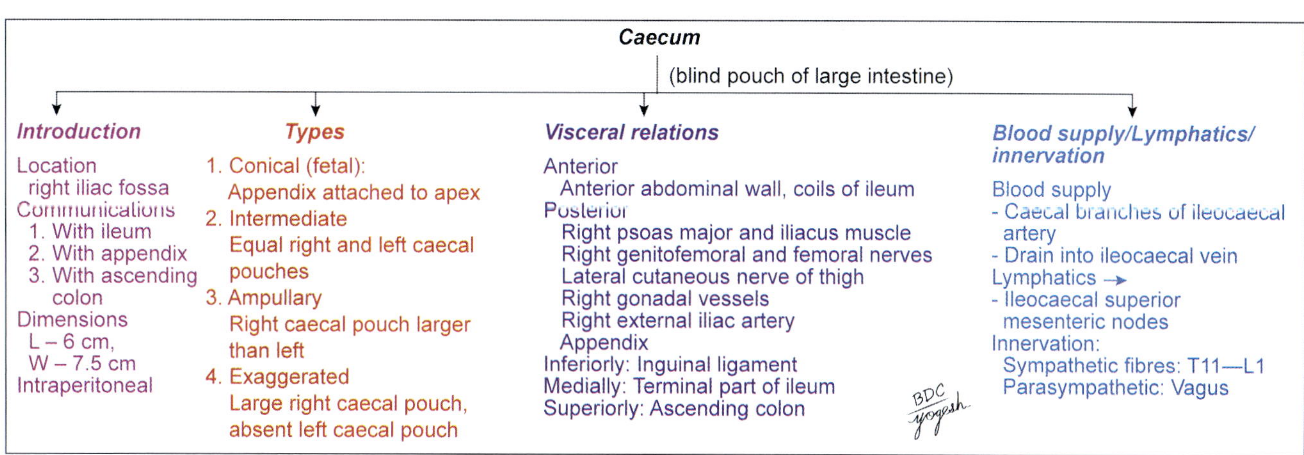

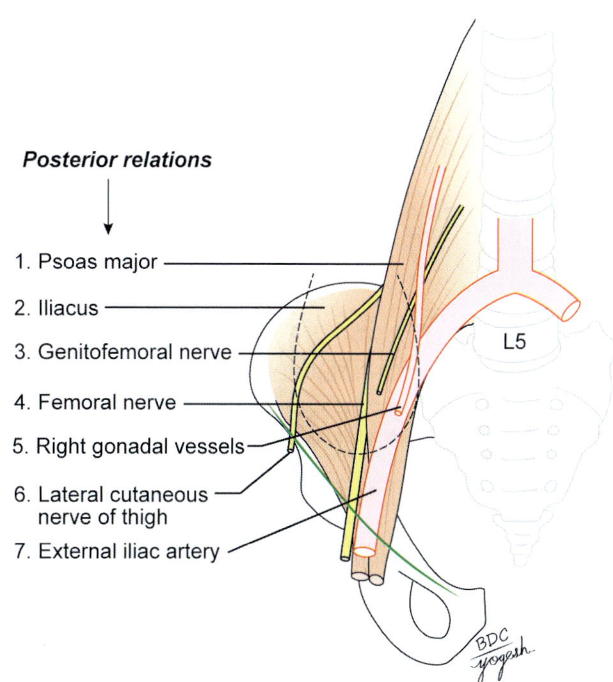

Fig. 20.17: Relations of caecum

Peritoneal Relations

The caecum is often completely covered by peritoneum. Peritoneal folds get reflected from caecum to the right iliac fossa and creates peritoneal recesses such as superior and inferior ileocaecal recesses and retrocaecal recesses.

Note:

Peritoneal folds related to caecum

From the caecum and terminal part of ileum, three peritoneal folds extend as follows (Plate 20.8):

1. ***Superior ileocecal fold*** (*vascular fold of caecum*): It connects the caecum with terminal part of ileum, mesentery and posterior abdominal wall. As it contains *anterior caecal artery*, it is called vascular fold of caecum. Superior ileocaecal recess lies deep to this fold.
2. ***Inferior ileocaecal fold*** *or bloodless fold of Treves*: It extends from anteroinferior aspect of terminal part of ileum to the caecum or appendix. As it does not contain any blood vessel, it is called bloodless fold of Treves. Inferior ileocaecal recess lies deep to this fold.
3. ***Caecal fold*** extends from posterior surface of caecum to the posterior abdominal wall. Posterior ileocaecal (retrocaecal) recess lies inferomedial to caecal fold.

Peritoneal recesses related to caecum

1. ***Superior ileocaecal recess*** is formed by a vascular fold of caecum, which arches over the anterior caecal artery. It lies between the ileum and ascending colon.
2. ***Inferior ileocaecal recess*** lies behind ileocaecal fold and mesoappendix. It lies behind the ileum and to the left of caecum.
3. ***Retrocaecal recess*** lies behind the caecum and may ascend behind the ascending colon. It often contains vermiform appendix.

Vessels and Nerves

The arterial supply of the caecum is derived from the caecal branches of the ***ileocolic artery*** (Fig. 20.18).

The veins drain into the superior mesenteric vein.

The nerve supply is same as that of the midgut (T11 to L1; parasympathetic, vagus).

Competency:

AN52.6 Describe the development and congenital anomalies of caecum.

Development and Types of Caecum

The caecum and appendix develop from the ***caecal bud*** arising from the *postarterial segment* of the midgut loop. The proximal part of the bud dilates to form the caecum. The distal part remains narrow to form the appendix.

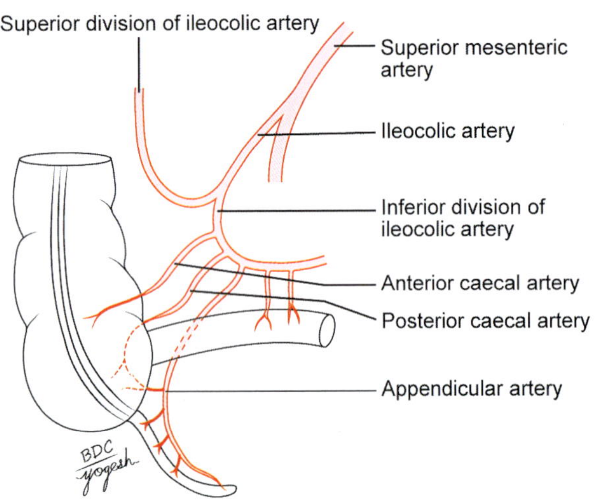

Fig. 20.18: Arterial supply of the caecum and appendix

Thus, initially the appendix arises from the apex of the caecum. However, due to rapid growth of the lateral wall of the caecum, the attachment of the appendix shifts.

Developmental arrest in the shift of appendix forms the basis of types of caecum (Fig. 20.19).

1. ***Conical*** *or foetal type* (13%): Caecum is conical, and the appendix is attached to its apex.
2. ***Intermediate*** *type* (9%): Caecum has right and left caecal pouches of same size and base of appendix is attached to the depression between them.
3. ***Ampullary*** *type* (73–74%): Caecum has the largest right caecal pouch than the left, and base of appendix is attached to posteromedial aspect of caecum, about 2 cm below the ileocaecal junction.
4. ***Exaggerated*** *type* (4–5%): The right caecal pouch is large (due to its exaggerated growth), and the left saccule is absent. The appendix is attached just below the ileocaecal junction.

Internal Appearance of Caecum

Interior of caecum shows two orifices: Ileocaecal and appendicular orifices. These can be visualised using *colonoscopy* (Plate 20.8).

Ileocaecal Orifice *(Ileal Papilla)*

The ***ileal papilla*** is a projecting terminal end of the ileum in the caecum, creating mucosal elevation and folds. It is situated at posteromedial wall of caecum, at its junction with ascending colon. It measures about 2.5 cm transversely. This orifice is guarded by *ileocaecal valve*.

Structure: The valve has upper lip, lower lip and two frenula.

1. *Upper lip of valve*: It is a horizontal mucosal fold at the junction of the ileum and colon.
2. *Lower lip of valve*: It is the longer and concave mucosal fold that lies at the junction of ileum and caecum.
3. *Two frenula of the valve*: The upper and lower lips fuse to form narrow mucosal ridges called frenula. These are right or posterior and left or anterior frenula.

Functions

1. It prevents reflux of faecal matter to ileum.
2. It regulates the flow of ileal contents to caecum.

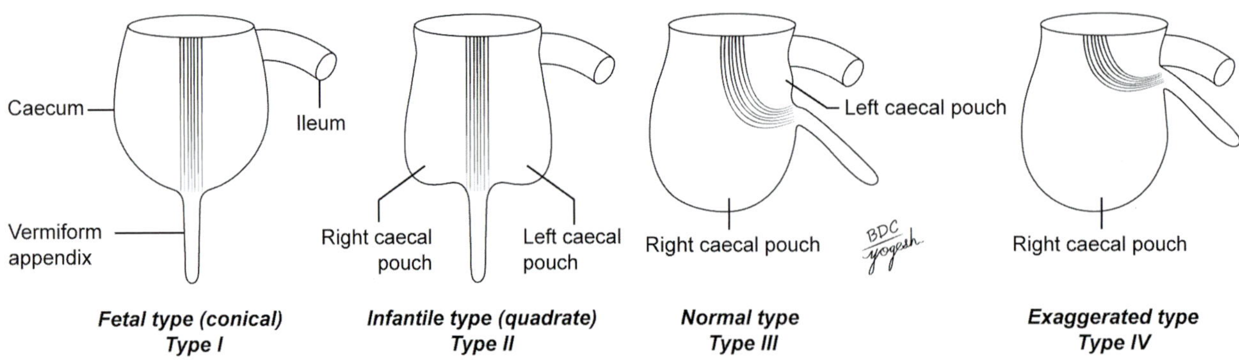

Fig. 20.19: Types of the caecum

Appendicular Orifice

It is a small circular opening situated about 2 cm below the ileocaecal orifice, on the posteromedial wall of caecum. The appendicular orifice is guarded by indistinct semilunar mucosal folds called ***valve of Gerlach***.

CLINICAL ANATOMY

- ***Typhlitis*** or *caecitis* is an inflammation of caecum.
- ***Caecal volvulus*** is a twisting of caecum. It usually occurs in case of persistent mesentery of caecum and ascending colon.
- Caecum may be a site for amoebic infection causing dysentery, intestinal tuberculosis and carcinoma.
- ***Surgical guide***: Caecum acts as a guide in the surgeries for intestinal obstructions. In large intestinal obstruction, caecum is distended and in small intestinal obstruction, caecum is empty.

DISSECTION

Turn the caecum upwards and identify its posterior relations.

Incise the lateral wall of the caecum and locate the ileocaecal orifice and its associated valve. Below the ileocaecal valve, identify the orifice of the vermiform appendix.

VERMIFORM APPENDIX

This is a worm-like (*Vermes in latin*) diverticulum arising from the posteromedial wall, of the caecum, about 2 cm below the ileocaecal orifice (Plate 20.8, Fig. 20.20, Flowchart 20.6).

Dimensions

Length: 6–10 cm in adults. The appendix grows in length up to 3 years of age [*Reference*: *Gray's Anatomy*, 42nd edn.].
Diameter: 5 mm
Lumen: Narrow, even obliterated after mid-adult life.

Parts of Appendix

The appendix is a tubular structure. It has three parts: base, body and tip.

1. ***Base*** *of appendix* is fixed and attached to the postero-medial wall of the caecum, at about 2 cm below the ileocaecal junction. It can be identified by the convergence at taenia coli at the base. It is useful surgical guide for appendicectomy.
2. ***Body*** *of appendix* is narrow, tubular and has uniform diameter.
3. ***Tip*** *of appendix* is a rounded blind end of tubular appendix. It is the least vascular part of appendix.

Positions

The base of the appendix is attached to the posteromedial wall of caecum and is fixed. The body of the appendix is directed in various directions as it is free due to the attachment of mesoappendix. Based on the position and its similarity to hourhand of clock, the positions are classified as follows (Fig. 20.20):

1. ***Paracolic*** *(11 o'clock) position* — appendix passes upward and to the right of ascending colon.
2. ***Retrocaecal*** or *retrocolic (12 o'clock position)* — appendix passes upward behind the caecum and ascending colon.
3. ***Splenic*** *(2 o'clock) position* — appendix passes upward and medially. It may pass anterior to the terminal part of ileum (*preileal appendix*) or posterior (*postileal appendix*).
4. ***Promonteric*** *(3 o'clock) position* — appendix passes horizontally to the left, toward the sacral promontory.
5. ***Pelvic*** *(4 o'clock) position* — appendix descend downward and medially. It crosses pelvic brim to enter true pelvis
6. ***Midinguinal*** *or subcaecal (6 o'clock) position* — appendix lies below the caecum, passes vertically downward and points toward midinguinal point.

Occurrences of Positions of Appendix

- The most common position of appendix is retrocaecal or retrocolic (12 o'clock) position, found in 65.28%.

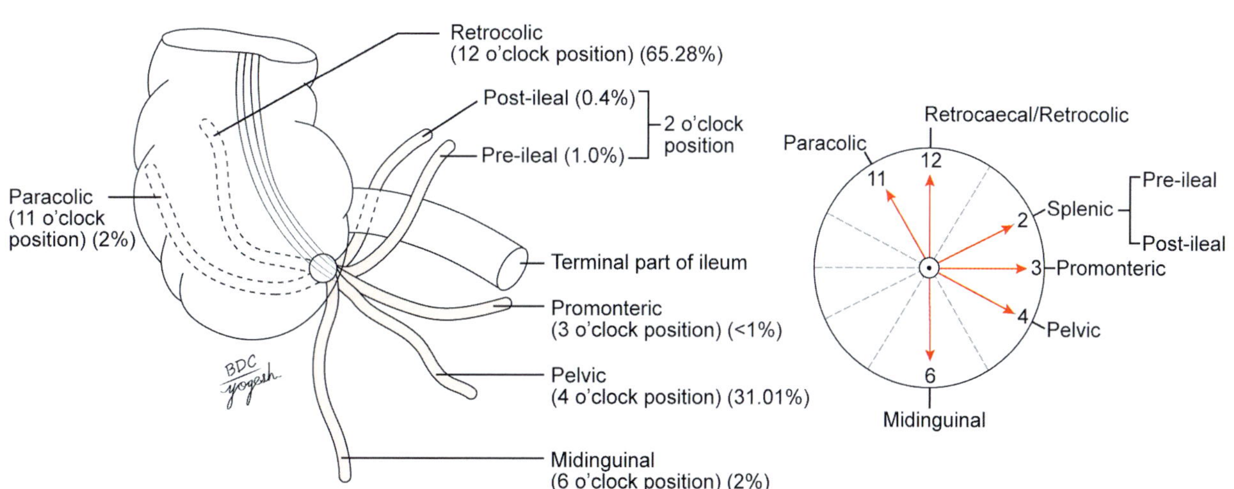

Fig. 20.20: Positions of vermiform appendix (after Treves)

Flowchart 20.6: Appendix

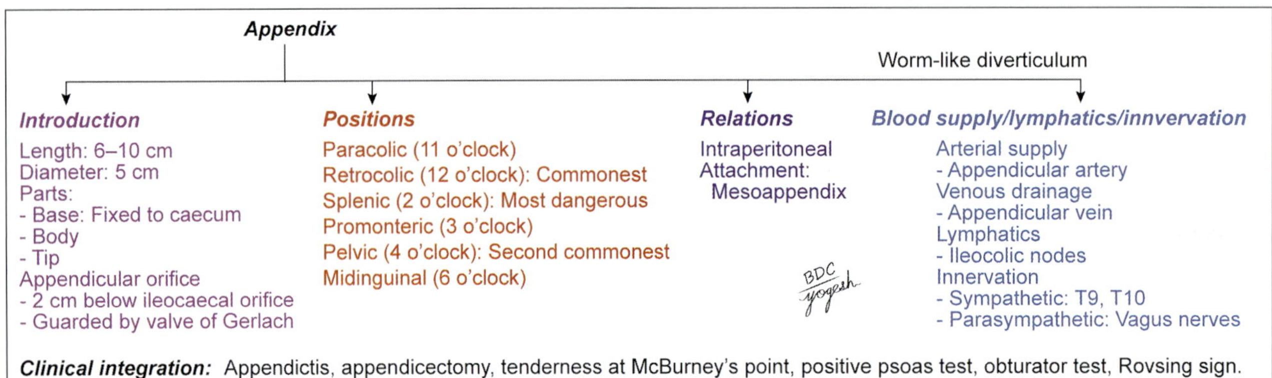

- The second most common position of appendix is pelvic (4 o'clock) position, found in 31.01%.
- The pre-ileal splenic (2 o'clock) position of the appendix is the most dangerous because, in this position, the infection from appendix may spread to general peritoneal cavity.

Appendicular Orifice

1. The appendicular orifice is situated on the posteromedial aspect of the caecum 2 cm below the ileocaecal orifice (Plate 20.8).
2. The appendicular orifice is occasionally guarded by an indistinct semilunar fold of the mucous membrane, known as the ***valve of Gerlach***.
3. ***Surface marking***: The orifice is marked on the surface by a point situated 2 cm below the junction of transtubercular and right lateral planes (Fig. 20.21).

Note: ***McBurney's point*** is the site of maximum tenderness in appendicitis. The point lies at the junction of lateral 1/3rd and medial 2/3rd of line joining the right anterior superior iliac spine to umbilicus (Fig. 20.21).

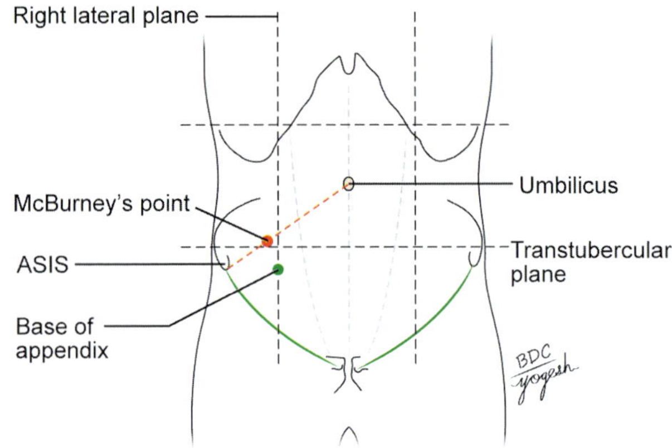

Fig. 20.21: McBurney's point (ASIS: Anterior superior iliac spine)

Lumen of Appendix

It is quite small and may be partially or completely obliterated after mid-adult life.

Peritoneal Relations

The appendix is an intraperitoneal organ. ***Mesoappendix*** is a small, triangular double-layered fold of the peritoneum which suspends the vermiform appendix from the posterior surface of the lower end of the mesentery, close to ileocecal junction (Plate 20.8).

Contents of Mesoappendix

1. Appendicular artery and vein
2. Autonomic nerves
3. Lymphatic vessels from appendix
4. Lymph nodes.

Blood Supply

The ***appendicular artery*** is a branch of the lower division of the ileocolic artery (Fig. 20.18).

Blood from the appendix is drained by the appendicular, ileocolic and superior mesenteric veins, to the portal vein.

Note: Features of appendicular artery:

1. It is a branch of lower division of ileocolic artery.
2. It runs behind the terminal part of ileum to enter the mesoappendix.
3. It runs toward the tip of appendix along the free margin of mesoappendix.
4. It gives recurrent branch that anastomoses with the branch of posterior caecal artery.
5. It is an ***end artery***.
6. It poorly supplies the tip of appendix; hence, it is prone for gangrenous changes in appendicitis.

Nerve Supply

1. Sympathetic nerves are derived from T9 and T10 segments through the coeliac plexus. These fibres carry pain sensation. Referred pain of appendix is felt at umbilicus, similar to that of small intestine and testis.
2. Parasympathetic nerves are derived from the vagus.

Lymphatic Drainage

Most of the lymphatics pass directly to the ileocolic nodes, but a few of them pass indirectly through the appendicular nodes situated in the mesoappendix.

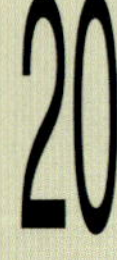

Competency:

AN52.1 Describe and identify the microanatomical features of vermiform appendix.

Histology of Appendix

Histologically, appendix shows four layers of gut: Mucosa, submucosa, muscularis externa and serosa (Plate 20.9).

1. ***Mucosa*** is lined by simple columnar epithelium with microvilli, ***goblet cells*** and M cells. *Lamina propria* contains short tubular intestinal glands lined by simple columnar epithelium with goblet cells. Lamina propria is mostly occupied by large and small ***lymphatic follicles*** that even may cross muscularis mucosa and extend into submucosa.
2. ***Submucosa*** consists of connective tissue. Many lymphatic follicles extend from lamina propria to submucosa.
3. ***Muscularis externa*** consists of inner circular and outer longitudinal muscle coat. *Note*: Though appendix is a part of large intestine, it does not have taenia coli.
4. ***Serosa:*** Appendix is entirely covered by peritoneum (serosa).

Plate 20.9: Histology of vermiform appendix

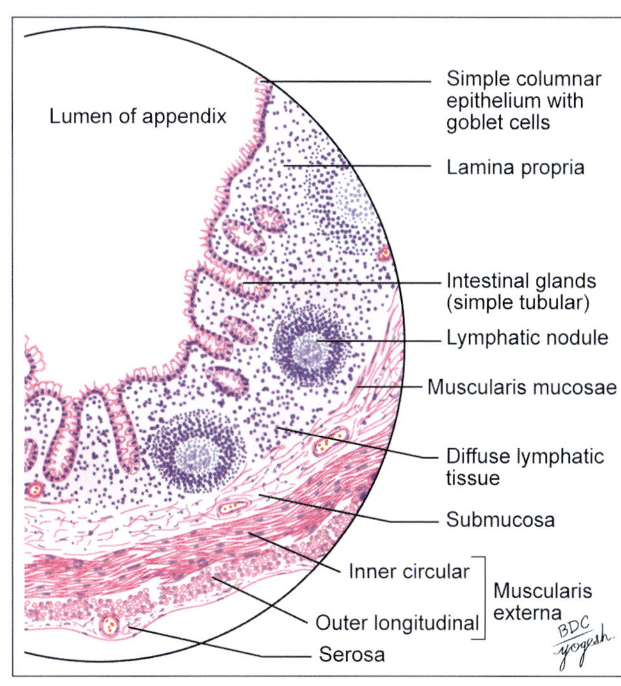

CLINICAL ANATOMY

- ***Appendicitis*** is an inflammation of appendix. The symptoms of appendicitis include right lower abdominal pain, nausea, vomiting and fever. Initially, pain may be felt around the umbilicus that later localizes at the right iliac fossa.

  Clinical examination

  1. Tenderness at McBurney's point (Fig. 20.21).
  2. *Psoas test*: In retrocaecal position of appendix, its inflammation may irritate the right psoas major muscle. In these patients, forced extension of the right thigh induces pain in the right iliac fossa.
  3. *Obturator test in appendicitis*: In pelvic position of appendix, the inflamed appendix may irritate the obturator internus muscle. In these patients, flexion and medial rotation of the right thigh induce pain in lower abdomen.
  4. *Rovsing sign*: Palpation of left iliac region induces pain in right iliac region of the abdomen in cases of appendicitis.

  Treatment: Appendicectomy is a surgical removal of appendix.
- *Appendicular dyspepsia:* Chronic appendicitis produces dyspepsia resembling disease of stomach, duodenum or gallbladder. It is due to passage of infected lymph to the subpyloric nodes which cause irritation of pylorus. There is history of earlier acute appendicitis.

ASCENDING COLON

Ascending colon is about 15–20 cm long and extends from the caecum to the inferior surface of the right lobe of the liver. Here it bends to the left to form the right colic flexure. It is covered by peritoneum on three sides (Plate 20.6, Fig. 20.13).

Anteriorly, it is related to the coils of small intestine, the right edge of the greater omentum and the anterior abdominal wall.

Posteriorly, it is related to the iliacus, the quadratus lumborum, the transversus abdominis, the lateral cutaneous, ilioinguinal and iliohypogastric nerves and the right kidney.

Right Colic Flexure (Hepatic Flexure)

Right colic flexure lies at the junction of the ascending colon and transverse colon. Here the colon bends forward, downwards and to the left. The flexure lies on the lower part of right kidney. Anterosuperiorly, it is related to the colic impression on inferior surface of the right lobe of liver (Plate 20.6, Fig. 20.13).

TRANSVERSE COLON

Transverse colon is about 50 cm long and extend across the abdomen from the right colic flexure to the left colic flexure. Actually, it is not transverse, but hangs low as a loop to a variable extent. It is suspended by the transverse mesocolon attached to the anterior border of pancreas and has a wide range of mobility (Plate 20.6, Fig. 20.13).

Anteriorly, it is related to the greater omentum and to the anterior abdominal wall.

Posteriorly, it is related to the second part of the duodenum, the head of the pancreas and to coils of small intestine. The differences between right two-thirds and left one-third of transverse colon are tabulated in Table 20.3.

TABLE 20.3: Differences between right 2/3rd and left 1/3rd of transverse colon

	Right two-thirds of transverse colon	*Left one-third of transverse colon*
Position	Descending till umbilicus	Ascending to left hypochondrium
Arterial supply	Middle colic branch of superior mesenteric artery	Ascending branch of left colic artery, branch of inferior mesenteric artery
Nerve supply and development	Branches of vagus, as it develops from midgut	Branches of pelvic splanchnic, S2, 3, 4, as it develops from hindgut

TABLE 20.4: Differences between hepatic flexure and splenic flexure

Feature	*Right colic flexure*	*Left colic flexure*
Alternate name	Hepatic flexure	Splenic flexure
Location	Right lumbar region	Left hypochondrium
Main visceral relation	Inferior surface of right lobe of liver	Spleen
Level	1 inch below the transpyloric plane	1 inch above the transpyloric plane
Vertebral level	L2	T12
Angulation	Wider	Acute
Peritoneal ligament	Absent	Phrenicocolic ligament
Blood supply	Right colic artery	Left colic artery

Left Colic Flexure (Splenic Flexure)

Left colic flexure lies at the junction of the transverse colon and the descending colon. Here the colon bends downwards and backwards. The flexure lies on the lower part of the left kidney and diaphragm, behind the stomach and below the anterior end of the spleen. The flexure is attached to the 11th rib (in the midaxillary line) by a horizontal fold of peritoneum, called the ***phrenicocolic ligament***. This ligament supports the spleen and forms a partial upper limit of the left paracolic gutter. Differences in hepatic flexure and splenic flexure are shown in Table 20.4.

DESCENDING COLON

Descending colon is about 25–30 cm long and extends from the left colic flexure to the sigmoid colon. It runs vertically up to the iliac crest and then inclines medially on the iliacus and psoas major to reach the pelvic brim, where it is continuous with the sigmoid colon. The descending colon is narrower than the ascending colon (Plate 20.6, Fig. 20.13).

Anteriorly, it is related to the coils of small intestine.

Posteriorly, it is related to the transversus abdominis, the quadratus lumborum, the iliacus and psoas muscles; the iliohypogastric, ilioinguinal, lateral cutaneous, femoral and genitofemoral nerves; the gonadal and external iliac vessels.

SIGMOID COLON (PELVIC COLON)

Sigmoid colon is about 37.5 cm long and extends from the pelvic brim to the third piece of the sacrum, where it becomes the rectum. It forms a sinuous loop and hangs down in pelvis over the bladder and uterus. Occasionally, it is very short and takes a straight course. It is suspended by the sigmoid mesocolon and is covered by coils of small intestine.

The **rectum** and the **anal canal** are described later.

Video 2.20 Small and Large Intestines: Duodenum, jejunum and ileum, large intestine.

Facts to Remember

- Small intestine is characterised by the evaginations called the *villi*.
- Most of the duodenum is fixed and retroperitoneal.
- Second part of duodenum contains the openings of bile and pancreatic ducts.
- Third part of duodenum is crossed anteriorly by superior mesenteric vessels.
- Duodenal cap is triangular shadow of its first part seen in barium meal X-ray. Transverse colon is the most mobile part of large intestine.
- Meckel's diverticulum is the proximal persistent part of vitellointestinal duct.
- Caecum is broader than longer.
- The most common position of vermiform appendix is retrocaecal.
- Pain of early appendicitis is referred to the region of umbilicus (T10 spinal segment).
- McBurney's point is a point at the junction of medial two-thirds and lateral one-third of a line joining umbilicus to the right anterior superior iliac spine.
- Ileocaecal junction is the most common site of tuberculosis (TB) of intestines.
- Cancer of colon mostly occurs at rectosigmoid junction.

BDC's Anatomy *e*-book

1. Development of intestines
2. Further reading
3. Viva voce questions

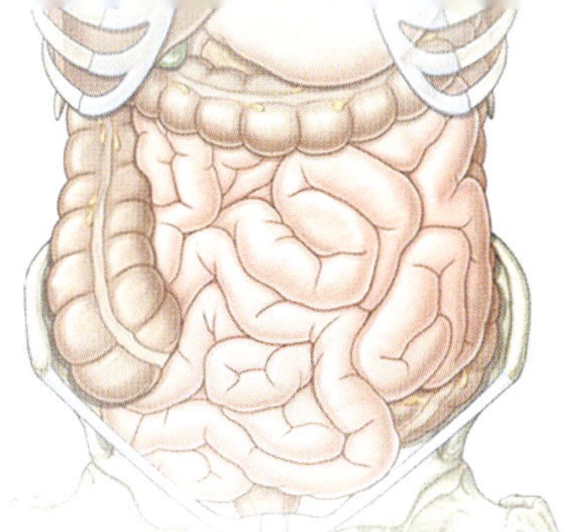

Chapter

21

Large Blood Vessels of the Gut

The three ventral branches of the abdominal aorta are coeliac trunk, superior mesenteric and inferior mesenteric arteries. These are the arteries of the foregut, midgut and hindgut, respectively. There are anastomoses between the branches of these three main arteries.

Competency:

AN47.9 Describe and identify the origin, course, important relations and branches of abdominal aorta, coeliac trunk, superior mesenteric, inferior mesenteric and common iliac artery.

COELIAC TRUNK

The coeliac trunk is the artery of the foregut (Figs 21.1 and 21.2). It supplies all derivatives of the foregut that lie in the abdomen, namely:

1. Lower end of the oesophagus
2. Stomach
3. Upper part of the duodenum up to the opening of the bile duct
4. Liver
5. Spleen
6. Greater part of the pancreas.

Origin and Length

The coeliac trunk arises from the front of the abdominal aorta just below the aortic opening of the diaphragm at the level of the disc between thoracic twelve and first lumbar vertebrae.

The trunk is only about 1.25 cm long.

Termination: It ends by dividing into its three terminal branches, namely the left gastric, common hepatic and splenic arteries (Fig. 21.3, Flowchart 21.1).

Relations

Coeliac trunk has the following relations (Fig. 21.2):

Anteriorly:	Lesser sac and parietal peritoneum
Posteriorly:	Abdominal aorta
Superiorly:	Median arcuate ligament
Inferiorly:	Body of pancreas, splenic vein
On the right:	Right crus of diaphragm, caudate process of liver
On the left:	Left crus of diaphragm.

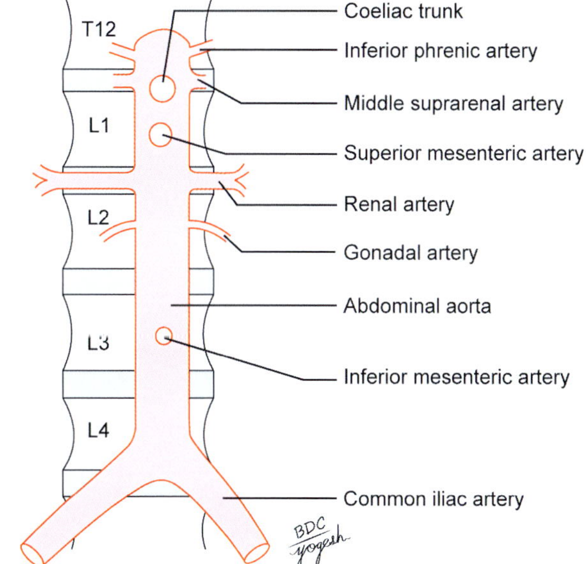

Fig. 21.1: Ventral and lateral branches of the abdominal aorta with their levels of origin

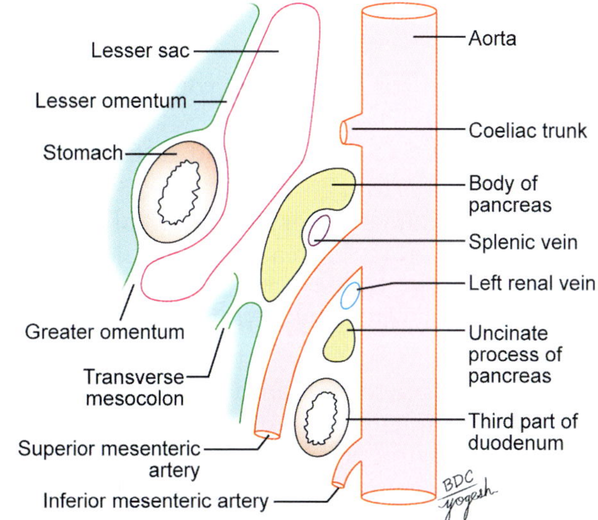

Fig. 21.2: Left view of a sagittal section through the abdominal aorta showing the origin of its three ventral branches

The coeliac trunk is surrounded by coeliac plexus of nerves and coeliac lymph nodes.

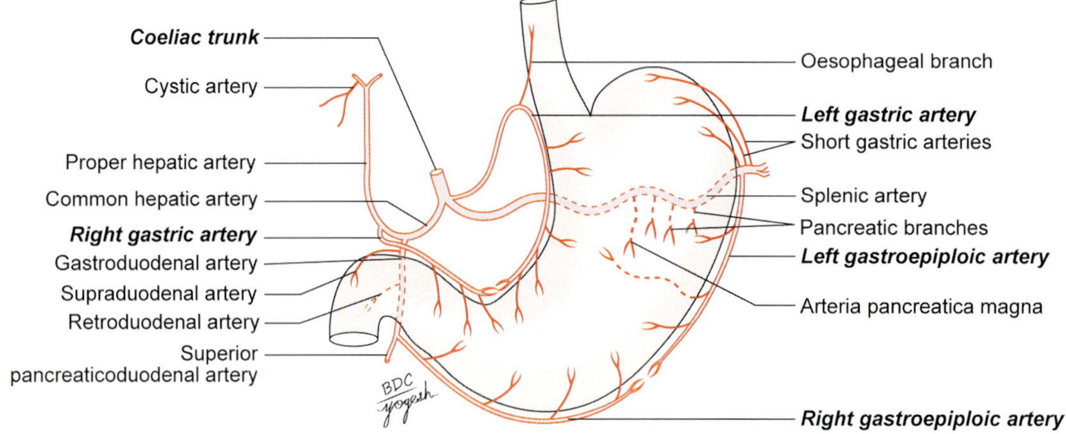

Fig. 21.3: Arteries arising from the branches of the coeliac trunk

Flowchart 21.1: Coeliac trunk

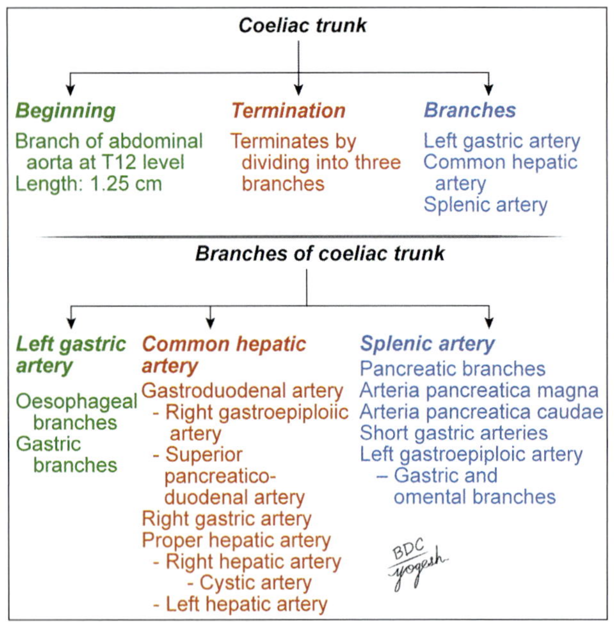

Branches

The branches and sub-branches of coeliac trunk are as follows:

1. *Left gastric artery*: Oesophageal and gastric branches
2. *Common hepatic artery*:
   a. Gastroduodenal artery—right gastroepiploic artery, superior pancreaticoduodenal artery
   b. Right gastric artery
   c. Proper hepatic artery—right and left hepatic arteries.
3. *Splenic artery*: Pancreatic branches, arteria pancreatica magna, arteria caudae pancreatis, short gastric arteries, left gastroepiploic artery.

Left Gastric Artery

The *left gastric artery* is the smallest of the three branches of the coeliac trunk. It runs upwards to the left behind the lesser sac to reach the cardiac end of the stomach where it turns forwards and enters the lesser omentum to run downwards along the lesser curvature of the stomach.

It gives off:

1. Two or three *oesophageal branches* at the cardiac end of the stomach.
2. Numerous *gastric branches* along the lesser curvature of the stomach (Fig. 21.4), supplying large part of body of stomach.

It ends by anastomosing with the right gastric artery.

Common Hepatic Artery

The *common hepatic artery* runs downwards, forwards and to the right, behind the lesser sac to reach the upper border of the 1st part of duodenum. Here, it enters the lesser omentum. It then runs upwards as proper hepatic artery in the right free margin of the lesser omentum, in front of the portal vein and to the left of the bile duct. Reaching the porta hepatis, it terminates by dividing into right and left hepatic branches.

Branches (Fig. 21.3)

1. The ***gastroduodenal artery*** is a large branch which arises at the upper border of the 1st part of the duodenum. The part of the hepatic artery till the origin of the gastroduodenal artery is called the *common hepatic artery*. The part distal to it is the ***proper hepatic artery***.

   The gastroduodenal artery runs downwards behind the 1st part of the duodenum and divides at its lower border into the right gastroepiploic and superior pancreaticoduodenal arteries.

   The ***right gastroepiploic artery*** enters the greater omentum, follows the greater curvature of the stomach and anastomoses with the left gastroepiploic artery.

   The ***superior pancreaticoduodenal artery*** (often represented by two arteries—anterior and posterior) runs downwards in the pancreaticoduodenal groove, and ends by anastomosing with the inferior pancreaticoduodenal artery, a branch of the superior mesenteric.
2. The ***right gastric artery*** is a small branch which arises from the proper hepatic artery close to the gastroduodenal artery. It runs to the left along the

lesser curvature and ends by anastomosing with the left gastric artery.

3. The ***cystic artery*** is a branch of the right hepatic artery. It passes behind the common hepatic and cystic ducts to reach the upper surface of the neck of the gallbladder where it divides into superficial and deep branches for the inferior and superior surfaces of the gallbladder, respectively.

Splenic Artery

The *splenic artery* is the largest branch of the coeliac trunk. It runs horizontally to the left along the upper border of the pancreas behind the lesser sac. It crosses the left suprarenal gland and the upper part of the left kidney to enter the lienorenal ligament, through which it reaches the hilum of spleen where it divides into 5 to 7 splenic branches (Fig. 21.3).

Branches: It gives off the following branches:

1. Numerous ***pancreatic branches*** which supply the body and tail of the pancreas. One of the branches to the body of the pancreas is large and is known as the ***arteria pancreatica magna***. Another large branch to the tail is known as the ***arteria caudae pancreatis*** (*see* Fig. 23.18). These large arteries anastomose (on the back of the pancreas) with the left branch of a *dorsal artery* which may arise from one of the following arteries—superior mesenteric, middle colic, hepatic or coeliac.
2. Five to seven ***short gastric arteries*** arise from the terminal part of the splenic artery, run in the gastrosplenic ligament and supply the fundus of the stomach.
3. The ***left gastroepiploic artery*** also arises from the terminal part of the splenic artery, runs downwards in the greater omentum, follows the greater curvature of the stomach and ends by anastomosing with the right gastroepiploic artery. As the name suggests, the gastroepiploic arteries supply both the stomach and greater omentum.

Note: The tortuosity of the splenic artery helps to regulate blood flow to the spleen in different metabolic activities. Its tortuosity allows distension of stomach without obstruction to the splenic blood flow.

SUPERIOR MESENTERIC ARTERY

The superior mesenteric artery is the artery of the midgut. It supplies all derivatives of the midgut, namely:

1. Lower part of the duodenum below the opening of the bile duct (Fig. 21.4).
2. Jejunum
3. Ileum
4. Appendix
5. Caecum
6. Ascending colon
7. Right 2/3rd of the transverse colon
8. Lower half of the head of the pancreas.

Origin, Course and Termination

The superior mesenteric artery arises from the front of the abdominal aorta, behind the body of the pancreas, at the level of vertebra L1, one centimetre below the coeliac trunk (Fig. 21.1). It runs downwards and to the right, forming a curve with its convexity towards the left.

At its origin, it lies 1st behind the body of the pancreas and then in front of the uncinate process. Next it crosses the third part of the duodenum, enters the root of mesentery and runs between its two layers. It terminates in the right iliac fossa by anastomosing with a branch of the ileocolic artery.

Branches

The superior mesenteric artery gives off five sets of branches both from its right and left sides (Fig. 21.4, Flowchart 21.2).

1. Those arising from its *right side* are:
   a. Inferior pancreaticoduodenal
   b. Middle colic
   c. Right colic
   d. Ileocolic.
2. Those arising from its *left side* are 12–15 jejunal and ileal branches.

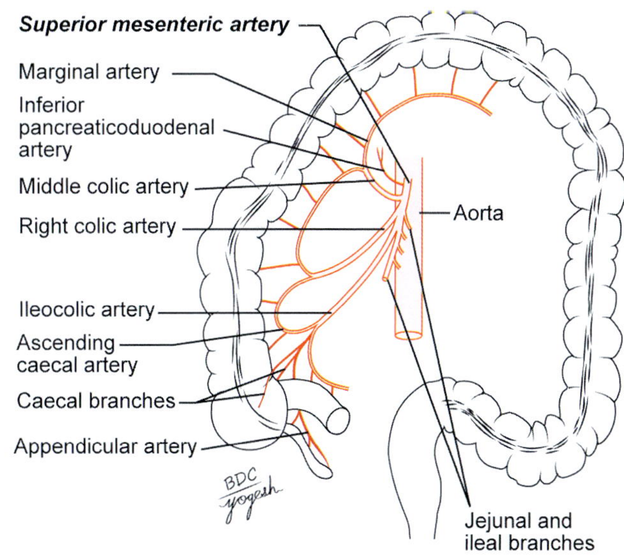

Fig. 21.4: Branches of the superior mesenteric artery

Flowchart 21.2: Superior mesenteric artery

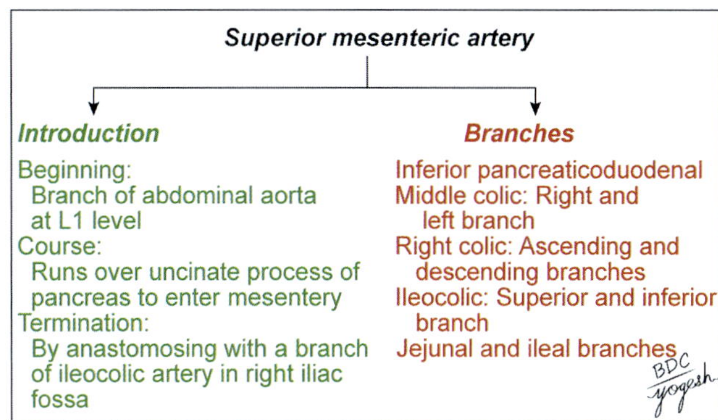

Inferior Pancreaticoduodenal Artery

Inferior pancreaticoduodenal artery arises from the superior mesenteric artery at the upper border of the 3rd part of the duodenum. The artery soon divides into ***anterior*** and ***posterior branches*** which run in the pancreaticoduodenal groove, supplies the head of the pancreas and the duodenum and end by anastomosing with the superior pancreaticoduodenal artery.

Middle Colic Artery

Middle colic artery arises from the right side of the superior mesenteric artery just below the pancreas. It runs downwards and forwards in the transverse mesocolon.

It divides into a ***right branch***, which anastomoses with the right colic artery, and a ***left branch***, which anastomoses with the left colic artery. Further branches arising from these form arcades and supply the transverse colon.

Right Colic Artery

Right colic artery arises near the middle of the concavity of the superior mesenteric artery. It passes to the right behind the peritoneum, and at the upper part of the ascending colon, it divides into a ***descending branch***, which anastomoses with the ileocolic artery, and an ***ascending branch***, which anastomoses with the middle colic artery. The branches form an arch, from the convexity of which smaller branches are distributed to the upper two-thirds of the ascending colon and the right flexure of the colon.

Ileocolic Artery

Ileocolic artery arises from the right side of the superior mesenteric artery. It runs downwards and to the right and divides into superior and inferior branches.

The ***superior branch*** anastomoses with the right colic artery, and the ***inferior branch*** anastomoses with the termination of the superior mesenteric artery.

The inferior branch of the ileocolic artery gives off:

a. Ascending colic branch to the ascending colon.
b. Anterior and posterior caecal branches to the caecum.
c. Appendicular branch which passes behind the ileum and reaches the appendix through its mesentery.
d. Ileal branch to the terminal portion of the ileum.

Jejunal and Ileal Branches

Jejunal and ileal branches are about 12 to 15 in number and arise from the left side of the superior mesenteric artery. They run between the two layers of the mesentery towards the gut. They anastomose with one another to form arterial arcades which give off straight branches or ***vasa recta*** to the gut. These branches supply the jejunum (Fig. 21.5a) and most of ileum (Fig. 21.5b). The terminal part of the ileum is supplied by the ileocolic artery.

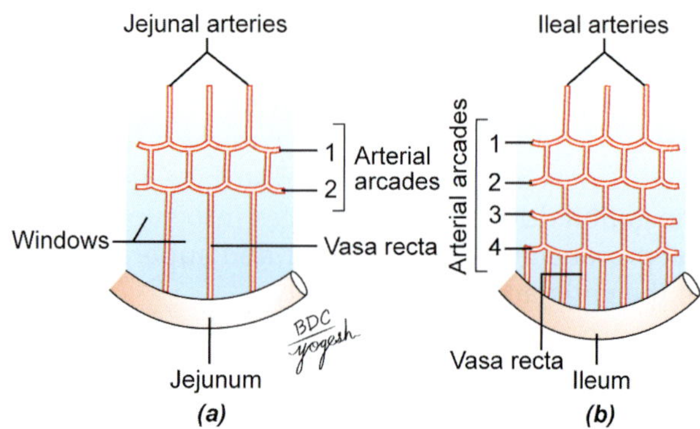

Figs 21.5a and b: Arterial arcades and vasa recta of: (a) Jejunum and (b) ileum

CLINICAL ANATOMY

- Acquired diverticula of small intestine are more common in upper jejunum. These occur on the side of the mesenteric border at the site of entry of vasa recta. Vulnerability of jejunum is due to relative weakness of the longitudinal muscle coat.
- Sudden occlusion of the superior mesenteric artery, vein or both may occur due to embolism or thrombosis. It is usually followed by a rapidly spreading form of intestinal obstruction due to the haemorrhagic infarction of the involved gut.
- Superior mesenteric artery crosses third part of duodenum. This part of duodenum may get obstructed as it lies between abdominal aorta and superior mesenteric artery. Duodenum behaves like a nut between the two tongs formed by these two arteries.

DISSECTION

Identify the short trunk of coeliac axis artery at the level of the intervertebral disc between T12 and L1 vertebrae arising from the aorta. Dissect its relations especially with the coeliac ganglion and identify its three branches and their further divisions.

Clean the superior mesenteric vessels with its branches both from its right and left surfaces. Dissect these branches and trace them till the organs of their supply.

Identify the inferior mesenteric artery arising at the L3 vertebra. Trace its course and branches.

Identify the large portal vein formed by the union of superior mesenteric and splenic vein posterior to the neck of pancreas. Trace it upwards towards the remains of free margin of lesser omentum till the porta hepatis where it divides into two branches. Identify the veins taking part in portosystemic anastomoses.

INFERIOR MESENTERIC ARTERY

The inferior mesenteric artery is the artery of the hindgut. It supplies the parts of the gut that are derivatives of the hindgut and posterior part of cloaca, the anorectal canal, namely (Fig. 21.6, Flowchart 21.3):

1. Left 1/3rd of the transverse colon
2. Descending colon

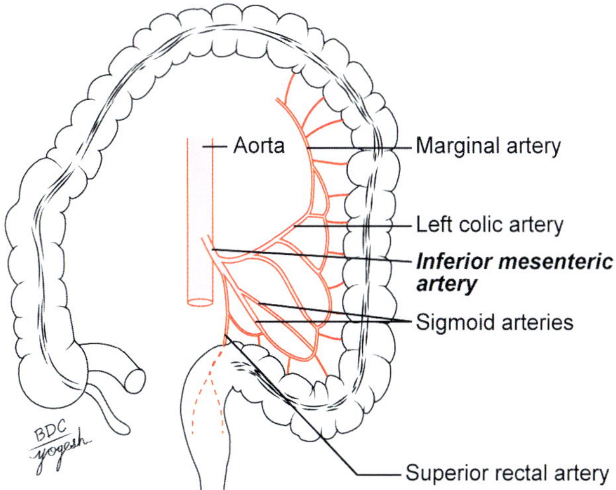

Fig. 21.6: Branches of the inferior mesenteric artery

Flowchart 21.3: Inferior mesenteric artery

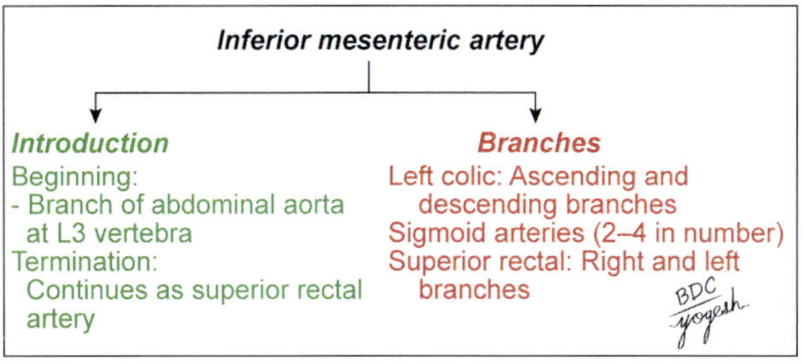

3. Sigmoid colon
4. Rectum
5. Upper part of the anal canal, above the anal valves.

Origin

Inferior mesenteric artery arises from the front of the abdominal aorta behind the third part of the duodenum, at the level of third lumbar vertebra and 3 to 4 cm above the bifurcation of the aorta.

Course and Termination

It runs downwards and to the left, behind the peritoneum, crosses the common iliac artery medial to the left ureter and continues in the sigmoid mesocolon as the superior rectal artery (Fig. 21.9).

Branches

The inferior mesenteric artery gives off the left colic and sigmoid branches (Fig. 21.10). It continues as superior rectal artery.

Left Colic Artery

Left colic artery is the 1st branch of the inferior mesenteric artery. It runs upwards and to the left, behind the peritoneum of the posterior wall of the left infracolic compartment and after a variable course divides into an ascending and a descending branch. The ***ascending branch*** enters the transverse mesocolon and anastomoses with the middle colic artery. The ***descending branch*** anastomoses with the highest sigmoid artery.

Sigmoid Arteries

Sigmoid arteries are 2 to 4 in number. They pass downwards and to the left and anastomose with each other to form the lower part of the marginal artery. The uppermost branch anastomoses with the descending branch of the left colic artery, whereas the lowest sigmoid artery sends a branch to anastomose with the superior rectal artery.

Superior Rectal Artery

Superior rectal artery is the continuation of the inferior mesenteric artery beyond the root of the sigmoid mesocolon, i.e. over the left common iliac vessels. It descends in the sigmoid mesocolon to reach the rectum. Opposite S3 vertebra, it divides into right and left branches which descend one on each side of the rectum. They pierce the muscular coat of the rectum and divide into several branches, which anastomose with one another at the level of the anal sphincter to form loops around the lower end of the rectum. These branches communicate with the middle and inferior rectal arteries in the submucosa of the anal canal.

MARGINAL ARTERY OF DRUMMOND

Marginal artery is an arterial arcade situated along the concavity of the colon (described by von Haller in 1803 and named by Sudeck in 1907). It is formed by anastomoses between the main arteries supplying the colon, namely the ileocolic, right colic, middle colic, left colic and sigmoid arteries.

It lies at a distance of 2.5 to 3.8 cm from the colon. It is closest to the colon in its descending and sigmoid parts. ***Vasa recta*** arise from the marginal artery and supply the colon (Fig. 21.7).

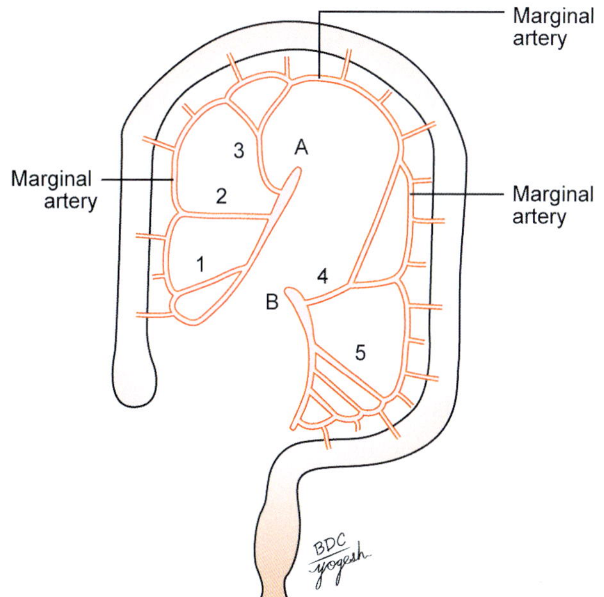

Fig. 21.7: The marginal artery. A Superior mesenteric artery, B inferior mesenteric artery. 1–ileocolic, 2–right colic, 3–middle colic, 4–left colic, 5–sigmoid arteries

The marginal artery is capable of supplying the colon even in the absence of one of the main feeding trunks. This fact is utilised in surgery. However, at the junctional points between the main vessels, there may be variations in the competence of the anastomoses.

Competency:
AN47.8 Describe and identify the formation, course, relations and tributaries of portal vein, inferior vena cava and renal vein.

SUPERIOR MESENTERIC VEIN

1. Superior mesenteric vein is a large vein which drains blood from the small intestine, the appendix, the caecum, the ascending colon and the transverse colon.
2. It begins in the right iliac fossa by the union of tributaries from the ileocaecal region. It accompanies the superior mesenteric artery. The vein lies on the right side of the artery. It terminates, behind the neck of the pancreas, by joining the splenic vein to form the portal vein (Fig. 21.8).
3. ***Tributaries***:
   a. Veins corresponding to the branches of the superior mesenteric artery
   b. Right gastroepiploic vein
   c. Inferior pancreaticoduodenal vein

INFERIOR MESENTERIC VEIN

1. The inferior mesenteric vein drains blood from the rectum, the anal canal, the sigmoid colon and the descending colon. It is longer than the artery.
2. It begins as the ***superior rectal vein*** from the upper part of the internal rectal venous plexus. In the plexus, it communicates with the middle and inferior rectal veins. The superior rectal vein crosses the left common iliac vessels medial to the left ureter and continues upwards as the inferior mesenteric vein. This vein lies lateral to the inferior mesenteric artery. The vein ascends behind the peritoneum and passes lateral to the duodenojejunal flexure in the free margin of paraduodenal fold and behind the body of the pancreas. It opens into the splenic vein (Fig. 21.8).
3. Its *tributaries* correspond to the branches of the inferior mesenteric artery.

PORTAL VEIN

Portal vein is a large vein which collects blood from:
1. Abdominal part of the alimentary tract
2. Gallbladder
3. Pancreas
4. Spleen.

It conveys this blood to the liver. In the liver, the portal vein breaks up into sinusoids which drained by the hepatic veins to the inferior vena cava (Figs 21.8 and 21.9, Flowchart 21.4).

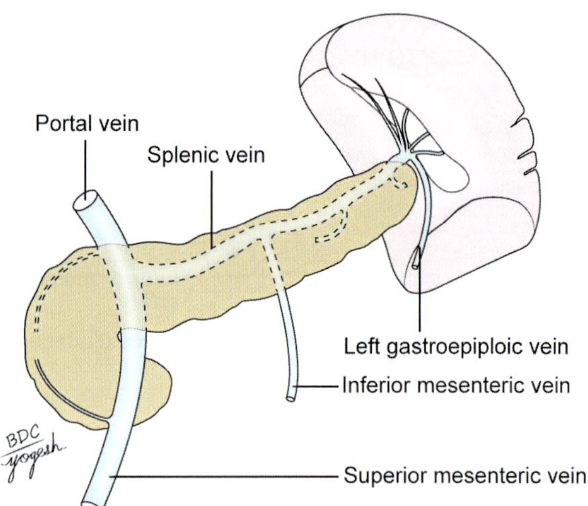

Fig. 21.8: Formation and course of the portal vein

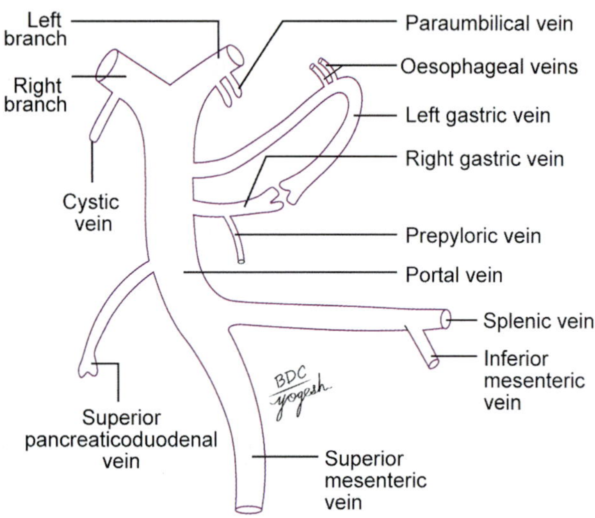

Fig. 21.9: Formation and tributaries of portal vein

It is called the portal vein because its main tributary, the superior mesenteric vein, begins in one set of capillaries (in the gut) and the portal vein ends in another set of capillaries in the liver.

Note: Mesenteric veins → Capillaries in intestine (first set) → Portal vein → Sinusoids in liver (second set) → Hepatic veins → Inferior vena cava.

Peculiarities of Portal Vein

1. Portal vein divides to supply liver similar to an artery.
2. It provides 80% of blood supply to the liver.
3. It is a reservoir of blood and contains up to 1/3rd of the total volume of the blood in the body.
4. Portal vein and its tributaries are devoid of valves.
5. It transports the absorbed nutrients from gut to liver.
6. *Two streams of blood* circulate through the portal vein. Its right branch primarily conveys the blood from the superior mesenteric vein, whereas its left branch primarily conveys the blood from the splenic vein.

Flowchart 21.4: Portal vein and portacaval anastomosis

Portal vein

- ***Peculiarities***
  - Supplies liver (80% of supply)
  - Reservoir of blood
  - Devoid of valves
  - Transports nutrients from gut to liver
- ***Formation***
  - By union of superior mesenteric and splenic vein behind neck of pancreas
  - Length: 8 cm
- ***Termination***
  - At porta hepatis divides into right and left branches
- ***Tributaries***
  - Superior mesenteric vein, splenic vein
  - Right and left gastric vein
  - Superior pancreaticoduodenal vein
  - Cystic vein, paraumbilical veins

Sites of portacaval anastomosis

collateral communication between portal and systemic veins

Umbilicus	*Lower end of oesophagus*	*Anal canal*	*The bare area of liver*	*Along posterior abdominal wall*
Paraumbilical veins (P)	Left gastric vein (P)	Superior rectal vein (P)	Portal radicles (P)	Splenic and colonic veins (P)
↕	↕	↕	↕	↕
Epigastric veins (S) Lateral thoracic vein (S)	Oesophageal vein (S)	Inferior and middle rectal veins (S)	Diaphragmatic veins (S)	Renal vein (S)

Functions: To provide alternate route of venous blood circulation in portal hypertension

Clinical integration: Portal hypertension: Portal venous blood pressure > 10 mm Hg
Effects: Splenomegaly, ascitis, caput medusae, oesophageal varices, hemorrhoids

BDC yogesh.

(P: Portal vein, S: Systemic vein)

Formation

The portal vein is about 8 cm long. It is formed by the union of the superior mesenteric and splenic veins behind the neck of the pancreas at the level of L2 vertebra. Inferior mesenteric vein drains into splenic vein.

Course

It runs upwards and a little to the right, first behind the neck of the pancreas, next behind the 1st part of the duodenum and lastly in the right free margin of the lesser omentum.

The blood flow in portal vein is slow. Blood of superior mesenteric vein drains into right lobe. Blood of splenic and inferior mesenteric vein drains into left lobe. This is called '***streamline flow***'.

The portal vein can thus be divided into infraduodenal, retroduodenal and supraduodenal parts.

Termination

The vein ends at the right end of the porta hepatis by dividing into ***right*** and ***left branches*** which enter the liver.

Relations

Infraduodenal Part

Anteriorly: Neck of pancreas.
Posteriorly: Inferior vena cava.

Retroduodenal Part

Anteriorly

1. First part of duodenum
2. Bile duct
3. Gastroduodenal artery.

Posteriorly: Inferior vena cava.

Supraduodenal Part

Anteriorly

1. Hepatic artery
2. Bile duct (within free margin of the lesser omentum).

Posteriorly: Inferior vena cava, separated by epiploic foramen.

Intrahepatic Course

After entering the liver, each branch divides and redivides along with the hepatic artery to end ultimately in the hepatic sinusoids, where the portal venous blood mixes with the hepatic arterial blood.

Branches

1. ***Right branch*** is shorter and wider than the left branch. After receiving the cystic vein, it enters the right lobe of the liver (Fig. 21.9).
2. ***Left branch*** is longer and narrower than the right branch. It traverses the porta hepatis from its right end to the left end and furnishes branches to the caudate and quadrate lobes. Just before entering the left lobe of the liver, it receives during foetal life:
   a. Paraumbilical veins along the ligamentum teres.
   b. Ductus venosus along ligamentum venosum.

Tributaries

Portal vein receives the following veins (Fig. 21.3):

1. Left gastric
2. Right gastric
3. Superior pancreaticoduodenal
4. Cystic vein in its right branch
5. Paraumbilical veins in its left branch.

Note: The ***left gastric vein*** accompanies the corresponding artery. At the cardiac end of the stomach, it receives a few oesophageal veins. The right gastric vein accompanies the corresponding artery. It receives the prepyloric vein.

The ***paraumbilical veins*** are small veins that run in the falciform ligament, along the ligamentum teres, and establish anastomoses between the veins of the anterior abdominal wall present around the umbilicus and the portal vein.

Development of Portal Vein

During the embryonic life, there are two *vitelline veins* (right and left) that pass on either side of gut tube (Fig. 21.10). The cranial parts of these veins form anastomosing network in the septum transversum that later develops liver sinusoids and ductus venosus.

Around the duodenum, infrahepatic parts of vitelline veins communicate by cranial ventral, middle dorsal and caudal ventral communicating channels. They further develop to form portal venous system as follows:

1. Infraduodenal part, from a part of the left vitelline vein distal to the dorsal anastomosis.
2. Retroduodenal part, from the dorsal anastomosis between the two vitelline veins.
3. Supraduodenal part, from the cranial part of the right vitelline vein.

Competencies:
AN47.10 Enumerate the sites of portosystemic anastomosis.
AN47.11 Explain the anatomic basis of hematemesis and caput medusae in portal hypertension.

PORTOSYSTEMIC COMMUNICATIONS (PORTOCAVAL ANASTOMOSES)

The communication or anastomosis sites between the tributaries of the portal and systemic veins are called sites of portosystemic shunts or portacaval anastomosis.

Important Sites of Portosystemic Shunts

The sites of portosystemic shunts include the following (Figs 21.11, 21.12, Table 21.1):

1. Umbilicus
2. Lower end of oesophagus
3. Anal canal
4. Extraperitoneal surfaces of retroperitoneal organs
5. The bare area of liver
6. At ligamentum venosum.

These communications form important routes of collateral circulation in portal obstruction.

CLINICAL ANATOMY

- ***Portal pressure:*** Normal pressure in the portal vein is about 5–10 mm Hg. It is usually measured by splenic puncture and recording the intrasplenic pressure.
- **Portal hypertension** (pressure above 10 mm Hg): It can be caused by the following conditions:
  a. Cirrhosis of liver, in which the vascular bed of liver is markedly obliterated.
  b. Banti's disease
  c. Thrombosis of portal vein.
- The effects of portal hypertension are as follows (Fig. 21.13):
  a. Congestive splenomegaly
  b. Ascites
  c. Collateral circulation through the portosystemic communications. It forms:

  Caput medusae around the umbilicus, which is of diagnostic value to the clinician.

  Oesophageal varices at the lower end of oesophagus which may rupture and cause dangerous or even fatal haematemesis.

  Haemorrhoids in the anal canal may be responsible for repeated bleeding felt per rectum.
- In cases of cirrhosis of liver, sometimes a shunt operation is done, where one of the main portal channels (splenic, superior mesenteric, or portal vein) is directly anastomosed with either inferior vena cava or the left renal vein (Fig. 21.14).
- Since the blood flow in portal vein is slow and streamlined, the toxic infective substances absorbed from small intestine pass via the superior mesenteric vein into the right lobe of liver leading to toxic changes or amoebic abscess in right lobe. The blood lacking in amino acids, etc. which is absorbed via the inferior mesenteric vein affect the left lobe, leading to its fibrosis or cirrhosis (Fig. 21.15).

Note: The lower end oesophagus is one of the sites of portocaval anastomoses. Some oesophageal veins drain into left gastric vein and then into portal vein. Other oesophageal veins drain into hemiazygos and then into vena azygos and superior vena cava. In liver cirrhosis, portal venous pressure is raised, leading to oesophageal varices, which may rupture leading to haematemesis.

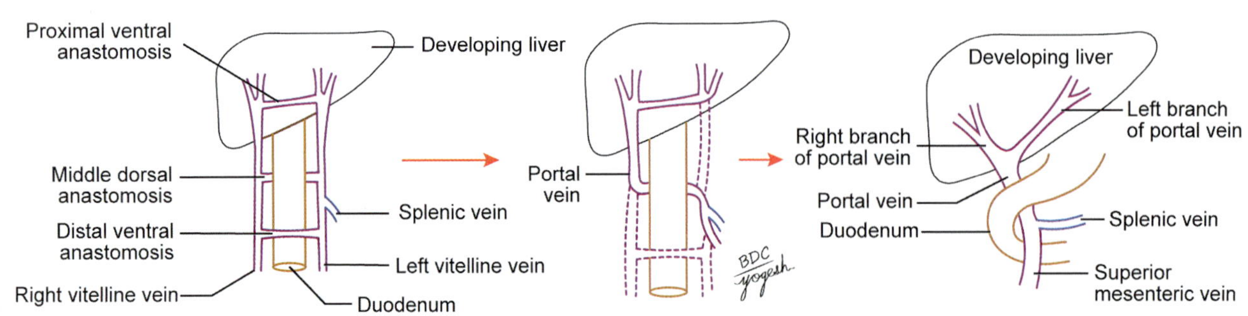

Fig. 21.10: Development of portal vein

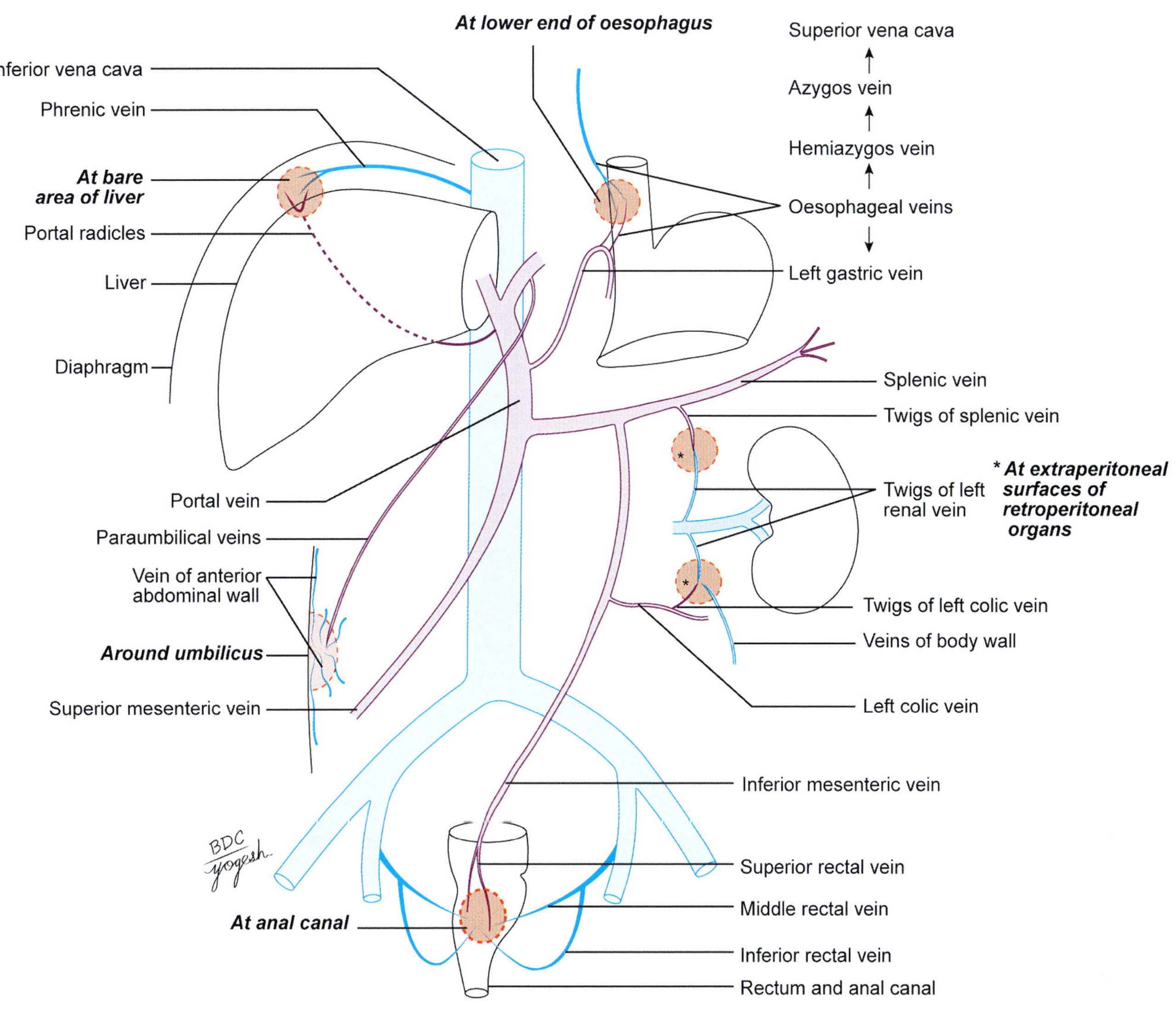

Fig. 21.11: Important sites of communication of portal and systemic veins

TABLE 21.1: Tributaries of portal venous system and systemic venous system including clinical conditions

Site	*Tributary of portal vein*	*Tributary of systemic vein*	*Clinical conditions*
Abdominal part of oesophagus	Left gastric vein	Oesophageal veins drain into hemiazygos → vena azygos → superior vena cava	*Oesophageal varices*, If ruptures, causes *haematemesis*
Umbilicus	Paraumbilical veins (run along ligamentum teres)	*Superiorly*: Superior epigastric and lateral thoracic veins *Inferiorly*: Superficial epigastric, inferior epigastric veins *On each side*: Posterior intercostals, lumbar veins	In liver cirrhosis, the paraumbilical veins open up to transfer portal venous blood into systemic circulation. It results in caput medusae (*see* Fig. 16.5)
Anal canal	Superior rectal vein → inferior mesenteric vein → portal vein	Middle and inferior rectal veins → inferior vena cava	Piles or haemorrhoids
Bare area of liver	Central veins and sublobular veins (portal radicles)	Intercostal veins and phrenic veins	—
Extraperitoneal connective tissue of posterior abdominal wall	Splenic and colonic veins	Left renal vein	—
Patent ductus venosus of liver	Left branch of portal vein	Inferior vena cava	Patent ductus venosus and other congenital anomalies

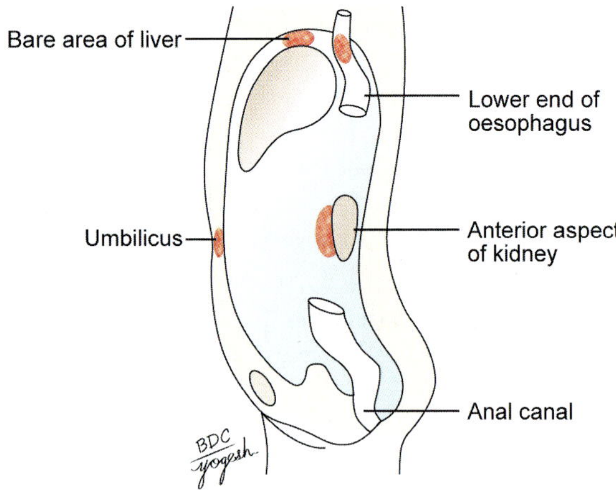

Fig. 21.12: Sites of portosystemic anastomoses

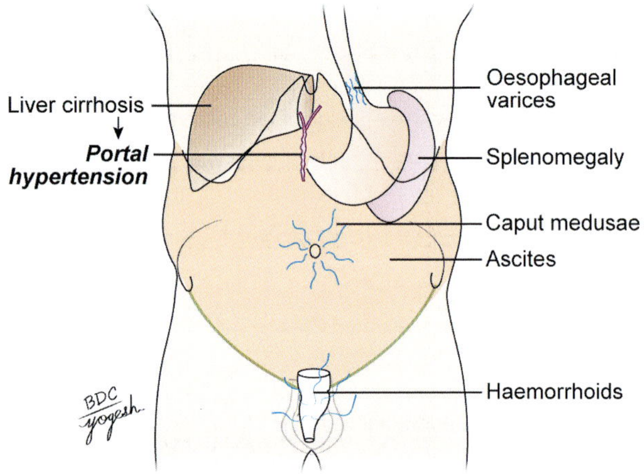

Fig. 21.13: Effects of the portal hypertension

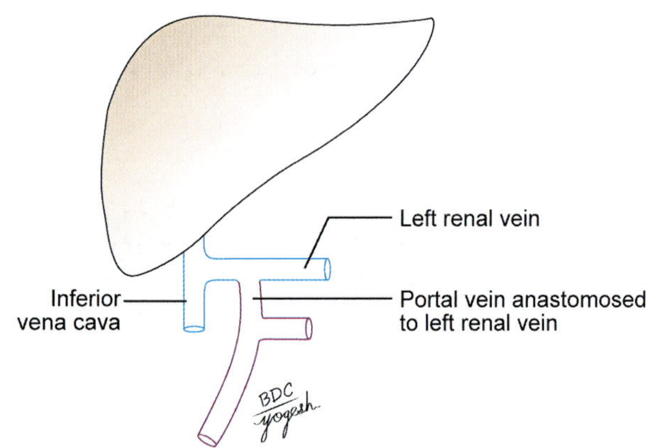

Fig. 21.14: Shunt operation between left renal vein and portal vein

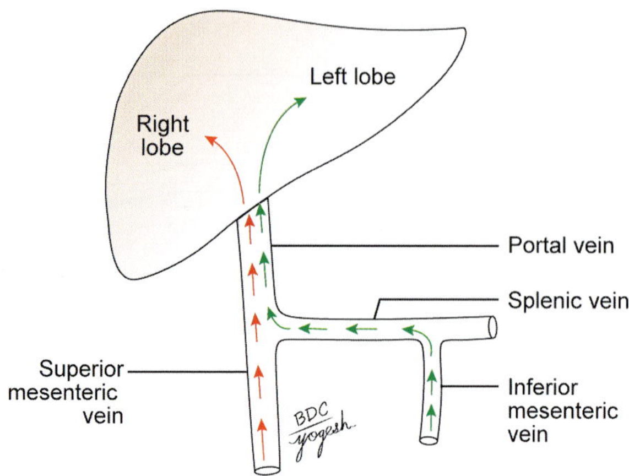

Fig. 21.15: Streamline flow of blood in the portal vein

Facts to Remember

- Coeliac trunk is the first short unpaired ventral visceral branch of the abdominal aorta which supplies structures derived from the foregut.
- Superior and inferior mesenteric arteries supply structures derived from midgut and hindgut, respectively.
- Branches of portal vein anastomose with the branches of systemic circulation at a few places.
- Portal vein supplies 80% blood to liver, while hepatic artery gives 20%.
- If the portal venous pressure increases above 10 mm Hg, it is considered as portal hypertension.
- *Opening of portosystemic shunts* that results in development of
  a. Caput medusae;
  b. Oesophageal varices; and
  c. Haemorrhoids.

BDC's Anatomy *e*-book

1. Intrahepatic part of portal vein
2. Details of portosystemic shunts
3. Further reading
4. Viva voce questions

Chapter

22

Extrahepatic Biliary Apparatus

The extrahepatic biliary apparatus collects bile from the liver, stores it in the gallbladder and transmits it to the second part of duodenum. The apparatus consists of (Figs 22.1 and 22.2, Flowchart 22.1):

1. Right and left hepatic ducts
2. Common hepatic duct
3. Gallbladder
4. Cystic duct
5. Bile duct.

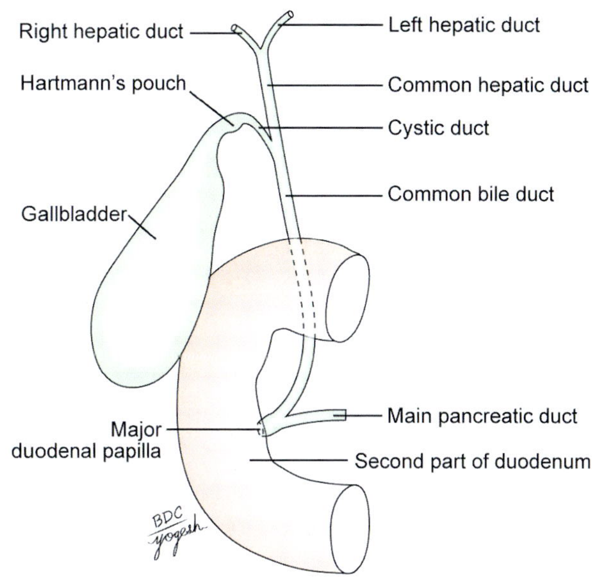

Fig. 22.1: Parts of the extrahepatic biliary apparatus

RIGHT AND LEFT HEPATIC DUCTS

The right and left hepatic ducts emerge at the porta hepatis from the right and left lobes of the liver.

The length of extrahepatic part of the right hepatic duct is about 1 cm and of the left hepatic duct is about 2.5 cm. At the porta hepatis, these ducts join to form *common hepatic duct*.

The arrangement of structures at the porta hepatis from behind forwards is (Figs 22.1 and 22.2):

1. Branches of the portal vein
2. Proper hepatic artery
3. Hepatic ducts.

Note: Accessory hepatic ducts are present in about 15% of subjects. They usually issue from the right lobe of the liver and terminate either in the gallbladder or in the common hepatic duct anywhere in its course, or even in the upper part of the bile duct (Fig. 22.3).

They are responsible for oozing of bile from the wound after cholecystectomy. Therefore, it is always better to use a drain to avoid retention of bile in the depths of the wound.

Cystohepatic angle is the angle between the cystic duct and the common hepatic duct. The common hepatic duct lies on the right of proper hepatic artery and anterior to the portal vein in the free margin of lesser omentum.

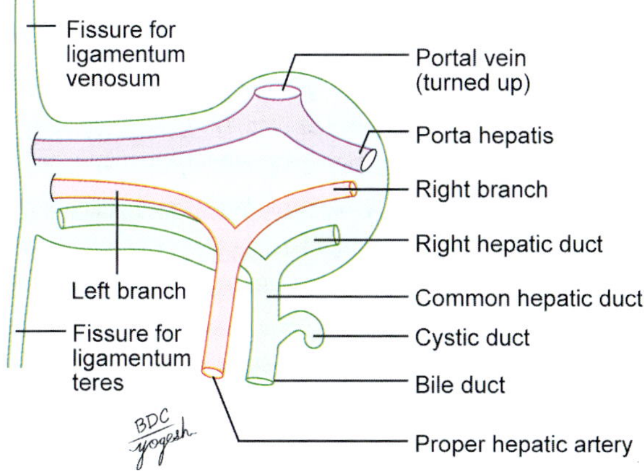

Fig. 22.2: Arrangement of structures in the porta hepatis

COMMON HEPATIC DUCT

It is formed by the union of the right and left hepatic ducts near the right end of the porta hepatis.

It runs downwards for about 3 cm and is joined on its right side at an acute angle by the cystic duct to form the common bile duct (CBD) (Figs 22.1 and 22.2).

GALLBLADDER

Gallbladder is a pear-shaped reservoir of bile situated in a fossa on the inferior surface of the right lobe of the liver.

The *fossa for the gallbladder* extends from the right end of the porta hepatis to the inferior border of the liver (Plate 22.1, Figs 22.1 and 22.4).

Flowchart 22.1: Extrahepatic biliary apparatus

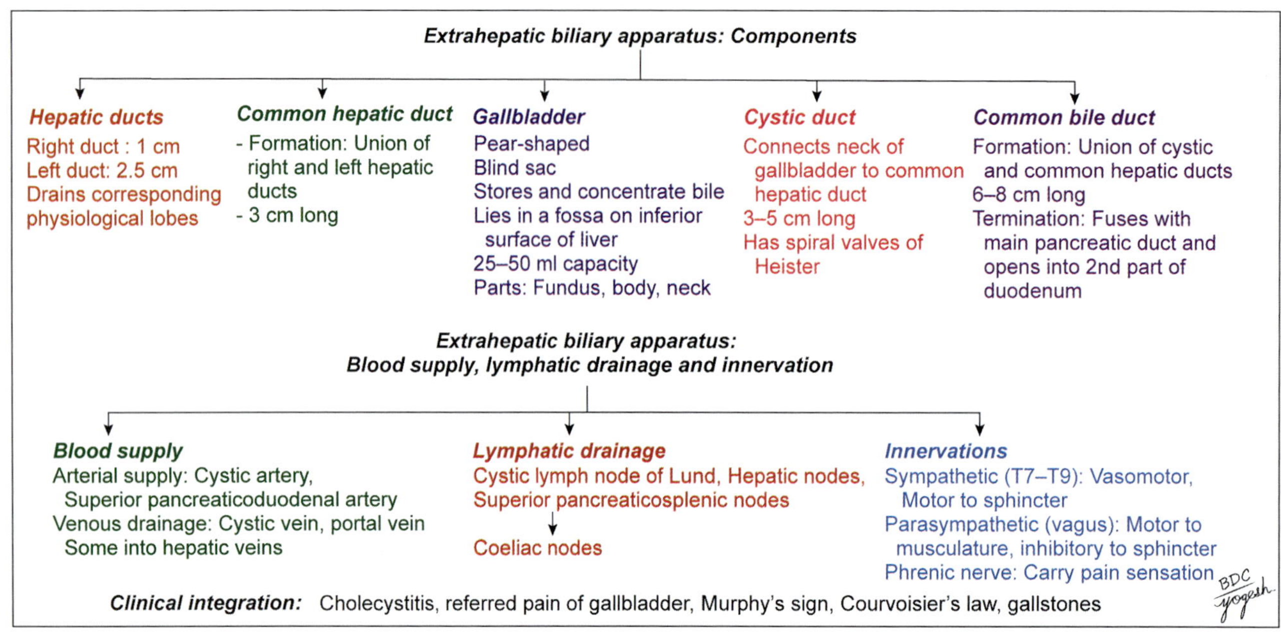

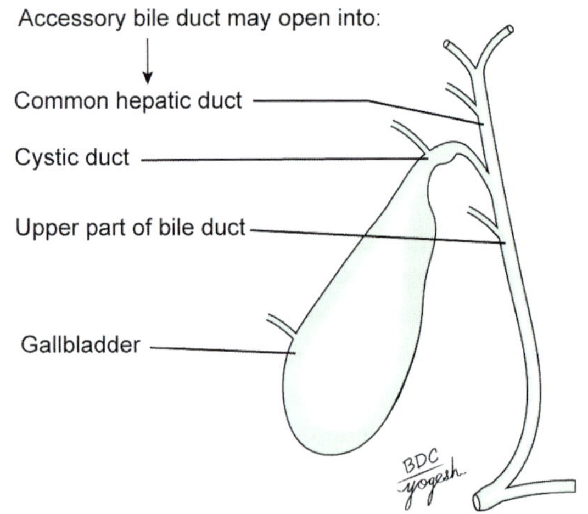

Fig. 22.3: The accessory hepatic ducts

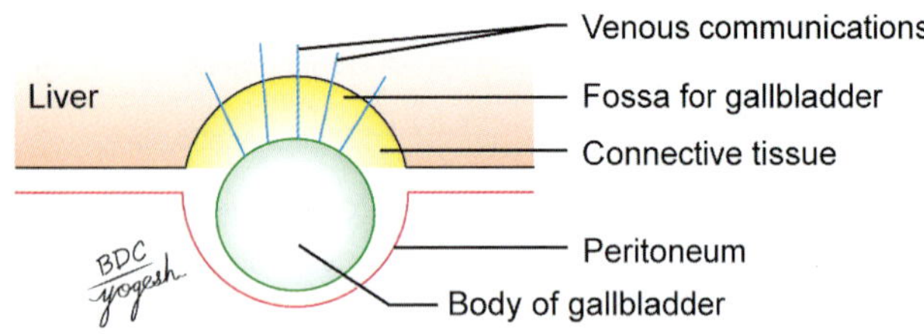

Fig. 22.4: Peritoneal relations of gallbladder

Functions of Gallbladder

The gallbladder performs the following functions:

1. Storage of bile
2. Concentrate the bile by absorbing water
3. Release of bile into duodenum on stimulation by cholecystokinin
4. Absorption of small amount of bile salt-cholesterol complex.

Dimensions and Capacity

Capacity: 25–50 ml
Length: 7–10 cm
Width: 3 cm

Parts

The gallbladder is divided into (Figs 22.5 to 22.7):

1. The fundus
2. The body
3. The neck.

Fundus

1. It projects beyond the inferior border of the liver, in the angle between the lateral border of the right rectus abdominis and the 9th costal cartilage.
2. It is entirely surrounded by peritoneum, and it is related anteriorly to the anterior abdominal wall and posteriorly to the beginning of the transverse colon.

Body

1. The body lies in the fossa for the gallbladder on the liver. The upper narrow end of the body is continuous with the neck at the right end of the porta hepatis.
2. It has two surfaces (Fig. 22.5):
   a. The *superior surface* of the body is devoid of peritoneum and is adherent to the liver.
   b. The *inferior surface* is covered with peritoneum and is related to the beginning of the transverse colon and the 1st and 2nd parts of the duodenum.

Neck

1. The neck is the narrow upper end of the gallbladder. It is situated near the right end of the porta hepatis.
2. It first curves anterosuperiorly and then postero-inferiorly to become continuous with the cystic

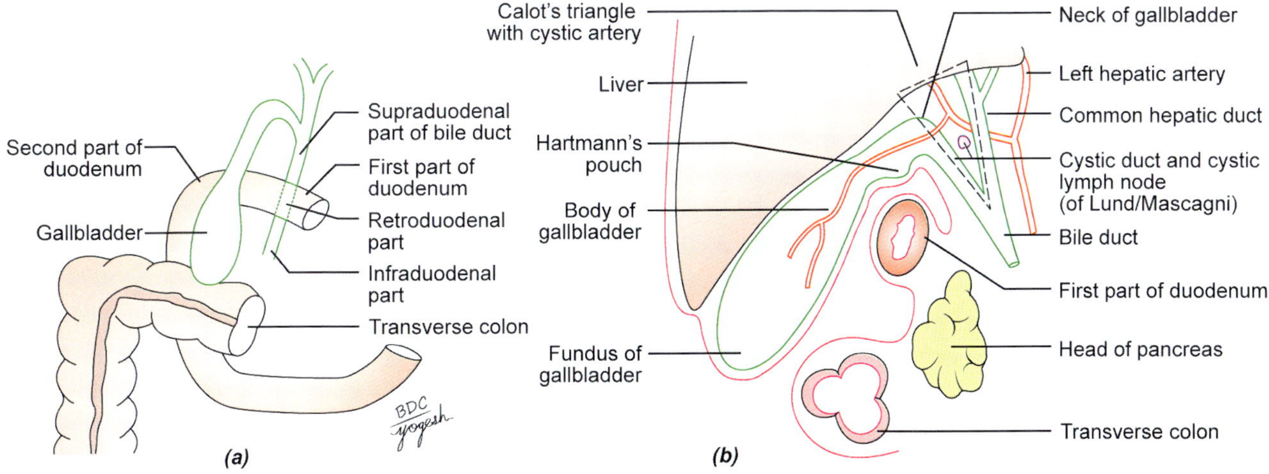

Figs 22.5a and b: Relations of the gallbladder: (a) Anterior view after removal of the liver and (b) left view of sagittal section through the gallbladder fossa including the Calot's triangle

duct. Its junction with the cystic duct is marked by a constriction (Fig. 22.7).

3. *Superiorly*, the neck is attached to the liver by areolar tissue in which the cystic vessels are embedded.
4. *Inferiorly*, it is related to the 1st part of the duodenum.
5. The mucous membrane of the neck is folded spirally to prevent any obstruction to the inflow or outflow of bile.
6. The posteromedial wall of the neck is dilated outwards to form a pouch called the ***Hartmann's pouch*** which is directed downwards and backwards. ***Gallstones*** may lodge in this pouch (Fig. 22.1).

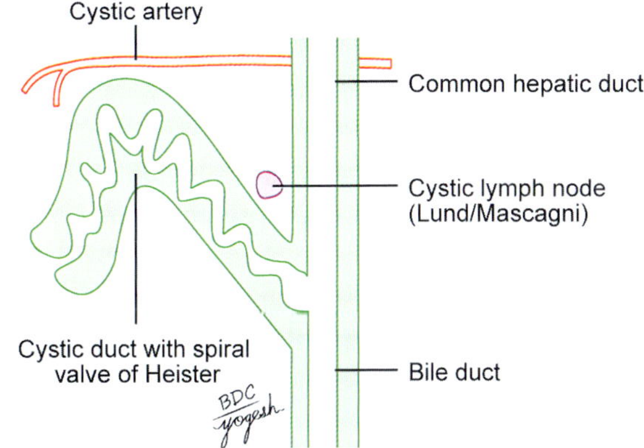

Fig. 22.6: The spiral valve of the cystic duct

CYSTIC DUCT

1. Cystic duct is about 3 to 4 cm long.
2. It begins at the neck of the gallbladder, runs downwards, backwards and to the left and ends by joining the common hepatic duct at an acute angle to form the bile duct.
3. The mucous membrane of the cystic duct forms a series of 5 to 12 crescentic folds, arranged spirally to form the so-called ***spiral valve of Heister***. This is not a true valve (Fig. 22.6).

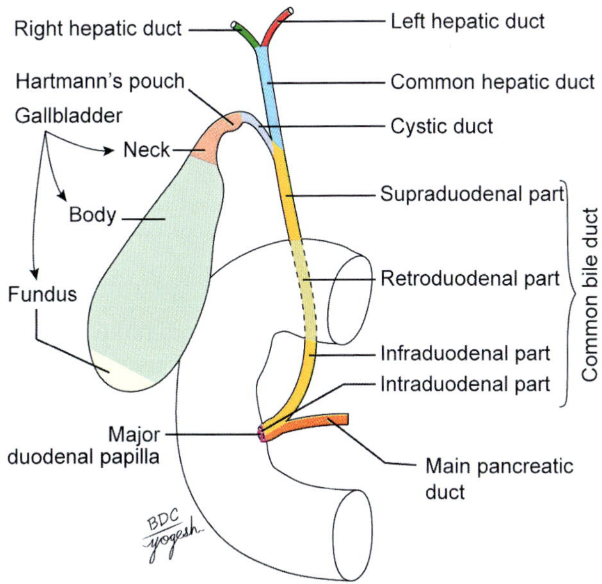

Fig. 22.7: Parts of gallbladder and common bile duct

COMMON BILE DUCT

Common bile duct is formed by the union of the cystic and common hepatic ducts near the porta hepatis. It is 6–8 cm long and has a diameter of about 7 mm.

Course

1. The bile duct runs downwards and backwards, first in the free margin of the lesser omentum, *supraduodenal part*;
2. Behind the first part of the duodenum, the *retroduodenal part*;
3. Then it lies behind, or embedded in, the head of pancreas, *infraduodenal part*; and
4. Near the middle of the left side of the 2nd part of the duodenum, it comes in contact with the pancreatic duct and accompanies it through the wall of the duodenum, the *intraduodenal part*.

Plate 22.1: Location of gallbladder on the inferior surface of liver

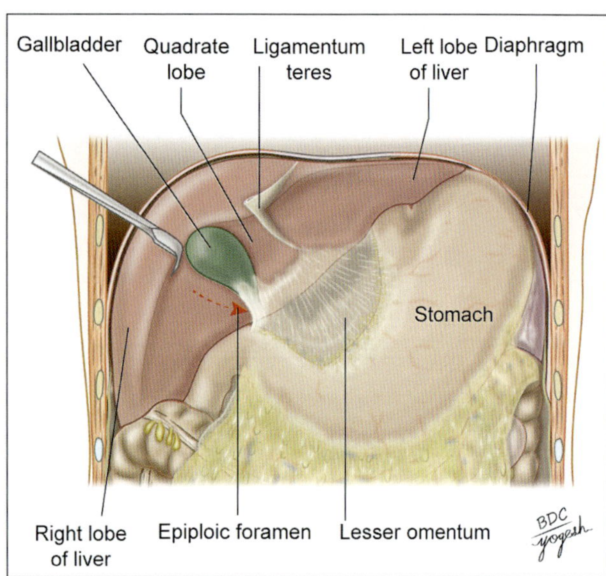

Plate 22.2: Sphincter of pancreaticobiliary junction

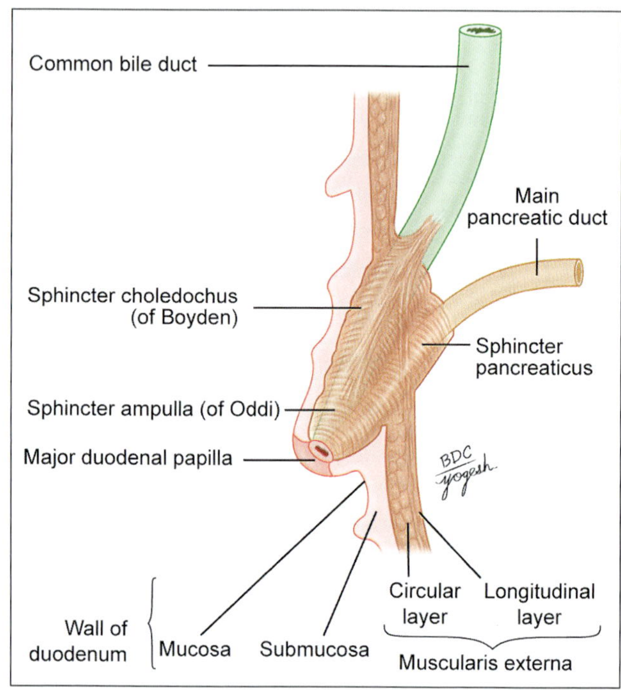

Relations

Supraduodenal Part

Supraduodenal part in the free margin of lesser omentum.

1. *Anteriorly:* Liver
2. *Posteriorly:* Portal vein and epiploic foramen
3. *To the left:* Hepatic artery.

Retroduodenal Part

1. *Anteriorly:* 1st part of duodenum
2. *Posteriorly:* Inferior vena cava
3. *To the left:* Gastroduodenal artery.

Infraduodenal Part

1. *Anteriorly:* A groove in the upper and lateral parts of the posterior surface of the head of the pancreas.
2. *Posteriorly:* Inferior vena cava.

Intraduodenal Part

The course of the duct through the duodenal wall is very oblique. Within the wall, the two ducts usually unite to form the ***hepatopancreatic ampulla***, or ***ampulla of Vater***.

The distal constricted end of the ampulla opens at the summit of the *major duodenal papilla* 8 to 10 cm distal to the pylorus.

Sphincters Related to the Bile and Pancreatic Ducts

The common bile duct and main pancreatic duct enter and join in the duodenal wall to form a short common channel called ***pancreaticobiliary junction***. The dilatation of this channel is called *hepatopancreatic ampulla of Vater* that opens into the posteromedial wall of duodenum at the *major duodenal papilla*.

The circularly arranged smooth muscles around this pancreaticobiliary junctions form the following sphincters (Plate 22.2):

1. *Sphincter choledochus* (*of Boyden*) around the bile duct
2. *Sphincter pancreaticus* around the main pancreatic duct
3. *Sphincter ampullae* (*of Oddi*) around the ampulla of Vater.

These three sphincters are independent of duodenal musculature. They remain closed until the digested contents from stomach enter the duodenum.

Innervation: Parasympathetic fibres and cholecystokinin hormone of duodenum relax the sphincters around the pancreaticobiliary junction.

CLINICAL ANATOMY

1. The division of upper part of sphincter of Oddi may be required during endoscopic retrograde cholangiopancreatography (ERCP).
2. The obstruction of the pancreaticobiliary junction leads to obstructive jaundice. It may occur due to carcinoma of head of pancreas, gallstone obstruction and periampullary tumours.

Competency:
AN47.7 Mention the clinical importance of Calot's triangle.

Calot's Triangle

Boundaries

The ***cystohepatic triangle of Calot*** is a triangular area that is bounded as follows (Fig. 22.8a):

- *On the right:* Cystic duct
- *On the left:* Common hepatic duct

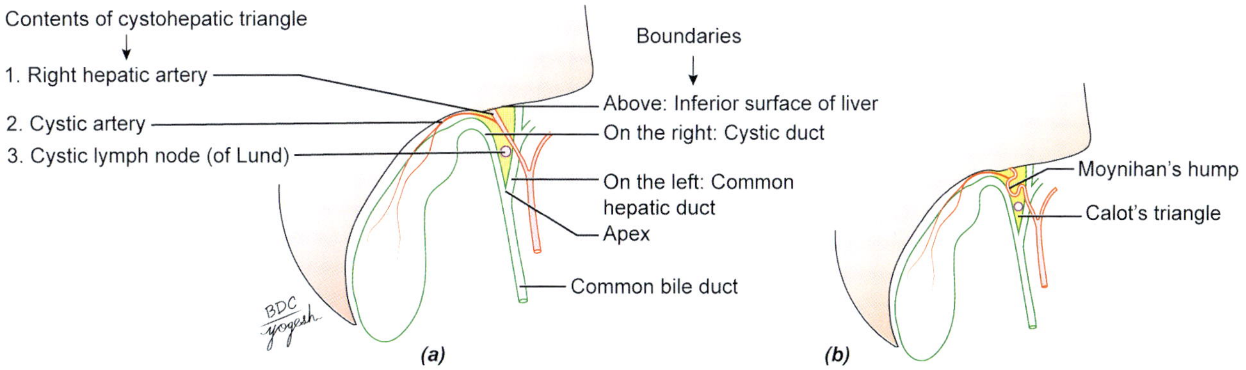

Figs 22.8a and b: Cystohepatic triangle (yellow colour-shaded area) and Moynihan's hump

- *Above*: Inferior surface of liver
- *Apex*: Directed downward between cystic and common hepatic ducts [Jean-François Calot, French surgeon, 1861–1944. *Note*: Calot originally described cystic artery as superior boundary of Calot's triangle].

Contents

1. Right hepatic artery
2. Cystic artery
3. Cystic nodes of Lund
4. Occasionally aberrant segmental right hepatic ducts and arteries.

CLINICAL ANATOMY

- In cholecystectomy surgery, the pedicle of gallbladder is located in Calot's triangle and ligated.
- *Moynihan's or caterpillar hump*: It is a caterpillar like loop of the right hepatic artery in the Calot's triangle (Fig. 22.8b). It may be mistakenly ligated along with cystic pedicle and cut during cholecystectomy that leads to profuse bleeding.
- Occasionally accessory hepatic duct may be left behind unattended during cholecystectomy that causes oozing of bile from the wound.
- Cystic nodes of Lund are often enlarged in cholecystitis.

VASCULAR AND NERVE SUPPLY

Arteries Supplying the Biliary Apparatus

1. The **cystic artery** is the chief source of the blood supply and is distributed to the gallbladder, the cystic duct, the hepatic ducts and the upper part of the bile duct (Fig. 22.9).
2. Several branches from the posterior superior pancreaticoduodenal artery supply the lower part of the bile duct.
3. The right hepatic artery forms a minor source of supply to the middle part of the bile duct.

Note: The *cystic artery* usually arises from the right hepatic artery, passes behind the common hepatic and cystic ducts and reaches the upper surface of the neck of the gallbladder, where it divides into superficial and deep branches.

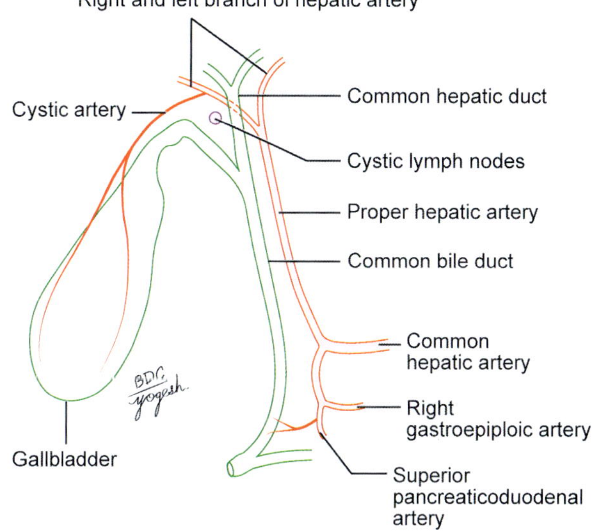

Fig. 22.9: Arterial supply of the gallbladder and bile ducts

Venous Drainage

- The superior surface of the gallbladder is drained by veins which enter the liver through the fossa for the gallbladder and join tributaries of hepatic veins.
- The rest of the gallbladder is drained by one or two ***cystic veins*** which open into the right branch of the portal vein.
- The lower part of the bile duct drains into the portal vein.

Lymphatic Drainage

1. Lymphatics from the gallbladder, the cystic duct, the hepatic ducts and the upper part of the bile duct pass to the ***cystic lymph node of Lund*** and *to the node on the anterior border of the epiploic* foramen. These are the most constant members of the upper hepatic nodes. The cystic node lies in the angle between the cystic and common hepatic ducts; it is constantly enlarged in cholecystitis (Fig. 22.9).
2. The lower part of the bile duct drains into the *lower hepatic* and *upper pancreaticosplenic nodes*.

Nerve Supply

1. The *cystic plexus* of nerves, supplying the territory of the cystic artery, is derived from the hepatic plexus,

which receives fibres from the coeliac plexus, the left and right vagi and the *right phrenic nerves*. The lower part of the bile duct is supplied by the nerve plexus over the superior pancreaticoduodenal artery.

2. *Parasympathetic nerves* are motor to the musculature of the gallbladder and bile ducts, but inhibitory to the sphincters.
3. *Sympathetic nerves* from T7 to T9 are vasomotor and motor to the sphincters.

Note: **Humoral control of the gallbladder**: The gallbladder contracts when food rich in fat enters the duodenum. The fat causes certain cells in duodenum to liberate a hormone called cholecystokinin-pancreozymin. The hormone is carried to the gallbladder and causes its contraction. It also causes dilatation of the sphincters.

Note: Pain from the gallbladder may travel along the vagus, the sympathetic nerves, or along the phrenic nerves. It may be referred to different sites through these nerves as follows:

1. Through vagus to the stomach (epigastrium).
2. Through the sympathetic nerves to the inferior angle of the right scapula. Lateral horn of T7 segment of spinal cord gives sympathetic fibres to coeliac ganglion through greater splanchnic nerve. T7 segment receives pain fibres from skin over inferior angle of scapula. So visceral pain is referred to somatic area.
3. Through the phrenic nerve to the right shoulder (C4 gives fibres to phrenic nerve and supraclavicular nerves).

DISSECTION

Locate the porta hepatis on the inferior surface of liver. Look for two hepatic ducts there. Follow them till these join to form common hepatic duct. Identify cystic duct and usually green-coloured gallbladder.

See the point of junction of cystic duct with common hepatic duct and the formation of bile duct. Trace the bile duct in relation to the duodenum. Its opening has been seen in dissection of the duodenum.

Trace the cystic artery supplying gallbladder, cystic duct, hepatic ducts and upper part of bile duct.

Competency:

AN47.6 Explain the anatomical basis of splenic notch, accessory spleens, Kehr's sign, different types of vagotomy, liver biopsy (site of needle puncture), referred pain in cholecystitis, obstructive jaundice, referred pain around umbilicus, radiating pain of kidney to groin and lymphatic spread in carcinoma stomach.

CLINICAL ANATOMY

- Inflammation of the gallbladder is called ***cholecystitis***. The patient complains of pain over the right hypochondrium radiating to the inferior angle of the right scapula, or to right shoulder. When a finger is placed just below the costal margin, at the tip of the 9th costal cartilage, the patient feels sharp pain on inspiration. He winces with a 'catch' in his breath. This is referred to as ***Murphy's sign*** (Fig. 22.10).
- ***Referred pain***: Pain of stretch of CBD or gallbladder is referred to as epigastrium. It is also referred to as right shoulder and inferior angle of right scapula (Fig. 22.11).
- The operation for removal of the gallbladder is called ***cholecystectomy***.
- The most significant lesions of ***typhoid*** fever occur in lymphoid tissue, bone marrow and gallbladder. Gallbladder is invariably infected in these cases, and the carrier state may be due to persistence of typhoid bacilli in this organ.
- Stones may form in the gallbladder. The condition is called ***cholelithiasis*** (Fig. 22.12). They typically occur in fat, fertile, females of forty (but also in males). The stones are responsible for the time to time spasmodic pain called biliary colic. Stones are common in human because of low fatty acid. They can give rise to severe spasmodic pain which is called ***biliary colic***.
- Gallstones may obstruct hepatopancreatic ampulla, causing pancreatitis or ***obstructive jaundice***.
- ***Courvoisier's law***: Dilatation of the gallbladder occurs only in extrinsic obstruction of the bile duct like pressure by carcinoma of head of pancreas. Intrinsic obstruction by stones does not cause any dilatation because of associated fibrosis.
- ***Imaging of biliary duct***
  1. *Cholecystography*: Gallbladder cannot be seen on plain radiographs. A radiopaque cholegraphic agent (iopanoic acid) is administered orally to visualize the gallbladder and biliary tree. It is absorbed by the intestine and excreted by the liver in bile. Then, the biliary tree is visualized on X-ray. This method is replaced by CT scan and ultrasound examination (Fig. 22.13).
  2. *Ultrasound* is the most commonly used and non-invasive technique to visualize the gallbladder and biliary tree.
  3. *Endoscopic retrograde cholangiopancreatography* (*ERCP*): Using endoscopy and fluoroscopy, the biliary tree and pancreatic ducts can be visualized. It is performed by gastroenterologist (Fig. 22.14).

     Procedure: Endoscope is introduced through mouth, oesophagus, stomach and duodenum to locate the major duodenal papilla. A cannula is inserted through the ampulla, and radiocontrast dye is injected into pancreaticobiliary tree. Fluoroscopy is used to visualize the pancreaticobiliary passage.
  4. *CT scan and MRI* are other noninvasive radiological methods used to visualize the pancreaticobiliary passage.

Competency:

AN52.1 Describe and identify the microanatomical features of gallbladder.

HISTOLOGY OF GALLBLADDER

Gallbladder shows three layers as follows (Plate 22.3):

1. ***Mucosa***: It is lined by tall columnar cells with striated borders because of the presence of microvilli. Nuclei

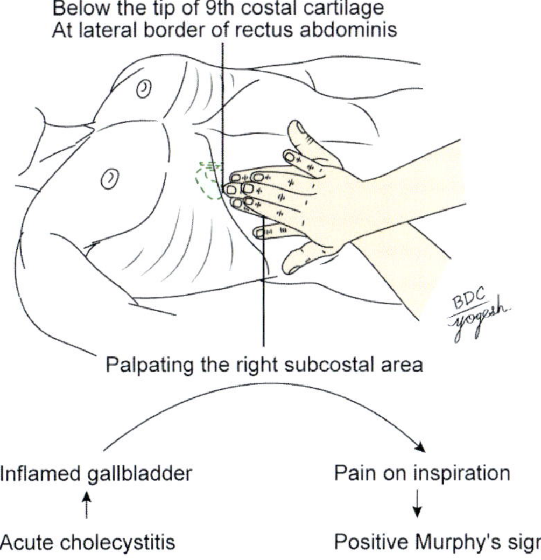

Fig. 22.10: Murphy's sign (cholecystitis)

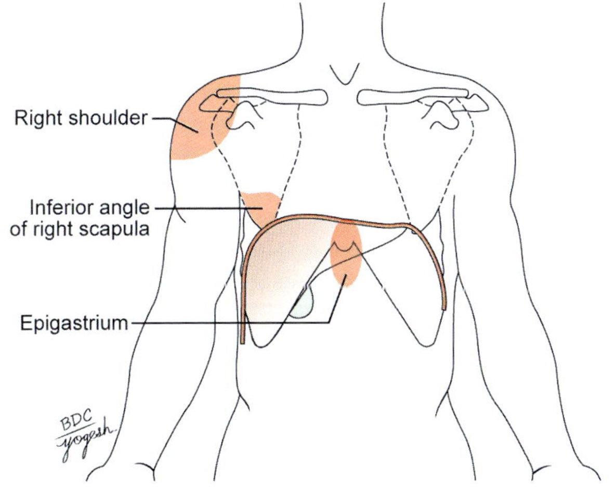

Fig. 22.11: Sites of referred pain due to stretch of bile duct or gallstone

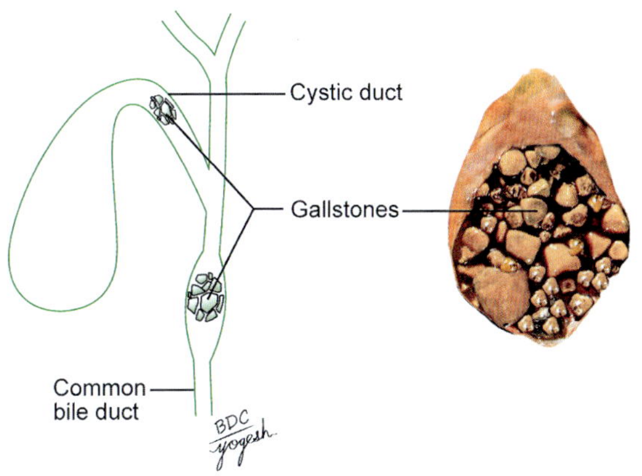

Fig. 22.12: Gallstones (cholelithiasis)

are elongated and basally placed. Cytoplasm is light eosinophilic (pink colour). Lamina propria consists of connective tissue.

2. ***Fibromuscular coat*:** It consists of bundle of smooth muscle fibres with interspaced collagen and elastic fibres.
3. ***Serosa/adventitia*:** Other than inferior surface (covered by peritoneum), gallbladder is covered by adventitia.

Plate 22.3: Histology of gallbladder

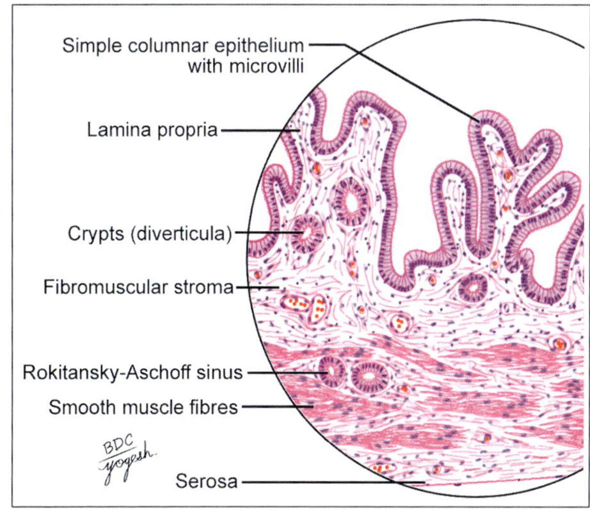

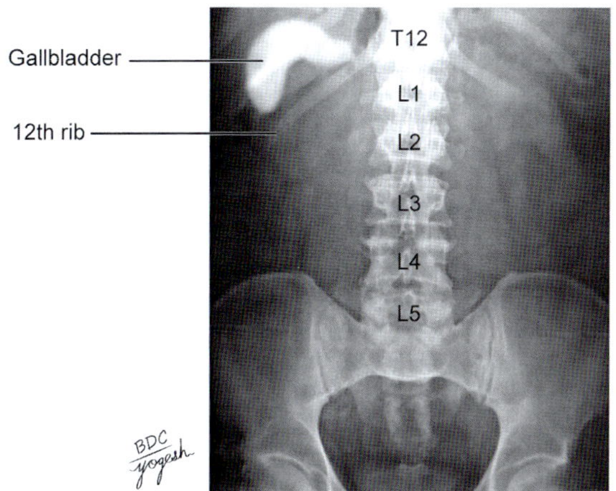

Fig. 22.13: Cholecystography: Visualization of gallbladder with an orally administered radiopaque cholegraphic agent (iopanoic acid)

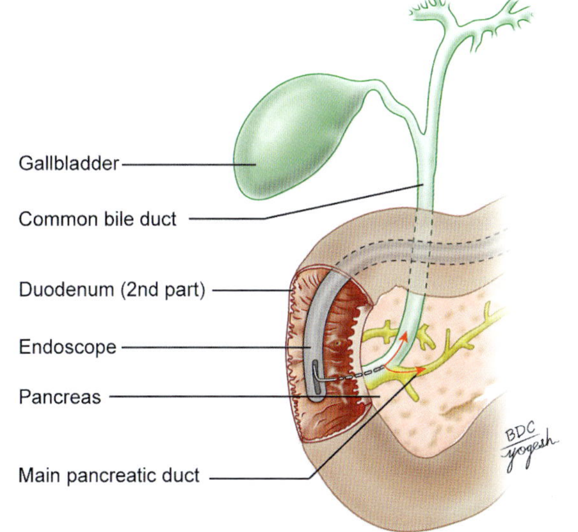

Fig. 22.14: Endoscopic retrograde cholangiopancreatography (ERCP)

Gallbladder shows absence of four that differentiate gallbladder from intestine: Villi, goblet cells, submucosa and properly organized muscularis externa.

Competency:
AN52.6 Describe the development of gallbladder.

DEVELOPMENT

Hepatic bud arises from the endoderm of caudal part of foregut. The bud elongates cranially. It gives rise to a small bud on its right side. This is called *pars cystica* and the main part is *pars hepatica*. *Pars cystica* forms the gallbladder and the cystic duct, which drains into the common hepatic duct (CHD). Pars hepatica forms CHD and divides into right and left hepatic ducts. These ducts reach *septum transversum* and proliferate to form the *hepatic parenchyma*. The entire epithelium is endodermal and other layers are of splanchnic origin.

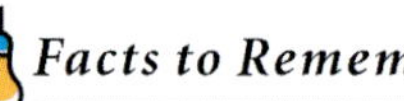

Facts to Remember

1. Gallbladder stores as well as concentrates bile. So it is more liable to have gallstones.
2. There are a lot of variations in the origin of cystic artery as well as in the pattern of joining of cystic duct. This has to be kept in mind during surgery of this region.
3. Pain of cholecystitis may be referred to epigastrium, right shoulder and inferior angle of right scapula.
4. *Cholelithiasis* is typically occur in fat, fertile, female of forty.

BDC's Anatomy *e*-book

1. Intrahepatic biliary tree
2. Further reading
3. Viva voce questions

Chapter

23

Spleen, Pancreas and Liver

SPLEEN

Location

The spleen is a wedge-shaped organ lying mainly in the left hypochondrium and partly in the epigastrium. It is wedged in between the fundus of the stomach and the diaphragm. The spleen is *tetrahedral* in shape (Fig. 23.1 and Flowchart 23.1).

Dimensions

The spleen is soft, highly vascular and dark purple in colour, normally it is nonpalpable.

- *Length*: 9–14 cm (~5 inches)
- *Breadth*: 6–8 cm (~3 inches)
- *Thickness*: 3–5 cm (~1 inch)
- *Weight*: 7 ounces (150 g).

[*Mnemonics*: For spleen dimensions: ***1, 3, 5, 7, 9, 11:*** **1** inch thick, **3** inches wide, **5** inches long. Weight is **7** ounces, underlies **9** to **11** ribs]

The size and weight of spleen vary with age and sex. Although its weight increases during puberty and tends to diminish in size and weight in old age.

Spleen lies opposite 10th, 11th and 12th ribs behind midaxillary line under the diaphragm, long axis lying along 11th rib (Refer to *Gray's Anatomy*, 42nd edition).

DISSECTION

Locate the spleen situated deep in the left hypochondrium. The gastrophrenic ligament has already been cut during removal of stomach. Now cut through the posteriorly placed lienorenal ligament taking care of the splenic vessels contained therein. See the close relation of spleen to the left costodiaphragmatic recess and the left lung.

Identify the viscera related to the spleen, e.g. stomach, tail of pancreas, left kidney and splenic flexure of colon.

Trace the branches of splenic artery into the substance of spleen as far as possible.

Cut the phrenicocolic ligament of peritoneum and deliver the spleen from the abdominal cavity.

Position (Axis of Spleen)

The spleen lies obliquely along the long axis of the 10th rib. Thus it is directed downwards, forwards and laterally, making an angle of about 45° with the horizontal plane (Fig. 23.2).

External Features

The spleen has the following presenting parts (Plate 23.1, Fig. 23.2)

Two ends: Anterior extremity, posterior extremity.

Two borders: Superior, inferior.

Two surfaces: Superolateral, inferomedial and hilum.

Ends

1. ***Anterior end*** or ***extremity*:** It is expanded and is more like a border. It is directed downwards and forwards and reaches the midaxillary line or even 3 cm beyond it.
2. ***Posterior end*** or ***extremity*:** It is rounded. It is directed upwards, backwards and medially and rests on the upper pole of the left kidney.

Borders

1. ***Superior border*** is characteristically notched near the anterior end.
2. ***Inferior border*** is rounded.

Surfaces

1. ***Diaphragmatic*** *surface* is convex and smooth.
2. ***Visceral*** *surface* is concave and irregular.

Hilum

The ***hilum*** lies on the visceral surface, in the inferomedial part of the gastric impression along the long axis of the spleen. It transmits the splenic vessels and nerves and provides attachment to the *gastrosplenic and lienorenal* ligaments.

Note: ***Anterobasal angle of spleen*** is the junction of superior border with lateral or anterior end. It is the most forward projecting part of spleen. When spleen is enlarged, this is felt first, so this is called '***clinical angle of spleen***'.

Posterobasal angle is the junction of inferior border with lateral or anterior end of spleen.

Spleen is not essential for life. But in cases of surgical removal of spleen, death due to sepsis is commonly observed.

Plate 23.1: External features of the spleen: (a) Visceral surface and (b) diaphragmatic surface

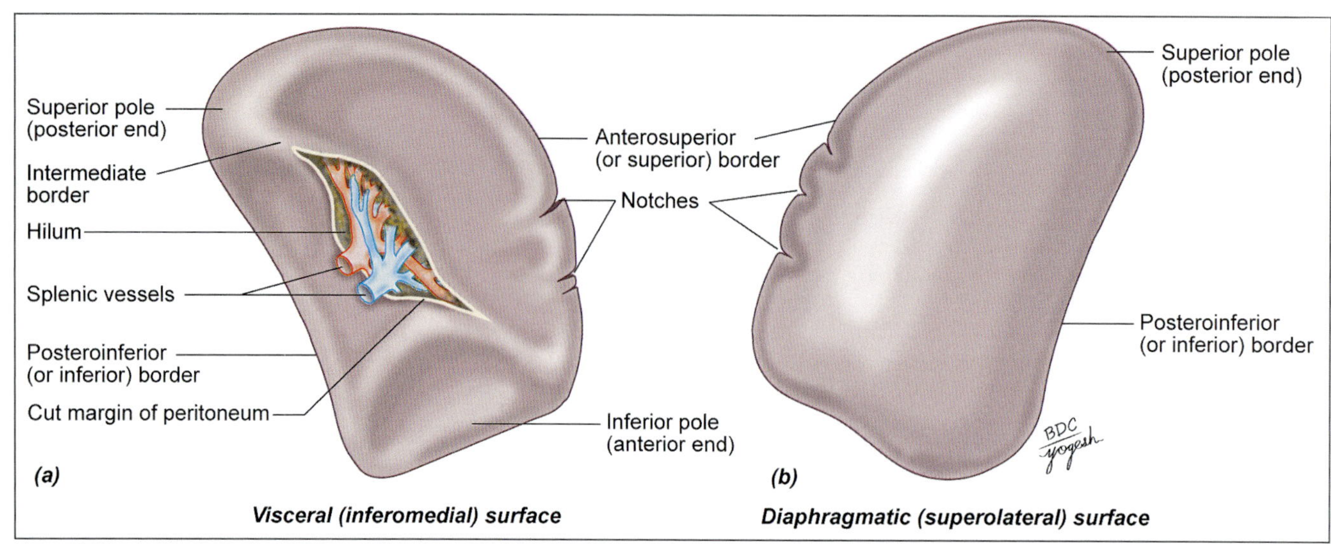

Flowchart 23.1: Spleen

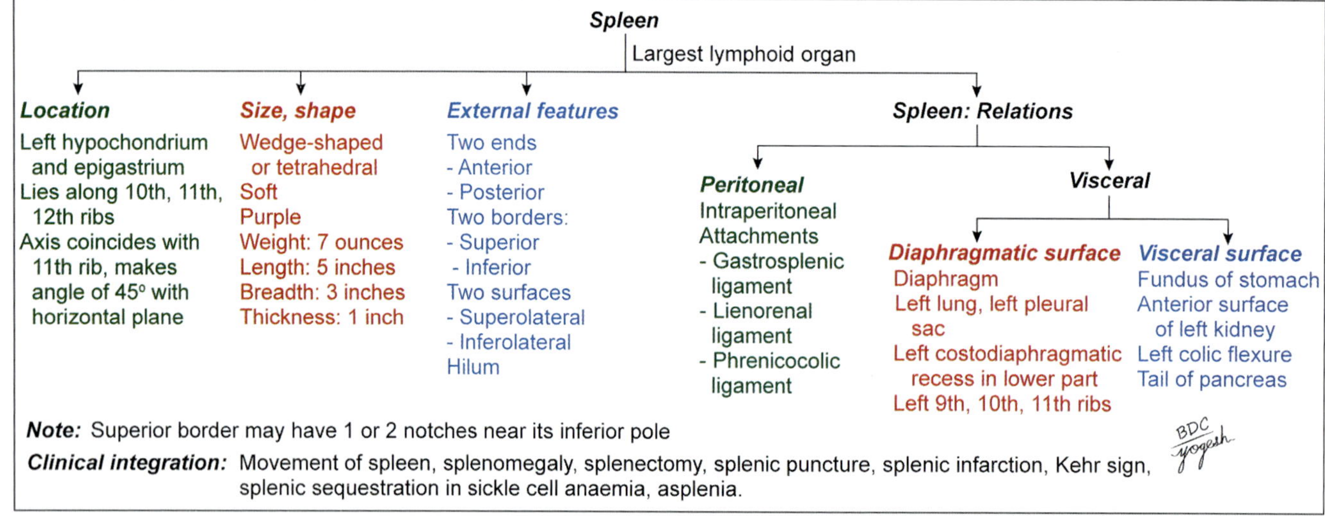

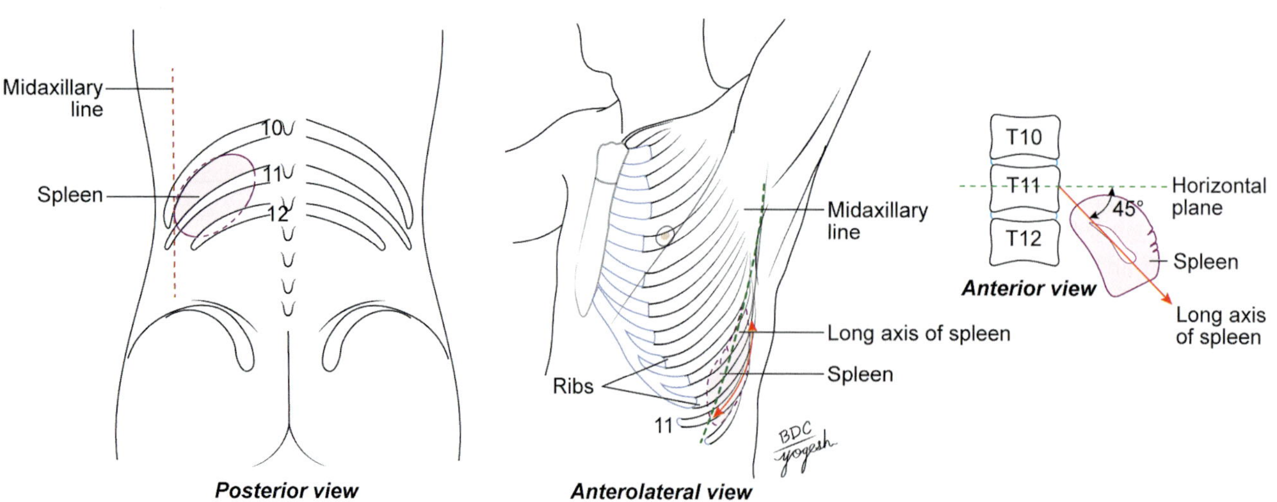

Fig. 23.1: Location of the spleen

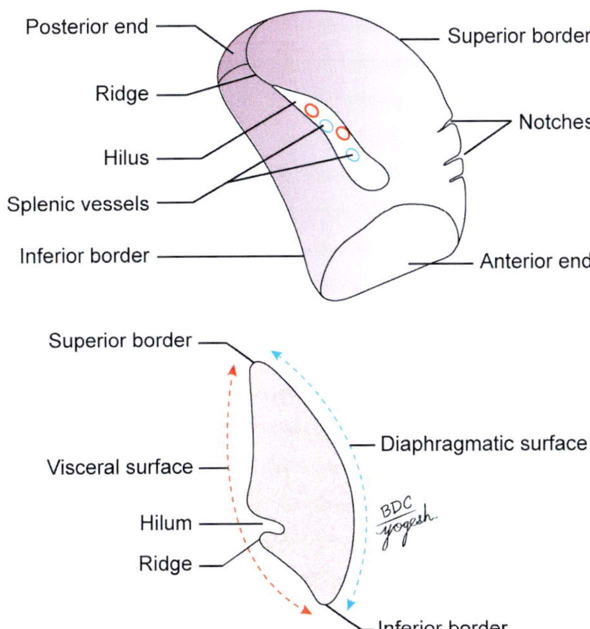

Fig. 23.2: External features of the spleen

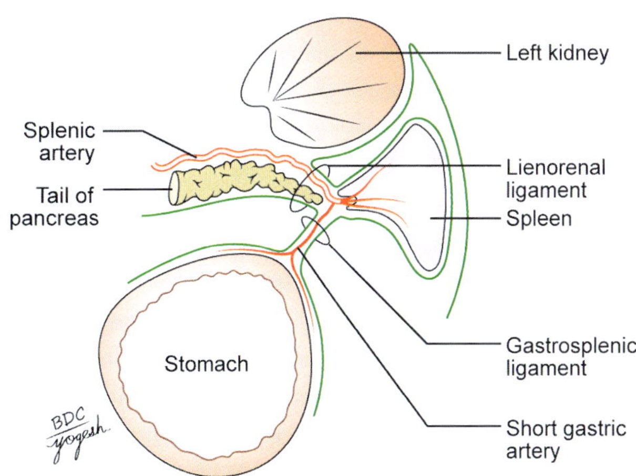

Fig. 23.3: Peritoneal ligaments attached to the spleen, and common sites of accessory spleen

Relations

Peritoneal Relations

The spleen is surrounded by peritoneum and is suspended by following ligaments (Plate 23.2, Fig. 23.3):

1. ***Gastrosplenic ligament*** extends from the hilum of the spleen to the greater curvature of the stomach. It contains the short gastric vessels and associated lymphatics and sympathetic nerves.
2. ***Lienorenal ligament*** extends from the hilum of the spleen to the anterior surface of the left kidney. It contains the tail of the pancreas, the splenic vessels and associated pancreaticosplenic lymph nodes, lymphatics and sympathetic nerves.
3. ***Phrenicocolic ligament*** is not attached to the spleen, but supports its anterior end. It is a horizontal fold of peritoneum extending from the splenic flexure of colon to the diaphragm, opposite the 11th rib in the midaxillary line. It limits the upper end of the left paracolic gutter. It is also called ***sustentaculum lienis***.

Visceral Relations

Visceral surface: The visceral surface is related to the fundus of the stomach, the anterior surface of the left kidney, the splenic flexure of the colon and the tail of the pancreas (Figs 23.4a and b).

1. The ***gastric impression***, for the fundus of the stomach, lies between the superior and intermediate borders. It is the largest and most concave impression on the spleen.
2. The ***renal impression***, for the left kidney, lies between the inferior and intermediate borders.
3. The ***colic impressions***, for the splenic flexure of the colon, occupies a triangular area adjoining the anterior end of the spleen. Its lower part is related to the *phrenicocolic ligament* (Fig. 23.5).
4. The ***pancreatic impression***, for the tail of the pancreas, lies between the hilum and the colic impression.

Diaphragmatic surface: The diaphragmatic surface is related to the diaphragm which separates the spleen from the costodiaphragmatic recess of pleura, lung and 10th, 11th and 12th ribs of the left side (Fig. 23.5).

Arterial Supply

The spleen is supplied by the ***splenic artery*** which is the largest branch of the *coeliac trunk*. The artery is tortuous

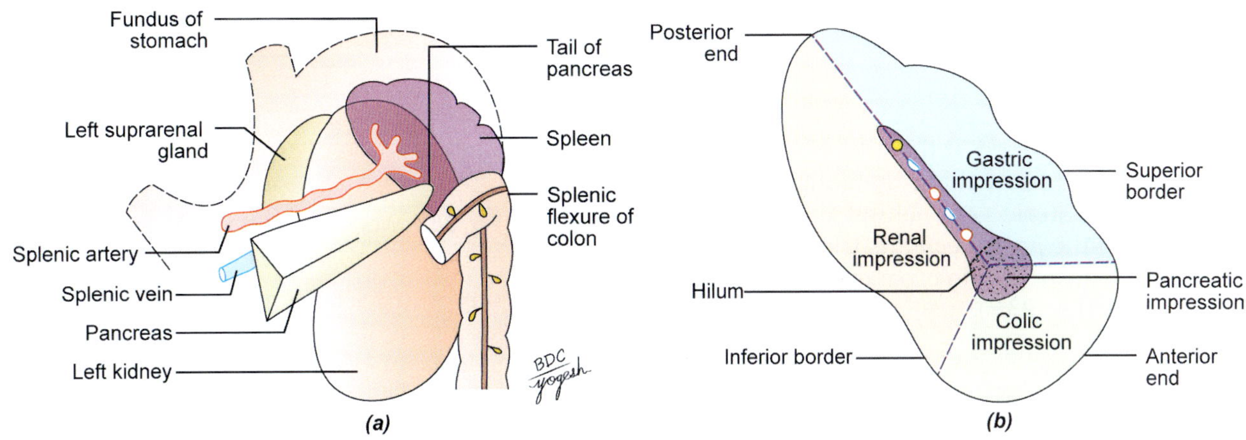

Figs 23.4a and b: Visceral relations of the spleen

Plate 23.2: Relations of the spleen

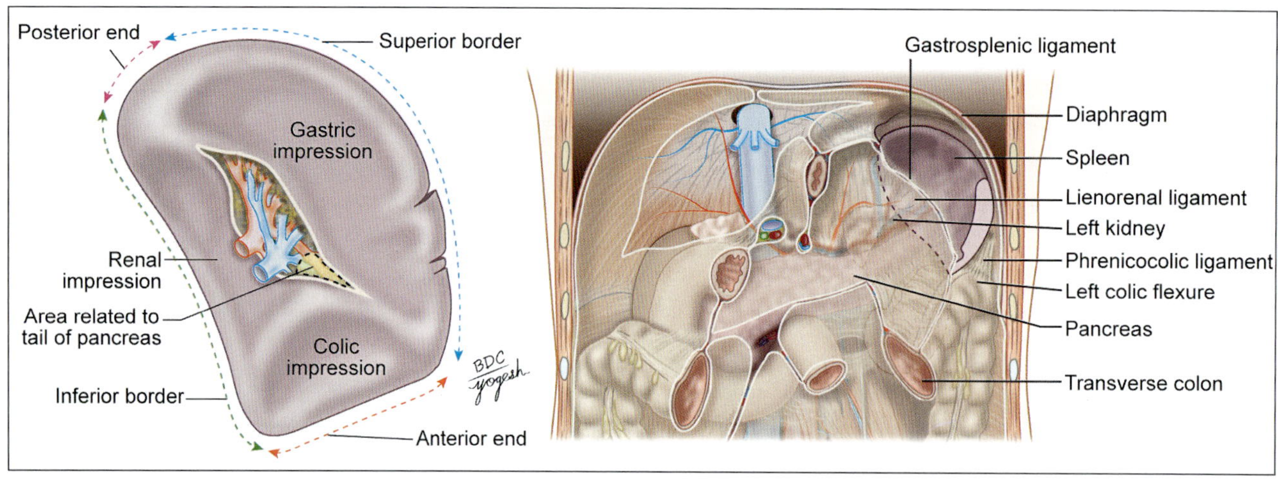

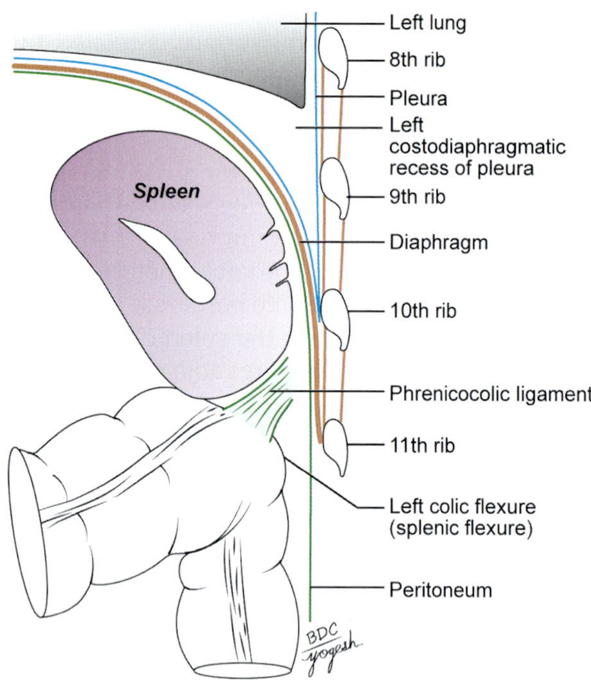

Fig. 23.5: Relations of diaphragmatic surface

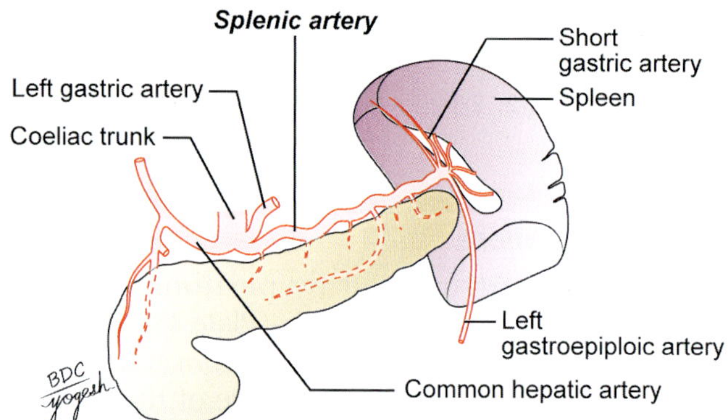

Fig. 23.6: Arterial supply of the spleen

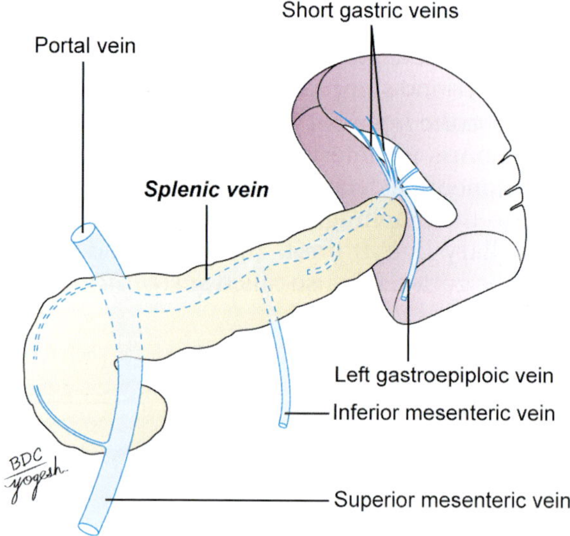

Fig. 23.7: Venous drainage of the spleen

in its course to allow movements of the spleen. It passes through the lienorenal ligament to reach the hilum of the spleen where it divides into five or more segmental branches (Fig. 23.6).

Venous Drainage

The ***splenic vein*** is formed at the hilum of the spleen. It runs a straight course behind the pancreas. It joins the superior mesenteric vein behind the neck of the pancreas to form the ***portal vein***. Its tributaries are the short gastric, left gastroepiploic, pancreatic and inferior mesenteric veins (Fig. 23.7).

Lymphatic Drainage

The lymphatics begin with the peri-arteriolar lymphoid sheaths (PALS) in the white pulp. The lymphatic vessels run along trabecular arteries in the trabeculae towards the hilum. The lymphatic vessels from the subcapsular plexus also run towards the hilum. Finally, the lymphatics from spleen drains to superior pancreatic, inferior pancreatic and pancreaticoduodenal nodes, and from there to coeliac nodes.

Note: There are no lymphatic vessels in the red pulp of spleen.

Nerve Supply

Sympathetic fibres are derived from the coeliac plexus. They are vasomotor in nature. They also supply some smooth muscle present in the capsule.

Functions of the Spleen

1. Removal of worn-out old RBCs by phagocytosis.
2. Haematopoiesis during foetal life and lymphopoiesis throughout the life.
3. Immune response by production of lymphocytes under antigen stimulation and production of plasma cells which produce antibodies.
4. Phagocytosis of microorganisms.
5. Reservoir of RBCs.

Vascular Segments of the Spleen

Splenic vascular segments: Before entering the spleen, the splenic artery gives superior and inferior branches (Fig. 23.8). These branches do not anastomose in the spleen; hence, avascular zone exists between their territories. Thus, spleen has superior and inferior segments separated by an avascular plane passing perpendicular to the long axis of spleen. It can be used for segmental resection of spleen.

Note: The spleen may be diffuse or compact based on branching pattern of splenic artery. In *diffuse type of spleen*, the terminal branches of splenic artery arise away from the hilum, whereas in the *compact type of spleen*, they arise near the hilum.

Competency:
AN52.1 Describe and identify the microanatomical features of spleen.

Histology of Spleen

The spleen is covered by dense connective tissue capsule that sends trabeculae into the parenchyma of spleen (Plate 23.3). Spleen shows:

1. *White pulp*: It consists of central arterioles surrounded by periarterial lymphatic sheaths of T lymphocytes.
2. *Splenic nodules / malpighian corpuscles* consist of B cells that aggregate with germinal centre around eccentric arterioles.
3. *Red pulp*: It consists of cords of Billroth (made up of RBCs, lymphocytes, macrophages and plasma cells).

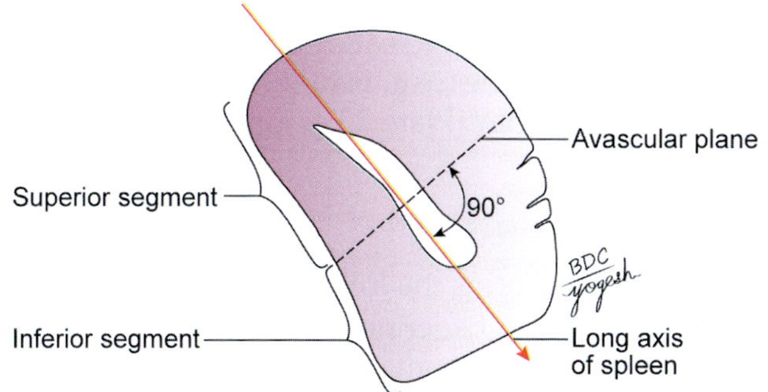

Fig. 23.8: Vascular segment of the spleen

Plate 23.3: Histology of spleen

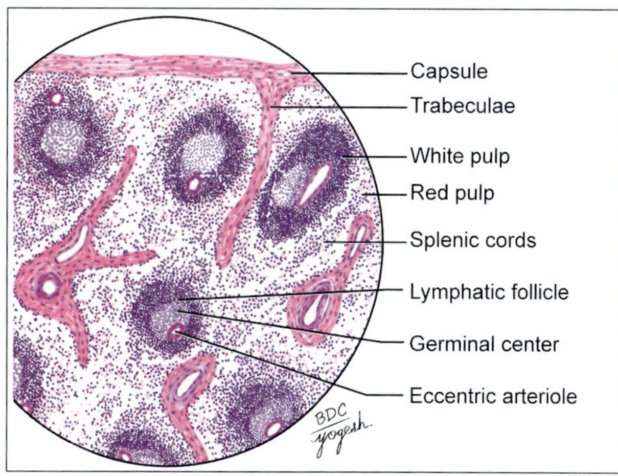

4. *Red pulp* has sinusoids that are lined by elongated stave cells (endothelial cells).
5. *Marginal zone* lies between red and white pulp and contains numerous antigen-presenting cells.

Competency:
AN52.6 Describe the development and congenital anomalies of spleen.

Development of Spleen

The spleen develops in the dorsal mesogastrium from mesoderm. In the 5th week of IUL, the mesenchymal cell condenses to form small masses called spleniculi which fuse to a single mass of spleen. Lobulated development of spleen in an adult is indicated by splenic notches. The spleen acts as haematopoietic organ in foetal life until birth.

Congenital Anomalies

1. *Accessory spleen*: Failure of fusion of spleniculi with the main splenic tissue gives rise to accessory spleen at the following sites: Hilus of spleen, gastrosplenic ligament, lienorenal ligament, tail of pancreas along the splenic artery and left spermatic cord.
2. *Lobulated spleen*: Incomplete fusion of spleniculi (persistent foetal spleen) produces lobulated spleen.
3. Right-sided bilaterality or isomerism is characterized by asplenia or hypoplastic spleen, whereas left-sided bilaterality is characterized by polysplenia.

Competency:
AN47.6 Explain the anatomical basis of splenic notch, accessory spleens, Kehr's sign, different types of vagotomy, liver biopsy (site of needle puncture), referred pain in cholecystitis, obstructive jaundice, referred pain around umbilicus, radiating pain of kidney to groin and lymphatic spread in carcinoma stomach.

CLINICAL ANATOMY

- ***Movements of spleen***: The spleen is intraperitoneal structure and related to the diaphragm. Hence, the spleen moves with respiration.

- ***Palpation of the spleen***: A normal spleen is not palpable. An enlarged spleen can be felt under the left costal margin during inspiration. Palpation is assisted by turning the patient to his right side. Note that the spleen becomes palpable only after it has enlarged about twice of its normal size (Fig. 23.9).
- ***Splenomegaly***: Enlargement of the spleen is called *splenomegaly* (Fig. 23.10). Sometimes the spleen becomes very large. It then projects towards the right iliac fossa in the direction of the axis of the tenth rib. The notches of enlarged spleen are easily palpable.
- ***Splenectomy***: Surgical removal of the spleen is called *splenectomy*. During this operation, damage to the tail of the pancreas has to be carefully avoided, as the tail of pancreas is very rich in islets of Langerhans. Spleen has two pedicles— gastrosplenic and lienorenal. Their contents are separated carefully before the ligaments are cut.
- ***Splenic puncture***: Spleen can be punctured through the left 9th or 10th intercostal space in the midaxillary line using a lumbar puncture needle. When enlarged, it can be punctured through the midaxillary line. To avoid laceration of spleen, the patient must hold his breath during the procedure.
- Intrasplenic pressure is an indirect record of the portal pressure. Splenic venography reveals and confirms the enlarged portosystemic communications in cases of portal hypertension.
- ***Splenic infarction***: The smaller branches of splenic artery are end arteries. Their occlusion by emboli causes splenic infarction.
- ***Kehr sign*** is the classical symptom of the ruptured spleen. It is the occurrence of acute pain in the tip of the shoulder due to presence of blood in the peritoneal cavity. Root value C3 and C4 and nerves involved are phrenic nerve and supraclavicular nerve. *Note*: Kehr sign is seen in ruptured spleen, renal calculi, subdiaphragmatic abscess and ruptured ectopic pregnancy.
- ***Sickle cell anaemia and splenic sequestration***: The splenic sequestration crisis is a life-threatening condition that occurs mostly in sickle cell anaemia and beta-thalassemia due to vaso-occlusion and trapping of large quantity of blood in the spleen. It may cause hypovolemic shock and death. In long term, small repeated splenic infarcts produce scaring and fibrosis of spleen.
- Spleen is in danger of trauma to the left lower thoracic cage. A ruptured spleen may cause severe haemorrhage, as it has a rich blood supply.
- ***Referred pain***: Pain of splenic tissue is poorly localised. It is also referred to the epigastrium. Stretch of the splenic capsule produces localized pain in the posterior part of left upper quadrant (hypochondrium).
- ***Splenic tear***: If there is a small tear in the spleen, it can be sutured with catgut and the greater omentum can be wrapped round the sutured tear.
- ***Partial splenectomy***: Since there are segmental branches of the splenic artery, only one segment can be removed according to the state of spleen.
- After splenectomy, spleen can be cut into small pieces and these can be implanted within the greater omentum. Because of vascularization, spleen survives and does its function of producing the antibodies.
- ***Banti's disease*** is a chronic congestive enlargement of spleen resulting in premature destruction of RBC.

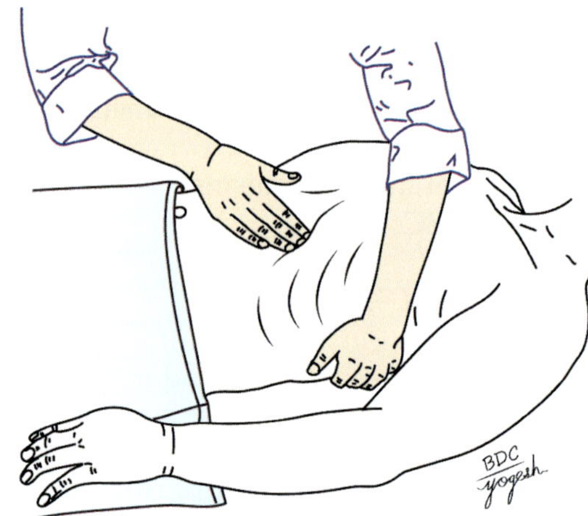

Fig. 23.9: Classic position for splenic palpation. As the patient inspires, the edge of an enlarged spleen descends to the examiner's fingertips. *Note*: A normal spleen is not palpable

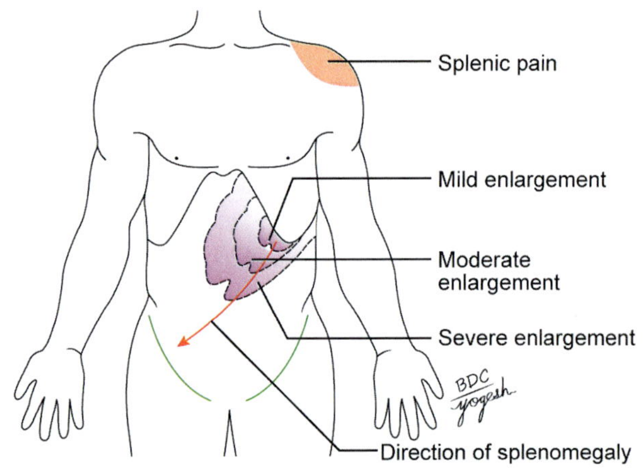

Fig. 23.10: Stages of enlargement of spleen towards right iliac fossa

PANCREAS

The pancreas (*pan* = all; *kreas* = flesh) is a gland that is partly exocrine and partly endocrine. The exocrine part secretes the digestive pancreatic juice; and the endocrine part secretes hormones, e.g. insulin. It is soft, lobulated and elongated organ (Plate 23.4, Fig. 23.11, Flowchart 23.2).

Functions of Pancreas

The pancreas performs the following functions:

1. *Exocrine function*: Exocrine pancreas secrete alkaline pancreatic juice that contains the following chemicals:
   a. Bicarbonates neutralize acidic content of stomach that enters the small intestine.

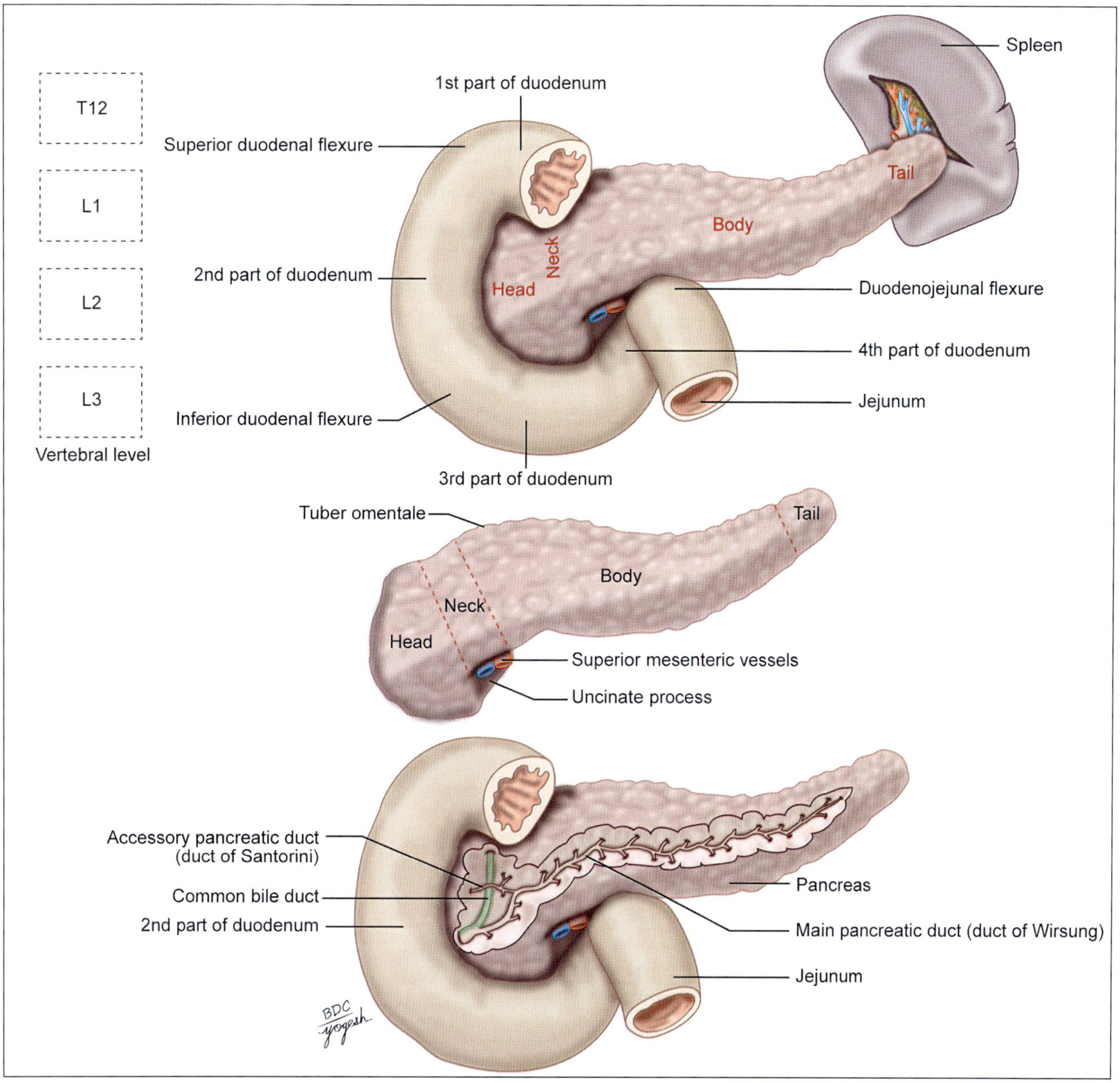

Plate 23.4: Pancreas

T12
L1
L2
L3
Vertebral level
1st part of duodenum
Superior duodenal flexure
2nd part of duodenum
Inferior duodenal flexure
3rd part of duodenum
Spleen
Tail
Body
Neck
Head
Duodenojejunal flexure
4th part of duodenum
Jejunum
Tuber omentale
Tail
Body
Neck
Head
Superior mesenteric vessels
Uncinate process
Accessory pancreatic duct (duct of Santorini)
Common bile duct
2nd part of duodenum
Pancreas
Main pancreatic duct (duct of Wirsung)
Jejunum
BDC Yogesh

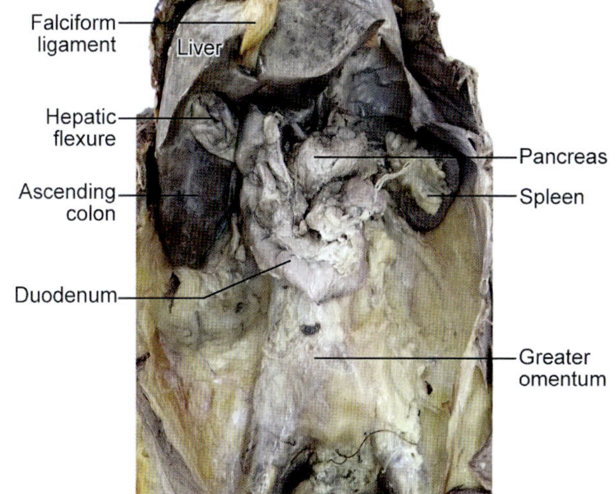

Fig. 23.11: Dissection showing liver, duodenum, pancreas and spleen

b. Pancreatic enzymes digest the food material; for example, proteases (trypsin, chymotrypsin) digest proteins, amylases hydrolyze carbohydrates, lipases break lipids.

2. *Endocrine function*: Islets of Langerhans secrete insulin, glucagon, somatostatin and pancreatic peptides.

Location

The pancreas lies more or less transversely across the posterior abdominal wall, at the level of L1 and L2 vertebrae.

Size and Shape

It is J-shaped or retort-shaped, set obliquely. The bowl of the retort represents its head, and the stem of the retort represents its neck, body and tail.

Length: 12–15 cm

Width: 3–4 cm

Flowchart 23.2: Pancreas

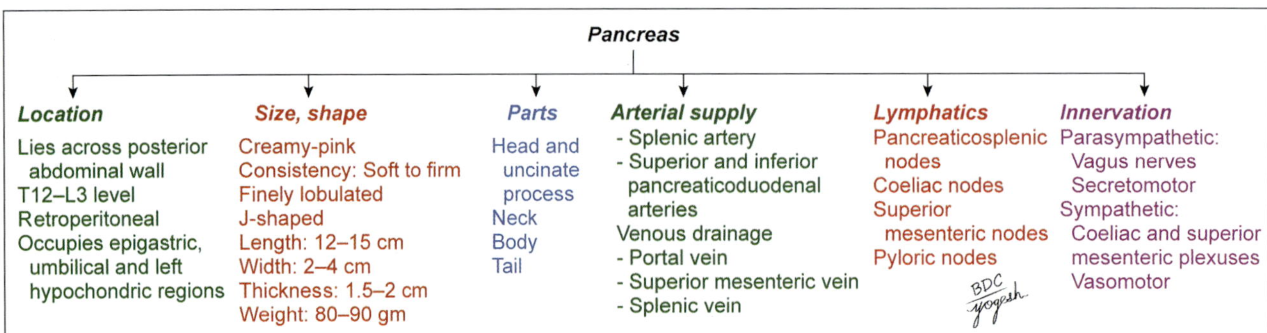

Thickness: 1.5–2 cm
Weight: 80–90 g
Volume: 70–80 cm^3

Parts of Pancreas

The pancreas is divided into four parts from right to left into the following (Plate 23.4, Figs 23.12 and 23.13):

1. *Head* is an enlarged part that lies in the concavity of the duodenum
2. *Neck* is a slightly constricted part
3. *Body* is elongated
4. *Tail* is a narrow, pointed part that reaches the hilus of spleen.

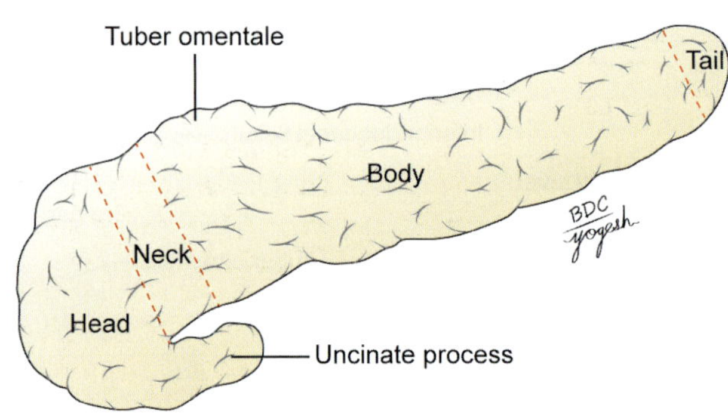

Fig. 23.12: Parts of pancreas

Peritoneal Relations of Pancreas

The ventral surface of pancreas is covered by parietal peritoneum and is crossed by the root of transverse mesocolon. The tail of the pancreas is its only intraperitoneal part and lies in the lienorenal ligament. Pancreas lies posterior to the lesser sac.

Head of the Pancreas

Head is the enlarged flattened right end of pancreas, situated within the 'C-shaped' curve of the duodenum.

External Features

The head of the pancreas has the following features:

1. *Three borders*: Superior, inferior and right-lateral
2. *Two surfaces*: Anterior and posterior
3. *One process*: Uncinate process.

Uncinate process is a hook-like projection at the lower end and left part of the head and it projects towards the left.

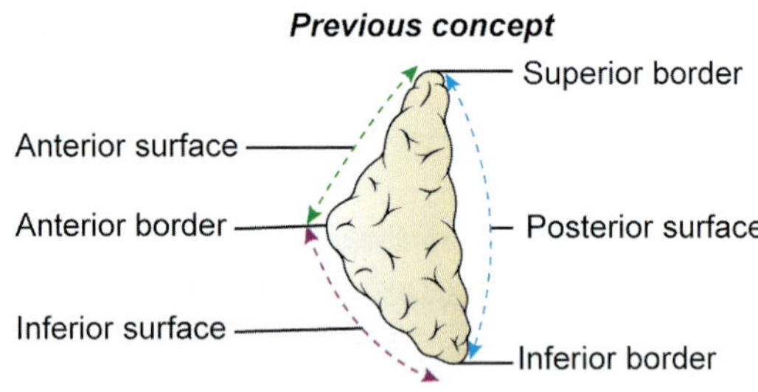

Fig. 23.13: Surfaces and borders of the body of pancreas as seen in cross section (*Previous concept*: The body of pancreas has three borders: Superior, inferior and anterior)

Relations of Head of Pancreas

(Figs 23.14a and b, Flowchart 23.3)

Three borders

1. ***Superior border*** is related to:
   - First part of the duodenum
   - Superior pancreaticoduodenal artery.
2. ***Inferior border*** is related to:
   - 3rd part of the duodenum
   - Inferior pancreaticoduodenal artery.
3. ***Right lateral border*** is related to:
   - 2nd part of the duodenum
   - Terminal part of the bile duct
   - Anastomosis between the two pancreaticoduodenal arteries.

Two surfaces:

1. ***Anterior surface*** is related, from above downwards, to:
   a. 1st part of duodenum
   b. Transverse colon
   c. Jejunum which is separated from it by peritoneum.

Flowchart 23.3: Relations of pancreas

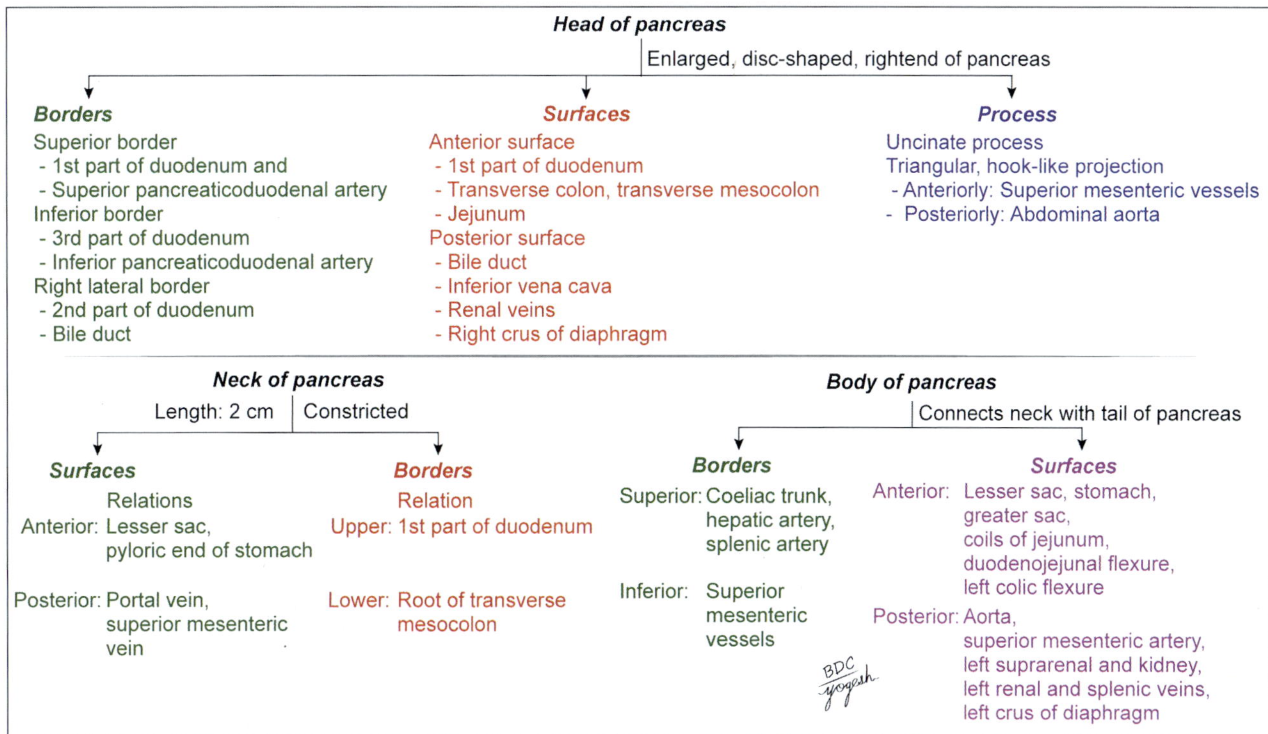

Figs 23.14a and b: Relations of head of the pancreas: (a) Anterior; (b) Posterior

2. ***Posterior surface*** is related to:
   a. Inferior vena cava
   b. Terminal parts of the renal veins
   c. Right crus of the diaphragm
   d. Bile duct which runs downwards and to the right and is often embedded in the substance of pancreas.

Uncinate process:

The uncinate process is a triangular, hook-like projection from lower part of the head. It is related

1. *Anteriorly* to the superior mesenteric vessels and
2. *Posteriorly* to the abdominal aorta.

Neck of the Pancreas

This is the slightly constricted part of the pancreas between its head and body. It is directed forwards, upwards and to the left. The neck has the following presenting parts:

1. *Two surfaces*: Anterior and posterior
2. *Two borders*: Upper and lower.

Relations of Neck

(Figs 23.15a and b, Flowchart 23.3)

1. ***Anterior surface*** is related to: The peritoneum covering the posterior wall of the lesser sac, and the pylorus.
2. ***Posterior surface*** is related to the termination of the superior mesenteric vein and the beginning of the portal vein.

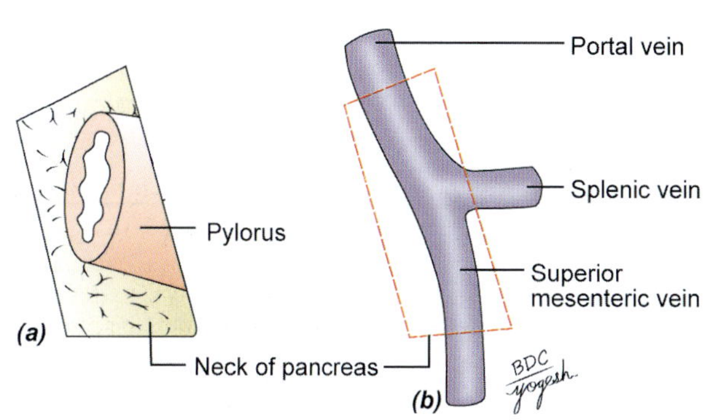

Figs 23.15a and b: Relations of the neck of the pancreas: (a) Anterior and (b) posterior

3. ***Upper border*** is related to the 1st part of duodenum.
4. ***Lower border*** is related to the root of transverse mesocolon.

Body of the Pancreas

The body of the pancreas is elongated. It extends from its neck to the tail. It passes towards the left with a slight upward and backward inclination.

External Features

The body of pancreas is slightly triangular in cross-section (Fig. 23.13). It has

1. *Two surfaces*: Anterior and posterior
2. *Two borders*: Superior and inferior [*Reference*: *Gray's Anatomy*, 42nd edn.].
   Previous concept: The body of pancreas has three surfaces: Anterior, inferior and posterior, and three borders: Superior, inferior and anterior.
3. *One process*: *Tuber omentale*: It is a rounded conical elevation from the right end of the superior border.

Relations of Body

(Figs 23.16a and b, Flowchart 23.3)

Superior border is related to coeliac trunk over the tuber omentale and hepatic artery to the right and splenic artery to the left of tuber omentale.

Inferior border is related to the superior mesenteric vessels at its right end.

As per previous concept: The anterior border provides the root of the transverse mesocolon and separates the anterior and inferior surfaces.

Anterior surface is covered by peritoneum and gives attachment to the transverse mesocolon [*Reference*: *Gray's Anatomy*, 42nd edn.].

Relations above the attachment of transverse mesocolon:

1. Lesser sac
2. Stomach

Relations below the attachment of transverse mesocolon:

1. Infracolic compartment of greater sac
2. Coils of jejunum
3. Duodenojejunal flexure
4. Left colic flexure.

Previous concept: The above-mentioned anterior surface is divided into anterior and inferior surfaces by the anterior border that provides attachment to the transverse mesocolon.

Posterior surface is devoid of the peritoneum. It lies on fusion fascia of Toldt. It is related to:

1. Aorta
2. Origin superior mesenteric artery
3. Left suprarenal gland
4. Upper pole of left kidney
5. Left renal vein
6. Splenic vein (may be embedded in the gland)
7. Left crus of diaphragm.

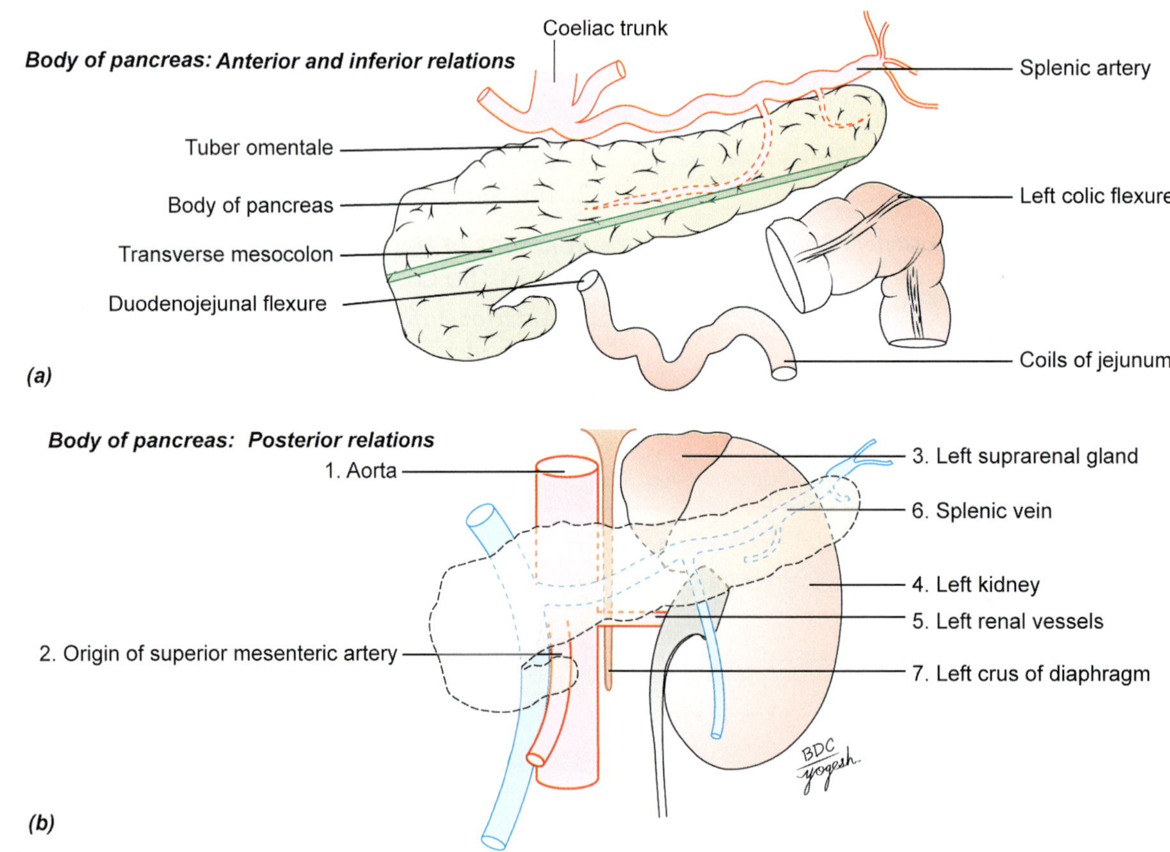

Figs 23.16a and b: Relations of the body of the pancreas: (a) Anterior and inferior and (b) posterior

Tail of the Pancreas

The tail of pancreas is the narrowest and the most left lateral portion of the pancreas. It is about 1.5 to 3.5 cm long. It lies in the splenorenal (lienorenal) ligament along with splenic vessels (Fig. 23.12). It is the only mobile part of pancreas. It contains the most significant number of islets of Langerhans.

Ducts of the Pancreas

The exocrine pancreas is drained by two ducts—main and accessory (Fig. 23.17).

Main Pancreatic Duct of Wirsung

- It is 3 mm in diameter and lies near the posterior surface of the pancreas and is recognised easily by its white colour. It begins at the tail; runs towards the right through the body; and bends at the neck to run downwards, backwards and to the right in the head.
- It receives many small tributaries which join it at acute angles to its long axis showing a 'V' shape pattern forming what has been described as a *herringbone pattern*.

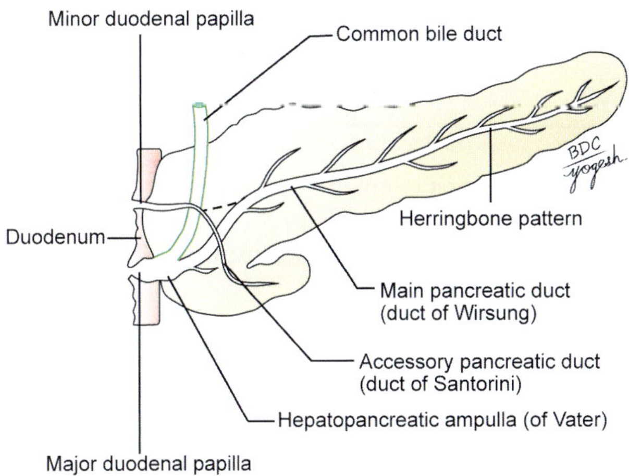

Fig. 23.17: The pancreatic ducts

- Within the head of the pancreas, the pancreatic duct is related to the bile duct which lies on its right side. The two ducts enter the wall of the 2nd part of the duodenum and join to form the ***hepatopancreatic ampulla of Vater*** which opens by a narrow mouth on the summit of the ***major duodenal papilla***, 8 to 10 cm distal to the pylorus.

Accessory Pancreatic Duct of Santorini

It begins in the lower part of the head, crosses the front of the main duct with which it communicates and opens into the duodenum at the ***minor duodenal papilla***. The papilla of accessory pancreatic duct is situated 6 to 8 cm distal to the pylorus.

Arterial Supply

The pancreas is supplied by the pancreatic branches of the following arteries (Fig. 23.18, Flowchart 23.2):

1. Splenic artery – branch of coeliac trunk.
2. Superior pancreaticoduodenal artery – branch of gastroduodenal artery.
3. Inferior pancreaticoduodenal artery – branch of superior mesenteric artery.

Venous Drainage

The venous blood from the pancreas drains into (Fig. 23.19, Flowchart 23.2):

1. Portal vein
2. Superior mesenteric vein
3. Splenic vein.

Lymphatic Drainage

The lymphatics from the pancreas drain into the following lymph nodes:

1. Pancreaticosplenic nodes [main lymphatic nodes]
2. Coeliac nodes
3. Superior mesenteric nodes
4. Pyloric nodes.

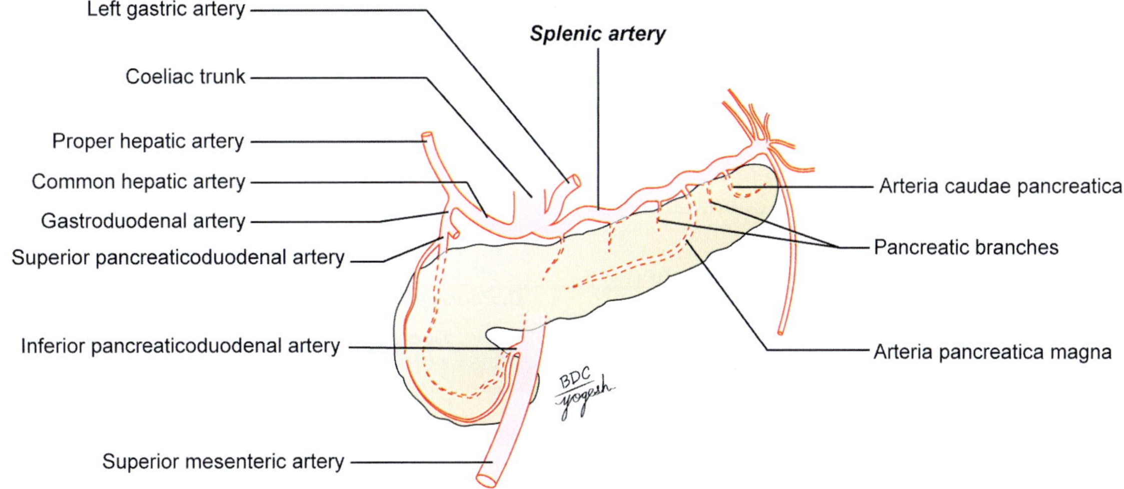

Fig. 23.18: Arterial supply of the pancreas

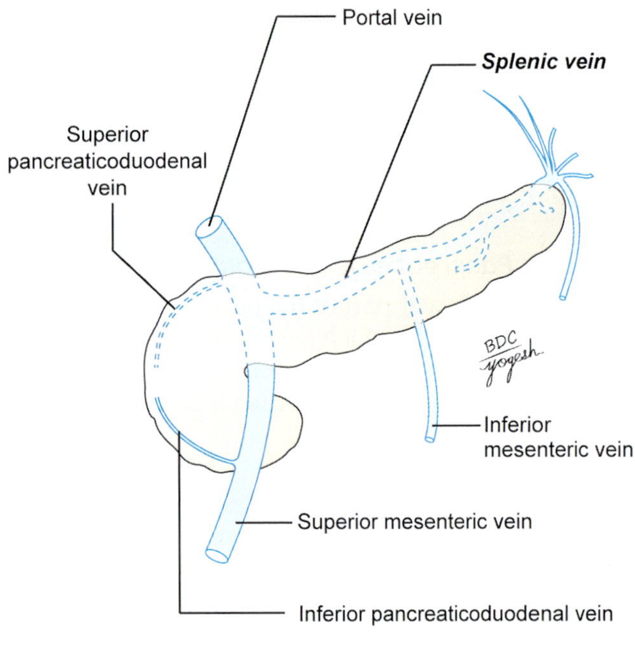

Fig. 23.19: Venous drainage of the pancreas

Plate 23.5: Histology of pancreas

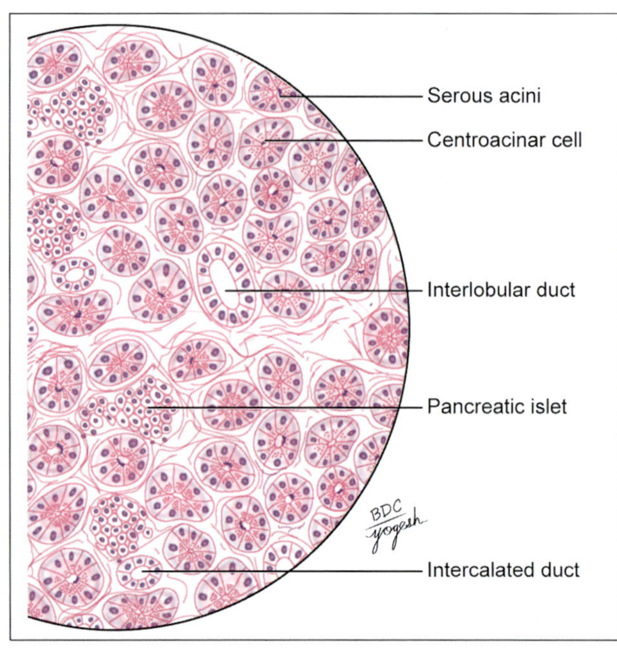

Nerve Supply

The pancreas is supplied by the following fibres:

1. *Parasympathetic fibres* from vagus nerve: These are secretomotor fibres that enhance pancreatic secretions along with cholecystokinin (produced by duodenum).
2. *Sympathetic fibres* from coeliac and superior mesenteric plexuses: These are vasomotor.

Competency:

AN52.1 Describe and identify the microanatomical features of pancreas.

Histology of Pancreas

The pancreatic parenchyma shows exocrine as well as endocrine components (Plate 23.5).

Exocrine pancreas (serous compound tubuloalveolar part): It secretes bicarbonates and digestive enzymes. It consists of:

1. *Serous acini* are lined by tall columnar cells that show basal basophilia (because of SER) apical eosinophilia (because of SER) and spherical basal nuclei. *Centroacinar cells* (simple squamous cells) line intercalated ducts.
2. Interlobular ducts are lined by simple cuboidal to low columnar epithelium.
3. Main and accessory pancreatic ducts are lined by simple columnar epithelium.

Endocrine pancreas (Islets of Langerhans): These are lightly stained clusters of polygonal cells. It consists of:

1. Alpha cells (A cells): Secrete glucagon
2. Beta cells (B cells): Secrete insulin
3. Delta cells (D cells): Secrete somatostatin.

Competency:

AN52.6 Describe the development and congenital anomalies of pancreas.

Development of Pancreas

Pancreas develops from endodermal ventral and dorsal pancreatic buds that arise from caudal part of the foregut (junctional zone of foregut and midgut) (Figs 23.20a to c, Table 23.1, Flowchart 23.4).

Proliferation of these endodermal buds form ducts, parenchyma (acini) and islets of Langerhans.

Flowchart 23.4: Development of pancreas

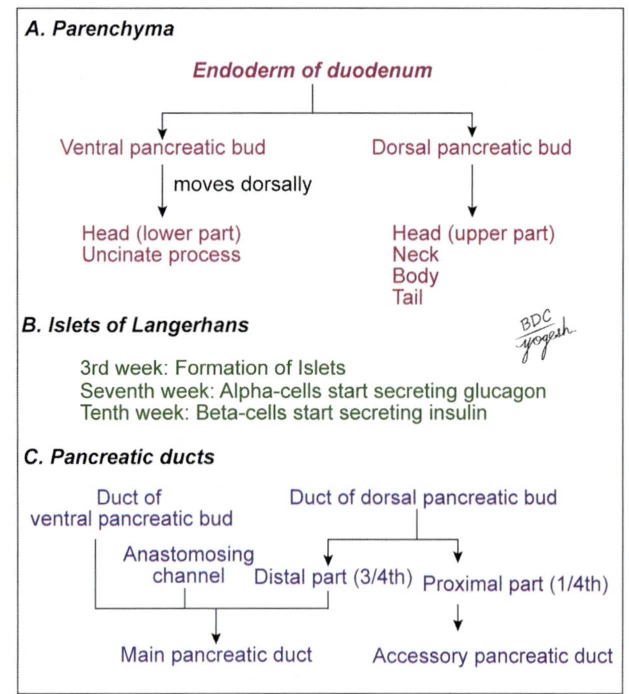

Section 2: Abdomen and Pelvis 23

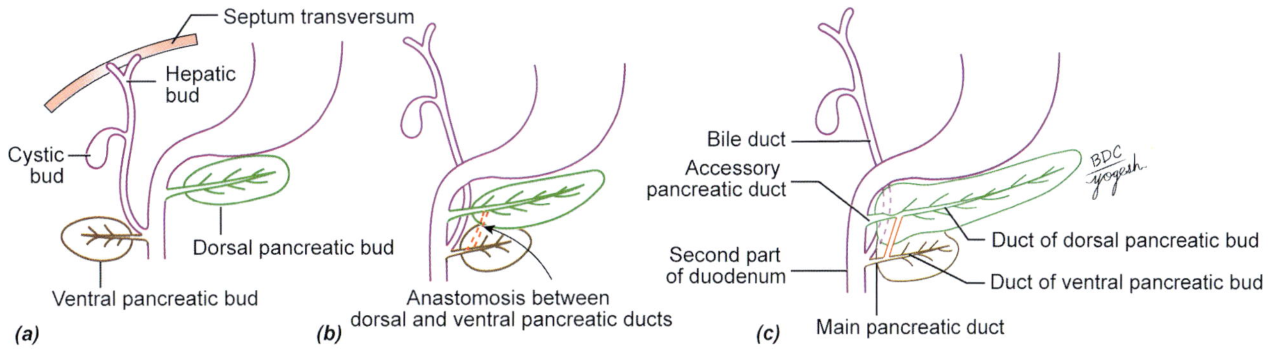

Figs 23.20a to c: Stages of development of pancreas

TABLE 23.1: Development of pancreas

Part	*Embryological source*
Lower part of head and uncinate process	Ventral pancreatic bud
Upper part of head, neck, body and tail	Dorsal pancreatic bud
Main pancreatic duct	Duct of ventral pancreatic bud Distal part of duct of dorsal pancreatic bud
Accessory pancreatic duct	Proximal part of duct of dorsal pancreatic bud
Connective tissue	Mesoderm

Note: The pancreatic acini and islets of Langerhans are derived from endodermal pancreatic buds. By 7th week, α-cells start secreting glucagon, and by 10th week, β-cells start secreting insulin. Glucagon can be detected in foetal plasma 15th week onward. (*Source*: *Textbook of Human Embryology*. Yogesh Sontakke, 2nd edn.)

Adjacent splanchnopleuric mesoderm condenses to form capsule, blood vessels and other connective tissue of pancreas.

Developmental anomalies of the pancreas include the following.

1. An *annular pancreas* encircling the second part of the duodenum. An annular pancreas may be the cause of duodenal obstruction.
2. *Accessory pancreatic tissue* may be present at various sites. These include the wall of the duodenum, the jejunum, the ileum, or of Meckel's diverticulum.
3. *Inversion of pancreatic ducts:* In this condition, the accessory duct is larger than the main duct, and the main drainage of the pancreas is through the minor duodenal papilla.

DISSECTION

Identify the pancreas—a retroperitoneal organ lying transversely across the posterior abdominal wall.

Head is easily identifiable in the concavity of duodenum. Uncinate process of the head is the part behind the upper part of superior mesenteric artery.

Portal vein is formed behind its neck. Rest of the part extending to the left is its body and tail reaching till the hilum of spleen.

Turn the descending part of the duodenum and the head of the pancreas to the left. Look for the posterior pancreaticoduodenal vessels and the bile duct on the head of the pancreas.

Expose the structures posterior to pancreas. Turn the tail and body of the pancreas to the right stripping the splenic artery and vein from its posterior surface and identify the vessels passing to the gland from them.

On the posterior surface of the pancreas, make a cut into the gland parallel to and close to the superior and inferior margins of the body. Pick away the lobules of the gland between the cuts to expose the greyish white duct and the interlobular ducts draining into the main duct.

CLINICAL ANATOMY

- ***Diabetes mellitus*** may occur due to deficiency of insulin.
- ***Carcinoma of head of pancreas*** may compress bile duct that leads to obstructive jaundice. It may also cause duodenal obstruction and compression of portal vein (resulting in ascites and portal hypertension).
- ***Acute pancreatitis*** is an acute inflammation of pancreas that has severe complications and high mortality (death) rate. It occurs because of abnormal activation of pancreatic proteolytic enzymes in the pancreas (usually, these enzymes get activated in the intestine). Activated enzymes cause inflammation, oedema and cellular death.
- ***Chronic pancreatitis*** is long-standing inflammation of pancreas (repeated attacks of mild acute pancreatitis).
- ***Pain from pancreatitis*** is poorly localized. Pain is referred to epigastrium. Pain is also referred to posterior paravertebral region and around the lower thoracic vertebrae, due to inflammation of soft tissues of retroperitoneum. Their afferents are being sent through lower intercostal nerves.
- ***Pancreatic resection*** is difficult due to its proximity to many large vessels.
- ***Pancreatic cysts*** are fluid-filled sacs within the pancreas. They may arise from benign or malignant tumours or dilatation of pancreatic ducts.
- ***Pseudocyst*** of pancreas is a circumscribed collection of fluid containing pancreatic enzymes, blood and necrotic tissue. It is located in lesser sac and may present symptoms similar to pancreatitis. It occurs as a complication of pancreatitis.

LIVER

The liver is a large and solid gland situated in the right upper quadrant of the abdominal cavity.

Liver consists of:

1. Exocrine part that secretes bile through biliary passage.
2. Endocrine part that liberates chemicals directly into the blood. These chemicals include glucose, heparin, plasma proteins (except immunoglobulins), cholesterol and so on.

The liver is also called the 'hepar' from which we have the adjective 'hepatic' applied to many structures connected with the organ.

Functions of Liver

Liver is an indispensable gland of the body.

1. *Metabolism* of carbohydrates, fats and proteins.
2. *Synthesis* of bile and prothrombin.
3. *Excretion* of drugs, toxins, poisons, cholesterol, bile pigments and heavy metals.
4. *Protective* by conjugation, destruction, phagocytosis, antibody formation and excretion.
5. *Storage* of glycogen, iron, fat, vitamins A and D.

Location

The liver occupies the whole of the right hypochondrium, the greater part of the epigastrium and extends into the left hypochondrium reaching up to the left lateral line. From the above, it will be obvious that most of the liver is covered by ribs and costal cartilages, except in the upper part of the epigastrium where it is in contact with the anterior abdominal wall (Plate 23.6, Fig. 23.21, Flowchart 23.5).

Size, Shape and Colour of Liver

In the living subject, the liver is reddish brown in colour, soft in consistency and very friable.

It weighs about 1600 g in males and about 1300 g in females. Weight of liver at birth is 150 g.

Note: The proportional weight of the liver is more in children (1/18th of body weight) than in adults (1/36th of the body weight). This is because of haematopoietic function of liver in foetal life.

Anatomical Position

Hold the liver in such a way that

1. Groove for the inferior vena cava on the posterior surface of liver should be vertically straight.
2. Broad base of wedge-shaped liver is on the right.
3. Smooth convexo-concavo-convex surface faces upward.

External Features

The liver is wedge-shaped. It resembles a four-sided pyramid laid on one side (Fig. 23.22).

It has the following features:

1. Five surfaces: Anterior, posterior, superior, inferior and right.

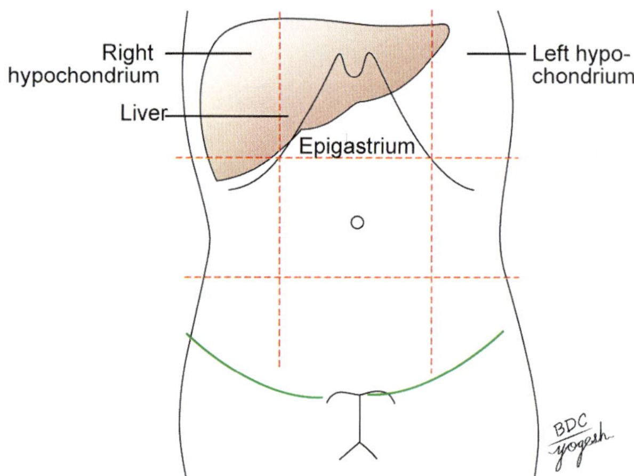

Fig. 23.21: Location of the liver

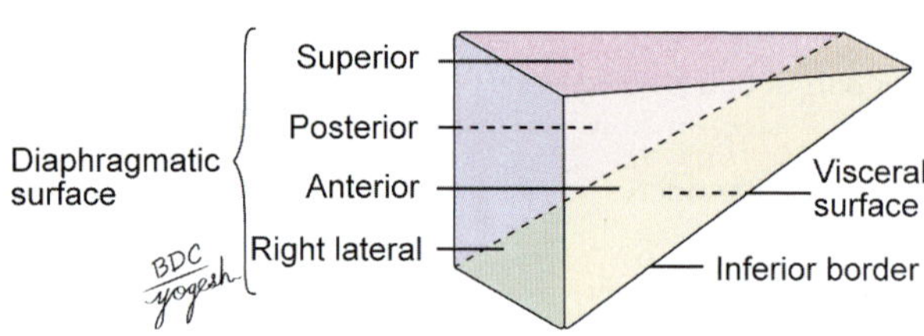

Fig. 23.22: Comparison of the orientation of the surfaces of the liver to those of a four-sided pyramid

Flowchart 23.5: Liver: Location, size, shape, external features

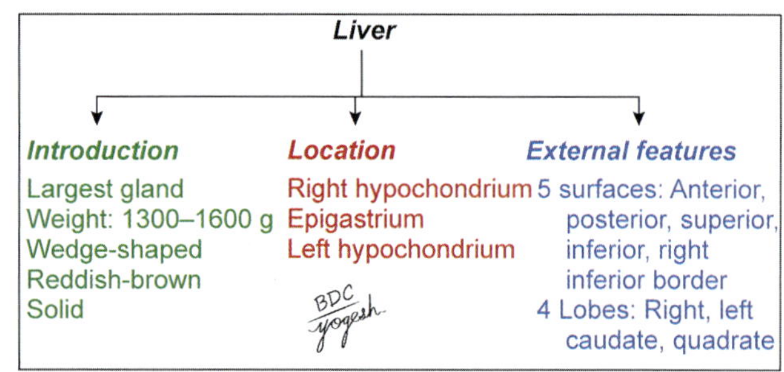

2. One border: Inferior.
3. Anatomical lobes: Right lobe, left lobe, caudate lobe and quadrate lobe.

Surfaces of Liver

It has five surfaces. These are (Figs 23.23 to 23.25, Flowchart 23.6):

1. Anterior
2. Posterior
3. Superior
4. Right
5. Inferior or visceral.

Note: Out of these, the ***inferior*** or ***visceral surface*** is well defined because it is demarcated, anteriorly, by a sharp inferior border. The other surfaces are more or less continuous with each other and are imperfectly separated from one another by ill-defined, rounded borders. It is more appropriate to group them as the ***diaphragmatic surface***, which is mostly separated from the inferior, or visceral surface by a narrow inferior border.

Plate 23.6: Liver

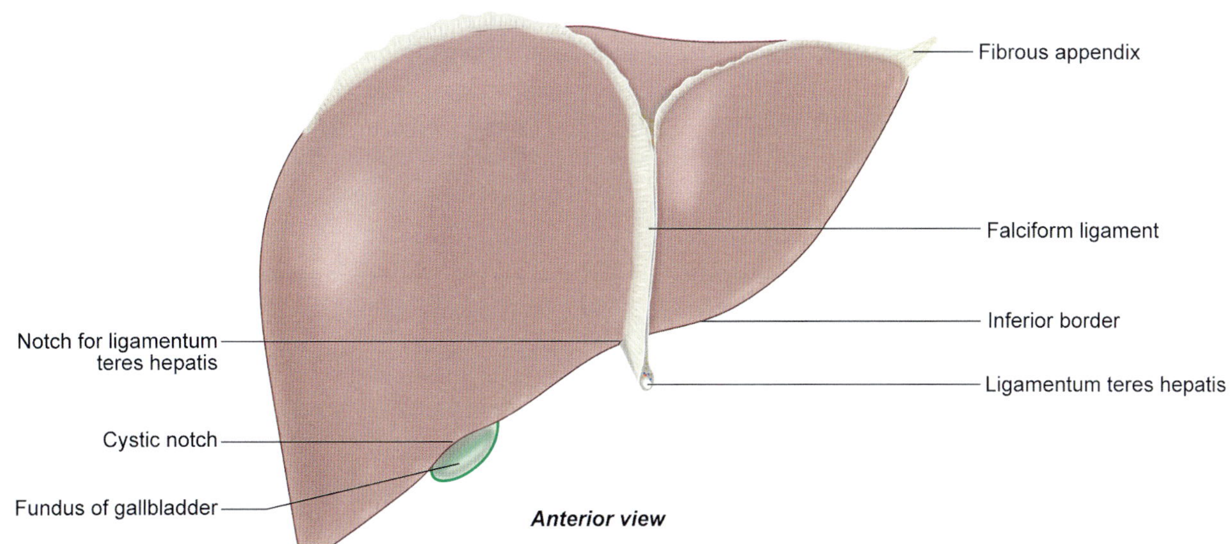

Anterior view

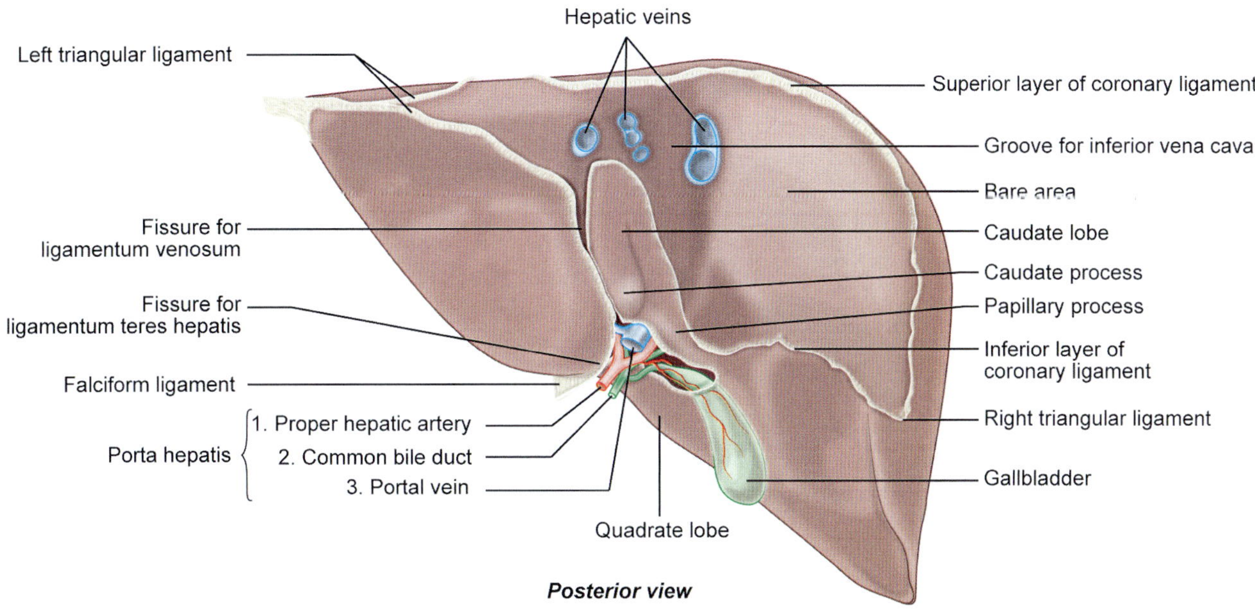

Posterior view

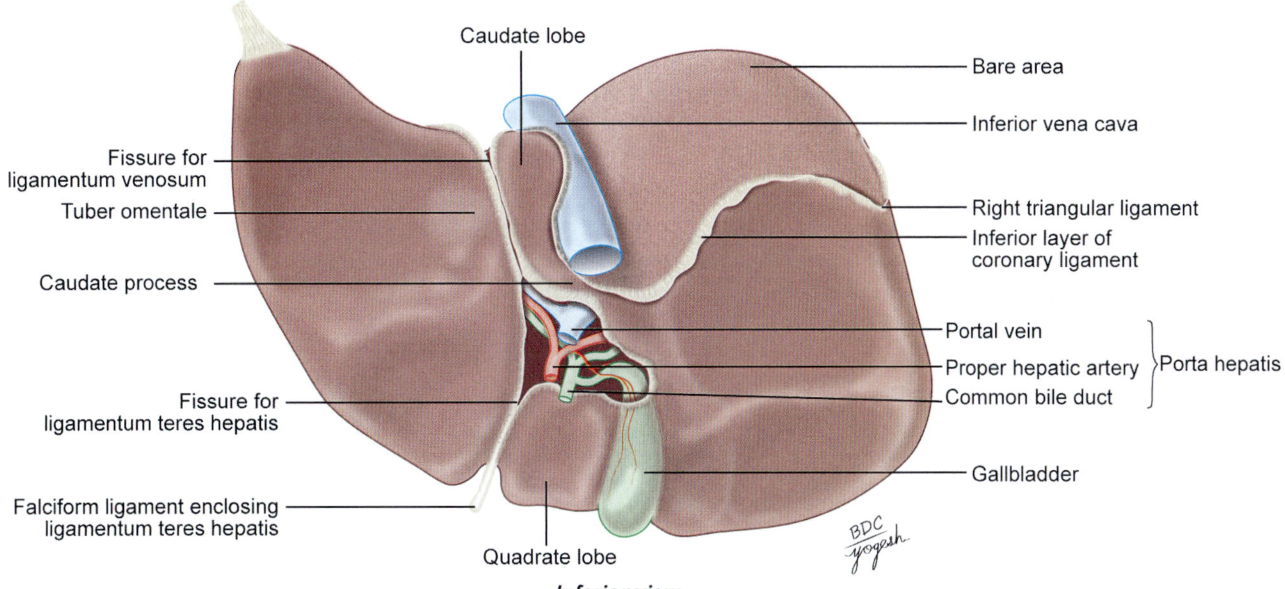

Inferior view

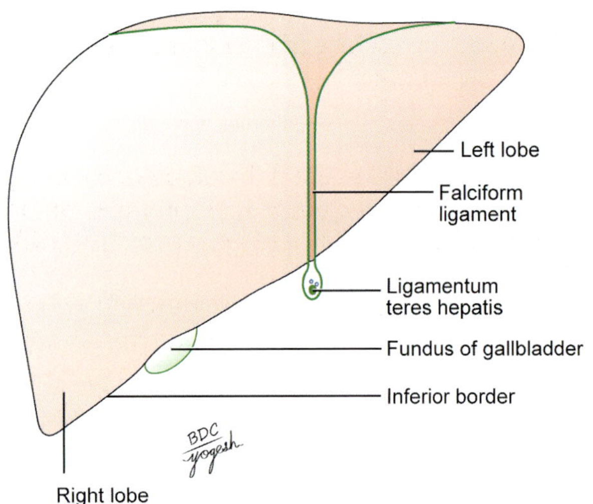

Fig. 23.23: Liver seen from the front

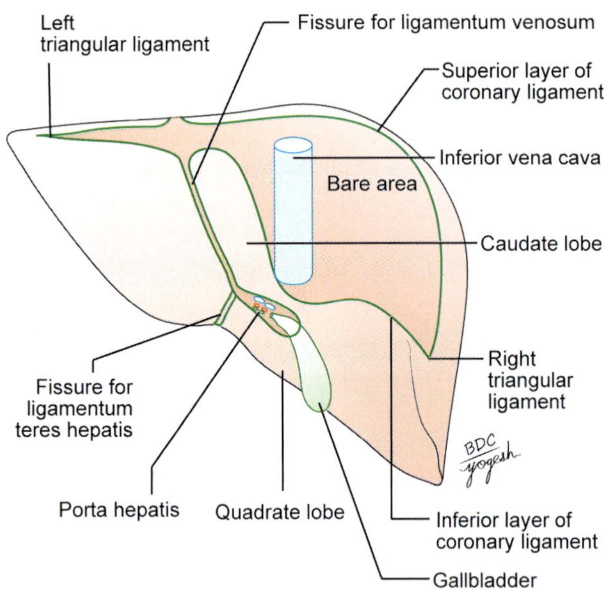

Fig. 23.24: Liver: Seen from behind

Inferior Border

The *inferior border* is sharp anteriorly where it separates the anterior surface from the inferior surface. It is somewhat rounded laterally where it separates the right surface from the inferior surface. The sharp anterior part is marked by:

a. ***Interlobar notch*** or the notch for the ligamentum teres.
b. ***Cystic notch*** for the fundus of the gallbladder (Plate 23.6).

In the epigastrium, the inferior border extends from the left 8th costal cartilage to the right 9th costal cartilage.

Flowchart 23.6: Surfaces of liver

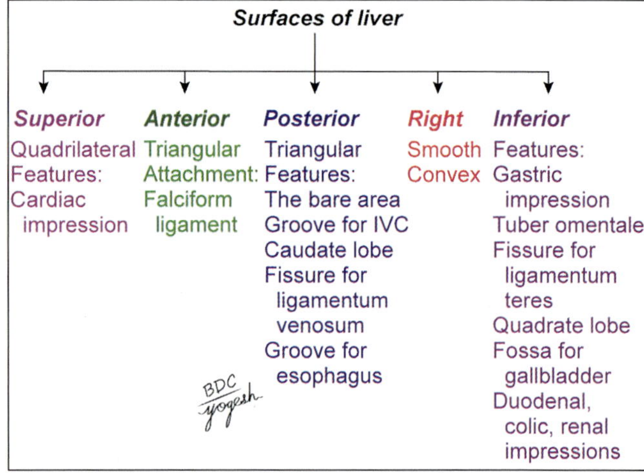

Lobes of Liver

The lobes of the liver are defined into two types (Flowcharts 23.7 to 23.9):

1. Anatomical lobes and
2. Physiological or functional lobes.

Anatomical Lobes

The liver is divided into right and left lobe as follows: Anteriorly and superiorly by the attachment of falciform ligament, inferiorly and posteriorly by the fissures for ligamentum teres and ligamentum venosum.

Right lobe: It is six times larger than the left lobe. It has two more lobes: Caudate and quadrate lobes.

a. *Caudate lobe:* It is situated on the posterior surface of liver, between the groove for inferior vena cava and fissure for ligamentum venosum above the porta hepatis.

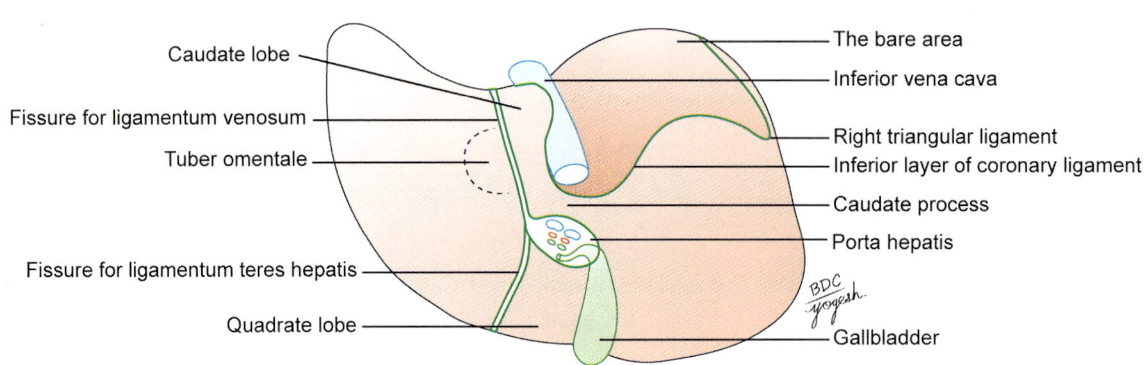

Fig. 23.25: Liver: Seen from below

Flowchart 23.7: Lobes of liver

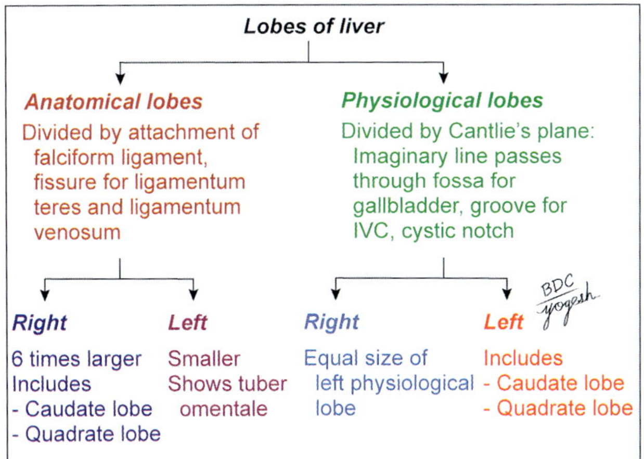

Flowchart 23.8: Caudate lobe

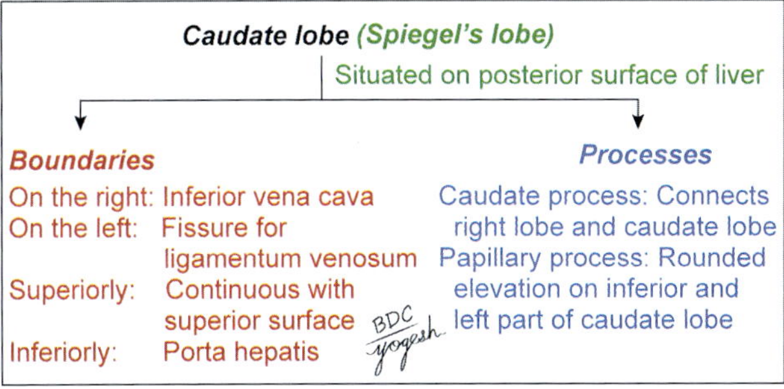

Flowchart 23.9: Quadrate lobe

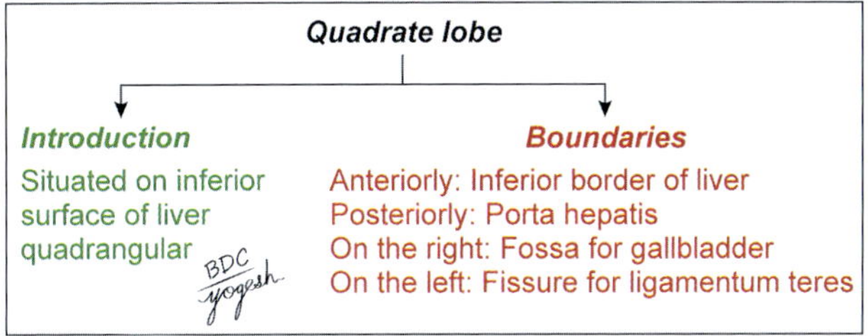

b. *Quadrate lobe*: It is quadrangular in shape and is situated on the inferior surface. It lies between fossa for gallbladder and fissure for ligamentum teres hepatis. It extends from inferior border of liver to porta hepatis.

Left lobe: It forms one-sixth of the liver. It is much smaller than the right lobe. It is flattened from above downward. *Tuber omentale* is rounded elevation on the inferior surface of left lobe of liver that comes in contact with lesser omentum.

Physiological Right and Left Lobes

The liver is divided into the right and left physiological lobes based on the intrahepatic distribution of branches of bile duct, hepatic artery and portal vein (Figs 23.26a and b).

Cantlie's plane/line is an imaginary line that divides right and left physiological lobes of the liver. This plane passes through the fossa for gallbladder, the groove for inferior vena cava and the cystic notch. It is present a little to the right of the falciform ligament.

Physiological right and left lobes of liver are approximately equal in size. Each physiological lobe is supplied by primary branch of hepatic artery and portal vein and drained by its own hepatic duct.

Relations

Peritoneal Relations and Bare Areas

(Plate 23.7, Flowchart 23.10)

Most of the liver is covered by peritoneum. The areas not covered by peritoneum are as follows:

1. *The bare area*: It is a triangular area, on the posterior surface of the right lobe, limited by the superior and inferior layers of the coronary ligament and by the right triangular ligament.
2. *Groove for the inferior vena cava*, on the posterior surface of the right lobe of the liver, between the caudate lobe and the bare area.
3. *Fossa for the gallbladder* which lies on the inferior surface of the right lobe to the right of the quadrate lobe.
4. The area of attachment of *lesser omentum* and the fissure for attachment of ligamentum venosum (Fig. 23.23).
5. Porta hepatis.

Ligaments of Liver

The liver is supported by false and true ligaments as follows (Plate 23.7, Figs 23.23 to 23.25, Flowchart 23.11):

A. ***False ligaments*** are folds of peritoneum. They include

1. ***Falciform ligament*** is a sickle-shaped peritoneal fold that connects the liver to the lower surface of the

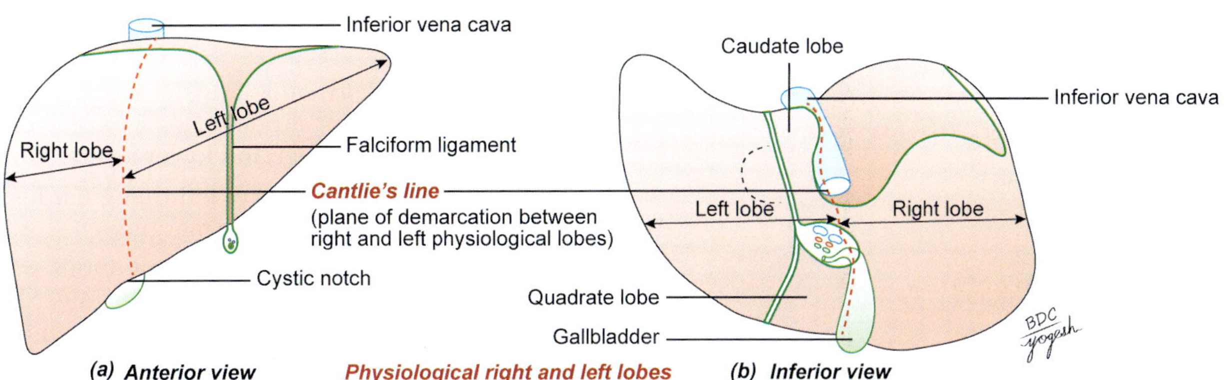

Figs 23.26a and b: Physiological lobes of the liver: (a) Anterior aspect and (b) inferior aspect

Plate 23.7: (a) Bare areas of liver (posterior view of liver); (b) Reflection of peritoneum of liver on the hepatic surface of diaphragm

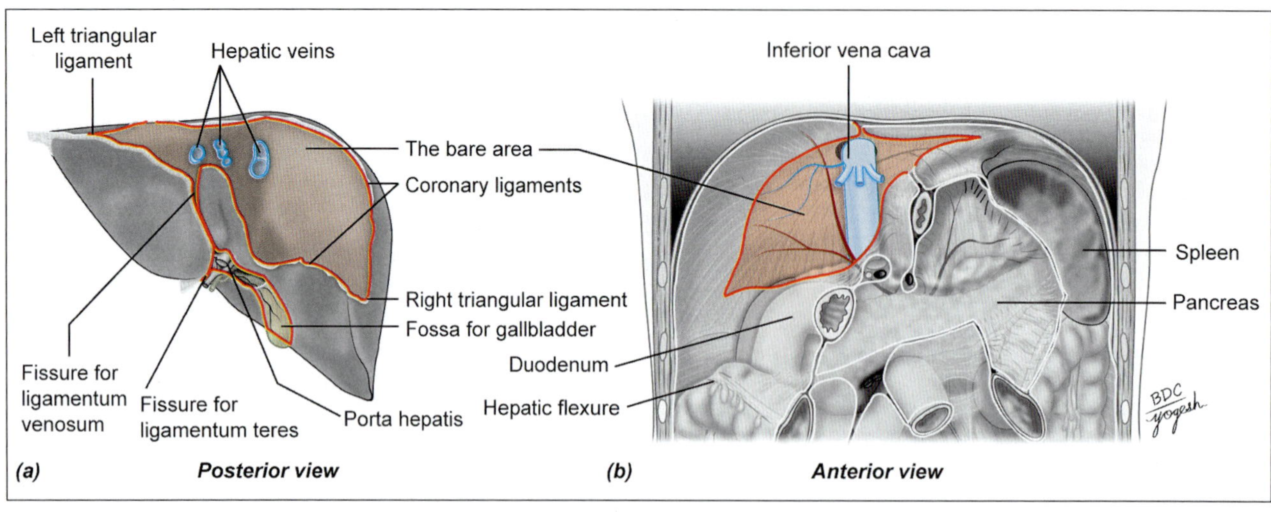

Flowchart 23.10: Bare areas of liver

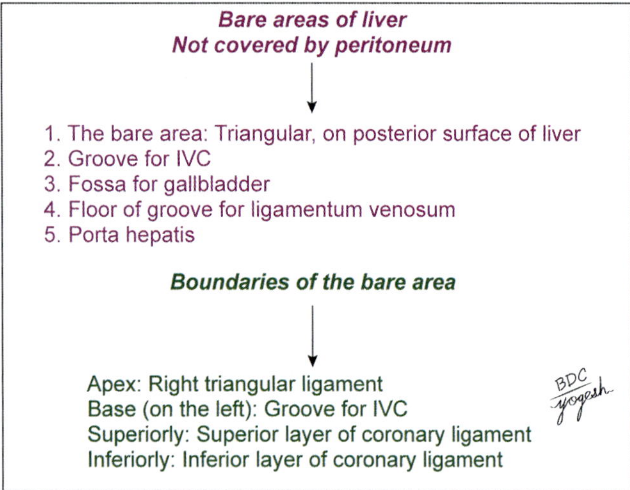

Flowchart 23.11: Ligaments of liver

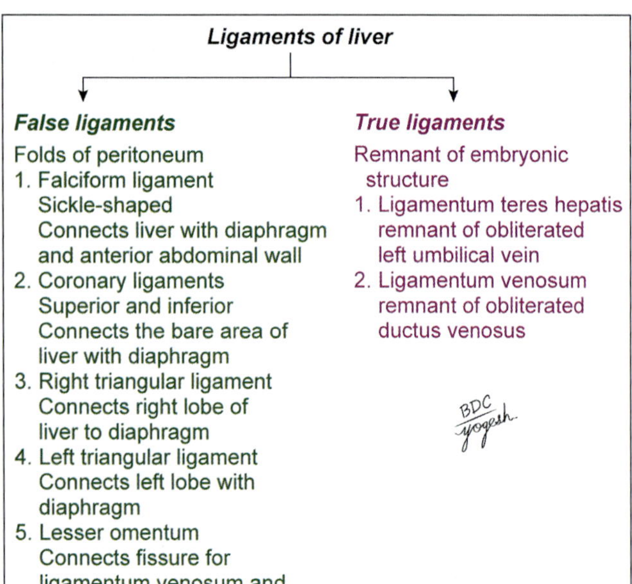

diaphragm and the anterior abdominal wall up to umbilicus. It develops from ventral mesogastrium.

Contents

- Ligamentum teres
- Paraumbilical vein (tributary of portal vein)
- Accessory portal system of Sappey, which communicates paraumbilical vein with diaphragmatic veins.

2. ***Coronary ligament*** is a triangular fold of peritoneum that connects the bare area of liver with the diaphragm. It consists of two layers — upper and lower. The *upper layer* (parietovisceral layer) is reflected from the diaphragm to the liver. The *lower layer* (inter-visceral layer) is reflected from the liver to the upper end of right kidney.

   On the right, both the layers fuse to form right triangular ligament.

   On the left, the upper layer is continuous with the right layers of the falciform ligament, and the lower layer is continuous with the peritoneal reflection along the right border of the caudate lobe.

   Contents

   - Connective tissue
   - Branches of the right phrenic artery.

3. ***Right triangular ligament*** is a small triangular fold of peritoneum that connects the right lobe of liver to the diaphragm. It encloses the apex of the bare area of liver.
4. ***Left triangular ligament*** is a small triangular fold that connects the superior surface of left lobe of liver to the diaphragm. It has upper and lower layers.

   On the left, both the layers of left triangular ligament are continuous to form a free margin.

   On the right, the upper layer is continuous with the left layer of the falciform ligament. Its lower layer is continuous with the anterior layer of lesser omentum along the fissure for ligamentum venosum.

5. ***Lesser omentum*** is a fold of peritoneum that connects the lesser curvature of stomach and proximal 1 inch

(2.5 cm) of duodenum to the liver. The lesser omentum is S-shaped, with the vertical limb being attached to the margins of porta hepatis.

Contents

- Along the lesser curvature of stomach, the anastomosis of right and left gastric vessels and branches of gastric nerves.
- Within the free margin portal vein, bile duct, hepatic artery and hepatic plexus of nerves and lymphatics.

B. *True ligaments* are remnants of foetal structures. They include:

1. ***Ligamentum teres hepatis*:** It is remnant of the obliterated left umbilical vein. It extends from the umbilicus to the left branch of the portal vein. It passes along the free margin of the falciform ligament.
2. ***Ligamentum venosum*:** It is the remnant of obliterated ductus venosus. In foetal life, it connects the left branch of portal vein with inferior vena cava and bypasses the hepatic circulation.

Visceral Relations (Fig. 23.27, Flowchart 23.12)

Anterior surface

The anterior surface is triangular and slightly convex. It is related to:

1. Xiphoid process and anterior abdominal wall in the median plane
2. Diaphragm on each side
3. Falciform ligament is attached to the anterior surface a little to the right of the median plane.

Superior surface

The superior surface is quadrilateral and shows a concavity in the middle.

This is the cardiac impression. On each side of the impression, the surface is convex to fit the dome of the diaphragm. The diaphragm separates this surface from the pericardium and the heart in the middle; and from pleura and lung on each side.

Right surface

The right surface is quadrilateral and convex. It is related to the diaphragm opposite the 7th to 11th ribs in the midaxillary line.

In the midaxillary line, it is separated by the diaphragm from

- Lungs and pleura in its upper 1/3rd
- Right costodiaphragmatic recess in middle 1/3rd
- 10th and 11th rib in the lower 1/3rd.

Posterior surface

The posterior surface is triangular. Its middle part shows a deep concavity for the vertebral column. The posterior surface presents the following features:

1. *Bare area of liver* that is related to diaphragm.
2. *Groove for inferior vena cava* that lodges the inferior vena cava and its floor is pierced by the hepatic veins.
3. *Caudate lobe* that is related to the superior recess of lesser sac.
4. *Fissure for ligamentum venosum* is very deep and extends to the front of the caudate lobe (Fig. 23.23). It contains two layers of the lesser omentum. The ligamentum venosum lies on its floor. The ligamentum venosum is a remnant of the ductus venosus of foetal life; it is connected below to the left branch of the portal vein and above to the inferior vena cava.
5. *Oesophageal impression* on the posterior surface of the left lobe.

Inferior surface

The inferior surface is quadrilateral and is directed downwards, backwards and to the left. It is marked by impressions for neighbouring viscera as follows (Fig. 23.27, Flowchart 23.12):

1. *Gastric impression* is shallow impression on the inferior surface of the left lobe of liver.
2. *Tuber omentale* is the rounded elevation that comes in contact with lesser omentum.
3. *Fissure for ligamentum teres.*
4. *Quadrate lobe* that is related to the pyloric end of stomach and first part of duodenum.
5. *Fossa for gallbladder* that lodges the gallbladder.
6. *Colic impression* that is related to right colic flexure.
7. *Duodenal impression*: Superior duodenal flexure (junction of 1st and 2nd part) is related to the upper part of fossa for gallbladder and adjoining part of right lobe.

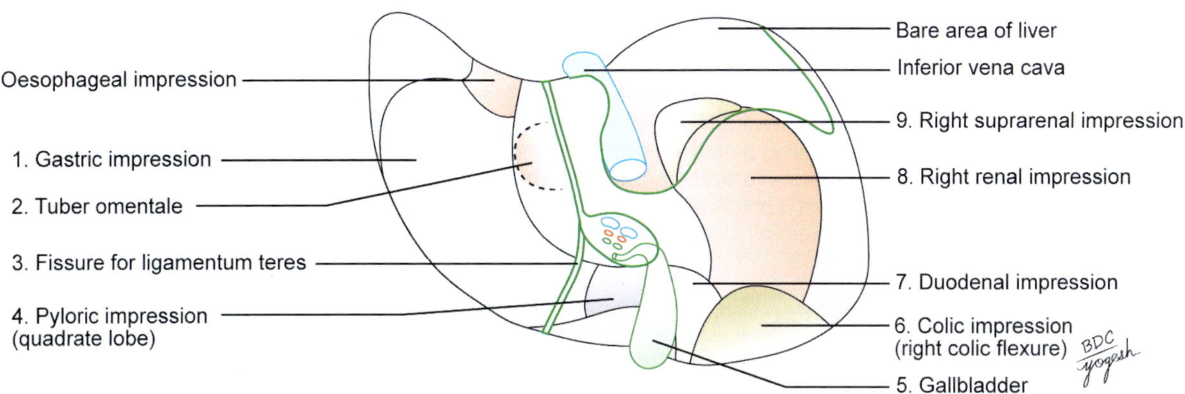

Fig. 23.27: Relations of the inferior surface of the liver

Flowchart 23.12: Visceral relations of inferior surface of liver

Visceral relations of inferior surface of liver

↓

1. Gastric, duodenal, colic, renal impressions
2. Tuber omentale
3. Fissures for ligamentum teres
4. Quadrate lobe—related to pylorus and 1st part of duodenum
5. Fossa for gallbladder
6. Porta hepatis

8. *Renal impression*: The part of inferior surface posterior to the colic impression is related to right kidney.
9. *Porta hepatis* is a horizontal fissure between the quadrate and caudate lobe of liver. It gives passage to right and left branches of hepatic artery and portal vein, and right and left hepatic ducts.

[*Mnemonics*: ***Structures at porta hepatis***: From anterior to posterior side – **DAV: D** – Hepatic **d**ucts, **A** – Hepatic **a**rtery, **V** – Portal **v**ein]

Arterial Supply

The liver has dual blood supply as follows (Flowchart 23.13):

- *Hepatic artery*: Liver receives 20% of its blood supply from hepatic artery. This is oxygenated blood.
- *Portal vein*: Liver receives 80% of its blood supply from portal vein. This is nutrient-rich venous blood.

Note: Before entering the liver, both the hepatic artery and the portal vein divide into right and left branches. Within the liver, they redivide to form segmental vessels which further divide to form interlobular vessels which run in the portal canals. Further ramifications of the interlobular branches open into the hepatic sinusoids. Thus the hepatic arterial blood mixes with the portal venous blood in the sinusoids. There are no anastomoses between adjoining hepatic arterial territories and hence each branch is an end artery.

Venous Drainage

Hepatic sinusoids drain into interlobular veins, which join to form sublobular veins. These in turn unite to form the ***hepatic veins*** which drain directly into the ***inferior vena cava***. Hepatic veins do not have extrahepatic course. They open directly into the inferior vena cava. These veins provide great support to the liver, besides the intra-abdominal pressure.

Note: The *hepatic veins* are arranged in three groups—right, left and middle.

The middle hepatic vein lies in the sagittal plane that divides the liver into right and left lobes.

The *left hepatic vein* lies between medial and lateral segments of left true lobe, the *middle hepatic vein* between anatomical right and left lobes, the *right hepatic vein* between anterior and posterior segments of right true lobe.

Lymphatic Drainage

1. *Superficial lymphatics* run on the surface of the liver beneath the peritoneum and terminate in caval, hepatic, paracardial and coeliac nodes (Flowchart 23.13).

Flowchart 23.13: Supply of liver

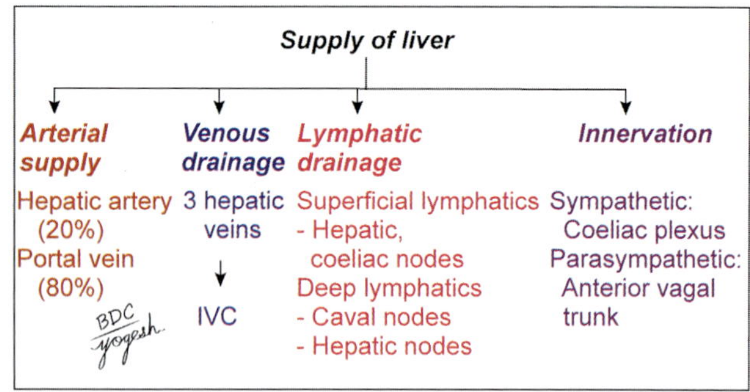

2. *Deep lymphatics* drain partly in the nodes around the end of inferior vena cava and partly in the hepatic nodes.

Nerve Supply

The liver supplied by (Flowchart 23.13)

1. *Sympathetic fibres* that are derived from the coeliac plexus. They run along the vessels in the free margin of the lesser omentum and enter the porta hepatis.
2. *Parasympathetic fibres* that are derived from hepatic branch of the anterior vagal trunk.
3. Pain sensation produced by distension of liver capsule or hepatitis runs along the sympathetic fibres and gets referred to epigastrium.

Hepatic Segments

Couinaud's division of liver is based on functional anatomy. He divided liver into right and left physiological lobes and further into total eight segments (Plate 23.8).

The right and left physiological lobes are divided by Cantlie's plane that passes on anterosuperior surface along the line joining cystic notch to the groove for the inferior vena cava. On the inferior surface, the plane passes through the fossa for gallbladder, and on the posterior surface, the plane passes through the middle of the caudate lobe.

These lobes are divided into eight segments as follows (*Reference*: *Gray's Anatomy*, 42nd edn.):

Left lobes:

I: Caudate lobe
II: Lateral superior
III: Medial inferior
IV: Medial superior.

Right lobe:

V: Medial (or anterior) inferior
VI: Lateral (or posterior) inferior
VII: Lateral (or posterior) superior
VIII: Medial (or anterior) superior.

CLINICAL ANATOMY

Liver resection: Liver resection for primary and secondary tumours is done commonly. 80% of liver mass can be removed safely. Liver can regrow to its original size within 6–12 months after resection. Major resections follow the planes between segments and are anatomical.

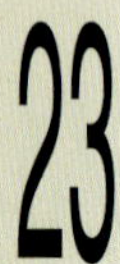

Plate 23.8: The segments of liver

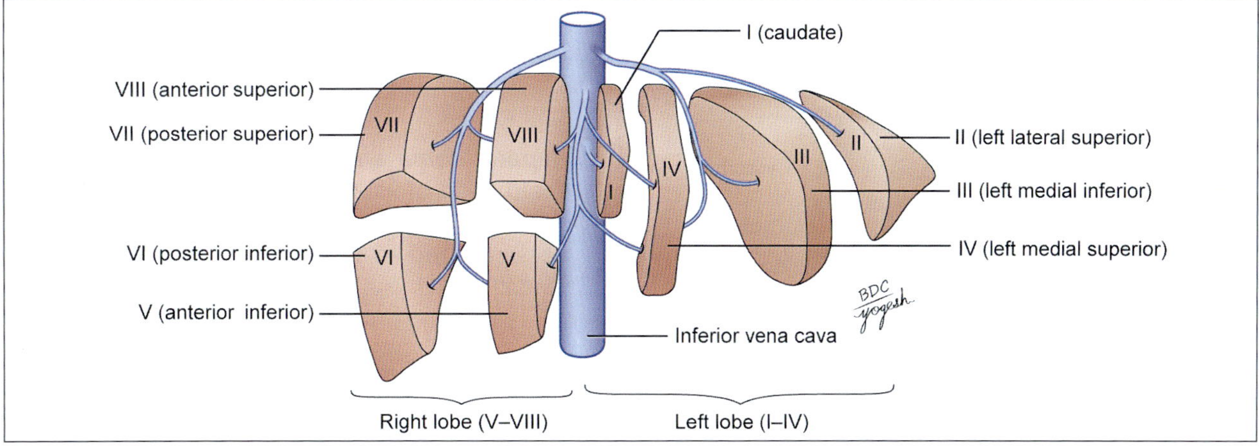

Competency:

AN52.1 Describe and identify the microanatomical features of liver.

Histology of Liver

The liver is covered by a thin connective tissue called ***Glisson's capsule***.

Liver shows classical hepatic lobules (hexagonal in shape) (Plate 23.9). Central vein lies in the form of space at the centre of lobule. The cords of hepatocytes are arranged radially, radiating away from central vein. Adjacent lobules are separated by thin connective tissue septa.

Portal triad: It consists of

1. Branch of portal vein (irregular lumen, simple squamous epithelium).
2. Branch of hepatic artery (circular lumen, simple squamous epithelium).
3. Interlobular bile duct (circular lumen, simple cuboidal to columnar epithelium).

Liver sinusoids: They separate cords of hepatocytes and are lined by discontinuous endothelium, Kupffer cells and discontinuous basal lamina.

Hepatocytes are large polygonal cells with large central nucleus and granular eosinophilic cytoplasm.

Competency:

AN52.6 Describe the development and congenital anomalies of liver.

Development of Liver

Liver develops from the following sources (Flowchart 23.14):

1. From the caudal end of foregut, an endodermal hepatic bud arises during 3rd week of development. The bud elongates cranially. It gives rise to a small bud on its right side. This is called *pars cystica* and the main part is *pars hepatica*. Pars cystica forms the gallbladder and the cystic duct which drains into common hepatic duct (CHD). The epithelial cells of pars hepatica proliferate to form the *parenchyma*.

Plate 23.9: Histology of liver

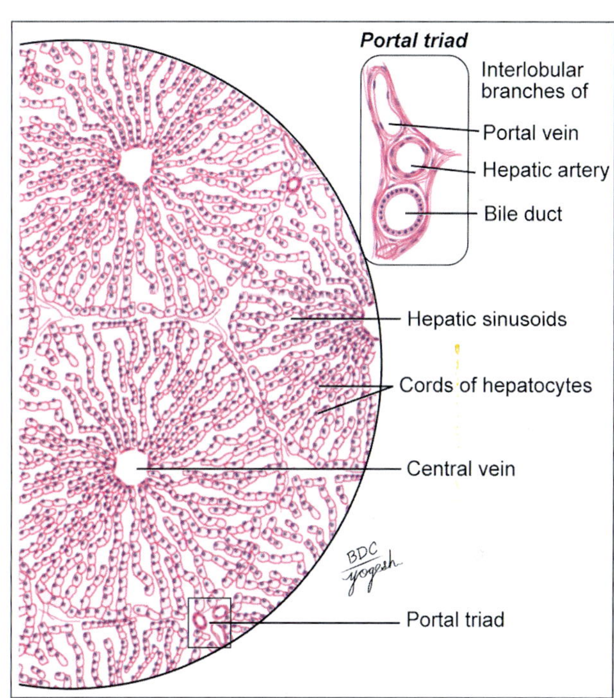

2. Septum transversum (mesoderm) forms connective tissue of liver including fibrous capsule, Kupffer's cells and blood vessels.
3. Vitelline and umbilical veins form sinusoids.
4. Ventral mesentery forms lesser omentum, falciform, coronary and triangular ligaments.

Competency:

AN47.6 Explain the anatomical basis of splenic notch, accessory spleens, Kehr's sign, different types of vagotomy, liver biopsy (site of needle puncture), referred pain in cholecystitis, obstructive jaundice, referred pain around umbilicus, radiating pain of kidney to groin and lymphatic spread in carcinoma stomach.

CLINICAL ANATOMY

- ***Palpation of liver:*** At the infrasternal angle, the liver is accessible for clinical examination (Fig. 23.28). The liver is *normally not palpable* because of softness

Flowchart 23.14: Development of liver

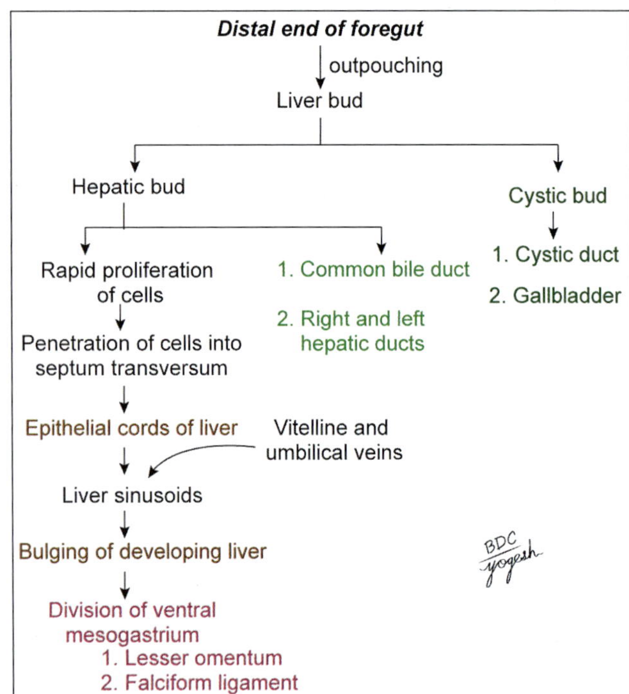

of liver and tone of rectus abdominis muscle. The liver enlarges downward toward the right iliac fossa (Fig. 23.29). The enlarged liver may become palpable.

- Inflammation of the liver is referred to as ***hepatitis***. It may be infective hepatitis or amoebic hepatitis.
- Under certain conditions, e.g. malnutrition, liver tissue undergoes fibrosis and shrinks. This is called ***cirrhosis*** of the liver.
- ***Liver biopsy:*** To avoid injury to the lung, during liver biopsy, the needle may be passed through 9th or 10th intercostal space at the midaxillary line during the forced expiration (Fig. 23.30). The needle traverses through skin, subcutaneous fat, intercostal muscles, pleural cavity and peritoneal cavity.
- Liver is the common site of metastatic tumours. Venous blood from GIT with primary tumour drains via portal vein into the liver.
- ***Pringle manoeuvre***: Bleeding from the liver can be stopped by compressing in hepatic artery and portal vein at the free margin of lesser omentum. These are major vessels supplying the liver.
- ***Liver transplantation:*** It can be done in patients with end stage liver disease. The implant of the graft requires an inferior caval anastomoses, followed by anastomosis of the portal vein. Finally, the arterial and biliary anastomoses are performed.
- ***Portal hypertension:*** It is an increased resistance to the flow of portal blood through the liver, causing increased blood pressure in portal vein. Cirrhosis or many other diseases produce portal hypertension. In portal hypertension, the portacaval anastomotic channels (veins) dilate. Liver cirrhosis causes 'caput medusae' at the umbilicus.
- ***Transjugular intraparenchymal portosystemic shunt*** (TIPS) for portal hypertension. In severe portal hypertension, balloon catheters are introduced from internal jugular vein → superior vena cava → inferior vena cava → hepatic veins → liver tissue → portal vein branch.
- ***Hepatic coma and liver failure:*** In cases of large destruction of liver cells (liver failure), liver cannot detoxify material; hence, waste products get accumulated in blood. It causes hepatic coma (unconsciousness) and even death.

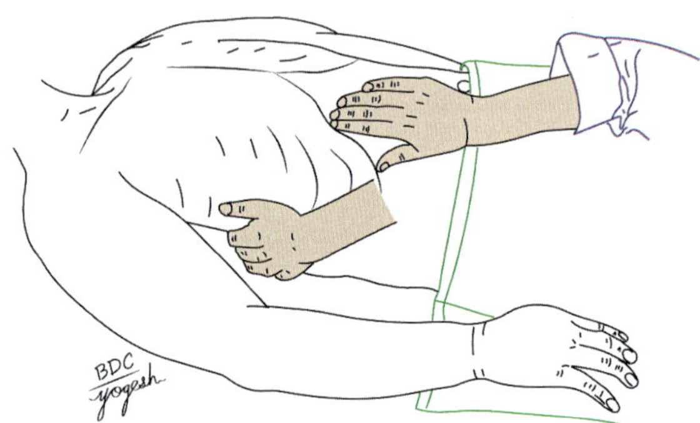

Fig. 23.28: Palpation of inferior margin of liver

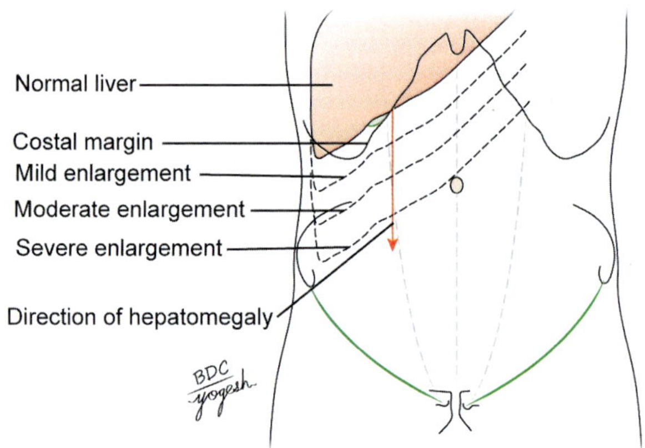

Fig. 23.29: Stages of liver enlargement

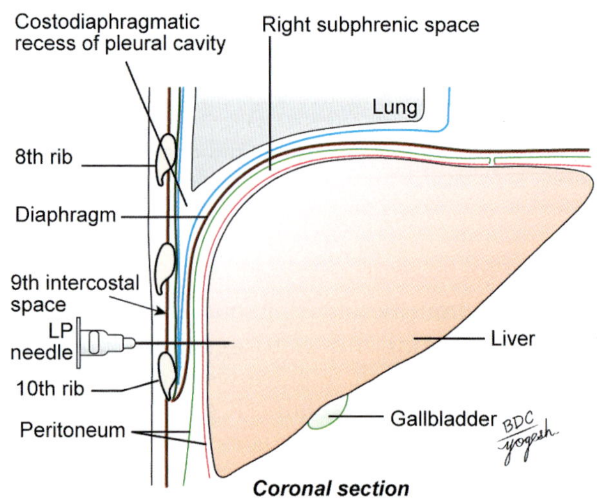

Fig. 23.30: Needle biopsy of the liver (coronal section passing through the midaxillary line)

DISSECTION

Pull the liver downwards and divide the anterior layers of the coronary and left triangular ligaments.

Identify the inferior vena cava between the liver and the diaphragm and separate the liver downwards from inferior vena cava. If the inferior vena cava happens to be deeply buried in the liver, divide it and remove a segment with the liver.

Expose the structures in the porta hepatis and follow them to their entry into the liver. Identify the viscera related to the inferior surface of the liver and see their demarcations on the liver.

Explore the extent of right and left pleural cavities and pericardium related to the superior and anterior surfaces of liver, though separated from it by the diaphragm.

Cut the structures close to the porta hepatis and separate all the peritoneal ligaments and folds of the liver.

Remove the liver from the body. Identify its various borders, surfaces and lobes.

Video 2.23 Glands of Abdominal Cavity: Liver, Gallbladder, Pancreas, Spleen.

Facts to Remember

- Spleen is a collection of lymphoid tissue with a lot of blood vessels.
- In case of rupture of spleen, it may be removed. Before cutting the lienorenal ligament, the tail of pancreas and splenic vessels need to be identified and not be injured.
- Spleen moves up and down with respiration. It is mesodermal in origin.
- Pancreas mainly develops from dorsal pancreatic bud. Only a part of head and its uncinate process develop from the ventral pancreatic bud.
- Islets of Langerhans are maximum in tail of a pancreas.
- Portal vein is formed by the union of splenic and superior mesenteric veins behind the neck of pancreas.
- Liver is the largest gland of the body. Liver is kept in position by the upper and lower groups hepatic veins which drain into the inferior vena cava.
- The bare area of liver is one of the sites of portosystemic anastomoses.
- There are 8 hepatic segments.
- Liver enlarges downwards right iliac fossa.
- The spleen also enlarges downwards and obliquely towards right iliac fossa. It is prevented from descending to left side by phrenicocolic ligament.

BDC's Anatomy *e*-book

1. Splenic microcirculation
2. Molecular regulation of development of pancreas
3. Molecular regulation of development of liver
4. Factors keeping the liver in position
5. Further reading
6. Viva voce questions

Chapter

24

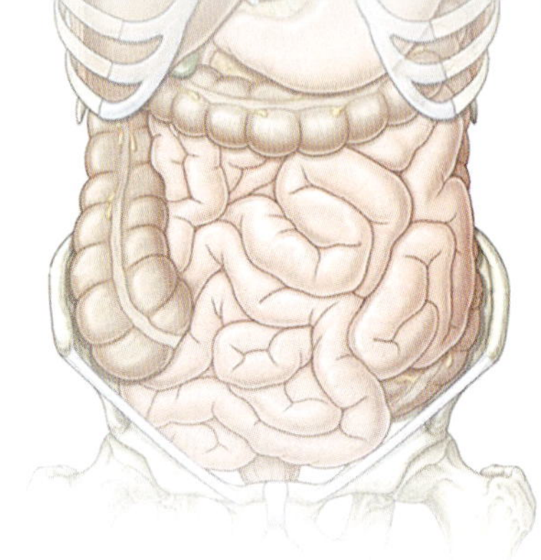

Kidney and Ureter

KIDNEY

Kidneys are a pair of excretory organs situated on the posterior abdominal wall, one on each side of the vertebral column, behind the peritoneum. They remove waste products of metabolism and excess water and salts from the blood and maintain its pH.

Synonyms

The kidneys are also called *renes* from which we have the derivative *renal*; and *nephros* from which we have the terms *nephron, nephritis*, etc.

Functions of Kidney

1. Kidney helps in purification of blood by ultrafiltration and removal of metabolic waste products.
2. Kidney conserves body fluid and electrolytes and maintains their balance.
3. Kidney also functions as an endocrine organ by production of the following:
   a. *Erythropoietin* helps in the formation of RBCs.
   b. *Renin* converts angiotensinogen to angiotensin, which helps in blood pressure regulation.
   c. *Vitamin D3*: Kidney enzyme 1-hydroxylase converts 25-hydroxy vitamin D3 (produced in liver) to active 1,25 dihydroxy vitamin D3.

Shape, Size, Weight

The kidneys are bean-shaped, reddish-brown organs.

Size

Length: 11 cm (left kidney is 1.5 cm longer than the right)
Breadth: 6 cm
Anteroposterior (thickness) diameter: 3 cm
Weight: 150 g in male and 135 g in female.

In the newborn, the kidney is lobulated, but in adults, its surface is smooth due to fusion of lobules.

In the foetus, the kidney is lobulated and is made up of about 12 lobules. After birth, the lobules gradually fuse, so that in adults the kidney is uniformly smooth. However, the evidence of foetal lobulation may persist.

Location

1. The kidneys occupy the epigastric, hypochondriac, lumbar and umbilical regions (Fig. 24.1, Flowchart 24.1).
2. *Vertebral level*: Kidneys lie opposite to T12 to L3 vertebrae (Fig. 24.2). The right kidney is slightly lower than the left, and the left kidney is a little nearer to the median plane than the right.
3. The transpyloric plane passes through the upper part of the hilus of the right kidney and through the lower part of the hilus of the left kidney.

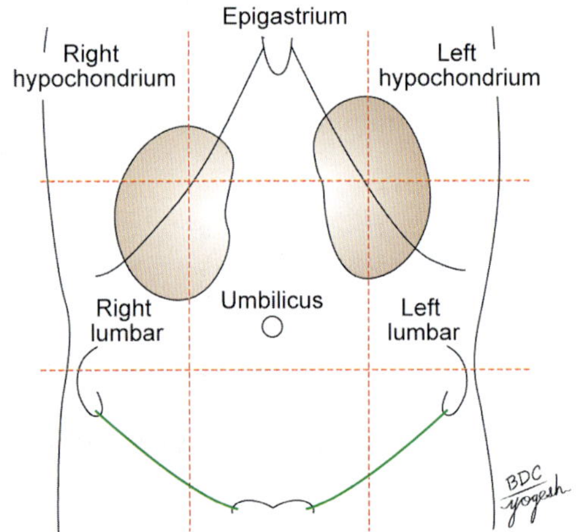

Fig. 24.1: Location of the kidneys

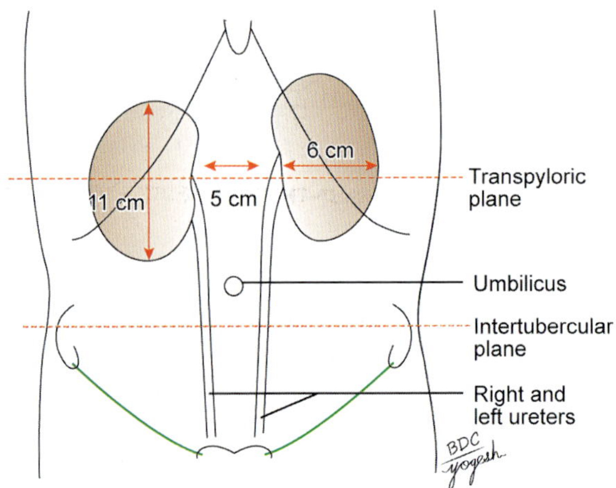

Fig. 24.2: Position of kidneys from anterior aspect

EXTERNAL FEATURES

Each kidney is bean-shaped. It has (Plate 24.1, Fig. 24.3):

1. *Two poles*: Superior and inferior
2. *Two borders*: Medial and lateral
3. *Two surfaces*: Anterior and posterior and
4. Hilum.

Poles

1. The *superior* or *upper pole* is broad and is in close contact with the corresponding suprarenal gland.
2. The *inferior* or *lower pole* is pointed.

Surfaces

1. The *anterior surface* is said to be irregular.
2. The *posterior surface* flat.

Borders

1. The *lateral border* is convex.
2. The *medial border* is concave. Its middle part shows a depression, the hilus or hilum.

Plate 24.1: Kidneys: External features

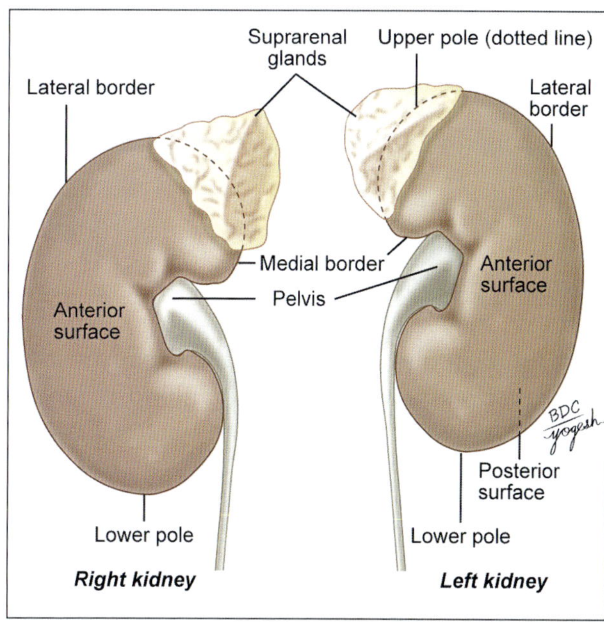

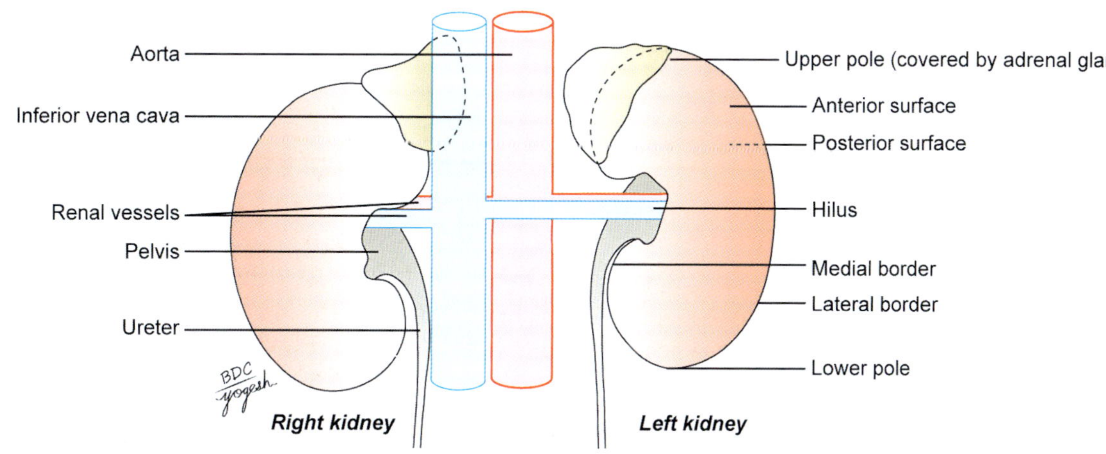

Fig. 24.3: External features of kidneys

Flowchart 24.1: Kidney: Parts, relations and coverings

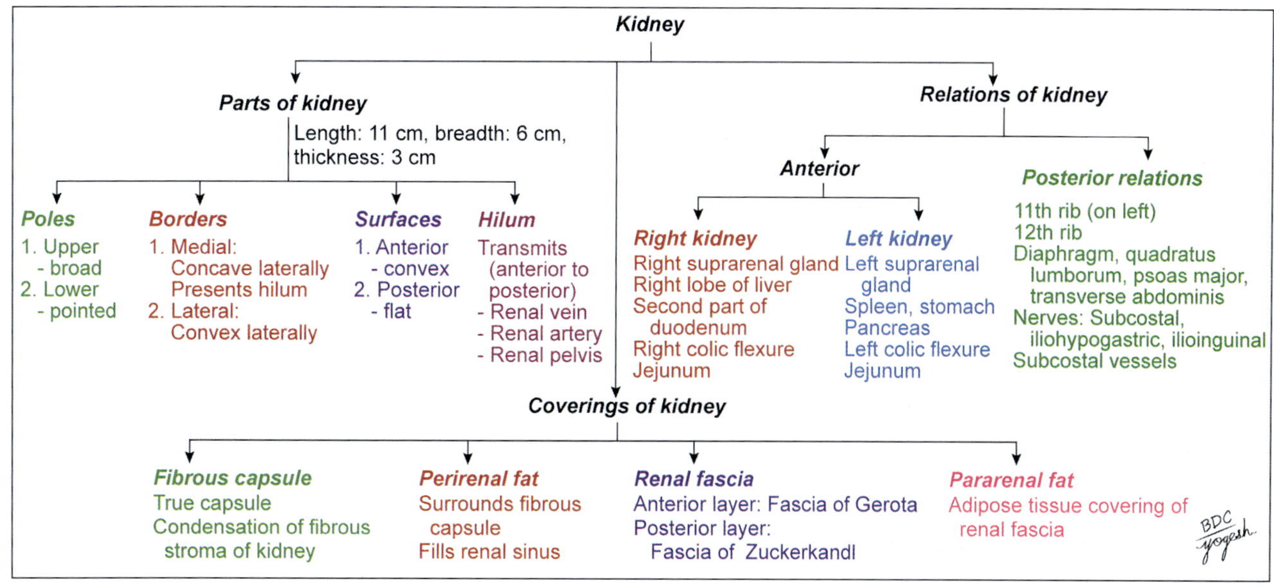

Hilum

The following structures are seen in the hilum from anterior side to posterior side:

1. Renal vein
2. Renal artery
3. Renal pelvis, which is the expanded upper end of the ureter.

Anatomical Position and Side Determination

Anatomical Position

Hold the kidney in such a way

1. Broad upper pole faces upward and slightly medially.
2. Convex, irregular surface faces anteriorly, and flat posterior surface faces posteriorly.
3. Concave border with hilum faces medially and directed to the opposite side of the kidney. For example, hilum of the right kidney is directed to the left.

Side Determination

For the side determination, observe the structures at hilum of kidney. These are arranged anterior to posterior as follows (Fig. 24.4):

1. Renal **v**ein: Thin-walled structure, may contain blood clots
2. Renal **a**rtery: Thick-walled, rounded structure
3. Renal **p**elvis: Dilated above, narrow downward and continues as ureter.
4. Sometimes a branch of renal artery passes behind the renal pelvis to enter the hilum.

[*Mnemonics*: ***VAP***: Vein – artery – pelvis]

Note: It is often difficult to recognize the anterior and posterior aspects of the kidney by looking at the surfaces. The proper way to do this is to examine the structures present in the hilum. As the pelvis is continuous inferiorly with the ureter, the superior and inferior poles of the kidney can also be distinguished by examining the hilum. Commonly, one of the branches of the renal artery enters the hilus behind the renal pelvis, and a tributary of the renal vein may be found in the same plane.

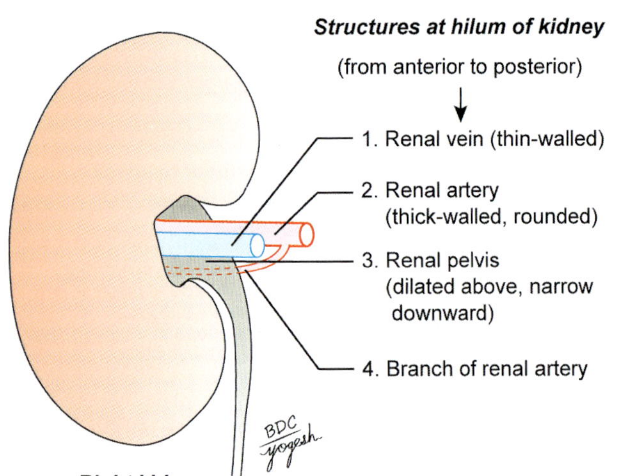

Fig. 24.4: Relationship of structures passing through the hilum of kidney

Axes of Kidney

- *Long axis*: It is directed downward and laterally so that the upper pole of kidney is nearer to the midline.
- *Transverse axis*: It is directed laterally and backward because the kidney rests on slopping muscles of posterior abdominal wall adjacent to vertebral bodies.

Movements during Respiration

Kidneys move vertically about 2.5 cm with respiration as their upper part of posterior surface is related to the diaphragm.

RELATIONS OF THE KIDNEYS

Peritoneal Relations

The kidney is a retroperitoneal organ; it is covered anteriorly by parietal peritoneum only at the following areas:

- *For right kidney*: Hepatic and jejunal areas.
- *For left kidney*: Gastric, splenic and jejunal areas.

Note: For right kidney, suprarenal gland, duodenum and colon come in direct contact, whereas for left kidney, left suprarenal gland, colon and pancreas come in indirect contact.

Anterior Relations

(Figs 24.5 and 24.6, Flowchart 24.1)

Anterior Relations of Right Kidney

The following structures are related anteriorly to the right kidney:

1. Right suprarenal gland
2. Right lobe of liver
3. Second part of duodenum
4. Right colic (hepatic) flexure
5. Jejunum.

Anterior Relations of Left Kidney

The following structures are related anteriorly to the left kidney:

1. Left suprarenal gland
2. Spleen
3. Stomach
4. Pancreas
5. Left colic (splenic) flexure
6. Jejunum.

Posterior Relations of Kidneys

The posterior relations of kidneys are as follows (Plate 24.2, Fig. 24.7):

1. 11th rib: Only to the left kidney
2. 12th rib
3. Muscles: Diaphragm, quadratus lumborum, psoas major and transverse abdominis
4. Nerves emerging from lateral border of psoas major (from above downward): Subcostal (T12), iliohypogastric (L1), ilioinguinal (L1) nerves.
5. Subcostal vessels.

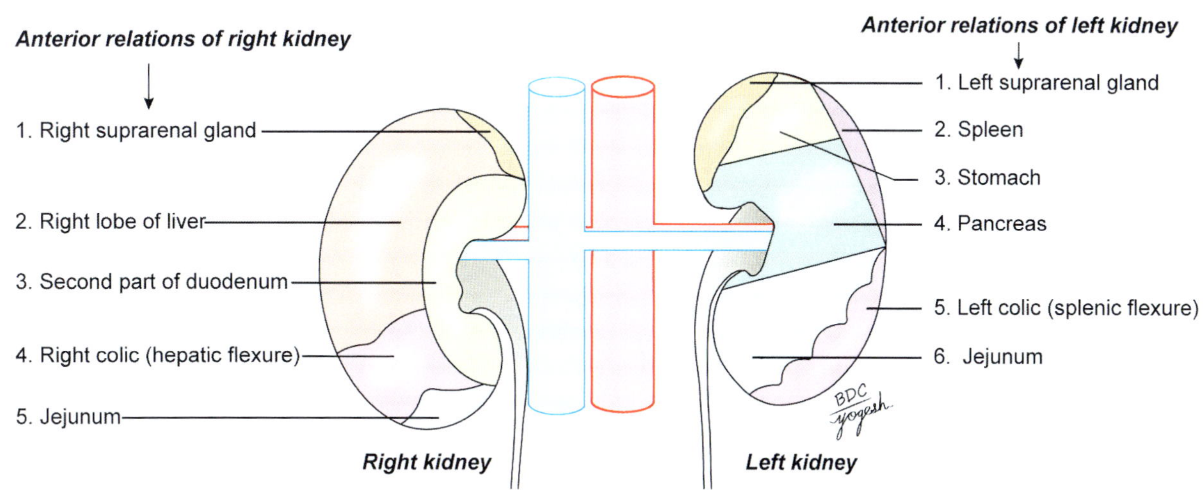

Fig. 24.5: Anterior relations of the kidneys. Areas covered by peritoneum are shaded

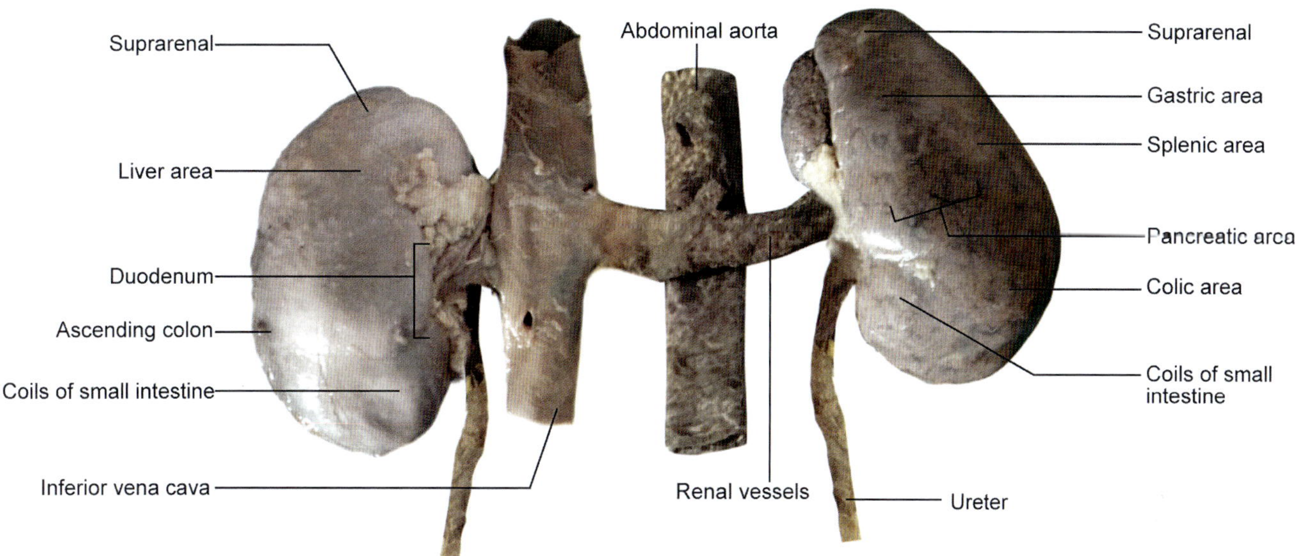

Fig. 24.6: Anterior relations of the kidneys

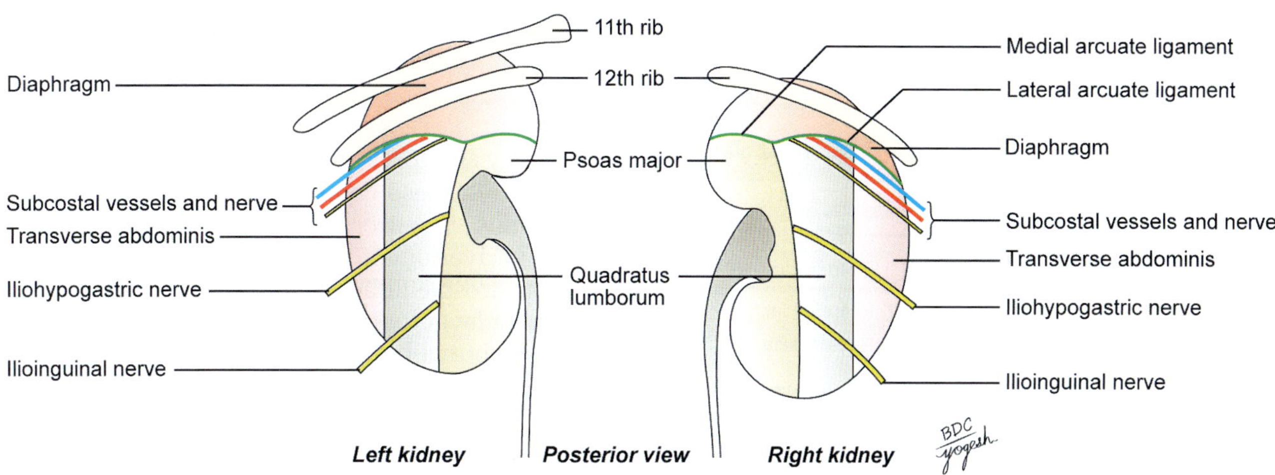

Fig. 24.7: Posterior relations of the left kidney and right kidney

Plate 24.2: Posterior relations and blood supply of kidneys

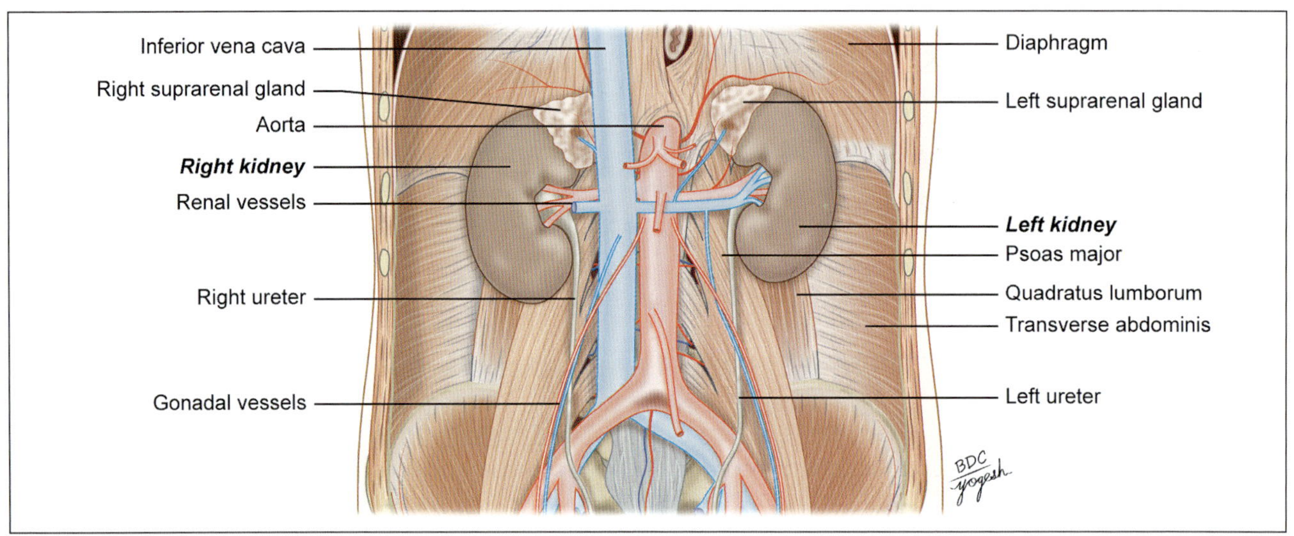

CAPSULES OR COVERINGS OF KIDNEY

From within outward, kidney is surrounded by four layers or coverings (Figs 24.8 and 22.9, Flowchart 24.3)

1. Fibrous capsule
2. Perirenal (perinephric) fat
3. Renal fascia
4. Pararenal fat.

1. *Fibrous capsule*: This is a thin membrane which closely invests the kidney and lines the renal sinus. Normally, it can be easily stripped off from the kidney (Figs 24.8 and 24.9).

2. *Perirenal or perinephric fat*: This is a layer of adipose tissue lying outside the fibrous capsule. It is thickest at the borders of the kidney and fills up the extra space in the renal sinus.

3. *Renal fascia*: The renal fascia is a dense, elastic connective tissue sheath that covers the kidney, suprarenal gland and perirenal fat. It consists of two layers:

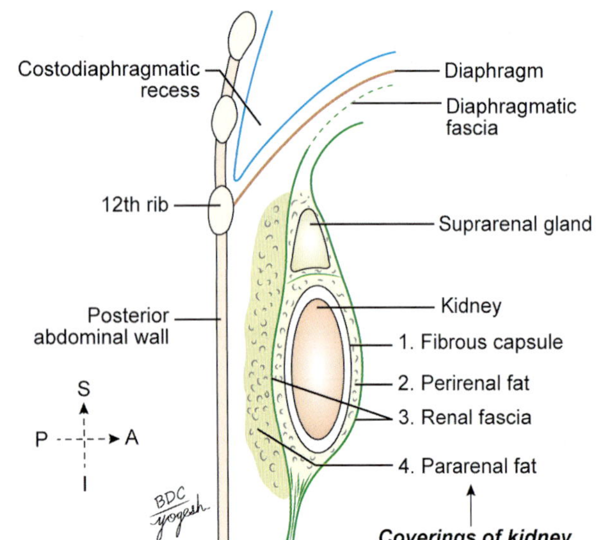

Fig. 24.8: Vertical section showing coverings of the kidney

Anterior layer or *fascia of Gerota* and posterior layer or *fascia of Zuckerkendl.*

4. *Pararenal or paranephric body* (*Fat*): It consists of a variable amount of fat lying outside the renal fascia. It is more abundant posteriorly and towards the lower pole of the kidney. It fills up the paravertebral gutter and forms a cushion for the kidney.

Renal Fascia

The renal fascia is a dense, elastic connective tissue sheath that covers the kidney, suprarenal gland and perirenal fat. It consists of two layers (Figs 24.8 and 24.9):

1. Anterior layer or fascia of Gerota.
2. Posterior layer or fascia of Zuckerkendl.

Attachments of Renal Fascia

(*Reference: Gray's Anatomy, 42nd edition*)

- *Laterally:* Both the layers fuse and continue behind the colon with parietal peritoneum.
- *Medially*

  Anterior layer covers the kidney and renal vessels and continues with similar layer of opposite renal fascia after crossing aorta and inferior vena cava. The *posterior layer* is attached to the bodies of lumbar vertebrae.

  Posteriorly: *Posterior layer* covers the posterior surface of kidney and fuses with fascia covering psoas major.
- *Superiorly:* These layers of fascia do not fuse with each other. Superiorly, the anterior layer fuses with inferior layer of coronary ligament on the right and with gastrosplenic ligament on the left. Superiorly, the posterior layer fuses with fascia covering psoas major and quadratus lumborum and with inferior phrenic fascia.
- *Inferiorly*

  Recent concept: Inferiorly, both the layers fuse to form a single multilaminar fascia and loosely attached to parietal peritoneum.

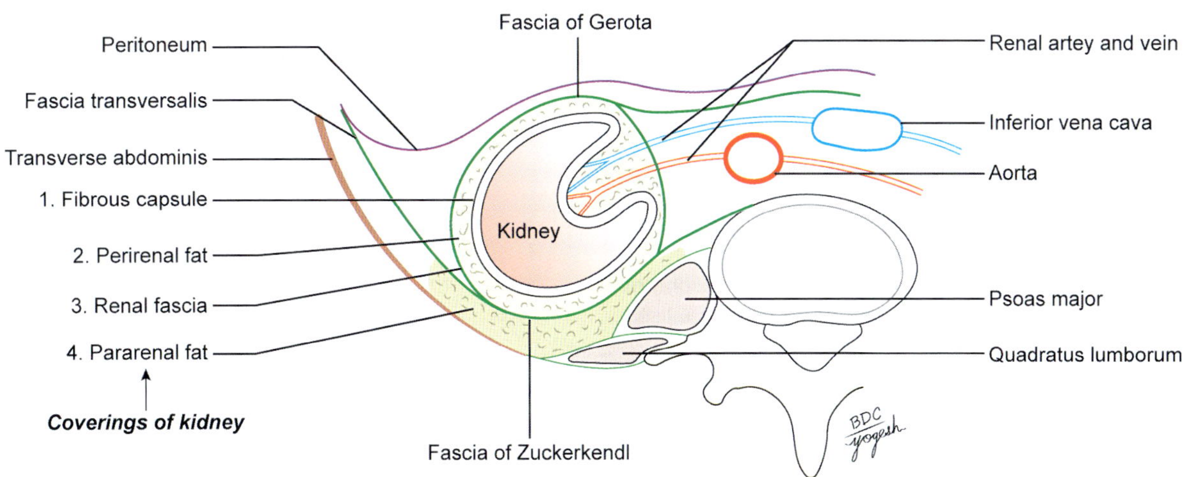

Fig. 24.9: Transverse section through the lumbar region showing the capsules of the kidney

- *Superiorly*, the peritoneal space is open and is continuous with connective tissue at bare area of liver on the right and subdiaphragmatic connective tissue on the left.

Note: There are different views about existence and attachments of renal fascia. Here, a simplified description is given to avoid the information overload. According to previous view, these two fasciae fused laterally to form lateral conal fascia which continued anterolaterally behind colon to blend with parietal peritoneum.

MACROSCOPIC STRUCTURE OF KIDNEY

The longitudinal section of the kidney on naked eye examination shows three zones as follows (Figs 24.10 and 24.11):

1. *Renal cortex*: It is a reddish-brown outer zone of kidney. It has two parts:
   a. *Cortical arches* or cortical lobules form a cap over the bases of pyramids of renal medulla.
   b. *Renal columns* are extensions of renal cortex in between renal pyramids.
2. *Renal medulla*: It is pale inner zone that consists of 5–10 conical masses called *renal pyramids*. Each renal pyramid has peripheral *base* and *apex*. Their *apices* converge to the renal sinus. The papillae are the projecting apices of renal pyramids into the minor calyces.
3. *Renal sinus*: It is a cavity of kidney that is continuous with the hilum of the kidney. It contains:
   a. The renal pelvis, minor and major calyces
   b. Renal vessels, lymphatics and nerves
   c. Fat
4. *Renal pelvis* is a funnel-shaped dilatation. It passes downward and medially through the hilum of kidney and continuous as the ureter at the lower pole of the kidney. The capacity of renal pelvis is 5–7 ml. It shows:
   a. *Major calyces*: The renal pelvis divides into two to three major calyces (cavities) (*kalyx* = cup of a flower).

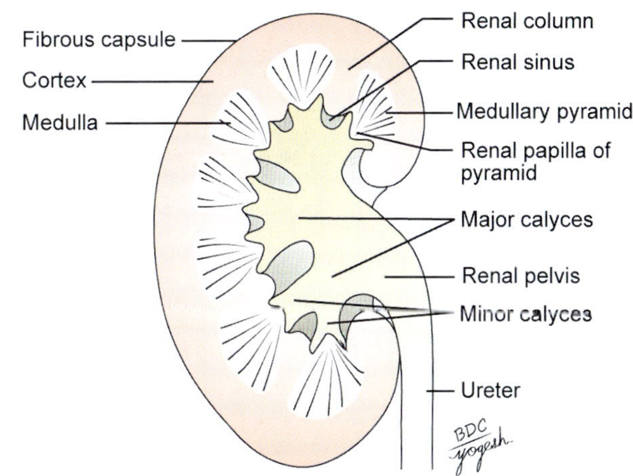

Fig. 24.10: A coronal section through the kidney showing the naked eye structure

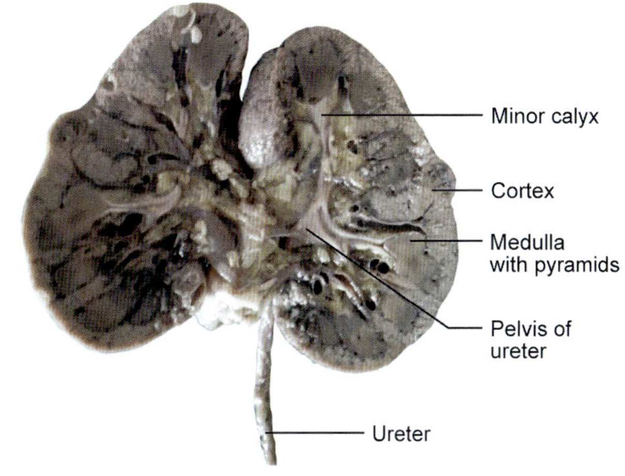

Fig. 24.11: Internal structure of kidney seen on a dissected specimen

   b. *Minor calyces* are 7–13 small cavities. They unite to form major calyces. The dilated outer part of minor calyces that receives renal papillae.
5. *Medullary rays of Ferrin* are the striations of renal cortex that are extensions of medulla into the cortex. They contain straight tubules and collecting ducts.

6. *Cortical labyrinth* is region of cortex between adjacent medullary rays.
7. *Area cribrosa* is a perforated area at the tip of each renal papilla because of collecting duct openings.

Note: *Kidney lobe*: Each pyramid with the surrounding cortical tissue forms a lobe of kidney. Each kidney contains 8–18 lobes. Lobulation is a prominent feature of foetal kidneys, but in adult kidneys, lobes are indistinct.

Kidney lobule: Similar to secretory unit of exocrine glands, collecting ducts of medullary ray and surrounding cortical tissue constitute kidney lobule.

Competency:

AN52.2 Describe and identify the microanatomical features of kidney.

HISTOLOGY OF KIDNEY

The kidney is covered by a connective tissue capsule. It has outer cortex and inner medulla. Kidney shows presence of renal corpuscles and renal tubules (Plate 24.3, Fig. 24.12a).

Renal corpuscle consists of the following:

a. Glomerulus: Tuft of capillaries
b. Bowman's capsule: It has outer parietal layer (simple squamous epithelium) and inner visceral layer (made up of podocytes). Bowman's space lies between visceral and parietal layers (urinary space).

Renal tubules consist of the following:

a. *Proximal convoluted tubules* have star-shaped indistinct lumen lined with simple cuboidal epithelium with prominent brush border.
b. Proximal straight tubule is lined with simple cuboidal epithelium and has less developed microvilli.
c. Loop of Henle:
   i. Thin segment of loop of Henle is lined with simple squamous epithelium.
   ii. Thick segment of loop of Henle is lined with cuboidal epithelium.
d. Distal convoluted tubules have regular oval/round lumen lined by simple cuboidal epithelium (no brush border).

- Collecting tubules and ducts: DCT continues as collecting tubules and later as ducts that finally open on the surface of renal pyramids. The collecting tubules and ducts are lined by simple cuboidal to columnar epithelium.
- Cortex and medulla show numerous sections of blood vessels.

Juxtaglomerular Apparatus

The juxtaglomerular apparatus is a group of specialized cells near the vascular pole of renal corpuscle. It consists of the following cells (Flowchart 24.2, Fig. 24.12b):

1. *Juxtaglomerular cells* are modified smooth muscle cells of wall of afferent arteriole. They secrete renin.

Plate 24.3: Histology of the kidney

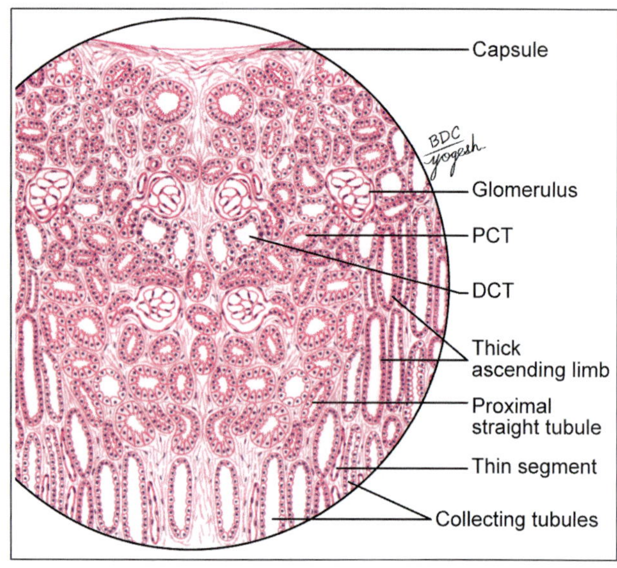

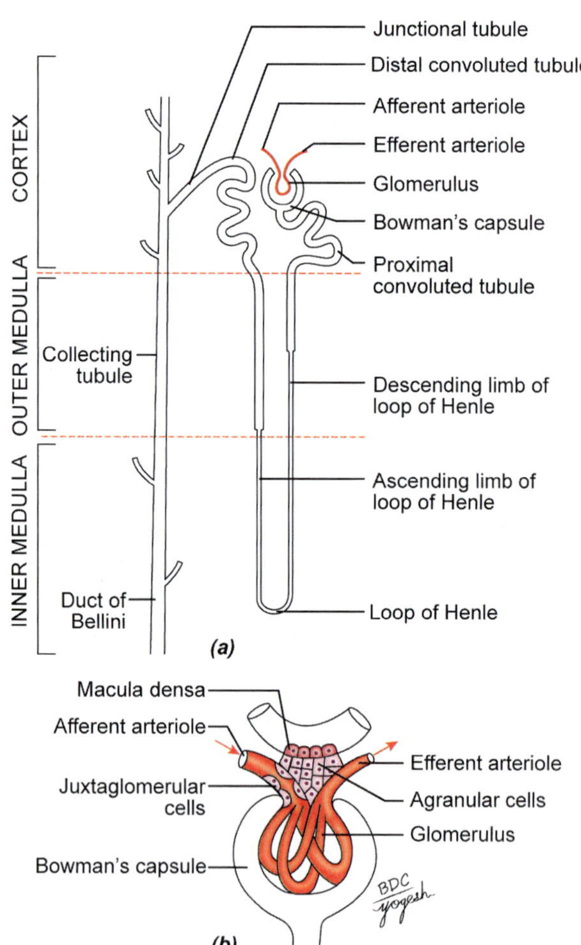

Figs 24.12a and b: (a) Placement of the uriniferous tubule/nephron in various zones of kidney and (b) renal corpuscle with juxtaglomerular apparatus

2. *Macula densa* are specialized cells of distal convoluted tubules that lie adjacent to afferent and efferent arteriole. They are narrow, columnar and crowded cells (other cells of DCT are cuboidal). The nuclei of

Flowchart 24.2: Juxtaglomerular apparatus

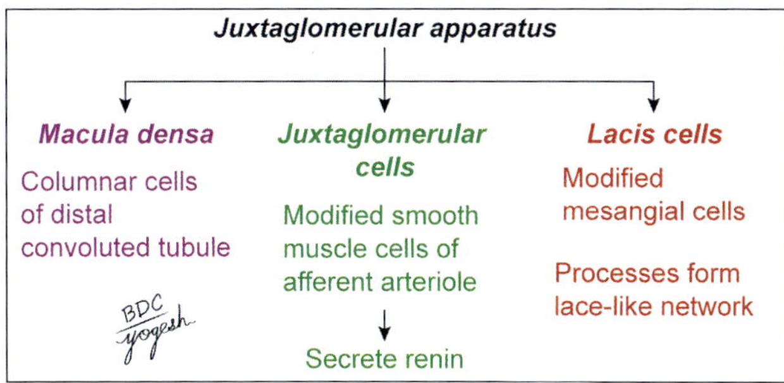

these cells are crowded and overlapping; hence, these cells are called macula densa.

3. *Lacis cells or extraglomerular mesangial cells* are the modified mesangial cells near the juxtaglomerular cells. These cells show receptors for angiotensin II and probably regulate glomerular filtration rate.

BLOOD SUPPLY, LYMPHATIC DRAINAGE AND INNERVATION

Blood Supply of Kidney

Each kidney is supplied by ***renal artery*** arising from abdominal aorta. Usually, there is a single renal artery for each kidney. In 30% individuals, an accessory renal artery is present.

Each kidney is drained by ***renal vein*** into the inferior vena cava. Left renal vein is longer. It crosses anterior to the aorta and also receives blood from left gonadal vein.

Lymphatic Drainage

The lymphatics of the kidney drain into the lateral aortic nodes located at the level of origin of the renal arteries (L2).

Nerve Supply

The kidney is supplied by the renal plexus, an off shoot of the coeliac plexus. It contains sympathetic (T10–L1) fibres which are chiefly vasomotor. The afferent nerves of the kidney belong to segments T10 to T12.

Microvasculature of Kidney

1. Each kidney is supplied by *renal artery*. It divides to form *lobar* and then *interlobar arteries* (Fig. 24.13, Flowchart 24.3). Interlobar artery divides to form *arcuate artery* along the base of pyramids.
2. The arcuate arteries form *interlobular arteries* that traverse cortex towards capsule. Interlobular arteries give *afferent arterioles*.
3. The afferent arterioles give rise to a network of *glomerular capillaries* that unite to form *efferent arteriole*.
4. The efferent arterioles form second set of capillaries called *peritubular capillary plexus*.
5. Efferent arterioles form the juxtamedullary glomeruli that form vasa recta and help in ***countercurrent exchange system***.
6. Peritubular capillaries in cortex drain into *interlobular vein*, later into *arcuate veins*, *interlobar veins*, and finally *renal veins*. Capsule drains into *stellate veins* and finally into *interlobar veins*.
7. ***Renal lobe*** is a portion of a kidney consisting of a renal pyramid and the renal cortex above it. In humans, there are 8 to 18 renal lobes.

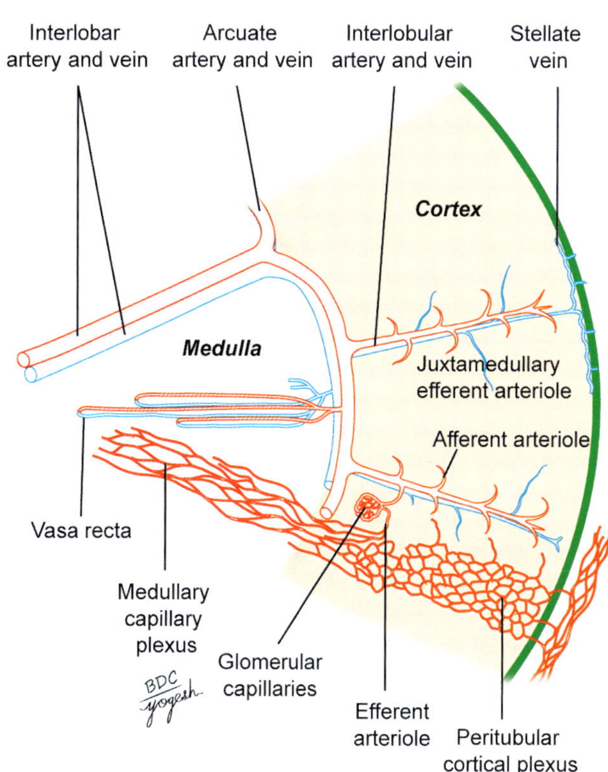

Fig. 24.13: Arrangement of the arteries in the kidney

Flowchart 24.3: Blood supply of kidney

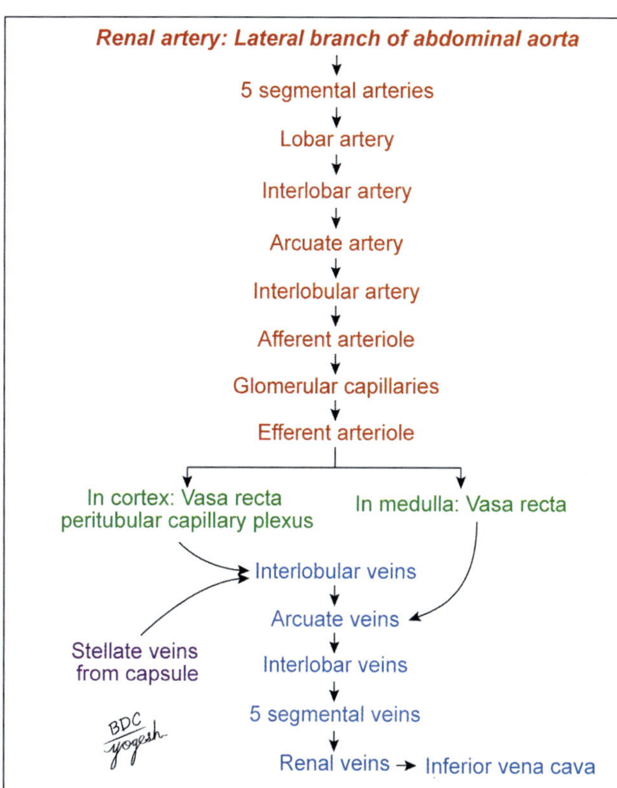

VASCULAR SEGMENTS OF KIDNEY

The vascular segment of the kidney is the area of the kidney supplied by the segmental branch of the renal artery (Figs 24.14a to d and 24.12b and 24.13). There are five arterial segments in each kidney as follows (*Reference*: *Gray's Anatomy*, 42nd edn.):

1. *Apical segment*: It occupies the anteromedial region of the superior pole.
2. *Superior segment*: It includes the rest of the superior pole and the middle part of anterosuperior region.
3. *Inferior segment*: It occupies the lower pole.
4. *Middle segment*: It lies between the superior and inferior segments.
5. *Posterior segment*: It includes the whole posterior area between the apical and inferior segments.

Each vascular segment is supplied by virtual end arteries. Intrarenal veins do not follow segmental organization and anastomose freely.

Bloodless line of Brödel: It is on the posterior aspect of the kidney at the junction of medial two-thirds and lateral one-third (Fig. 24.15). It indicates a relatively avascular longitudinal zone along the convex renal border. It is considered the most suitable site for surgical incision.

Note: The knowledge of segmental anatomy of kidney is useful for partial nephrectomy for renal cell cancers. It is also useful for nephrolithotomy (to remove the renal stones).

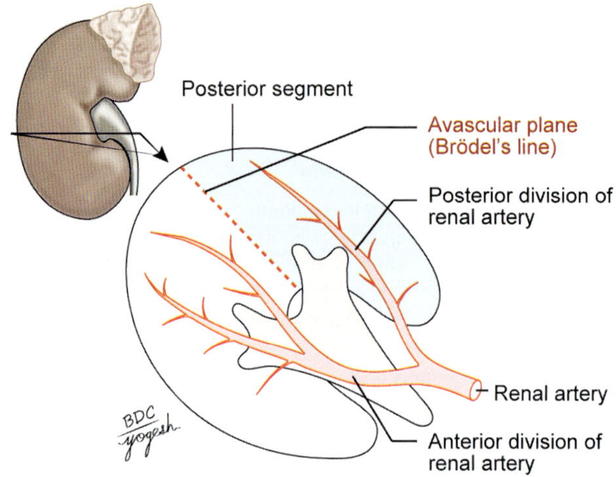

Fig. 24.15: Schematic diagram showing avascular plane of the kidney (Brödel's line)

DISSECTION

Remove the fat and fascia from the anterior surface of left and right kidneys and suprarenal glands. Find left suprarenal vein and left testicular or ovarian vein and trace both to left renal vein. Follow this vein from the left kidney to inferior vena cava and note its tributaries. Displace the vein and expose left renal artery, follow its branches to the left suprarenal gland and ureter. Follow the ureter in abdomen.

Identify the structures related to the anterior surface of both the kidneys. Turn the left kidney medially to expose its posterior surface and note the relation of its vessels and the ureter. Identify the muscles, vessels and nerves which are posterior to the kidneys.

Carry out the same dissection on the right side. Note that the right testicular or ovarian and suprarenal veins drain directly into the inferior vena cava.

Cut through the convex border of the kidney till the hilus. Look at its interior. Identify the cortex, pyramids and calyces.

Follow the ureters in the renal pelvis, in the abdomen, in the pelvic cavity and finally through the wall of urinary bladder.

EXPOSURE OF THE KIDNEY FROM BEHIND

In exposing the kidney from behind, the following layers have to be reflected one by one (Fig. 24.16).

1. Skin
2. Superficial fascia
3. Posterior layer of thoracolumbar (lumbar) fascia with latissimus dorsi and serratus posterior inferior

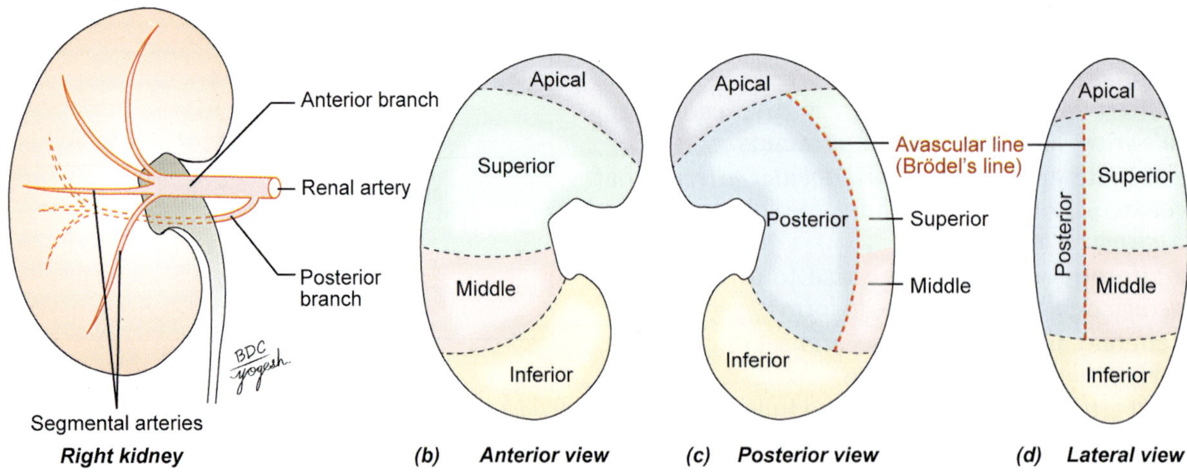

Figs 24.14a to d: Vascular segments of the kidney as seen in a sagittal section: (a) Branches of the renal artery and (b to d) the segments as seen from anterior, lateral and posterior aspects of the kidney, respectively

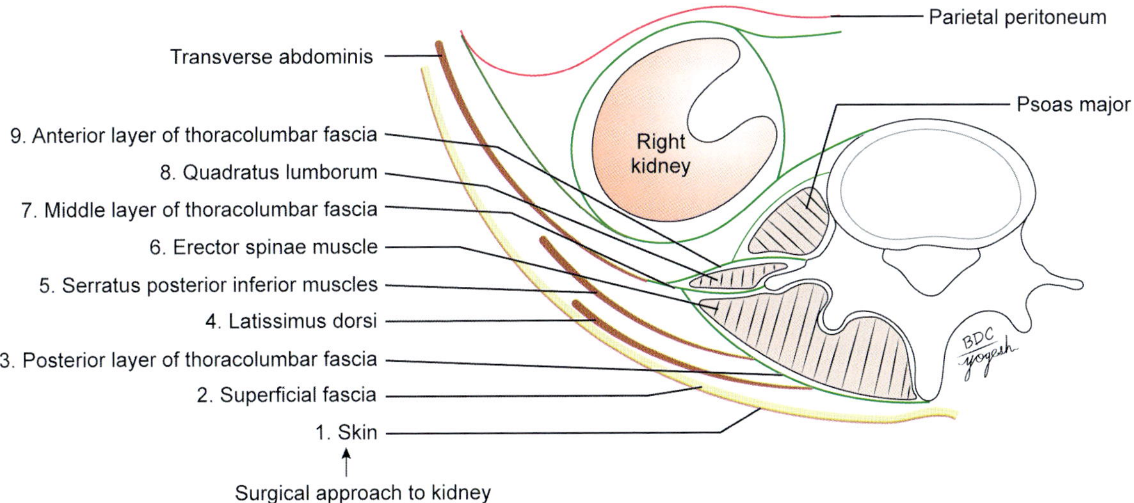

Fig. 24.16: Transverse section through the upper lumbar region showing the layers of thoracolumbar fascia encountered during exposure of the kidney from behind

4. Erector spinae, which can be removed for convenience
5. Middle layer of thoracolumbar fascia
6. Quadratus lumborum
7. Anterior layer of thoracolumbar fascia in which the related nerves are embedded.

CLINICAL ANATOMY

- ***Renal pain***: Pain sensation from kidney is carried by sympathetic fibres to T10–L1 spinal segment. It is referred to loin, anterior abdominal wall, and it radiates down into the groin. It ranges from dull aching to severe spasmodic pain. It occurs due to stretching of renal capsule and spasm of smooth muscles of the wall of renal pelvis.
- ***Palpation of kidney***: Kidney is palpated bimanually; that is, with one hand placed anteriorly and one hand behind the flank in supine position of patient (Fig. 24.17). Normal kidney is not palpable except in very thin person and position children.
- ***Renal angle***: The angle between the lower border of the 12th rib and the outer border of the erector spinae is known as the *renal angle*. It overlies the lower part of the kidney. Tenderness in the kidney is elicited by applying pressure over this angle, with the thumb (Fig. 24.18).
- On deep inspiration, the kidney moves downward, and its lower pole becomes palpable in
  1. thin persons
  2. children
  3. enlarged kidney
- ***Floating kidney***: It is the hypermobility of the kidney. If there is decrease in perinephric fat, the mobility of the kidney increases. It can be moved up and down within the renal fascia. Normally, kidney moves 2.5 cm vertically with respiration.
- ***Trauma to the kidney***: Usually, kidneys are protected from trauma due to their deep locations. Sometimes penetrating from trauma injuries may damage kidney that may cause severe blood loss.
- One common congenital condition of kidney is ***polycystic kidney*** which leads to hypertension (Fig. 24.19).

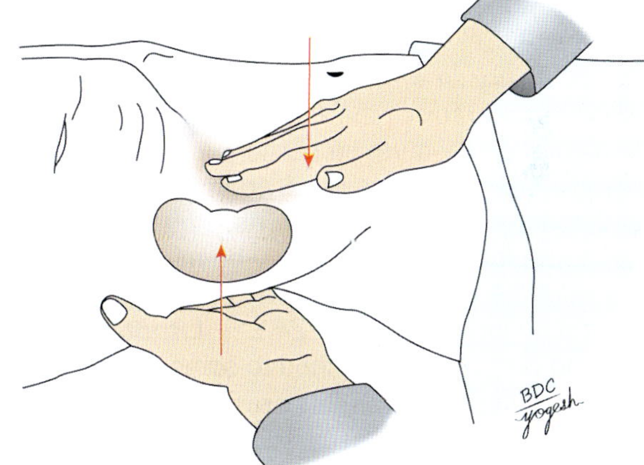

Fig. 24.17: Bimanual palpation of the kidney

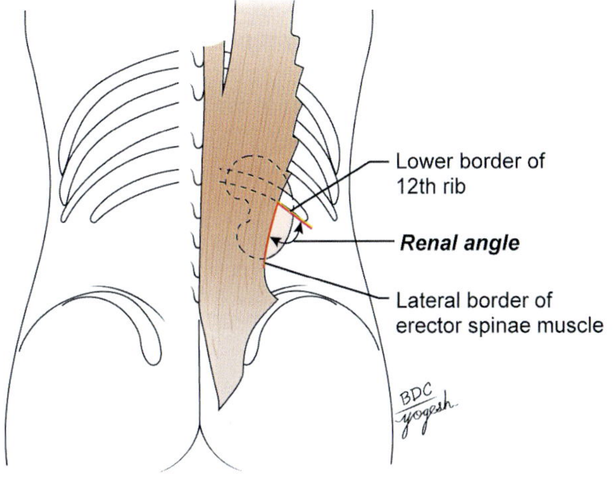

Fig. 24.18: Renal angle

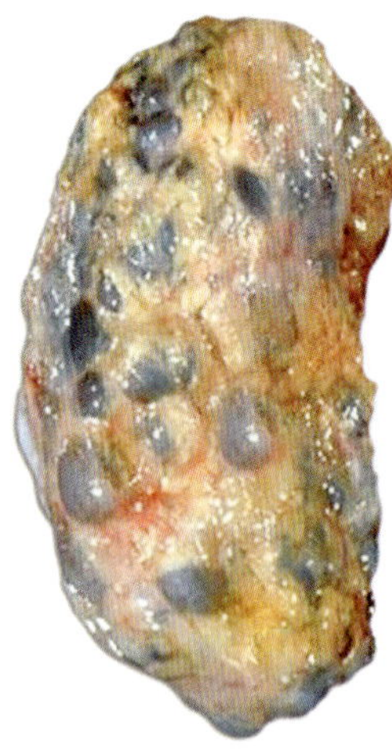

Fig. 24.19: Polycystic kidney

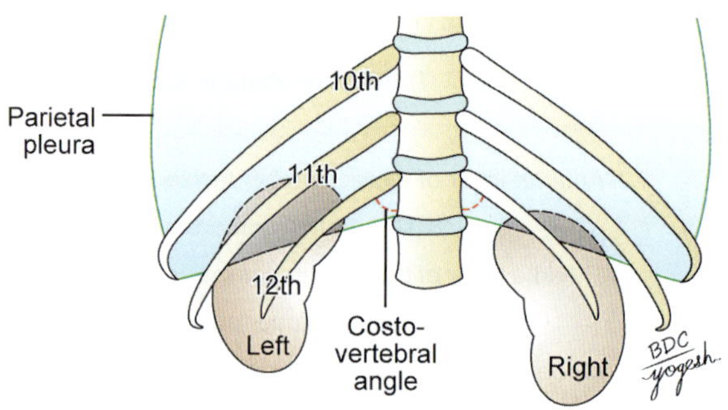

Fig. 24.21: Relation of twelfth rib to pleural cavity and kidney

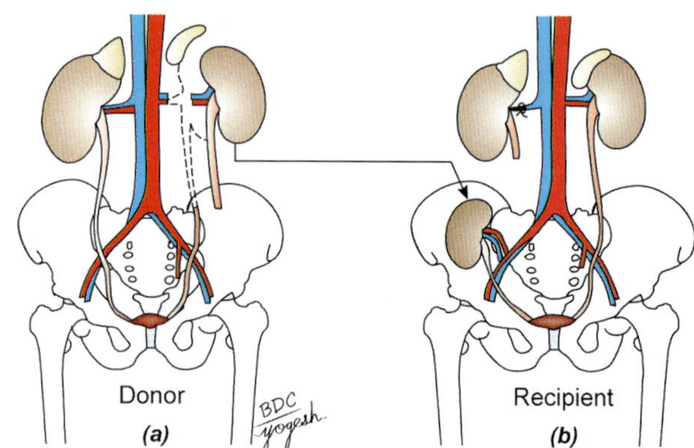

Figs 24.22a and b: (a) Donor's left kidney transplanted and (b) recipient's right kidney

- ***Renal stones***: Renal pelvis is a common site for renal stones. Staghorn calculus is a big venal calculus that obtains characteristic shape of renal pelvis and calyces. Kidneys stone lies on the body of vertebra (Fig. 24.20). Gallstones lie anterior to body of vertebra.
- ***Pleural injury in kidney surgery***: In the posterior surgical exposures of the kidney, *danger of opening the pleural cavity* must be borne in mind. The lower border of the pleura lies in between the 12th rib and the diaphragm. When the 12th rib is absent or is too short to be felt, the 11th rib may be mistaken for the 12th, and the chances of opening the pleural cavity are greatly increased (Fig. 24.21). ***Lithotripsy*** has replaced conventional method to some degree.
- ***Kidney transplantation***: In chronic renal failure and end-stage kidney diseases, kidney transplantation can be performed.

  Selection of donor's kidney: The left kidney is preferred for donation as the left renal vein is longer (right renal vein is short) (Fig. 24.22).

  Procedure: Donated kidney is placed retroperitoneally in the iliac fossa. The renal artery is connected with internal iliac artery and renal vein with external iliac vein. Ureter is fixed into the urinary bladder.
- ***Dialysis***: It is done to purify the blood and clear the waste products and excess water in case of renal failure (Fig. 24.23). There are two methods of dialysis – haemodialysis and peritoneal dialysis.

  For peritoneal dialysis, dialysis fluid is injected into peritoneal cavity and drained back. Draining takes around 20 minutes. *Principal*: The peritoneal surface helps to excrete water and waste products from blood into dialysis fluid.

  For haemodialysis, patient's blood is pumped through the dialyzer machine that filters the blood with the help of semipermeable membranes and dialysis fluid. Cleaned blood is sent back to the body (Fig. 24.24).

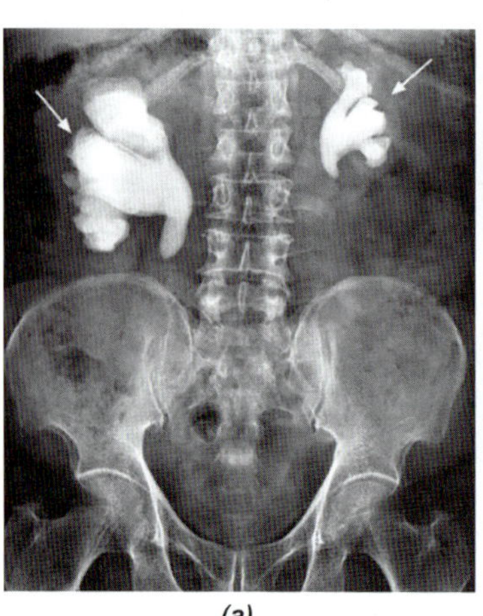

(a)

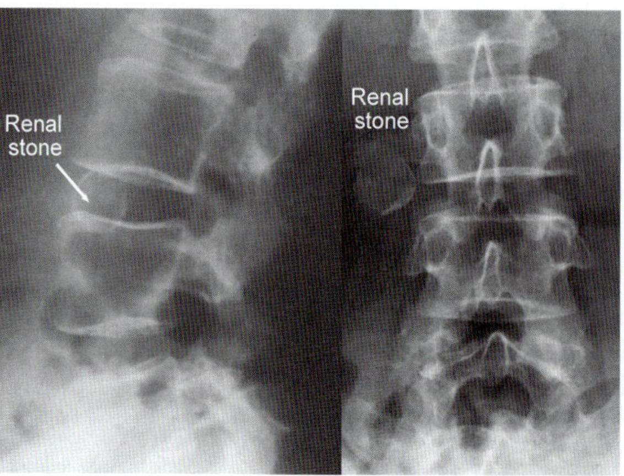

(b)

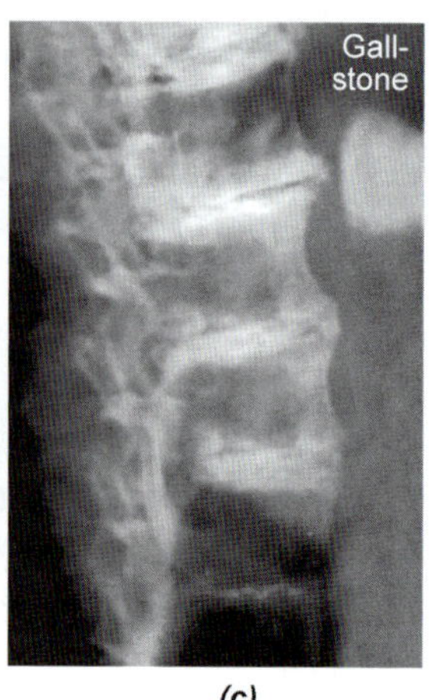

(c)

Figs 24.20a to c: (a) Staghorn renal stone, (b) renal stone on the body of vertebra and (c) gallstone anterior to the vertebra

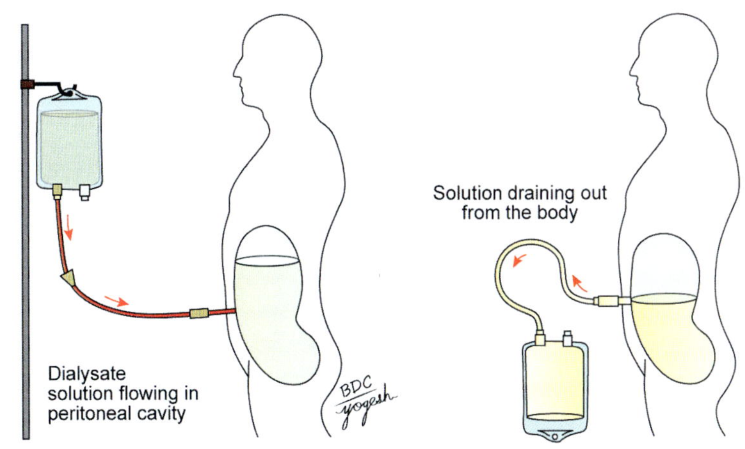

Fig. 24.23: Peritoneal dialysis

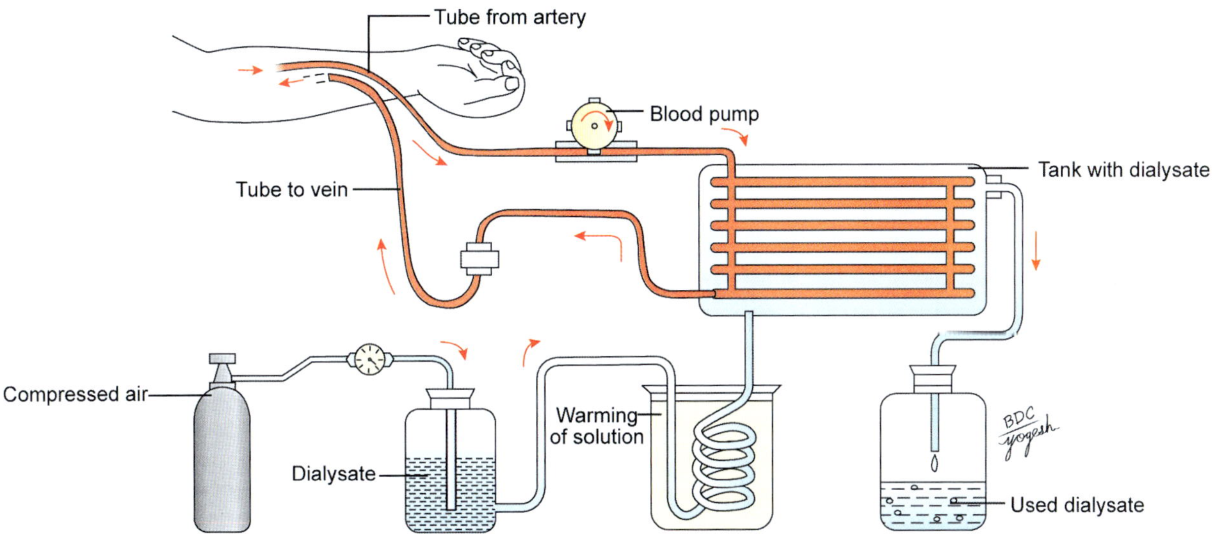

Fig. 24.24: Haemodialysis

URETER

The ureters are a pair of narrow, thick-walled muscular tubes which convey urine from the kidneys to the urinary bladder (Plate 24.4, Fig. 24.25, Flowchart 24.4).

They lie deep to the peritoneum, closely applied to the posterior abdominal wall in the upper part, and to the lateral pelvic wall in the lower part.

Dimensions

Length: About 25–30 cm (10 inches)
Diameter: About 3 mm.

Parts of Ureter

The ureter extends from renal pelvis to the urinary bladder. It crosses the abdominal cavity and enters the pelvic cavity to open into the urinary bladder. Due to its course, ureter is divided for descriptive purposes into three parts (Flowchart 24.4):

1. Abdominal,
2. Pelvic and
3. Intravesical parts.

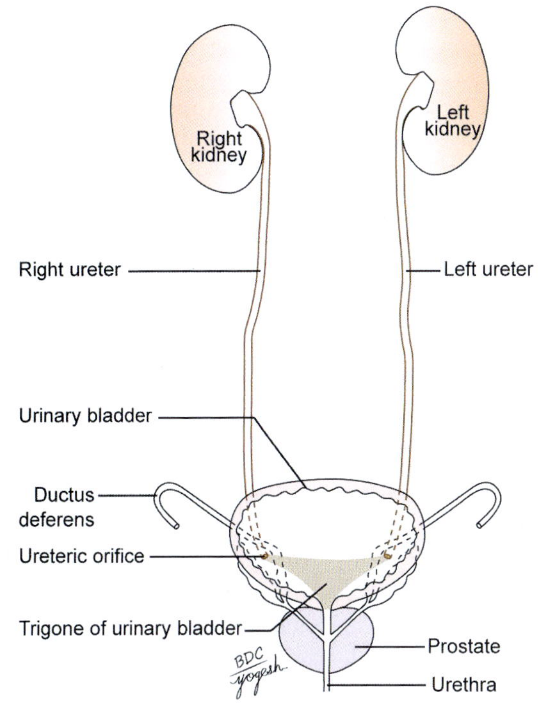

Fig. 24.25: Ureters in male

Plate 24.4: Ureters

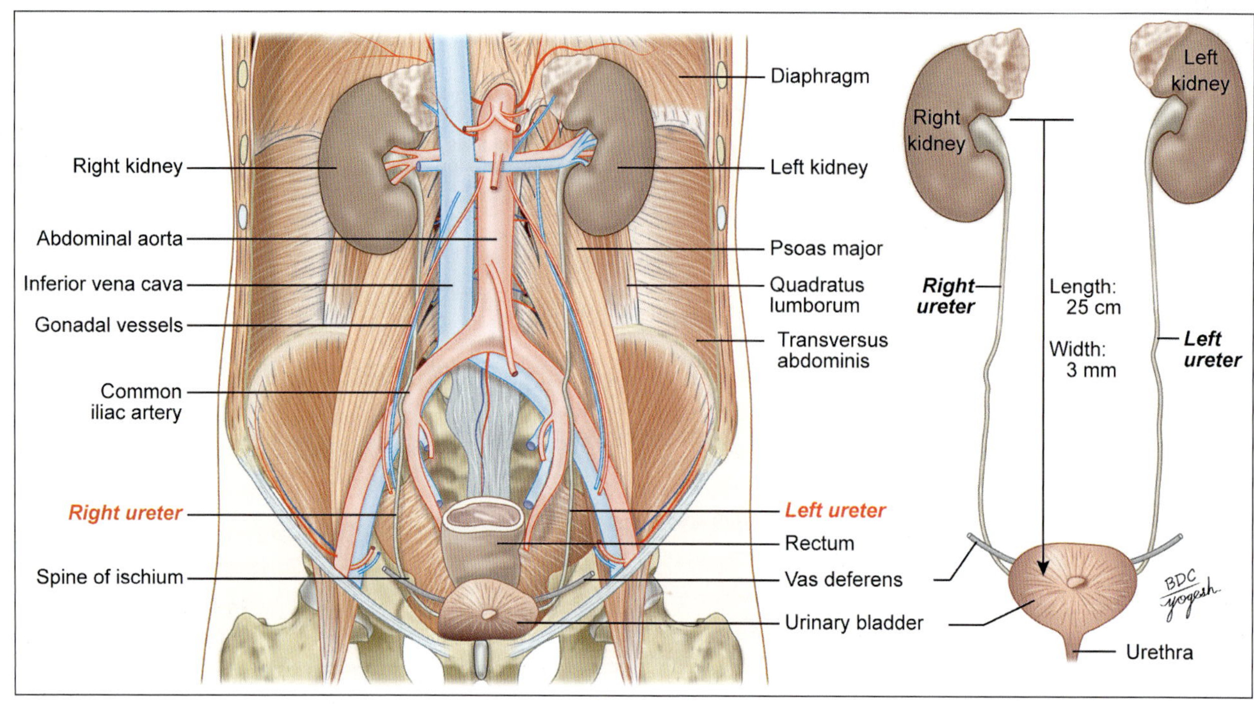

Flowchart 24.4: Ureter

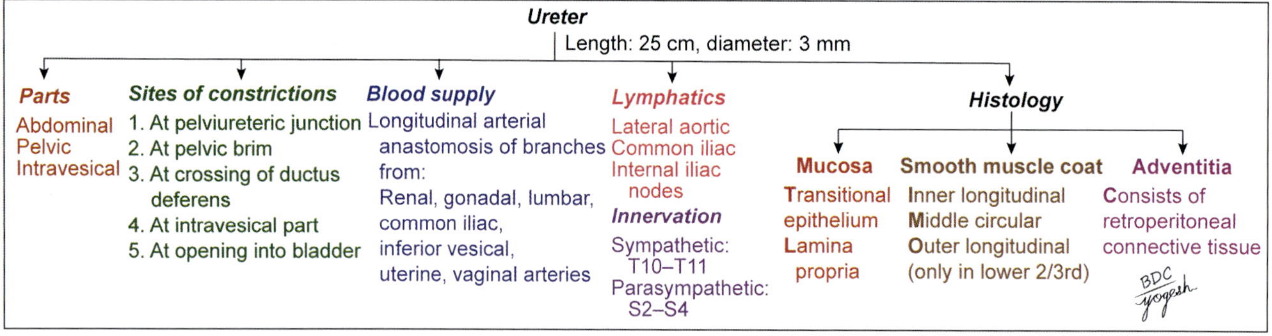

Course

The ureter begins within the renal sinus as a funnel-shaped dilatation, called the *renal pelvis*. The pelvis issues from the hilus of the kidney, descends along its medial margin, or partly behind it. Gradually, it narrows till the lower end of the kidney where it becomes the ureter proper.

The ureter passes downwards and slightly medially on the tips of transverse processes and the psoas major muscle, and enters the pelvis by crossing in front of the termination of the common iliac artery (Fig. 24.26).

In the lesser or true pelvis, the ureter at first runs downwards, and slightly backwards and laterally, following the anterior margin of the greater sciatic notch. Opposite the ischial spine, it turns forwards and medially to reach the base of the urinary bladder.

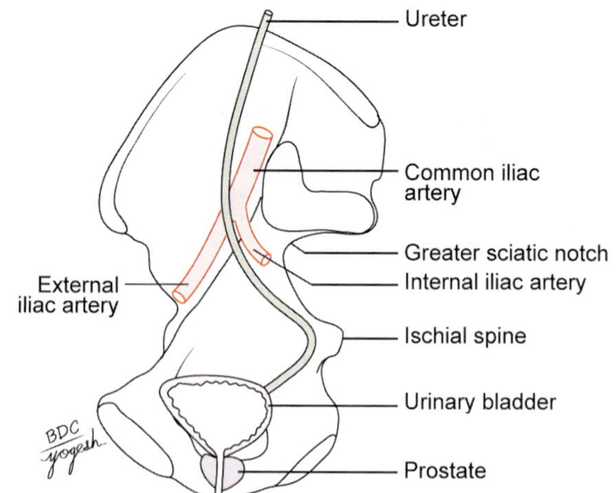

Fig. 24.26: Course of the pelvic part of the ureter

Normal Constrictions

The ureter is slightly constricted at five places.

1. At the pelviureteric junction (Fig. 24.27).
2. At the brim of the lesser pelvis.
3. Point of crossing of ureter by ductus deferens or broad ligament of uterus.
4. During its oblique passage through the bladder wall.
5. At its opening in lateral angle of trigone.

Relations of Ureter

The relations of the ureter are listed in Table 24.1.

TABLE 24.1: Relations of the ureter

Part of ureter			
Abdominal	***Anterior*:** On the *right side:* 1. Third part of the duodenum (Fig. 24.28) 2. Peritoneum 3. Right colic vessels 4. Ileocolic vessels 5. Gonadal vessels 6. Root of the mesentery 7. Terminal part of the ileum On the *left side*: 1. Peritoneum 2. Gonadal artery 3. Left colic vessels 4. Sigmoid colon 5. Sigmoid mesocolon	***Posterior*:** 1. Psoas major 2. Tips of transverse processes (Fig. 24.29) 3. Genitofemoral nerve	***Medial*:** On the *right side:* Inferior vena cava On the *left side:* Left gonadal vein, inferior mesenteric vein
Pelvic It extends from pelvic brim to the base of urinary bladder. The pelvic course of ureter is divided into vertical and oblique parts. (Figs 24.30 and 24.31)	***Relations of vertical part*:** It extends from pelvic brim to the ischial spine. ***Anterior*:** Covered by peritoneum ***Posterior*:** 1. Internal iliac artery and its anterior division 2. Internal iliac vein 3. Lumbosacral trunk 4. Sacroiliac joint ***Medial*:** Covered by peritoneum ***Lateral*:** 1. Fascia covering the obturator internus 2. Superior vesical artery 3. Obturator nerve 4. Obturator vessels 5. Inferior vesical artery 6. Middle rectal artery 7. In females: Uterine and vaginal arteries	***Relations of oblique part:*** It extends from ischial spine to the base of urinary bladder. It lies in extraperitoneal connective tissue in both sexes. ***In male*** • *Superomedial*: Covered by peritoneum. At the lateral angle of base of urinary bladder superomedially, the ureter is crossed by vas deferens. • *Inferolateral*: Levator ani muscle, seminal vesicle. Vesical plexus of veins surrounds the ureter.	***In female*** • *Superior*: Broad ligament of uterus, uterine artery (crosses ureter from lateral to medial) • *Inferior*: Mackenrodt's ligament, lateral fornix of vagina and levator ani muscle • *Medial*: Supravaginal part of uterine cervix, anterior vaginal wall • *Lateral*: Uterine artery
Intravesical (1.5–2.0 cm)	Pierces the wall of urinary bladder obliquely. The oblique course closes the ureter on contraction of urinary bladder during urination and prevents the regurgitation of urine into the ureter. Distance between two ureteric openings in the urinary bladder: It is about 5 cm in distended bladder and 2.5 cm in empty bladder.		

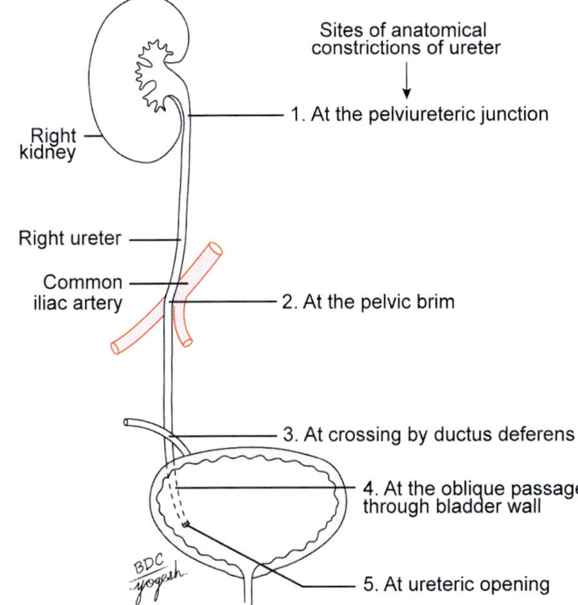

Fig. 24.27: Sites of anatomical constrictions of ureter (in male)

Blood Supply

The ureter is supplied by longitudinal arterial anastomosis. The anastomosis is contributed by branches of renal, gonadal, lumbar, common iliac, inferior vesical, uterine and vaginal arteries (Fig. 24.32).

Note: The ureter receives vessels that are closely attached to the peritoneum. Hence, it is advised not to detach ureter from the peritoneum during surgeries.

Lymphatic Drainage

Lymphatics from upper abdominal part of ureter drain into lateral aortic nodes, from lower abdominal part of ureter into common iliac nodes and from pelvic ureter into the common and internal iliac nodes.

Nerve Supply

The ureter is innervated by autonomic nerves as follows:

A. *Sympathetic fibres* from T10–L1 spinal segments through renal, aortic and hypogastric plexuses.
B. *Parasympathetic fibres* from S2–S4 spinal segment through pelvic splanchnic nerves.

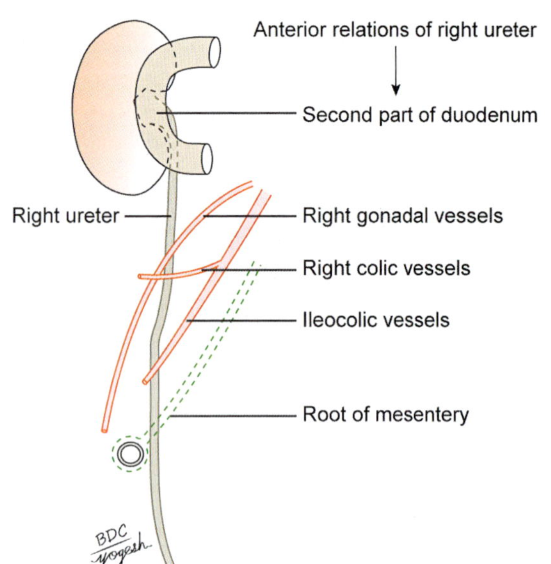

Fig. 24.28: Anterior relations of the abdominal part of the right ureter

Fig. 24.29: Anterior relations of the abdominal part of the left ureter

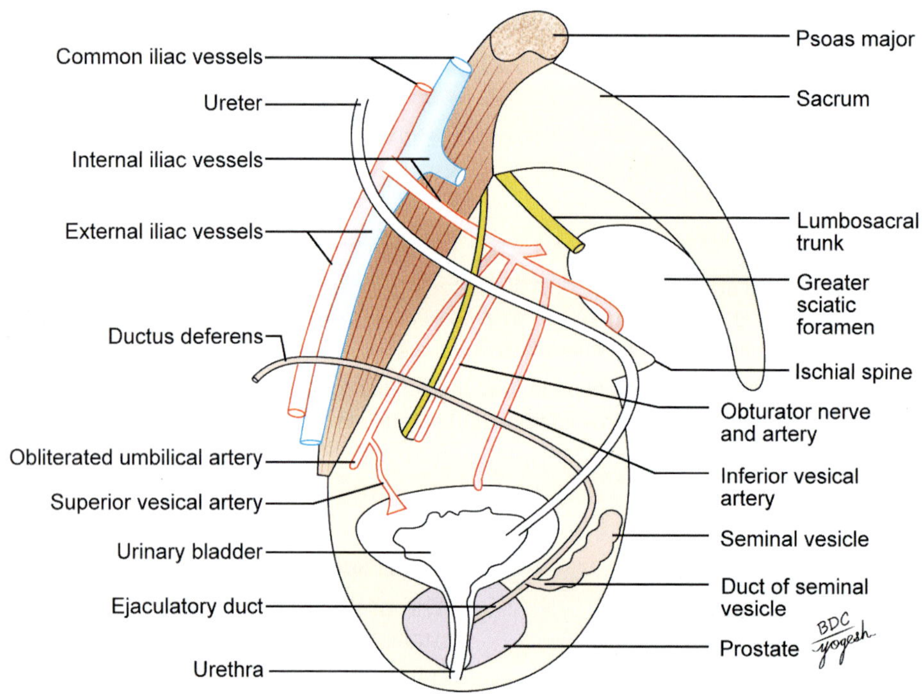

Fig. 24.30: Relations of the pelvic part of the ureter

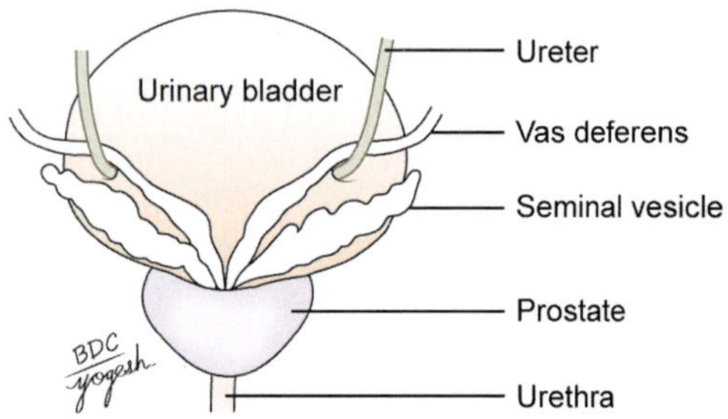

Fig. 24.31: Posterior view of the male urinary bladder showing the relations of the ureter to the vas deferens and the seminal vesicle

Competency:
AN52.2 Describe and identify the microanatomical features of ureter.

Histology of Ureter

The ureter is a mucomuscular tube with star-shaped lumen (Plate 24.5). It has three layers.

1. *Inner mucous membrane* is lined by transitional epithelium and lamina propria (shows longitudinal folding).
2. *Middle smooth muscle layer* having inner longitudinal, middle circular and outer longitudinal layers.
3. *Outer adventitia*: Connective tissue coat having blood vessels, nerves and lymphatics.

Plate 24.5: Histology of the ureter

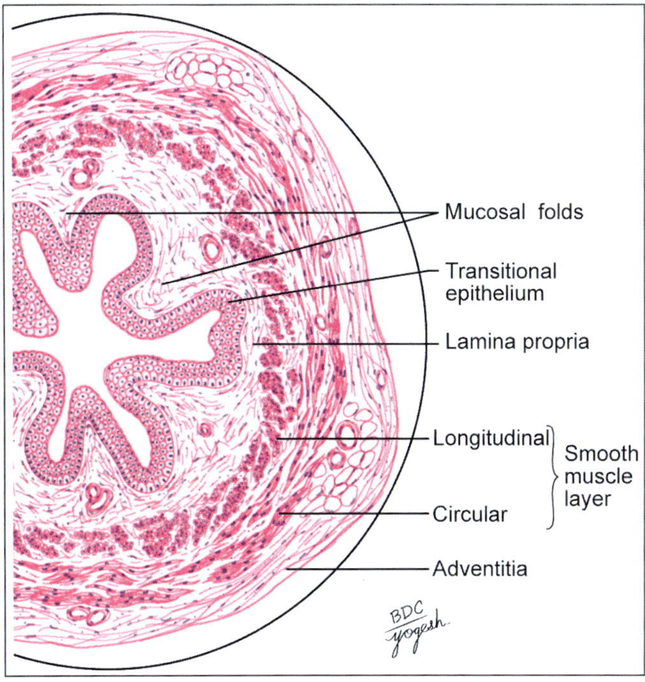

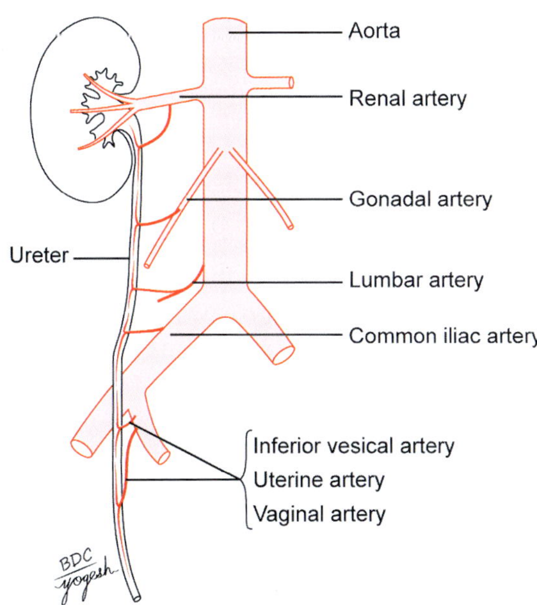

Fig. 24.32: Arterial supply of the ureter

CLINICAL ANATOMY

- ***Ureteric colic***: The sympathetic fibres (T10–L1) carry the pain sensation from ureter. Hence, colic pain from ureter gets referred to the loin and infraumbilical part of the anterior abdominal wall and groin.
- ***Ureteric peristalsis*** is a contraction wave that proceeds towards urinary bladder. The pacemaker for ureteric peristalsis lies in the smooth muscles of minor calyces. The pressure within the ureter at the time of each peristalsis is 20–80 cm H_2O.
- ***Renal stones*** may get impacted at the sites of anatomical constrictions of ureter.
- ***Lithotripsy*** (breaking in Greek) is a physical destruction of renal stones.
- ***Extracorporeal shockwave therapy*** (ESWT) is used for lithotripsy. In this procedure, highly focused, high-intensity acoustic pulse is applied to break the renal stone. It is also helpful for bile stones.
- In ***laser lithotripsy***, laser light is directly emitted on the stone using cystoscope or ureteroscope to break the stone.
- ***Surgical identification of ureter***: It is a thick-walled mucomuscular tube that can be identified by its worm-like peristaltic movements in the living individuals during surgery.
- ***Surgical approach to ureter***: Excess mobilization of ureter may cause avascular necrosis. Abdominal part of ureter is supplied by arteries from its medial side, whereas the pelvic part from its lateral side. This knowledge should be used for surgical approach of ureter with minimal mobilization through extraperitoneal plane.
- ***Visualization of ureter***: The ureter can be visualized by:
  1. Ultrasonography
  2. CT scan
  3. MRI
  4. Ureteroscopy
  5. Pyelography
- ***Pyelography*** is a radiological method for visualization of urinary tract. Pyelogram is a radiograph obtained on pyelography. Pyelography is of two types:
  1. Descending or intravenous pyelography
  2. Retrograde or ascending pyelography: In this method, a dye is injected directly into the ureter through cystoscope and ureteric catheter.

Competency:

AN52.7 Describe the development of urinary system.

DEVELOPMENT OF KIDNEY AND URETER

Human kidney shows two developmental parts as (Figs 24.33 and 24.34, Flowchart 24.5):

1. *Collecting part:* It consists of collecting tubules, collecting ducts, minor and major calyces, renal pelvis and ureter.
2. *Secretory part:* It consists of glomeruli, Bowman's capsule, proximal and distal convoluted tubules and loop of Henle.

Embryological sources:

1. Ureteric bud forms collecting part of kidney.
2. Metanephric blastema forms secretory part of kidney.

The kidney ascends from sacral region to thoracolumbar region to get better blood supply. The primitive kidney

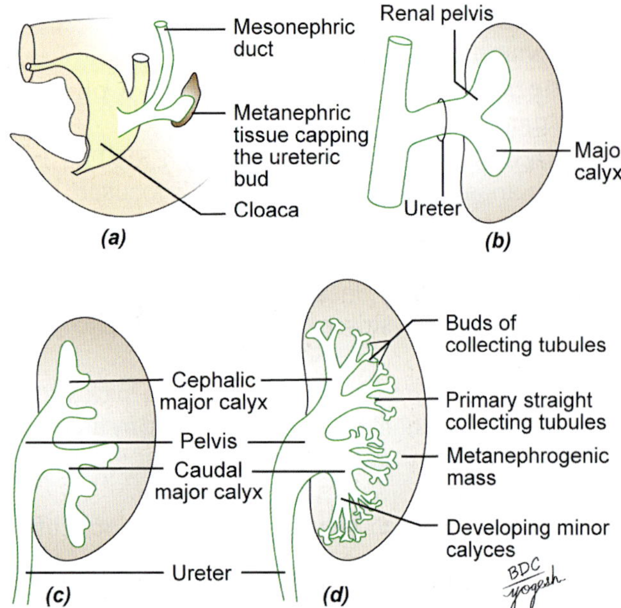

Figs 24.33a to d: Development of collecting system of permanent kidney: (a) Formation of ureteric buds, (b) capping of ureteric bud by metanephros and (c and d) formation of ureter, renal pelvis, major calyces, minor calyces and collecting tubules

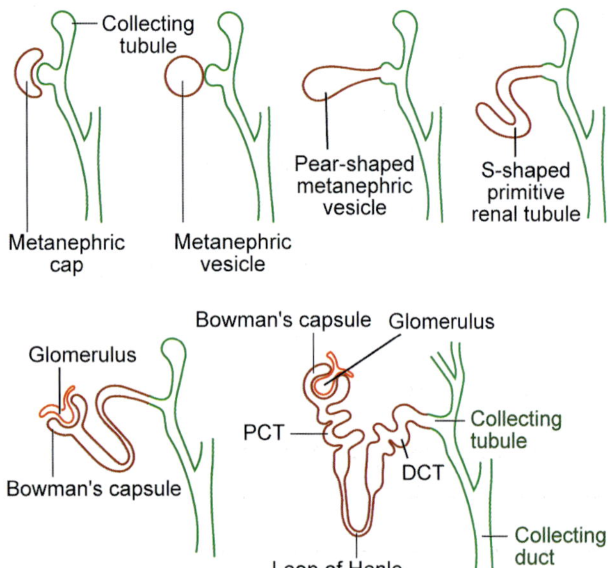

Fig. 24.34: Development of nephron

initially gets supply from median sacral artery via renal artery. Later receives from common iliac artery. On ascent, kidney receives supply from lateral splanchnic branches of the aorta as renal artery. On rotation of kidney by 90° medially, hilum turns from ventral to medial side. The foetal kidney starts functioning by 12th week of IUL and excretes urine into amniotic cavity.

Ureter: It develops from ureteric bud that arises from mesonephric or Wolffian duct. The part of ureteric bud that lies between renal pelvis and vesicourethral canal (part of cloaca) forms ureter.

Flowchart 24.5: Development of kidney

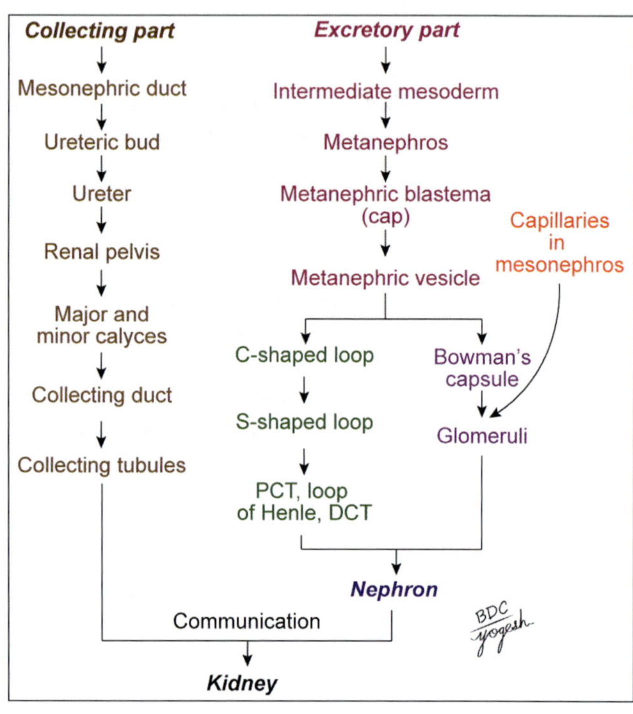

Anomalies of the Kidney and Ureter

1. Non-union of the excretory and collecting parts of the kidney results in the formation of ***congenital polycystic kidney***.
2. Fusion of the lower poles may occur, resulting in a ***horseshoe kidney or pancake kidney***. In these cases, the ureters pass anterior to the isthmus of the kidney (Fig. 24.35).
3. The early *pelvic position* of the kidney may persist. The renal artery then arises from the common iliac artery.
4. Unilateral *aplasia* or *hypoplasia* of the kidney may occur. Sometimes both kidneys may lie on any one side of the body.
5. Obstruction to the ureter may give rise to hydroureter. The ureter may be double ureter partly or completely or may be blind (Figs 24.36a to c).

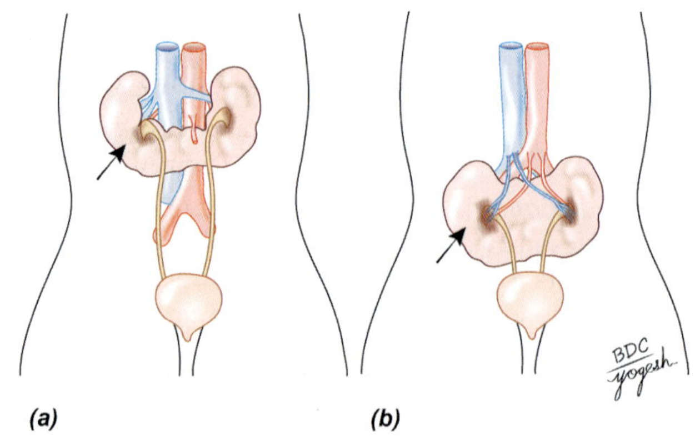

Figs 24.35a and b: (a) Horseshoe kidney (arrow) and (b) pancake kidney (arrow)

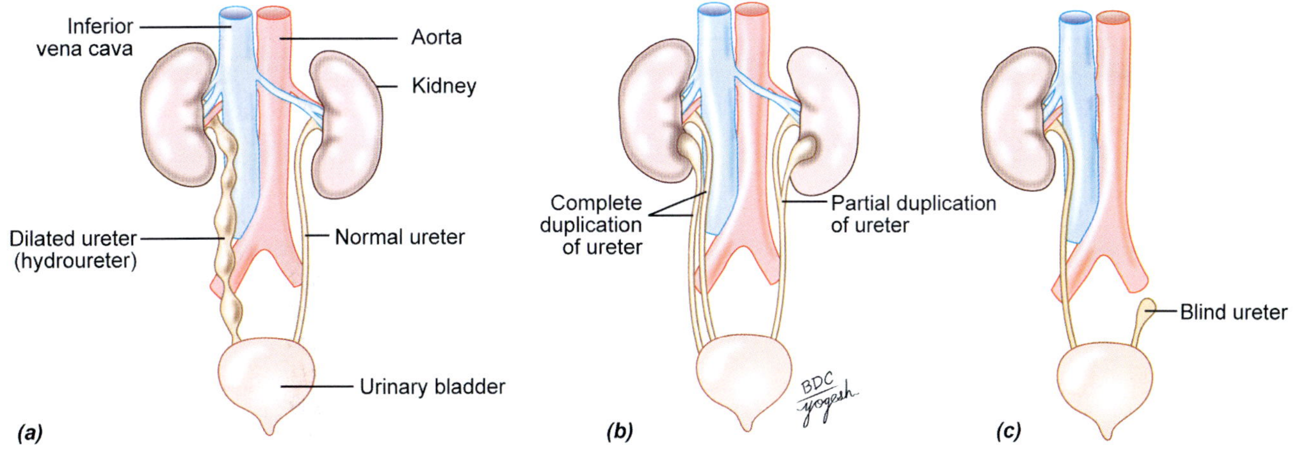

Figs 24.36a to c: Anomalies of ureter include hydroureter (a), partial or complete duplication of ureter (b); and blind ureter (c)

Video 2.24 Kidney and Ureter: Kidneys, Ureters.

Facts to Remember

- Order of structures at the hilum of kidney is renal vein, renal artery and pelvis of ureter from before backwards.
- Kidney is kept in position by intra-abdominal pressure, pararenal fat, renal fascia, perirenal fat, renal capsule.
- There are 5 renal segments—apical, upper, middle, lower and posterior.
- Ureter shows 5 constrictions. These are at pelviureteric junction, at the brim of pelvis, at crossing with ductus deferens or broad ligament, intravesical course and at its termination at the trigone of the urinary bladder.
- Most of the renal stones are radio-opaque, while most of the gallstones are non-radio-opaque.
- Excretory part of kidney develops from metanephros; collecting part of kidney develops from ureteric bud, arising from mesonephric duct.

BDC's Anatomy *e*-book

1. Work of Zuckerkandl
2. Molecular regulation of kidney development
3. Factors preventing reflux of urine from urinary bladder to urethra
4. Molecular regulation of kidney development
5. Developmental anomalies of ureter
6. Further reading
7. Viva voce questions

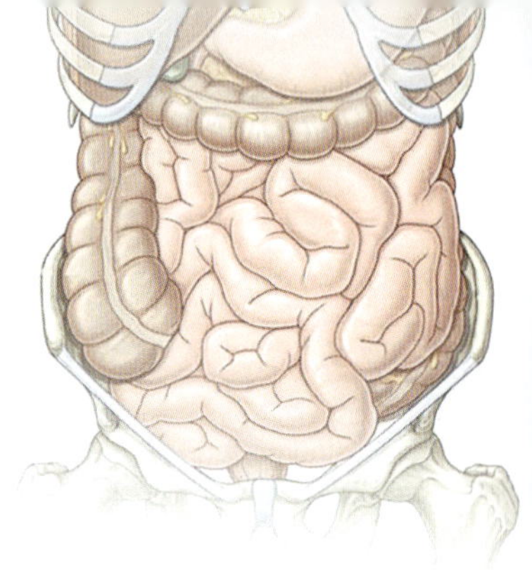

Chapter

25

Suprarenal Gland and Chromaffin System

SUPRARENAL GLAND

Suprarenal or adrenal glands are a pair of endocrine glands located at the upper pole of kidneys (Plate 25.1, Flowchart 25.1). It consists of outer cortex and inner medulla.

Location

Each gland lies in the epigastrium, at the upper pole of the kidney, in front of the crus of the diaphragm, opposite the vertebral end of the 11th intercostal space and the 12th rib, at the level of T12 vertebra (Fig. 25.1).

Size, Shape and Weight

Each suprarenal gland is flattened anteroposteriorly. The right suprarenal gland is triangular or pyramidal and the left suprarenal gland is semilunar or crescentic in shape.

Measurements

- Length: 60–80 mm
- Breadth: 30 mm
- Thickness: 5 mm
- Weight: 5 g
- Volume: 3–6 cm^3

Note: The medulla of the adrenal gland contributes about 1/10th of the total gland weight. The gland is approximately 1/3rd of the size of kidney at birth and about 1/13th of it in adults.

Sheaths

The suprarenal gland is surrounded by two sheaths as follows (Fig. 25.1):

1. *Sheaths of perirenal fat*: It is a layer of loose areolar tissue that surrounds kidney and suprarenal gland.
2. *Renal fascia*: It encloses suprarenal gland, kidney and peritoneal fat. It is open superiorly. The suprarenal gland is separated from the kidney by a *septum* (*Reference:* Gray's Anatomy, 42nd edition).

Right Suprarenal Gland

The right suprarenal gland is triangular to pyramidal in shape. It has (Figs 25.2a and b):

1. Apex
2. Base
3. Two surfaces: Anterior and posterior
4. Two borders: Medial and lateral.

Plate 25.1: Suprarenal glands

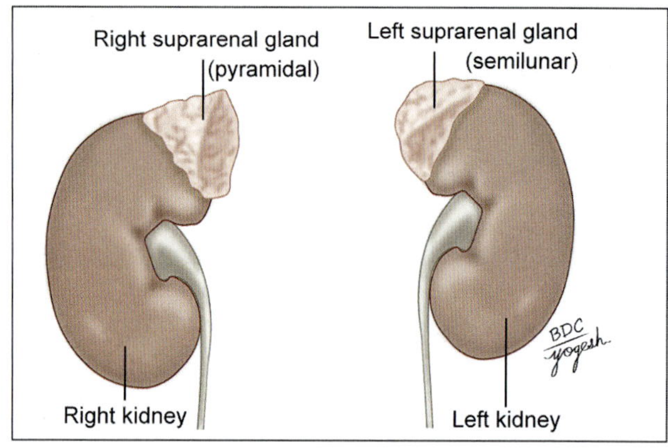

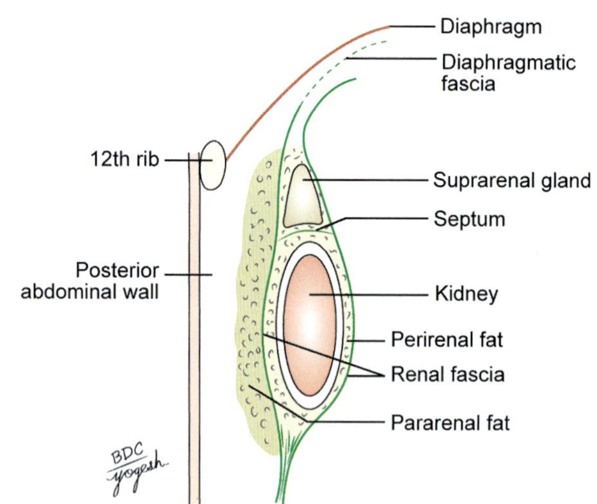

Fig. 25.1: Kidney and suprarenal glands enclosed in the renal fascia with a septum intervening

Left Suprarenal Gland

The *left gland* is semilunar. It has (Figs 25.2a and b):

1. *Two ends*: Upper (narrow end) and lower (rounded end).

Flowchart 25.1: Suprarenal glands

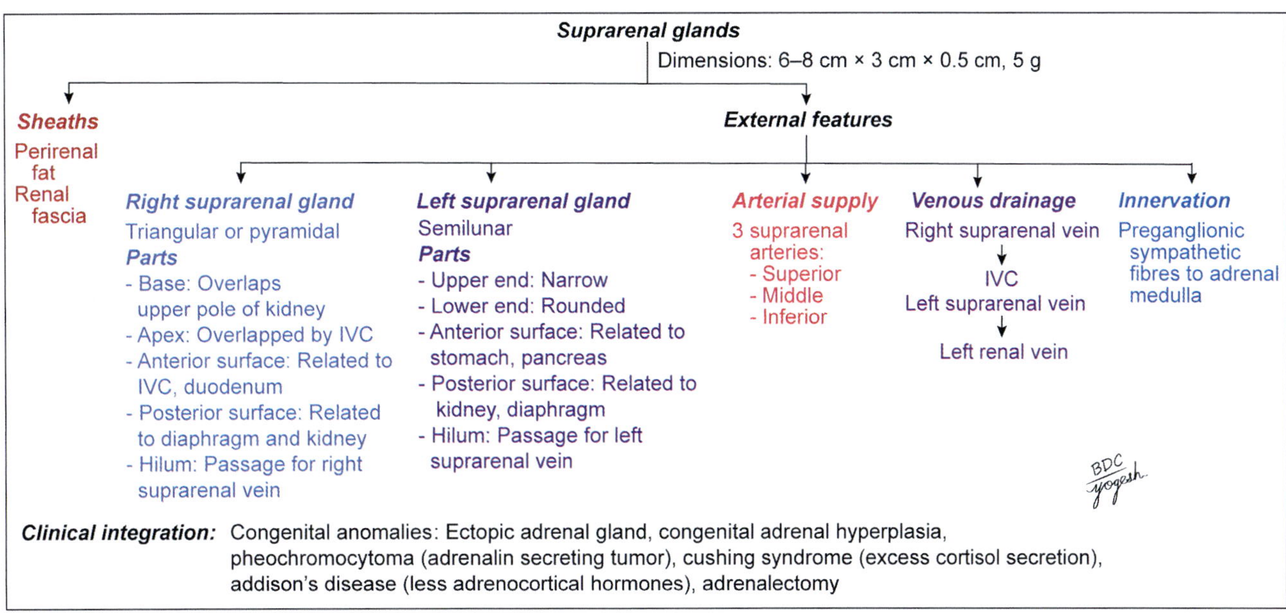

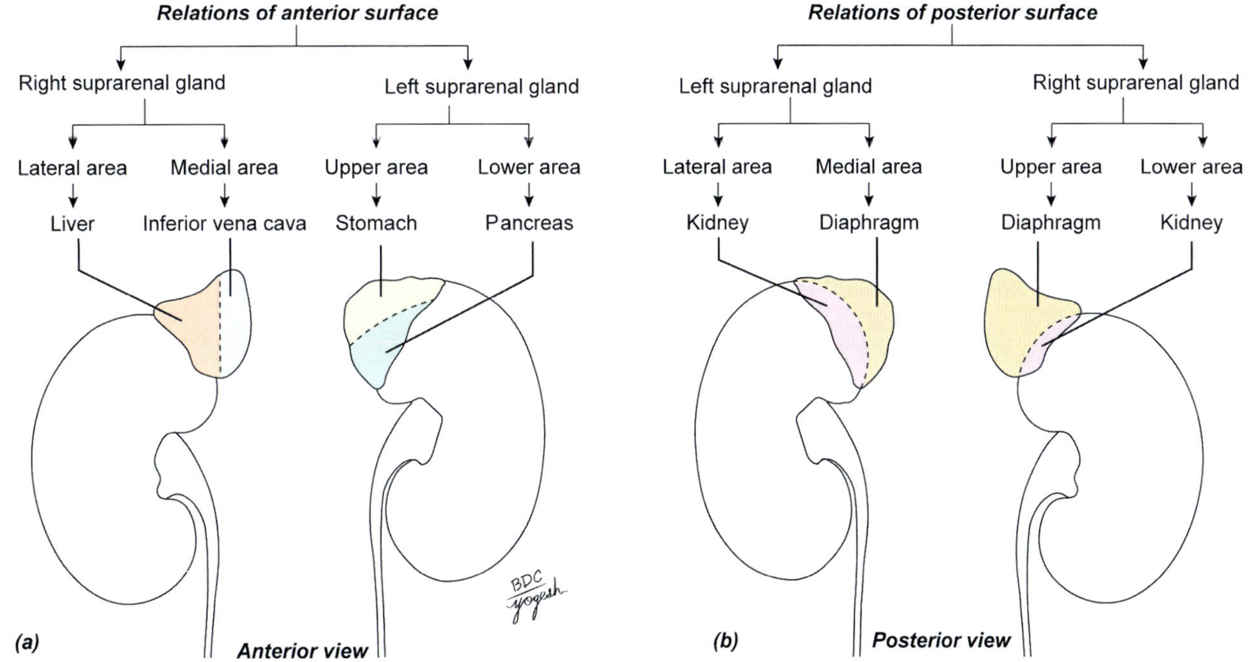

Figs 25.2a and b: Relations of the suprarenal glands: (a) Anterior view of right suprarenal gland and anterior view of left suprarenal gland and (b) posterior view of left suprarenal gland and posterior view of right suprarenal gland

2. *Two borders*: Medial—convex and lateral—concave
3. *Two surfaces*: Anterior and posterior.

Comparison and relations of right and left suprarenal glands are given in Table 25.1.

Arterial Supply

Each gland is supplied by:

1. The *superior suprarenal artery*, a branch of the inferior phrenic artery.
2. The *middle suprarenal artery*, a branch of the abdominal aorta.
3. The *inferior suprarenal artery*, a branch of the renal artery (Fig. 25.3).

Venous Drainage

Each gland is drained by one vein (Fig. 25.4). The right suprarenal vein drains into the inferior vena cava, and the left suprarenal vein drains into the left renal vein.

Lymphatic Drainage

Lymphatics from the suprarenal glands drain into the lateral aortic nodes.

TABLE 25.1: Comparison of right and left suprarenal glands

	Right suprarenal gland	*Left suprarenal gland*
Shape	Pyramidal	Semilunar
Parts and relations	*Apex*: Bare area of liver *Base*: Upper pole of right kidney	*Upper end*: Close to spleen *Lower end*: Presents hilum, left vein emerges from here
Anterior surface	*Medial area*: Inferior vena cava *Lateral area*: Bare area of liver	*Upper area*: Stomach *Lower area*: Pancreas with splenic artery
Posterior surface	*Upper area*: Right crus of diaphragm *Lower area*: Right kidney	*Medial area*: Left crus of diaphragm *Lateral area*: Left kidney
Borders	*Medial border*: Thin, related to coeliac ganglion *Lateral border*: Related to liver	*Medial border:* Convex and related to coeliac ganglion *Lateral border:* Concave and in contact with kidney
Hilum	Lies near upper end of anterior surface Right suprarenal vein emerges	Lies near lower end of anterior surface Left suprarenal vein emerges

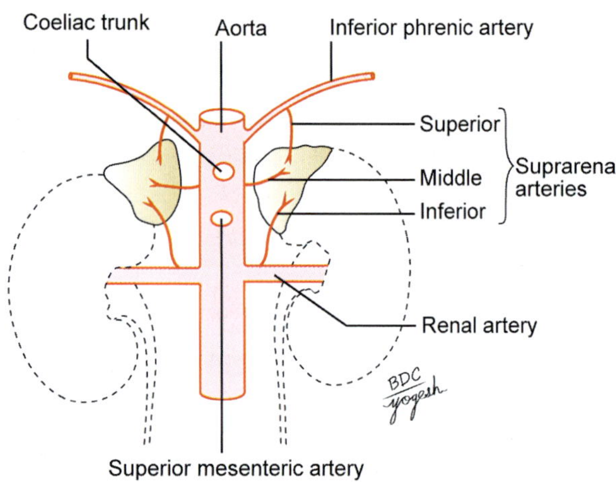

Fig. 25.3: Arterial supply of the suprarenal glands

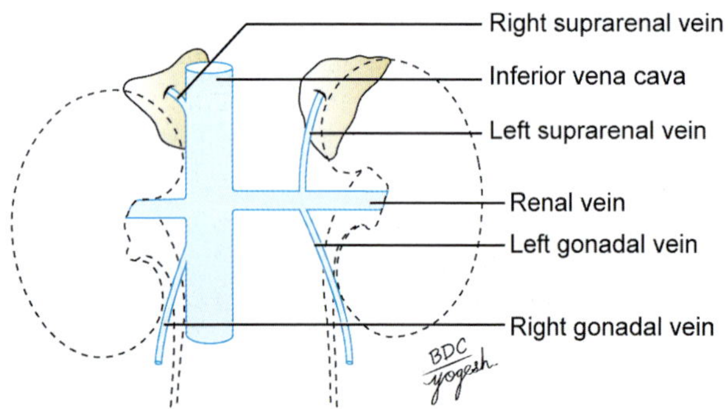

Fig. 25.4: Venous drainage of the suprarenal glands

Nerve Supply

The suprarenal medulla has a rich nerve supply through myelinated *preganglionic* sympathetic fibres. The chromaffin cells in it are considered homologous with postganglionic sympathetic neurons.

Competency:
AN52.1 Describe and identify the microanatomical features of suprarenal gland.

Histology of Adrenal Gland

The adrenal gland is surrounded by thick connective tissue capsule, outer cortex and inner medulla (Plate 25.2).

Plate 25.2: Histology of suprarenal gland

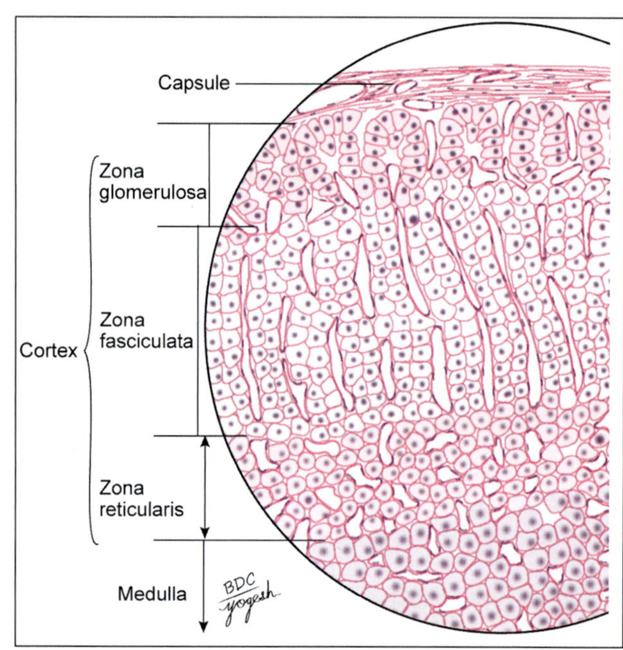

The adrenal ***cortex*** shows:

1. Outer zona glomerulosa (15%): Ovoid clusters or curved columns of small acidophilic cells.
2. Middle zona fasciculata (80%): Long straight columns of large polyhedral light-pink cells separated by sinusoidal capillaries.
3. Inner zona reticularis (5%): Anastomosing cords of small cells separated by fenestrated capillaries.

The adrenal ***medulla*** consists of ovoid groups of pale staining epithelioid cells (positive for chromaffin reaction; hence, called pheochromocytes).

Competency:
AN52.7 Describe the development of suprarenal gland.

Development of Adrenal Gland

Adrenal cortex: It develops from coelomic epithelium (mesoderm) that forms suprarenal ridge. Initially formed cortex gets replaced by definitive cortex, which

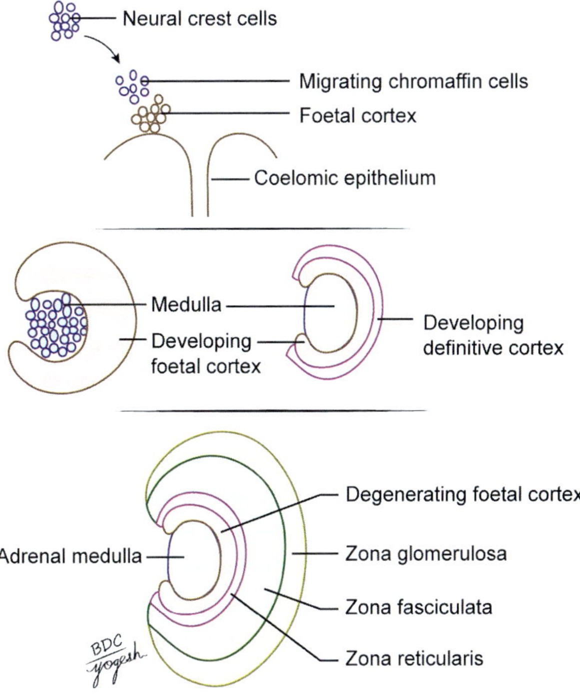

Fig. 25.5: Development of adrenal gland

Flowchart 25.2: Development of adrenal gland

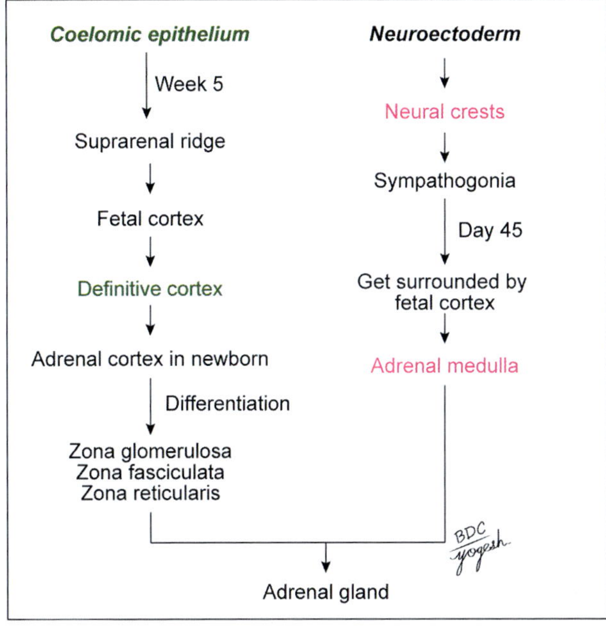

differentiates into zona glomerulosa, zona fasciculata and zona reticularis (Fig. 25.5, Flowchart 25.2).

Adrenal medulla: It develops from sympathochromaffin cells derived from neural crest cells.

Functions of Adrenal Glands

- Adrenal cortex has three parts:
  1. Outer *zona glomerulosa* produces mineralocorticoids which maintain water and electrolyte balance.
  2. Middle *zona fasciculata* produces glucocorticoids.
  3. Inner *zona reticularis* produces sex steroid hormones.
- Adrenal medulla produces adrenaline and noradrenaline.

DISSECTION

Locate the suprarenal glands situated along the upper pole and medial border of the two kidneys. Identify the structures related to the right and left suprarenal glands.

CLINICAL ANATOMY

- ***Congenital anomalies of adrenal gland***
  – ***Ectopic adrenal gland*** may be present deep to the renal capsule or fused with the kidney or liver.
  – ***Congenital adrenal hyperplasia*** involves deficiency of 21-hydroxylase enzyme (essential for steroid hormone synthesis). It results in elevation of androgens and causes pseudo-intersexuality as follows:

    In males, it causes the early development of secondary sexual characters, which is called adrenogenital syndrome.

    In females, it causes enlargement of clitoris, and the condition is called pseudo-hermaphroditism.
- ***Pheochromocytoma*** is a tumour of chromaffin cells. It produces a large quantity of adrenaline and noradrenaline (Fig. 25.6). It is usually benign (non-spreading) tumour. It leads to high blood pressure, increased heart rate, palpitations, headache, episodic sweating (most common symptom) and so on. Surgical resection of the tumour is the treatment of choice.
- ***Cushing's syndrome (hyperadrenalism)*** is produced by excess secretion of adrenal cortical hormones, primarily cortisol. It may occur because of excess ACTH secretion of pituitary (Cushing's disease), tumours of adrenal cortex, or ectopic ACTH secreting tumours. Features of Cushing's syndrome include weight gain, buffalo hump (deposition of fat on the back of neck), moon face (deposition of fat on the face), excess sweating, facial plethora, decreased libido, thin skin, menstrual irregularities, abdominal red-purple stria, osteoporosis and so on.
- ***Addison's disease***: Hypoadrenalism causes Addison's disease because of insufficient production of adrenocortical hormone. Features of Addison's disease include fatigue, weakness, anorexia, postural hypotension, hyperpigmentation, vitiligo, gastrointestinal disturbances and so on.

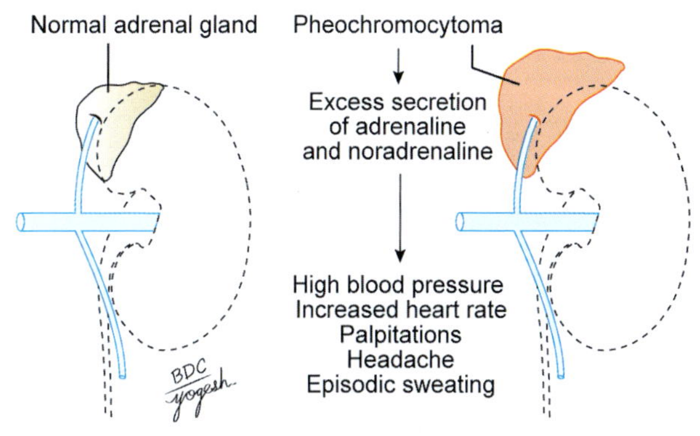

Fig. 25.6: Pheochromocytoma

- ***Adrenalectomy*** is surgical removal of adrenal gland. During this surgery, the adrenal vein is ligated first to prevent the sudden release of catecholamines while manipulating the gland.

CHROMAFFIN SYSTEM

Chromaffin system is made up of cells which have an affinity for certain salt of chromic acid. Such cells are called chromaffin cells or pheochromocytes. These are situated close to sympathetic ganglia because both of them develop from the cells of the neural crest. Chromaffin cells secrete adrenaline and noradrenaline. This system includes the following groups of cells.

1. Suprarenal medulla (described above)
2. Paraganglia
3. Para-aortic bodies
4. Coccygeal body
5. Small masses of chromaffin cells scattered irregularly amongst ganglia of sympathetic chain, splanchnic nerves, autonomic plexuses and may be closely related to various organs like heart, liver, kidney, ureter, prostate, epididymis, etc.

Paraganglia

These are rounded nodules of chromaffin tissue, about 2 mm in diameter, situated inside or closely related to the ganglia of the sympathetic chain. In adults, they are generally represented by microscopic remnants only.

Para-aortic Bodies

Two para-aortic bodies, each about 1 cm long, lie on each side of the origin of the inferior mesenteric artery. They are connected together above the artery to form an inverted horseshoe, or an H-shaped body. They develop during foetal life, attain their maximum size in the first three years of life and gradually atrophy to disappear by the age of 14 years. The chromaffin cells of the para-aortic bodies secrete noradrenaline.

Other small chromaffin bodies are found in the foetus in all parts of the prevertebral sympathetic plexuses of the abdomen and pelvis. They reach their maximum size between the 5th and 8th months of foetal life. In adults, they can be made out only in the vicinity of the coeliac and superior mesenteric arteries.

Coccygeal Body (Glomus Coccygeum)

Also known as glomus coccygeum, it is a small oval body about 2.5 cm in diameter situated in front of the coccyx. It is closely connected to the termination of the *median sacral artery* and to the *ganglion impar*. It is made up of epithelioid cells grouped around a sinusoidal capillary. Thus it does not clearly belong to the chromaffin system.

Facts to Remember

- Suprarenal gland sustains the body during stress by its cortical and medullary hormones.
- Suprarenal gland is drained by one vein which ends in inferior vena cava on the right side and in left renal vein on the left side.
- Each suprarenal is supplied by 3 arteries.
- Adrenal cortex secretions:
  1. *Zona glomerulosa:* Mineralocorticoids
  2. *Zona fasciculata:* Glucocorticoids
  3. *Zona reticularis:* Sex steroid hormones.
  4. Adrenal medulla: Adrenaline and noradrenaline.

BDC's Anatomy *e*-book

1. Molecular regulation of adrenal gland development
2. Further reading
3. Viva voce questions

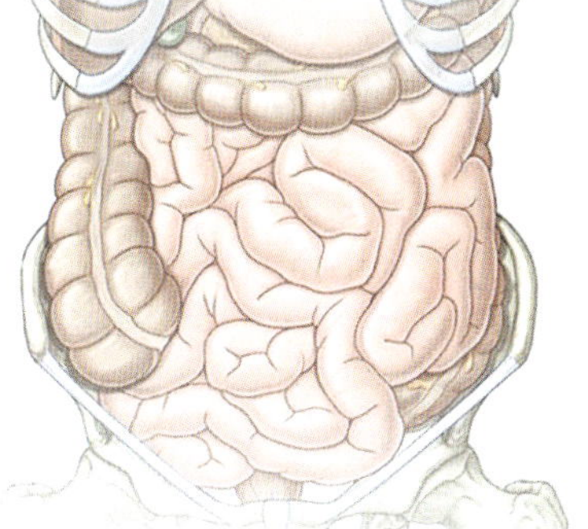

Chapter

26

Thoracoabdominal Diaphragm

Competency:

AN47.13 Describe and demonstrate the attachments, openings, nerve supply and action of the thoracoabdominal diaphragm.

The thoracoabdominal diaphragm is a dome-shaped muscle forming the partition between the thoracic and abdominal cavities. It is the chief muscle of respiration.

Muscle fibres form the periphery of the partition. They arise from circumference of the thoracic outlet and are inserted into a central tendon (Fig. 26.1).

Origin

- The domes of diaphragm projects into thoracic cavity. It has three groups of fibres (Figs 26.1 and 26.2, Flowchart 26.1):
  1. *Sternal part*: It consists of two fleshy slips that arise from back of xiphoid process.
  2. *Costal part*: It arises from inner surface of lower six ribs and their costal cartilages.
  3. *Vertebral part*: It consists of right and left crura and five arcuate ligaments.
- ***Crura*** are elongated muscular slips.
  - ***Right crus*** arises from right side of anterior surface of L1–L3 vertebrae and corresponding intervertebral discs.
  - ***Left crus*** is smaller than the right. It arises from left side of anterior surface of L1 and L2 vertebrae and corresponding intervertebral disc.
- ***Arcuate ligaments*:** There are 5 arcuate ligaments.
  - One ***median arcuate ligament*** arches between upper ends of right and left crura.
  - Two ***medial arcuate ligaments*** arch between L2 vertebra to the tip of transverse process of L1 vertebra.
  - Two ***lateral arcuate ligaments*** arch between tip of transverse process of L1 vertebra and the 12th rib.

Insertion

All the fibres converge and insert into central tendon. It is an aponeurotic sheet. It is ***trifoliate-shaped***: Has a single triangular median/anterior leaflet and two tongue-shaped posterior leaflets (right and left). It is fused superiorly with fibrous pericardium.

Nerve Supply

- *Motor supply:* Phrenic nerve (C3, C4, C5)
- *Sensory supply:* Central part of diaphragm by phrenic nerve. Peripheral part by lower 6–7 intercostal nerves.

Note: The phrenic nerves also supply sensory fibres to the mediastinal and diaphragmatic pleurae, the fibrous pericardium, the parietal layer of serous pericardium and the part of the parietal peritoneum lying below the central part of the thoracoabdominal diaphragm. Through its communications with the phrenic branches of the coeliac plexus, the phrenic nerve is also distributed to the falciform and coronary ligaments of the liver, the inferior vena cava, the suprarenal glands and the *gallbladder*.

Blood Supply

- Branches of internal thoracic artery
  1. Musculophrenic artery
  2. Pericardiophrenic artery
- Branches of aorta
  3. Lower five posterior intercostal and subcostal arteries
  4. Superior phrenic artery
  5. Inferior phrenic artery
- Veins correspond to arteries and drain into systemic veins.

Lymphatic Drainage

Diaphragm is drained into the following group of lymph nodes:

1. Anterior diaphragmatic lymph nodes
2. Posterior diaphragmatic lymph nodes
3. Right lateral diaphragmatic lymph nodes
4. Left lateral diaphragmatic lymph nodes.

STRUCTURES PASSING THROUGH THE DIAPHRAGM

There are three large and several small openings in the diaphragm which allow passage to structures from thorax to abdomen or *vice versa* (Figs 26.1 and 26.3, Flowchart 26.2).

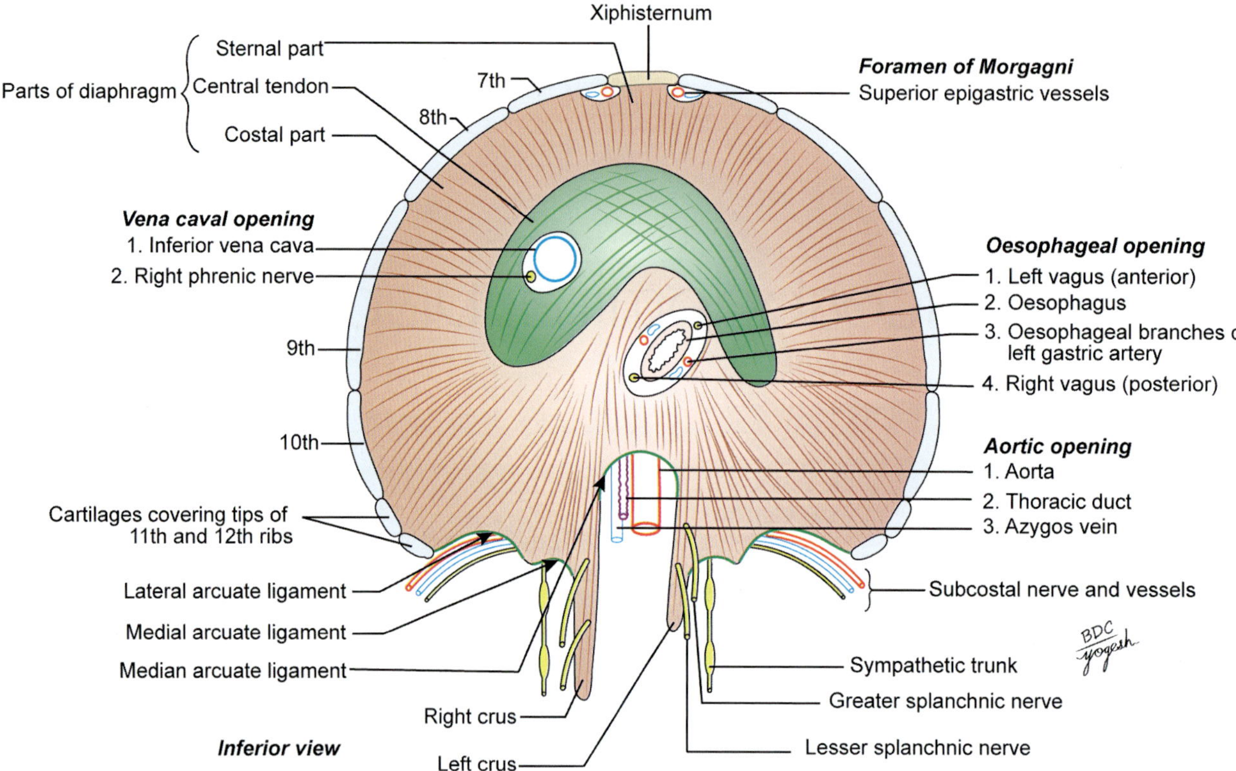

Fig. 26.1: The thoracoabdominal diaphragm: Openings in the diaphragm and structures passing through these openings (as seen from below)

Flowchart 26.1: Thoracoabdominal diaphragm

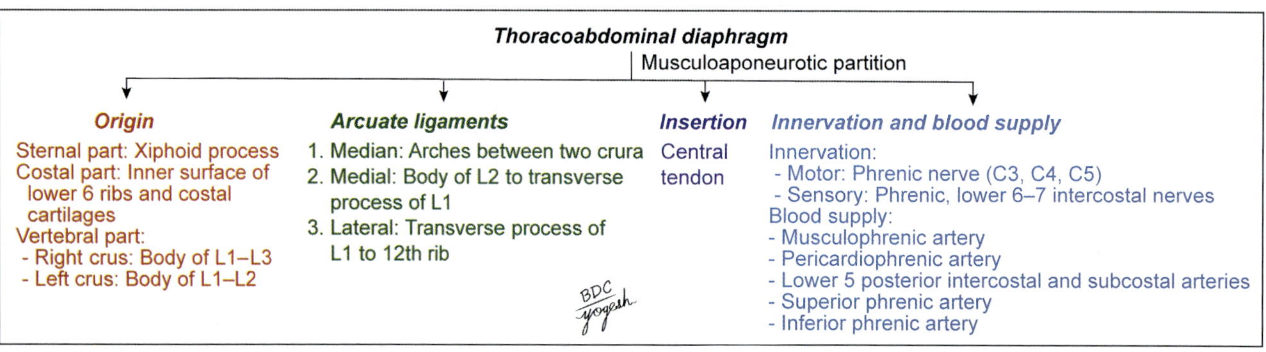

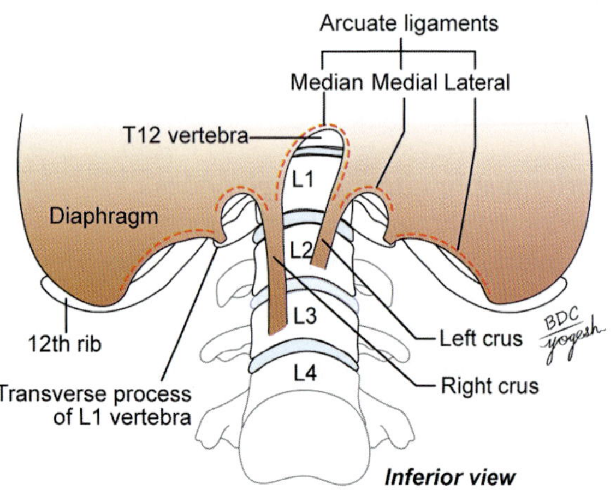

Fig. 26.2: Arcuate ligaments and crura of diaphragm

Flowchart 26.2: Openings in diaphragm

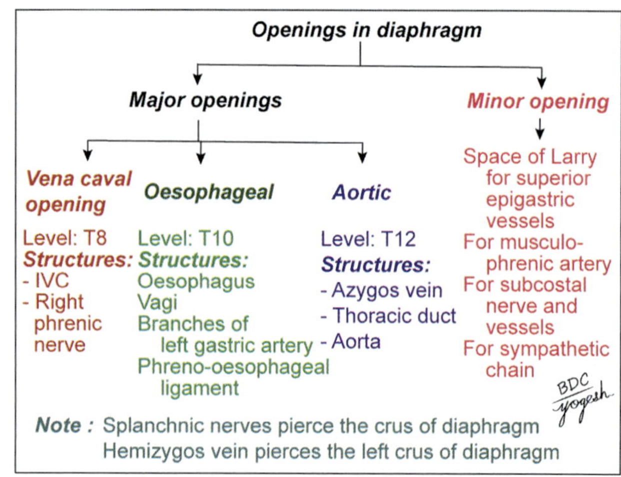

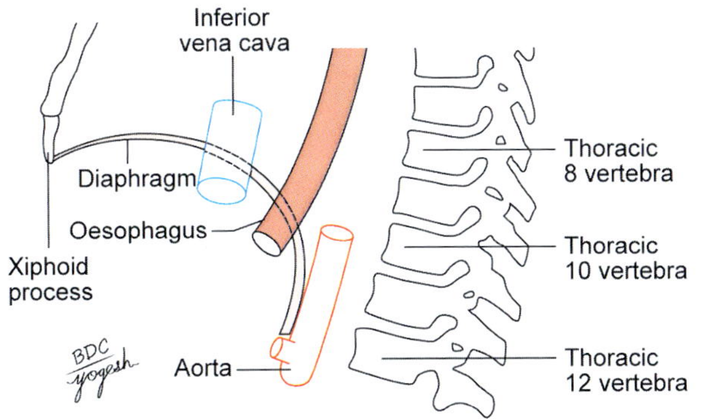

Fig. 26.3: Main openings in the thoracoabdominal diaphragm

Large Openings

1. Vena caval opening in the central tendon
2. Oesophageal opening in the right crus of diaphragm
3. Aortic opening behind the median arcuate ligament.

The structures passing through large openings are put in Table 26.1.

Small Openings

1. ***Superior epigastric artery*** passes in ***space of Larrey*** present between slip of xiphoid process and 7th costal cartilaginous slip of the diaphragm. When foramen is enlarged, it is known as ***foramen of Morgagni***. Musculophrenic artery perforates diaphragm at the level of 9th costal cartilage.
2. ***Lower 5 intercostal vessels and nerves*** pass between costal origins of diaphragm and transversus abdominis.
3. ***Subcostal vessels and nerves*** pass behind lateral arcuate ligament.
4. ***Sympathetic trunk*** passes behind medial arcuate ligament.
5. ***Greater and lesser splanchnic nerves*** pierce each crus.
6. ***Left phrenic nerve*** pierces left cupola.

Relations

Superiorly

1. Pleurae and lungs
2. Pericardium.

Inferiorly

1. Peritoneum
2. Liver
3. Fundus of the stomach
4. Spleen
5. Kidneys
6. Suprarenals.

Actions of Diaphragm

1. *Inspiration*: Diaphragm is the principal muscle of respiration. On contraction, the diaphragm descends downward and vertical diameter of thoracic cavity increases. It helps to create more negative intrathoracic pressure and inhalation of air.
2. *Other actions*
   a. Helps in micturition, defecation, vomiting and parturition.
   b. Supports vertebral column by increasing intra-abdominal pressure in weightlifting.
   c. Helps in venous return to heart by decreasing intrathoracic pressure (suction action) and increasing intra-abdominal pressure (compresses abdominal veins).
   d. Oesophageal sphincteric action by contraction of arching fibres of right crus over the diaphragmatic oesophageal opening.

DISSECTION

Strip the peritoneum from the under aspect of the thoracoabdominal diaphragm and expose its crura on the anterior surfaces of the upper 2 or 3 lumbar vertebrae. Dissect the arcuate ligaments.

Expose the slips of thoracoabdominal diaphragm arising from the internal surfaces of the remaining costal cartilages and identify the intercostal vessels and nerves entering the abdominal wall between them.

Locate the main openings in the thoracoabdominal diaphragm and identify the structures passing through each one of them. Explore the other minor openings and the structures traversing these.

TABLE 26.1: Large openings in thoracoabdominal diaphragm

Opening	*Location*	*Shape*	*Structures passing*	*Effect on contraction*
Vena cava	T8, right part of central tendon	Quadrilateral	IVC Right phrenic nerve Lymphatic of liver	Dilation
Oesophageal	T10, splitting of right crus	Elliptical	Oesophagus Both vagal trunks Left gastric vessels	Constriction
Aortic	T12, behind median arcuate ligament	Rounded	Aorta Thoracic duct Azygos vein	No change

[*Mnemonics:* ***Diaphragm apertures: Spinal levels: I 8** eggs **10** at **12:*** **I**nferior vena cava **(8)**, **O**esophagus **(10)**, **A**orta **(12)**]

Competencies:

AN47.14 Describe the abnormal openings of thoracoabdominal diaphragm and diaphragmatic hernia.

AN52.5 Describe the development and congenital anomalies of thoracoabdominal diaphragm.

AN52.5 Describe the development of diaphragm.

Development of Diaphragm

Various parts of diaphragm develop as follows (Fig. 26.4):

1. Central tendon from pleuro-peritoneal membranes.
2. Crura of diaphragm from dorsal mesentery of oesophagus.
3. Muscular components form cervical somites (level C3–C5).
4. Ventrolateral peripheral part from mesoderm of lateral body wall.

For details, refer to *source*: *Textbook of Human Embryology*, Yogesh Sontakke.

Note: Previous concept: Central tendon develops from septum transversum.

CLINICAL ANATOMY

- ***Paralysis of diaphragm***: Damage to the nerve supply (phrenic nerve) leads to paralysis of diaphragm. In ***unilateral paralysis of diaphragm***, the paralyzed dome of diaphragm remains elevated during inspiration and moves downward in expiration. This is called ***paradoxical movements*** (Fig. 26.5). It can be observed on radiological fluoroscopy (real-time viewing). Bilateral paralysis may lead to respiratory failure.
- ***Hiccups***: Irritation of diaphragm may cause spasmodic involuntary contraction of diaphragm and produce hiccups.

  It may be:

  a. *Peripheral*, due to local irritation of the thoraco-abdominal diaphragm or its nerve.

  b. *Central*, due to irritation of the hiccough centre in the medulla. Uraemia is an important cause of hiccough.
- ***Shoulder tip pain***: Irritation of the thoracoabdominal diaphragm may cause referred pain in the shoulder because the phrenic and supraclavicular nerves have the same root values (C3, C4, C5).

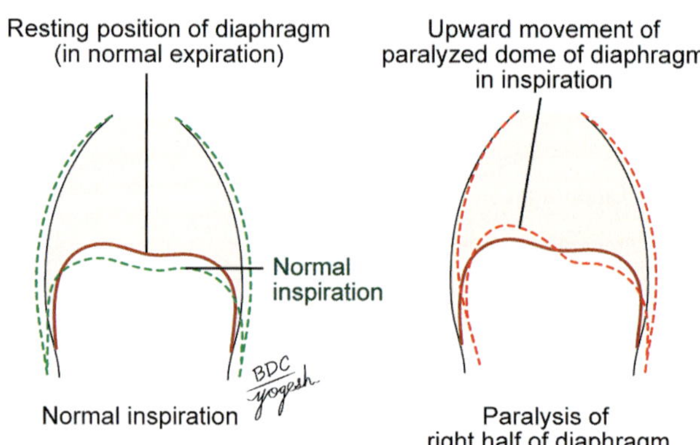

Fig. 26.5: Normal and paradoxical movement of diaphragm

- ***Diaphragmatic hernia***: It is the protrusion of abdominal contents into the chest through a defective diaphragm. It may be congenital or acquired.
- ***Congenital diaphragmatic hernia*** (CDH) occurs due to failure of proper formation of the diaphragm (Fig. 26.6).

  Congenital diaphragmatic hernia has three types:

  a. ***Bochdalek hernia (posterolateral hernia):*** About 95% cases of CDH are Bochdalek hernia. It occurs due to the failure of contribution of pleuroperitoneal membrane to the diaphragm.

  b. ***Morgagni hernia (retrosternal or parasternal hernia):*** It occurs through foramen of Morgagni or space of Larry.

  c. ***Diaphragmatic eventration***: It refers to abnormal contour of diaphragmatic dome because of paralysis, aplasia, or atrophy to varying degrees of muscle fibres.

  Acquired diaphragmatic hernia may be (traumatic hernia) sliding hiatal hernia or rolling hiatal hernia (Fig. 26.7).

  a. In ***sliding hernia***, a part of stomach protrudes into thoracic cavity through oesophageal opening of the diaphragm. It occurs due to old age, obesity, chronic cough and so on. It may result in *gastroesophageal reflux disease* (*GERD*) and gastric ulcers. Sliding hernia is the commonest of all the internal hernias.

  b. ***Rolling hiatal hernia***: In this, paraesophageal junction remains within the abdominal cavity and fundus of stomach bulges into the thoracic cavity.

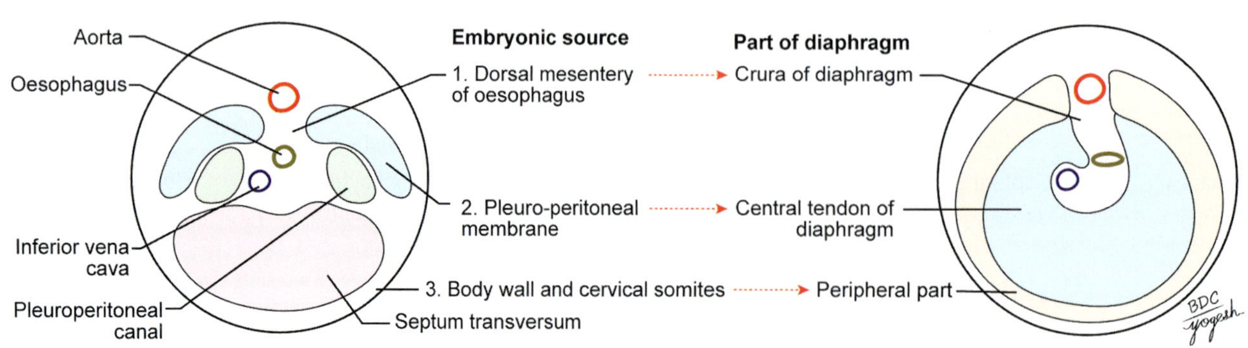

Fig. 26.4: Development of diaphragm (*Previous concept*: Septum transversum forms the central tendon of the diaphragm)

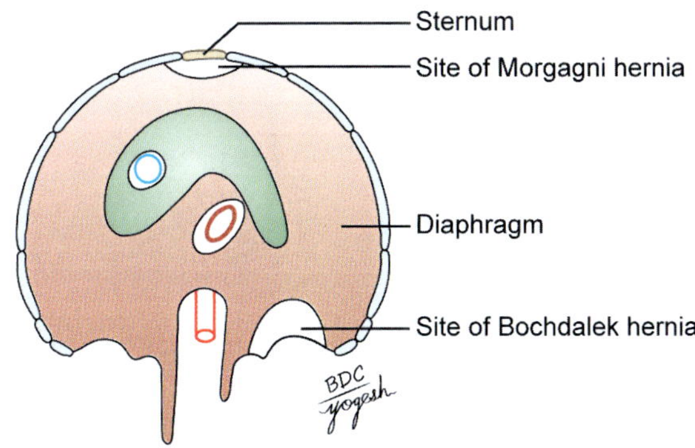

Fig. 26.6: Sites of Bochdelek and Morgagni hernia

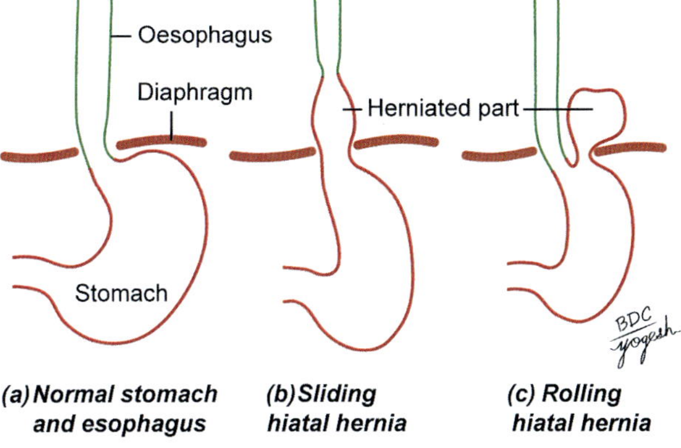

Figs 26.7a to c: Acquired diaphragmatic hernia

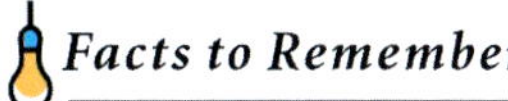

Facts to Remember

- Diaphragm is the principal muscle of inspiration.
- Right dome of diaphragm lies higher than left due to location of liver.
- The sole motor nerve supply of the diaphragm is phrenic nerve (C4). It develops in the neck, but is carried downwards due to developmental factors.
- Inferior vena caval opening is in the central tendon. During inspiration, the opening gets dilated allowing increased venous return.
- Right crus of diaphragm acts as a sphincter at the gastro-oesophageal junction.
- Hiatal hernia may be of rolling or sliding type. The rolling type is usually congenital while the sliding type is usually acquired.

BDC's Anatomy *e*-book

1. Diaphragmatic hernia
2. Further reading
3. Viva voce questions

Chapter

27

Posterior Abdominal Wall

The posterior abdominal wall extends from the 12th rib above to the pelvic brim below. It includes iliac fossa or false pelvis. The demarcation between the posterior abdominal wall and anterolateral abdominal wall is not clearly defined.

The posterior abdominal wall consists of several layers such as (posterior to anterior):

1. Skin
2. Superficial fascia
3. Deep fascia
4. Muscles
5. Extraperitoneal fat
6. Parietal peritoneum.

The posterior abdominal wall consists of the following parts (Plate 27.1):

1. ***Bony part***: It lies in the median plane. It consists of five lumbar vertebra and their intervertebral discs.
2. ***Muscular part***: It is supported by psoas major, quadratus lumborum and transverse abdominis. In the false pelvis, it is supported by iliacus. Posterior to these muscles, the muscles of back (erector spinae, latissimus dorsi and serratus posterior inferior) also support the posterior abdominal wall.
3. ***Fasciae***: The muscles of posterior abdominal wall are supported by fascia iliaca and thoracolumbar fascia.

The posterior abdominal wall includes the study of the following structures:

1. Muscles of the posterior abdominal wall and thoracolumbar fascia
2. Abdominal aorta
3. Inferior vena cava
4. Abdominal parts of the azygos and hemiazygos veins
5. Lymph nodes of posterior abdominal wall and cisterna chyli
6. Nerves of the posterior abdominal wall including lumbar plexus and the abdominal part of autonomic nervous system.

Competency:

AN45.3 Mention the major subgroups of back muscles, nerve supply and action.

MUSCLES OF THE POSTERIOR ABDOMINAL WALL

The posterior abdominal wall consists of muscles (Flowchart 27.1):

1. Psoas major
2. Iliacus
3. Quadratus lumborum
4. Psoas minor (frequently absent).

Their origin and insertion are described in Table 27.1 and nerve supply and actions are given in Table 27.2. Some additional facts about the psoas major (Fig. 27.3) are given below.

Note: The psoas and the iliacus are together known as the ***iliopsoas***, due to their common insertion and actions (Plate 27.2).

Flowchart 27.1: Muscles of the posterior abdominal wall

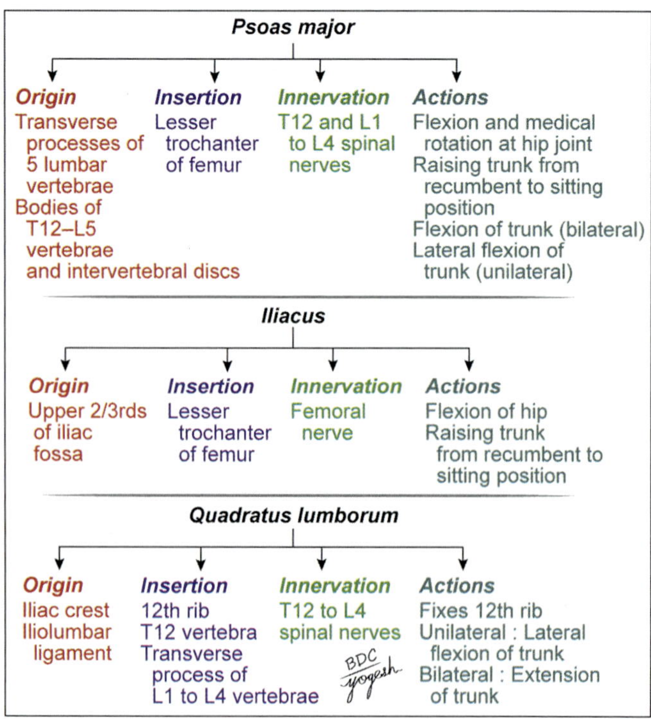

Plate 27.1: Bones and muscles forming the posterior abdominal wall

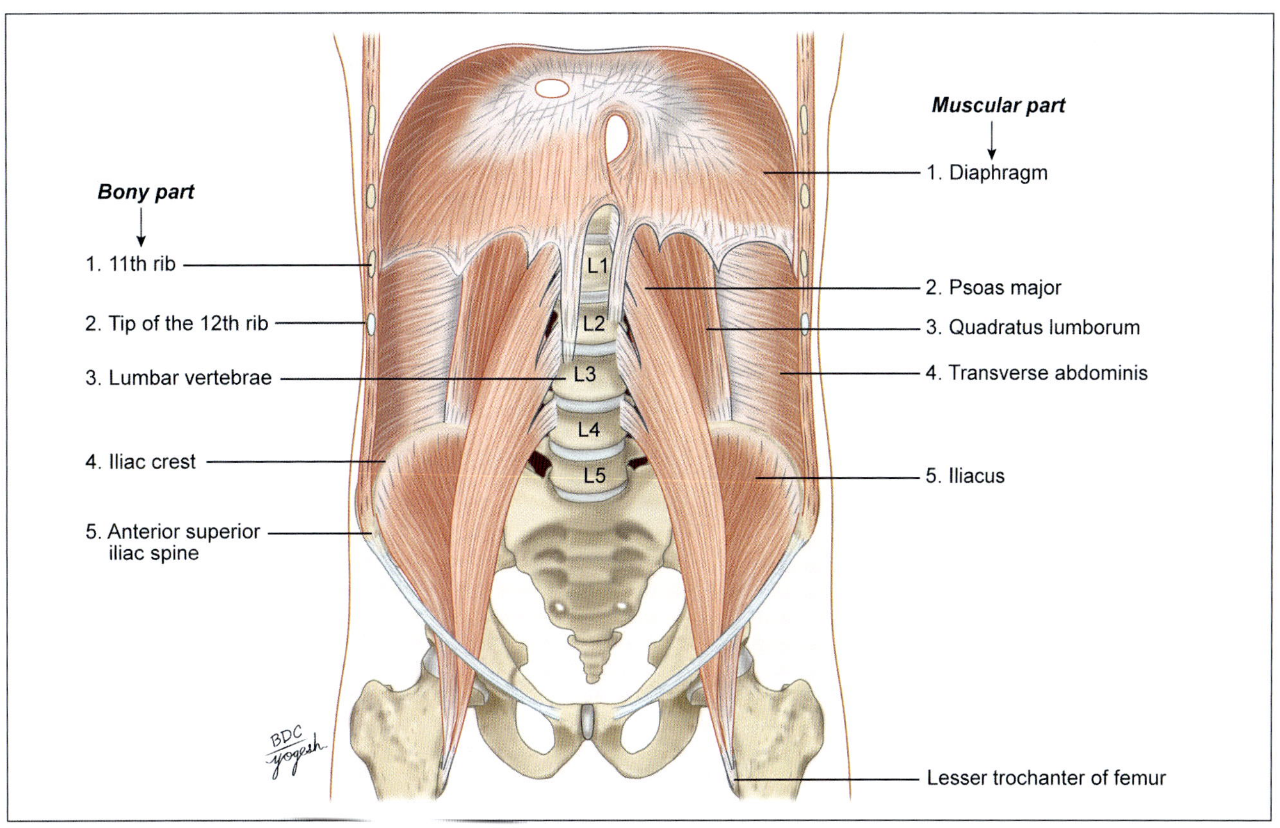

TABLE 27.1: Origin and insertion of muscles of the posterior abdominal wall

Muscle	*Origin*	*Insertion*
1. **Psoas major** Fusiform muscle, placed on the side of the lumbar spine and along the brim of the pelvis	a. From anterior surfaces and lower borders of transverse process of all ***lumbar vertebrae***. b. By ***5 slips***, one each from the bodies of two adjacent vertebrae and their intervertebral discs, from vertebrae T12 to L5 c. From ***4 tendinous arches*** extending across the constricted parts of the bodies of lumbar vertebrae, between the preceding slips. The origin is a continuous one from the lower border of T12 to upper border of L5	The muscle passes behind the inguinal ligament and in front of the hip joint to enter the thigh. It ends in a tendon which receives the fibres of the iliacus on its lateral side to form ***iliopsoas tendon***. It is then inserted into the tip and medial part of the anterior surface of the ***lesser trochanter of the femur*** (*see* Fig. 2.11a)
2. **Iliacus** Triangular muscle	a. Upper 2/3rd of ***iliac fossa*** b. Inner lip of the iliac crest and the ventral sacroiliac and iliolumbar ligaments c. Upper surface of the lateral part of the sacrum	Lateral part of anterior surface of the ***lesser trochanter***. The insertion extends for 2.5 cm below the trochanter
3. **Quadratus lumborum** Quadrate muscle, lying in the lumbar region. Note: Its origin lies below and the insertion is above (Plate 27.3)	a. Transverse process of ***L5 vertebra*** b. Iliolumbar ligament c. Adjoining 5 cm of the inner lip of the ***iliac crest***	a. Transverse processes of ***L1 to L4 vertebrae*** b. Medial half of the lower border of anterior surface of the ***12th rib***
4. **Psoas minor** A small muscle which lies in front of the psoas major. It is frequently absent.	Sides of the bodies of vertebrae ***T12 and L1*** and the disc between them	The muscle ends in a long, flat tendon which is inserted into the ***pecten pubis*** and the ***iliopubic eminence***

Plate 27.2: Iliacus and psoas major muscles

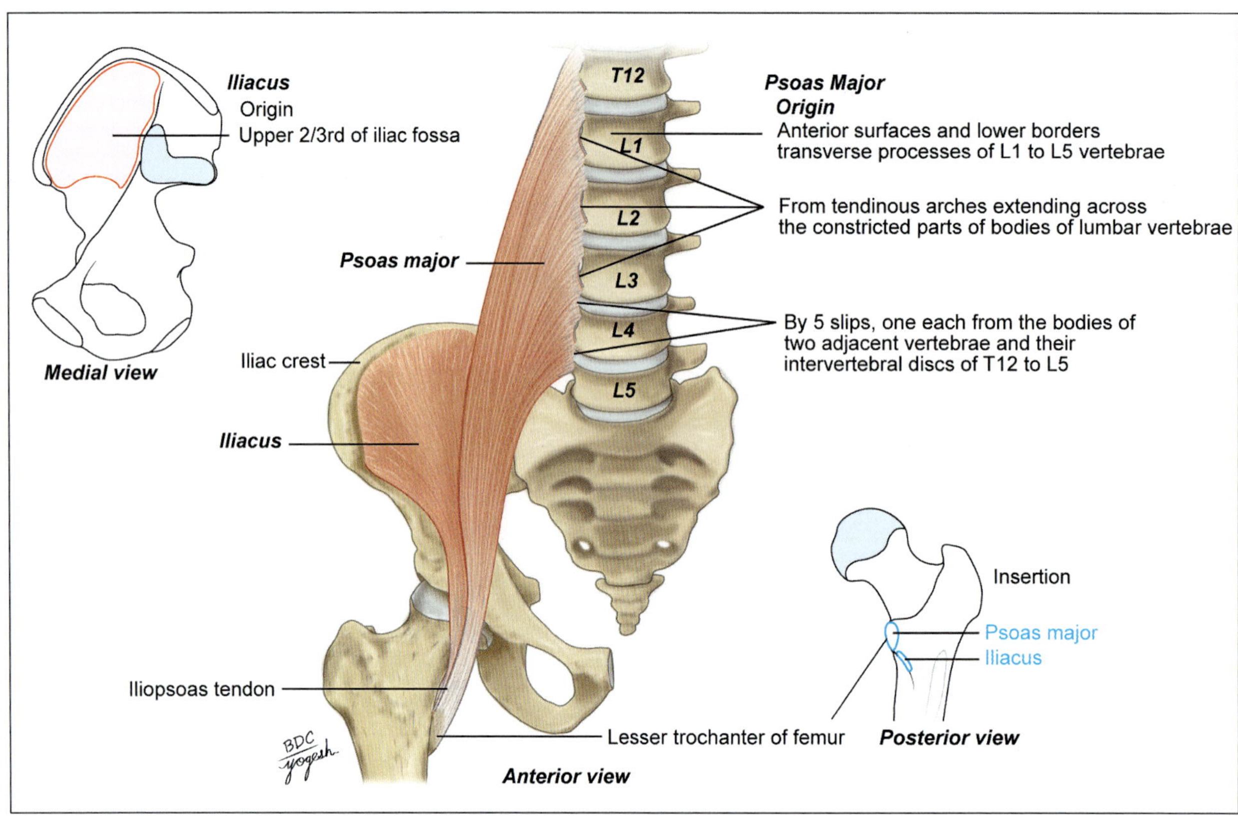

TABLE 27.2: Nerve supply and actions of muscles of the posterior abdominal wall

Muscle	*Nerve supply*	*Actions*
1. **Psoas major**	Ventral rami of L2, 3 and L4 spinal nerves	1. With the iliacus, it acts as a powerful flexor of the hip joint as in raising the trunk from recumbent to sitting posture 2. Helps in maintaining stability at the hip. Balances the trunk while sitting 3. When the muscle of one side acts alone, it brings about lateral flexion of the trunk on that side 4. It is a weak medial rotator of the hip. After fracture of the neck of the femur, the limb rotates laterally
2. **Iliacus**	Femoral nerve (L2, 3)	With the psoas, it flexes the hip joint
3. **Quadratus lumborum**	Ventral rami of T12 to L4 spinal nerves	1. Fixes the last rib during inspiration so that the contraction of the diaphragm takes place more effectively 2. When the pelvis is fixed, it may cause lateral flexion of the vertebral column 3. The muscles of both sides acting together can extend the lumbar vertebral column
4. **Psoas minor**	Ventral ramus of L1 spinal nerve	Weak flexor of the trunk

Nerves Emerging from the Psoas Major Muscle

From the lateral border (above downwards) (Plate 27.4, Fig. 26.3)

1. Subcostal nerve (T12)
2. Iliohypogastric nerve (L1)
3. Ilioinguinal nerve (L1)
4. Lateral cutaneous nerve of thigh (L1 and L2)
5. Femoral nerve (L2, L3 and L4).

From anterior surface

1. Genitofemoral nerve (L1 and L2).

From medial border

1. Lumbosacral trunk
2. Obturator nerve (L2, L3, L4).

Note: Subcostal nerve runs along with subcostal vessels.

CLINICAL ANATOMY

Psoas abscess (Fig. 27.1)**:** The psoas is enclosed in the psoas sheath, a part of the lumbar fascia. The sheath is formed by psoas fascia. The attachments of fascia:

Plate 27.3: Quadratus lumborum

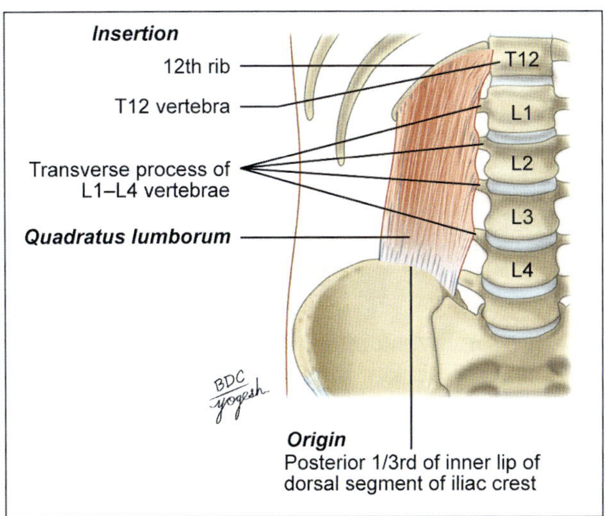

Plate 27.4: Nerves piercing the psoas major muscle

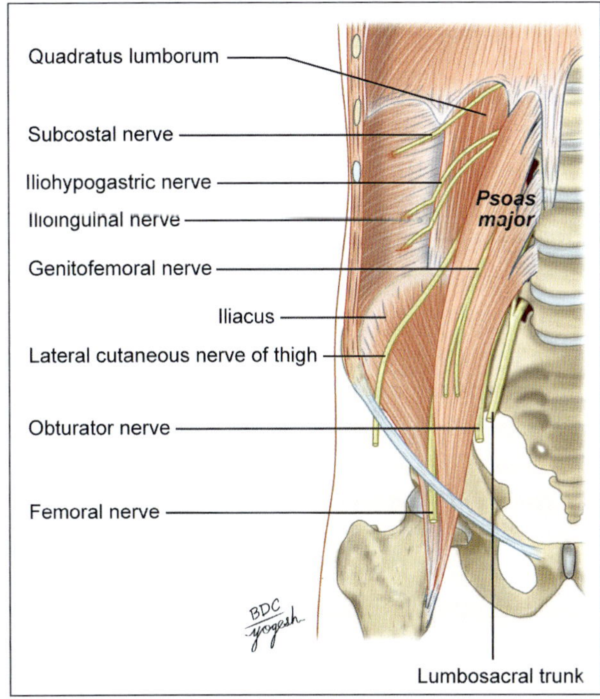

a. *Medial*: Bodies of lumbar vertebrae with intervertebral discs and 4 tendinous arches.
b. *Lateral*: Fuses with anterior layer of thoracolumbar fascia.
c. *Superior*: It is thickened to form medial arcuate ligament extending between body of L1 vertebra and transverse process of L1.
d. *Inferior*: Fuses with fascia covering iliacus muscle. Pus from tubercular infection of the thoracic and lumbar vertebrae may track down through the sheath into the thigh, producing a soft swelling in the femoral triangle.

The typical posture of a laterally rotated lower limb following fracture of the neck of the femur is produced by contraction of the psoas muscle.

Lumbosacral Triangle of Marcille

It is a triangular space located on each side of L5 vertebra (Fig. 27.2).

Boundaries

Medial: Body of L5 vertebra

Lateral: Medial border of psoas major muscle *Inferior* (base): Ala of sacrum

Apex is directed upward.

Floor (posterior wall): Transverse process of L5 vertebra and iliolumbar ligament.

Contents

It contains four structures (medial to lateral):

1. **S**ympathetic trunk
2. **L**umbosacral trunk
3. **I**liolumbar artery
4. **O**bturator nerve [*Mnemonics*: **SLIO**].

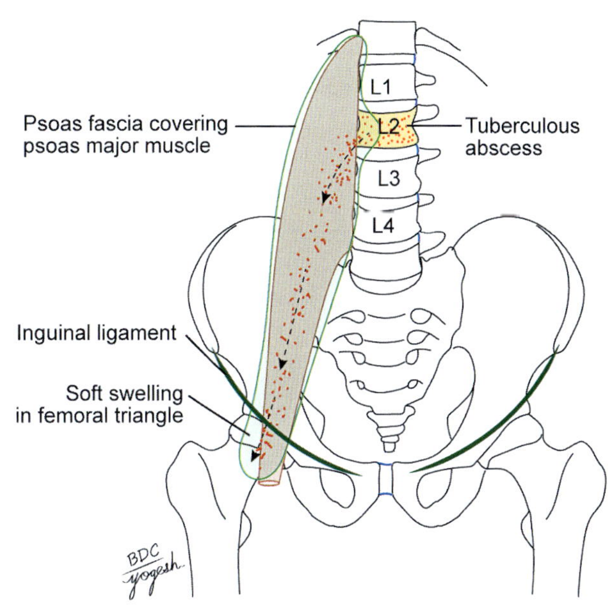

Fig. 27.1: Psoas abscess

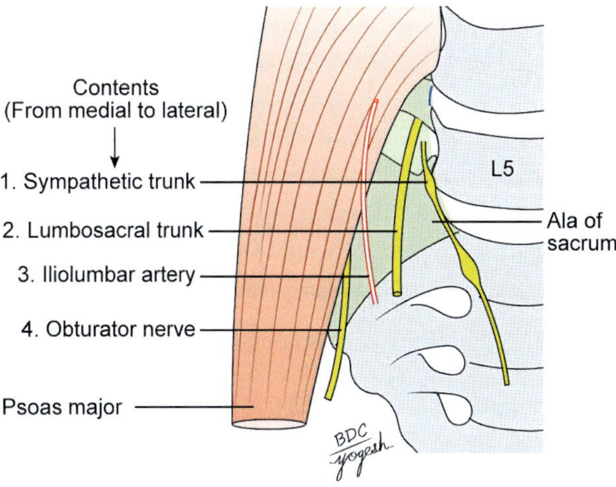

Fig. 27.2: Lumbosacral triangle (of Marcille)

Competency:
AN45.1 Describe thoracolumbar fascia.

FASCIAE OF THE POSTERIOR ABDOMINAL WALL

The fasciae of posterior abdominal wall are:
1. Psoas fascia
2. Fascia iliaca
3. Thoraco-lumbar fascia.

Psoas Fascia

It covers the anterior surface of psoas major muscle.

Attachments

- *Superiorly*: It merges with medial arcuate ligament.
- *Inferiorly*: It extends downward in the thigh around the iliopsoas tendon.
- *Medially*: It is attached to the bodies and discs of lumbar vertebrae and tendinous arches.
- *Laterally*: It blends with anterior layer of thoracolumbar fascia and iliac fascia.

Iliac Fascia

It covers the anterior surface of iliacus.

Attachments

- *Superiorly*: It blends with psoas fascia.
- *Inferiorly*: It continues in thigh to form posterior layer of femoral sheath.
- *Medially*: It is attached to ala of sacrum, pelvic brim and iliopubic eminence.
- *Laterally*: It is attached to iliac crest and fascia transversalis.

Structures of Piercing Iliopsoas Fascia

1. Genitofemoral nerve
2. Iliohypogastric nerve
3. Ilioinguinal nerve
4. Fourth lumbar artery
5. Lumbosacral trunk
6. Iliolumbar artery
7. Obturator nerve.

Thoracolumbar Fascia (Lumbar Fascia)

Lumbar fascia is the fascia enclosing the deep muscles of the back. It has thoracic and lumbar parts (Fig. 27.3, Flowchart 27.2).

Extent

The posterior layer covers the loin and is continued upwards on the back of the thorax and neck. The middle and anterior layers are confined to the lumbar region.

Thoracic Part of the Thoracolumbar Fascia

Attachments

Medially: To the spines of thoracic vertebrae.

Laterally: To the angles of the ribs.

Above: Extends into the cervical region deep to the serratus posterior superior to fuse with fascia of the neck.

Lumbar Part of the Thoracolumbar Fascia

It is made up of three layers—posterior, middle and anterior. The posterior layer is the thickest and the anterior layer is the thinnest. Their attachments are as follows:

Posterior layer

Medially: To the tips of the lumbar and sacral spines and the interspinous ligaments.

Laterally: Blends with the middle layer at the lateral border of the erector spinae.

Superiorly: Continues onto the back of the thorax where it is attached to the vertebral spines and the angles of the ribs.

Inferiorly: To the posterior 1/4th of the outer lip of the iliac crest.

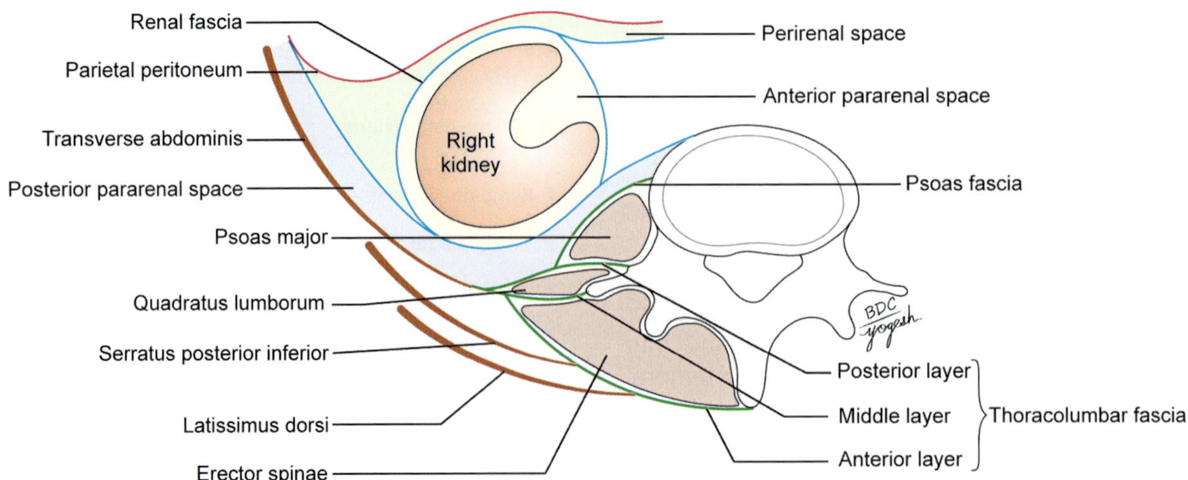

Fig. 27.3: Thoracolumbar fascia and spaces of peritoneum (transverse section through lumbar region)

Flowchart 27.2: Thoracolumbar fascia

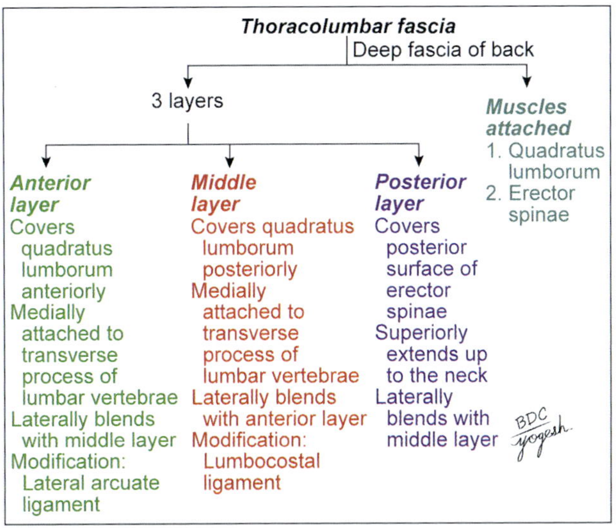

Middle layer

Medially: To the tips of the lumbar transverse processes and the intertransverse ligaments.

Laterally: Blends with the anterior layer at the lateral border of the quadratus lumborum.

Superiorly: To the lower border of the 12th rib and to the lumbocostal ligament.

Inferiorly: To the posterior part of the intermediate area of the iliac crest.

Anterior layer

Medially: To the vertical ridges on the anterior surface of the lumbar transverse processes.

Laterally: Blends with the middle layer at the lateral border of the quadratus lumborum.

Superiorly: Forms the lateral arcuate ligament, extending from the tip of the first lumbar transverse process to the 12th rib.

Inferiorly: It is attached to the inner lip of the iliac crest and the iliolumbar ligament.

DISSECTION

Expose the centrally placed abdominal aorta and inferior vena cava to the right of aorta. Trace the ventral, lateral, posterior and terminal branches of abdominal aorta and the respective tributaries of inferior vena cava. Remove the big lymph nodes present in the posterior abdominal wall.

Identify the muscles of the posterior abdominal wall by removing their fascial coverings. These are psoas major, quadratus lumborum and iliacus. Avoid injury to the vessels and nerves related to the muscles.

Detach psoas major from the intervertebral discs and vertebral bodies and trace the lumbar vessels and the rami communicantes posteriorly deep to the tendinous arches from which psoas major arises. Dissect the genitofemoral nerve seen on the anterior surface of psoas major.

Trace the various branches of lumbar plexus, e.g. iliohypogastric, ilioinguinal, lateral cutaneous nerve of thigh and femoral nerve. These exit from the lateral border of psoas major. Identify obturator and lumbosacral trunk seen on the medial aspect of the muscle.

Locate the lumbar part of the right and left sympathetic chains. Trace their branches into the coeliac and superior mesenteric plexuses of nerves in addition to giving rami communicantes to the lumbar spinal nerves.

BLOOD VESSELS, MUSCLES AND NERVES

Competency:

AN47.9 Describe and identify the origin, course, important relations and branches of abdominal aorta, coeliac trunk, superior mesenteric and inferior mesenteric artery.

ABDOMINAL AORTA

Beginning, Course and Termination

Beginning: The abdominal aorta begins in the midline at the aortic opening of the diaphragm, opposite the lower border of vertebra T12 (Flowchart 27.3).

Course and termination: It runs downwards and slightly to the left in front of the lumbar vertebrae and ends in front of the lower part of the body of vertebra L4, about 1.25 cm to the left of the median plane, by dividing into the right and left common iliac arteries.

Due to the forward convexity of the lumbar vertebral column, aortic pulsations can be felt in the region of the umbilicus, particularly in slim persons.

Measurements

- *Length:* 10–11 cm
- *Width*: 2 cm.

Relations

Anteriorly

From above downwards, the aorta is related to:

1. Coeliac and aortic plexuses.
2. Body of the pancreas, with the splenic vein embedded in its posterior surface.
3. Third part of the duodenum.

Posteriorly

The aorta is related to:

1. Bodies of L1 to L4 vertebrae and the corresponding intervertebral discs
2. Anterior longitudinal ligament.

Right Side

To the right side of the aorta, there are:
Inferior vena cava.

Left Side

To the left side of the aorta, there are:

1. Left sympathetic chain
2. Left crus of the diaphragm.

Flowchart 27.3: Abdominal aorta

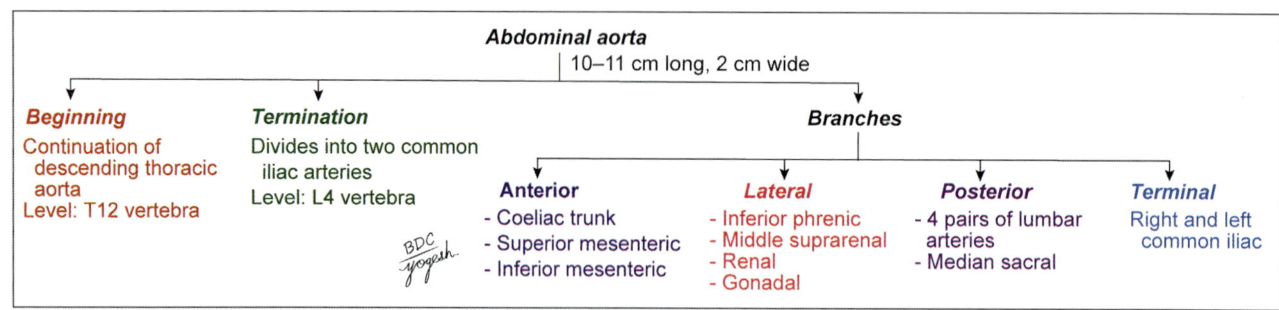

Branches

Ventral or anterior branches: They develop from *ventral splanchnic* or *vitelline arteries* and supply the gut. These are as follows (Plate 27.5, Fig. 27.4):

a. Coeliac trunk (*see* Chapter 21, page 288) gives left gastric, common hepatic and splenic branches.
b. Superior mesenteric artery (*see* Chapter 21, page 289) gives inferior pancreaticoduodenal, middle colic, right colic, ileocolic and 12–15 jejunal and ileal branches.
c. Inferior mesenteric artery (*see* Chapter 21, page 290) gives left colic, sigmoid arteries and continues as superior rectal artery.

Lateral branches: They develop from the *lateral splanchnic* or *mesonephric arteries* and supply the viscera derived from the intermediate mesoderm. These are right and left:

a. Inferior phrenic arteries
b. Middle suprarenal arteries
c. Renal arteries
d. Testicular or ovarian arteries.

Dorsal or posterior branches: They represent the *somatic intersegmental* arteries and are distributed to the body wall.

These are:

a. Lumbar arteries—four pairs.
b. Median sacral artery—unpaired.

Terminal branches: They are a pair of common iliac arteries. They supply the pelvis and lower limbs.

Note:

1. ***Inferior phrenic arteries*** arise from the aorta just above the coeliac trunk. Each artery runs upwards and laterally on the corresponding crus of the diaphragm, medial to the suprarenal gland. Each artery gives off two to three ***superior suprarenal arteries*** and is then distributed to the diaphragm.
2. **Middle *suprarenal arteries*** arise at the level of the superior mesenteric artery. Each passes laterally and slightly upwards over the corresponding crus of the diaphragm, to reach the gland (*see* Fig. 25.3).
3. ***Renal arteries*** are large arteries, which arise from the abdominal aorta just below the level of origin of the superior mesenteric artery. The ***right renal artery*** passes laterally behind the inferior vena cava to reach the hilum of the right kidney. The ***left renal artery*** runs behind the left renal vein and the splenic vein. Each artery gives off the ***inferior suprarenal*** and ***ureteral branches*** and is then distributed to the kidney (Fig. 27.1).

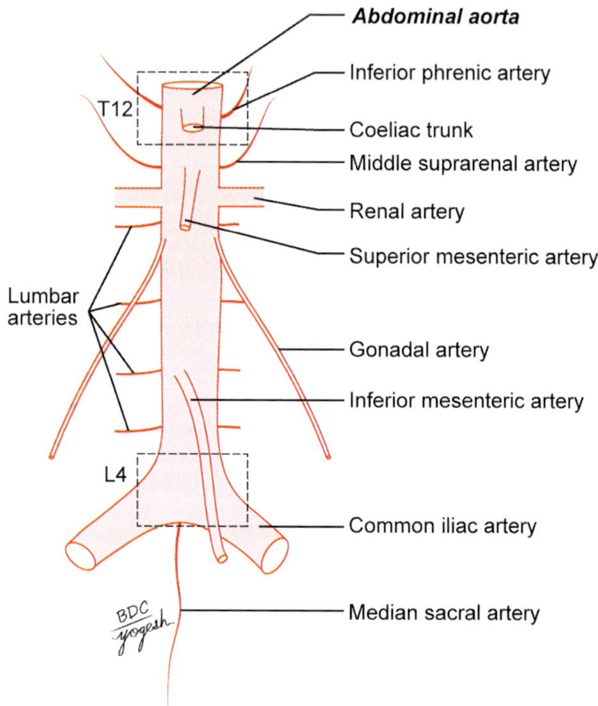

Fig. 27.4: Branches of abdominal aorta

4. **Gonadal (Testicular or Ovarian) arteries** are small and arise from the front of the aorta a little below the origin of the renal arteries. Each artery runs downwards and slightly laterally on the psoas major. On the right side, the artery crosses in front of the inferior vena cava, the ureter and the genitofemoral nerve. It passes deep into the ileum. On the left side, the artery crosses in front of the ureter and the genitofemoral nerve; and passes deep into the colon.

   The ***testicular artery*** joins the spermatic cord at the deep inguinal ring and traverses the inguinal canal. Within the cord, it lies anterior to the ductus deferens. At the upper pole of the testis, it breaks up into branches which supply the testis and the epididymis.

   The ***ovarian artery*** crosses the external iliac vessels at the pelvic brim to enter the suspensory or infundibulopelvic ligament of the ovary. It thus enters the broad ligament and runs below the uterine tube to reach the ovary through the mesovarium. The artery gives a branch, which continues medially to anastomose with the uterine artery, and supplies twigs to the uterine tube and to the pelvic part of the ureter.
5. ***Lumbar arteries*:** Four pairs of lumbar arteries arise from the aorta opposite the bodies of the upper four lumbar vertebrae. The small 5th pair is usually represented by the lumbar branches of the iliolumbar arteries (Fig. 27.1).

Plate 27.5: Branches of abdominal aorta

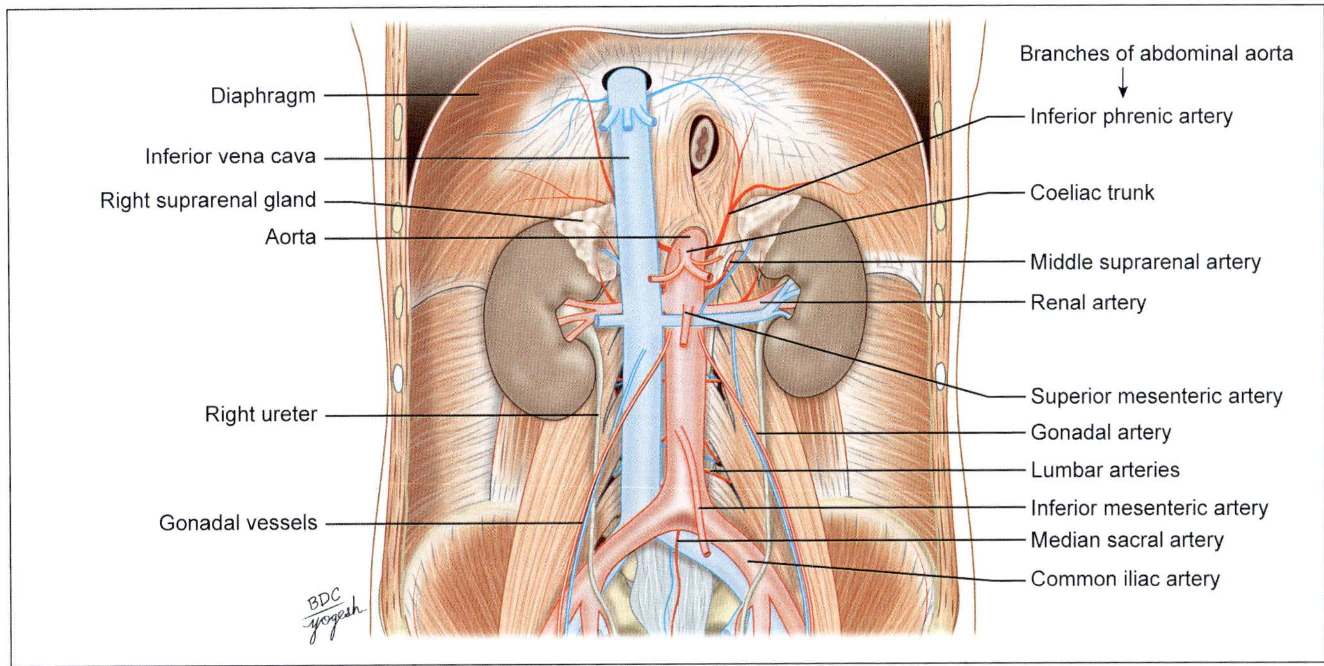

The ***upper four lumbar arteries*** run across the sides of the bodies of the upper four lumbar vertebrae, passing deep to the crura (upper arteries only), deep to the psoas major and the quadratus lumborum to end in small branches between the transversus and internal oblique muscles. Each artery gives off a dorsal branch, which arises at the root of the transverse process. The dorsal branch gives off a spinal branch to the vertebral canal and then runs backwards to supply the muscles and skin of the back.

6. ***Median sacral artery*** represents the continuation of the primitive dorsal aorta. It arises from the back of the aorta just above the bifurcation of the latter and runs downwards to end in front of the coccyx. It supplies the rectum and anastomoses with the iliolumbar and lateral sacral arteries (*see* Table A2.1; Appendix 2).

Competency:
AN47.9 Describe and identify the origin, course, important relations and branches of common iliac artery.

Common Iliac Arteries

These are the terminal branches of the abdominal aorta, beginning in front of vertebra L4, 1.25 cm to the left of the median plane.

On each side, it passes downwards and laterally and ends in front of the sacroiliac joint, at the level of the lumbosacral intervertebral disc, by dividing into the external and internal iliac arteries.

The ***right common iliac artery*** passes in front of the commencement of the inferior vena cava. The right common iliac vein is posterior to the vena cava above and medial to it below.

The ***left common iliac artery*** is shorter than the right artery. It is crossed at its middle by the inferior mesenteric vessels. The left common iliac vein is medial to it. The structures lying on the left ala of the sacrum, i.e. sympathetic trunk, lumbosacral trunk, iliolumbar artery and obturator nerve are deep to it.

CLINICAL ANATOMY

- ***Aortic aneurysm*** is localized dilatation of abdominal aorta (Fig. 27.5). It usually occurs in infrarenal part of abdominal aorta and commonly in elderly men those who are suffering from atherosclerosis.
- ***Pulsation of abdominal aorta***: In normal individual, the abdominal pulsation cannot be felt. Pulsation of abdominal wall aorta can be felt in the following cases:
  - Tumours of structures overlying the aorta
  - Aortic aneurysm.
- ***Fatal rupture of aortic aneurysm***: If rupture is suspected in aortic aneurysm, it is fatal in about 90% cases due to heavy blood loss.

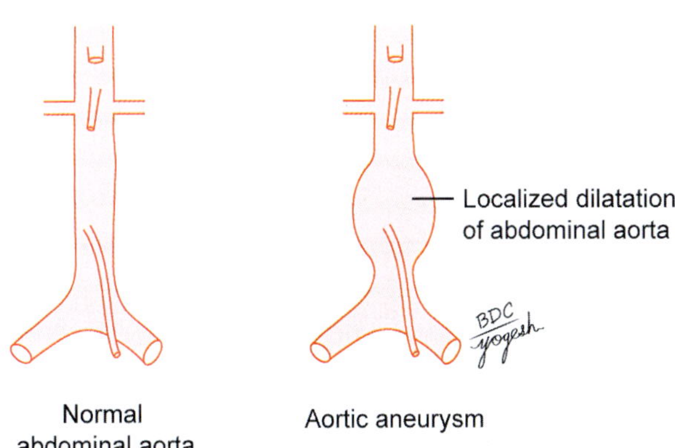

Fig. 27.5: Aortic aneurysm

Competency:

AN47.8 Describe and identify the formation, course relations and tributaries of portal vein, inferior vena cava and renal vein.

INFERIOR VENA CAVA

The inferior vena cava is formed by the union of the right and left common iliac veins on the right side of the body of vertebra L5 (Flowchart 27.4).

It ascends in front of the vertebral column, on the right side of the aorta, grooves the posterior surface of the liver, pierces the central tendon of the diaphragm at the level of vertebra T8 and opens into the lower and posterior part of the right atrium (*see* Fig. 26.1).

Relations

Anteriorly

From above downwards, inferior vena cava is related to:
1. Posterior surface of the liver
2. Epiploic foramen
3. First part of the duodenum and the portal vein
4. Head of the pancreas along with the bile duct
5. Third part of duodenum
6. Right gonadal artery.

Posteriorly

The IVC is related to the following structures posteriorly from above downward:
1. Right crus of diaphragm
2. Right suprarenal gland
3. Right renal, middle suprarenal and phrenic arteries
4. Bodies of lower three lumbar vertebrae
5. Right psoas major
6. Right sympathetic trunk.

On the Right

1. Bare of area of liver
2. Hepatorenal pouch of Morrison
3. Second part of duodenum
4. Right kidney
5. Right ureter.

On the Left

1. Caudate lobe of liver
2. Lesser sac
3. Right crus of diaphragm
4. Cisterna chyli
5. Aorta.

Tributaries (Fig. 27.6)

A. Formative tributaries
   1. Right common iliac vein
   2. Left common iliac vein
   3. Median sacral vein.

B. From abdominal wall
   1. Inferior phrenic vein
   2. Third and fourth lumbar veins.

C. From abdominal viscera
   1. Right suprarenal vein
   2. Right and left renal veins
   3. Right testicular or ovarian vein
   4. From liver: Right, middle and left hepatic veins.

[*Mnemonics*: ***Inferior vena cava tributaries "I** like **To Rise So High":*** **I**liac veins, **L**umbar veins, **T**esticular veins, **R**enal veins, **S**uprarenal veins, **H**epatic veins]

Note:
1. ***Common iliac veins*** formed by the union of the external and internal iliac veins unite to form the inferior vena cava. Each vein receives an iliolumbar vein. The median sacral vein joins the left common iliac vein (Fig. 27.1).
   a. The ***third*** and ***fourth lumbar veins*** run along with the corresponding arteries and open into the posterior aspect of the inferior vena cava. The veins of the left side cross behind the aorta to reach the vena cava. The *first* and *second lumbar veins* end in the ascending lumbar vein, on the right and the left sides. The ***ascending lumbar vein*** is an anastomotic channel which connects the lateral sacral, iliolumbar and the subcostal veins. It lies within the psoas muscle in front of the roots of the transverse processes of the lumbar vertebrae. On joining the subcostal vein, it forms the azygos vein on the right side and the hemiazygos vein on the left side.
2. The ***right testicular*** or ***ovarian vein*** opens into the inferior vena cava just below the entrance of the renal veins. *The left gonadal vein drains into the left renal vein* (Fig. 27.1).
3. The ***renal veins*** join the inferior vena cava just below the transpyloric plane. Each renal vein lies in front of the corresponding artery. The right vein is shorter than the left and lies behind the second part of the duodenum. The left vein crosses in front of the aorta and lies behind the pancreas and the splenic vein. It receives the left suprarenal and gonadal veins (Fig. 27.1).

Flowchart 27.4: Inferior vena cava

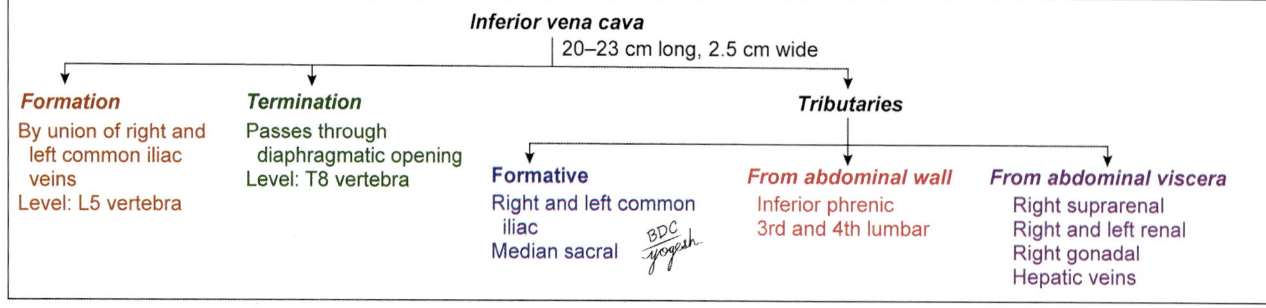

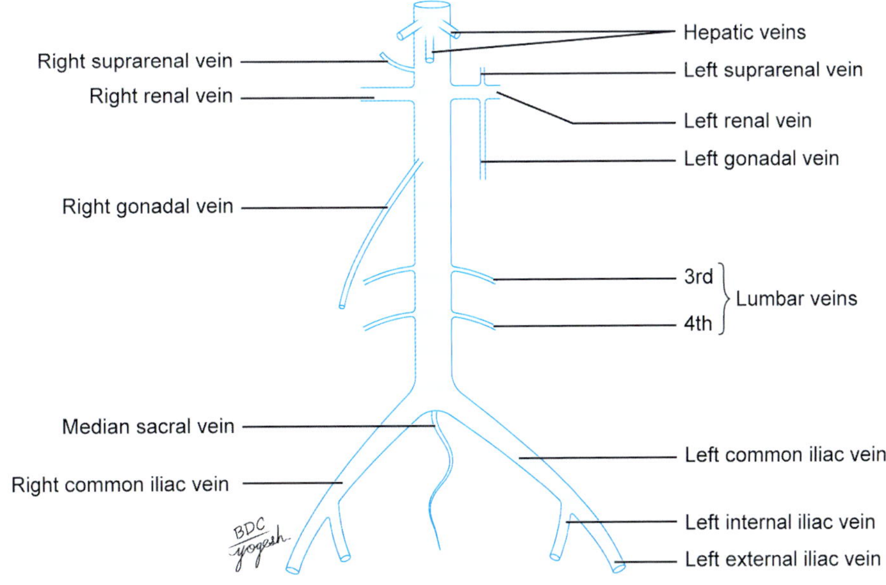

Fig. 27.6: Tributaries of the inferior vena cava

4. The ***right suprarenal vein*** is extremely short. It emerges from the hilum of the gland and soon opens into the inferior vena cava. The left suprarenal vein opens into the left renal vein (*see* Fig. 25.4).
5. The ***hepatic veins*** are three large and many small veins which open directly into the anterior surface of the inferior vena cava just before it pierces the diaphragm. These act as important support of liver.

Flowchart 27.5: Development of inferior vena cava

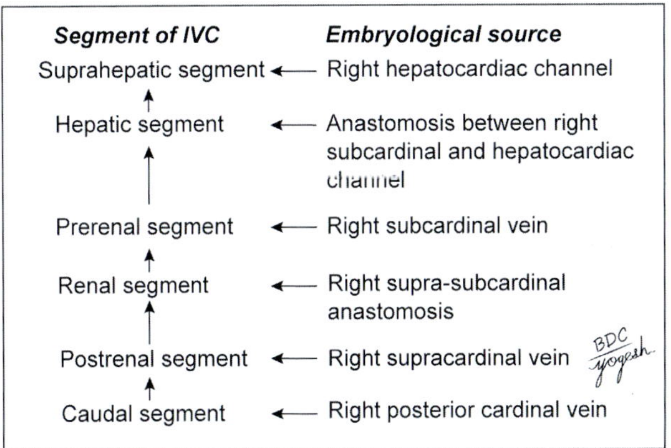

Segment of IVC	*Embryological source*
Suprahepatic segment ←	Right hepatocardiac channel
Hepatic segment ←	Anastomosis between right subcardinal and hepatocardiac channel
Prerenal segment ←	Right subcardinal vein
Renal segment ←	Right supra-subcardinal anastomosis
Postrenal segment ←	Right supracardinal vein
Caudal segment ←	Right posterior cardinal vein

Development of Inferior Vena Cava

The inferior vena cava develops from the following components (Fig. 27.7, Flowchart 27.5):

1. *Caudal segment of IVC*: From caudal part of right posterior cardinal vein (between transverse inter-posterior cardinal veins and caudal to junction of right supracardinal vein with right posterior cardinal vein).
2. *Postrenal segment of IVC*: From right supracardinal vein.
3. *Renal segment*: From right supra-subcardinal anastomosis.
4. *Prerenal segment*: From right subcardinal vein.
5. *Hepatic segment*: From anastomosis between right subcardinal vein and right vitelline veins (common hepatic veins).
6. *Suprahepatic segment*: From right vitelline vein or right hepatocardiac channel (left hepatocardiac channel disappears due to regression of left horn of sinus venosus).

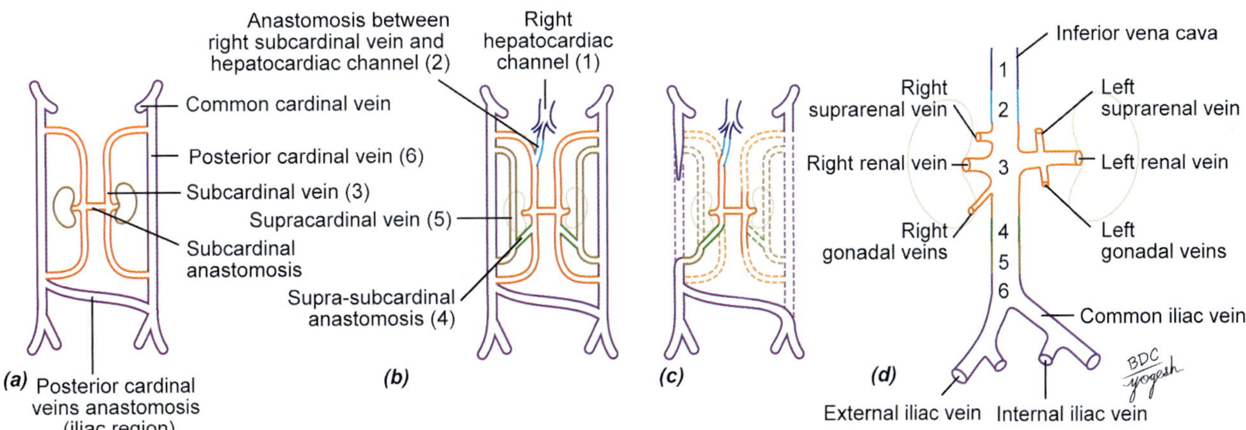

Figs 27.7a to d: Development of inferior vena cava

CLINICAL ANATOMY

Thrombosis in the inferior vena cava causes oedema of the legs and back. The collateral venous circulation between the superior and inferior venae cavae (***caval-caval shunt***) is established through the superficial or deep veins, or both (Fig. 27.8).

The participating main superficial veins include

- Superficial epigastric
- Thoracoepigastric
- Lateral thoracic.
- Internal thoracic, posterior intercostal, external pudendal and lumbovertebral veins.

The deep veins are the azygos, hemiazygos and lumbar veins. The vertebral venous plexus may also provide an effective collateral circulation between the two venae cavae.

Most common site of abdominal aneurysm (dilatation of the vessel) is between the renal arteries and bifurcation of the abdominal aorta.

LYMPH NODES OF POSTERIOR ABDOMINAL WALL

The lymphatic vessels from the abdominal and pelvic viscera are drained by the following group of lymph nodes (Plate 27.6):

1. External iliac nodes
2. Common iliac nodes
3. Aortic lymph nodes: Preaortic and para-aortic.

Plate 27.6: Lymphatics and lymph nodes of the posterior abdominal wall

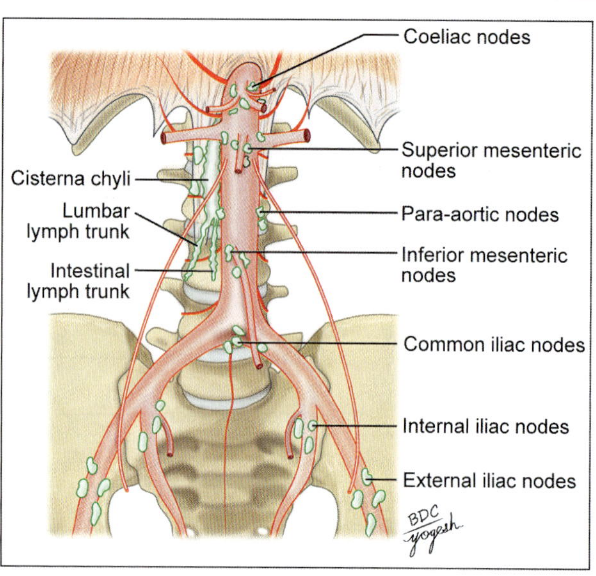

External Iliac Nodes

The *external iliac nodes,* 8 to 10 in number, lie along the external iliac vessels, being lateral, medial and anterior to them. They receive afferents from:

1. Inguinal lymph nodes
2. Deeper layers of the infraumbilical part of the anterior abdominal wall
3. Adductor region of the thigh

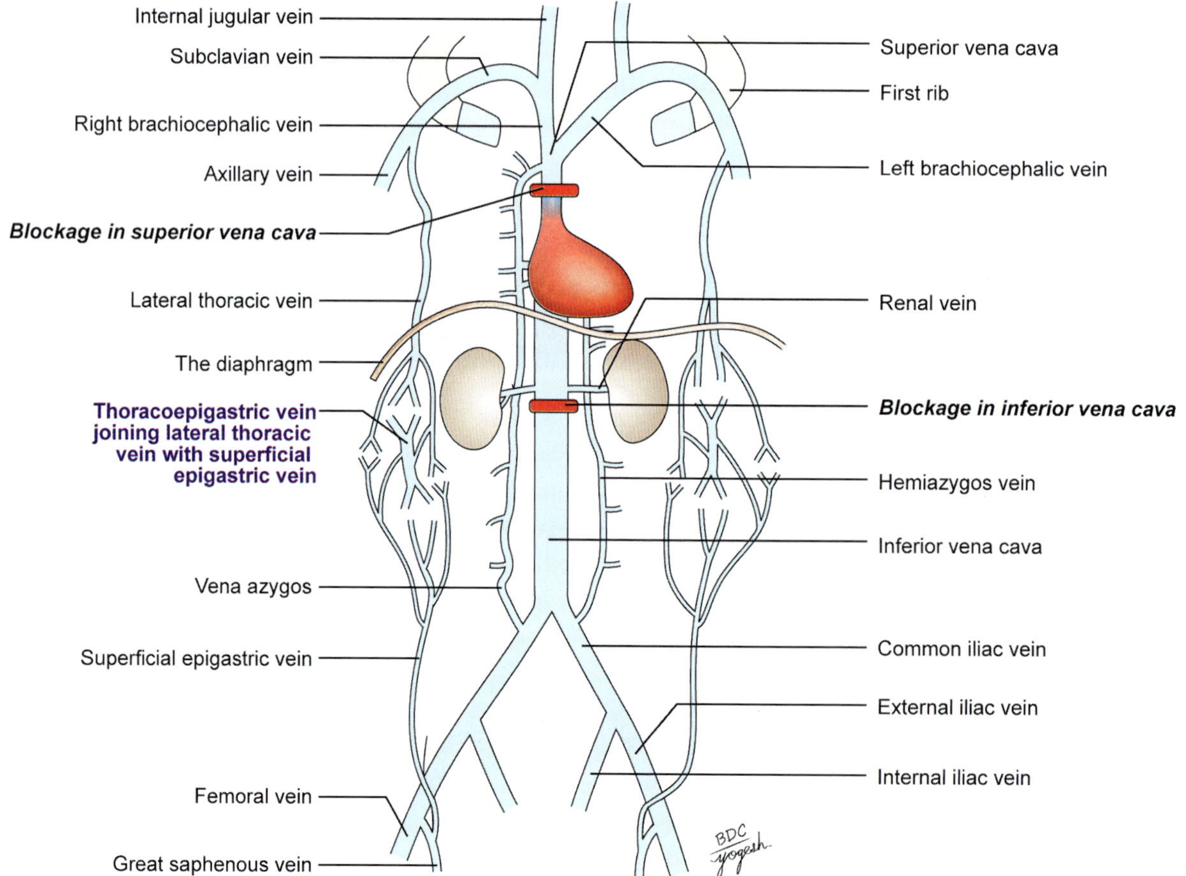

Fig. 27.8: Dilated veins in thrombosis of inferior vena cava or in obstruction of superior vena cava

4. Glans penis or clitoris
5. Membranous urethra
6. Prostate
7. Fundus of the urinary bladder
8. Cervix uteri
9. Part of the vagina.

Their efferents pass to common iliac nodes. The inferior epigastric and circumflex iliac nodes are outlying members of the external iliac group.

Common Iliac Nodes

The *common iliac nodes*, 4 to 6 in number, lie along the common iliac artery below the bifurcation of the aorta in front of vertebra L5 or in front of the sacral promontory. They receive afferents from the external and internal iliac nodes and send their efferents to the lateral aortic nodes (Fig. 27.1).

Aortic Lymph Nodes

The *lumbar* or *aortic nodes* are divided into preaortic and lateral aortic groups.

1. The ***preaortic nodes*** (Fig. 27.1) lie directly anterior to the abdominal aorta and are divisible into coeliac, superior mesenteric and inferior mesenteric groups. They receive afferents from intermediate nodes associated with the subdiaphragmatic part of the gastrointestinal tract, the liver, the pancreas and the spleen. Their efferents form the ***intestinal trunks*** which enter the cisterna chyli.
2. The ***lateral aortic nodes*** lie on each side of the abdominal aorta (Fig. 27.1). They receive afferents from the structures supplied by the lateral and dorsal branches of the aorta and from the common iliac nodes. Their efferents form a ***lumbar trunk*** on each side, both of which terminate in the cisterna chyli.

CISTERNA CHYLI

This is an elongated lymphatic sac, about 2 cm long and 1 cm wide (Plate 27.6).

It is situated in front of the L1 and L2 vertebrae, immediately to the right of the abdominal aorta. It is overlapped by the right crus of the diaphragm. Its upper end is continuous with the thoracic duct.

Tributaries

1. *Right and left intestinal lymphatic trunks*: The intestinal trunk brings lymph from the stomach, the intestine, the pancreas, the spleen and the anteroinferior part of the liver.
2. *Right and left lumbar trunks*: The lumbar trunks arise from the lateral aortic nodes and bring lymph from the lower limbs, the pelvic wall and viscera, the kidneys, the suprarenal glands, the testes or ovaries and the deeper parts of the abdominal wall.
3. A pair of lymphatic vessels form lower intercostal lymph nodes.

Competency:
AN45.2 Describe and demonstrate lumbar plexus for its root value, formation and branches.

NERVES OF THE POSTERIOR ABDOMINAL WALL

Lumbar Plexus

Lumbar plexus is a plexus of nerves formed in the substance of psoas major muscle by the ventral primary rami of L1 to L4 spinal nerve with a contribution of the subcostal nerve (Fig. 27.9).

Formation

The lumbar plexus is contributed by fibres of ventral primary rami of T12 and L1–L4 spinal nerves as follows:

1. Fibres of T12 and L1 form a common trunk that divides into:
   a. Larger upper branch which gives: *Iliohypogastric, ilioinguinal nerves*.
   b. Small lower branch that receives fibres from L2 nerve and continues as *genitofemoral nerve*.
2. Ventral rami of L2, L3 and L4 nerves divides into anterior and posterior divisions
   a. Anterior divisions of L2, L3 and L4 nerves join to form *obturator nerve*.
   b. Posterior divisions of L2 and L3 nerves join to form *lateral cutaneous nerve of thigh*.
   c. Posterior divisions of L2, L3 and L4 nerves join to form *femoral nerve*.
3. Lumbosacral trunk: Fibres of L4 nerve join with ventral ramus of L5 nerve to form lumbosacral trunk that enters in pelvis to contribute in sacral plexus.

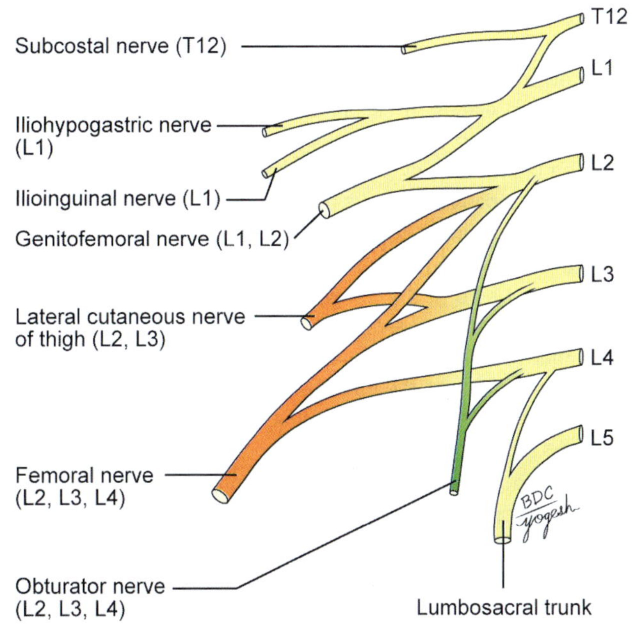

Fig. 27.9: Right lumbar plexus of nerves (dorsal divisions are shown by orange colour and ventral divisions by green colour)

Branches of Lumbar Plexus

The branches of lumbar plexus are:
1. Iliohypogastric nerve (L1)
2. Ilioinguinal nerve (L1)
3. Genitofemoral nerve (L1, L2)
4. Lateral cutaneous nerve of thigh (L2, L3)
5. Femoral nerve (L2, L3, L4)
6. Obturator nerve (L2, L3, L4)
7. Accessory obturator nerve (occasional) (L3, L4).

Note:
1. ***Iliohypogastric nerve (L1)***: It emerges at the lateral border of the psoas, runs downwards and laterally in front of the quadratus lumborum, and behind the kidney and colon, pierces the transversus abdominis a little above the iliac crest and runs in the abdominal wall supplying the anterolateral muscles (*see* Fig. 16.12).
2. ***Ilioinguinal nerve (L1)***: It has the same course as the iliohypogastric nerve, but on a slightly lower level. It exits through superficial inguinal ring.
3. ***Genitofemoral nerve*** (L1, L2 ventral divisions): It emerges on the anterior surface of the psoas muscle near its medial border and runs downwards in front of the muscle. Near the deep inguinal ring, it divides into femoral and genital branches.
   a. The ***femoral branch*** passes through the arterial compartment of the femoral sheath and is distributed to the skin of the upper part of the front of the thigh.
   b. The ***genital branch*** pierces the psoas sheath and enters the inguinal canal through the deep inguinal ring. In the male, it supplies the cremaster muscle, and in the female, it gives sensory branches to the round ligament of the uterus and to the skin of the labium majus.
4. **Lateral cutaneous nerve of the thigh** (L2, 3; dorsal divisions): It emerges at the lateral border of the psoas, runs downwards and laterally across the right iliac fossa, over the iliacus and reaches the anterior superior iliac spine. Here it enters the thigh by passing behind the lateral end of the inguinal ligament (*see* Fig. 3.15).
5. **Femoral nerve** (L2, 3, 4; dorsal divisions): It emerges at the lateral border of the psoas below the iliac crest and runs downwards and slightly laterally in the furrow between the psoas and iliacus. It lies under cover of the fascia iliaca. It passes deep to the inguinal ligament to enter the thigh lying on the lateral side of the femoral sheath. Before entering the thigh, it supplies the iliacus and pectineus. In thigh, it supplies quadriceps femoris and sartorius (*see* Fig. 3.28).
6. **Obturator nerve** (L2, 3, 4; ventral divisions): It emerges on the medial side of the psoas muscle and runs forwards and downwards on the pelvic wall, below the pelvic brim. Near its commencement, it is crossed by the internal iliac vessels and the ureter. It enters the thigh by passing through the obturator canal. It supplies 3 adductor muscles, obturator externus and gracilis (*see* Fig. 4.4).
7. **Lumbosacral trunk** (L4, 5 ventral rami): It is formed by union of the descending branch of nerve L4 with nerve L5. It enters the lesser pelvis by passing over and grooving the lateral part of the ala of the sacrum, posterior to the common iliac vessels and the medial part of the psoas. It is related medially to the sympathetic chain; and laterally to the iliolumbar artery and the obturator nerve (*see* Fig. 15.13). In the pelvis, it takes part in the formation of the sacral plexus.

Competency:
AN47.12 Describe important nerve plexuses of posterior abdominal wall.

ABDOMINAL PART OF THE AUTONOMIC NERVOUS SYSTEM

The abdomen is supplied by both sympathetic and parasympathetic nerves.

A. ***Sympathetic nerves***: The *sympathetic nerves* are derived from two sources:
   1. The ***lumbar sympathetic trunk*** supplies somatic branches to the lower abdominal wall and the lower limb; and visceral branches for the pelvic organs (Fig. 27.4).
   2. The ***coeliac plexus***, formed by splanchnic nerves from the thorax, supplies all the abdominal organs, including the gonads.

      Aortic plexus continues as superior hypogastric plexus supplemented by branches from L4, 5 ganglia.
B. ***Parasympathetic nerves***: The *parasympathetic nerves* are also derived from two sources.
   1. ***Vagus*** nerves — join the coeliac plexus.
   2. The ***pelvic splanchnic nerves*** join the inferior hypogastric plexus.

Lumbar Sympathetic Chain

It is a ganglionated chain situated on either side of bodies of lumbar vertebrae (Fig. 27.10).

Course and Relations

Each lumbar sympathetic chain is a downward continuation of thoracic sympathetic chain deep to the medial arcuate ligament of the diaphragm.

It runs vertically downward along the sides of bodies of lumbar vertebrae. On the right, it is overlapped by inferior vena cava and on the left, by the abdominal aorta.

Termination

It continues downward as *sacral sympathetic chain* in front of the ala of sacrum. These sacral sympathetic chains (right and left) converge in front of the coccyx to form *ganglion impar*.

Structure

Each lumbar sympathetic chain consists of *four ganglia*, the 1st and 2nd often fused together.

Branches

1. *White rami* communicantes: These are *preganglionic* sympathetic fibres from ventral primary rami of L1 and L2 spinal nerves. It also carries sensory fibres from abdominal viscera.
2. *Grey rami* communicantes: These are postganglionic fibres from sympathetic chain to the lumbar nerves.

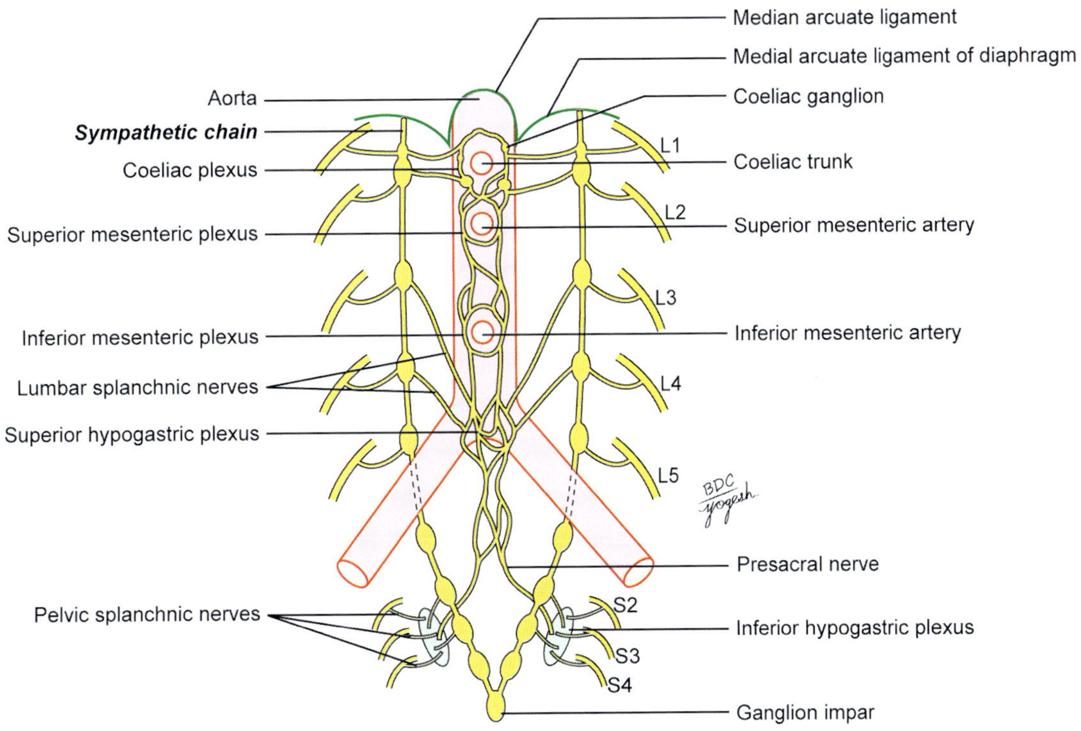

Fig. 27.10: Lumbar sympathetic chain and autonomic plexuses of the posterior abdominal wall

3. *Lumbar splanchnic nerves*: These are four lumbar splanchnic nerves that arise as medial branches of lumbar sympathetic chain. The upper two splanchnic nerves join coeliac and aortic plexuses, whereas lower two join the superior hypogastric plexus.

Autonomic Plexuses of the Posterior Abdominal Wall

There are three primary autonomic plexuses at the posterior abdominal wall (Fig. 27.10):

1. Coeliac plexus
2. Superior hypogastric plexus
3. Inferior hypogastric plexus.

Coeliac or Solar Plexus

It is the largest autonomic plexus.

Location: It is located around the coeliac trunk and root of superior mesenteric artery. Coeliac plexus is located at the level of T12 and L1 vertebrae.

Source of fibres: The following fibres contribute to the coeliac plexus:

1. Preganglionic sympathetic fibres from greater and lesser splanchnic nerves
2. Postganglionic sympathetic fibres from coeliac ganglia
3. Preganglionic parasympathetic fibres from vagus nerves
4. Some sensory fibres from the diaphragm.

Coeliac Ganglion

It is irregular neural mass situated one on each side of coeliac trunk. It is the largest ganglion in the body (Figs 27.11 and 27.12). It has two parts:

A. *Upper part*: It receives fibres from greater splanchnic nerves.

B. *Lower part* is called *aorticorenal ganglion*: It receives fibres from lesser splanchnic nerves and mostly contributes to renal plexus.

Branches

Coeliac plexus forms number of secondary plexuses that surround the branches abdominal aorta. These are as follows (Table 27.3):

1. Phrenic plexus
2. Hepatic plexus
3. Left gastric plexus
4. Splenic plexus
5. Suprarenal plexus
6. Renal plexus
7. Testicular plexus
8. Ovarian plexus
9. Superior mesenteric plexus
10. Intermesenteric plexus
11. Inferior mesenteric plexus.

Superior Hypogastric Plexus (Presacral Nerve)

Location: It lies in front of the bifurcation of the abdominal aorta at the level of body of L5 vertebra (Fig. 27.11).

Formation (Fig. 27.12)**:** It is formed by the following fibres:

1. *Sympathetic fibres* from aortic plexus and third and fourth lumbar splanchnic nerves.
2. *Parasympathetic fibres* from pelvic splanchnic nerves through inferior hypogastric plexus.

Branches

1. *Right and left hypogastric nerves* descend in the pelvis to form two inferior hypogastric plexuses.

TABLE 27.3: Secondary autonomic plexuses arising from coeliac plexus

Plexus	*Location (related blood vessel)*	*Distribution*
Phrenic plexus	Inferior phrenic artery	To diaphragm, suprarenal gland
Hepatic plexus	Hepatic artery	Receives fibres from right and left vagus nerves and right phrenic nerve To liver, gallbladder and bile duct
Left gastric plexus	Left gastric artery	To stomach
Splenic plexus	Splenic artery	To spleen
Suprarenal plexus	Suprarenal artery	To suprarenal gland. This plexus contains mainly preganglionic sympathetic fibres
Renal plexus	Renal artery	To kidney and upper part of ureter. It arises from aorticorenal ganglion and lower thoracic splanchnic nerves, first lumbar splanchnic nerve
Testicular plexus	Testicular artery	To epididymis and vas deferens
Ovarian plexus	Ovarian artery	To ovary and uterine tube
Superior mesenteric plexus	Superior mesenteric plexus	To the territory of superior mesenteric artery. It contains superior mesenteric ganglion
Intermesenteric or abdominal wall aortic plexus	In front of aorta, between superior and inferior mesenteric arteries	It is not a discrete structure. Connected with coeliac and inferior mesenteric plexus and to adjacent other plexuses
Inferior mesenteric plexus	Inferior mesenteric artery	To the territory of inferior mesenteric artery

2. Branches to ureteric, gonadal and common iliac plexuses.

Note: Superior hypogastric plexus is called *presacral nerve*, but the plexus does not form a single definable nerve. This plexus is located at the level of L5 vertebra. Hence, the name presacral nerve for this plexus is inappropriate.

Inferior Hypogastric Plexuses

There are two inferior hypogastric plexuses: Right and left. This plexus contains numerous small ganglia (Fig. 27.11).

Location: Inferior hypogastric plexuses lie in extraperitoneal connective tissue of the pelvis, on the side of the rectum.

Formation (Fig. 27.12)**:** It receives both sympathetic and parasympathetic fibres as follows:

1. *Sympathetic fibres* from superior hypogastric (presacral) nerve and from superior hypogastric plexuses.
2. *Parasympathetic fibres* from pelvic splanchnic nerves (S2, S3, S4).
3. Sensory fibres from viscera.

Branches: The branches from inferior hypogastric plexuses give rise to:

1. *Rectal plexus*: It lies around the middle rectal artery and supplies rectum.
2. *Vesical plexus*: It lies around vesical arteries and supplies urinary bladder, adjoining part of ureters, ejaculatory ducts and seminal vesicle.
3. *Prostatic plexus*: It lies around the prostate and supplies prostate, seminal vesicles and ejaculatory ducts.
4. *Uterine and vaginal plexuses*: They lie around the uterine and vaginal arteries and supply uterus and vagina.

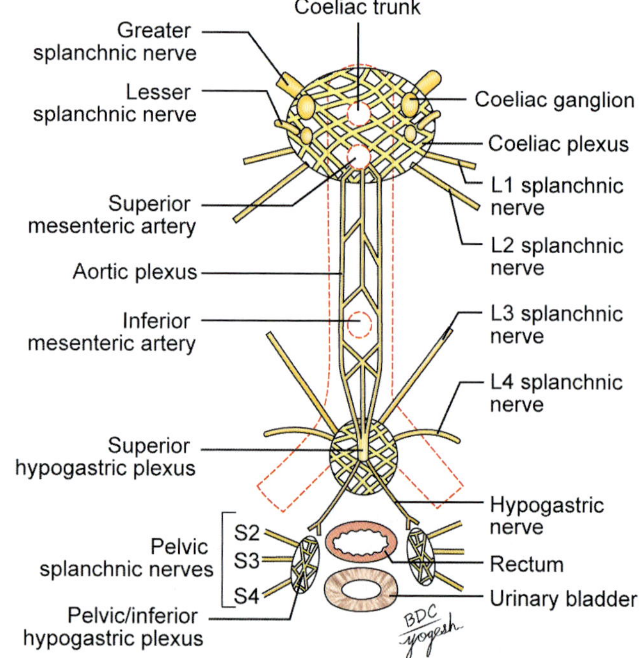

Fig. 27.11: The coeliac, superior hypogastric and inferior hypogastric plexuses

Note:

Para-aortic bodies: There are two para-aortic bodies: They are also called paraganglion or organ of Zuckerkandl. These are neural crest derived chromaffin tissue. Para-aortic bodies are relatively large in the fetus, reach maximum size by 3 years of age and regress by adulthood. They lie anterolateral to the aorta in the region of inferior mesenteric and superior hypogastric= plexuses. *Function*: Secretion of adrenalin.

Coccygeal body: It is called *glomus coccygeum*. It is a small oval body situated in front of coccyx. It also contains chromaffin cells derived from neural crest cells.

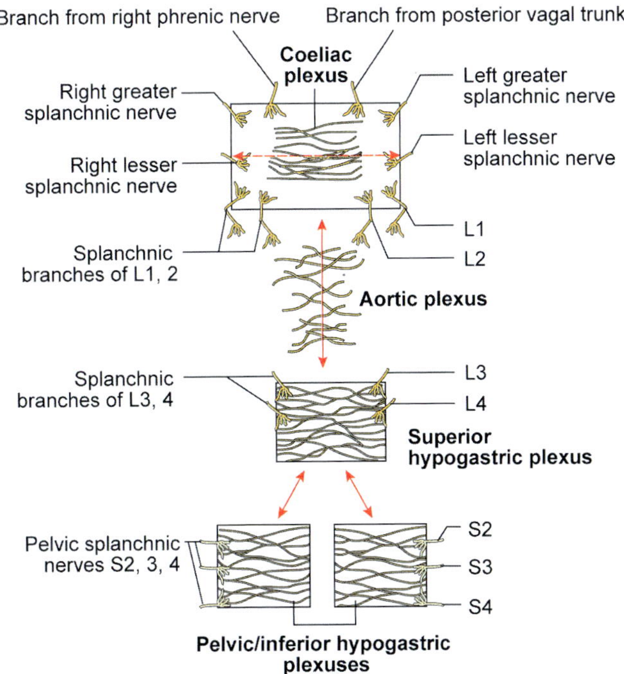

Fig. 27.12: Formation of plexuses

CLINICAL ANATOMY

- ***Visceral pain***: Viscera are insensitive to cutting, crushing or burning. However, visceral pain is caused by:
  a. Excessive distension
  b. Spasmodic contraction of smooth muscle
  c. Ischaemia.

  The pain felt in the region of the viscus itself is known as true visceral pain. It is poorly localized and is dull or heavy. Pain arising in viscera may also be felt in the skin or other somatic tissues, supplied by somatic nerves arising from the same spinal segment. This kind of pain is called ***referred pain*** (Fig. 27.13).
- ***Lumbar sympathectomy:*** It is done for vaso-occlusive disease of the lower limb (Buerger's disease). Usually, the second, third and fourth lumbar ganglia are removed with the intervening chain, via an extraperitoneal approach. It is a preganglionic resection after which the skin becomes warm, pink and dry.
- *Note*: The first lumbar ganglion is preserved because it plays an important role in ejaculation. In fact, it is not concerned with vasomotor and sudomotor functions in the foot and leg below the knee and its resection is not necessary. Removal of this ganglion results in dry coitus. Normally, during ejaculation, it keeps the sphincter vesicae closed and thus prevents entry of semen into the urinary bladder.
- ***Presacral neurectomy:*** Division of the superior hypogastric plexus is known as presacral neurectomy. It does not completely relieve pain associated with disease of the pelvic organs because many pain fibres pass in the pelvic splanchnic nerves. However, the operation is successful in cases of intractable dysmenorrhoea because the pain fibres from the body of uterus pass in the sympathetic nerves via the superior hypogastric plexus.
- In males, presacral neurectomy is followed by loss of the power of ejaculation because the sympathetic pathways to the seminal vesicle, vasa deferentia and prostate are interrupted.

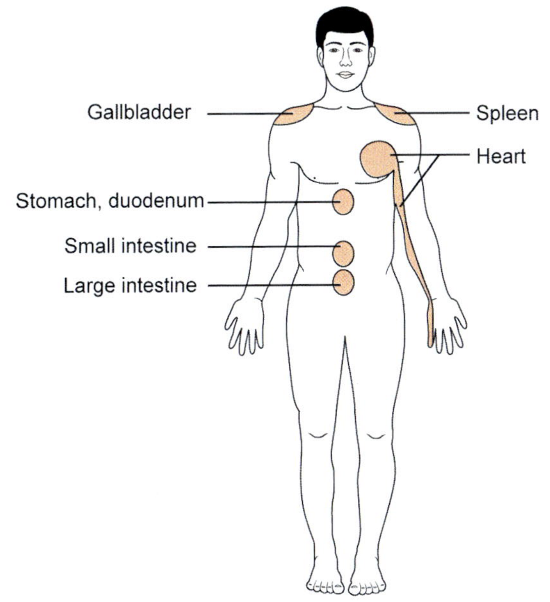

Fig. 27.13: Sites of referred pain

Facts to Remember

- Branches of abdominal aorta are:
  - 3 ventral unpaired visceral: Coeliac axis, superior mesenteric and inferior mesenteric arteries
  - 4 lateral paired visceral: Inferior phrenic, middle suprarenal, renal and gonadal arteries
  - 4 dorsal paired: 4 pairs of lumbar arteries
  - 3 terminal: One medial sacral and 2 common iliac arteries
- Inferior vena cava is the largest and the widest vein.
- Coeliac plexus is chiefly sympathetic. It also contains fibres of parasympathetic system through vagus nerve.
- Pelvic splanchnic nerves arise from S2, 3, 4 segments and supply parasympathetic fibres to the distal parts of digestive tube, urinary bladder, urethra, prostate including the genital organs.
- Cisterna chyli is the largest lymphatic sac.

BDC's Anatomy *e*-book

1. Retroperitoneum
2. Relations of the psoas major
3. Retroperitoneal fusion fascia
4. Lateroconal fascia
5. May-Thurner syndrome
6. Abdominal parts of azygos and hemiazygos veins
7. Branches of coeliac plexus
8. Layers of the abdomen
9. Further reading
10. Viva voce questions

Chapter

28

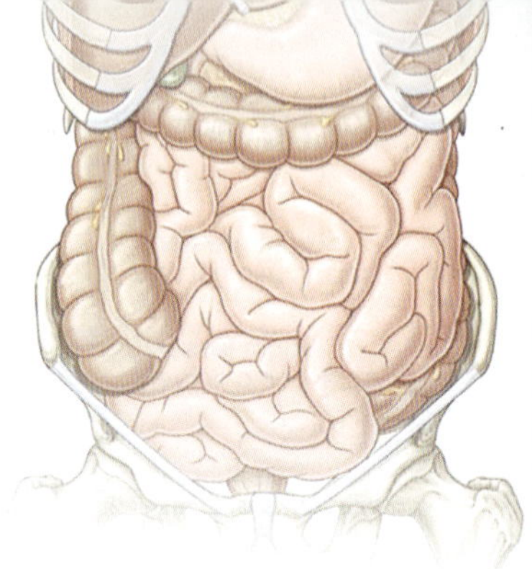

Perineum

Perineum is the region at the lower end of the trunk, in the interval between the two thighs. The external genitalia are located in the perineum. The perineum forms the lower division of the pelvis that lies below the pelvic diaphragm (formed by the levator ani and coccygeus) and the pelvic outlet or inferior aperture of the pelvis (Fig. 28.1).

In males, there are two openings—one of the gastrointestinal system and the other being the common opening of urinary and genital systems. In females, there are three separate openings—one each of the gastrointestinal, genital and urinary systems. The perineal body supports the reproductive system. Its injury without repair may lead to prolapse of the uterus. Pudendal nerve supplies muscles, skin, mucous membrane of both anal and urogenital triangles comprising the perineum. Pudendum means 'to be ashamed of'.

Gynaecological perineum: In female, the median region between vagina and anus is considered as gynaecological perineum and it contains perineal body.

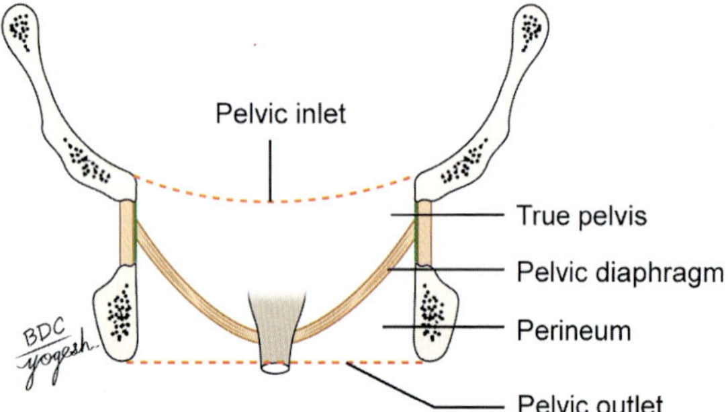

Fig. 28.1: Boundaries of perineum

Superficial Boundaries (Figs 28.1 and 28.2)

Anteriorly: Scrotum in males, and mons pubis in females

Posteriorly: Buttocks

On each side: Upper part of the medial side of the thigh.

Deep Boundaries of the Perineum

The deep boundaries of the perineum are the same as those of the pelvic outlet (Plate 28.1, Fig. 28.3, Flowchart 28.1).

Anteriorly: Lower border of pubic symphysis, arcuate pubic ligament

Posteriorly: Tip of the coccyx.

On each side:

Anterolaterally: Conjoint ischiopubic ramus and ischial tuberosity

Posterolaterally: Sacrotuberous ligament.

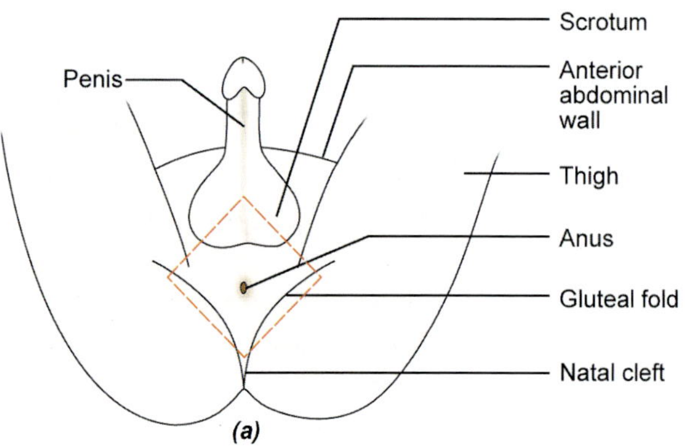

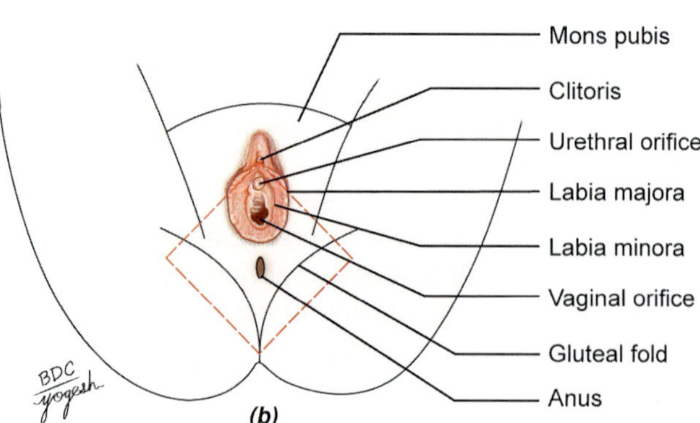

Figs 28.2a and b: (a) The male perineum: Dotted lines indicate the outlines of pelvic outlet and (b) the female perineum: Dotted lines indicate the position of pelvic outlet

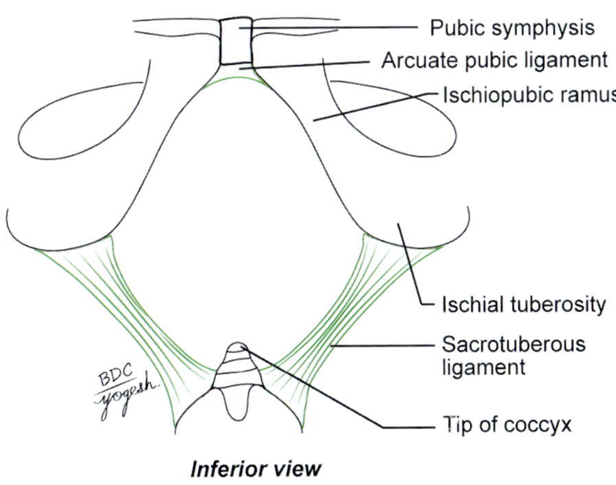

Fig. 28.3: Boundaries of perineum

Divisions of Perineum

A transverse line joining the anterior parts of the ischial tuberosities, and passing immediately anterior to the anus, divides the perineum into two triangular areas (Fig. 28.4):

- Posterior *anal region* or triangle
- Anterior *urogenital region* or triangle.

1. ***Anal triangle*** contains the termination of the anal canal in the median plane and an ischioanal fossa on each side.

Plate 28.1: Deep boundaries of perineum (red dotted line shows the division of perineum into urogenital and anal triangles)

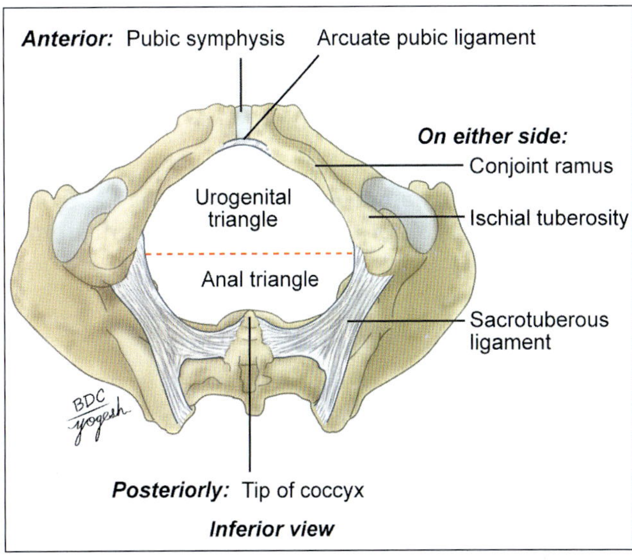

2. ***Urogenital region*** contains the external urogenital organs. In males, the urethra enclosed in the root of penis, partly hidden anteriorly by the scrotum; and in females, the female external genital organs.

Flowchart 28.1: Perineum: Boundaries and division

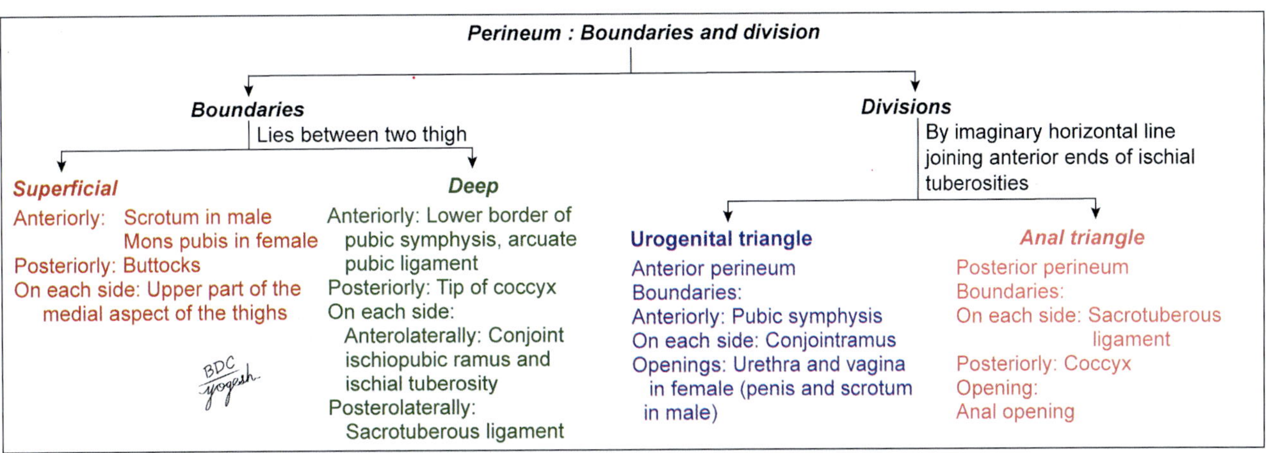

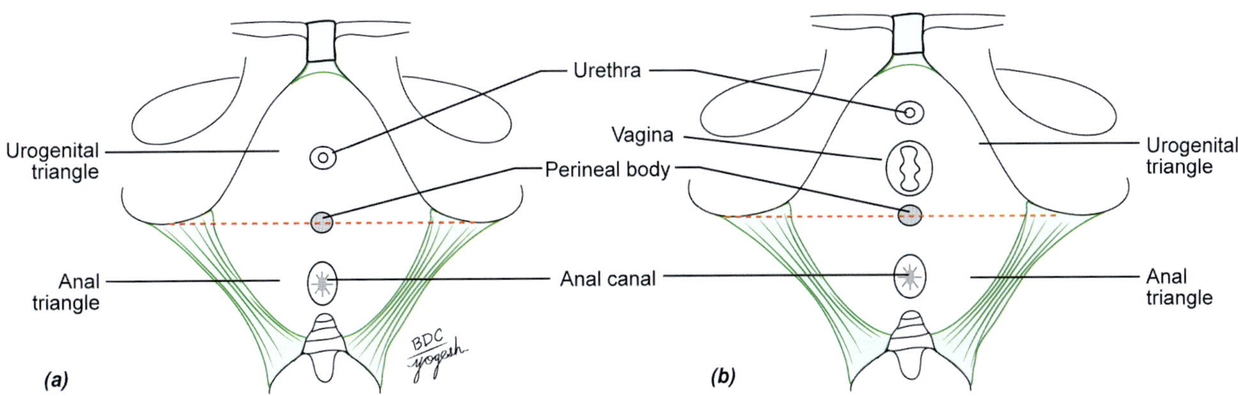

Figs 28.4a and b: Subdivision of the perineum: (a) Male perineum and (b) female perineum (inferior view, red dotted line shows the division of perineum)

UROGENITAL TRIANGLE

The urogenital triangle is also called anterior perineum. It is a triangular area that is bounded as follows:

Anterior: Lower margin of pubic symphysis and arcuate pubic ligament

On each side: Conjoint ischiopubic rami

Posterior: Imaginary line joining the anterior ends of ischial tuberosities.

The urogenital triangle in male has penis and scrotum and in female, orifices of urethra, vagina and female external genital organs.

Layers of Urogenital Triangle

The layers of the urogenital triangle from above downwards are as follows (Fig. 28.5):

7. Superior fascia of urogenital diaphragm
6. Deep perineal pouch
5. Perineal membrane (inferior fascia of urogenital diaphragm)
4. Superficial perineal pouch
3. Colles' fascia/membranous layer of superficial fascia
2. Fatty layer of superficial fascia
1. Skin

Note: These are numbered in reverse order as they encounter in this order during surgeries or dissection from superficial to deep.

Layers of the urogenital triangle
7. Superior fascia of urogenital diaphragm
6. Deep perineal pouch
5. Perineal membrane
4. Superficial perineal pouch
3. Colles' fascia
2. Fatty layer of superficial fascia
1. Skin
BDC yogesh

Fig. 28.5: Layers of the urogenital triangle (from above downwards, coronal section)

Skin

1. In male, the skin of the perineum presents a *midline raphe*, which is continuous with the *median raphe of scrotum*.
2. In female, the skin of the perineum presents a median cleft called *vestibule* that lies between two labia minora. The urethra and vagina open in the vestibule.

Cutaneous Innervation

The skin of the perineum is supplied by (Fig. 28.6)

1. Dorsal nerves of penis or clitoris
2. Ilioinguinal nerves
3. Genital branch of the genitofemoral nerve
4. Perineal branch of posterior cutaneous nerve of thigh
5. Posterior scrotal or labial nerves.

Note:

1. *Dorsal nerve of penis or clitoris* is a branch of pudendal nerve. It supplies the skin of penis or clitoris except its root.
2. *Ilioinguinal nerve* and *genital branch of genitofemoral nerve* supply the skin of anterior 1/3rd of the scrotum or labium major and the root of the penis or clitoris.
3. *Perineal branch of the posterior cutaneous nerve of thigh* supplies the skin of the lateral part of the urogenital region and the lateral part of the posterior 2/3rds of scrotum or labium major.
4. *Posterior scrotal or labial nerve* is a branch of pudendal region and medial part posterior 2/3rds of the scrotum or labium major.
5. *Perineal branch of pudendal nerve* supplies the mucous membrane of urethra.

CLINICAL ANATOMY

The cutaneous nerves of perineum are derived from the sacral nerves (S2–S4). These segments also supply parasympathetic fibres to the pelvic organs. Diseases of these organs may, therefore, cause *referred pain* in the perineum.

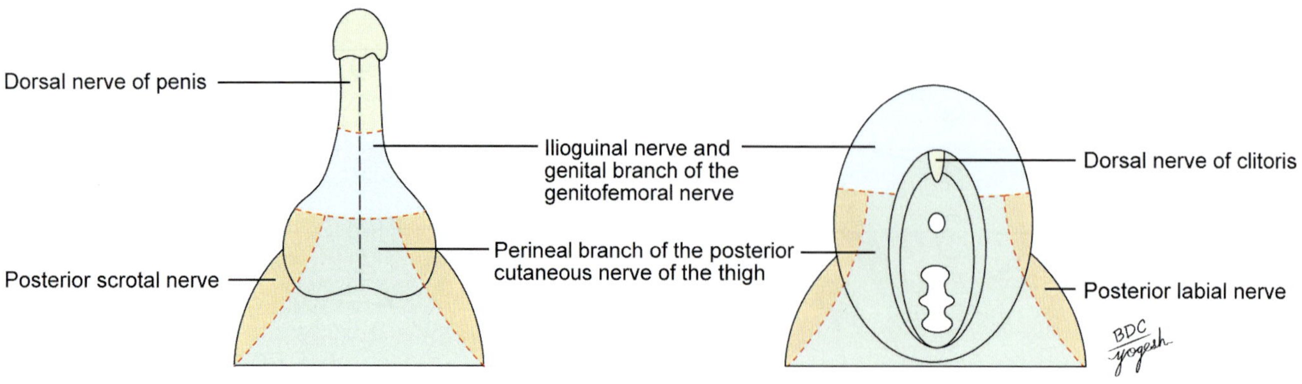

Fig. 28.6: Cutaneous innervation of the male and female urogenital region

Competency:

AN49.3 Describe and demonstrate perineal membrane in male and female.

FASCIA OF PERINEUM

The perineum has the following layes of fascia from superficial to deep:

1. Superficial fascia: Fatty layer and Colles' fascia/ membranous layer
2. Deep fascia or perineal membrane (inferior fascia of urogenital diaphragm)
3. Superior fascia of urogenital diaphragm.

Superficial Fascia

The perineum has two layers of superficial facia: Superficial fatty and deep membranous layer (Fig. 28.8).

Fatty Layer of Superficial Fascia

It is continuous with subcutaneous tissue of the adjacent area.

Colles' Fascia

(Membranous Layer of Superficial Fascia)

It is a strong sheet that lies in the pubic arch. It forms the inferior boundary of superficial perineal pouch.

Attachment

On each side: Colles' fascia is attached to ischiopubic ramus.

Anteriorly: Continuous with dartos muscle of scrotum, fascia of penis and fascia of Scarpa of the anterior abdominal wall.

Posteriorly: Continuous with posterior margin of perineal membrane.

Structures piercing Colles' fascia

1. Perineal branch of posterior cutaneous nerve of thigh
2. Urethra
3. Vagina in female.

Deep Fascia or Perineal Membrane

The perineal membrane is a strong sheet of deep fascia of the perineal region that extends between pubic arch and separates superficial and deep perineal pouches (Figs 28.7 and 28.8).

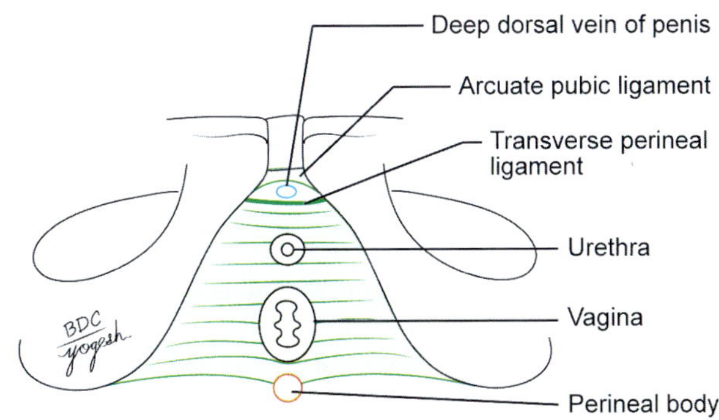

Fig. 28.7: Perineal membrane

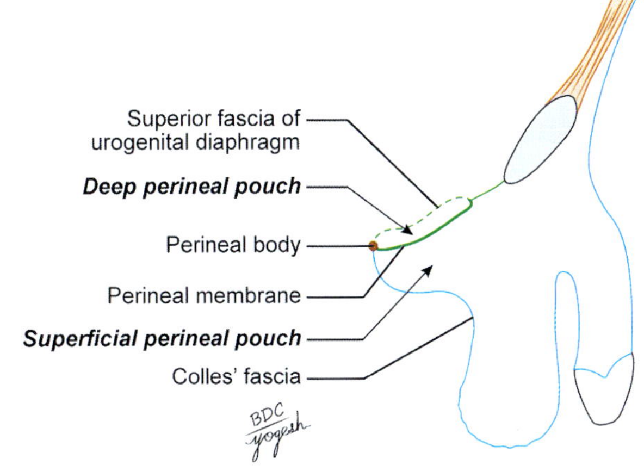

Fig. 28.8: Superficial and deep perineal pouches (sagittal section of the urogenital region of male perineum)

The perineal membrane or inferior layer of urogenital diaphragm is a strong fascial sheet that lies across the urogenital triangle in between the ischiopubic rami. It separates superficial and deep perineal pouches (Fig. 28.12, Flowchart 28.2).

Attachments

Anteriorly: It is thickened to form *transverse perineal ligament* and is continuous with superior fascia of urogenital diaphragm.

On each side: It is attached to ischiopubic ramus.

Posteriorly: It is fixed to the perineal body in the midline and split into two layers:

- Upper layer is continuous with superior fascia of urogenital diaphragm
- Lower layer is continuous with Colles' fascia.

Flowchart 28.2: Perineal membrane

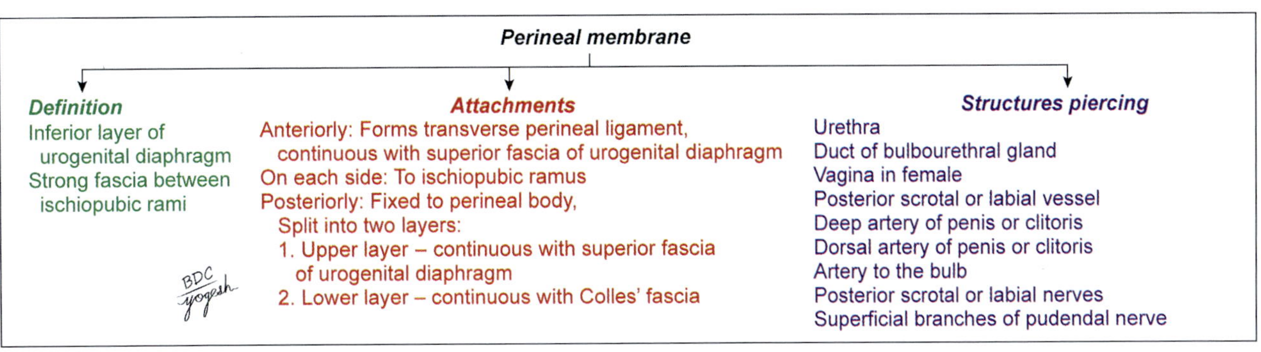

Superior Fascia of Urogenital Diaphragm

It is a thin fascia covering the upper surface of muscles of urogenital diaphragm. It is derived from the pelvic fascia (Figs 28.7 to 28.11, Flowchart 28.2). It encloses a space called *deep perineal pouch*.

Attachments

Anteriorly: Blends with perineal membrane
Posteriorly: Continuous with perineal membrane
On each side: Attached to the ischiopubic ramus.

Structures Piercing Perineal Membrane

Structures piercing or traversing perineal membrane in male and female are partially different. They are as follows (Fig. 28.11, Flowchart 28.2 and Table 28.1):

1. Urethra
2. Duct of bulbourethral gland in male
3. Vagina in female
4. Vessels
   a. Posterior scrotal or labial vessel
   b. Deep artery of penis or clitoris
   c. Dorsal artery of penis or clitoris
   d. Artery to the bulb of penis or bulb of vestibule of vagina.
5. Nerves
   a. Posterior scrotal or labial nerves
   b. Superficial branches of pudendal nerve.

CLINICAL ANATOMY

Rupture of the urethra leads to extravasation of urine, which may be superficial or deep. In *superficial extravasation*, the urine spreads downwards deep to the membranous layer of the superficial fascia. It first fills the superficial perineal space; and then the scrotum, the penis and the lower part of the anterior abdominal wall.

It is prevented from going to the ischioanal fossa or the thigh by the firm attachment of the membranous layer of superficial fascia to their boundaries.

In *deep extravasation*, the urine spreads upwards into the extraperitoneal space of the pelvis around bladder and prostate into the anterior abdominal wall (Fig. 28.16).

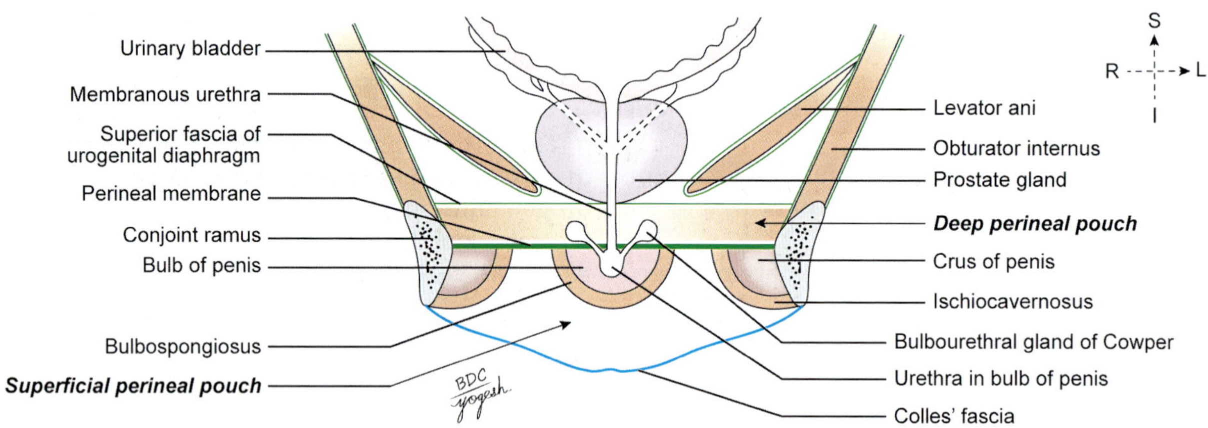

Fig. 28.9: Coronal section of the urogenital region in male

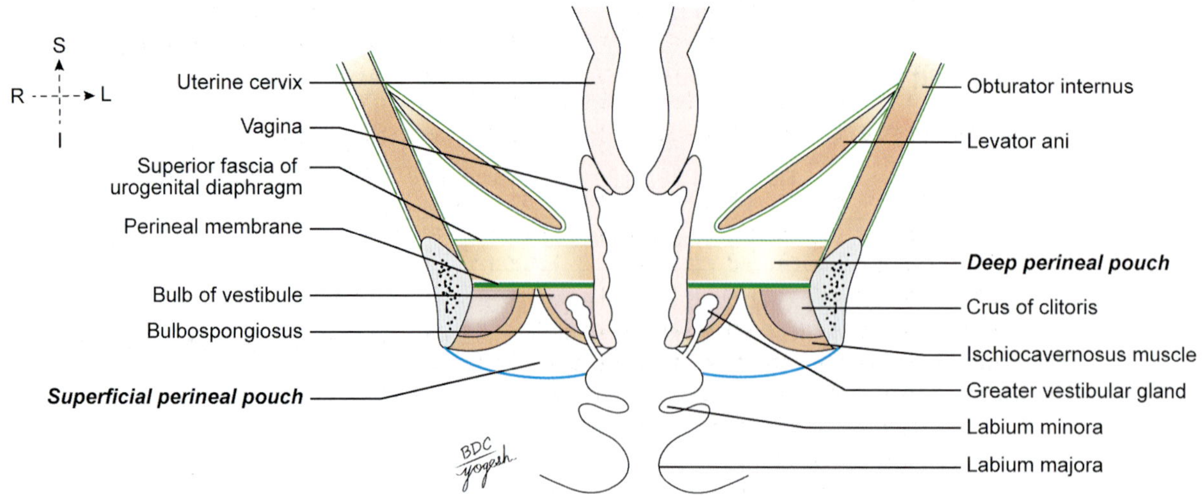

Fig. 28.10: Coronal section of the urogenital region in female

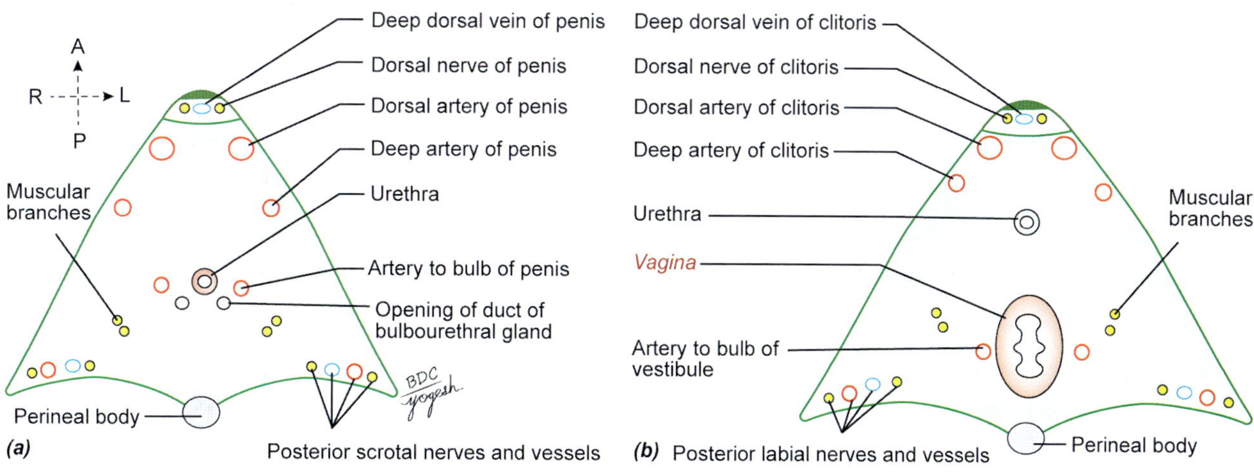

Figs 28.11a and b: Structures piercing the perineal membrane: (a) In male and (b) in female (inferior view of perineal membrane)

TABLE 28.1: Structures piercing or traversing perineal membrane in male and female

Male	***Female***
Urethra	Urethra Vagina
Duct of bulbourethral glands	
Vessels a. Posterior scrotal vessels b. Deep artery of penis c. Dorsal artery of penis d. Artery to the bulb of penis	 a. Posterior labial vessels b. Deep artery of penis c. Dorsal artery of penis d. Artery to the bulb of vestibule
Nerve a. Posterior scrotal nerves b. Superficial branches of pudendal nerve	 a. Posterior labial nerve b. Superficial branches of pudendal nerve

TABLE 28.2: Superficial perineal space in male and female

Feature	***Male***	***Female***
Definition	Lies superficial to the perineal membrane	Lies superficial to the perineal membrane
Boundaries		
Superficial	Colles' fascia	
Deep	Perineal membrane	
On each side	Ischiopubic ramus	
Anterior	Open, continuous with superficial inguinal space	Transverse perineal ligament
Posterior	Fusion of Colles' fascia and perineal membrane	
Contents		
Muscles	Ischiocavernosus Superficial transverse perinei Bulbospongiosus	
Nerves	Posterior labial nerves Perineal branch of posterior cutaneous nerves of thigh	Posterior labial nerves Perineal branch of posterior cutaneous nerves of thigh
Vessels	Two posterior scrotal vessels Artery to bulb of penis Deep and dorsal arteries of penis	Two posterior labial vessels Artery to bulb of clitoris Deep and dorsal arteries of clitoris
	Transverse perineal vessels Urethral artery	
Other structures	Crus of penis Bulb of penis	Crus of clitoris Bulb of vestibule Vagina Greater vestibular gland
	Urethra	

Competency:

AN49.1 Describe and demonstrate the superficial and deep perineal pouch (boundaries and contents).

PERINEAL POUCHES

These are the interfascial spaces located in the urogenital region. They include:

a. Superficial perineal pouch
b. Deep perineal pouch.

Superficial Perineal Pouch

It is a superficial interfascial space situated in the lower part of the perineum, superficial to the perineal membrane (Table 28.2, Flowchart 28.3).

Boundaries

Superficial (inferior): Colles' fascia

Deep (superior): Perineal membrane

On each side: Ischiopubic ramus

Anteriorly: It is open and is continuous with the superficial inguinal space of scrotum in male and of clitoris in female.

Posteriorly: Fusion of Colles' fascia and perineal membrane.

Plate 28.2: Superficial muscles of perineum in male and female

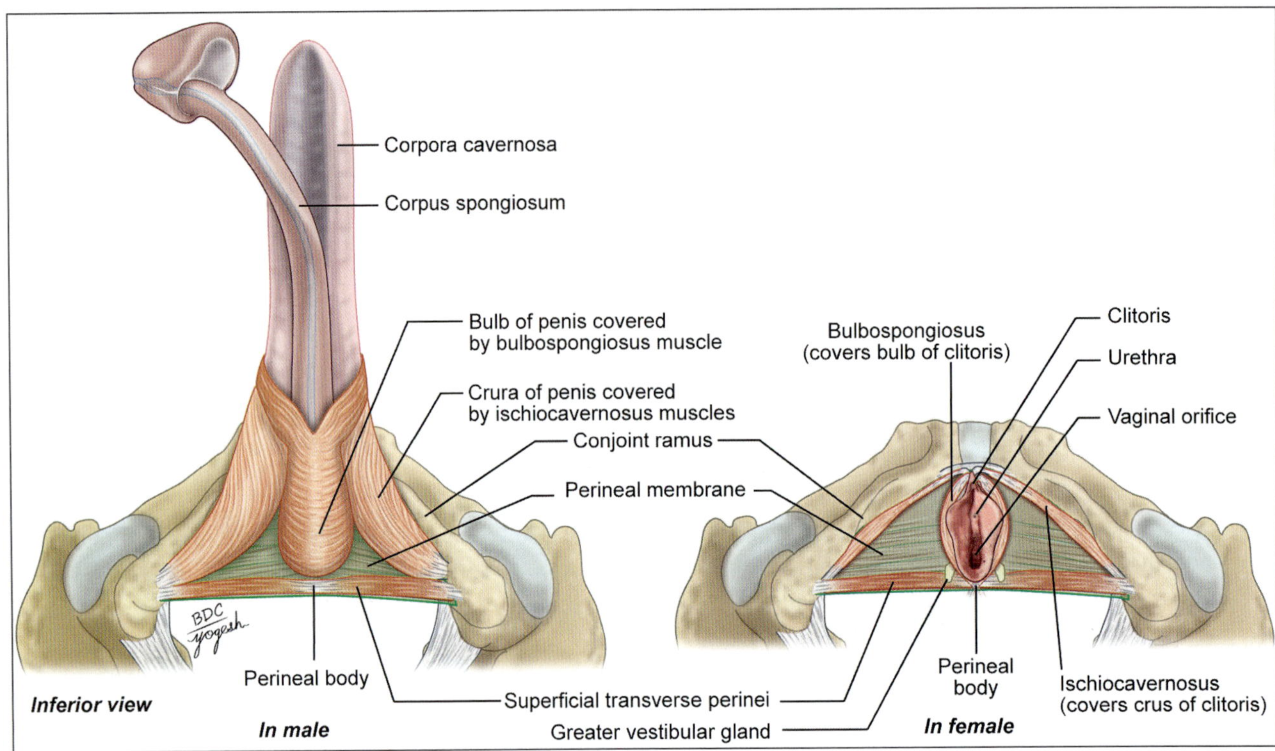

Flowchart 28.3: Superficial perineal pouch

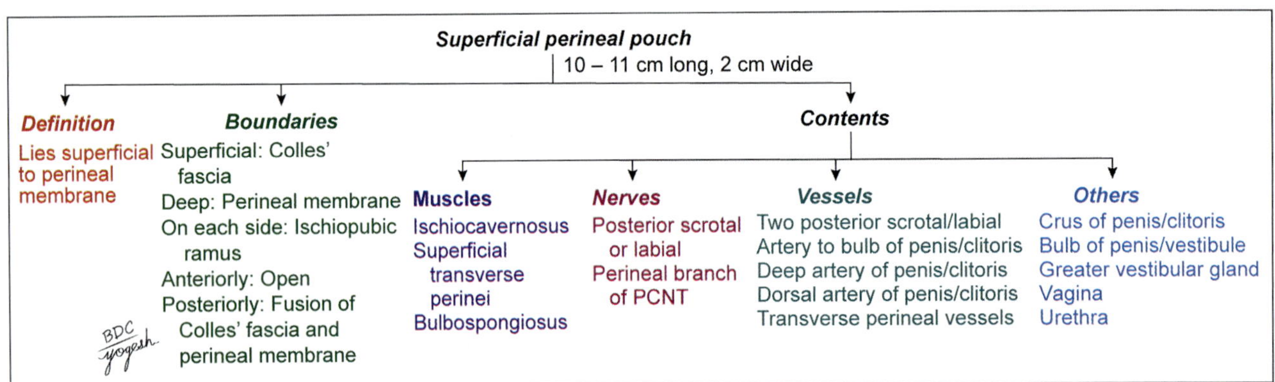

Contents (Table 28.2)

Muscles (Figs 28.15 to 28.18)

1. Ischiocavernosus covering crus of penis or clitoris
2. Superficial transverse perinei
3. Bulbospongiosus covering the bulb of penis or bulb of vestibule.

Note: In male, right and left bulbospongiosus muscles fuse in the midline, whereas in female, they remain separated to give passage to the urethra and vagina.

Nerves

1. Posterior scrotal or labial nerves (branches of perineal nerve).
2. Perineal branch of posterior cutaneous nerve of thigh.

Vessels

1. Two posterior scrotal or labial vessels
2. Artery to the bulb of penis or clitoris
3. Deep artery of penis or clitoris
4. Dorsal artery of penis or clitoris
5. Transverse perineal vessels
6. Urethral artery.

Other structures

1. Crus of penis or clitoris
2. Bulb of penis traversed by urethra in male
3. Bulb of vestibule, greater vestibular gland, vagina, urethra in female.

Deep Perineal Pouch

It is a deep *interfascial closed* space situated in the upper part of the perineum, deep to the perineal membrane (Fig. 28.19, Flowchart 28.4, Table 28.3).

Boundaries

Superficial (inferior): Perineal membrane

TABLE 28.3: Deep perineal space

Features	*Male*	*Female*
Definition	This is the thin space of the urogenital region situated deep to the perineal membrane Contributes to pelvic floor	Same
Boundaries		
a. Superficial	Perineal membrane (Fig. 28.12)	
b. Deep	Open above	
c. On each side	Ischiopubic rami	
d. Anteriorly	Gap between perineal membrane and inferior pubic ligament	
Contents		
1. Tubes	Part of urethra	Parts of urethra and vagina
2. Muscles	a. Sphincter urethrae or distal urethral sphincter within the wall of urethra b. Deep transversus perinei. Mainly skeletal muscle (Fig. 28.12)	a. Sphincter urethrae within the wall of urethra b. Deep transversus perinei. Mainly smooth muscle c. Compressor urethrae d. Sphincter urethrovaginalis (Fig. 28.20)
3. Nerves on each side	a. Dorsal nerve of penis b. Muscular branches from perineal nerve	a. Dorsal nerve of clitoris b. Muscular branches from perineal nerve
4. Vessels	a. Artery of penis b. Stems of origin of four branches, namely artery to the bulb of penis, urethral artery, deep and dorsal arteries of penis	a. Artery of clitoris b. Stems of origin of four branches, namely artery to bulb of vestibule, urethral artery, deep and dorsal arteries of clitoris
5. Glands	Bulbourethral glands	No glands

Flowchart 28.4: Deep perineal pouch

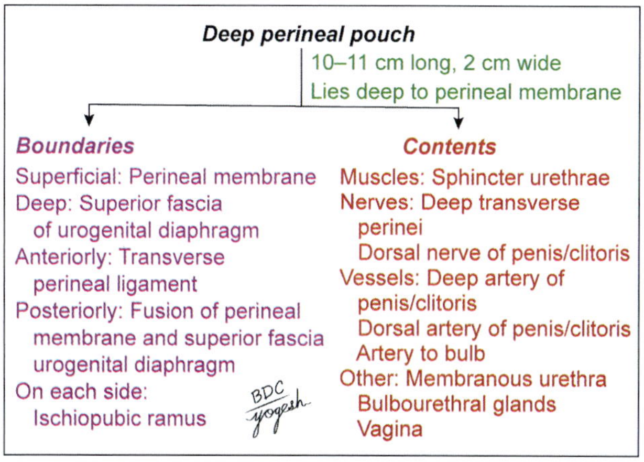

Deep perineal pouch
10–11 cm long, 2 cm wide
Lies deep to perineal membrane

Boundaries
Superficial: Perineal membrane
Deep: Superior fascia of urogenital diaphragm
Anteriorly: Transverse perineal ligament
Posteriorly: Fusion of perineal membrane and superior fascia urogenital diaphragm
On each side: Ischiopubic ramus

Contents
Muscles: Sphincter urethrae
Nerves: Deep transverse perinei
Dorsal nerve of penis/clitoris
Vessels: Deep artery of penis/clitoris
Dorsal artery of penis/clitoris
Artery to bulb
Other: Membranous urethra
Bulbourethral glands
Vagina

BDC yogesh

Deep (superior): Superior fascia of urogenital diaphragm

Anteriorly: Transverse perineal ligament

Posteriorly: Fusion of perineal membrane and superior fascia urogenital diaphragm

On each side: Ischiopubic ramus.

Contents

Muscles

1. Sphincter urethrae muscle
2. Deep transverse perinei.

Nerves: Dorsal nerve of penis or clitoris

Vessels: Three terminal branches of internal pudendal artery

1. Deep artery of penis or clitoris
2. Dorsal artery of penis or clitoris
3. Artery to the bulb of penis or bulb of vestibule.

Other structures

1. Membranous urethra
2. Bulbourethral glands in male
3. Vagina in female.

Note:

Previous concept: Deep perineal pouch is a closed space that lies between superficial fascia of urogenital diaphragm and perineal membrane. The space contains urethral sphincter.

Recent concept: As there is no superficial fascia of urogenital diaphragm, the deep perineal pouch is open above. *There is no existence of urogenital diaphragm.* The sphincter urethrae muscle lies inside the urethral wall itself (*Reference*: *Gray's Anatomy*, 42nd edn.).

Urogenital Diaphragm

It is a musculo-fascial partition across the pubic arch that consists of

- two fascias – superior and inferior fascias of urogenital diaphragm, and
- two muscles – sphincter urethrae and deep transverse posterior.

Note: As per the recent concept, the urogenital diaphragm does not exist. Here, it is described as per previous concept (*Reference*; *Gray's Anatomy*, 42nd edition).

MUSCLES OF PERINEUM

The perineum contains the following two groups of muscles (Plate 28.3):

1. Superficial perineal muscles (Figs 28.12 and 28.13, Table 28.4)
   a. Ischiocavernosus
   b. Bulbospongiosus
   c. Superficial transverse perinei.
2. Deep perineal muscles (Figs 28.14 and 28.15, Table 28.5)
   a. Deep transverse perinei
   b. Sphincter urethrae.

Note:

1. ***Rhabdosphincter***: These are circularly arranged striated muscle fibres that surround the membranous urethra and form main part of distal urethral sphincter mechanism.
2. ***Compressor urethrae*** arises from ischiopubic rami of each side the fibres pass anteriorly and meet their counterparts anterior to the urethra.
3. ***Sphincter urethrae vaginalis*** arises from perineal body. Its fibres pass anterior on either side of urethra and vagina to meet their counterparts.

The compressor urethrae and sphincter urethrae vaginalis help continence in female by compressing the membranous urethra. These muscles are supplied by perineal branch of pudendal nerve.

TABLE 28.4: Muscles of the superficial perineal spaces in male and female
(*Note*: All these muscles are supplied by perineal branch of pudendal nerve.)

Muscle	*Origin*	*Fibres*	*Insertion*	*Actions*
1. **Ischiocavernosus** It covers the crus penis or crus clitoridis; smaller in females	a. Medial surface of ischial ramus behind the crus b. Posterior part of perineal membrane	Fibres run forwards and spiral over the crus	Inserted by an aponeurosis into the sides and undersurface of the anterior part of the crus	It helps in maintaining erection of the penis by compressing the crus Causes erection of clitoris in female
2. **Bulbospongiosus** It covers the bulb of penis and the two muscles are united by a median raphe (Fig. 28.14)	a. Perineal body b. Median raphe over the bulb of penis	a. Posterior fibres embrace the posterior end of the bulb b. Middle fibres embrace the corpus spongiosum c. Anterior fibres embrace the entire body of penis	a. Posterior *fibres,* into the perineal membrane b. Middle fibres embrace the bulb and corpus spongiosum, and the raphe on their upper surface c. Anterior fibres are inserted into the raphe on the dorsal surface of the penis	1. Helps in ejaculation of semen and ejecting the last drops of urine 2. Middle fibres assist in the erection of the penis by compressing the bulb 3. Anterior fibres also help in the erection of penis by compressing the deep dorsal vein of penis
In females, it covers the bulb of vestibule and the two muscles are separated by the vagina and urethra	Perineal body	Fibres pass anteriorly	a. Perineal membrane b. Bulb of vestibule c. Body of clitoris and corpus spongiosum	In females, it acts as sphincter of vagina and assists in erection of clitoris
3. **Superficial transversus perinei** Narrow slip running transversely in front of anus on either side	Medial surface of the root of ischial ramus	Fibres run medially	Inserted into the perineal body where it interlaces with other converging muscles	Steadies the perineal body

TABLE 28.5: Deep perineal muscles
(Deep transverse perinei and sphincter urethrae are supplied by muscular branches of perineal nerve.)

Muscle	*Origin*	*Fibres*	*Insertion*	*Actions*
Deep transverse perinei	Ramus of ischium	Fibres run transversely	Perineal body	Steadies the perineal body
Sphincter urethrae Encircles membranous urethra	*Superficial fibres*: Transverse perineal ligament and pubic arch	Pass backward	Perineal body	Forms voluntary external urethral sphincter
	Deep fibres: Inner surface of ischiopubic ramus	Pass horizontally and encircle urethra	Similar fibres of opposite side	

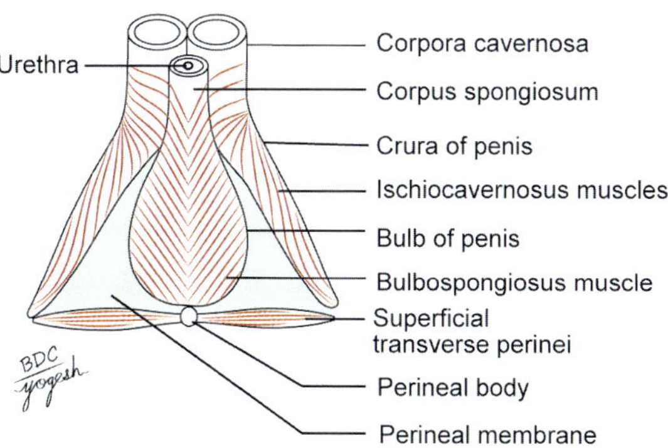

Fig. 28.12: Superficial muscles of the male perineum

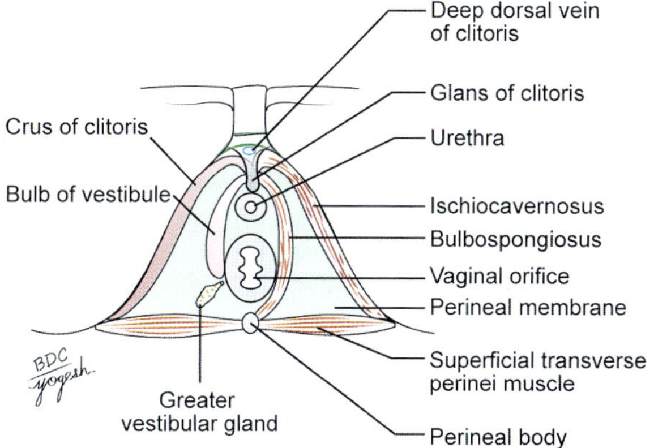

Fig. 28.13: Structures in superficial perineal pouch in female

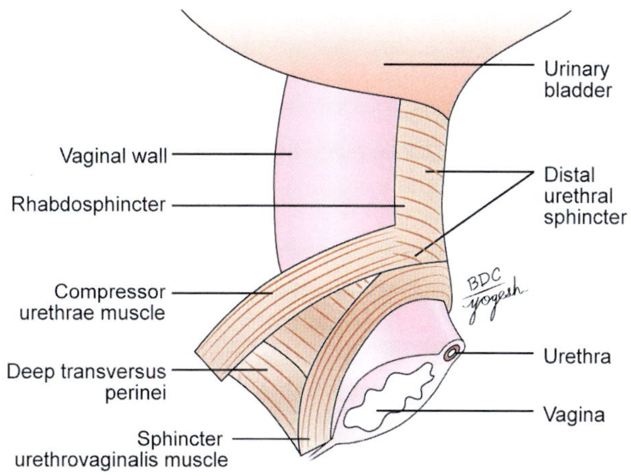

Fig. 28.14: Muscles in the deep perineal pouch in female

Plate 28.3: Attachments of perineal muscles

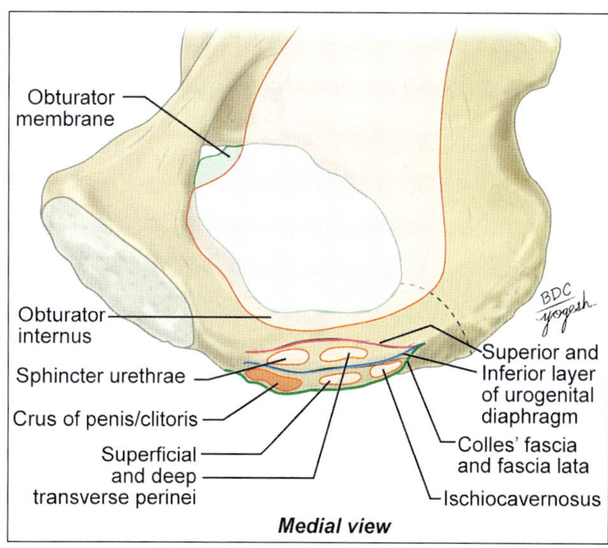

Competency:

AN49.2 Describe and identify perineal body.

PERINEAL BODY

The perineal body, or the central point of the perineum, is a fibromuscular node situated in the median plane, about 1.25 cm in front of the anal margin and close to the bulb of the penis. Ten muscles of the perineum converge and interlace in the perineal body (Fig. 28.16, Flowchart 28.5).

Two unpaired:

1. External anal sphincter
2. Fibres of longitudinal muscle coat of anal canal.

Four paired:

1. Bulbospongiosus
2. Superficial transversus perinei
3. Deep transversus perinei
4. Levator ani.

All these converge and interlace in the perineal body.

The perineal body is very important in the female for support of the pelvic organs. Sphincter urethrovaginalis

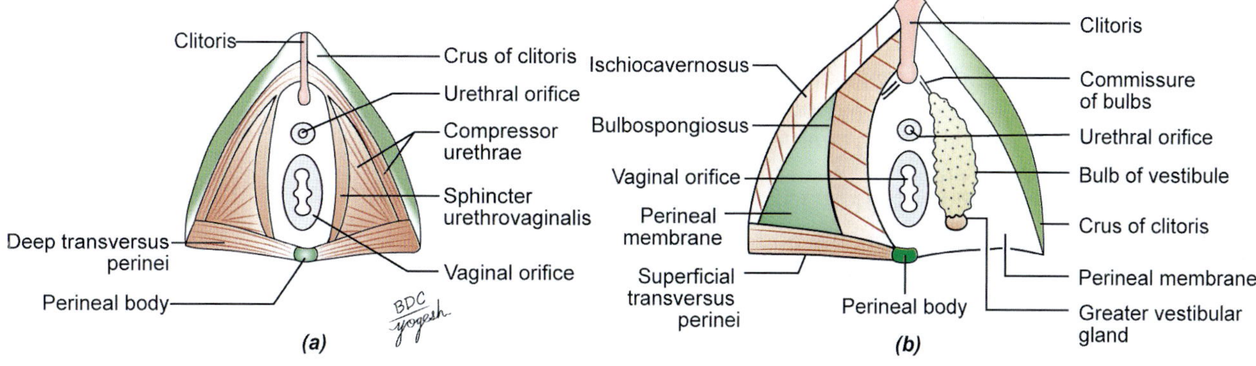

Figs 28.15a and b: (a) Female perineum showing the deep perineal muscles and (b) female perineum showing superficial perineal muscles, bulb of vestibule

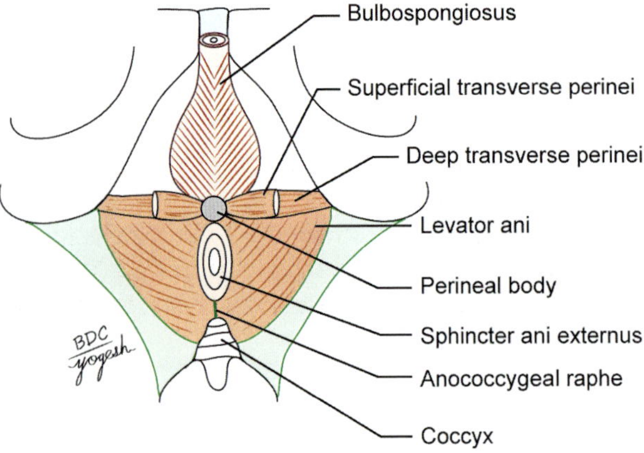

Fig. 28.16: Muscles attached to perineal body (in male)

Flowchart 28.5: Perineal body

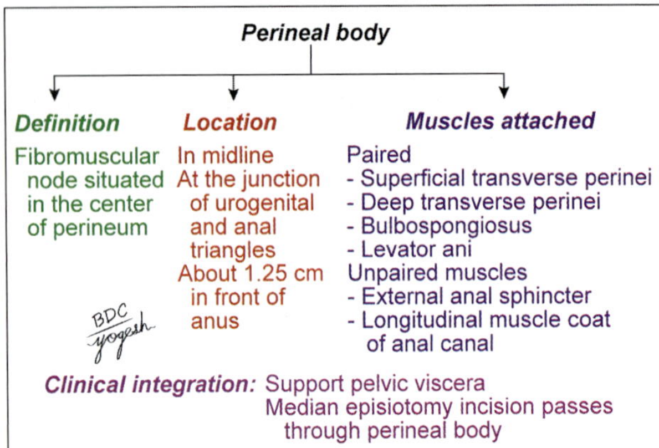

in female is also attached here. It may be damaged during parturition or childbirth. This may result in prolapse of the urinary bladder, the uterus, the ovaries and even of the rectum.

CLINICAL ANATOMY

Episiotomy is an incision in perineum made to enlarge the vaginal orifice to facilitate the passage of fetus during childbirth (Fig. 28.17). *Median episiotomy* involves the incision through frenulum of labia minora to the external anal sphincter including perineal body. *Lateral episiotomy incision* is more preferred as it saves the perineal body.

DISSECTION

Clean the sacrotuberous and sacrospinous ligaments. Identify coccyx in the midline posteriorly and locate the ischial tuberosity. Define the ischiopubic rami till the lower margins of pubic symphysis anteriorly.

Identify the openings of urethra, anal canal and vagina, if it is a female cadaver. Define perineal body in the centre of perineum. Dissect the parts of external anal sphincter.

Pass a forceps downwards and backwards deep to the membranous layer of the superficial fascia of the anterior abdominal wall.

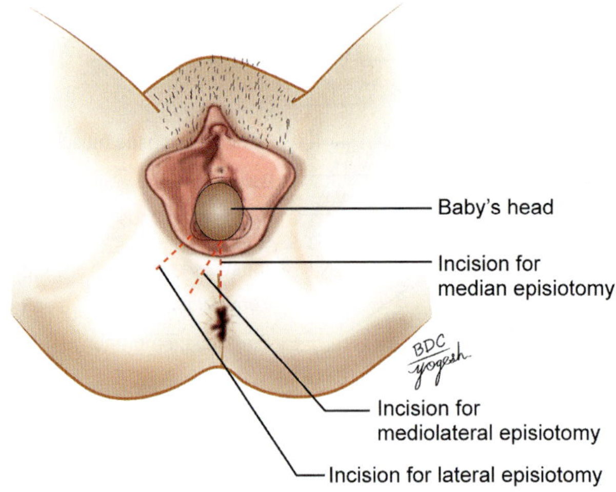

Fig. 28.17: Episiotomy

In the male, expose the membranous layer in the perineum. Make an incision in the membranous layer on one side and dissect the ischiocavernosus, bulbospongiosus and superficial transversus perinei muscles, nerves, blood vessels present in the superficial perineal space (Fig. 28.4). The posterior scrotal vessels and nerves pierce the posterolateral corner of perineal membrane to enter the superficial perineal space.

In the female, remove the fat from the labium majus and expose the membranous layer. Incise it and expose the posterior part of this space and all its contents. Note the posterior limit where the membranous layer passes superiorly to fuse with the perineal membrane. Identify the various female external genital organs.

Identify the structures piercing the perineal membrane in both male and female. Note the ill-defined nature of the perineal membrane in female as it is pierced by vagina in addition to urethra.

Dissect the inferior rectal vessels and nerve and follow them to the lateral wall of the ischioanal fossa. Remove the fat from the ischioanal fossa. Identify and trace the pudendal nerve and vessels in the fascial pudendal canal on the lateral wall of the ischioanal fossa.

ANAL REGION

The ***anal triangle*** is located in the posterior part of the perineum. It is a triangular zone that has the following boundaries (Figs 28.18 and 28.19):

Anteriorly: A horizontal line joining the anterior ends of ischial tuberosities
On each side: Sacrotuberous ligaments
Posteriorly: Coccyx

Contents

It contains the anal canal in the middle and ischioanal fossae, one on each side of the anal canal.

Skin

The skin of the anal region shows external *anal opening* (anus). The skin surrounding the anal orifice is pigmented

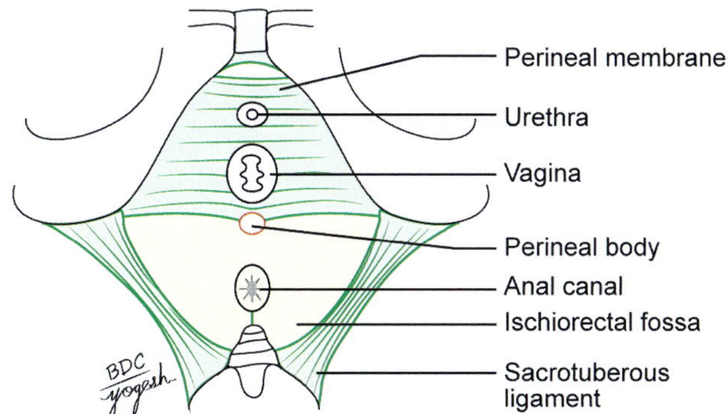

Fig. 28.18: Location of ischiorectal fossa and perineal membrane

and thrown into radiating folds due to pull exerted by underlying subcutaneous muscle called ***corrugator cutis ani***.

Cutaneous Innervation

The skin of anal region is supplied by:

1. *Inferior rectal nerve* (S2, S3, S4) is a branch of pudendal nerve. It supplies the skin around the anus and the overlying ischioanal fossae.
2. *Perineal branch of S4 nerve*: It supplies the skin posterior to the anus.

Superficial Fascia

It contains a large amount of fat which fills the ischioanal fossa.

Deep Fascia

It is formed by the inferior fascia of the pelvic diaphragm and the fascia covering the obturator internus below the attachment of the levator ani.

Anococcygeal Ligament

It is a fibrofatty mass permeated with muscle fibres derived from the levator ani and the external anal sphincter. It extends from the anus to the tip of the coccyx, and supports the rectum (Fig. 28.4).

External Anal Sphincter

Anal canal is surrounded in its upper three-fourths by the internal anal sphincter which ends below at the level of white line of Hilton.

The external anal sphincter surrounds the whole length of the anal canal. It is supplied by the inferior rectal nerve and by the perineal branch of the fourth sacral nerve. It is under voluntary control and keeps the anus and anal canal closed. It is described in detail in Chapter 33.

Competency:
AN49.4 Describe and demonstrate boundaries, content and applied anatomy of ischioanal fossa.

ISCHIOANAL FOSSA

The ischioanal fossa is a wedge-shaped space situated one on each side of the anal canal below the pelvic diaphragm. Its base is directed downwards, towards the surface. The apex is directed upwards (Figs 28.18 to 28.20).

Dimensions

It is a wedge-shaped space. It has:

Base: Directed downward, toward the skin
Apex: Directed upward
Length (anteroposterior): 5 cm
Width (side to side): 2.5 cm
Depth: 5 cm or slightly more.

Boundaries

The ischioanal fossa has base, apex, roof, floor and three walls (medial, lateral and posterior) as follows (Fig. 28.19, Flowchart 28.6):

Base (floor): Skin of perineum
Anteriorly: It extends up to posterior border of perineal membrane
Posteriorly: Sacrotuberous ligament

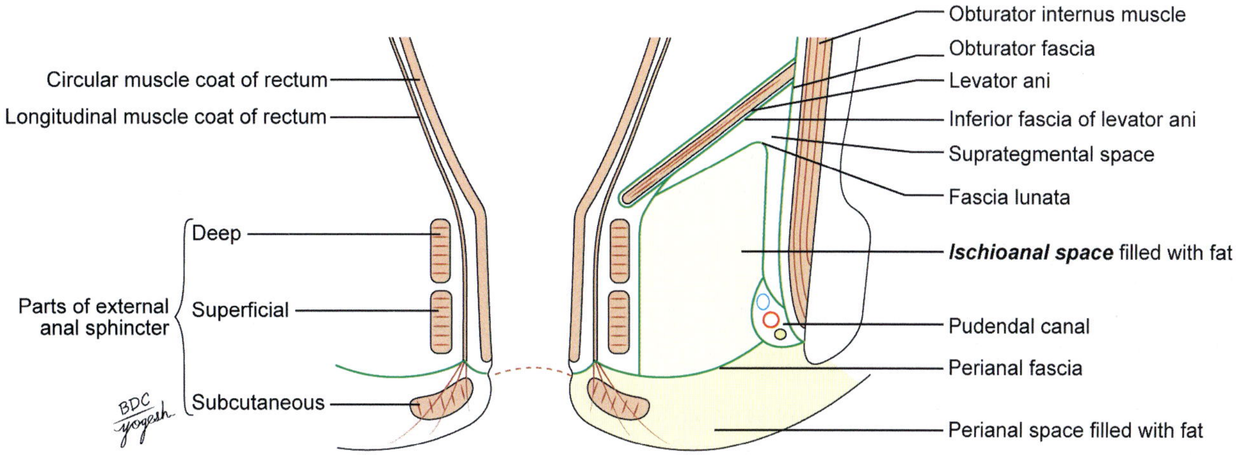

Fig. 28.19: Ischioanal fossa (coronal section through the anal triangle)

Flowchart 28.6: Ischioanal fossa

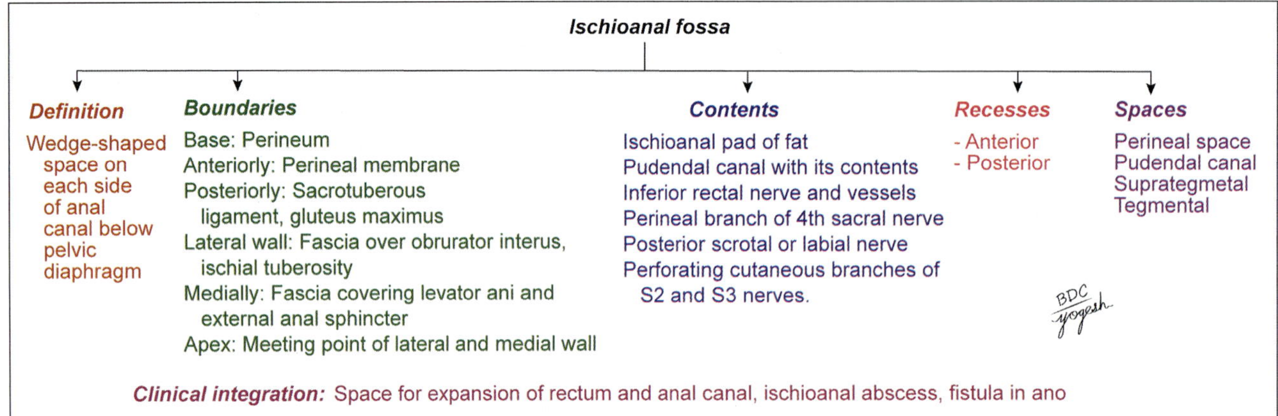

Lateral wall: It is vertical and bounded by fascia covering the obturator internus and medial surface of ischial tuberosity

Medial wall: It is slopping and bounded by fascia covering levator ani and external anal sphincter

Apex: It is formed by a line where obturator fascia meets the fascia covering the inferior surface of levator ani muscle (inferior fascia of pelvic diaphragm)

Contents of Ischioanal Fossa (Fig. 28.20)

1. Ischioanal pad of fat.
2. Inferior rectal nerve and vessels. They pass through the fossa from lateral to medial side. They arch upwards above the fat (Fig. 28.9) to supply mucous membrane, external sphincter and the skin around the anus.
3. Pudendal canal with its contents. This canal lies along the lateral wall of the fossa.
4. Posterior scrotal or posterior labial (in females) nerves and vessels. They cross the anterolateral part of the fossa and enter the urogenital triangle.
5. Perineal branch of the fourth sacral (S4) nerve. It enters the posterior angle of the fossa and runs over the levator ani to the external anal sphincter.
6. Perforating cutaneous branches of nerves S2, 3. They appear at the lower border of the gluteus maximus, in the posterior part of the fossa.

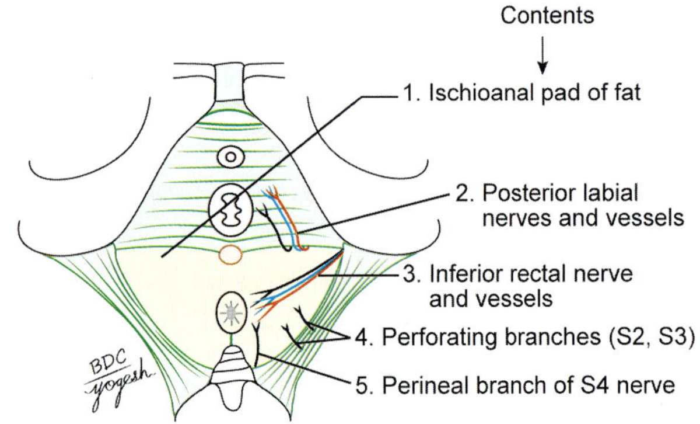

Fig. 28.20: Contents of the ischioanal fossa

Recesses

These are narrow extensions of the fossa beyond its boundaries.

1. *Anterior recess*: It extends forward above the perineal membrane and reaches up to the body of pubis.
2. *Posterior recess*: It extends deep to sacrotuberous ligaments.
3. *Horse-shaped posterior midline recess*: It connects the two ischioanal fossae behind the anal canal.

Spaces and Canals of the Fossa

The fascial arrangements in perianal region create the following spaces:

1. Perianal space
2. Pudendal canal
3. Ischioanal space that includes suprategmental and tegmental spaces.

Perianal Space

The perianal fascia is in the form of a septum that passes laterally from the lower end of the longitudinal coat of the anal canal. It extends medially from the white line of Hilton to the pudendal canal laterally. It separates a shallow subcutaneous *perianal space* from the deep *ischioanal space*. Perianal space is small and shallow. The fat in the perianal space is tightly arranged in small loculi formed by complete septa. The infections of this space are, therefore, very painful due to the tension caused by swelling (Fig. 28.7).

Ischioanal Space

This is large and deep. The fat in this space is loosely arranged in large loculi formed by incomplete delicate septa. The infections of this space are, therefore, least painful because swelling can occur without tension (Fig. 28.21). The *lunate fascia* arches over the ischioanal fat. It begins laterally at the pudendal canal and merges medially with the fascia covering the deep part of the external anal sphincter. The fascia divides the ischioanal space into:

a. *Suprategmental space*, above the fascia.
b. *Tegmental space*, below the fascia.

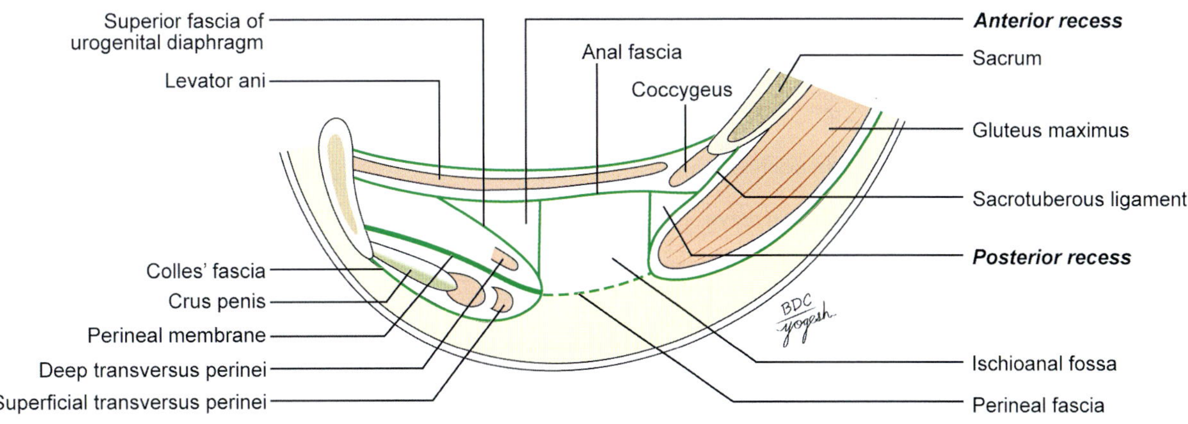

Fig. 28.21: Parasagittal section through the ischioanal fossa, showing its recesses

Pudendal Canal

This is a fascial canal in the lateral wall of the ischioanal fossa, enclosing the pudendal nerve and internal pudendal vessels. The fascia of the canal is fused with the lower part of the obturator fascia laterally, with the lunate fascia above, with the perianal fascia medially, and with the falciform process of the sacrotuberous ligament below.

Competency:

AN49.5 Explain the anatomical basis of perineal tear, episiotomy, perianal abscess and anal fissure.

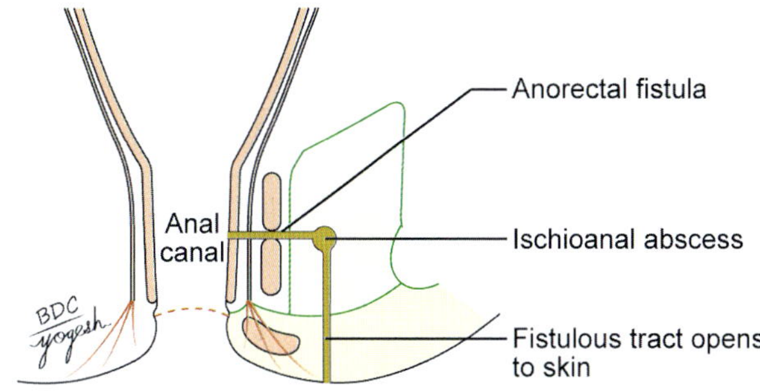

Fig. 28.22: Ischiorectal type of fistula in ano. Internally, it usually opens into one of anal crypts. The track traverses the superficial parts of external anal sphincter and lower part of internal anal sphincter. A blind sinus lies high up in the ischiorectal fossa

CLINICAL ANATOMY

- ***Space for expansion of rectum and anal canal***: The fat in ischioanal fossa provides cushion-like support and space for expansion of rectum and anal canal during defecation. Loss of the fat may cause diarrhea or rectal prolapse.
- ***Ischioanal abscess***: Infection of ischioanal fossa is common due to its location (Fig. 28.21). Source of infection: Boil or aberrations in the perineal skin, lesions of anal canal, sometimes spreads from blood. Infection of perineal fat often results into ischioanal or ischiorectal abscess.
- ***Spread of ischioanal abscess***: As one ischioanal fossa communicates with another fossa, through horseshoe-shaped posterior recess, the infection from one fossa may spread to another (horseshoe-shaped abscess).
- ***Fistula in ano***: It may occur due to bursting of ischioanal abscess in the anal canal. The most common site of internal opening is in the floor of anal crypts (Fig. 28.22).
- ***Hiatus of Schwalbe***: It is an occasional gap between the tendinous origin of the levator ani and obturator fascia. Ischioanal hernia is the herniation of pelvic organs through hiatus of Schwalbe.

DISSECTION

Place a finger in the ischioanal fossa and push it gently forwards. It will pass easily above the urogenital diaphragm, lateral to levator ani. Strip the ischiocavernosus muscles from the crus of the penis or clitoris.

Trace them to their termination.

Detach the superficial perineal muscles, including right crus of the penis from the ischiopubic rami. Turn it forwards to expose the deep artery and vein on the superior surface of perineal membrane also called inferior fascia of urogenital diaphragm. In the male, detach the bulb of the penis from the central perineal tendon. Turn it forwards to expose the urethra and the artery of the bulb.

In the female, raise the posterior end of the bulb of the vestibule to expose the greater vestibular gland.

Detach the perineal membrane from the pubic arch on the right side. Carefully reflect the membrane medially to visualize the urethra and a pair of posteriorly placed deep transversus perinei muscles.

Remove the exposed muscles of the deep perineal space including the endopelvic fascia. Clean the area to see the perineal surface of the levator ani.

PUDENDAL CANAL (ALCOCK'S CANAL)

This is a fascial tunnel present in the lateral wall of the ischioanal fossa, just above the sacrotuberous ligament. It transmits the pudendal nerve and the internal pudendal vessels.

The canal extends from the lesser sciatic notch to the posterior border of the perineal membrane (Plate 28.4)

Plate 28.4: Location of pudendal canal

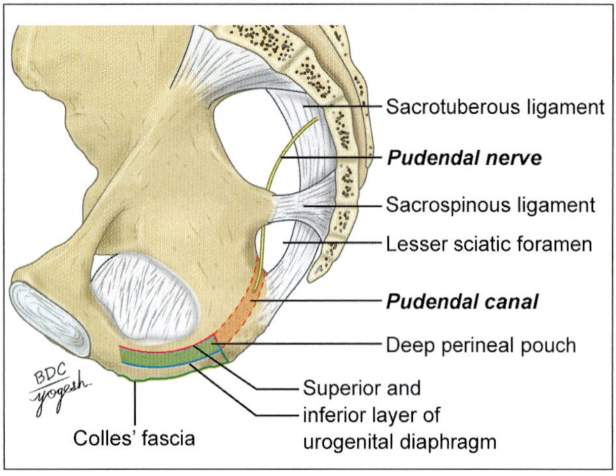

Formation

The pudendal canal is a space between obturator fascia and the lunate fascia. Others believe that it is formed by splitting of the obturator fascia.

Contents

Pudendal nerve (S2–S4): In the posterior part of the canal, pudendal nerve gives off the inferior rectal nerve and then soon divides into a larger perineal nerve and a smaller dorsal nerve of penis.

Internal pudendal artery: This artery gives off the inferior rectal artery in the posterior part of the canal. In the anterior part of the canal, the artery divides into the perineal artery and the artery of penis. Vein accompanies the artery.

PUDENDAL NERVE

Pudendal nerve is the chief nerve of the perineum and of the external genitalia. It is accompanied by the internal pudendal vessels.

Origin

Pudendal nerve arises from the sacral plexus in the pelvis. It is derived from spinal nerves S2, S3 and S4.

Course

It originates in the pelvis, enters gluteal region through greater sciatic notch, leaves it through lesser sciatic notch to enter the pudendal canal in the lateral wall of ischioanal fossa. It terminates by dividing into branches (Fig. 28.23, Flowchart 28.7).

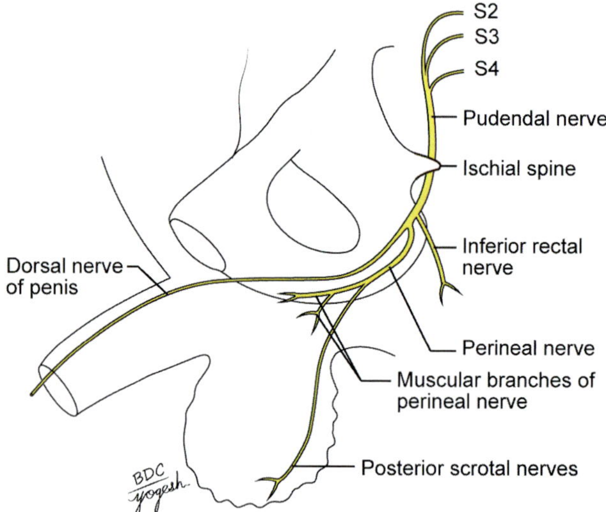

Fig. 28.23: Course and branches of pudendal nerve

Flowchart 28.7: Pudendal nerve

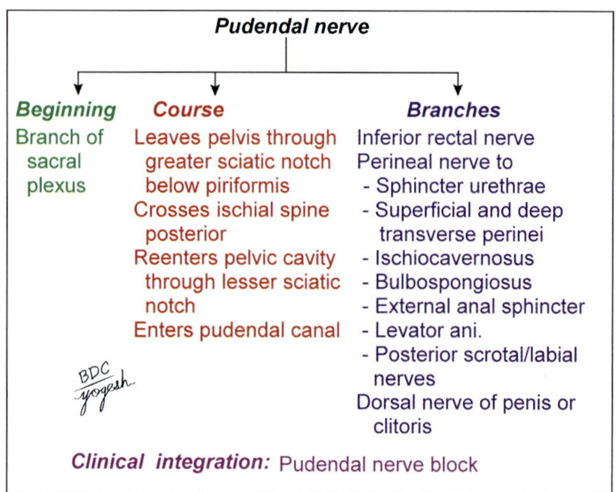

Relations

In the pelvis, the pudendal nerve descends in front of the piriformis deep to its fascia. It leaves the pelvis, to enter the gluteal region, by passing through the lower part of the greater sciatic foramen, between the piriformis and the coccygeus, medial to internal pudendal vessels (*see* Figs 5.14 and 5.15).

1. *In the gluteal region*, the pudendal nerve crosses the apex of the sacrospinous ligament, under cover of gluteus maximus. Here it lies medial to the internal pudendal vessels which cross the ischial spine. Accompanying these vessels, the nerve leaves the gluteal region by passing through the lesser sciatic foramen, and enters the pudendal canal.
2. *In the pudendal canal*, the neurovascular bundle lies in the lateral wall of the ischioanal fossa.

Branches

It gives the following branches:

Inferior rectal nerve: It supplies external anal sphincter, skin around the anus, lining of anal canal below the pectinate line, and lower 2.5 cm of vagina.

Two terminal branches

a. *Perineal nerve*:
   - *Muscular branches* to supply sphincter urethrae, superficial and deep transverse perinei, ischiocavernosus, bulbospongiosus, anterior part of external anal sphincter, levator ani.
   - *Cutaneous branches*: Posterior scrotal or labial nerves for posterior 2/3rd of scrotum or labia majora.

b. *Dorsal nerve of penis or clitoris* enters the deep perineal pouch and runs forward. It leaves the deep perineal pouch to reach the dorsal surface of penis through a trianglar gap between transverse perineal ligament and arcuate pubic ligament. It supplies skin of penis, prepuce and glans.

Note:

1. ***Inferior rectal nerve*** along with inferior rectal vessels pierce the medial wall of pudendal canal, traverse the ischiorectal fossa to reach the anal canal.
2. ***Perineal nerve*** is divided into superficial and deep branch. The deep branch supplies muscle and superficial branch is cutaneous and gives rise to two posterior scrotal or labial nerve.

CLINICAL ANATOMY

Pudendal nerve block

The pudendal nerve can be blocked by infiltration of anaesthetic agent near the ischial spine (Fig. 28.24).

Procedure: The ischial spine is palpated by a finger through vagina (in female) or anal canal (in male). A long needle is passed through the vaginal wall (in female) or skin (in male) to the ischial spine guided by the finger and the anaesthetic agent is infiltrated.

Area anesthetized: Lower part of the vagina and vulva, relaxation of muscle of pelvic floor, and loss of anal reflex.

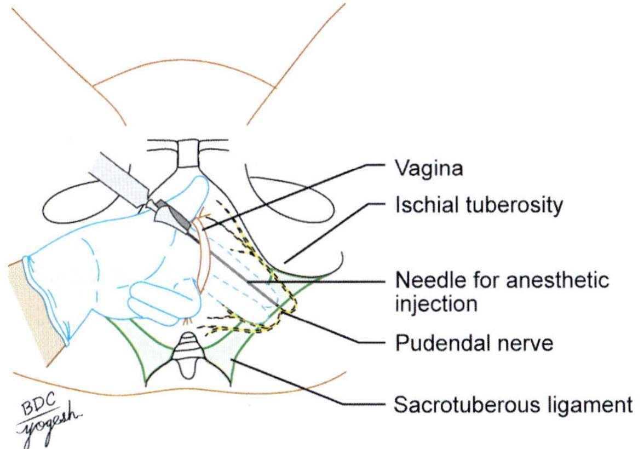

Fig. 28.24: Pudendal nerve block in female

INTERNAL PUDENDAL ARTERY

This is the chief artery of the perineum and of the external genital organs. It is smaller in females than in males (Fig. 28.25, Flowchart 28.8).

Beginning

The artery is the smaller terminal branch of the anterior division of the internal iliac artery, given off in the pelvis; the larger branch is the inferior gluteal.

Course

The course of internal pudendal artery is similar to the course of pudendal nerve. It enters the gluteal region through greater sciatic notch, leaves it through lesser sciatic notch to enter the pudendal canal.

Relations

In the pelvis, the artery runs downwards in front of the piriformis, the sacral plexus and the inferior gluteal artery. It leaves the pelvis by piercing the parietal pelvic fascia and passing through the greater sciatic foramen, below the piriformis, thus entering the gluteal region.

In the ***gluteal region***, the artery crosses the dorsal aspect of the tip of the ischial spine, under cover of the gluteus maximus. Here it lies between the pudendal nerve medially and the nerve to the obturator internus laterally. It leaves the gluteal region by passing through

Flowchart 28.8: Internal pudendal artery

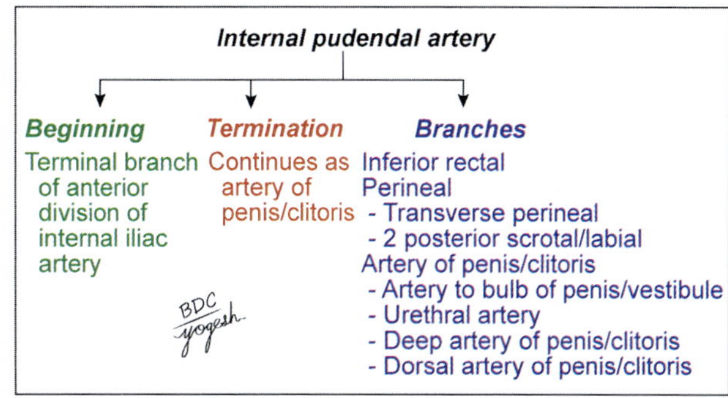

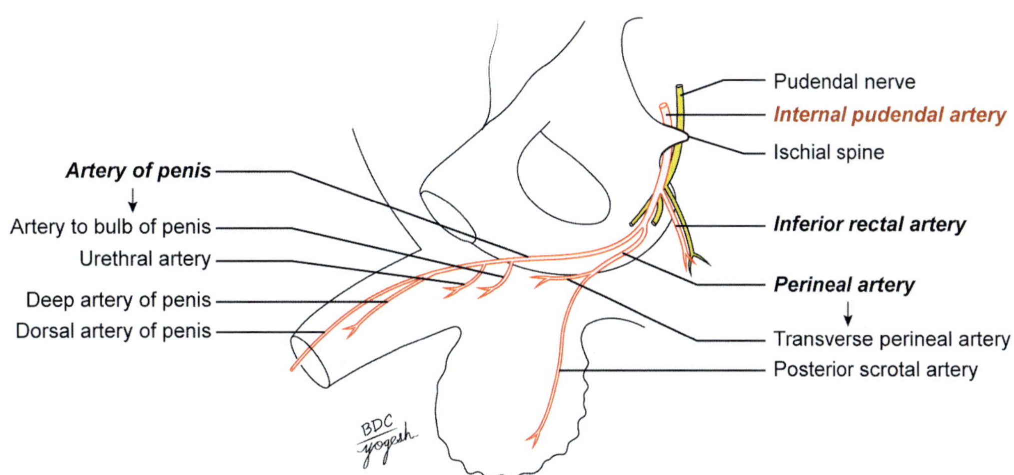

Fig. 28.25: Course and branches of internal pudendal artery

the lesser sciatic foramen, and thus enters the pudendal canal (*see* Figs 5.14 ad 5.15).

In the ***pudendal canal***, the artery runs downwards and forwards in the lateral wall of the ischioanal fossa, about 4 cm above the lower margin of the ischial tuberosity. Here it is related to the dorsal nerve above and the perineal nerve below. The artery gives off the inferior rectal artery in the posterior part of the canal, and the perineal artery in the anterior part. The internal pudendal artery continues into the deep perineal space as the artery of the penis or of the clitoris (Fig. 28.24).

In the ***deep perineal space***, the artery of the penis or clitoris, which is continuation of internal pudendal artery, runs forwards close to the side of pubic arch, medial to the dorsal nerve of penis or of clitoris. The artery ends a little behind the arcuate pubic ligament by dividing into the deep and dorsal arteries of penis or of the clitoris (Fig. 28.27).

Branches

1. Inferior rectal artery
2. Perineal artery
   a. Transverse perineal artery
   b. Two posterior scrotal or labial arteries
3. Artery of penis or clitoris
   a. Artery to the bulb of penis or bulb of vestibule
   b. Urethral artery
   c. Deep artery of penis or clitoris
   d. Dorsal artery of penis or clitoris.

Note:

1. The ***inferior rectal artery*** arises near the posterior end of the pudendal canal, and accompanies the nerve of the same name. The artery supplies the skin, muscles and mucous membrane of the anal region, and anastomoses with the superior and middle rectal arteries (Fig. 28.24).
2. The ***perineal artery*** arises near the anterior end of the pudendal canal, and pierces the base of the perineal membrane to reach the superficial perineal space. Here it divides into the *transverse perineal* and the *posterior scrotal* or *posterior labial* branches.
3. The ***artery of the penis*** or *the* ***clitoris*** runs in the deep perineal space and gives off: Artery to the bulb, urethral artery, deep artery of the penis or the clitoris, and dorsal artery of the penis or the clitoris. All of them pierce the perineal membrane and reach the superficial perineal space.
   a. The ***artery to the bulb*** supplies the bulb of the penis or bulb of vestibule and the posterior part of the urethra or only the urethra.
   b. The ***urethral artery*** supplies the corpus spongiosum and the anterior part of the urethra.
   c. The ***deep artery of the penis*** or *the* ***clitoris*** traverses and supplies the crus and the corpus cavernosum.
   d. The ***dorsal artery of the penis*** or *the* ***clitoris*** supplies the skin and fasciae of the body of the penis and of the glans or the glans clitoridis.

INTERNAL PUDENDAL VEIN

The tributaries of internal pudendal vein follow the branches of the internal pudendal artery. The vein drains into internal iliac vein.

Facts to Remember

- Perineum is divided into anteriorly placed urogenital triangle and posteriorly placed anal triangle.
- Sphincter urethrae is within the wall of urethra. So there is thin deep perineal space.
- Perineal membrane is the key structure in urogenital triangle.
- Key structure and central tendon of perineum is perineal body. Muscles attached here are external anal sphincter, fibres of longitudinal muscle coat of anal canal, pair of levater ani, bulbospongiosus and superficial and deep transversus perinei.
- Body of clitoris in female is made up of only two corpora cavernosa and *no* corpus spongiosum.
- Clitoris is much smaller than the penis and is *not traversed by the urethra*. Urethral orifice lies 2 cm behind clitoris.
- Bulbspongiosus of two sides is separate in female and overlie the bulb of vestibule. In male, the two are united by a median septum and overlie the bulb of penis.

BDC's Anatomy *e*-book

1. Histology of body of penis/clitoris
2. Rupture of the urethra
3. Further reading
4. Viva voce questions

Chapter

29

Preliminary Consideration of Boundaries and Contents of Pelvis

Pelvis is formed by articulation of each of the two hip bones with the sacrum behind and with each other in front (Fig. 29.1).

The bony pelvis is formed by *four bones* united at *four joints*. The bones are the two hip bones in front and on the sides and the sacrum and coccyx behind. The joints are the two sacroiliac joints, the pubic symphysis and the sacrococcygeal joint.

The pelvis is divided by the plane of the ***pelvic inlet*** or ***pelvic brim***, or superior aperture of the pelvis into two parts:

a. Upper part is known as the ***greater*** or ***false pelvis***, which lodges the abdominal viscera.
b. Lower part is known as the ***lesser*** or ***true pelvis***.

The plane of the pelvic inlet passes from the sacral promontory to the upper margin of the pubic symphysis. The *greater* or *false pelvis* includes the two iliac fossae and forms a part of the posterior abdominal wall. The *lesser* or *true pelvis* contains the pelvic viscera.

Competency:

AN53.2 Demonstrate the anatomical position of bony pelvis and show boundaries of pelvic inlet, pelvic cavity and pelvic outlet.

TRUE OR LESSER PELVIS

The true pelvis lies below the pelvic brim and is enclosed within the bony walls formed by sacrum, coccyx and hip bones.

Pelvic Walls

The pelvic walls are made up of bones, ligaments, membranes and muscles.

Bony Walls

These are formed:

1. *Anteriorly* by the pubic symphysis and bodies of the pubic bones.
2. *Posteriorly* by the sacrum and coccyx.
3. *On each side* by the two rami of the pubis, the ischium with its ramus, and the lower part of the ilium (Plate 29.1).

Plate 29.1: Pelvic bones and ligaments seen from the medial side

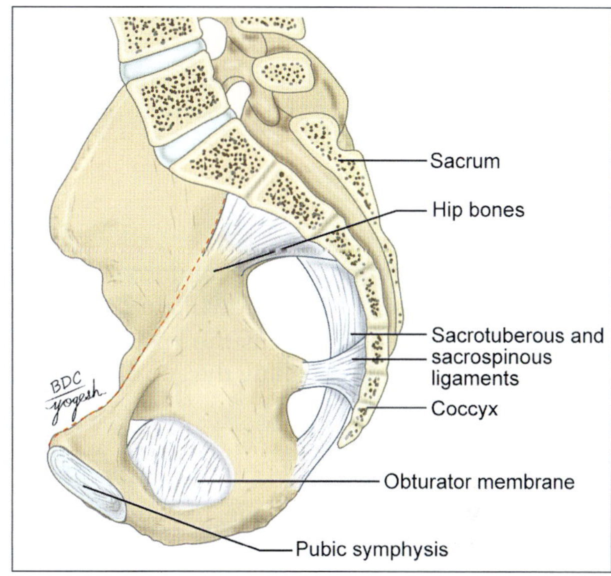

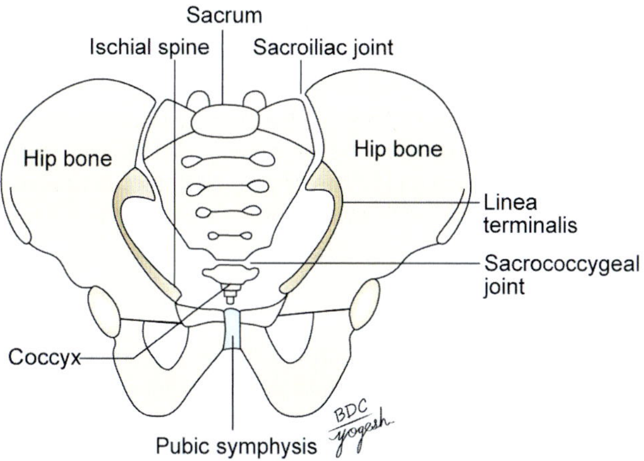

Fig. 29.1: Anterior view of the male pelvis

Ligaments and Membranes

1. *Obturator membrane* closes the greater part of the obturator foramen and completes the lower part of the lateral wall of the pelvis (Plate 29.1).

Plate 29.2: Obturator internus and piriformis muscles of the pelvic wall seen from the medial side

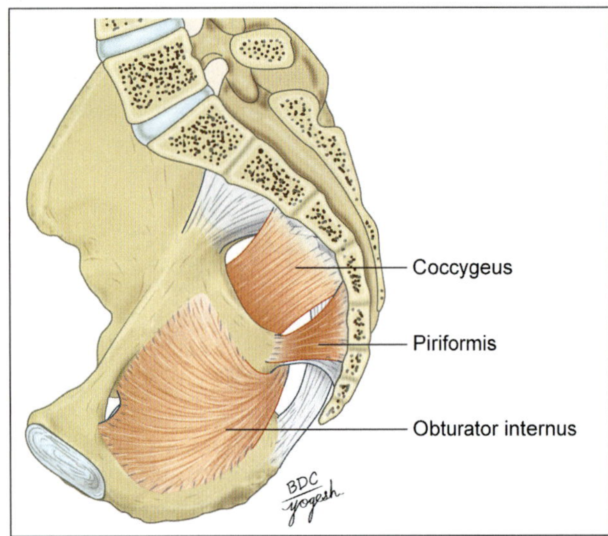

2. *Sacrotuberous* and *sacrospinous* ligaments bridge the gap between the hip bone and the sacrum, and convert the greater and lesser sciatic notches into the foramina of the same name (Plate 29.2).

Muscles

1. *Obturator internus* with its fascia reinforces the lateral wall of the pelvis from the inside (Plate 29.2).
2. *Piriformis* with its fascia forms the posterior wall of the pelvis. It also helps in filling the gap of the greater sciatic foramen.

Pelvic Inlet (Superior Aperture of Pelvis)

The pelvic inlet is an oblique plane, making an angle of 50° to 60° with the horizontal plane.

Boundaries

Posteriorly: Sacral promontory

Anteriorly: Upper margin of the pubic symphysis

On each side: Linea terminalis that includes the anterior margin of the ala of the sacrum, the arcuate line or lower part of the medial border of the ilium, the pectineal line of the pubis or pecten pubis, and the pubic crest (Fig. 29.2).

Shape

The pelvic inlet is heart-shaped *in the male*, and is widest in its posterior part. *In the female*, it is oval, and is widest more anteriorly than in the male. Posteriorly, the inlet is indented by the sacral promontory, more so in the male than in the female (Fig. 29.3).

Pelvic Outlet (Inferior Aperture of Pelvis)

Boundaries

Anteriorly: Arcuate or inferior pubic ligament

Posteriorly: Coccyx

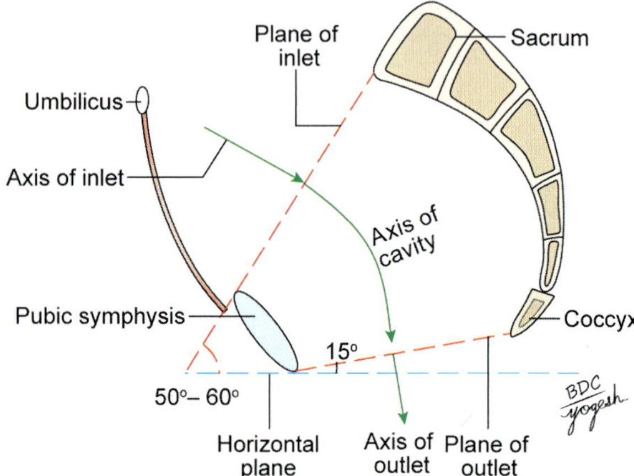

Fig. 29.2: Sagittal section of the pelvis showing the planes of its inlet and outlet and their axes. The axis of the pelvic cavity is J-shaped

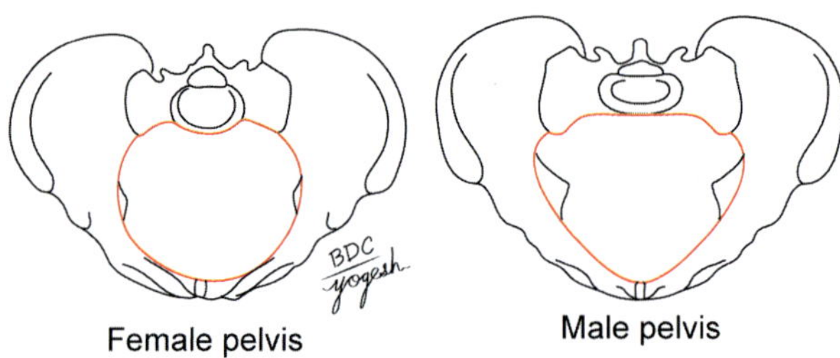

Fig. 29.3: Shape of pelvic inlet in the male and female

On each side: Ischiopubic rami or side of the pubic arch, the ischial tuberosities and the sacro-tuberous ligaments.

Dimensions of pelvis in females, classification of pelvis and sex differences are given in Chapter 15.

CLINICAL ANATOMY

- The pelvis is a basin with various walls and many openings. The posterior wall contains five pairs of anterior sacral foramina. The greater and lesser sciatic notches are converted into foramina of the same name with the help of sacrotuberous and sacrospinous ligaments. Greater sciatic foramen is the 'doorway' of the gluteal region. Pudendal nerve enters the region through the greater sciatic notch and quickly leaves it through lesser sciatic notch to enter the perineum. The lateral wall contains obturator foramen for the passage of obturator nerve, which supplies adductors of the hip joint.
- Fracture may occur in the true (ring-like) pelvis. If fracture is at one point, the fracture will be stable.
- In athletes, anterior superior iliac spine may be pulled off by forcible contraction of sartorius. Similarly, anterior inferior iliac spine or ischial tuberosity may get **avulsed** by the contraction of their attached muscles.

Pelvic Floor

The pelvic floor is formed by the pelvic diaphragm, which consists of the levator ani and the coccygeus.

Plate 29.3: Pelvic floor: Levator ani and coccygeus muscles

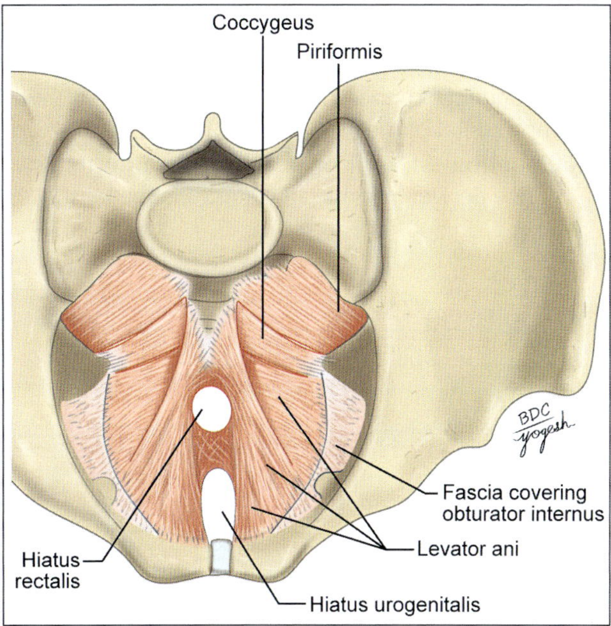

It resembles a hammock, or a gutter, because it slopes from either side towards the median plane, where it is traversed by the urethra and the anal canal, and also by the vagina in the female. The pelvic diaphragm separates the perineum below from the pelvis above (Plate 29.3).

The muscles of the true pelvis, its blood vessels and nerves are considered in Chapter 34.

CLINICAL ANATOMY

- Pelvic floor is formed by two gutter-shaped levator ani muscles that support the pelvic viscera, especially during raised intra-abdominal pressure.
- The foetal head travels in the axis of pelvic cavity. Sometimes episiotomy is given to enlarge the perineum (Plate 29.3).
- Injury to pelvic floor, which mostly occurs during vaginal delivery, may cause uterine, vaginal or even rectal prolapse.
- The 2nd to 4th sacral nerves and coccygeal nerve can be anaesthetised by the anaesthetic agent put into the sacral canal. It is called *caudal anaesthesia* and is used in obstetrics practice.
- Pain in the sacroiliac joint is felt on pressing the posterior superior iliac spine presents as a dimple on the lower back.

Pelvic Cavity

The pelvic cavity is continuous above with the abdominal cavity at the pelvic brim, and is limited below by the pelvic diaphragm. The cavity is curved in such a way that it is first directed downwards and backwards, and then downwards and forwards (J-shaped). It has unequal walls, measuring only about 5 cm anteriorly and 15 cm posteriorly. The cavity is more roomy or larger in the female than in the male.

Contents

1. Sigmoid colon and rectum occupy the posterior part of the pelvis.
2. Urinary bladder lies anteriorly. The prostate lies below the neck of urinary bladder.
3. In between the bladder and rectum, there is a transverse septum or *genital septum* made up of connective tissue. In the male, the septum is small. It contains the ductus deferens, the seminal vesicle and the ureter on each side.

In the female, the septum is large, and contains uterus, uterine tubes, round ligament of the uterus, ligaments of the ovary, ovaries, vagina and ureters.

These contents are considered in detail in Chapters 31 and 32.

Structures Crossing the Pelvic Inlet/Brim of the Pelvis

From posterior median plane sweeping laterally and anteriorly (Fig. 29.4):

1. Median sacral vessels
2. Sympathetic trunk
3. Lumbosacral trunk

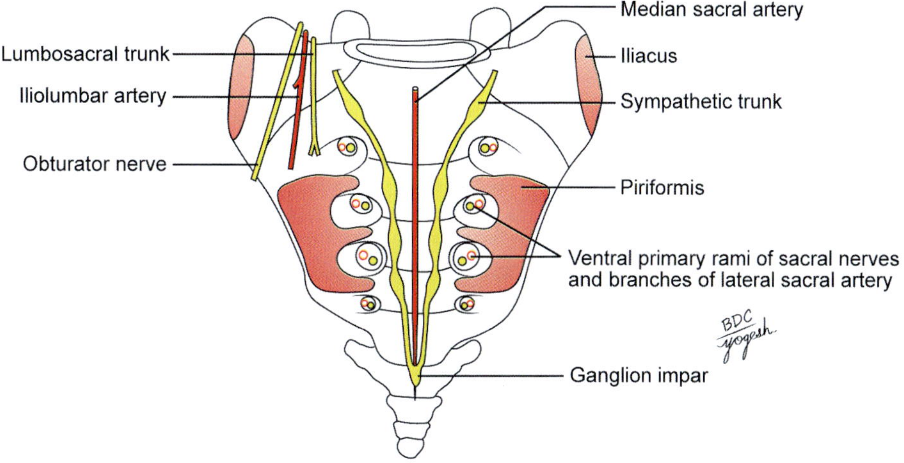

Fig. 29.4: Anterior (pelvic) view of the sacrum and its attachments

4. Iliolumbar artery
5. Obturator nerve
6. Internal iliac vessels
7. Medial limb of sigmoid mesocolon with superior rectal vessels—left side only
8. Ureter
9. Sigmoid colon—on left side only
10. Ovarian vessels in female
11. Ductus deferens in male/round ligament of uterus in female
12. Obliterated umbilical artery
13. Median umbilical ligament or urachus
14. Autonomic nerve plexuses
15. Coils of intestine and pregnant uterus
16. Full urinary bladder.

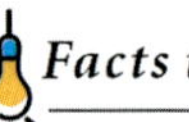

Facts to Remember

- Axis of pelvic cavity is 'J' shaped. Plane of outlet of pelvis makes an angle of 15° with the horizontal plane. Plane of inlet of pelvis makes an angle of 50°–60° with the horizontal plane.
- The shallowest wall of pelvis is its anterior wall. Distance between two ischial spines is the least.

BDC's Anatomy *e*-book

1. Urachus and obliterated umbilical artery
2. Further reading
3. Viva voce questions

Chapter

30

Urinary Bladder and Urethra

URINARY BLADDER

The urinary bladder is a mucomuscular temporary reservoir of urine, which lies in the anterior part of the pelvic cavity. The detrusor muscle of urinary bladder is arranged in whorls and spirals and is adapted for mass contraction rather than peristalsis.

Size, Shape and Position

The bladder varies in its size, shape and position according to the amount of urine it contains.

When empty, it lies entirely within the pelvis; but as it fills it expands and extends upwards into the abdominal cavity, reaching up to the umbilicus or even higher (Figs 30.1 to 30.3, Plate 30.1, Flowchart 30.1).

Note: *In children*, the bladder is an abdominopelvic organ even when it is empty, because of smaller pelvic cavity. In children, the neck of bladder lies at the level of upper border of pubic symphysis. The descent of bladder begins after birth and continues up to puberty.

Capacity

The mean capacity of urinary bladder is about 220 ml (120–320 ml) (Flowchart 31.1).

1. The sense of bladder filling first starts at a capacity of 100–150 ml.
2. First desire for micturition initiates at a capacity of 150–250 ml.
3. A filling beyond 500 ml causes pain due to distention of the bladder wall. Referred pain is felt in the lower part of the anterior abdominal wall, perineum and penis (T11–L2; S2–S4).
4. Collection of about 800 ml of urine initiates micturition as it is beyond one's voluntary control.

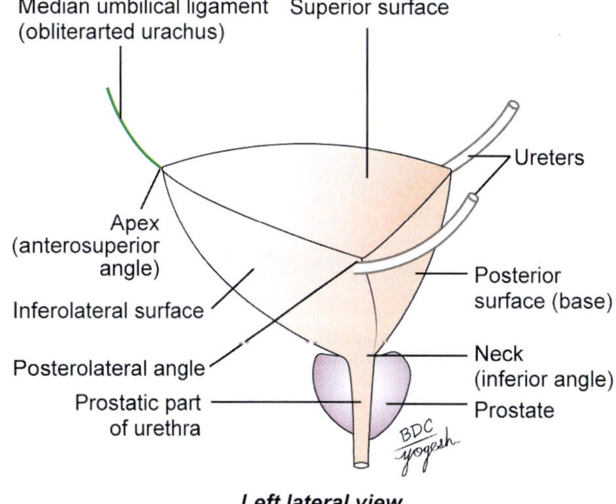

Fig. 30.1: Shape of the urinary bladder

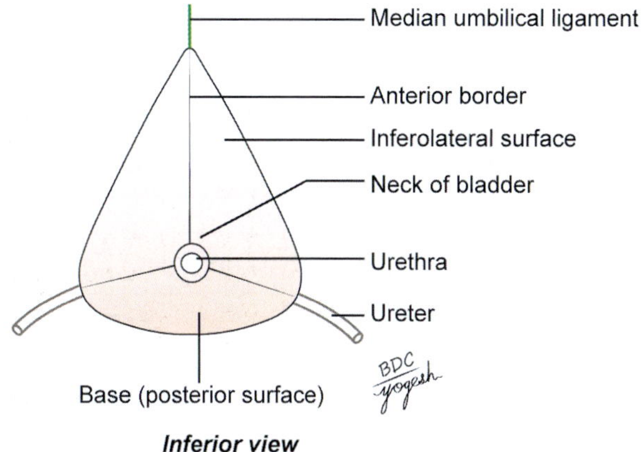

Fig. 30.2: Urinary bladder seen from below

External Features

Empty bladder is *tetrahedral* in shape and has (Plates 30.2 and 30.3):

1. *Apex* — directed forwards.
2. *Base* or *fundus* — directed backwards.
3. *Neck* — the lowest and most fixed part of the bladder.
4. *Three surfaces* — superior, right and left inferolateral.
5. *Four borders* — two lateral, one anterior and one posterior (Figs 30.1 and 30.2).

Full bladder is *ovoid* in shape and has the following:

1. *Apex* — directed upwards towards the umbilicus.
2. *Neck* — directed downwards.
3. *Two surfaces* — anterior and posterior.

Plate 30.1: Location of the urinary bladder in male (midsagittal section)

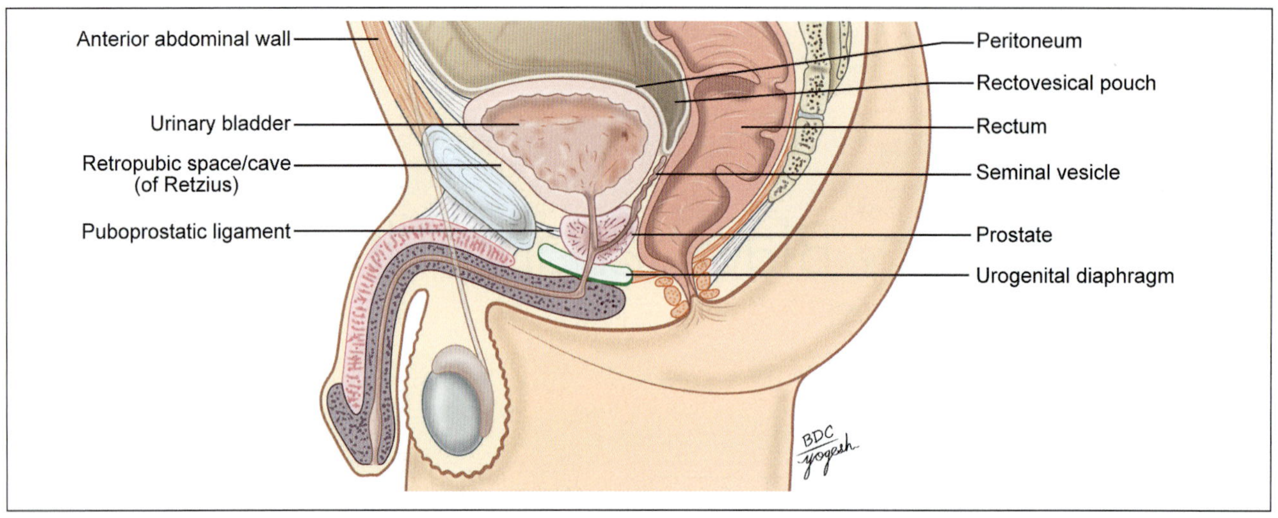

Plate 30.2: External features of empty bladder (left lateral view)

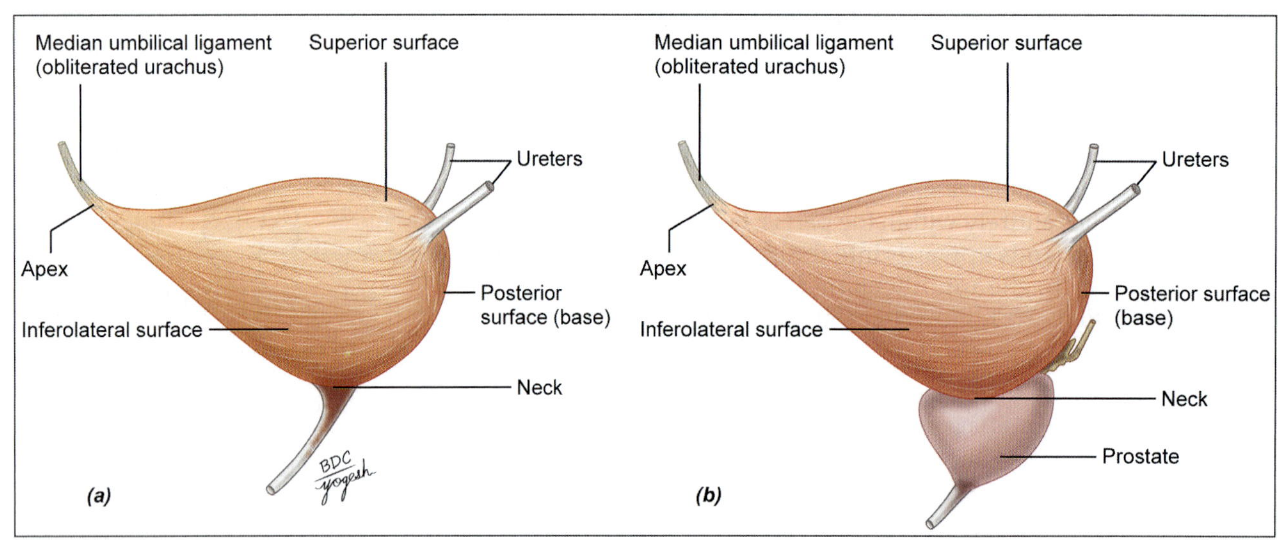

Plate 30.3: Male urinary bladder: (a) Base and (b) interior

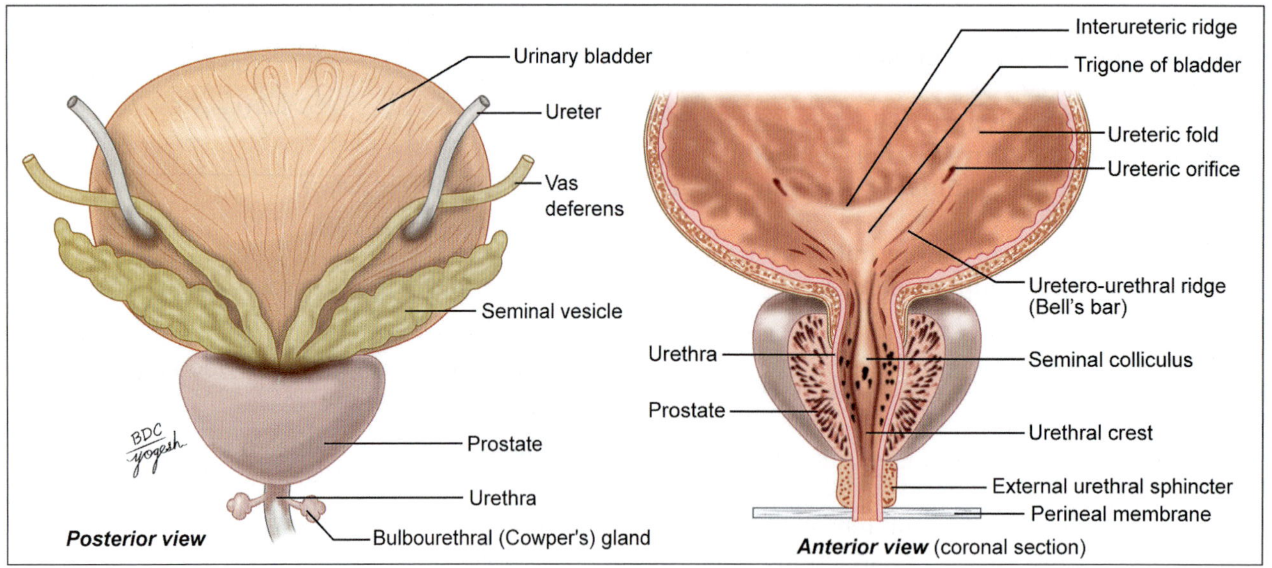

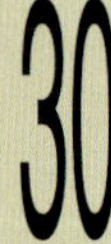

Flowchart 30.1: Urinary bladder

Urinary bladder
Mucomuscular bag

- ***Capacity***
  - 220 ml
- ***Location***
  - Empty bladder in lesser pelvis, behind pubic symphysis
  - Full bladder reaches up to umbilicus behind the anterior abdominal wall
- ***Parts***
  - Empty bladder
  - - Apex
  - - Base
  - - Neck
  - - 3 surface: superior and two in ferolateral
  - - 4 borders: two lateral, one anterior, one posterior

Ligaments of bladder

- ***True***
  - Median umbilical ligament
  - Two medial puboprostatic or pubovesical ligaments
  - Two lateral puboprostatic or pubovesical ligaments
  - Two lateral ligaments
  - Two posterior ligaments
- ***False***
  - Median umbilical fold
  - Two medial umbilical folds
  - Two lateral false ligaments
  - Two posterior false ligaments

Relations of urinary bladder

- ***Apex***
  - Directed upward
  - Connected to umbilicus by median umbilical ligament
- ***Base***
  - In male
  - - Rectovesical pouch
  - - Seminal vesicles
  - - Vas deferens
  - In female
  - - Vescicouterine pouch
- ***Neck***
  - Directed inferiorly
  - - Fixed
  - - Lies 3–4 cm behind the pubic symphysis
  - - In male: surrounded by prostate
  - - In female: surrounded by pelvic fascia
- ***Superior surface***
  - Triangular
  - Covered by peritoneum
- ***Inferolateral surface***
  - Directed inferolaterally
  - Related to
  - - Retropubic pad of fat
  - - Puboprostatic ligament
  - - Obturator internus
  - - Levator ani

Interior of urinary bladder

- ***Vesical mucosa***
  - Irregular folds ↑ Loose attachment of mucosa with muscular layer
- ***Trigone of bladder***
  - Triangular area
  - Located at posteroinferior part of bladder
  - Shows
  - - Internal urethral orifice
  - - Two ureteric openings
  - - Uvula vesicae
- ***Interureteric crest***
  - Bar of Mercier
  - Mucosal bridge
- ***Ureteric fold***
  - Oblique mucosal folds ↑ intramural course of ureters
- ***Ureterourethral ridges***
  - Called Bell's bars
  - Mucosal folds
  - Extend from ureteric orifice to urethral orifice

Supply of urinary bladder

- ***Arterial supply***
  - Superior and inferior vesical arteries
  - Obturator, inferior gluteal, uterine, vaginal
- ***Venous drainage***
  - Vesical venous plexus ↓ Internal iliac veins
- ***Lymphatics***
  - External iliac nodes
- ***Innervation***
  - ***Motor***
  - Parasympathetic: S2, S3, S4
  - Sympathetic: T10–T12, L1 and L2
  - Somatic: S1, S2, S3
  - ***Sensory*** by parasympathetic

BDC yogesh

Anatomical Position

Hold the cadaveric bladder in such a way that:

1. Its apex is directed upwards, and base is directed posteromedially.
2. Triangular superior surface faces upwards and narrow neck downwards.
3. Convex inferolateral surfaces face inferolateral (face the palm while holding in hand).

Relations

Apex

The apex is connected to the umbilicus by the ***median umbilical ligament***, which represents the obliterated embryonic urachus (Fig. 30.1).

Base

The base of the urinary bladder is triangular and directed posteroinferiorly.

- *In the **female**,* it is related to the uterine cervix and vagina.
- *In the **male**:*
  - The ***upper part*** of the base is separated from the rectum by the ***rectovesical pouch*** and the contained coils of the intestine
  - The ***lower part*** is related to the seminal vesicles and the terminations of the vas deferens (Fig. 30.3). The triangular area between the two ductus deferens is separated from the rectum by the ***rectovesical fascia of Denonvilliers***.

Neck

The neck is the lowest and most ***fixed*** part of the bladder. It lies 3 to 4 cm behind the lower part of the pubic symphysis, a little above the plane of the pelvic outlet. It is pierced by the internal urethral orifice.

- *In **males**,* it is surrounded by the prostate.

Note: The smooth muscle bundles surround the bladder neck and preprostatic urethra. These are arranged as distinct circular collar with their own distinct adrenergic innervations. This is the preprostatic sphincter and is devoid of parasympathetic cholinergic nerves. It is part of proximal urethral sphincter mechanism.

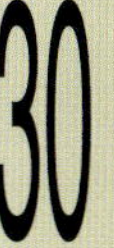

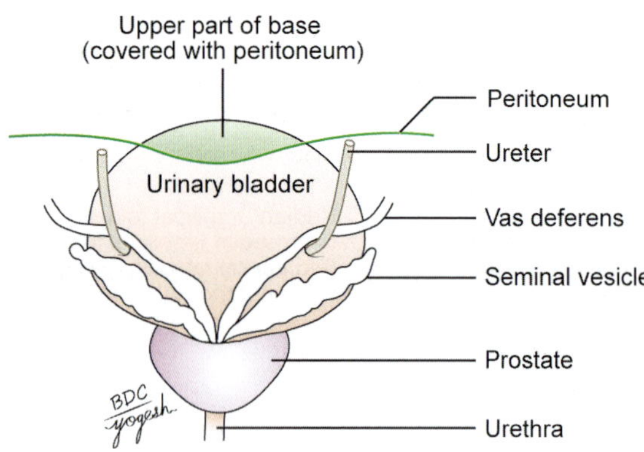

Fig. 30.3: Posterior view of a male urinary bladder and its relation

- *In* ***females***, neck is related to the pelvic fascia, which surrounds the upper part of the urethra.
- In ***infants***, the bladder lies at a higher level. The internal urethral orifice lies at the level of the superior border of the pubic symphysis. It gradually descends to reach the adult position after puberty.

Superior Surface

It is triangular and bounded on each side by lateral borders and posteriorly by the posterior border.

- *In* ***males***, it is completely covered by peritoneum, and is in contact with the sigmoid colon and coils of the terminal ileum.
- *In* ***females***, peritoneum covers the greater part of the superior surface, except for a small area near the posterior border, which is related to the supravaginal part of the uterine cervix. The peritoneum from the superior surface is reflected to the isthmus of the uterus to form the ***vesicouterine pouch***.

Inferolateral Surfaces

These are devoid of peritoneum, and are separated from each other anteriorly by the anterior border and from the superior surface by the lateral borders.

- *In the* ***male***, each surface is related to (Plate 30.4):
  1. Pubis
  2. Puboprostatic ligaments
  3. Retropubic fat
  4. Obturator internus muscle
  5. Levator ani muscle.
- *In the* ***female***, the relations are same, except that the puboprostatic ligaments are replaced by the pubovesical ligaments.

Space of Retzius or Retropubic Space

This is a perivesical horseshoe-shaped space. It lies between anterolateral wall of pelvis and sides of urinary bladder and prostate. It allows distension of the bladder.

Boundaries

Anteriorly: Pubic symphysis and anterior abdominal wall
Posteriorly: Inferolateral surface of urinary bladder
Superiorly: Peritoneum of paravesical fossa
Inferiorly: Puboprostatic or pubovesical ligaments.

Plate 30.4: Relations of inferolateral surface of urinary bladder

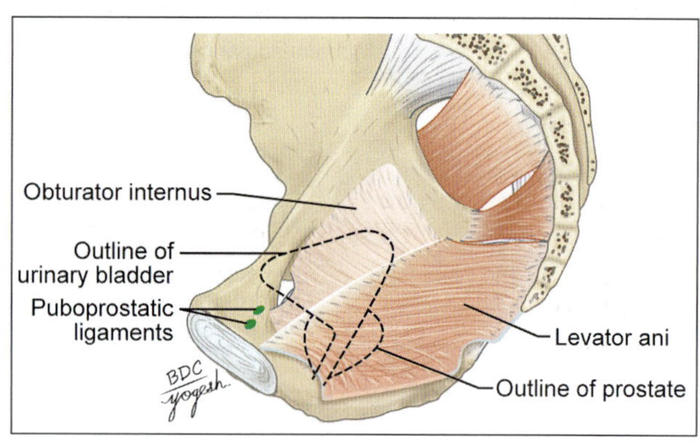

Contents: Retropubic pad of fat and vesical venous plexus.

Note: As the bladder fills, the inferolateral surfaces form the anterior surface of the distended bladder, which is covered by peritoneum only in its upper part. The lower part comes into direct contact with the anterior abdominal wall, there being no intervening peritoneum.

Suprapubic cystostomy *or suprapubic catheterisation*: Distended bladder can be approached surgically through this space retroperitoneally (without entering in the peritoneal cavity). This is commonly used for suprapubic catheterisation of urinary bladder (*see* Fig. 30.8).

Ligaments of the Bladder

The ligaments of urinary bladder are classified as *true and false.*

True Ligaments

These are condensations of pelvic fascia around the neck and base of the bladder. They are continuous with the fascia on the superior surface of the levator ani (Fig. 30.4).

1. ***Median umbilical ligament*** is the fibrous remnant of the urachus.
2. ***Medial puboprostatic ligaments*** *(right and left)* are directed downwards and backwards. They extend from the back of the pubic bone (near the pubic symphysis) to the prostatic sheath. The ligaments of

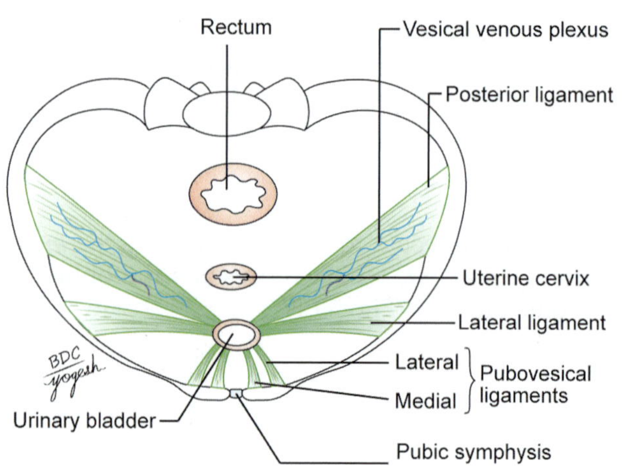

Fig. 30.4: True ligaments of the bladder in female

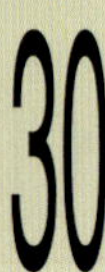

the two sides form the floor of the retropubic space. In females, bands similar to the puboprostatic ligaments are known as the ***pubovesical ligaments***. They end around the neck of the bladder.

3. ***Lateral puboprostatic ligaments*** *(right and left)* are directed medially and backwards. They extend from the anterior end of the tendinous arch of the pelvic fascia to the upper part of the prostatic sheath.
4. ***Lateral true ligaments*** *(right and left)* of the bladder extend from the side of the bladder to the tendinous arch of the pelvic fascia.
5. ***Posterior ligaments*** *(right and left)* of the bladder are directed backwards and upwards along the vesical plexus of veins. They extend on each side from the base of bladder to the wall of pelvis.

False Ligaments

These are peritoneal folds, which do not form any support to the bladder. They include:

1. Median umbilical fold
2. Medial umbilical folds (*right and left*)
3. Lateral false ligaments (*right and left*)
4. Posterior false ligaments (*right and left*).

Note: The *median umbilical fold* is a fold of peritoneum that covers median umbilical ligament. The m*edial umbilical folds* cover the obliterated umbilical arteries. The l*ateral false ligaments* extend from the bladder to the lateral pelvic wall and form the floor of paravesical fossae. The p*osterior false ligaments* are sacrogenital folds that extend from the side of bladder posteriorly to the third sacral vertebra. They lie on either side of rectum.

Interior of the Bladder

The interior of the bladder can be visualized using cystoscopy in living individuals. It shows the following features (Fig. 30.5):

1. ***Vesical mucosa***: In an empty bladder, the mucosa shows irregular folds that stretch flat as the bladder fills. Mucosa is loosely attached to the subadjacent muscles of bladder wall. Hence, mucosal folds are visible on empty bladder.

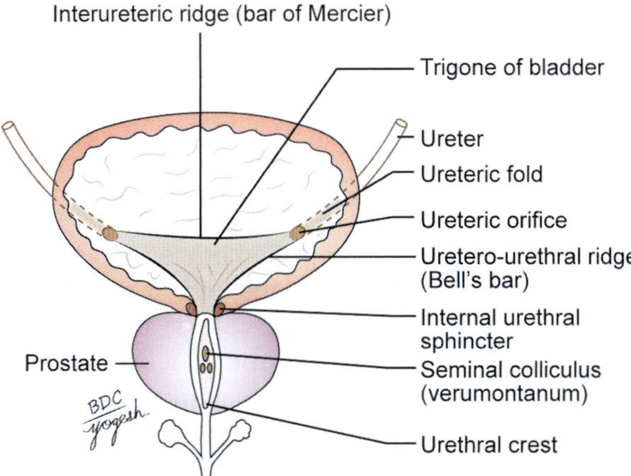

Fig. 30.5: Coronal section through the bladder and prostate to show the interior of the bladder

2. ***Trigone of bladder***: This is a small triangular area located on the posteroinferior part of interior of the bladder. At the trigone, the mucosa is firmly adherent to the muscular wall of the bladder; hence, do not show mucosal folds.

   Feature of trigone:
   - Anteroinferior angle of trigone has *internal orifice of urethra.*
   - Two posterosuperior angles of trigone have *openings of ureters.*
   - ***Uvula vesicae*** is a slight elevation on the trigone of bladder immediately posterior to the urethral orifice. It is produced by the median lobe of prostate.
3. ***Interureteric ridge*** or ***crest*** is a ridge of mucosa extending between two ureteric orifices and it forms the base of trigone. It is also called ***bar of Mercier***.
4. ***Ureteric folds*** are the lateral extensions of interureteric ridges beyond the openings of ureters. They are produced by oblique course of ureters within the bladder wall.
5. *Two* ***uretero-urethral ridges*** (*Bell's bars*): These are mucosal folds that extend from ureteric orifice to the urethral orifice. They are produced by the longitudinal fibres of ureter that extend downwards.

Note:

Embryologically, the trigone of urinary bladder is derived from absorption of mesonephric ducts, whereas rest of the bladder develops from endodermal cloaca.

The ureteric orifices are slit-like openings, about 2.5 cm in the empty bladder, and 5 cm apart in a distended bladder.

Arterial Supply

1. The main supply comes from the superior and inferior vesical arteries, branches of anterior trunk of the internal iliac artery.
2. Additional supply is derived from the obturator, and inferior gluteal arteries; and in females from the uterine and vaginal arteries instead of inferior vesical.

Venous Drainage

Lying on the inferolateral surfaces of the bladder, there is a ***vesical venous plexus***. Veins from this plexus pass backwards in the posterior ligaments of the bladder, and drain into the internal iliac veins.

Lymphatic Drainage

Most of the lymphatics from the urinary bladder terminate in the external iliac nodes. A few vessels may pass to the internal iliac nodes or to the lateral aortic nodes.

Nerve Supply

The urinary bladder is supplied by the vesical plexus of nerves, which is made up of fibres derived from the inferior hypogastric plexus. The vesical plexus contains both sympathetic and parasympathetic

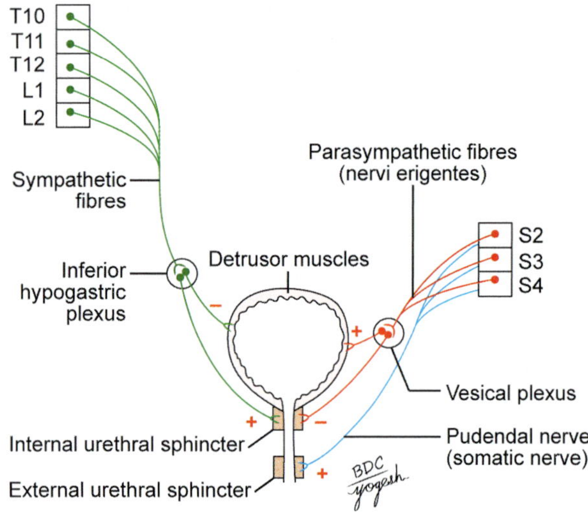

Fig. 30.6: Nerve supply of urinary bladder

components, each of which contains motor or efferent and sensory or afferent fibres. The sympathetic innervation is responsible for the filling of the bladder and parasympathetic innervation for the emptying of the bladder. The somatic innervation is responsible for voluntary control of micturition (Fig. 30.6).

1. *Parasympathetic efferent* fibres or nervi erigentes, S2, 3, 4 are motor to the detrusor muscle. These are stimulatory to the detrusor muscles and inhibitory to internal urethral sphincter.
2. *Sympathetic efferent* fibres (T11 to L2) are said to be inhibitory to the detrusor and motor to the preprostatic sphincter mechanism.
3. The somatic *pudendal nerve* (S2–4) supplies the sphincter urethrae, which is voluntary and situated within the wall of urethra.
4. *Sensory nerves:* Pain sensations, caused by distension or spasms of the bladder wall, are carried mainly by parasympathetic nerves and partly by sympathetic nerves.

Competency:
AN52.2 Describe and identify the microanatomical features of urinary bladder.

HISTOLOGY OF URINARY BLADDER

The urinary bladder has three layers: Inner mucous layer, middle thick smooth muscle coat and outer serous layer (Plate 30.5).

1. Interior of urinary bladder is lined by 3 to 6-cell-layered thick transitional epithelium. Superficial cells are umbrella-shaped and covered by thick eosinophilic plaques. Transitional epithelium rests on thick coat of lamina propria.
2. The urinary bladder has thick muscle coat with inner and outer layers arranged longitudinally, and middle run obliquely.
3. External surface of bladder is covered by connective tissue serosa or adventitia.

Plate 30.5: Urinary bladder

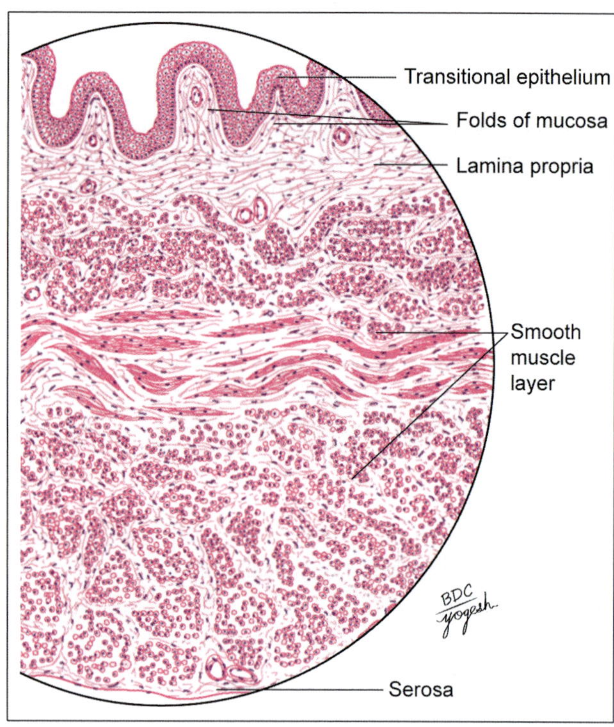

Competency:
AN48.6 Describe the neurological basis of automatic bladder.

CLINICAL ANATOMY

- The interior of the bladder can be examined in the living by ***cystoscope*** (Fig. 30.7).
- A distended bladder may be *ruptured* by injuries to the lower abdominal wall. The peritoneum may or may not be involved.
- Chronic obstruction to the outflow of urine by an enlarged prostate causes hypertrophy of bladder leading to ***trabeculated bladder***.
- In the operation of ***suprapubic cystotomy or catheterisation***, the bladder is distended with about 300 ml of fluid. As a result, the anterior aspect of the bladder comes into direct contact with the anterior abdominal wall, and can be approached without entering the peritoneal cavity (Fig. 30.8).
- Urinary bladder is one of sites for ***urinary stone*** formation as concentrated urine lies here.

DISSECTION

Clean and define the muscles, membranes and ligaments in the pelvic cavity. These are the levator ani, obturator internus muscles; medial and lateral puboprostatic ligaments, median and medial umbilical folds.

Identify the peritoneum on the superior surface of the bladder situated just behind the pubic symphysis. Identify and follow the median umbilical ligament from the apex of bladder. Define the surfaces, blunt borders and the openings in the urinary bladder.

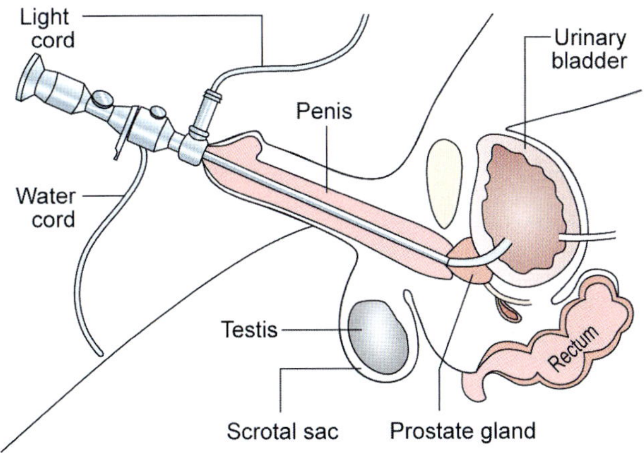

Fig. 30.7: Cystoscopy

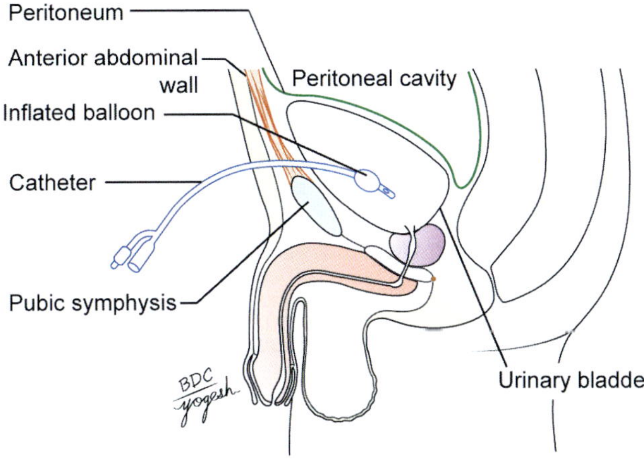

Fig. 30.8: Suprapubic catheterisation of urinary bladder

In the male, trace the ductus deferens and ureter to the base of the bladder on both sides. Pull the bladder medially and identify the structures on its lateral surface, e.g. the levator ani, obturator vessels and nerve, superior vesical branch of umbilical artery and the obliterated umbilical artery.

In females, the cervix and vagina lie behind the urinary bladder.

Make the incision through the bladder wall along the junction of the superior and inferolateral surfaces on both sides. Extend these incisions to the lateral extremities of the base. Incise the superior wall of the bladder to be able to visualise its interior.

In the male, make a median section through the penis, opening the entire length of the spongy part of the urethra. Examine the internal structure of the urethra.

URETHRA

MALE URETHRA

Male urethra is 18–20 cm long that extends from the internal urethral orifice in the urinary bladder to the external opening (meatus) at the end of the penis (Plate 30.6, Figs 30.9 and 30.10, Flowchart 30.2).

Plate 30.6: Urethra in male (midsagittal section)

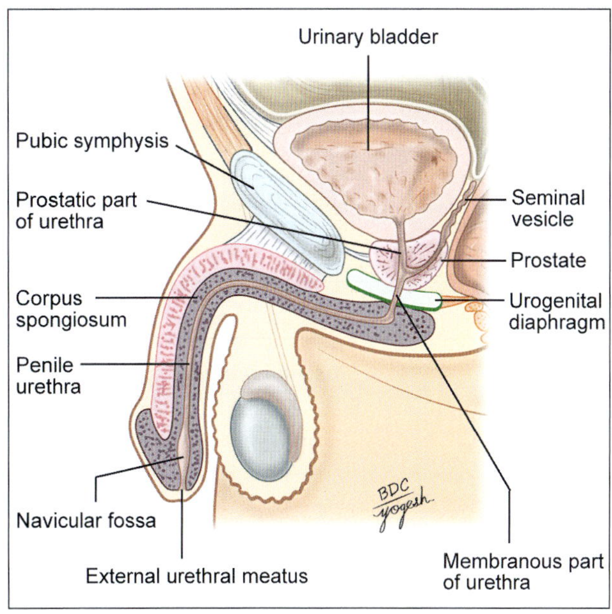

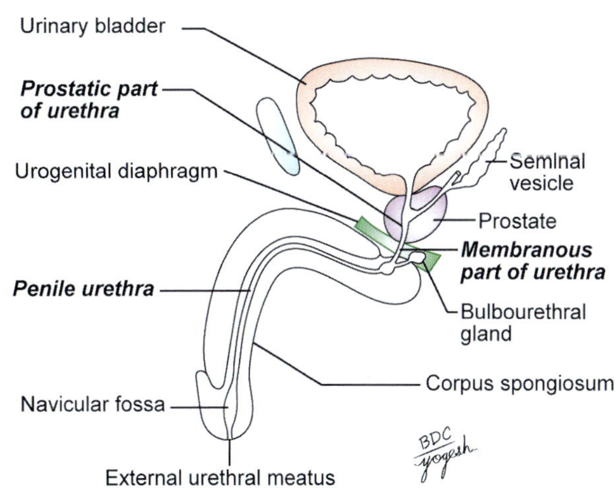

Fig. 30.9: Left view of a sagittal section through the male urethra showing its subdivisions

Parts of Urethra

For descriptive purposes, the urethra is divided into two parts: Posterior part and anterior part.

Posterior Urethra

It is 4 cm long, lies in the pelvis proximal to corpus spongiosum and is acted upon by urogenital sphincter mechanisms and also acts as a conduit (Fig. 30.9).

Posterior urethra has three parts:

a. Preprostatic part.
b. Prostatic part.
c. Membranous part.

Anterior Urethra

It is 16 cm long within the perineum (proximally) and penis (distally). It is surrounded by corpus spongiosum and is functionally a conduit.

Flowchart 30.2: Male urethra

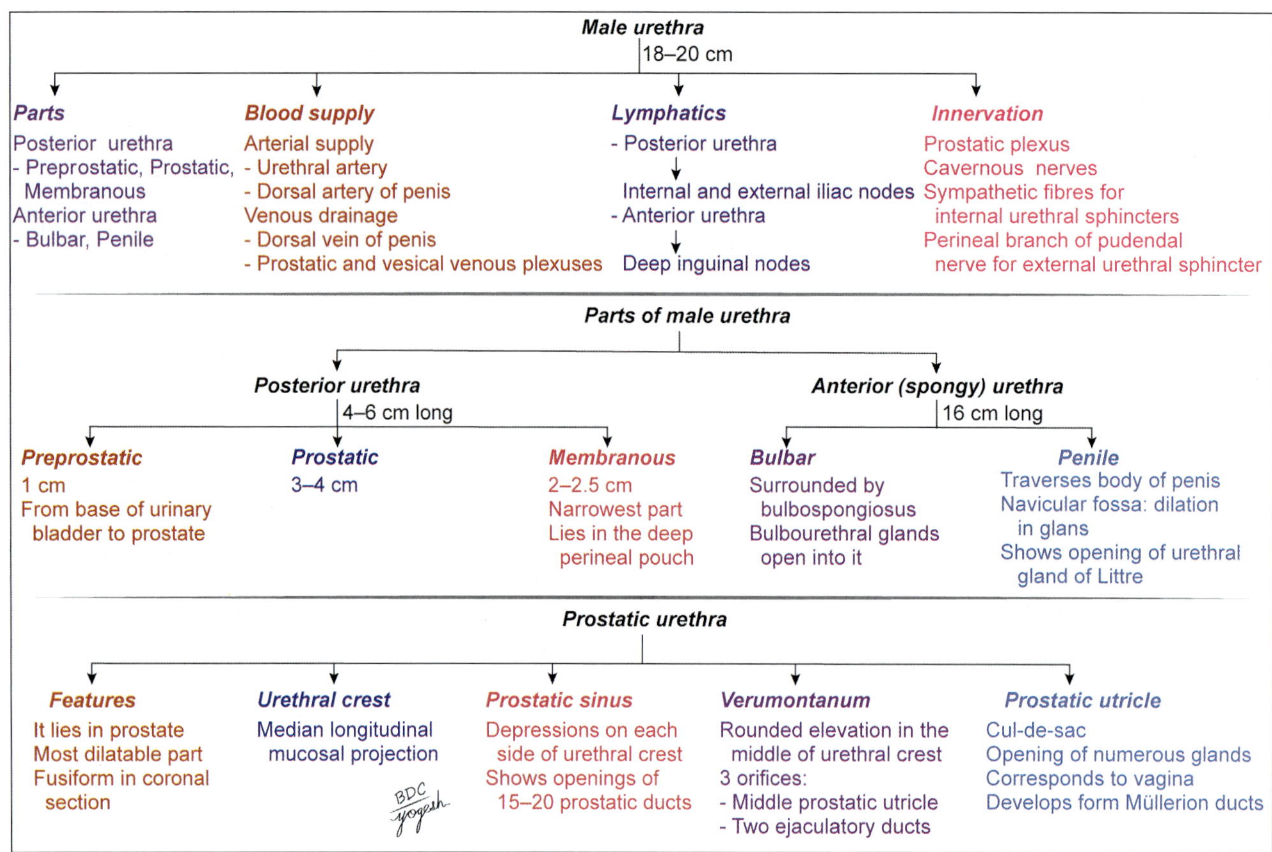

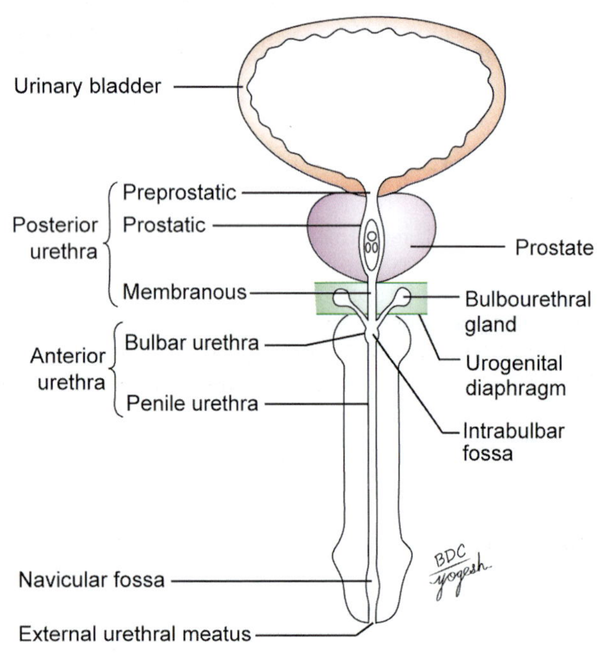

Fig. 30.10: Parts of male urethra (anterior view of the male urethra straightened and cut open)

Anterior urethra has two parts:

a. ***Bulbar urethra*** (proximal) — surrounded by bulbospongiosus. Entirely within perineum (Fig. 30.11).
b. ***Pendulous/penile component*** — continues to the tip of penis.

Shape of Urethra

In flaccid penis, urethra as a whole represents double curve except during the passage of fluid along it. The urethral canal is a mere slit.

In transverse section:

1. The urethral slit is crescentic or transversely arched in prostatic part (Fig. 30.11).
2. In the preprostatic and membranous parts, it is stellate.
3. In bulbar and penile portions, it is transverse.
4. In external urethral orifice, it is sagittal.

Passage of urine through different shapes of urethra causes it to flow in a continuous stream.

Features of Urethra

Posterior Urethra

It has three segments: Preprostatic, prostatic and membranous.

Preprostatic urethra: It is about 1 cm long. It extends from the base of urinary bladder to the prostate. It is surrounded by proximal urethral sphincter in males.

Prostatic urethra: It is 3–4 cm long. It traverses through the substance of prostate closer to the anterior than the posterior surface of gland. It is concave anteriorly. It emerges from prostate slightly anterior to the apex of prostate and continues as membranous urethra.

Membranous urethra: It is about 2–2.5 cm long. It is the second narrowest part of urethra (*Note*: External

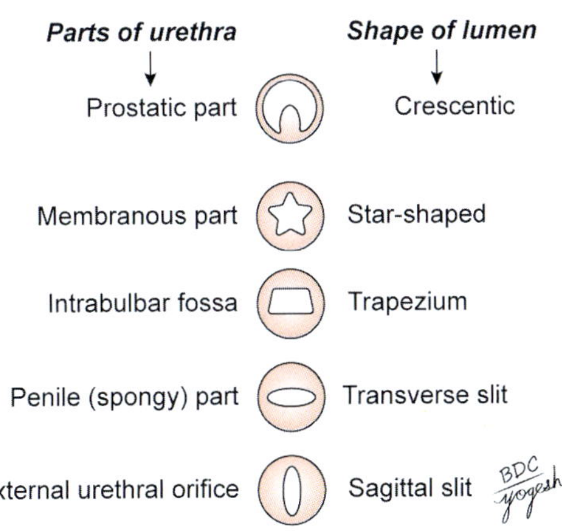

Fig. 30.11: Shape of different parts of the male urethra

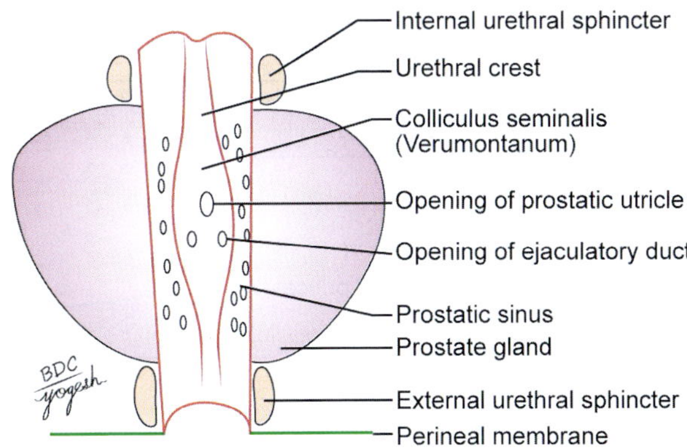

Fig. 30.12: Features of the posterior wall of the prostatic urethra (anterior view, coronal section)

urethral orifice is the narrowest part of urethra). It passes downwards and forward from the prostate to the bulb of penis. It pierces perineal membrane about 2.5 cm behind the pubic symphysis.

Anterior Urethra (Spongy Part)

It is about 15 cm long and traverses the corpus spongiosum through the penis. It consists of two parts: Bulbar urethra and penile urethra.

Bulbar urethra: It is surrounded by bulbospongiosus. The bulbourethral glands open into the bulbar urethra, 2.5 cm below the perineal membrane.

Penile or pendulous urethra

It is a narrow, slit-like passage up to the external urethral orifice. It shows the following features:

1. ***Navicular fossa*** is a dilatation of terminal part of penile urethra within the glans penis.
2. ***External urethral orifice*** is the narrowest part of urethra. It is a slit-like opening (6 mm long) and bounded on each side by small *labium.*
3. ***Urethral glands of Littre*** are simple tubular mucous glands that open in the entire anterior or spongy urethra.
4. ***Urethral lacunae*** are the pit-like recesses of urethral mucosa which project from entire urethra except in the navicular fossa.
5. ***Lacuna magna*** or ***sinus of Guerin*** is the largest urethral lacuna located on the roof of the navicular fossa. Its mouth is guarded by mucous fold called *valvule of Guérin.*

Features of Prostatic Urethra

It is the widest and most dilatable part of male urethra. It is fusiform in coronal section and the lumen is crescentic on transverse section (Plate 30.7, Fig. 30.12). Lowermost part of prostatic urethra is fixed by puboprostatic ligaments and is, therefore, immobile.

It shows the following features:

1. ***Urethral crest:*** It is a median longitudinal mucosal crest that projects posteriorly into the lumen making the lumen crescentic in transverse section.
2. ***Prostatic sinuses:*** On each side of prostatic crest, there are shallow depressions called prostatic sinuses. It receives openings of 15–20 prostatic ducts.
3. ***Verumontanum*** (seminal colliculus; previous name: Colliculus seminalis): It is a round elevation at the middle of urethral crest. Embryologically, this colliculus corresponds to the Müllerian eminence. It presents three orifices of:
   - *Middle prostatic utricle*
   - Two *ejaculatory ducts,* one on each side of the prostatic utricle.
4. ***Prostatic utricle:*** It is cul-de-sac (6 mm long) located in the midline at the middle of verumontanum. It extends upward and backward from the colliculus in the substance of median lobe of the prostate. It has openings of numerous small glands. It develops from united caudal ends of two Müllerian ducts. It corresponds with the vagina of female; hence, called ***vaginus masculinus.***

Arteries

1. Urethral artery arises from internal pudendal artery just below perineal membrane and travels through corpus spongiosum to reach glans penis.
2. Dorsal penile artery via circumflex branches on each side.

Veins

1. Anterior urethra → dorsal vein of penis → internal pudendal vein which drains into prostatic venous plexus → internal iliac veins.
2. Posterior urethra → prostatic and vesical venous plexus → internal iliac veins.

Lymphatic Drainage

1. Prostatic urethra → internal iliac.
2. Membranous urethra → internal iliac.
3. Anterior urethra → accompany that of glans → deep inguinal.

Innervation

1. Prostatic plexus supplies the smooth muscle of prostate and prostatic urethra. Parasympathetic

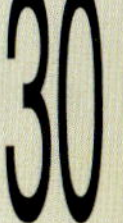

Plate 30.7: Features of the posterior wall of the prostatic urethra (anterior view, coronal section)

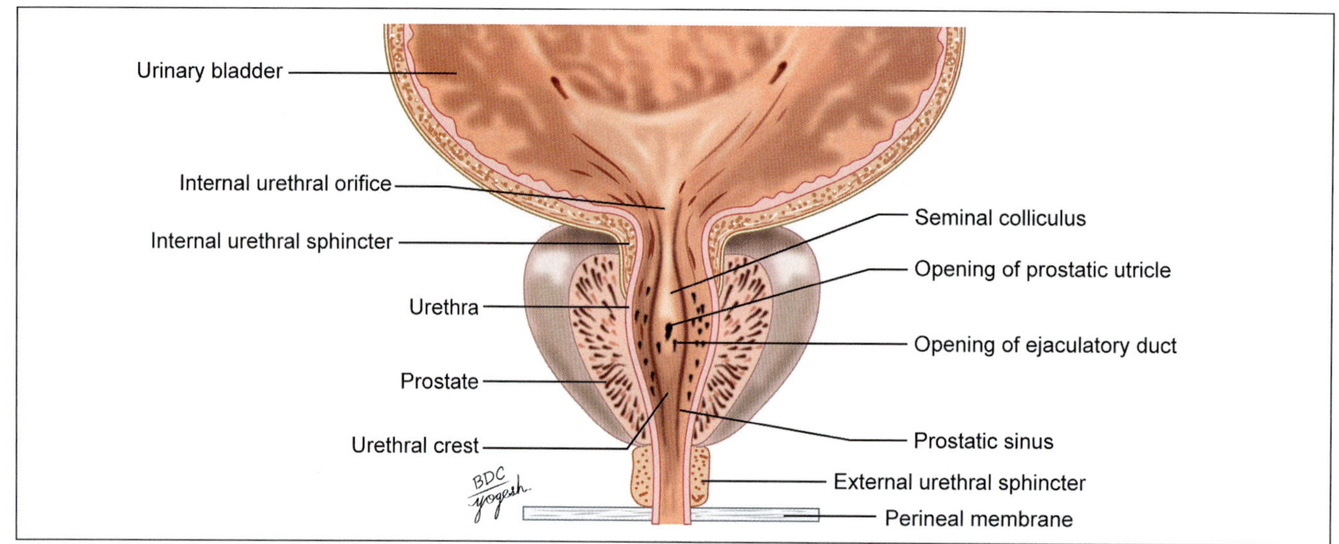

nerves are from 2nd–4th sacral segments. Greater cavernous nerves are sympathetic to preprostatic sphincter during ejaculation.

2. Nerve supply of rhabdosphincter is controversial but is said to be by neurons in Onuf's nucleus situated in 2nd sacral segment of spinal cord; fibres pass via perineal branch of pudendal nerve.

Histology of Urethra

The urethra consists of three coats: Inner mucous membrane, middle submucosa, and outer muscle layer.

1. *Mucous membrane*: Urethra is mostly lined by pseudostratified columnar epithelium except at the following sites:
   a. Adjacent to urinary bladder—lined by transitional epithelium.
   b. Near external opening — lined by stratified squamous epithelium.
2. *Submucosa*: It consists of loose connective tissue.
3. *Muscle coat*: It consists of inner longitudinal and outer circular coat of smooth muscle fibres. Terminal part of urethra is surrounded by striated muscle fibres that form *external urethral sphincter*.

Sphincters of Urethra

The urethra has two sphincters: Internal and external urethral sphincters (Plate 30.8).

Internal (Proximal) Urethral Sphincter

- It is a distinct circular collar of smooth muscle fibres located at the junction of urinary bladder and urethra. These fibres surround the internal urethral orifice. It is also called *preprostatic sphincter* or sphincter vesicae.
- *Innervation*: It is devoid of parasympathetic cholinergic nerves. It is supplied by *sympathetic fibres* from lower thoracic and upper lumbar segments of spinal cord (T11 to T12).

Plate 30.8: Urethral sphincter (in male)

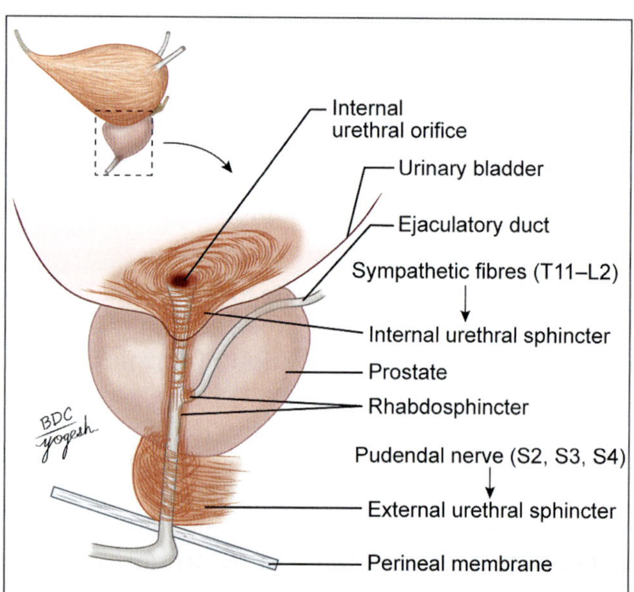

- *Functions*: Its contraction prevents retrograde flow of semen into the bladder. It maintains continence (holding the urine).

External (Distal) Urethral Sphincter (Sphincter Urethrae)

- It consists of *striated muscle fibres* that are circularly arranged around the membranous part or urethra. Its *superficial fibres* arise from transverse perineal ligament and pubic arch and *deep fibres* arise from inner surface of ischiopubic ramus.
- *Insertion*: Superficial fibres pass backward and insert on the perineal body. Deep fibres pass horizontally, encircle the membranous urethra, and interdigitate with similar fibres on opposite side.
- *Innervation*: It is supplied by perineal branch of the pudendal nerve.

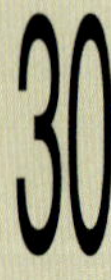

TABLE 30.1: Differences between internal and external urethral sphincters

Internal urethral sphincter	*External urethral sphincter*
Surrounds the internal urethral orifice	Surrounds the membranous urethra
Also called preprostatic sphincter in men or sphincter vesicae	Also called sphincter urethrae
Involuntary	Voluntary
Consists of smooth muscle fibres	Consists of striated muscle fibres
Innervated by sympathetic fibres (T11–L2)	Innervated by pudendal nerve (S2, 3, 4)
Functions: • Continence of urine • Prevention of retrograde ejaculation	*Functions*: • Continence of urine • Voluntary voiding of urine

The differences between the internal and external urethral sphincter are listed in Table 30.1.

Note: *Recent concept*: There is no existence of separate sphincter urethrae muscle in deep perineal pouch. These are the fibres that lie inside the urethral wall itself (*Reference*: *Gray's Anatomy*, 42nd edn.).

Rhabdosphincters are parts of the external urethral sphincter that continue superiorly as a trough-like extension running vertically across the anterior aspect of the prostate to reach the neck of the bladder.

CLINICAL ANATOMY

- ***Urethritis*** is an infection of urethra.
- ***Rupture of urethra***: The urethra is commonly ruptured by a fall on a sharp object. The most common site of urethral rupture is the bulb of the penis, just below the urogenital diaphragm. On rupture extravasated urine goes to superficial perineal pouch, scrotum, penis, and infraumbilical part of anterior abdominal wall in the thigh up to Holden's line.
- ***Catheterisation of bladder in male***: If the patient is unable to pass urine leading to retention of urine, the catheterisation of bladder is needed (Fig. 30.13a). Catheter is a soft rubber tube that has round tip, opening for urine, balloon, urine drainage port and balloon port. This catheter is passed into the bladder through urethra. While passing the catheter, the curvatures of urethra should be kept in mind. Balloon is inflated with the normal saline that helps to hold the catheter in position.
- ***Foley catheter*** is commonly used for urinary bladder catheterisation (Fig. 30.13b).
- ***Stricture***: A constriction of the urethra is called *stricture* of the urethra. It is usually a result of infection.
- ***Hypospadias***: It is a common anomaly in which the urethra opens on the undersurface of the penis or in the perineum. Hypospadias may be glandular (on ventral surface of glans), balanic (at base of glans), penile (on ventral surface of penis), penoscrotal (at junction of penis and scrotum), and perineal (at unfused part of scrotum) (Fig. 30.14).
- ***Epispadias*** is rare condition that causes failure of development of infraumbilical part of anterior abdominal wall that leads to opening of urethra or bladder on the dorsum of penis. It may be associated with ectopia vesicae.
- ***Posterior urethral*** valve is an obstructive membrane that develops in the urethra, close to the internal urethral orifice. It occurs if the Wolffian ducts open too anteriorly on the primitive prostatic urethra.

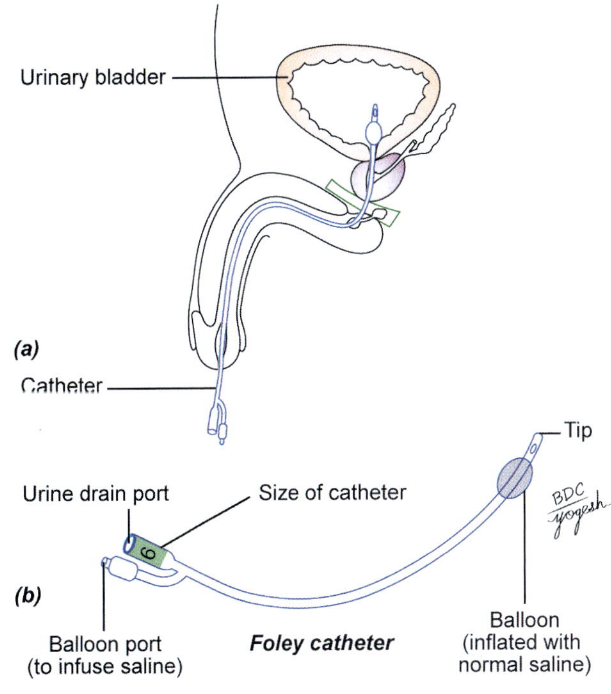

Figs 30.13a and b: (a) Catheterisation of urinary bladder in male and (b) Foley catheter

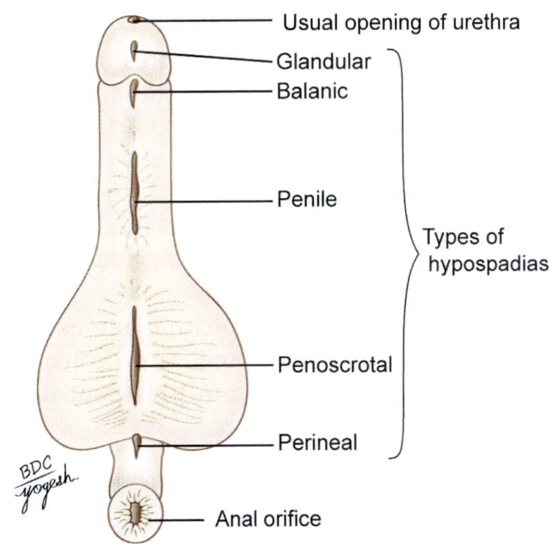

Fig. 30.14: Types of hypospadias

FEMALE URETHRA

Female urethra is only 4 cm long and 6 mm in diameter (Plate 30.9).

Course

It begins at the neck of bladder. It passes downward and forward. It pierces perineal membrane and opens in the vestibule of vagina. External urethral orifice is located anterior to the opening of vagina, 2.5 cm behind the glans clitoris.

Parts and Shape

The female urethra consists of the following parts:

1. *Upper part*: It has crescentic-shaped lumen.
2. *Middle part*: It traverses the deep perineal pouch. It has star-shaped lumen.
3. *Lower part*: It lies in the perineal region. Its lumen is like a transverse slit.
4. *External urethral orifice*: It lies between the clitoris and the vagina, in the vestibule. It is sagittal slit.

Glands around the Female Urethra

1. *Urethral glands*: These are small tubular mucous secreting glands that surround the entire urethra.
2. *Paraurethral glands of Skene* (*lesser vestibular glands*): These are mucous glands around the upper part of the urethra. They are homologous to male prostate.
3. *Urethral lacunae* are the pit-like mucosa recesses along the entire urethra.

Arteries

Superior vesical and vaginal arteries.

Veins

Venous plexus around urethra → vesical venous plexus → internal pudendal vein → internal iliac vein.

Lymphatic Drainage

Internal and external iliac nodes.

Innervation

1. Parasympathetic preganglionic fibres from 2nd–4th sacral segments of spinal cord. These run through pelvic splanchnic nerves and synapse in vesical venous plexus. Postganglionic fibres reach smooth muscles.
2. Somatic fibres from same segments (S2–S4) reach the striated muscles through pelvic splanchnic nerves that do not synapse in vesical plexus.
3. Sensory fibres in pelvic splanchnic nerves reach to 2nd–4th sacral segments of spinal cord. Postganglionic sympathetic fibres arise from plexus around the vaginal arteries.

CLINICAL ANATOMY

- ***Catheterisation*** of female urethra is easier due to its short course.

Plate 30.9: Female urethra (midsagittal section through the female pelvic cavity viewed from the left)

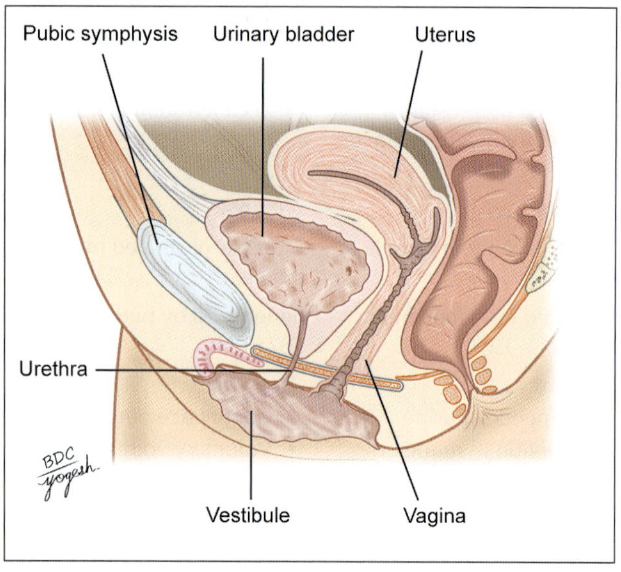

- Urinary tract infections (**UTI**) are more common in females because of shorter urethra.
- ***Urinary incontinence*** is common in females due to weak external urethral sphincter and damages to it during childbirth.

MICTURITION AND NEURONAL CONTROL

The process of micturition involves the following steps (Flowchart 30.3).

1. *Sense of filling*: The filling of urinary bladder beyond 220 ml distends the bladder and sends the signals of filling through stretch receptors in bladder wall. These receptors stimulate afferent fibres, mostly parasympathetic fibres (S2, S3, S4).
2. *Perception of fullness of bladder*: Sensory fibres from S2, S3 and S4 spinal segments ascend upward in ipsilateral tract of Goll to nucleus Gracilis (→ internal arcuate → medial lemniscus → thalamus) and finally reach to paracentral lobule. This paracentral lobule perceives the fullness of bladder and initiates the desire to micturate.
3. *Holding of urine*: Detrusor centre of paracentral lobule inhibits the sacral neurons (lateral horn cells of S2, S3, S4) until suitable space and time available for micturition.
4. *Voiding or micturition*: Parasympathetic fibres (S2, S3, S4) get stimulated by inputs from sensory fibres carrying filling sensation. In absence of inhibition from paracentral lobule, these fibres contract detrusor muscle and relax preprostatic sphincter. Entry of urine in proximal part of urethra stimulates the urethral stretch receptors that also send signals through parasympathetic fibres (S2, S3, S4) and inhibits pudendal nerve (S2, S3, S4). This inhibition pudendal nerve causes relaxation of external urethral sphincter and initiates micturition.

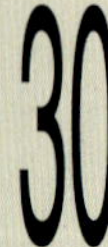

Flowchart 30.3: Neuronal control of micturition

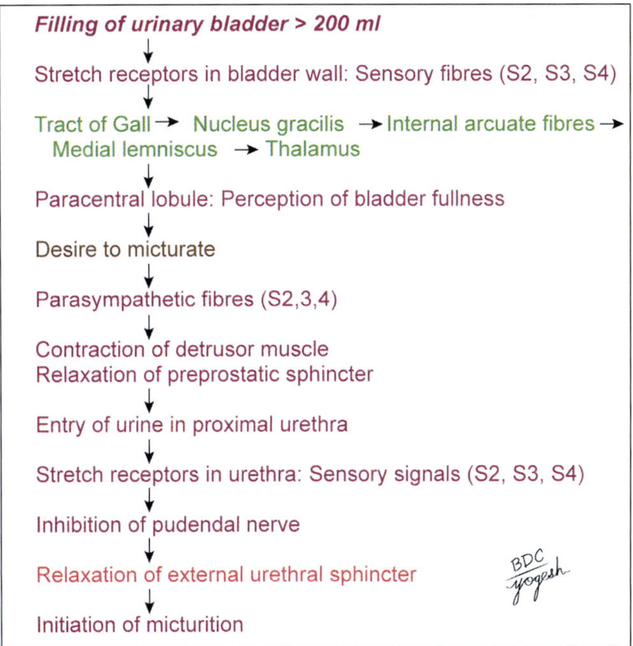

CLINICAL ANATOMY

- ***Automatic or reflex bladder***: It occurs on removal of higher centre control over sacral nerves (S2, S3, S4). For example, transection of spinal cord above the S2 segment. It results in:
  - Loss of voluntary control and initiation of micturition.
  - On filling, distended bladder sends signals that reflexly contract the detrusor muscle to initiate micturition.
  - Automatic bladder is normal in early infancy.
- ***Atonic bladder***: Due to the lesion involving damage to sensory (afferent) fibres of bladder, it results into atonic bladder. In this condition:
  1. Bladder remains distended, thin-walled and hypotonic.
  2. Overflow incontinence is present.
- ***Autonomous bladder***: It occurs due to loss of innervation of the bladder (may be due to pelvic surgeries or damage to S1 to S3 segments of spinal cord). In this condition:
  1. Bladder becomes flaccid, and capacity of bladder increases.
  2. Voluntary and reflex control of micturition is lost.
  3. There is continuous dribbling of urine.
  4. Bladder is emptied by overfilling or by increasing abdominal pressure.
  5. Patient requires continuous catheter.
- ***Uninhibited bladder***: It occurs due to damage to the brain by stroke or brain tumour. In this condition sudden uncontrolled evacuation of bladder (urge incontinence) is observed.

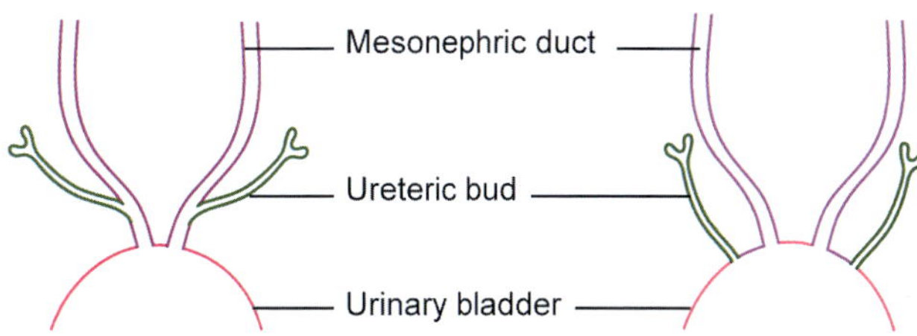

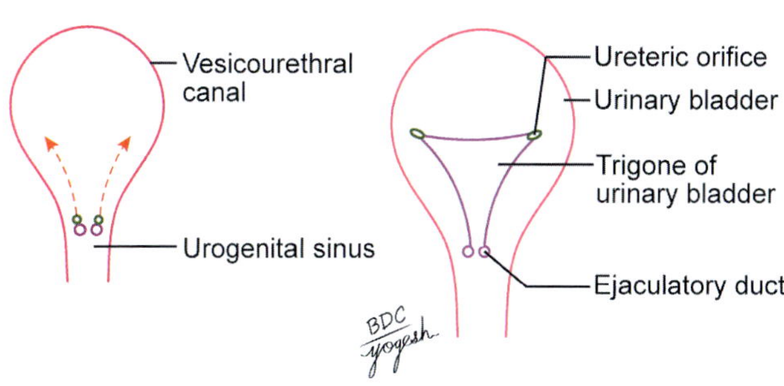

Fig. 30.15: Development of urinary bladder

DEVELOPMENT OF URINARY BLADDER AND URETHRA

Development of Urinary Bladder

Cloaca (Latin *sewer*) is divided by the *urorectal septum* into posterior *anorectal canal* and anterior *primitive urogenital sinus*. The cranial and largest part of primitive urogenital sinus called the *vesicourethral canal* forms most of the urinary bladder. It is connected with the *allantois*.

Developmentally, bladder shows the following sources (Fig. 30.15):

1. *Lining epithelium of bladder except for trigone* is derived from cranial dilated part of vesicourethral canal (endoderm).
2. *Lining epithelium of trigone* develops from mesoderm by absorption of mesonephric ducts in dorsal wall of vesicourethral canal.
3. *Muscles and connective tissue coats* develop from mesoderm — splanchnopleuric intraembryonic mesoderm surrounding vesicourethral canal.
4. Urachus (median umbilical ligament) is derived from allantois.

Development of Urethra

1. Vesicourethral canal formed by endoderm forms the anterior wall of prostatic urethra above the opening of prostatic utricle.
2. Absorbed portions of the mesonephric ducts, i.e. mesoderm, form posterior wall of prostatic urethra above the opening of prostatic utricle.
3. Definitive urogenital sinus formed by endoderm forms the lower part of prostatic urethra and the membranous urethra.
4. Urethral plate or endoderm forms most of the anterior part of urethra.
5. Surface epithelium of glans penis or ectoderm forms the terminal portion of penile urethra.

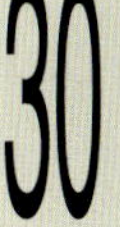

Facts to Remember

- Most fixed part of urinary bladder is the neck of bladder.
- The male urethra subserving the functions of urination and ejaculation. Male urethra is 18–20 cm long, whereas the female urethra is 4 cm long.
- The widest part of male urethra is prostatic part. The narrowest part of urethra is external urethral orifice.
- Least dilatable part of male urethra is the membranous part.
- Prostatic utricle represents the vagina of female.
- Proximal urethral sphincter is lacking in the female.
- Prostatic utricle corresponds with the vagina of female; hence, called *vaginus masculinus*.
- *Paraurethral glands of Skene* (*lesser vestibular glands*) are homologous to male prostate.

BDC's Anatomy e-book

1. Urethral sphincter mechanism
2. Walls of urethra
3. Further reading
4. Viva voce questions

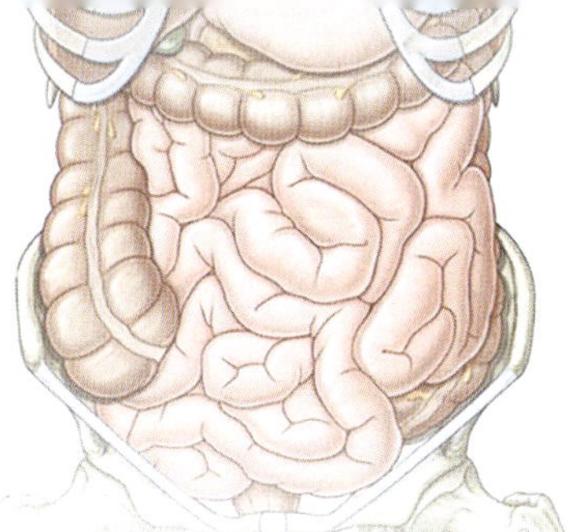

Chapter

31

Female Reproductive Organs

Female reproductive organs include external and internal genital organs (Plate 31.1):

External genital organs are called *vulva*. It consists of:

1. Mons pubis
2. Labia majora
3. Labia minora
4. Clitoris
5. Vestibule of vagina
6. Greater vestibular glands.

Internal genital organs are situated within the pelvis. These includes:

1. Pair of ovaries
2. Pair of uterine tubes
3. Uterus
4. Vagina.

FEMALE EXTERNAL GENITAL ORGANS

The female external genital organs are called ***vulva*** or ***pudendum***. They include mons pubis, labia majora, labia minora, clitoris, vestibule of vagina, bulb of vestibule, and pair of greater vestibular glands (Plate 31.1, Figs 31.1 and 31.2).

Mons Pubis

Mons pubis is a rounded eminence present in front of the pubic symphysis. It is formed by accumulation of subcutaneous fat.

Labia Majora

- Labia majora are two thick folds of skin enclosing fat. They form the lateral boundaries of the *pudendal cleft*. Their outer surfaces are covered with hair, and the inner surfaces are studded with large sebaceous glands.
- The larger anterior ends are connected to each other below the mons pubis to form the ***anterior commissure***. The skin connecting the less prominent posterior ends of the labia is known as the ***posterior commissure***.
- The area between the posterior commissure and the anus which is about 2.5 cm long constitutes the ***gynaecological perineum***.

Labia Minora

- Labia minora are two thin folds of skin, which lie within the pudendal cleft.
- *Anteriorly*, each labium minus splits into two layers; the upper layer joins the corresponding layer of the opposite side to form the ***prepuce of the clitoris***. Similarly, the lower layers of the two sides join to form the ***frenulum of the clitoris***.
- *Posteriorly*, the two labia minora meet to form the ***frenulum of the labia minora***.
- The inner surface of the labia minora contains numerous sebaceous glands.

Clitoris

- The clitoris is an erectile organ, homologous with the penis. However, *it is not traversed by urethra*. It lies in the anterior part of pudendal cleft.
- The body of clitoris is made up of two ***corpora cavernosa*** enclosed in a fibrous sheath and partly separated by an incomplete ***pectiniform septum***. *The corpus spongiosum is absent*. Each corpus cavernosum is attached to the ischiopubic rami.
- The down-turned free end of clitoris is formed by a rounded tubercle, ***glans clitoridis***, which caps the free ends of corpora. The glans is made up of erectile tissue continuous posteriorly with the commissural venous plexus uniting right and left bulbs of vestibule called ***bulbar commissure***. The surface of glans is highly sensitive and plays an important role in sexual responses.

Vestibule of the Vagina

Vestibule of the vagina is space between two labia minora. Its features are as follows:

1. Clitoris placed most anteriorly.
2. The ***urethral orifice*** lies about 2.5 cm behind the clitoris and just in front of the vaginal orifice.
3. ***Vaginal orifice*** or *introitus* lies in the posterior part of the vestibule, and is partly closed, in the virgin, by a thin membrane called the ***hymen***. In married women, the hymen is represented by rounded tags of tissue called the ***carunculae hymenales***.

Plate 31.1: Female genital organs

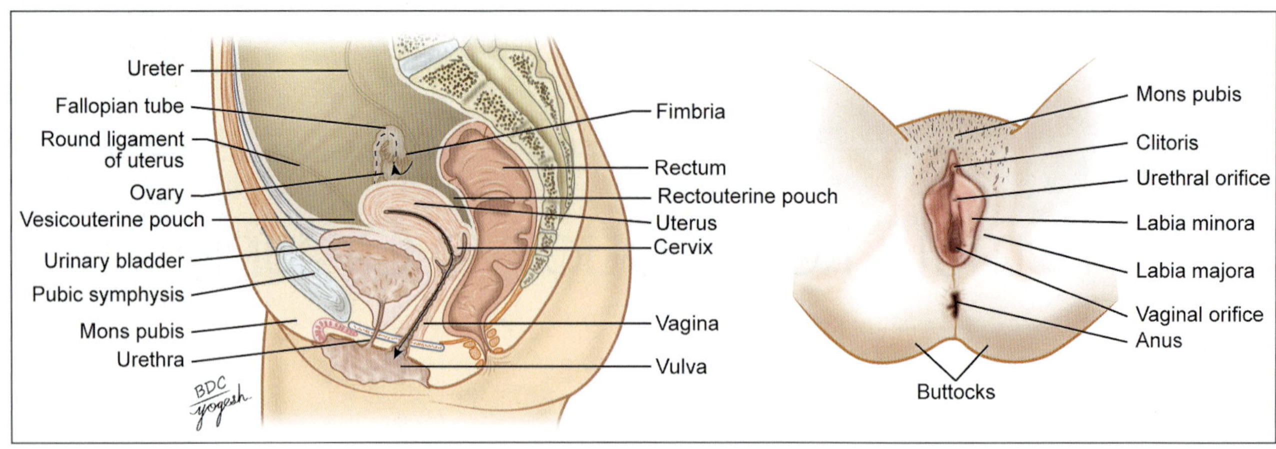

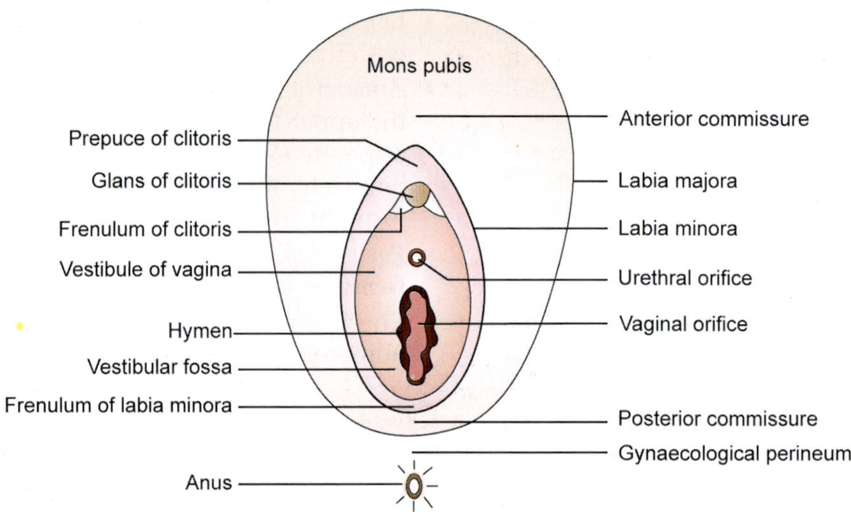

Fig. 31.1: The female external genital organs

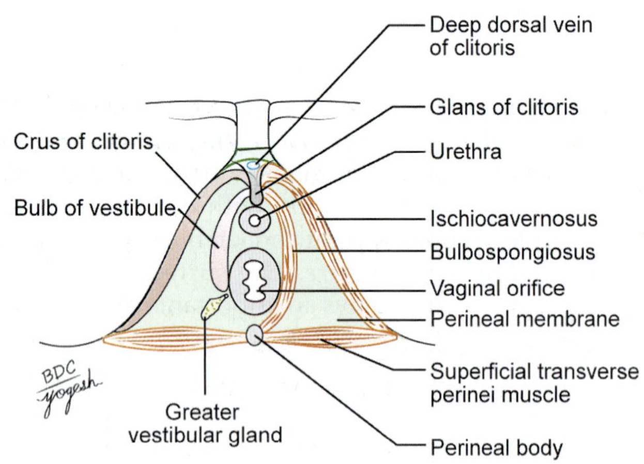

Fig. 31.2: Bulb of vestibule, greater vestibular gland (superficial perineal pouch in female)

4. ***Orifices of the ducts of greater vestibular glands*** lie one on each side of vaginal orifice, between the hymen and labium minus.
5. Numerous *lesser vestibular* or *mucous glands* open on the surface of vestibule.
6. The posterior part of vestibule between vaginal orifice and frenulum of labia minora forms a shallow depression known as ***vestibular fossa***.

Bulbs of the Vestibule

Bulbs of the vestibule are two oval bodies of erectile tissue that correspond to the two halves of the bulb of the penis (Fig. 31.2). The bulbs lie on either side of the vaginal and urethral orifices, superficial to the perineal membrane.

The tapering anterior ends of the bulbs are united in front of the urethra by a venous plexus, called the ***bulbar commissure***. The expanded posterior ends of the bulbs partly overlap the greater vestibular glands.

Greater Vestibular Glands of Bartholin

Greater vestibular glands are homologous with the bulbourethral glands of Cowper in the male. These lie in the superficial perineal space. Each gland has a long duct about 2 cm long which opens at the side of the hymen, between the hymen and the labium minus.

These are tubuloacinar glands that secret mucus, especially during sexual arousal.

Competency:

AN48.2 Describe and demonstrate the position, features, important peritoneal and other relations, blood supply, nerve supply, lymphatic drainage and clinical aspects of important female pelvic viscera.

INTERNAL GENITAL ORGANS

The internal genital organs are situated within the pelvis. These includes a pair of ovaries, pair of uterine tubes, uterus and vagina (Plate 31.2, Fig. 31.3).

OVARIES

The ovaries are the female gonads.

Functions of Ovary

1. *Production of oocytes*: The ovaries produce oocytes (female gametes) during reproductive life, one secondary oocyte per ovarian cycle.
2. *Production of hormones*: Ovaries produce:
   A. *Oestrogen* that promotes the growth of reproductive organs and mammary glands.
   B. *Progesterone* that prepares the internal genital organs for reproduction in each menstrual cycle.

Location

Each ovary lies in the ***ovarian fossa*** on the lateral pelvic wall. The ovarian fossa is bounded (Fig. 31.4):

Anteriorly: Obliterated umbilical artery.
Posteriorly: Ureter and the internal iliac artery
Inferiorly: Uterine tubes
Floor: Obturator nerve and vessels.

Position

The position of the ovary is variable (Figs 31.5a and b).

1. In *nulliparous* women, its long axis is nearly vertical, so that the ovary is usually described as having an upper pole and a lower pole.
2. In *multiparous* women, the long axis becomes horizontal; so that the upper pole points laterally and the lower pole medially.

External Features

In young girls, *before the onset of ovulation*, the ovaries have smooth surfaces which are greyish-pink in colour. *After puberty*, the surface becomes uneven and the colour changes from pink to grey.

Their average dimensions are 4 × 2 × 3 cm in reproductively mature woman. During pregnancy, the size of the ovary becomes double.

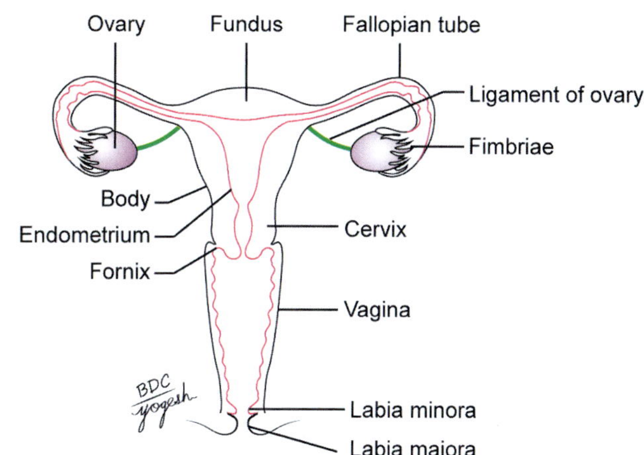

Fig. 31.3: Female internal genital organs

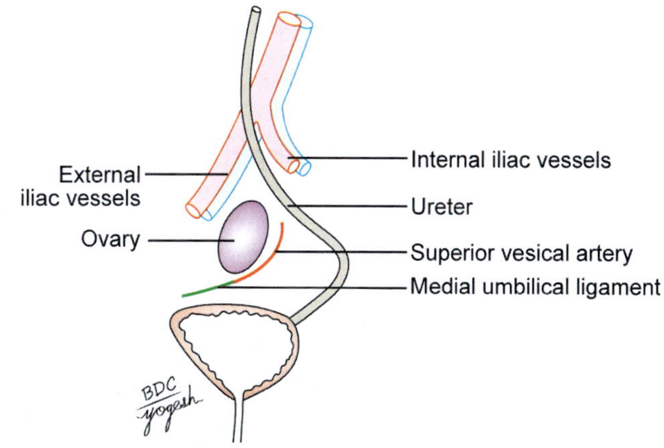

Fig. 31.4: Medial view of boundaries of the ovarian fossa is seen in a sagittal section

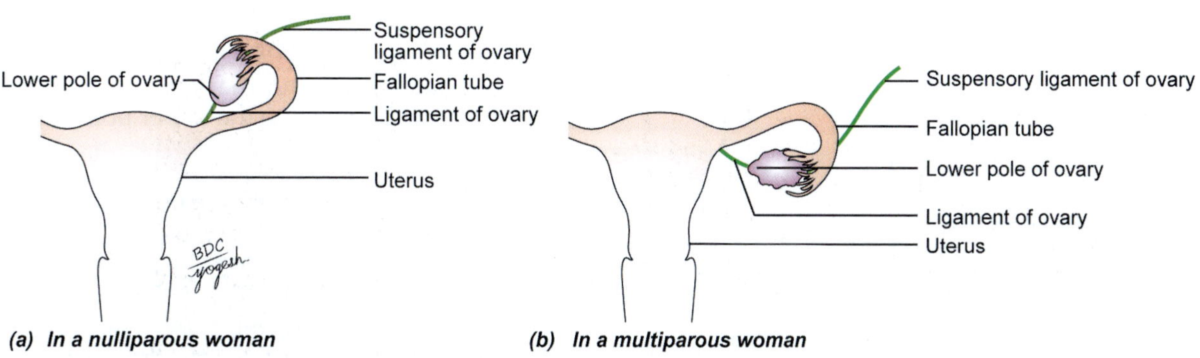

Figs 31.5a and b: Positions of the ovary: (a) It is vertical in nullipara and (b) horizontal in multipara (after one or more deliveries) due to the pull of the pregnant uterus

Plate 31.2: Uterus and fallopian tube

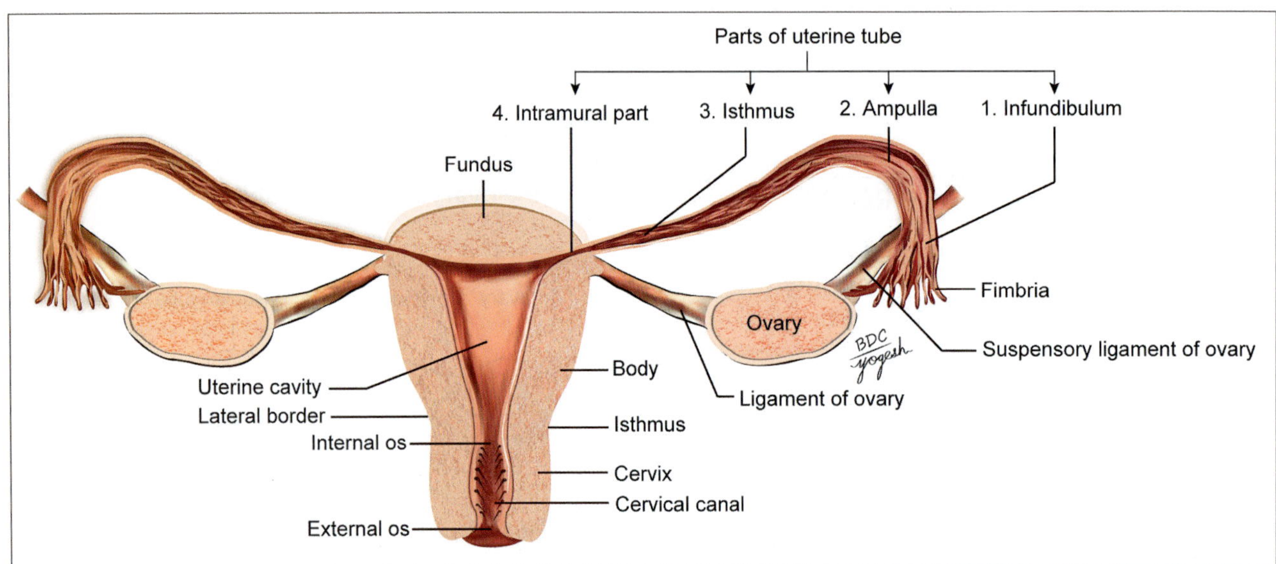

Presenting Parts

Each ovary has:

1. *Two poles or extremities:* Upper or tubal pole, and lower or uterine pole.
2. *Two borders:* Anterior or mesovarian border, and posterior or free border.
3. *Two surfaces:* Lateral and medial.

Relations

Peritoneal Relations

The ovary is almost entirely covered with peritoneum, except along the mesovarian or anterior border where the two layers of the covering peritoneum are reflected onto the posterior layer of the broad ligament of the uterus.

The ovary is connected to the posterior layer of the broad ligament by a short fold of peritoneum, called the ***mesovarium*** (Fig. 31.6). The mesovarium transmits the vessels and nerves to and from the ovary.

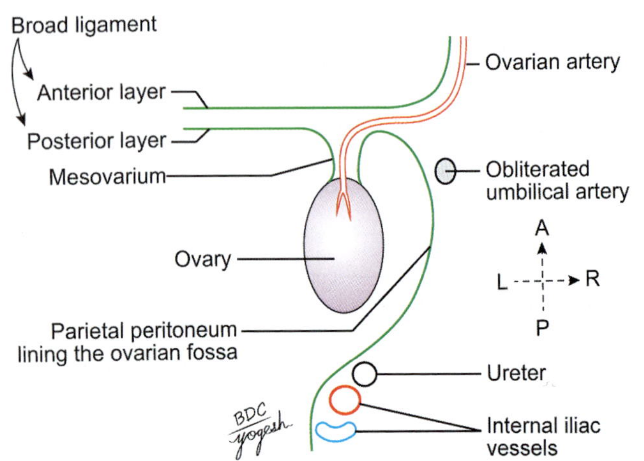

Fig. 31.6: Superior view of a horizontal section through the right ovarian fossa and the lateral part of the broad ligament

Suspensory ligament of the ovary or ***infundibulopelvic ligament*** is the distinct fold of peritoneum (lateral part of the broad ligament of uterus), extending from the infundibulum of the uterine tube and the upper pole of the ovary, to the external iliac vessels. It contains the ovarian vessels and nerves (Fig. 31.4).

Ovarian ligament (*ligament of ovary*) extends from inferior (uterine) pole of the ovary to the lateral angle of uterus, just posteroinferior to the uterine tube. It lies in the broad ligament. Its medial end is continuous with the round ligament of uterus.

Note:

1. The squamous epithelium of the *mesovarium* is continuous with the cubical epithelium of the ovary.
2. ***White line of ovary*** (***line of Furre***) marks the junction between the flattened mesothelium of peritoneum and the cuboidal germinal epithelium of ovary.
3. Ovarian and round ligaments are the remnants of the gubernaculum.

Visceral Relations

Poles or extremities

Upper or tubal pole

- It is broader than the lower pole, and is related to the uterine tube and the external iliac vein (Flowchart 31.1).
- The right ovary may be related to the appendix, if the latter is pelvic in position.
- The ovarian *fimbria* and the ***suspensory ligament of the ovary*** are attached to the upper pole of the ovary.

Lower or uterine pole

- It is narrower than the upper pole and is related to the pelvic floor.
- It is connected, by the ***ligament of the ovary***, to the lateral angle of the uterus, posteroinferior to the attachment of the uterine tube. The ligament lies between the two layers of the broad ligament of the uterus and contains some smooth muscle fibres (Flowchart 31.1).

Flowchart 31.1: Ovaries

Ovaries
Female gonads

- ***Location***
  In ovarion fossa on lateral pelvic wall
- ***Position***
  In nulliparous:
  - Vertical long axis
  In multiparous:
  - Horizontal long axis
- ***Relations***
  - ***Peritoneal***
    Covered by peritoneum
    Mesovarium
    Suspensory ligament of ovary
    Ovarian ligament
  - ***Visceral***
    Upper pole: Uterine tube
    Lower pole: Related to pelvic diaphragm
    Anterior border: Mesovarium is attached
    Posterior border: Free
- ***Supply and Innervation***
  Arteries: Ovarian, uterine
  Veins: Pampiniform plexus ovarian vein
  Lymphatics: Pre- and para-aortic nodes
  Innervation: Sympathetic (T10, T11) Parasympathetic (S2–S4)

Clinical Integration: Ovarian cyst, PCOD, ovarian torsion, prolapse of ovaries, ovarian carcinoma, ovarian teratoma

BDC yogesh

Borders

Anterior or mesovarian border

- It is straight and is related to the uterine tube and the obliterated umbilical artery.
- It is attached to the back of the broad ligament of the uterus by the mesovarium, and forms the ***hilus*** of the ovary (Flowchart 31.1).

Posterior or free border

It is convex and is related to the uterine tube and the ureter.

Surfaces

Lateral surface

It is related to the ovarian fossa, which is lined by parietal peritoneum. This peritoneum separates the ovary from the obturator vessels and nerve (Fig. 31.1b).

Medial surface

It is largely covered by the uterine tube.

Note: The peritoneal recess between the mesosalpinx and this surface is known as the ovarian bursa.

Only the lower pole and lateral surfaces are not related to uterine tube, remaining two borders, upper pole and medial surface are related to the tube.

Arterial Supply

Ovarian artery: It arises from the abdominal aorta just below the renal artery, at the level of L1 vertebra. It descends over the posterior abdominal wall and enters the suspensory ligament of the ovary. It sends branches to the ovary through the mesovarium, and continues medially through the broad ligament of the uterus to anastomose with the uterine artery (Fig. 31.6).

Uterine artery: It gives some branches, which reach the ovary through the mesovarium.

Venous Drainage

The veins emerge at the hilus and form a ***pampiniform plexus*** around the artery. The plexus condenses into a ***single ovarian vein*** near the pelvic inlet (Flowchart 31.1).

This ovarian vein ascends on the posterior abdominal wall and drains into the *inferior vena cava* on the right side and into the *left renal vein* on the left side.

Lymphatic Drainage

The lymphatics from the ovary communicate with the lymphatics from the uterine tube and fundus of the uterus. They ascend along the ovarian vessels to drain into the *lateral aortic* and *preaortic nodes*.

Nerve Supply

The *ovarian plexus*, derived from the renal, aortic and hypogastric plexuses, accompanies the ovarian artery.

It contains both sympathetic and parasympathetic nerves. Sympathetic nerves (T10, T11) are afferent for pain as well as efferent or vasomotor. Parasympathetic nerves (S2–S4) are vasodilator.

Note: Pain sensation (visceral sensation) from the ovary is carried by sympathetic fibres (T10, T11). Hence, the ovarian pain is referred to the umbilical region being supplied by ***T10*** spinal segment.

Competency:

AN52.2 Describe and identify the microanatomical features of ovary.

Histology of Ovary

- Ovary has an outer ***cortex*** that shows follicles of various sizes and an inner ***medulla*** that consists of connective tissue, blood vessels, and nerves. Ovary is covered with ***cuboidal germinal epithelium*** (Plate 31.3).
- A layer of connective tissue that lies deep to germinal epithelium is called *tunica albuginea*.

Ovarian follicles: One follicle matures every month and sheds an oocyte. Total of 400 oocytes are ovulated in the reproductive life.

- *Primordial follicle:* Primary oocyte covered by a flattened layer of follicular cells.
- *Primary follicle:* Primary oocyte covered by zona pellucida and single cell thick cuboidal follicular cells.
- *Secondary follicle:* In secondary follicle, the primary oocyte is covered by zona pellucida, granulosa cells with follicular antrum, theca interna (vascular) and theca externa (fibrous) layers.
- *Graafian follicle:* It is about 10 mm or more in size and shows secondary oocyte with first polar body.

Plate 31.3: Histology of ovary

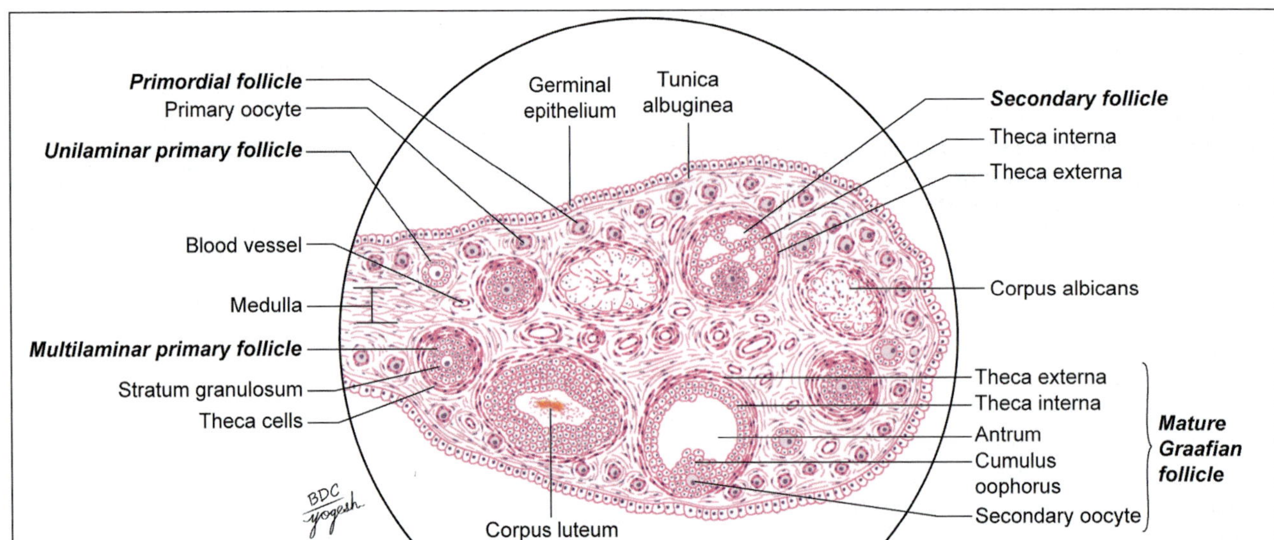

- *Corpus haemorrhagicus:* It is a follicle just after ovulation. It is filled with blood.
- *Corpus luteum:* Follicle after ovulation, consists of luteal cells (yellow pigments in cytoplasm), secretes progesterone.
- *Corpus albicans:* If ovum does not get fertilized, the corpus luteum degenerates and forms fibrous corpus albicans (white body).

Competency:
AN52.8 Describe the development of female reproductive system.

Development of Ovary

The components of ovary are derived as follows (Fig. 31.7, Flowchart 31.2):

1. Oocytes develop from primordial germ cells that migrate from yolk sac.
2. Follicular cells are derived from cortical sex cords that are raised from the coelomic epithelium.

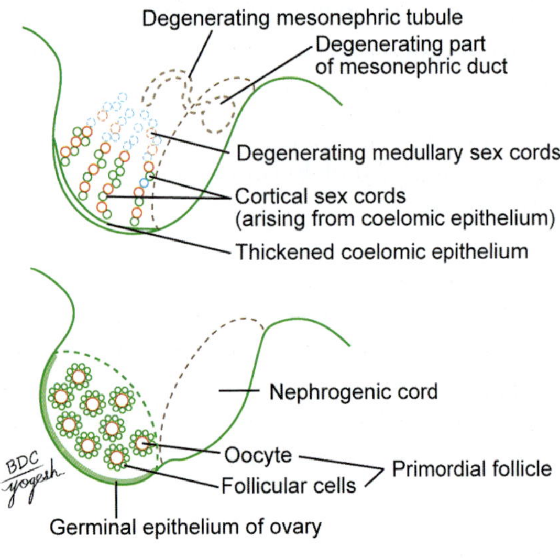

Fig. 31.7: Development of ovary

Flowchart 31.2: Development of ovary

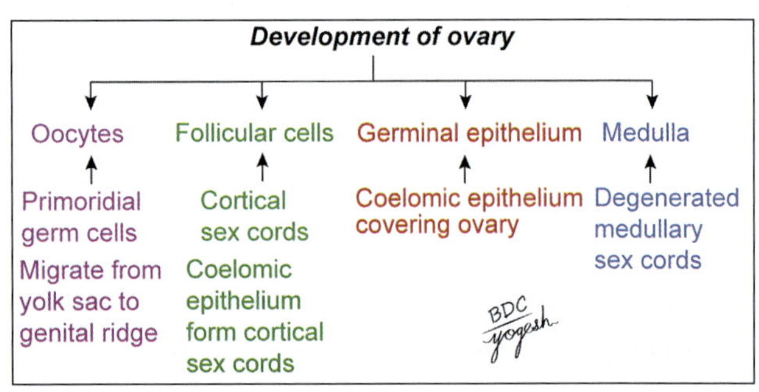

3. Germinal epithelium (cuboidal epithelium covering the ovaries) is derived from coelomic epithelium that covers genital ridge.
4. Medulla of ovary is derived from degenerated medullary sex cords.

CLINICAL ANATOMY

- ***Determination of ovulation***: In cases of sterility, the ovulation can be determined by repeated ultrasonography.
- ***Ovarian torsion***: It may occur due to unusual long mesovarium and suspensory ligament of ovary.
- ***Prolapse of ovaries***: Ovaries are frequently displaced to the pouch of Douglas where they can be palpated by a PV or per vaginal examination.
- ***Polycystic ovary syndrome (PCOD)***: It is the most common endocrine disorder in females during reproductive age. It is characterised by multiple ovarian cysts. It may result in irregular menstrual periods, menorrhagia (excessive menstrual bleeding), hirsutism (excess hair growth), acne, and infertility.
- Multiple small theca lutein cysts involve both the ovaries in cases with ***Stein-Leventhal syndrome***. The syndrome is characterised by mild hirsutism, deep voice, secondary amenorrhoea, and cystic enlargement of both the ovaries.

- Ovaries are the most common site in the abdomen for endometriosis. The endometrial cysts in the ovary are called the ***chocolate cysts***.
- ***Carcinoma of ovary*** is common, and accounts for 15% of all cancers and 20% of gynaecological cancers.
- *Ovarian teratoma* (*dermoid cyst of ovary*): It is a benign tumour of ovary that contains different types of tissues, such as hairs, teeth, bone and so on.

DISSECTION

Cut through the pubic symphysis with a knife in the median plane and extend the incision into the urethra. Make a median dorsal cut with a saw through the fourth and fifth lumbar vertebrae, the sacrum and coccyx to meet the knife. Cut through the soft tissues.

Separate the two halves of the pelvis and examine the cut surface of all the tissues.

Locate the ovary on the lateral wall of pelvis in the female cadaver. Identify the ovarian vessels in the infundibulopelvic ligament and trace these to the ovary and uterine tube. Follow the ovarian artery till its anastomosis with the uterine artery.

Identify the uterus and follow the peritoneum on its superior and inferior surfaces which is thus free to move. Trace the uterus downwards till the supravaginal part of cervix which is attached to the lateral pelvic wall by transverse cervical ligaments and to the sacrum by uterosacral ligaments.

The vaginal part of cervix is surrounded on all sides by fornices of the vagina. The posterior fornix is the deepest. These can be felt by putting index and middle fingers through the vagina.

Identify the broad ligament attaching uterus to the lateral pelvic wall and note various structures present in its borders and surfaces.

UTERINE TUBES

Uterine tubes are tortuous ducts, which convey oocyte from the ovary to the uterus. Spermatozoa introduced into the vagina pass up into the uterus, and from there into the uterine tubes. Fertilization usually takes place in the lateral part of the tube (Plate 31.2, Fig. 31.8, Flowchart 31.3).

Synonym

Fallopian tubes, salpinx.

Situation

These are situated in the free upper margin of the broad ligament of uterus.

Dimensions

Each uterine tube is about 10 cm long.

At the lateral end, the uterine tube opens into the peritoneal cavity through its ***abdominal ostium***. This ostium is about 3 mm in diameter.

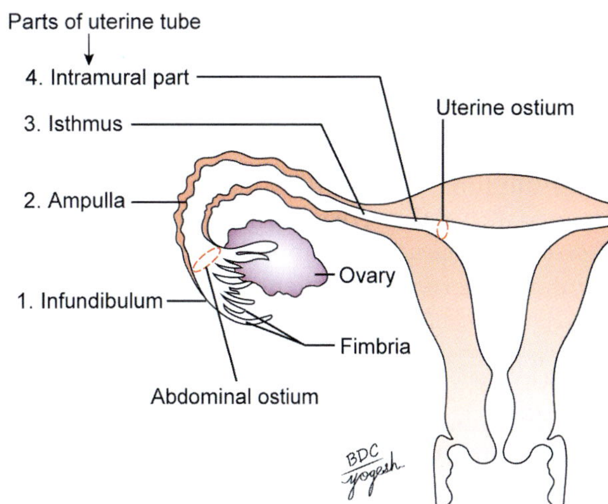

Fig. 31.8: Parts of uterine tube

Flowchart 31.3: Uterine tubes

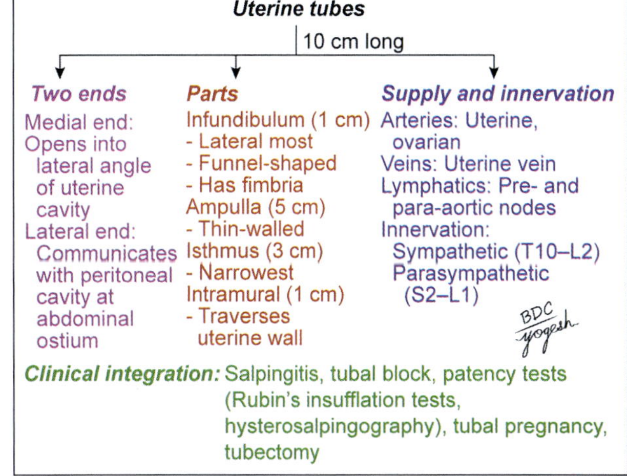

Subdivisions

1. ***Infundibulum***: The lateral end of the uterine tube is shaped like a funnel and is, therefore, called the *infundibulum*. It bears a number of finger-like processes called ***fimbriae*** and is, therefore, called the *fimbriated end*. One of the fimbriae is longer than the others and is attached to the tubal pole of the ovary. It is known as the ***ovarian fimbria***.
2. ***Ampulla***: The part of the uterine tube medial to the infundibulum is called the *ampulla*. It is thin-walled, dilated and tortuous, and forms approximately the lateral two-thirds or 6 to 7 cm of the tube. It arches over the upper pole of the ovary. The ampulla is about 4 mm in diameter .This is the ***site for fertilization***.
3. ***Isthmus***: It succeeds the ampulla. It is narrow, rounded and cord-like. It forms approximately the medial one-third or 2 to 3 cm of the tube.
4. ***Intramural*** or ***interstitial part***: It is about 1 cm long and lies within the wall of the uterus. It opens at the superior angle of the uterine cavity by a narrow ***uterine ostium***. This ostium is about 1 mm in diameter.

Blood Supply

The ***uterine artery*** supplies approximately the medial two-thirds, and the ovarian artery supplies the lateral one-third of the tube. The *veins* run parallel with the arteries and drain into the pampiniform plexus of the ovary and into the uterine veins (*see* Fig. 31.15).

Lymphatic Drainage

Most of the tubal lymphatics join the lymphatics from the ovary and drain with them into the *lateral aortic* and *preaortic nodes*. The lymphatics from the isthmus accompany the round ligament of the uterus and drain into the *superficial inguinal nodes*.

Nerve Supply

The uterine tubes are supplied by both the sympathetic and parasympathetic nerves running along the uterine and ovarian arteries.

1. The *sympathetic nerves* from T10 to L2 segments are derived from the hypogastric plexuses. They contain both visceral afferent and efferent fibres. The latter are vasomotors and perhaps stimulate tubal peristalsis. However, peristalsis is mainly under hormonal control.
2. *Parasympathetic nerves* are derived from the vagus for splanchnic nerves from S2–S4 segments of spinal cord for the medial half. They inhibit peristalsis and produce vasodilatation.

Competency:
AN52.2 Describe and identify the microanatomical features of uterine tube.

Histology of Fallopian Tubes

Uterine tube is made up of the following coats from inside outwards: Mucosa, muscle layer and serosa (Plate 31.4).

1. *Mucosa*: It consists of thin projecting longitudinal folds that fill the lumen. It is lined by simple ciliated columnar epithelium with few nonciliated secretory cells or peg cells. Core of mucosal fold consists of highly cellular and vascular connective tissue.
2. *Muscle layer*: Muscle coat consists of two layers of smooth muscle: Inner thick circular and outer thin longitudinal layers.
3. *Serosa or peritoneal coat*: Fallopian tube is covered by a thin layer of connective tissue and mesothelium.

Note: ***Transport of ovum***: The transport of ovum is chiefly due to muscular contractions. The ciliary movements create an effective stream of lymph towards the uterus, which assists in the nourishment of ovum in the lumen of the tube over the mucosal ridges.

Competency:
AN48.5 Explain the anatomical basis of suprapubic cystostomy, retroverted uterus, prolapse uterus, internal and external haemorrhoids, anal fistula, tubal pregnancy and tubal ligation.

CLINICAL ANATOMY

- ***Salpingitis***: Inflammation of the uterine tube is called salpingitis (Salpinx = trumpet or tube).
- ***Sterility***: Inability to have a child is called sterility.

Plate 31.4: Histology of fallopian tube

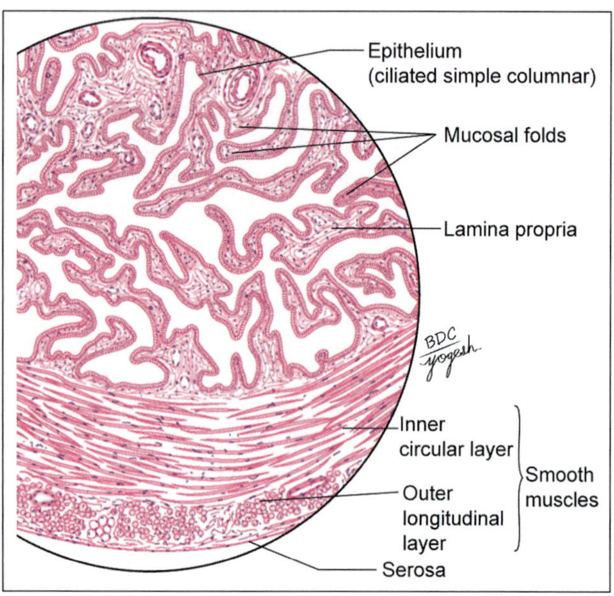

- The most common cause of sterility in the female is tubal blockage which may be congenital, or caused by infection.
- ***Test for patency***: The patency of the tube can be investigated by:
  1. *Insufflation test* or *Rubin's test*. Normally, air pushed into the uterus passes through the tubes and leaks into the peritoneal cavity. This leakage produces a hissing or bubbling sound which can be auscultated over the iliac fossae.
  2. *Hysterosalpingography* is a radiological technique by which the cavity of the uterus and the lumina of the tubes can be visualized, after injecting a radio-opaque oily dye into the uterus (Fig. 31.9).
- ***Tubal pregnancy***: Sometimes the fertilised ovum instead of reaching the uterus adheres to the walls of the uterine tube and starts developing there. This is known as *tubal pregnancy*. The enlarging embryo may lead to rupture of tube.

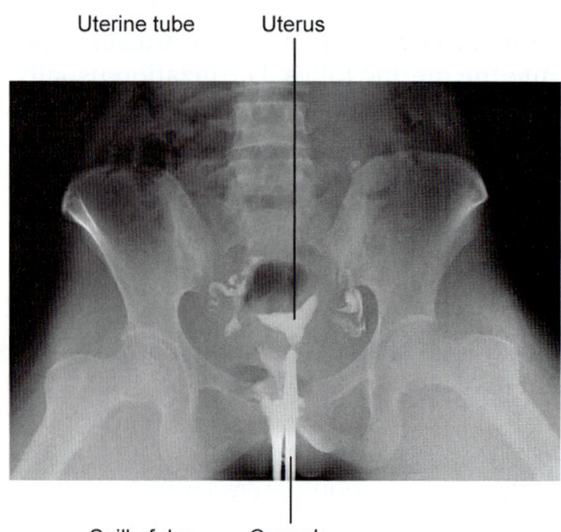

Fig. 31.9: Hysterosalpingogram

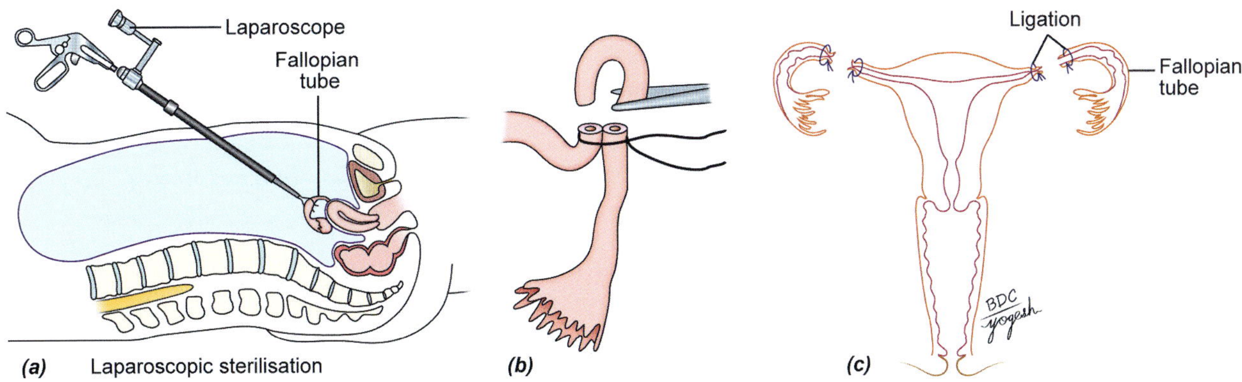

Figs 31.10a to c: Tubectomy

- ***Tubectomy***: For purposes of family planning, a woman can be sterilized by removing a segment of the uterine tube on both sides. This can be done by laparoscopy (Fig. 31.10a) or through an incision in abdominal wall (Figs 31.10a to c).

UTERUS

Uterus is a child-bearing organ in females, situated in the pelvis between bladder and rectum. Though hollow, it is thick walled, firm, muscular organ.

It is the organ which protects and provides nutrition to a fertilized ovum, enabling it to grow into a fully formed foetus. At the time of childbirth or parturition, contractions of muscle in the wall of the organ result in expulsion of the foetus from the uterus (Fig. 31.11).

Synonym

In layman's language, the uterus is called the womb. It is also called *hystera*, on which word hysterectomy is based.

Size and Shape

The uterus is pyriform in shape. Its dimensions are:

- *Length*: 3 inches (7.5 cm)
- *Breadth*: 2 inches (5 cm)
- *Thickness*: 1 inch (2.6 cm)
- *Weight*: 30–40 g
- *Consistency*: Firm.

Subdivisions or Parts of Uterus

Uterus is divided into two regions (parts):

1. Muscular *body of uterus* — forms upper 2/3rd part
2. Fibrous *cervix* — forms lower 1/3rd part.

The junction of the body and cervix is marked by a circular constriction called *isthmus*.

Part of uterus above the opening of fallopian tube is called the *fundus*.

The *superolateral angle* of the body project outwards at the junction of body and fundus and is called ***cornua of uterus***. The uterine tube, ligament of ovary and round ligament are attached to it on each side.

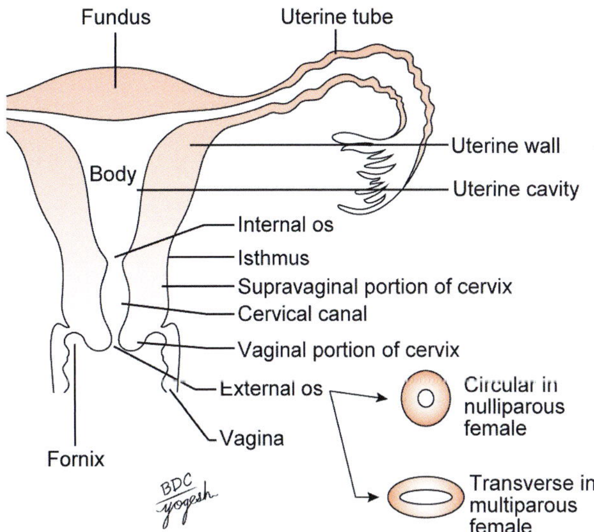

Fig. 31.11: Different parts of the uterus and shapes of external os in nulliparous and multiparous females

Communications

Superiorly, the uterus communicates on each side with the uterine tube, and inferiorly, with the vagina (Figs 31.12a and b).

Normal Position and Angulation

1. The ***angle of anteversion*** is a forward angle between the long axis of body of uterus and the long axis of vagina. Normally, it measures about 90° and open forwards. The forward tilting of the uterus relative to the vagina is called ***anteversion***.
2. The ***angle of anteflexion*** is a forward angle between the long axis of the body of uterus and the long axis of the cervix at the isthmus. It measures about 120°–170°. The uterus is also slightly flexed at the level of internal os of cervix; this is referred to as ***anteflexion***.

Note: Roughly, the long axis of the uterus corresponds to the axis of the pelvic inlet, and the axis of the vagina to the axis of the pelvic cavity and of the pelvic outlet. It is normally deviated to right side and is called ***dextrorotation***.

Retroversion: In retroverted (tilted or tipped) uterus, the uterus is tilted backward relative to the vagina. Long axis of the uterus corresponds to the axis of the pelvic inlet and the axis of the vagina to the axis of the pelvic cavity and the pelvic outlet.

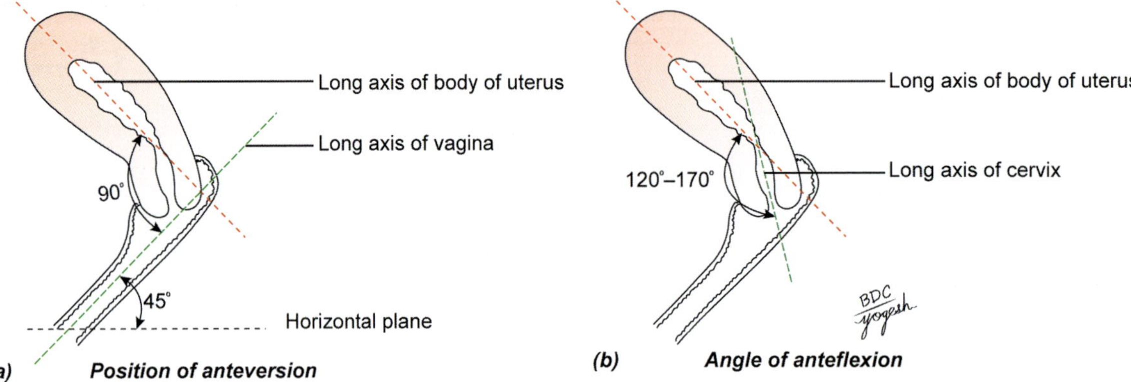

Figs 31.12a and b: (a) Angulations of the uterus and vagina, and their axes and (b) angle of anteversion

Features of Uterus

The uterus comprises:

1. Body: It has:
   a. Fundus
   b. Two surfaces: Anterior or vesical and posterior or intestinal
   c. Two lateral borders
2. Cervix.

Body of Uterus

Fundus

The *fundus* is formed by the free upper end of the uterus. Fundus lies above the openings of the uterine tubes. It is convex like a dome. It is covered with peritoneum and is directed forward when the bladder is empty. The fertilized oocyte is usually implanted in the posterior wall of the fundus or upper part of body of uterus (Plate 31.5, Fig. 31.13).

Surfaces and borders

1. The ***anteroinferior surface*** of the body is flat and related to the urinary bladder. It is covered with peritoneum and forms the posterior or superior wall of the uterovesical pouch.
2. The ***posterosuperior surface*** is convex and is related to coils of the terminal ileum and to the sigmoid colon. It is covered with peritoneum and forms the anterior wall of the rectouterine pouch.
3. Each ***lateral border*** is rounded and convex.

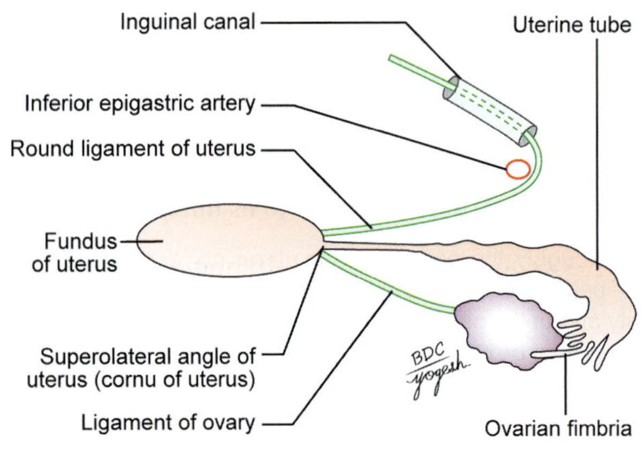

Fig. 31.13: Fundus of the uterus seen from above

Attachments

a. The lateral border provides attachment to the *broad ligament* of the uterus which connects it to the lateral pelvic wall.
b. The *uterine tube* opens into the uterus at the upper end of this border.
c. This end of the border gives attachment to the *round ligament of the uterus*, anteroinferior to the tube; and to the ligament of the ovary posteroinferior to the tube.
d. The uterine artery ascends along the lateral border of the uterus between the two layers of the broad ligament (Fig. 31.12).

Note: Usual site of implantation: On seventh day after fertilisation, blastocyst usually implants in endometrium of uterus at posterior wall of superior part of uterus (Plate 31.5).

Cervix of Uterus

The cervix is the lower, cylindrical part of the uterus. It is less mobile than the body. It is about 2.5 cm long, and is slightly wider in the middle than at either end. The lower part of the cervix projects into the anterior wall of the vagina, which divides it into supravaginal and vaginal parts.

A. ***Supravaginal part of the cervix*** is related:
   1. Anteriorly to the bladder.
   2. Posteriorly to the rectouterine pouch, containing coils of intestine and to the rectum.
   3. On each side, to the ureter and to the uterine artery, embedded in parametrium. The fibrofatty tissue between the two layers of the broad ligament and below it, is called the *parametrium*. It is most abundant near the cervix and vagina.

B. ***Vaginal part of the cervix*** projects into the anterior wall of the vagina. The spaces between it and the vaginal wall are called the ***vaginal fornices***. The cervical canal opens into the vagina by an opening called the ***external os***.

Cavity of Uterus

Cavity of Body of Uterus

1. In sagittal section, the cavity of the body of the uterus is seen as a mere slit because the uterus is compressed anteroposteriorly.

Plate 31.5: Usual site of implantation

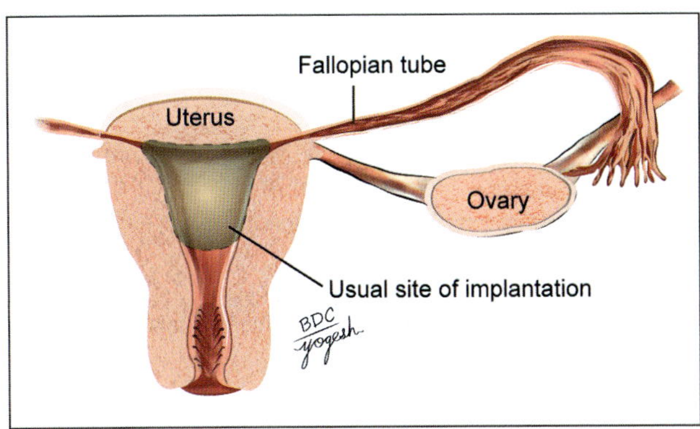

2. In coronal section, the cavity is seen to be triangular in shape, the apex being directed downwards.
3. At the apex, the cavity becomes continuous with the canal of the cervix. The junction is called the ***internal os***.
4. The superolateral angles of the cavity receive the openings of the right and left uterine tubes (*see* Fig. 31.11).

Cervical Canal

- The cavity of the cervix, is fusiform in shape.
- It communicates above with the cavity of the body of the uterus, through the ***internal os***, and below with the vaginal cavity through the ***external os***.
- The canal is flattened from before backwards so that it comes to have anterior and posterior walls. These walls show mucosal folds, which resemble the branches of a tree called the ***arbor vitae uteri***. The folds in the anterior and posterior walls interlock with each other and close the canal.

Note: In a nulliparous woman, i.e. a woman who has not borne children, the *external os* is small and circular (Figs 31.5a and b). However, in multiparous women, the *external os* is bounded by anterior and posterior lips, both of which are in contact with the posterior wall of the vagina.

Relations of the Uterus

Relations of Body (Fig. 31.14)

Anterior

- Uterovesical pouch
- Surface of urinary bladder.

Posterior

- Rectouterine pouch
- Coils of ileum, sigmoid colon.

Lateral

- Broad ligament
- Ureter
- Uterine vessels.

Relations of Cervix (Fig. 31.14)

Anterior

- The supravaginal part of cervix is related to posterior surface of urinary bladder.

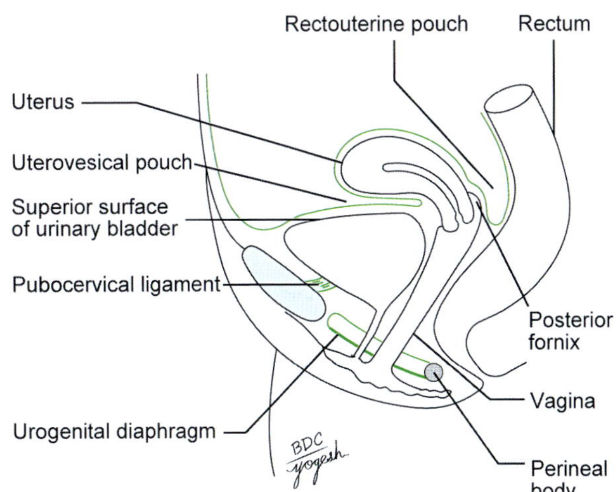

Fig. 31.14: Relations of the uterus

- The vaginal part of cervix is related to the anterior fornix of vagina.

Posterior

- The supravaginal part of the cervix is related to rectouterine pouch with the ileum and sigmoid colon coils in it.
- The vaginal part of cervix is related to posterior fornix of vagina.

Laterally

- The supravaginal part of cervix is related to ureter and uterine vessels.
- The vaginal part of cervix is related to fornixes of the vagina.

Ligaments of Uterus

Peritoneal Ligaments

These are mere peritoneal folds which do not provide any support to the uterus.

1. *Anterior ligament* — consists of the uterovesical fold of peritoneum.
2. *Posterior ligament* — consists of the rectovaginal fold forming rectovaginal pouch of peritoneum.
3. The right and left *broad ligaments* — are folds of peritoneum which attach the uterus to the lateral pelvic wall.
4. *Rectouterine folds (right and left).*

Fibromuscular Ligaments

The fibromuscular ligaments are:

1. Round ligaments of the uterus
2. Transverse cervical ligaments
3. Uterosacral ligaments.

These are described separately under the heading of 'supports' of uterus.

Broad Ligament of Uterus

These are pairs of folds of peritoneum extending from the lateral borders of uterus to the lateral wall of the pelvis on each side (Plate 31.6, Flowchart 31.4).

Plate 31.6: Broad ligament of uterus (Posterosuperior view)

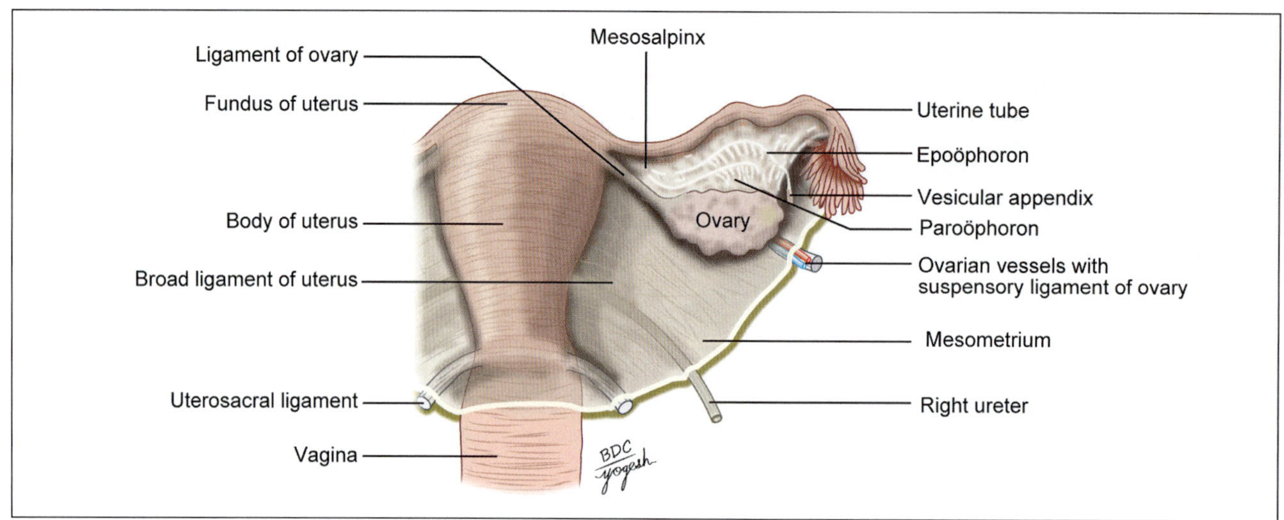

Flowchart 31.4: Broad ligament

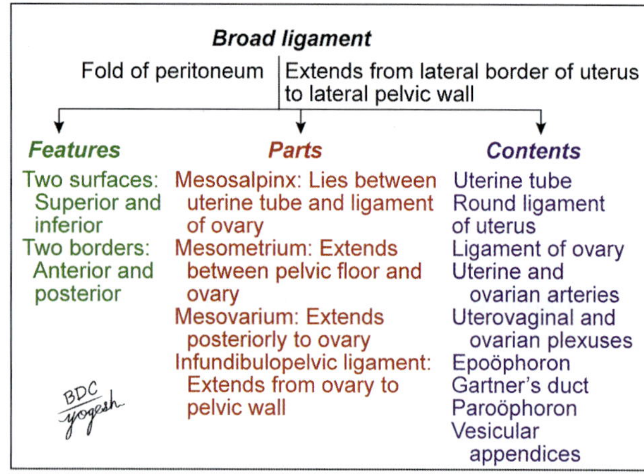

External features

Each broad ligament has:

Two surfaces:

- Superior and inferior (when bladder is empty)
- Anterior and posterior (when bladder is full).

Two borders:

- When bladder is empty: Anterior free border and posterior attached borders.
- When bladder is full: Upper free border and inferior attached borders.

Parts of broad ligament

The broad ligament has four parts: Mesosalpinx, mesometrium, mesovarium, and infundibulopelvic ligament.

1. ***Mesosalpinx*** is a part of broad ligament between the uterine tube and the ligament of ovary.
2. ***Mesometrium*** is a part of broad ligament extending from the pelvic floor to the ovary, the ligament of ovary, and the body of uterus.
3. ***Mesovarium*** is a fold of peritoneum that extends posteriorly from the broad ligament to the ovary.
4. ***Infundibulopelvic ligament*** (*suspensory ligament of ovary*) is a part of broad ligament that extends from infundibulum of uterine tube to the upper pole of the lateral wall of the pelvis.

Contents of broad ligament

1. One tube: Uterine tube (Figs 31.15 and 31.16)
2. Two ligaments: Round ligament of uterus, ligament of ovary
3. Arteries: Uterine and ovarian
4. Nerve plexuses: Uterovaginal and ovarian
5. Embryological remnants: Epoöphoron and Gartner's duct, paroöphoron, vesicular appendices
6. Lymph nodes and lymphatic vessels
7. Fibrofatty tissue or parametrium.

Arterial Supply

The uterus is supplied:

1. Chiefly by the two uterine arteries which are markedly enlarged during pregnancy (Fig. 31.17).
2. Partly by the ovarian arteries.

Note: The *uterine artery* is a branch of the anterior division of the internal iliac artery. It first runs medially towards the cervix, crossing the ureter above the lateral fornix of the vagina and 2 cm lateral to the cervix. Then the artery ascends along the side of the uterus, with a tortuous course. Finally, it runs laterally towards the hilus of the ovary, and ends by anastomozing with the ovarian artery. The tortuosity of the artery permits expansion of the uterus during pregnancy without stretching the artery (Fig. 31.14). Apart from the uterus, the artery also gives branches to vagina, medial 2/3rd of the uterine tube, ovary, ureter and structures present in the broad ligament.

Venous Drainage

The veins form a plexus along the lateral border of the uterus. The plexus drains through the uterine, ovarian and vaginal veins into the internal iliac veins.

Lymphatic Drainage

Lymphatics of the uterus begin at three intercommunicating networks—endometrial, myometrial and subperitoneal.

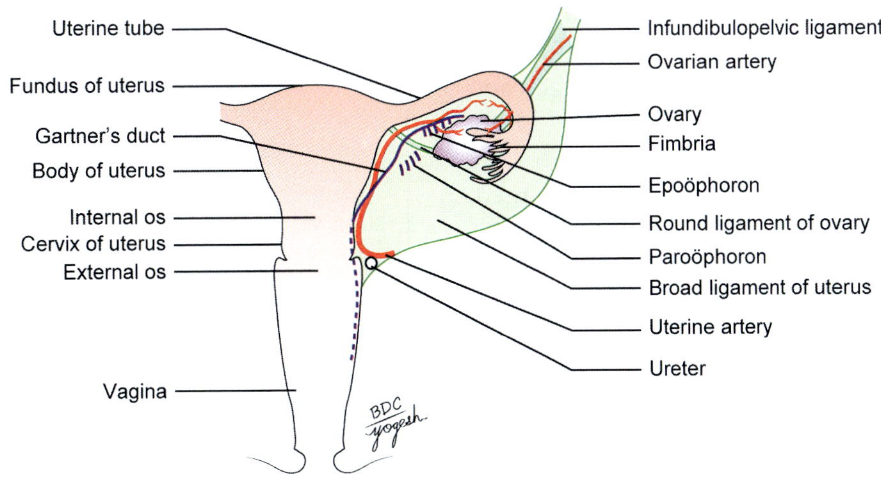

Fig. 31.15: Contents of the broad ligament (posterosuperior view of the right broad ligament of the uterus)

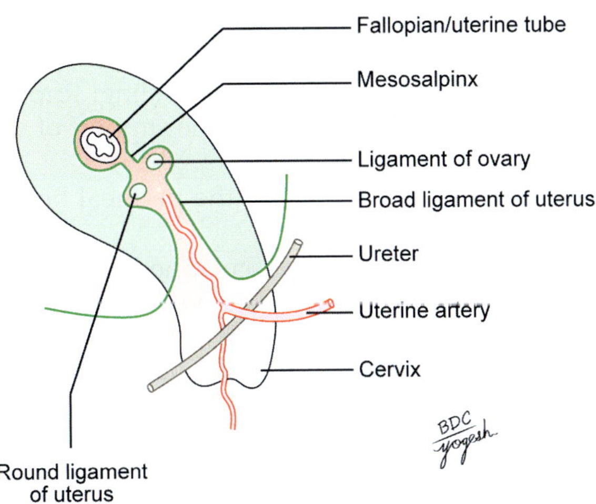

Fig. 31.16: Contents of the broad ligament (sagittal section through the broad ligament of the uterus)

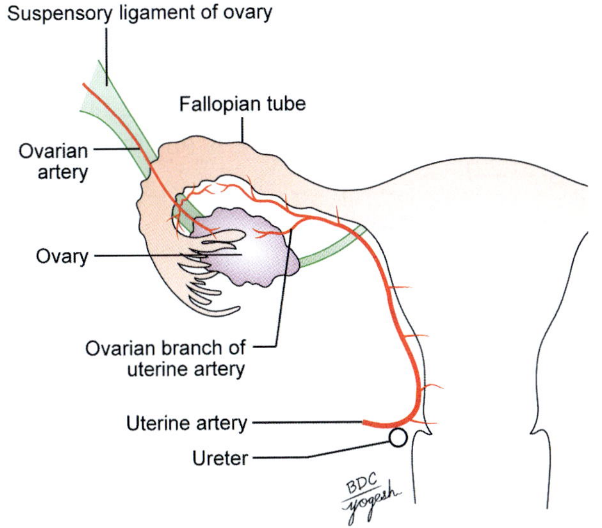

Fig. 31.17: Arterial supply of uterus and ovary

These plexuses drain into lymphatics on the side of the uterus as follows (Fig. 31.18):

1. The *upper lymphatics* from the fundus and upper part of the body drain mainly into the aortic nodes, and only partly to the superficial inguinal nodes along the round ligament of the uterus.

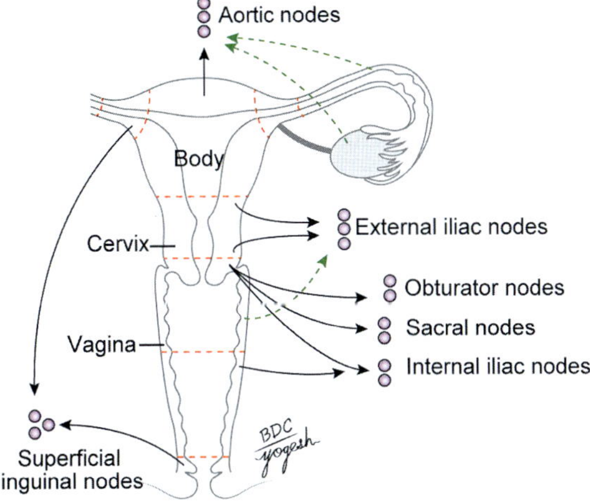

Fig. 31.18: Lymphatic drainage of uterus and vagina

2. The *middle lymphatics* from the lower part of body drain into the external iliac nodes.
3. The *lower lymphatics* from the cervix drain into the internal iliac and sacral nodes.

Nerve Supply

The uterus is richly supplied by both sympathetic and parasympathetic nerves, through the inferior hypogastric and ovarian plexuses as follows:

1. *Sympathetic* nerves from T12, L1 segments of spinal cord produce uterine contraction and vasoconstriction.
2. The *parasympathetic* nerves (S2–S4) produce uterine inhibition and vasodilatation. However, these effects are complicated by the pronounced effects of hormones on the genital tract.
3. *Pain sensations* from the body of the uterus pass along the sympathetic nerves, and from the cervix, along the parasympathetic nerves.

Age and Reproductive Changes

In foetal life: The cervix is larger than the body which projects a little above the pelvic brim.

At puberty: The uterus enlarges and descends to the adult position. The arbor vitae uteri also appear.

During menstruation: The uterus is slightly enlarged and becomes more vascular. The lips of the *external os* are swollen.

During pregnancy: The uterus is enormously enlarged, mainly due to hypertrophy of the smooth muscle fibres and partly due to hyperplasia. As pregnancy advances, the uterine wall becomes progressively thinner. After parturition, the uterus gradually involutes and returns almost to the non-pregnant size.

In old age: The uterus becomes atrophic and smaller in size and more dense in texture. The *internal os* is frequently obliterated. The lips of the *external os* disappear, and the *os* itself may be obliterated.

Supports of the Uterus

The uterus is a mobile organ which undergoes extensive changes in size and shape during the reproductive period of life. It is supported and prevented from sagging down by a number of factors which are chiefly muscular and fibromuscular (Flowchart 31.5).

Primary Supports

1. ***Muscular or active supports***
   a. Pelvic diaphragm
   b. Perineal body
   c. Distal urethral sphincter mechanism
2. ***Fibromuscular or mechanical supports***
   a. Uterine axis
   b. Pubocervical ligaments
   c. Transverse cervical ligaments of Mackenrodt
   d. Uterosacral ligaments
   e. Round ligaments of uterus.

Secondary Supports

These are of doubtful value and are formed by peritoneal ligaments.

1. Broad ligaments (Plate 31.6)
2. Vesicouterine pouch and fold of peritoneum
3. Rectovaginal or rectouterine pouch and fold of peritoneum.

Flowchart 31.5: Supports of uterus

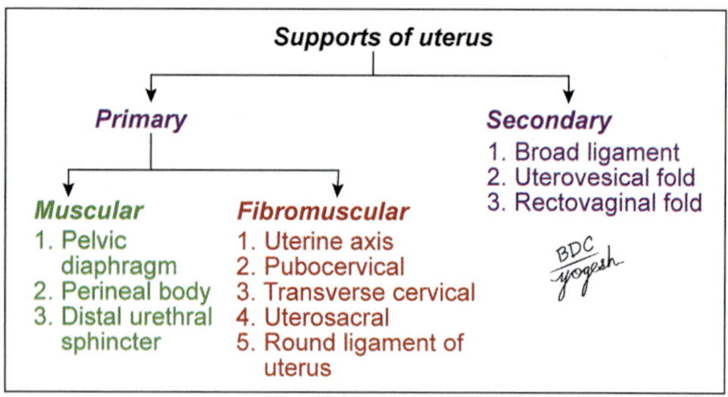

Role of Individual Supports (Figs 31.19 to 31.23)

1. ***Pelvic diaphragm***: It supports the pelvic viscera and resists raised abdominal pressure. Pubococcygeus (part of levator ani) inserts on the perineal body and supports the vagina by forming a sling. Rupture of these fibres during childbirth, the support of vagina is lost, and it may prolapse. (Fig. 31.19)
2. ***Levator ani muscle***: It fixes the perineal body and supports the pelvic viscera.
3. ***Perineal body***: It is fibromuscular node located in the centre of perineum between vagina and rectum. It gives attachments to perineal muscles and pelvic diaphragm and maintains the integrity of the pelvic floor.
4. ***Sphincter urethrae fibres***: The compressor urethrae and sphincter urethrovaginalis fibres are inserted into the vagina, and hence, they support the uterus and vagina.
5. ***Uterine axis***: The anteverted and anteflexed position of uterus prevents the organ from sagging down through the vagina. Increased intra-abdominal pressure further accentuates anteversion of uterus and prevents the prolapse of uterus.
6. ***Pubocervical ligaments***: They connect the cervix to the posterior surface of the pubic bone. They are a pair of fibrous bands derived from endopelvic fascia. They correspond to the puboprostatic ligaments in males (Fig. 31.22).

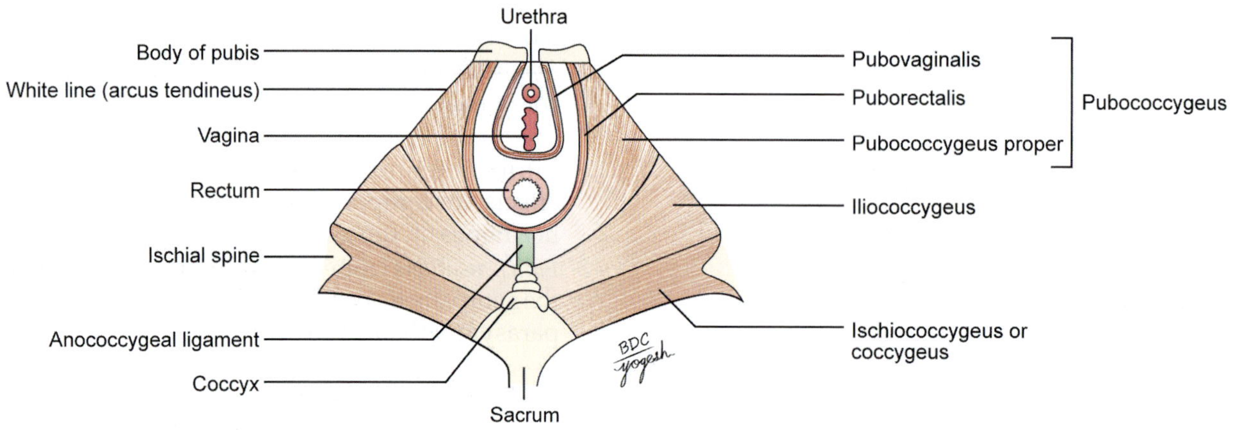

Fig. 31.19: Superior view of the pelvic diaphragm (the levator ani and coccygeus)

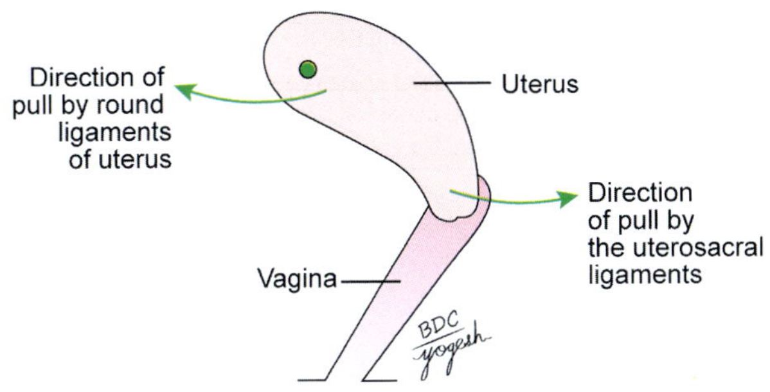

Fig. 31.20: Anteversion of the uterus is maintained by the couple of forces provided by the pull of the uterosacral ligament and the round ligament of the uterus.

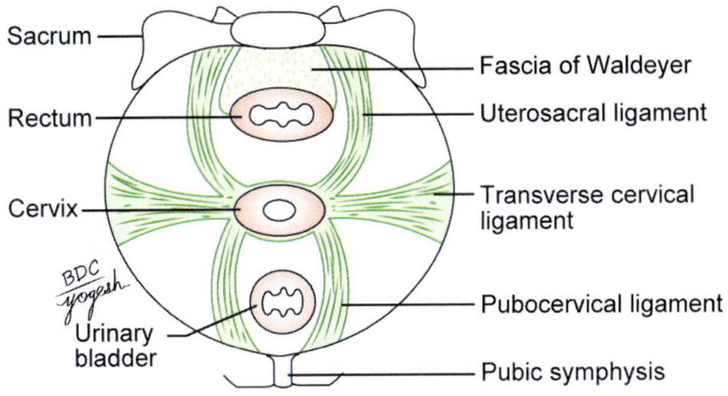

Fig. 31.21: Ligamentous (fibromuscular) supports of the uterus (superior view)

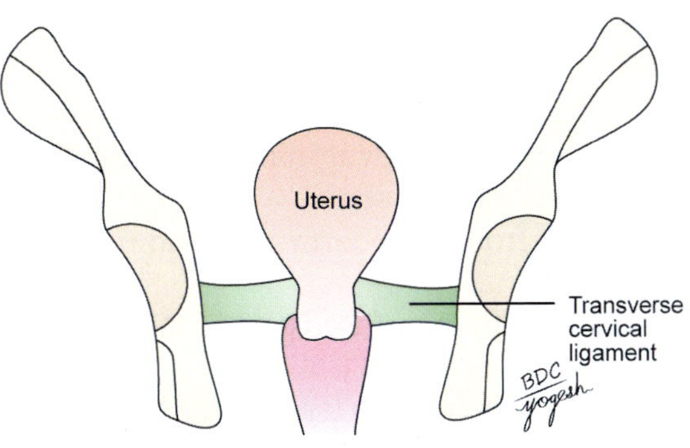

Fig. 31.22: Cervical ligaments supporting the uterus

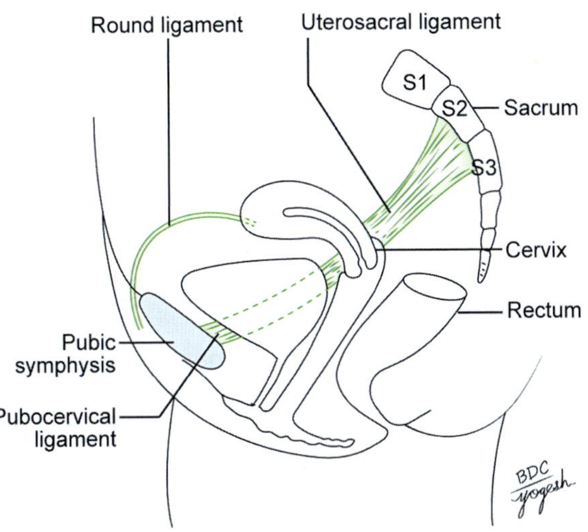

Fig. 31.23: Ligamentous (fibromuscular) supports of the uterus

7. ***Transverse cervical ligaments of Mackenrodt:*** These are called *cardinal ligaments, cervical ligaments, paracervical ligaments*, or *retinacula uterine sustentaculum of Bonny*. These are fibrous bands derived from endopelvic fascia. They are fan-shaped bands. They connect the lateral aspect cervix and upper vaginal wall to the lateral pelvic wall. They form a *hammock* which supports the uterus and prevents its prolapse.
8. ***Uterosacral ligaments:*** It is a pair of fibrous bands derived from condensation of endopelvic fascia. They connect the cervix to the second and third sacral vertebrae (Fig. 31.20).
9. ***Round ligaments of uterus:*** These are pairs of fibromuscular bonds. They extend from the lateral angle of uterus, run forward and laterally, then pass through the deep inguinal ring, traverse the inguinal canal, and merge with connective tissue of labia majora. Round ligament pulls the fundus forward and helps to maintain the anteversion and anteflexion of the uterus (Fig. 31.20).

Note:

Surgical tightening of Mackenrodt's ligament is commonly done for repair of prolapsed uterus.

Round ligaments pull the cervix forward, whereas uterosacral ligaments pull backward. They help to maintain the anteflexed and anteverted position of the uterus.

Canal of Nuck is patent extension of peritoneum in the inguinal canal, along with the round ligament. It extends externally up to the labia majora. It is homologous to processus vaginalis in males.

Competency:

AN52.2 Describe and identify the microanatomical features of uterus.

Histology of Uterus

The body and fundus of the uterus has three layers: Endometrium, myometrium and perimetrium.

The endometrium consists of simple columnar epithelial lining, simple tubular glands and connective tissue stroma (Plate 31.7).

Myometrium consists of smooth muscle cells showing inner and outer longitudinal fibres and middle spirally arranged fibres.

Perimetrium consists of connective tissue layer covered by mesothelium.

Endometrium shows cyclic changes as follows:

- In proliferative phase, glands are long with narrow lumen; thick stroma with less coiled spiral arteries (Plate 31.7).
- In secretory phase, glands are highly coiled with wide lumen and secretions, stroma with coiled spiral arteries (Plate 31.8).
- In menstrual phase, the endometrium becomes ischaemic and starts being shed. The vessel wall gets necrosed and blood enters the stroma and menstrual flow starts.

Plate 31.7: Histology of proliferative phase of uterine endometrium

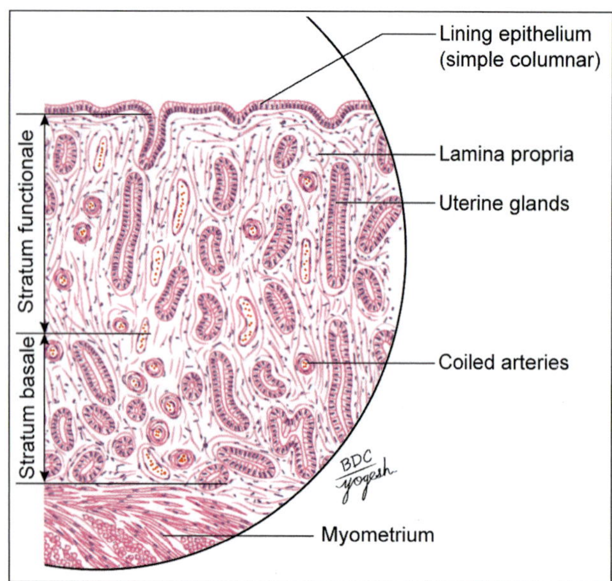

Plate 31.8: Histology of secretory phase of uterine endometrium

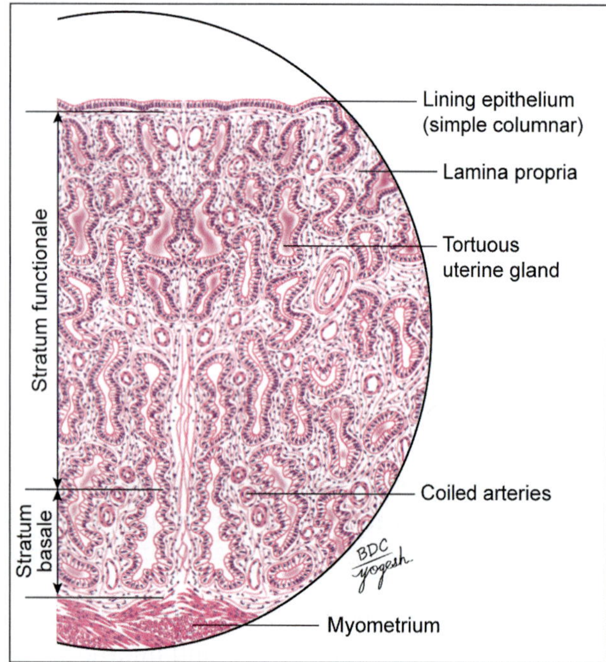

Histology of Cervix of Uterus

The cervix shows endocervix (mucous membrane) and muscle layer (Plate 31.9).

1. *Endocervix*: The cervical canal is lined by *tall columnar* mucus secreting epithelium. The epithelium rests on *lamina propria* (loose areolar tissue). *Cervical glands* are small, branched tubular glands that lie in lamina propria. These glands secrete cervical mucus that is rich in lysozyme.
2. *Muscle coat:* Mucosa rests on thick layer of fibroelastic tissue and smooth muscles (6%–25%). The elastic component of cervix is essential for stretching of the cervix during childbirth.

Plate 31.9: Histology of uterine cervix

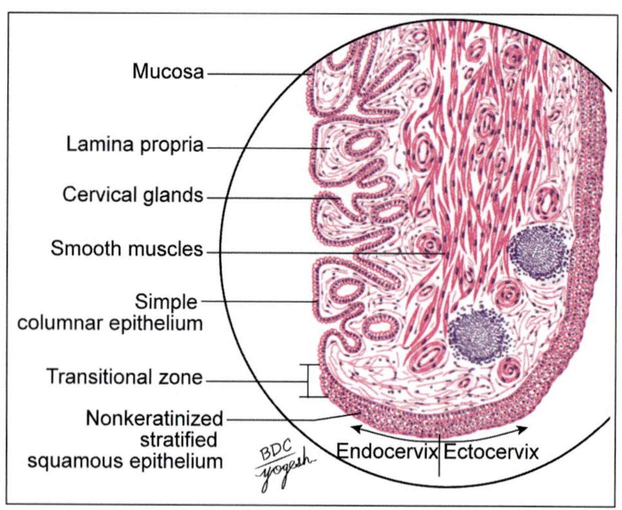

3. *Ectocervix/Portio vaginalis:* The portion of cervix that projects into the vagina is called ectocervix. Ectocervix shows transformation zone where the simple columnar epithelium of cervical canal becomes stratified squamous epithelium that continues with vaginal epithelium.

Competency:
AN52.8 Describe the development of female reproductive system.

Development of Uterus and Fallopian Tubes

Uterus develops from the following sources (Fig. 31.24):

1. Epithelium from uterovaginal canal (fused part of paramesonephric ducts).
2. Myometrium from mesoderm surrounding paramesonephric ducts.
3. Fallopian tubes from unfused part of paramesonephric ducts.
4. At birth, cervix is twice in length than body of uterus. After puberty, the body of uterus elongates and becomes longer than the cervix.

Competencies:
AN48.5 Explain the anatomical basis of suprapubic cystostomy, urinary obstruction in benign prostatic hypertrophy, retroverted uterus, prolapse uterus, internal and external haemorrhoids, anal fistula, vasectomy, tubal pregnancy and tubal ligation.
AN48.8 Mention the structures palpable during vaginal and rectal examination.

CLINICAL ANATOMY

- ***Uterine fibroids*** are benign smooth muscle tumours of the uterus. These are primarily asymptomatic. Sometimes they may cause painful, excessive menstrual bleeding (Fig. 31.25).
- ***Cervical carcinoma*** is the most common cancer in females (11%). The second most common is breast cancer (8%). It spreads directly to adjacent

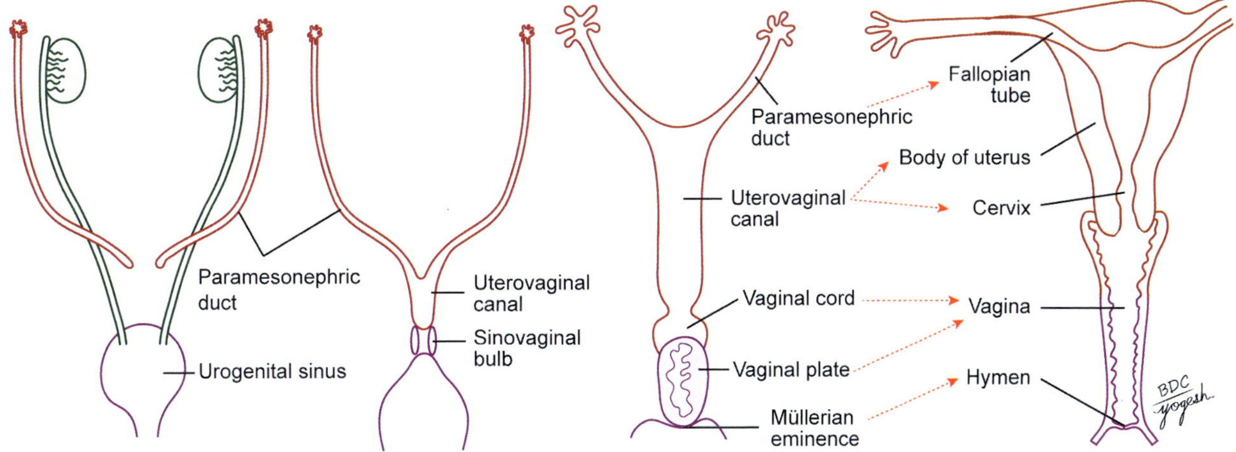

Fig. 31.24: Development of uterus and vagina

structures. It may metastasize via lymphatics. It causes abnormal vaginal bleeding, postcoital bleeding, and weight loss.

- ***Caesarean section*** (*C-Section*) is a surgical procedure by which baby is delivered through horizontal incision in mother's anterior abdominal wall and anterior wall of uterus. It is required in case of placenta previa, transverse lie of baby, multiple pregnancies, disproportionate baby's head, and mother's pelvis and so on.
- ***Endometritis*** is an inflammation of the endometrium.
- ***Colpotomy** and **colporrhaphy**:* Posterior colpotomy is done to drain the pus from the pouch of Douglas.
- ***Intrauterine contraceptive device*** is used to prevent implantation of fertilized oocyte (Fig. 31.26).
- Perineal body is one of the chief supports of pelvic organs. Damage to the perineal body often leads to prolapse of the uterus and of other pelvic organs.
- ***Prolapse of uterus*:** Uterine prolapse is the herniation of the uterus from its normal anatomical position into the vaginal canal.

  Causes: Uterine prolapse is due to weakening of the supports of the uterus. It usually occurs due to successive vaginal deliveries, obese female, advancing age or connective tissue disorders.

  Signs and symptoms:
  - Sensation of heaviness and pressure in vagina.
  - Bulging lump into vagina or protruding out of vagina.
  - Painful sexual intercourse.

  Treatment: Treatment depends on the extent of prolapse and symptoms. It includes:
  - Pelvic floor exercises
  - Vaginal pessaries (silicon object) are inserted into the vagina to provide support for prolapsed uterus.
  - *Surgical treatments* include sacrohysteropexy (resuspension of prolapsed uterus using a strip of synthetic mesh to the anterior longitudinal ligament over sacral promontory) and hysterectomy (surgical removal of uterus).

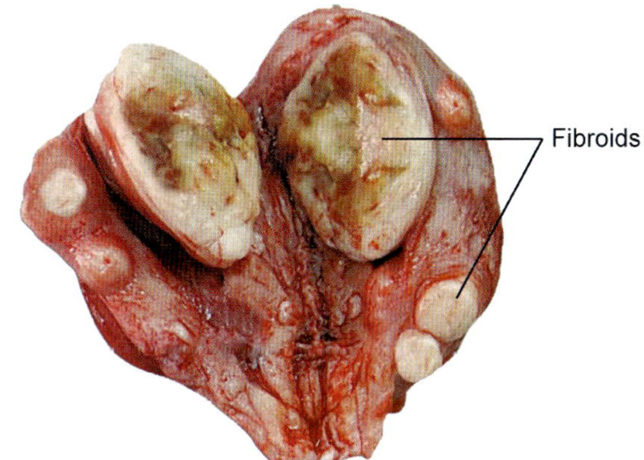

Fig. 31.25: Uterine fibroids

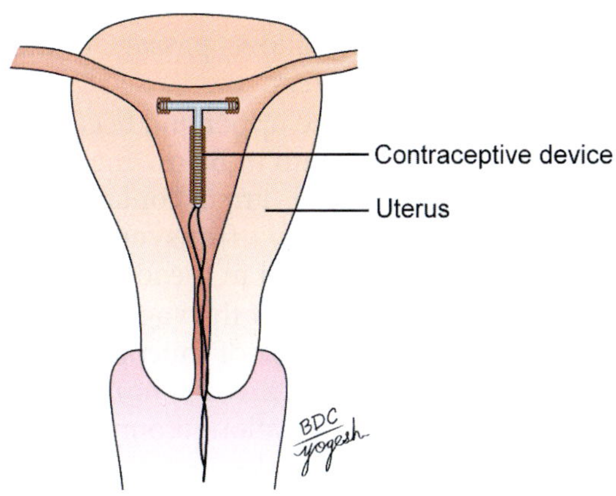

Fig. 31.26: Intrauterine contraceptive device

VAGINA

The vagina is a fibromuscular canal, forming the female copulatory organ. The term 'vagina' means a sheath (Fig. 31.27).

Synonym

Kolpos = Vagina (use of the terms colposcopy, colpotomy and colporrhaphy).

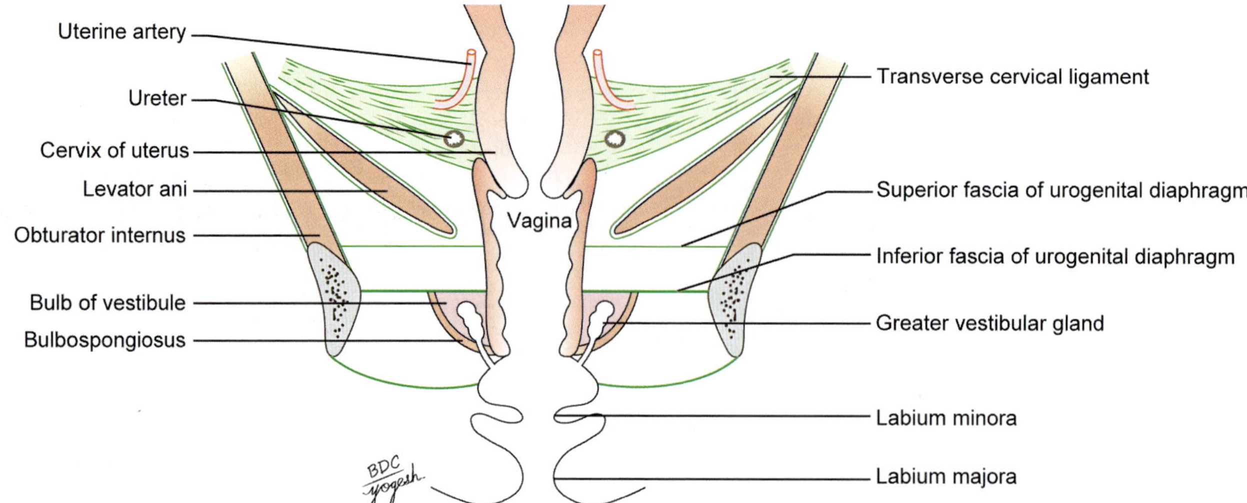

Fig. 31.27: Vagina and some related structures as seen in coronal section

Extent and Situation

The vagina extends from the vulva to the uterus, and is situated behind the bladder and the urethra, and in front of the rectum and anal canal.

Direction

In the erect posture, the vagina is directed upwards and backwards. Long axis of uterus and cervix forms an angle of 90° with long axis of vagina (Figs 31.12a to b).

Size and Shape

1. The anterior wall of the vagina is about 8 cm long and the posterior wall about 10 cm long.
2. The *diameter* of the vagina gradually increases from below upwards. The upper end or vault is roughly 5 cm twice the size of the lower end (2.5 cm). However, it is quite distensible and allows passage of the head of the foetus during delivery.
3. The *lumen* is circular at the upper end because of the protrusion of the cervix into it. Below the cervix, the anterior and posterior walls are in contact with each other, so that the lumen is a transverse slit in the middle part, and is H-shaped in the lower part.
4. In the virgin, the lower end of the vagina is partially closed by a thin annular fold of mucous membrane called the *hymen*. In married women, the hymen is represented by rounded elevations around the vaginal orifice, the *caruncular hymenales*.

Fornices of Vagina

The interior of the upper end of the vagina or vaginal vault is in the form of a circular groove that surrounds the protruding cervix. The groove becomes progressively deeper from before backwards and is arbitrarily divided into four parts called the vaginal fornices.

1. The *anterior fornix* lies in front of the cervix and is the shallowest.
2. The *posterior fornix* lies behind the cervix and is the deepest.
3. The *lateral fornices* lie one on each side of the cervix.

Relations

Anterior Wall

1. Upper half is related to the base of the bladder.
2. Lower half to the urethra (Fig. 31.27).

Posterior Wall

1. Upper 1/4th is separated from the rectum by the rectouterine pouch.
2. Middle 2/4th are separated from the rectum by loose connective tissue.
3. Lower 1/4th is separated from the anal canal by the perineal body and the muscles attached to it.

Lateral Walls

On each side:

1. Upper 1/3rd is related to the transverse cervical ligament of pelvic fascia in which are embedded a network of vaginal veins, and the *ureter gets crossed by the uterine artery.*
2. Middle 1/3rd is related to the pubococcygeus part of the levator ani.
3. Lower 1/3rd pierces the perineal membrane, below which it is related to the bulb of the vestibule, the bulbospongiosus and the duct of greater vestibular gland of Bartholin.

Arterial Supply

The vagina is a very vascular organ, and is supplied by the following arteries.

1. The main artery supplying it is the vaginal branch of the internal iliac artery.
2. In addition, the upper part is supplied by the cervico-vaginal branch of the uterine artery.

The lower part is supplied by the middle rectal and internal pudendal arteries.

Branches of these arteries anastomose to form anterior and posterior midline vessels called the ***vaginal azygos arteries***.

Venous Drainage

The rich vaginal venous plexus drains into the internal iliac veins through the vaginal veins which accompany the vaginal arteries.

Lymphatic Drainage

Lymphatics from the upper one-third of the vagina drain into the external iliac nodes; from the middle one-third into the internal iliac nodes; and from the lower 1/3rd into the medial group of superficial inguinal nodes.

Nerve Supply

1. The lower 1/3rd of the vagina is pain sensitive and is supplied by the pudendal nerve through the inferior rectal and posterior labial branches of the perineal nerve.
2. The upper 2/3rd of the vagina are pain insensitive and are supplied by sympathetic L1, 2 and parasympathetic segments S2–S4. Nerves are derived from the inferior hypogastric and uterovaginal plexuses. Sympathetic nerves are vasoconstrictor and parasympathetic nerves are vasodilator. The fibres, which accompany the vaginal arteries form the vaginal nerves.

Competency:

AN52.2 Describe and identify the microanatomical features of vagina.

Histology of Vagina

The vagina has three layers: Mucosa, muscle layer, and adventitia (Plate 31.10).

1. *Mucosa*: It shows numerous longitudinal folds lined with non-keratinized stratified squamous epithelium resting on highly vascular lamina propria.
2. *Muscular layer*: It consists of smooth muscle fibres arranged as inner circular and outer longitudinal layers. Muscle layer also contains many elastic fibres.
3. *Adventitia*: The vagina is surrounded by adventitia that is made up of connective tissue and blood vessels.

Note: There are no glands in the vaginal mucosa. It is kept moist by the cervical glands from above and the greater vestibular glands from below. The vaginal fluid is acidic in nature because of the fermentation of glycogen (in vaginal cells) by the Doderlein's bacilli.

Plate 31.10: Histology of vagina

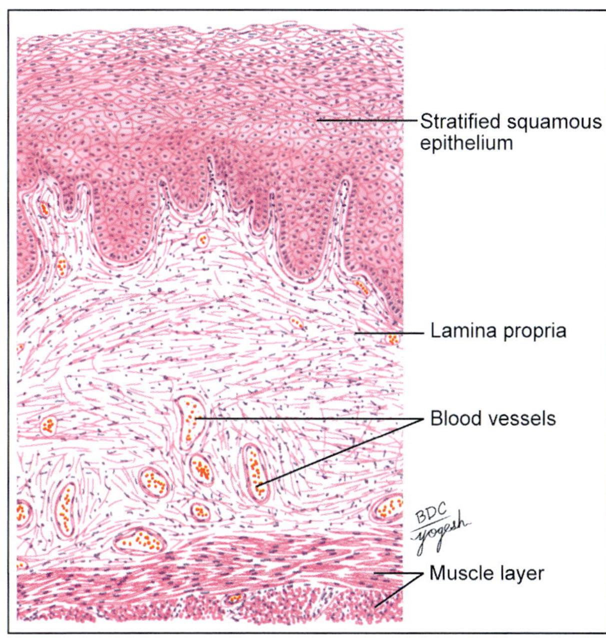

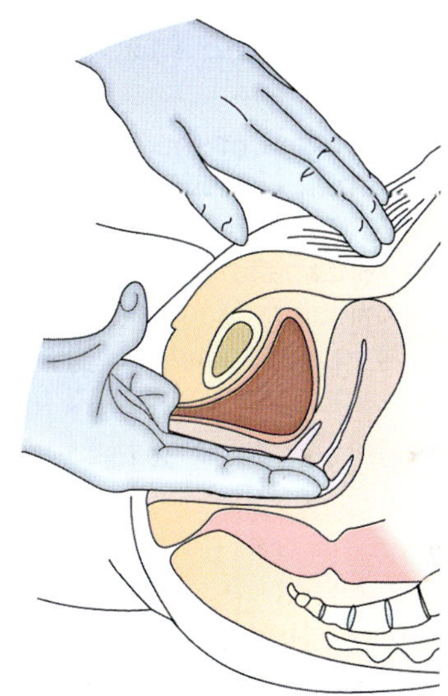

Fig. 31.28: Bimanual examination of the female internal genital organs

CLINICAL ANATOMY

- ***Vaginal examination***
  a. *Inspection:* Vagina is first inspected at the introitus by separating the labia minora with the left hand. Next the speculum examination is done to inspect the cervix and vaginal vault, and to take the vaginal swab.
  b. *Palpation* of the pelvic organs can be done by a per vaginal (PV) digital examination (Fig. 31.28). With the examining fingers, one can feel:
     - *Anteriorly,* the urethra, bladder and pubic symphysis;
     - *Posteriorly,* the rectum and pouch of Douglas;
     - *Laterally,* the ovary, tube, lateral pelvic wall, thickened ligaments, and ureters; and
     - *Superiorly,* the cervix.

  Bimanual (abdominovaginal) examination helps in the assessment of the size and position of the uterus, enlargements of the ovaries and tubes, and the other pelvic masses (Fig. 31.28).
- ***Vaginal lacerations***: Traumatic lacerations of vagina are common, and may be caused by forcible coitus (rape), during childbirth, or by accidents. This may give rise to profuse bleeding.
- Hymen is examined in medicolegal cases to confirm virginity.
- ***Vaginitis***: It is common before puberty and after menopause because of the thin delicate epithelium.

In adults, the resistant squamous epithelium prevents the infection. Vaginitis is commonly caused by the trichomonal, monilial and gonococcal infections. It causes leucorrhoea or white discharge.

- ***Culdocentesis*** is a clinical procedure of fluid extraction from the pouch of Douglas through a needle inserted through the vaginal wall just below the uterus. This area is called the cul-de-sac. It is also useful to obtain oocytes for *in vitro* fertilization.
- ***Colpotomy*** is a procedure by which an incision is made in the posterior fornix of the vagina to visualise the structures or to drain the pus from the pouch of Douglas.
- ***Colporrhaphy*** is a surgical repair of a defect in the wall of vagina.
- ***Prolapse***: Prolapse of the anterior wall of vagina drags the bladder (cystocoele) and urethra (urethrocoele); the posterior wall drags the rectum (rectocoele). Weakness of supports of uterus can give rise to different degrees of prolapse.

  Similarly, trauma to the anterior and posterior walls of vagina can cause the vesicovaginal, urethrovaginal and rectovaginal fistulae.
- ***Neoplasms***: Primary new growths of vagina, like the infections, are uncommon. However, secondary involvement of vagina by the cancer cervix is very common.
- ***Episiotomy*** is an incision in perineum made to enlarge the vaginal orifice to facilitate the passage of fetus during childbirth. Median episiotomy involves the incision through frenulum of labia minora to the external anal sphincter, including perineal body. Lateral episiotomy incision is more preferred as it saves the perineal body.

Video 2.31 **Female Reproductive System**

Facts to Remember

- Cervix is the least movable part of uterus.
- Main ligamentous support of uterus is the transverse cervical ligament.
- Site of implantation of the blastocyst is posterior wall of fundus of uterus, close to its body.
- Uterine artery crosses ureter from lateral to medial side anteriorly to run tortuously along lateral surface of uterus.
- Broad ligament has four parts: infundibulopelvic ligament, mesovarium, mesosalpinx, and mesometrium.
- Round ligament is 10–12 cm long with one end attached to uterine cornua and other to anterior third of labia majora.
- Transverse cervical ligaments (of Mackenrodt) is the most important ligamentous support of the uterus. Before PV examination, the urinary bladder must be emptied.
- Caesarean section is the delivery of the baby by cutting open the anterior abdominal wall and the uterus.

BDC's Anatomy *e*-book

1. Structures under cover of the trapezius
2. Course and relations of fallopian tubes
3. Molecular regulation
4. Ureter in female pelvis
5. Genital ducts
6. Comparison between the derivatives of female and male urogenital structures
7. Intrinsic circulation of the uterus
8. Further reading
9. Viva voce questions

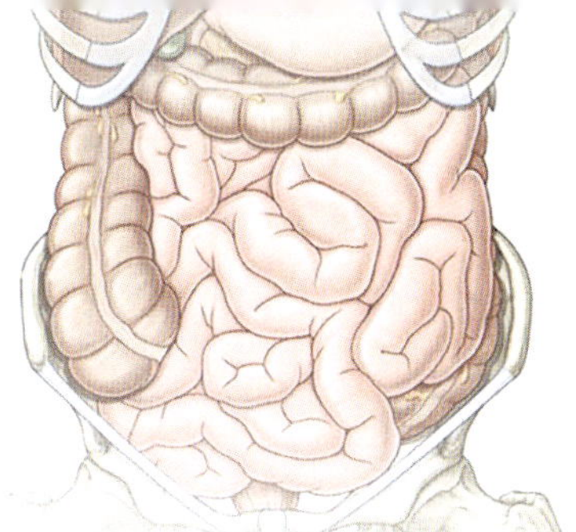

Chapter

32

Male Internal Genital Organs

The male reproductive organs include the external and internal genitalia (Plate 32.1).

Male external genitalia: It includes:

1. Penis
2. Scrotum – containing testis, epididymis and part of ductus deferens.

Male internal genitalia: It includes (on each side)

1. Part of ductus deferens
2. Seminal vesicle
3. Ejaculatory ducts
4. A prostate gland
5. Bulbourethral glands.

The external genitalia have been described in Chapter 17, and the male urethra in Chapter 30. The remaining structures are considered below.

Competency:

AN48.2 Describe and demonstrate the position, features, important peritoneal and other relations, blood supply, nerve supply, lymphatic drainage and clinical aspects of important male pelvic viscera.

Plate 32.1: Male reproductive organs (midsagittal section through the male pelvic cavity viewed from the left)

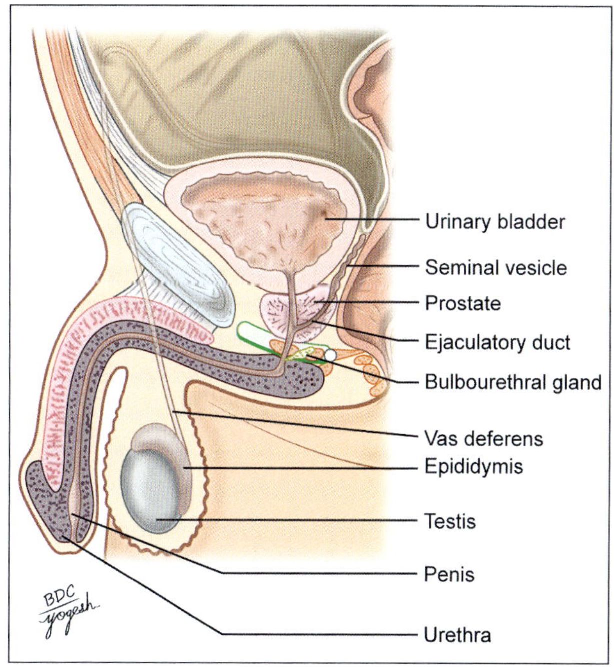

DUCTUS DEFERENS

The ductus deferens is a thick-walled, muscular tube, which transmits spermatozoa from the epididymis to the ejaculatory duct (Fig. 32.1). It feels cord-like at the upper lateral part of scrotum. Ductus deferens has a narrow lumen except at the terminal dilated part called the ampulla.

Synonyms

The *ductus deferens* is also called the *vas deferens* or the *deferent duct*.

Length

The ductus deferens is about 45 cm long when straightened.

Location and Course

In its course, the vas lies successively (Fig. 32.1):

1. Within the scrotum along the posterior border of the testis.

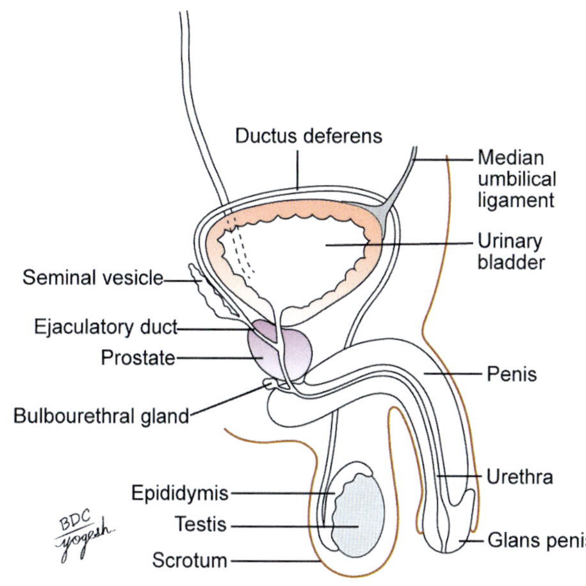

Fig. 32.1: Course of ductus deferens

2. In the inguinal canal as part of the spermatic cord
3. In the greater pelvis
4. In the lesser pelvis.

Course and Relations

The ductus deferens begins as a continuation of the tail of the epididymis (Figs 32.1 and 32.2).

External Course of Vas Deferens

1. ***Along the posterior border of the testis:*** At first, it is very tortuous, but gradually straightens as it ascends along the posterior border of the testis, medial to the epididymis.
2. ***In the spermatic cord:*** The ductus deferens lies vertically in posterior part of spermatic cord. It runs upwards to the superficial inguinal ring, and then traverses the inguinal canal. In the vertical part of its course, it can be felt as a cord-like structure within the spermatic cord.

Internal Course of Vas Deferens

1. ***In the greater pelvis:*** At the deep inguinal ring, it leaves the spermatic cord, and hooks round the lateral side of the inferior epigastric artery. It then passes backwards and medially, across the external iliac vessels, and enters the lesser pelvis.
2. ***In the lesser pelvis:*** The ductus deferens runs downwards and backwards on the lateral pelvic wall, deep to the peritoneum. Here it crosses the obliterated umbilical artery, the obturator nerve and vessels and the vesical vessels. It then crosses the ureter and bends medially at right angles, to enter the sacrogenital fold of peritoneum. Reaching the base of the urinary bladder, the ductus runs downwards and forwards medial to the seminal vesicle. Here it approaches the opposite duct and reaches the base of the prostate.
3. At the base of the prostate, the ductus deferens is joined at an acute angle by the ***duct of the seminal vesicle*** to form the ***ejaculatory duct***.
4. The part of the ductus lying behind the base of the bladder, is dilated and tortuous, and is known as the ***ampulla***.

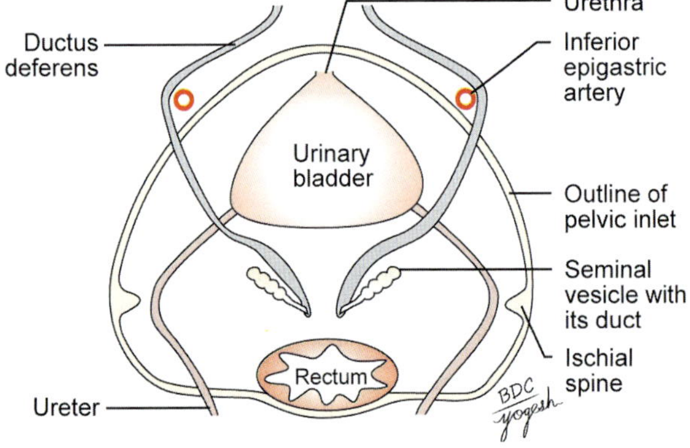

Fig. 32.2: Schematic diagram to show the course of the ductus deferens

Arterial Supply

It receives branches from:
1. Superior vesical artery
2. Inferior vesical artery
3. Middle rectal artery.

Venous Drainage

Veins from the ductus join the vesical venous plexus, which opens into the internal iliac vein.

Competency:
AN52.2 Describe and identify the microanatomical features of vas deferens.

Histology of Ductus Deferens

Vas deferens is a thick-walled muscular tube (star-shaped lumen) having three layers (Plate 32.2):
1. Mucosa: Lined by pseudostratified columnar epithelium with stereocilia.
2. Smooth muscle coat arranged as inner and outer longitudinal and middle thick circular layers.
3. Adventitia consists of loose areolar tissue.

Development of Ductus Deferens

Ductus deferens develops from the mesonephric duct.

Competency:
AN48.5 Explain the anatomical basis of suprapubic cystostomy, urinary obstruction in benign prostatic hypertrophy, retroverted uterus, prolapse uterus, internal and external haemorrhoids, anal fistula, tubal pregnancy and tubal ligation.

CLINICAL ANATOMY

- ***Vasectomy*** or removing part of the vas deferens is one of the commonest operations being done for purposes of family planning. It is a minor operation, which is done under local anaesthesia. A median incision is made in the upper part of the scrotum, just below the penis. Through this incision, both the ductus deferens are operated. A short segment of each duct is excised, and the cut ends are ligated. The operation is reversible, and recanalisation can be done, if required (Fig. 32.3).
- After vasectomy, the testes continue to produce the hormones normally to maintain the male characteristics. The hormones pass out through the veins. Sperms are present in the ejaculations after vasectomy for 2–3 months as it is an emptying process. Newly formed sperms are destroyed in the epididymis and are removed by phagocytosis.

Competency:
AN52.8 Describe the development of vas deferens.

DISSECTION

The ductus deferens has been seen till the deep inguinal ring in the anterior abdominal wall (Fig. 32.1). Follow it from there as it hooks round the lateral side of inferior

Plate 32.2: Histology of ductus deferens

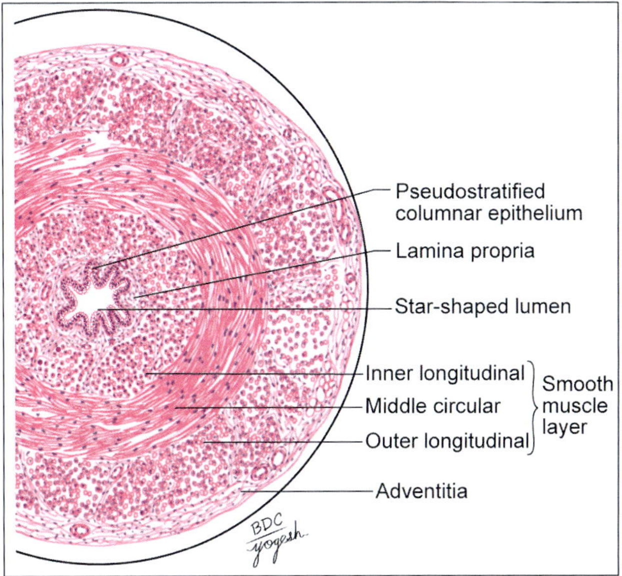

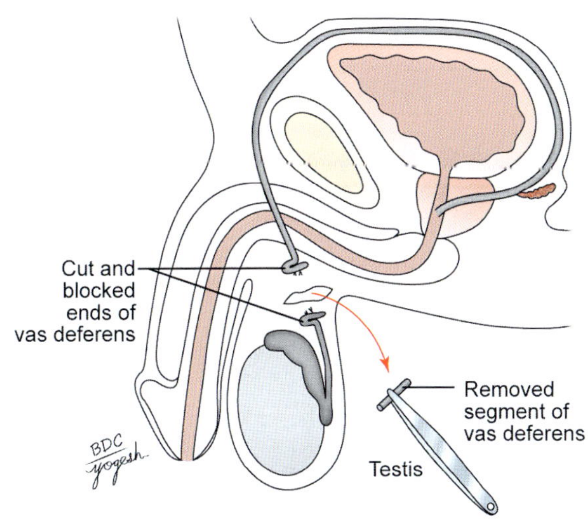

Fig. 32.3: Vasectomy

epigastric artery to pass backwards and medially across the external iliac vessels to enter into the lesser pelvis. There it crosses the ureter and lies on the posterior surface of urinary bladder medial to the seminal vesicle (Fig. 32.2). Separate the ductus from the adjacent seminal vesicle and trace these till the base of the prostate gland.

Follow the deep dorsal vein of the penis and its two divisions into the prostatic venous plexus situated in the angle between the bladder and the prostate.

Feel the thickened puboprostatic ligaments. Feel the firm prostate lying just at the neck of the urinary bladder.

Identify the levator prostatae muscle lying inferolateral to the prostate. This is identifiable by pulling both the bladder and prostate medially. The first part of urethra traverses the prostate. Cut through the anterior one-third of the gland to expose the prostatic urethra.

PROSTATE

The prostate is an accessory gland of the male reproductive system. It is a globular fibromuscular gland that surrounds the proximal part of male urethra (Flowchart 32.1).

Note: In the female, the prostate is represented by the paraurethral glands of Skene.

Functions

1. *Prostatic fluid* forms major part of semen (10–30%).
2. Prostatic alveoli secrete prostatic fluid that contains prostatic acid phosphatase (PAP), fibrinolysin, citric acid, and prostate-specific antigen (PSA).
3. Prostatic secretions are pumped by contractions of smooth muscles that lie in fibromuscular stroma.
4. Prostatic fibrinolysin helps in liquefaction of semen.

Situation

The prostate lies in the lesser (true) pelvis, below the neck of the urinary bladder, behind the lower part of the pubic symphysis and the upper part of the pubic arch. It lies in front of the ampulla of the rectum (Figs 32.4 and 32.5).

Shape, Size and Weight

It resembles an inverted cone shaped.

Measurements

- *Width* (at base): 4 cm transversely
- *Anteroposterior* (thickness): 2 cm
- *Vertical* (length): 3 cm
- *Weight* in youth: 8 g.

External Feature

The prostate gland has the following features:
1. Base
2. Apex
3. Four surfaces: Anterior, posterior, two inferolateral.

Base

The *base* is directed upwards, and is structurally continuous with the neck of the bladder.

Note: The junction is marked by a circular groove, which lodges venules of the vesical and prostatic plexuses.

Apex

The *apex* is directed downwards surrounds the junction of prostatic and membranous parts of posterior urethra. It is separated from the anal canal by the perineal body.

Surfaces

Anterior surface: It is narrow and convex from side-to-side. It lies 2 cm behind the pubic symphysis, with retropubic fat intervening. Its upper part is connected to the pubic bones by the puboprostatic ligaments. The lower end of this surface is pierced by the urethra. The lower end of urethra emerges from this surface anterosuperior to the apex of gland. This surface is composed of fibrous tissue.

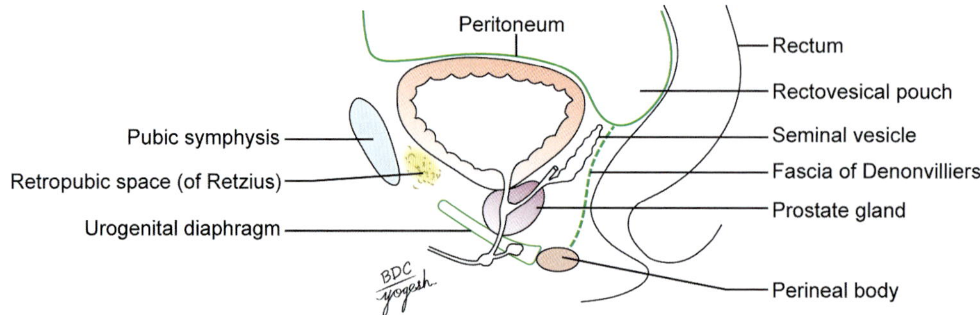

Fig. 32.4: Location of prostate gland (midsagittal section)

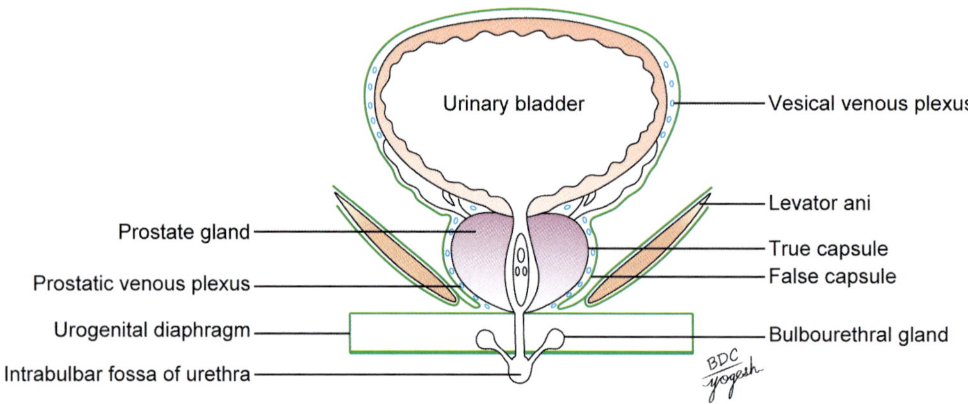

Fig. 32.5: Location of prostate and related structures (coronal section of the male pelvis)

Flowchart 32.1: Prostate gland

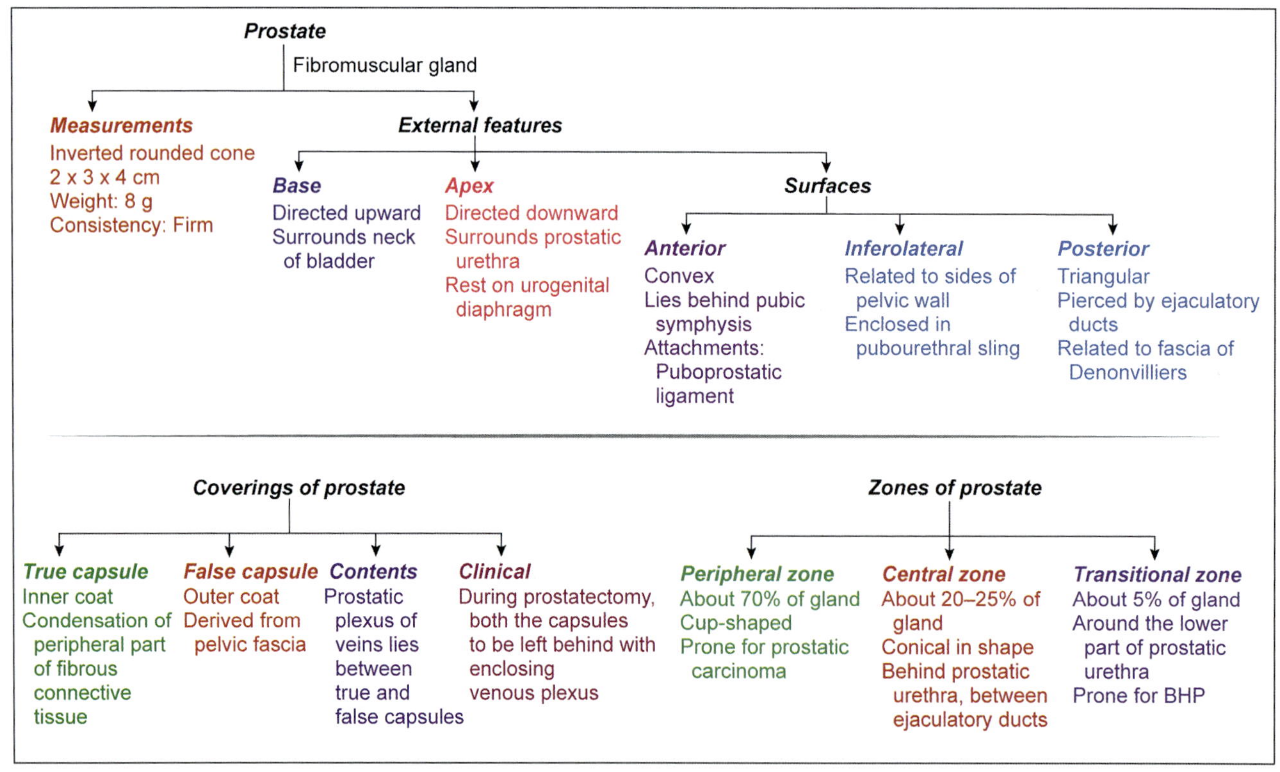

Posterior surface: It is triangular in shape. It is flattened from side-to-side and convex from above downwards. It is separated from the rectum by the *fascia of Denonvilliers* which is the obliterated rectovesical pouch of peritoneum. Near its upper border, it is pierced on each side of the median plane by the ejaculatory duct. This surface lies 4 cm from the anus, and can be easily palpated on digital examination through the rectum (Fig. 32.6, Plate 32.3).

Plate 32.3: Relations of the prostate gland and urinary bladder in the male (posterior view of urinary bladder, male)

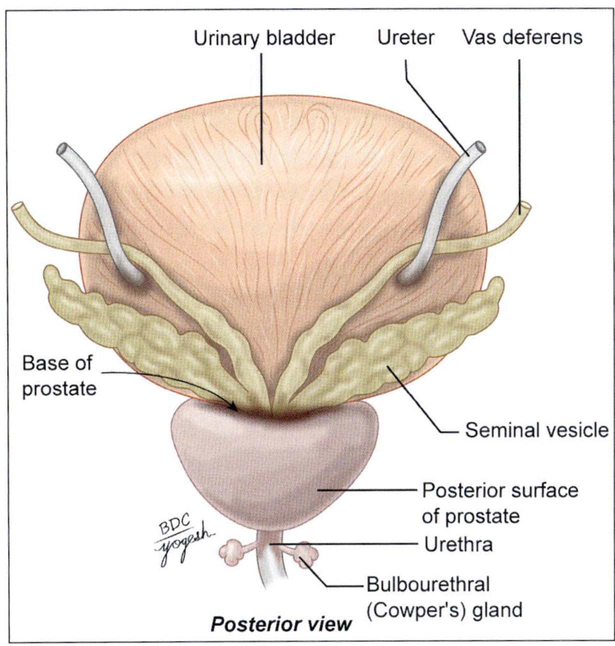

Inferolateral surfaces: These are related to the side walls of pelvis. The anterior fibres of the levator ani enclose the gland in pubourethral sling. They are separated from the muscle by a plexus of veins embedded in its sheath (Fig. 32.6).

Sphincters Related to Prostate

1. In the preprostatic part of urethra, there is internal urethral sphincter mechanism that subserves sexual function of closing during ejaculation. If this sphincter gets resected, retrograde ejaculation occurs.
2. Distal urethral sphincter mechanism is seen at the junction of prostatic and membranous parts of urethra. It is horseshoe shaped, with most of the bulk lying anteriorly. It is distinct from muscle of pelvic floor.

Lobes

The *foetal prostate* up to 20 weeks of gestation: It shows 5 lobes: Median, anterior, posterior and two lateral.

The prostate after 20 weeks gestation and throughout the life shows three lobes: Median and two lateral lobes as follows (Figs 32.7 and 32.8):

1. *Median lobe* is a wedge-shaped lobe with the apex directed downwards. Median lobe is bounded in front by urethra and on each side by ejaculatory ducts.
2. *Two lateral lobes* cover the sides of urethra and anteriorly connected with each other by median fibromuscular stroma or isthmus.

Capsules of Prostate

The prostate is covered by inner true capsule and outer false capsule (Fig. 32.9)

1. ***True capsule:*** It is formed by condensation of the peripheral part of the gland. It is fibromuscular in structure and is continuous with stroma of the gland. The venous plexus lies between true and false capsules.
2. ***False capsule:*** It lies outside the true capsule and is derived from the endopelvic fascia.

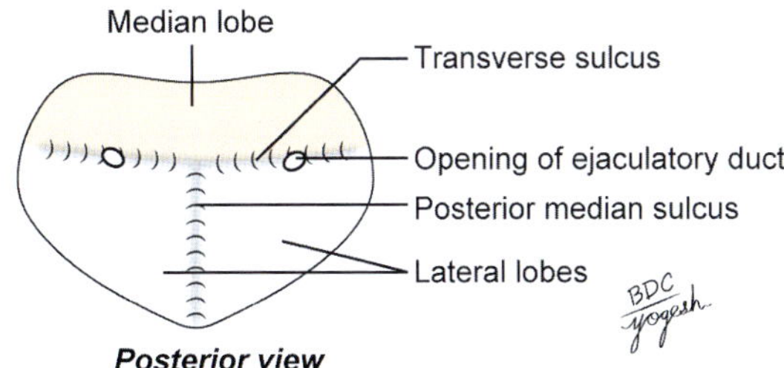

Fig. 32.6: Features of the posterior surface of the prostate

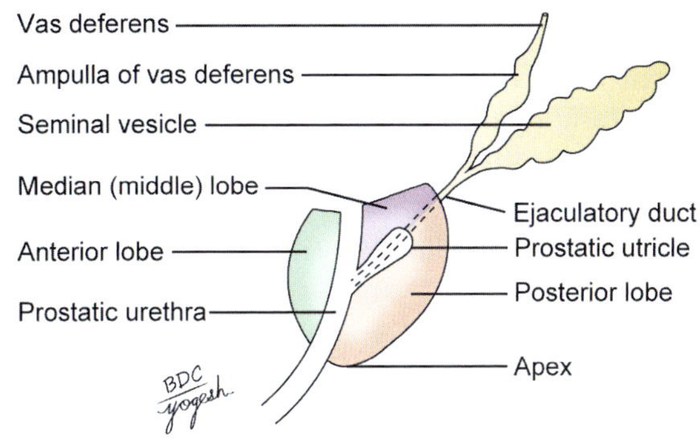

Fig. 32.7: Lobes of the prostate gland (left view of a sagittal section)

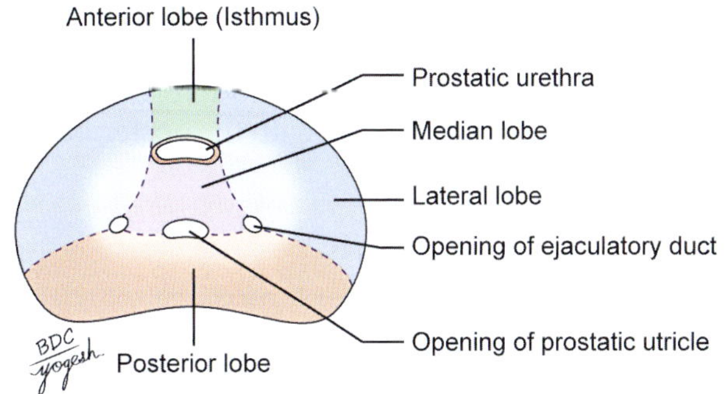

Fig. 32.8: Lobes of the prostate gland (transverse section)

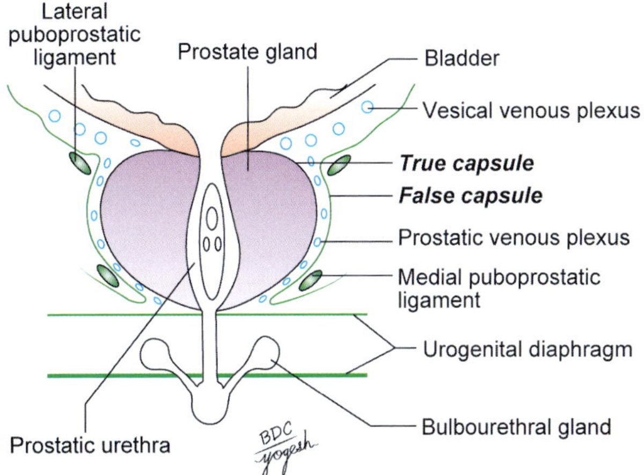

Fig. 32.9: Capsules, ligaments and venous plexus of the prostate gland

Anteriorly, it is continuous with the puboprostatic ligaments. On each side, the prostatic venous plexus is embedded in between false and true capsules.

Posteriorly, it is avascular, and is formed by the rectovesical fascia of Denonvilliers.

Note: ***Surgical or pathological capsule*:** The enlarged adenoma of the gland compresses the peripheral part of the gland. This compressed part of the gland is called surgical or pathological capsule.

Ligaments of Prostate

A pair of medial puboprostatic and a pair of lateral puboprostatic ligaments extend from the false capsule to the back of pubic bone. The medial pair lies near the apex while lateral pair is close to the base. These four ligaments support the gland (Fig. 32.9).

Supports of the Prostate

The prostate is supported by (Fig. 32.9):

1. Urogenital diaphragm
2. Four puboprostatic ligaments: Two medial and two lateral
3. Rectovesical fascia of Denonvilliers.

Structures within the Prostate

1. *Prostatic urethra* traverses the gland vertically at the junction of its anterior 1/3rd with the posterior 2/3rd (Fig. 32.12).

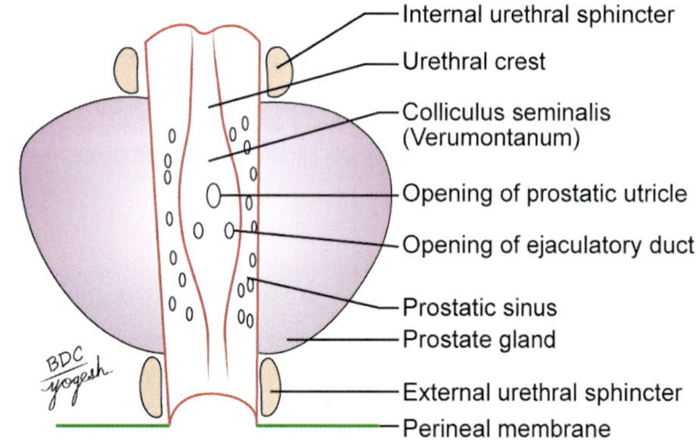

Fig. 32.10: Features of the posterior wall of the prostatic urethra (anterior view, coronal section)

2. *Prostatic utricle* is a blind sac directed upwards and backwards. It opens at the middle of the urethral crest.
3. *Ejaculatory ducts* pass downwards and forwards, and open into the prostatic urethra on each side of the opening of the prostatic utricle (Fig. 32.10).

Zones of the Prostate

According to McNeal, the gland is divided into (Fig. 32.11):

1. **Peripheral zone** forms 70% of glandular tissue. It is situated posteriorly and is cancer vulnerable.
2. **Central zone** constitutes 25% of glandular tissue situated posterior to urethral lumen and above the ejaculatory ducts. The two zones are like an egg in its egg-cup. The central zone is not involved in disease and is of wolffian duct origin.
3. **Periurethral transition zone** (5%) from which benign prostatic hyperplasia arises. The central zone and transition zone constitute 'central gland'.

The space between the peripheral zones, anterior to the prostatic urethra, is filled by non-glandular fibromuscular stroma. This stroma includes smooth muscle fibres of urethral sphincter.

Arterial Supply

The prostate is supplied by branches from the inferior vesical, middle rectal and internal pudendal arteries. Branches of these arteries form a large outer or *subcapsular plexus*, and a small inner or *periurethral plexus*. The greater part of the gland is supplied by the subcapsular plexus.

Venous Drainage

The *veins* form a rich ***plexus*** around the sides and base of the gland. The plexus communicates with the vesical plexus and with the internal pudendal vein, and drains into the vesical and internal iliac veins.

Note: Valveless communications exist between the prostatic and vertebral venous plexuses through which prostatic carcinoma can spread to the vertebral column and to the skull (Fig. 32.12).

Lymphatic Drainage

Lymphatics from the prostate drain chiefly into the internal iliac and sacral nodes; and partly into the external iliac nodes.

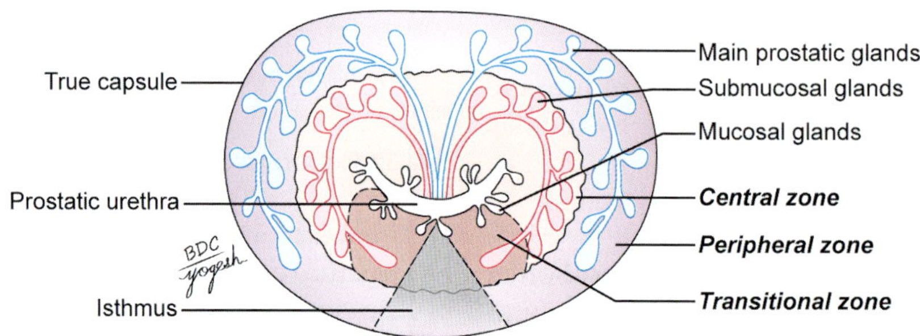

Fig. 32.11: Horizontal section through the prostate gland showing the histological zones and the glands in them

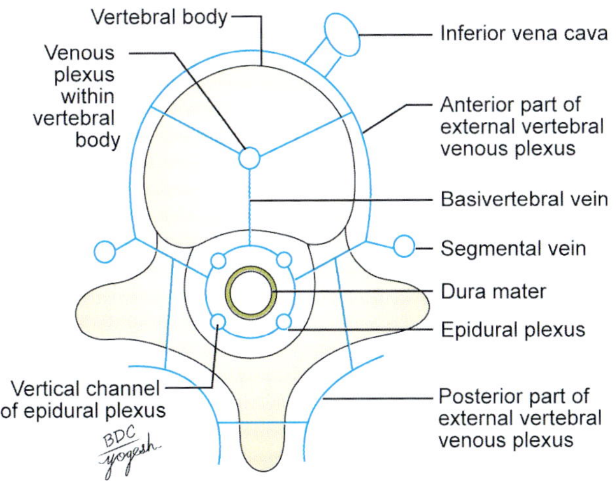

Fig. 32.12: The vertebral system of veins

Flowchart 32.2: Age changes in prostate

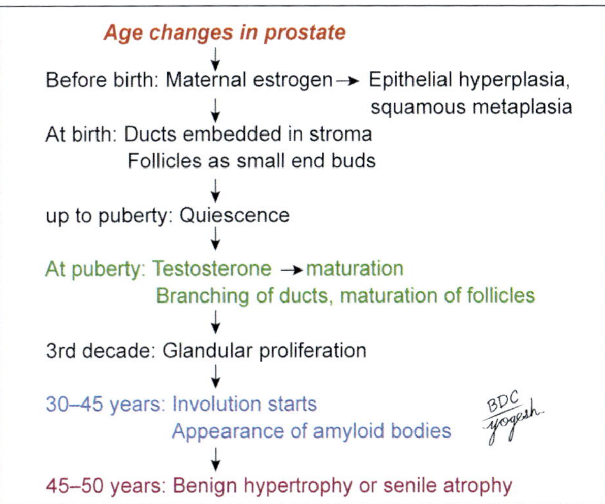

Nerve Supply

The prostate is supplied by prostatic plexus of nerves that is contributed by:

1. Numerous nerve fibres and ganglia located in prostatic capsule.
2. Fibres from inferior hypogastric plexus.

Sympathetic fibres from L1 and L2 spinal segments and *parasympathetic fibres* from S2, S3 and S4 spinal segments. This plexus supplies autonomic fibres to prostate urethra, ejaculatory ducts, corpora cavernosa, corpus spongiosum, membranous and penile urethra and bulbourethral glands.

Note: The prostate gland contains numerous end-organs, impulses from which are relayed to the L3–L5 and S2–S4 spinal segments. Secretions of the prostate are produced and discharged after stimulation of both the parasympathetic and sympathetic nerves.

Age Changes in Prostate

The age-related changes are as follows (Flowchart 32.2):

1. ***Before birth***: Under the influence of maternal oestrogen, the prostate shows epithelial hyperplasia and squamous metaplasia.
2. ***At birth***: The prostate is small in size, and is made up mainly of stroma in which a simple duct system is embedded. During the first 6 weeks after birth, the epithelium of the ducts and of the prostatic utricle undergoes hyperplasia and squamous metaplasia, under the stimulation of maternal oestrogens. Thereafter, up to the age of 9 years, changes are negligible. Between 9 and 14 years, the duct system becomes more elaborate by formation of side buds, and the gland slowly increases in size.
3. ***At puberty***: The male hormones bring about rapid changes in the gland. In about one year, it becomes double its prepubertal size due to rapid growth of the follicles and condensation and reduction of the stroma.
4. ***From 20 to 30 years***: There is marked proliferation of the glandular elements with infolding of the glandular epithelium into the lumen of the follicles, making them irregular.
5. ***From 30 to 45 years***: The size of the prostate remains constant, and involution starts. The epithelial infoldings gradually disappear and amyloid bodies increase in number.
6. ***After 45 to 50 years***: The prostate is either enlarged called the benign hypertrophy or reduced in size called the senile atrophy or undergo malignant changes.

Competency:

AN52.2 Describe and identify the microanatomical features of prostate.

Histology of Prostate

1. The prostate consists of 30–50 tubuloalveolar glands embedded in fibromuscular stroma (Plate 32.4).
2. Glandular epithelium: Simple columnar to pseudostratified columnar epithelium.
3. Ducts are lined by simple columnar or stratified columnar epithelium (opens into prostatic urethra).
4. Fibromuscular stroma: Contains smooth muscles, collagen fibres, elastic fibres, blood vessels and lymphatics.
5. Corpora amylacea are concentric lamellated eosinophilic structures that lie in prostatic alveoli in old age.

Development of Prostate

Prostate develops from the following sources (Fig. 32.13):

1. Outer glandular zone: It develops from buds arising from prostatic urethra (endodermal in origin).
2. Inner glandular zone: It develops from buds arising from mesodermal posterior wall of urethra above the openings of ejaculatory ducts. There are total five buds arising from the prostatic urethra, namely one anterior, two posterior and two lateral.
3. Muscle, connective tissue, and capsule: They develop from surrounding mesoderm of urethra.
4. Prostatic utricle develops in the region of Müllerian tubercle similar to vagina in females. The central zone of glandular tissue is of wolffian duct system.

Plate 32.4: Histology of prostate gland

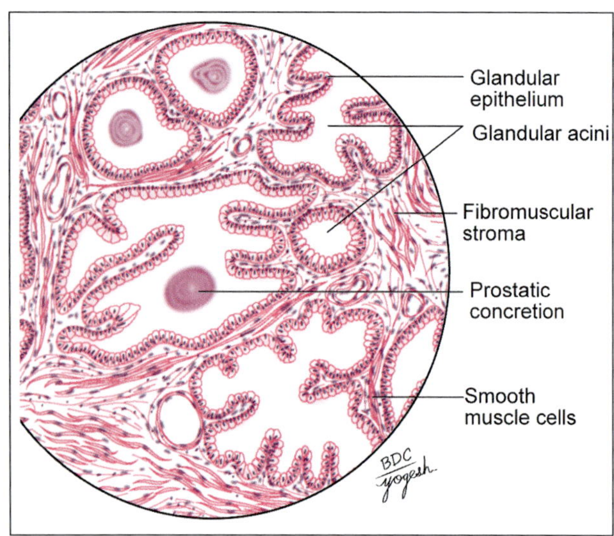

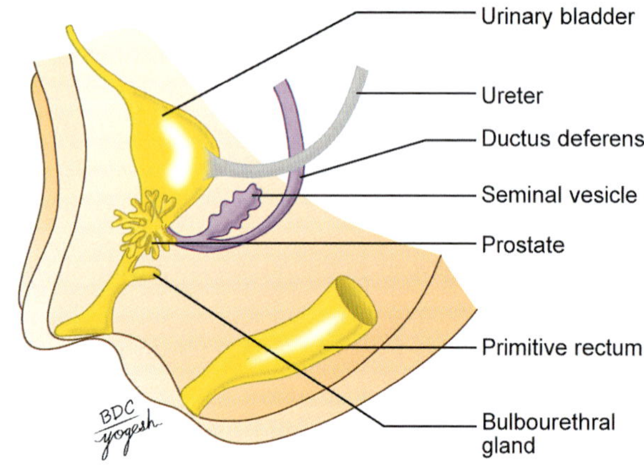

Fig. 32.13: Development of seminal vesicle, prostate and bulbourethral gland

Competency:

AN48.7 Mention the lobes involved in benign prostatic hypertrophy and prostatic cancer.

CLINICAL ANATOMY

- ***Senile enlargement of prostate***: After 50 years of age, the prostate is often enlarged due to ***benign hypertrophy of prostate (BHP)*** or due to the formation of an adenoma. This causes retention of urine due to distortion of the urethra. Enlargement of the median lobe not only projects into bladder, but forms a sort of valve over the internal urethral orifice, so that more patient strains, more it obstructs the passage. Urine passes when the patient relaxes. (Fig. 32.17)
- Benign prostatic hyperplasia occurs in periurethral zone. Carcinoma of prostate occurs in peripheral zone (Fig. 32.14).
- Digital examination of the rectum is very helpful in the diagnosis of an enlarged prostate (Fig. 32.15).
- If symptoms are mild, BPH can be treated with medicines (selective α_1 blockers, 5α-reductase inhibitors)
- Surgical removal of a prostate called ***prostatectomy.*** It relieves the urinary obstruction in BHP. During removal, the enlarged gland is enucleated, leaving behind both the capsules and venous plexus between them.
- The prostate can be removed through bladder (transvesical), through prostatic capsule (retropubic), or through perineum and fascia of Denonvilliers (perineal approach) or through urethra (TUR—***transurethral resection***).
- Inflammation of the prostate is referred to as ***prostatitis***. It may be acute or chronic.
- The prostate is a common site of ***carcinoma***. It usually occurs after the age of 50–55 years.
- Rectal examination reveals an irregular hard and fixed prostate. Metastatic spread occurs to the vertebral column through the valveless connections between the prostatic and vertebral venous plexuses.
- *Prostate-specific antigen* (*PSA*)/*kallikrein-3* is a glycoprotein enzyme secreted by prostatic epithelium. In prostatic cancers, PSA level increases significantly.

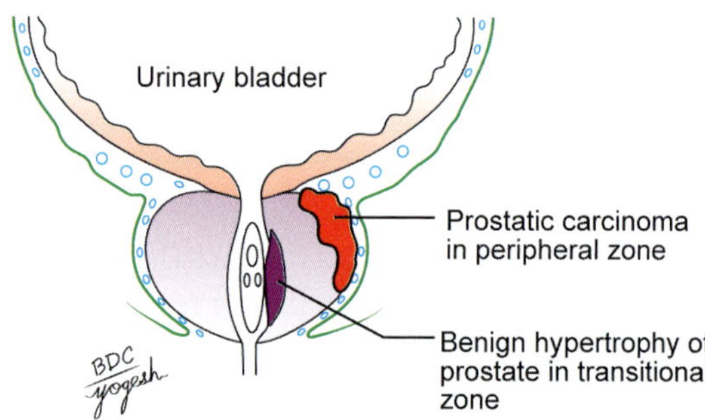

Fig. 32.14: Zonal preponderance of diseases in the prostate gland

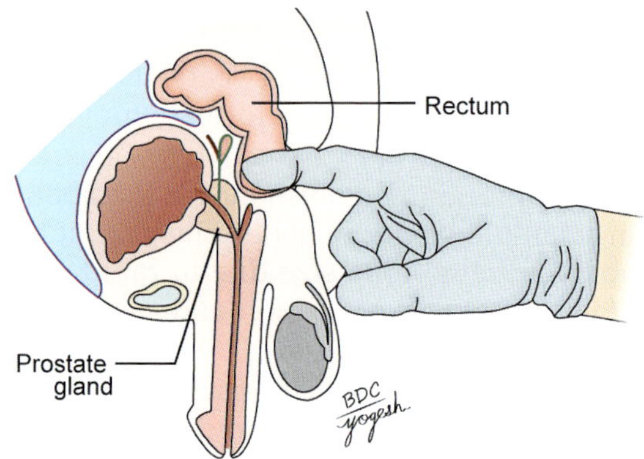

Fig. 32.15: Per rectal (PR) examination for prostate gland

SEMINAL VESICLES

Seminal vesicles are two lobulated sacs situated between the base of urinary bladder and rectum.

Measurements

- Length: 5 cm
- Diameter: 3 cm
- Volume: 13 ml.

Features

Each seminal vesicle is a coiled tube with irregular diverticula. This tube is surrounded by dense fibromuscular sheath. Each seminal vesicle has two ends:

- *Upper pole* is cul-de-sac
- *Lower pole* is narrow and joins with ductus deferens to form the ejaculatory duct.

Blood Supply

It is supplied by vesiculodeferential artery (a branch of umbilical artery) and inferior vesical artery (a branch of internal iliac artery).

Nerve Supply

It is supplied by preganglionic parasympathetic fibres from pelvic splanchnic nerves, and sympathetic fibres from hypogastric plexus.

Functions

Seminal vesicles are not the reservoir of the sperms. They secrete ***seminal fluid***. It is rich in ***fructose*** (main energy source for sperms) and prostaglandins. Seminal fluid is alkaline in nature that helps to neutralize vaginal secretions. Seminal fluid contains lipochrome pigments that impart yellowish color to semen.

EJACULATORY DUCT

There are two ejaculatory ducts, one on each side. Each ejaculatory duct is about 2 cm long, and formed by fusion of terminal part of vas deferens with the duct of seminal vesicle.

The ejaculatory ducts pass downwards and medially through the prostate towards prostatic urethra. These ducts open into the prostatic urethra at the verumontanum.

BULBOURETHRAL GLANDS (COWPER'S GLAND)

These are pairs of small, round, yellow, lobulated glands. They are situated in the deep perineal pouch, one on each side of membranous urethra.

Size: 1 cm in diameter.

The ducts of bulbourethral glands are 3 cm long. They pierce the perineal membrane and open into the intrabulbar fossa of the spongy urethra. These are tubuloalveolar glands. They secrete neutral mucus into the urethra prior ejaculation (lubricating function). It comprises 5–10% of total ejaculate volume.

PERIURETHRAL GLANDS

These are *glands of Littre*. These are numerous in penile urethra. They secrete mucous into the urethra prior to the ejaculation.

Video 2.32 Male Reproductive System.

Facts to Remember

- Prostate comprises three lobes: One median, and two lateral.
- Benign hypertrophy of prostate occurs in the median lobe; carcinoma occurs in the peripheral zone of prostate.
- Per-rectal examination is an important examination to judge the prostate, or anal canal pathology.
- Prostatic adenoma is enucleated, both the capsules are left behind in the patient.
- Cancer of prostate may metastasise to distant parts through vertebral venous plexus.
- Most common approach to remove adenoma of prostate is transurethral resection.

BDC's Anatomy *e*-book

1. Vertebral system of veins (Batson's plexus)
2. Further reading
3. Viva voce questions

Chapter

33

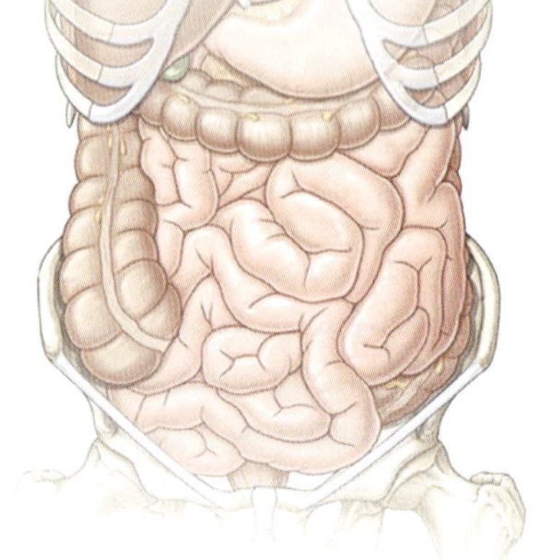

Rectum and Anal Canal

RECTUM

The rectum is the distal part of the large gut. It is placed between the sigmoid colon above and the anal canal below. Distension of the rectum causes the desire to defaecate (Plate 33.1, Fig. 33.1, Flowchart 33.1).

The rectum in man is not straight as the name implies. In fact it is curved in an anteroposterior direction and also from side-to-side. The three cardinal features of the large intestine, e.g. sacculations, appendices epiploicae and taeniae, are absent in the rectum.

Location

The rectum is situated in the posterior part of the lesser pelvis, in front of the lower three pieces of the sacrum and the coccyx (Plate 33.1, Fig. 33.1, Flowchart 33.1).

Extent

- The rectum *begins* as a continuation of the sigmoid colon at the level of S3 vertebra.
- The ***rectosigmoid junction*** is indicated by the lower end of the sigmoid mesocolon.
- The rectum *ends* by becoming continuous with the anal canal at the ***anorectal junction***. The junction lies 2 to 3 cm in front of and a little below the tip of the coccyx. In males, the junction corresponds to the apex of the prostate.

Dimensions

The rectum is 12 cm long. In the upper part, it has the same diameter of 4 cm as that of the sigmoid colon, but in the lower part, it is dilated to form the ***rectal ampulla***.

Course and Direction

In its course, the rectum runs first downwards and backwards, then downwards, and finally downwards and forwards.

The beginning and the end of the rectum lie in the median plane, but it shows two types of curvatures in its course.

Two anteroposterior curves:

a. The *sacral flexure* of the rectum follows the concavity of the sacrum and coccyx.

Plate 33.1: Location and relations of rectum

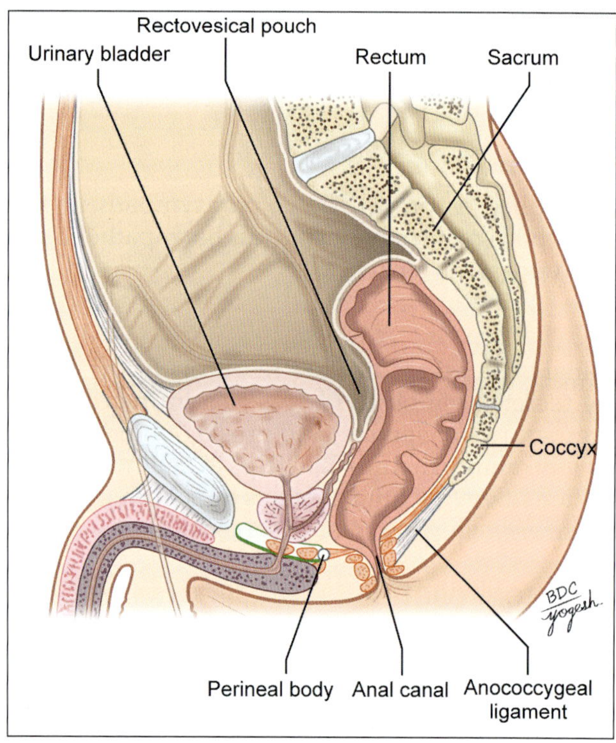

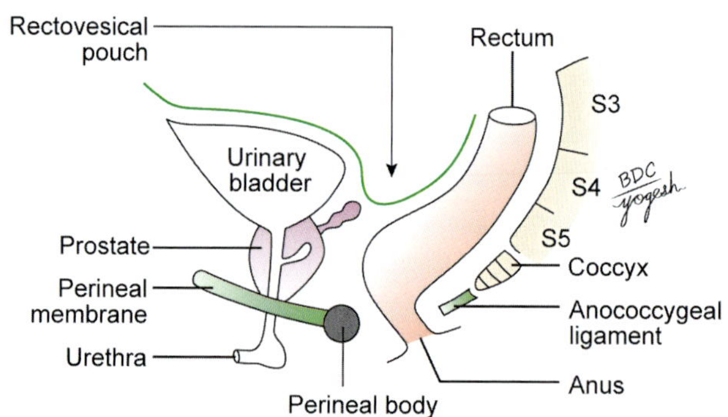

Fig. 33.1: Sagittal section through the male pelvis showing the location of the rectum and some of its anterior and posterior relations

b. The *perineal flexure* of the rectum is the backward bend at the anorectal junction (Figs 33.2a and b).

Flowchart 33.1: Rectum

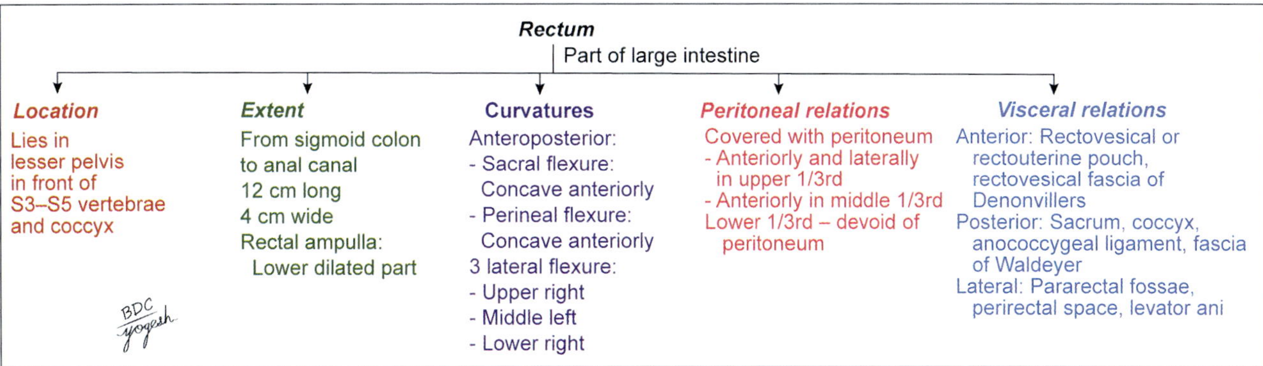

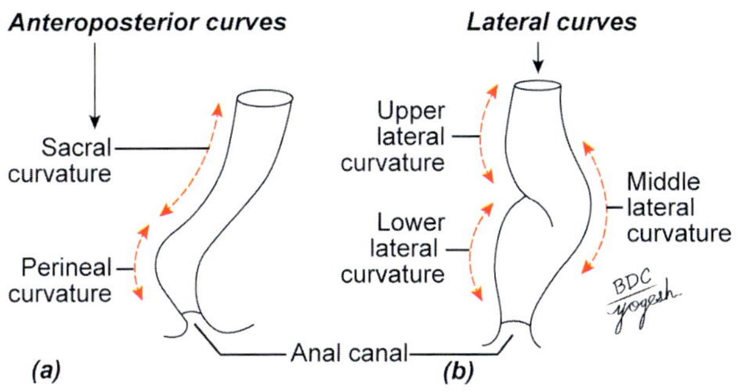

Figs 33.2a and b: Curvatures of the rectum: (a) Anteroposterior curves and (b) side-to-side (lateral) curves

Three lateral curves

a. Upper lateral curve of rectum is convex to the right.
b. Middle lateral curve is convex to the left and is most prominent.
c. Lower lateral curve is convex to the right.

Relations

Peritoneal Relations (Figs 33.3a and b)

1. Upper 1/3rd of the rectum is covered with peritoneum in front and on the sides.
2. Middle 1/3rd is covered only in front.
3. Lower 1/3rd, which is dilated to form the ampulla, is devoid of peritoneum, and lies below the rectovesical pouch in males and below the rectouterine pouch in females. The distance between the anus and the floor of the pouch is 7.5 cm in males but only 5.5 cm in females.

Visceral Relations

Anteriorly in males

1. *Upper 2/3rd of the rectum* are related to the rectovesical pouch with coils of intestine and sigmoid colon.
2. *Lower 1/3rd of the rectum* is related to the base of the urinary bladder, the terminal parts of the ureters, the seminal vesicles, the ductus deferens and the prostate.

Anteriorly in females

1. *Upper 2/3rd* of the rectum are related to the rectouterine pouch with coils of intestine and sigmoid colon. The pouch separates the rectum from the uterus, and from the upper part of the vagina.
2. *Lower 1/3rd* of the rectum is related to the lower part of the vagina.

Posteriorly: The relations are the same in the male and female. They are as follows (Fig. 33.4):

1. Lower three pieces of the sacrum, the coccyx and the anococcygeal ligament.
2. Piriformis, the coccygeus and the levator ani.
3. The median sacral, the superior rectal and the lower lateral sacral vessels.
4. The sympathetic chain with the ganglion impar; the anterior primary rami of S3, S4, S5, coccygeal 1 and the pelvic splanchnic nerves; lymph nodes, lymphatics and fat.

Interior of Rectum

The mucous membrane of an empty rectum shows two types of folds: Longitudinal and transverse (Figs 33.5a and b, Flowchart 33.2).

1. The ***longitudinal folds*** are transitory. They are present in the lower part of an empty rectum, and are obliterated by distension.
2. The *transverse* or *horizontal folds* or **Houston's valves** or *plicae transversales* are permanent and most marked when the rectum is distended.
   a. *First transverse fold* lies near the upper end of the rectum, and projects from the left wall situated about 15 cm above anus. Sometimes, it may encircle and partially constrict the lumen (Figs 33.5a and b).
   b. *Second transverse fold*, the largest and most constant, lies at the upper end of the rectal ampulla, about 8 cm from anus and projects from the anterior and right walls.

Flowchart 33.2: Interior of rectum

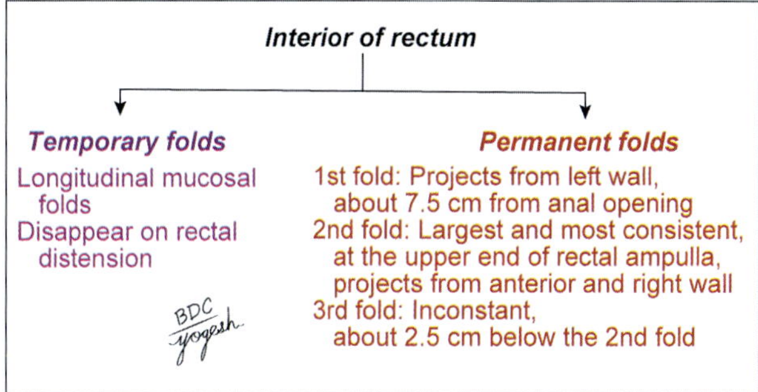

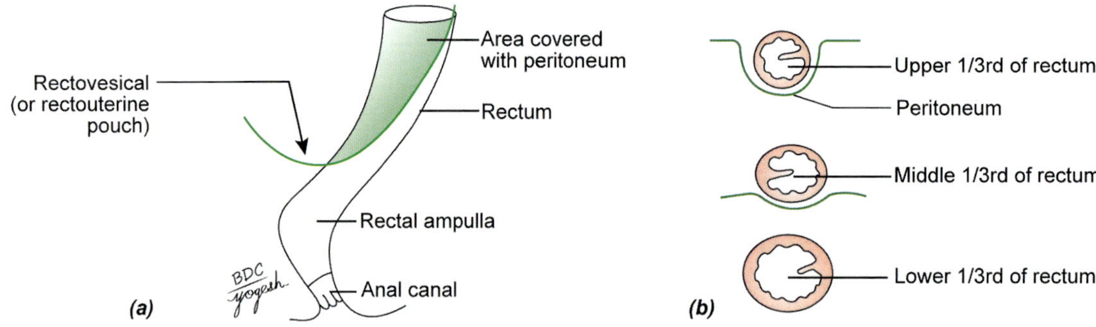

Figs 33.3a and b: Peritoneal relations of the rectum

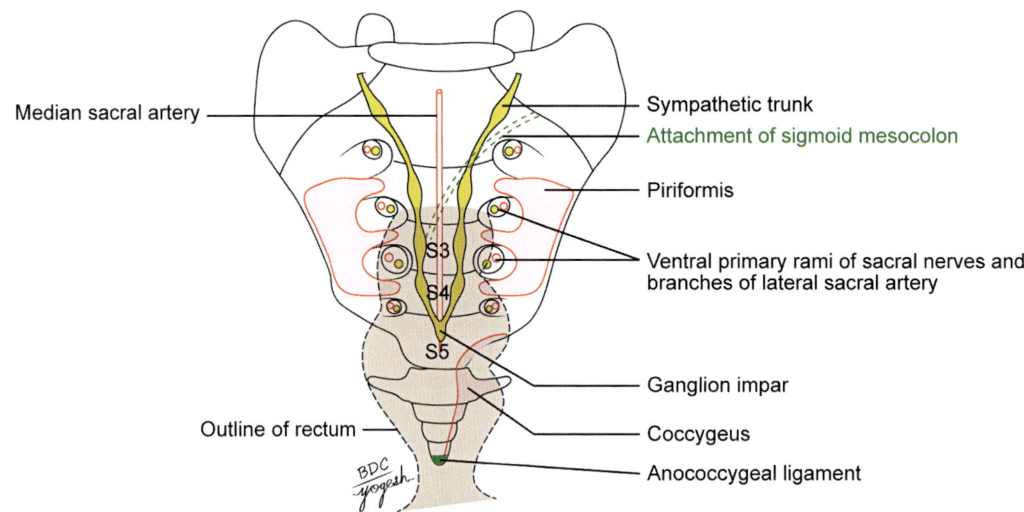

Fig. 33.4: Posterior relations of the rectum

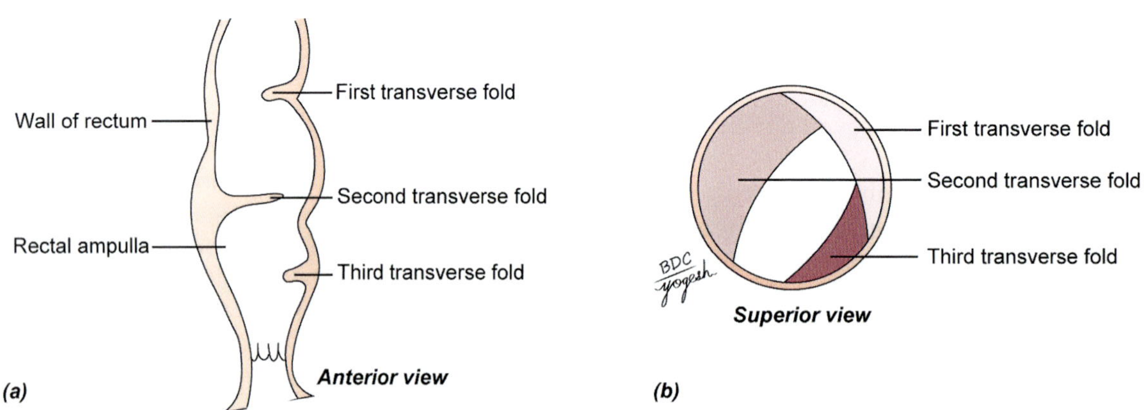

Figs 33.5a and b: Superior view of the transverse mucosal folds of the rectum

Note: The rectum has two developmental parts. The upper part related to the peritoneum develops from the hindgut and lies above the third transverse fold of the rectum. The lower part devoid of peritoneum develops from the cloaca and lies below the third transverse fold.

Functionally, the sigmoid colon is the faecal reservoir and the whole of the rectum is empty in normal individuals, being sensitive to distension. Passage of faeces into the rectum, therefore, causes the desire to defaecate.

c. *Third transverse fold* which is inconstant lies 2.5 cm below the second fold, and projects from the left wall.

Note: Current concept: The number of horizontal folds in rectum is variable. Mostly they are three in number as described above [*Reference*: *Gray's Anatomy*, 42nd edn.].

Arterial Supply

1. ***Superior rectal artery:*** This is the chief artery of the rectum. It is the continuation of the inferior mesenteric artery (Fig. 33.6).

   Note: It arises at the pelvic brim, medial to the left ureter. It lies in medial limb of pelvic mesocolon and divides opposite the third sacral vertebra into right and left branches, which run on each side of the rectum. Each branch breaks up at the middle of the rectum into several small branches, which pierce the muscular coats and run in the anal columns up to the anal valves where they form looped anastomoses.

2. ***Middle rectal arteries:*** They arise from the anterior division of the internal iliac artery, run in the lateral ligaments of rectum and supply only superficial muscle coats of the lower part of the rectum (Fig. 33.6). Their anastomoses with the adjacent arteries are poor.
3. ***Median sacral artery:*** This is a small branch arising from the back of the aorta near its lower end.

Venous Drainage

1. ***Superior rectal vein:*** The tributaries of this vein begin in the anal canal, from the internal rectal venous plexus, in the form of about three veins of considerable size. They pass upwards in the rectal submucosa, pierce the muscular coat about 7.5 cm above the anus and unite to form the superior rectal vein which continues upwards as the inferior mesenteric vein to end in the splenic vein (Fig. 33.7).
2. ***Middle rectal vein:*** The tributaries of this vein drain, chiefly, the muscular walls of the rectal ampulla and open into the internal iliac veins (Fig. 33.7).
3. ***Median sacral vein:*** It joins left common iliac vein.

Lymphatic Drainage

1. Lymphatics from more than the *upper half* of the rectum pass along the superior rectal vessels to the inferior mesenteric nodes after passing through the pararectal and sigmoid nodes (Fig. 33.8).
2. Lymphatics from the *lower half* of the rectum pass along the middle rectal vessels to the internal iliac nodes.
3. Lymphatics from the lower part of anal canal drain into superficial inguinal nodes.

Nerve Supply

1. The rectum is supplied by both sympathetic (L1, 2) and parasympathetic (S2, 3, 4) nerves through the superior rectal or inferior mesenteric and inferior hypogastric plexuses.
2. Sympathetic nerves are vasoconstrictor, inhibitory to the rectal musculature and motor to the internal sphincter. Parasympathetic nerves are motor to the musculature of the rectum and inhibitory to the internal sphincter.
3. Sensations of distension of the rectum pass through the parasympathetic nerves, while pain sensations are carried by both the sympathetic and parasympathetic nerves.

Supports of Rectum

1. Pelvic floor formed by levator ani muscles.
2. *Fascia of Waldeyer:* It attaches the lower part of the rectal ampulla to the sacrum. It is formed by condensation of the pelvic fascia behind the rectum. It encloses the superior rectal vessels and lymphatics.
3. *Lateral ligaments of the rectum:* They are formed by condensation of the pelvic fascia on each side of the rectum. They enclose the middle rectal vessels, and branches of the pelvic plexuses, and attach the rectum to the posterolateral walls of the lesser pelvis.
4. *Rectovesical fascia of Denonvilliers:* It extends from the rectum behind to the seminal vesicles and prostate in front.
5. The *pelvic peritoneum* and the related *vascular pedicles* also help in keeping the rectum in position.
6. Perineal body with its muscles.

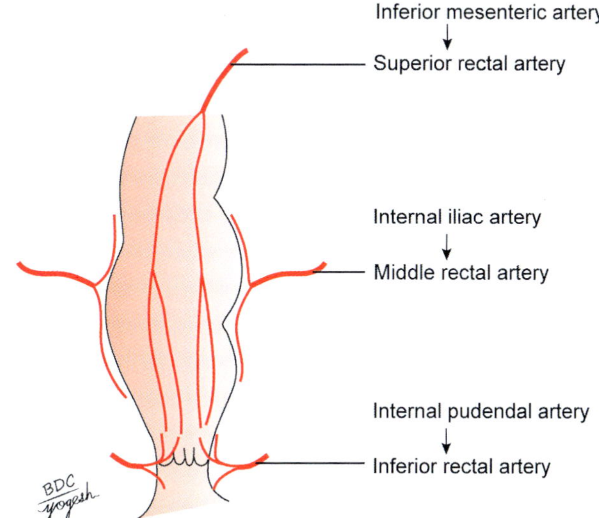

Fig. 33.6: Arterial supply of rectum and anal canal

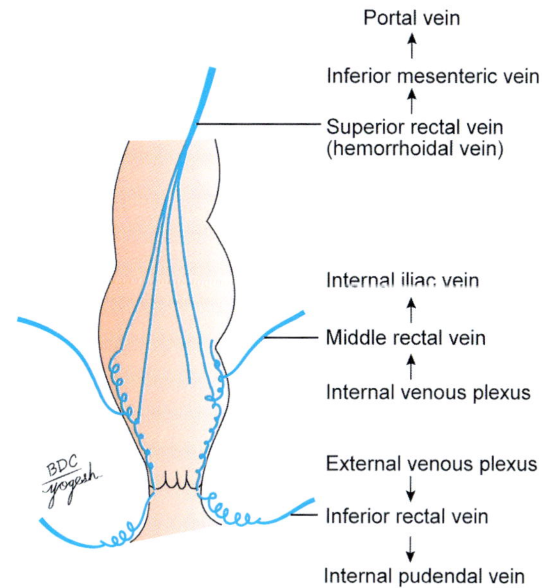

Fig. 33.7: Venous drainage of rectum and anal canal

Competency:

AN48.8 Mention the structures palpable during vaginal and rectal examination.

CLINICAL ANATOMY

- ***Digital per rectum (PR) examination:*** In PR examination, the finger enters anal canal before reaching lower end of rectum. In a normal person, the following

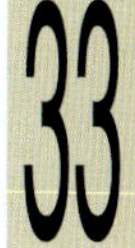

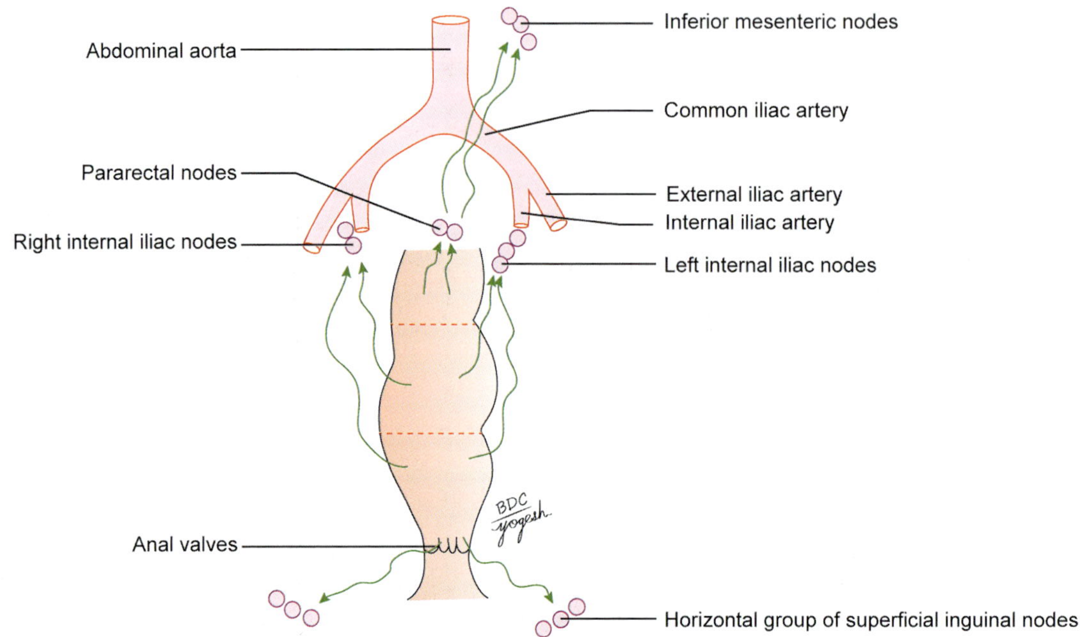

Fig. 33.8: Lymphatic drainage of rectum and anal canal

structures can be palpated by a finger passed per rectum.

In males (Fig. 33.9):

1. Posterior surface of prostate
2. Seminal vesicles
3. Vas deferens

In females (Fig. 33.10):

1. Perineal body
2. Cervix
3. Presenting part of the foetus during delivery.

In both sexes:

1. Anorectal ring
2. Coccyx and sacrum
3. Ischioanal fossae and ischial spines

- In patients, a PR examination can help in the palpation of the following abnormalities:
  1. Within the lumen: Faecal impaction and foreign bodies, bleeding piles or haemorrhoids.
  2. In the rectal wall: Rectal growths and strictures, and thrombosed piles.
  3. Outside the rectal wall: In males, the enlargements of prostate, seminal vesicles and bulbourethral glands, and stone in membranous urethra; in females, enlargements of uterus, tubes and ovaries, and abnormalities in the pouch of Douglas; and in both sexes, the distended bladder, lower ureteric stones, and tumours of the bony pelvis.
  4. During parturition, the dilatation of cervix is commonly assessed through the rectal wall to avoid infection by repeated vaginal examinations.
- ***Proctoscopy and sigmoidoscopy:*** The interior of the rectum and anal canal can be examined under direct vision with special instruments, like a proctoscope or a sigmoidoscope. Proctoscopy shows internal piles and growths in lower part of rectum. Sigmoidoscopy helps in revealing the ulcers, growths and diverticula, and in taking a rectal biopsy.
- ***Prolapse of rectum:***
  1. ***Incomplete*** or ***mucosal prolapse*** of the rectum through the anus may occur following violent straining. This is due to imperfect support of the rectal mucosa by the submucosa which is made up of loose areolar tissue.
  2. ***Complete prolapse*** or *procidentia* is the condition in which the whole thickness of the rectal wall protrudes through the anus. The contributory factors in its causation are:
     - Laxity of the pelvic floor.
     - Excessively deep rectovesical or rectouterine pouch.
     - Inadequate fixation of the rectum in its presacral bed.
- ***Neurological disturbances of the rectum:*** Neurological disturbances of rectum: Sacral denervation results in automatic evacuation of rectum as reflex activity. Transverse lesions of spinal cord cause constipation or reflex defecation.
- ***Carcinoma of rectum:*** Carcinoma of rectum: It occurs frequently in elderly. It causes bleeding per rectum. It needs surgical removal.
- ***Colostomy***: It is a surgical procedure for creating an opening for large intestine on the anterior abdominal wall mostly in the left iliac fossa. It may be temporary or permanent. It is required after surgeries of rectal carcinoma.
- ***Rectal continence:*** Rectal continence depends solely on the anorectal ring. Damage to the ring results in rectal incontinence. The surgeon has to carefully protect the anorectal ring in operating on the region.

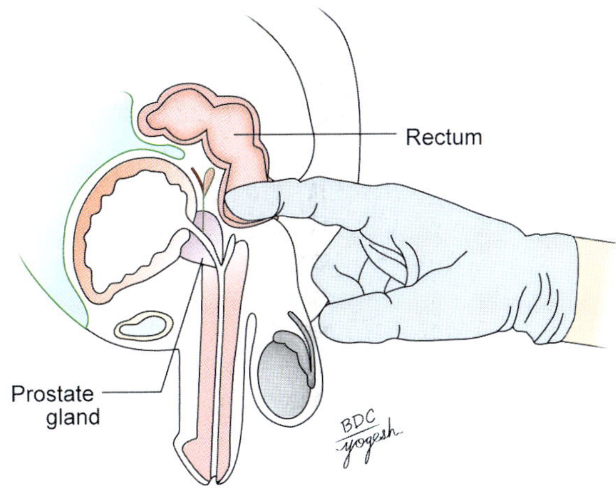

Fig. 33.9: Digital per rectal (PR) examination in male

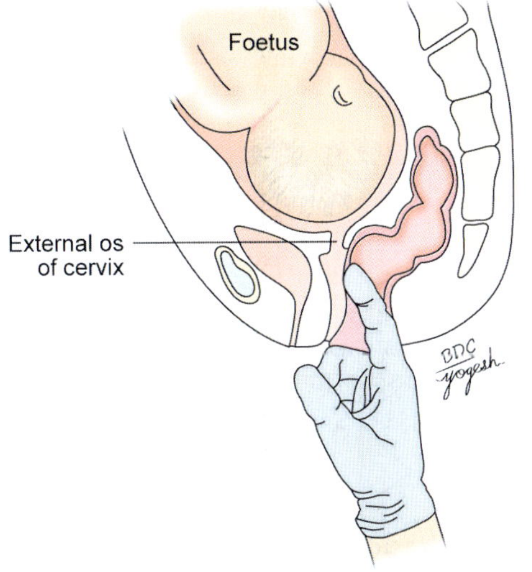

Fig. 33.10: Digital per rectal (PR) examination in female

DISSECTION

Identify the relation of the peritoneum to the upper two-thirds of the rectum. See the structures/viscera related to the rectum both in male and female cadavers. Cut through the rectum and examine its mucous membrane with a hand lens.

Find the superior rectal artery, as the continuation of the inferior mesenteric artery. Trace it onto the posterior surface of the upper part of rectum and follow its branches downwards on the posterolateral surfaces till the lowest part of the rectum. Trace the middle rectal artery from its origin from the internal iliac artery till the wall of the rectum.

ANAL CANAL

Anal canal is the terminal part of gastrointestinal tract and is situated below the level of the pelvic diaphragm.

It lies in the anal triangle of perineum in between the right and left ischioanal fossae, which allows its expansion during passage of the faeces. The sacculations and taeniae are absent here also.

Length, Extent and Direction

1. The anal canal is 3.8 cm long.
2. It extends from the anorectal junction to the anus. It is directed downwards and backwards. The anal canal is surrounded by inner involuntary and outer voluntary sphincters which keep the lumen closed in the form of an anteroposterior slit.
3. The ***anorectal junction*** is marked by the forward convexity of the perineal flexure of the rectum (Fig. 33.2) and lies 2–3 cm in front of and slightly below the tip of the coccyx. Here, the ampulla of the rectum suddenly narrows and pierces the pelvic diaphragm. In males, it corresponds to the level of the apex of the prostate.
4. The ***anus*** is the surface opening of the anal canal, situated about 4 cm below and in front of the tip of the coccyx in the cleft between the two buttocks. The surrounding skin is pigmented and thrown into radiating folds and contains a ring of large apocrine glands.

Relations of the Anal Canal

Anteriorly

1. *In both sexes:* Perineal body
2. *In males:* Membranous urethra and bulb of penis
3. *In females:* Lower end of the vagina.

Posteriorly

1. Anococcygeal ligament
2. Tip of the coccyx.

Laterally: Ischioanal fossae.

All-round: Anal canal is surrounded by the sphincter muscles, the tone of which keeps the canal closed.

Interior of the Anal Canal

The interior of the anal canal shows many important features and can be divided into three parts:

- Upper part about 15 mm long
- Middle part about 15 mm long
- Lower part about 8 mm long.

Each part is lined by a characteristic epithelium and reacts differently to various diseases of this region (Plate 33.2, Fig. 33.11).

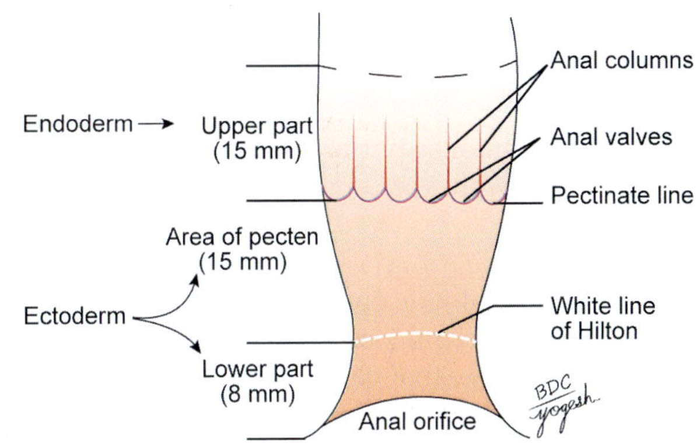

Fig. 33.11: Interior of the anal canal

Plate 33.2: Internal features of lower part of rectum and anal canal (coronal section)

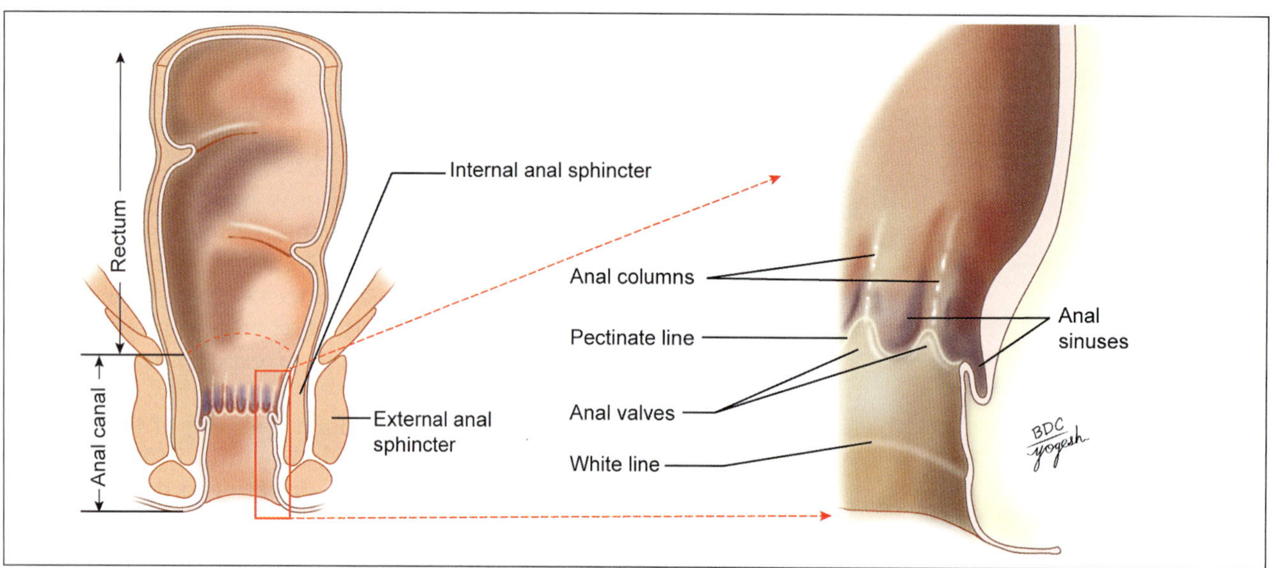

Upper Mucous Part

1. This part is about 15 mm long. It is lined by mucous membrane, and is of endodermal origin (Figs 33.12 and 33.13).
2. The mucous membrane shows:
   a. ***Anal columns of Morgagni*:** These are permanent longitudinal mucosal folds. They are 6–10 in number. Anal columns contain terminal branch of superior rectal artery and vein.
   b. ***Anal valves*** (*valves of Ball*): These are crescentic mucous folds connecting the lower ends of the anal columns. These anal valves have free margin, and upper and lower surfaces.
   c. ***Pectinate line** or dentate line*: The free margin of the anal valve forms a line called pectinate or dentate line (Flowchart 33.3).
   d. ***Anal sinuses*:** These are depressions (recesses) above the anal valves. The ducts of the submucosal tubular *anal glands* open in the floor of the anal sinuses.
   e. ***Anal papillae*:** These are occasional epithelial projections from the free margin anal valves. Anal papillae represent the remnant of embryonic *anal membrane*.
   f. ***Anal glands*:** These are tubular submucosal glands. Their ducts open in the floor of the anal sinuses.

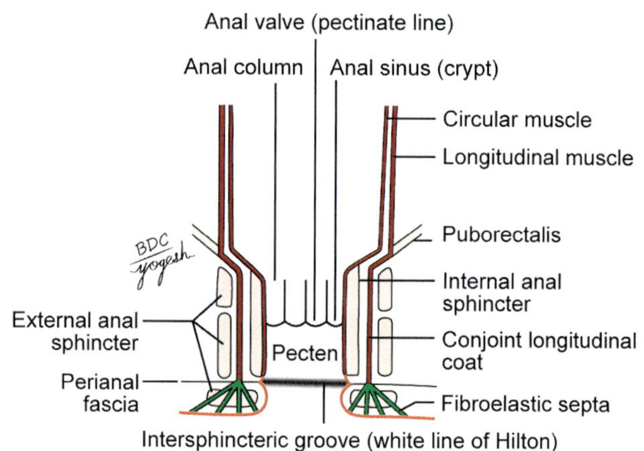

Fig. 33.12: Coronal section through the wall of the anal canal

Flowchart 33.3: Significance of pectinate line

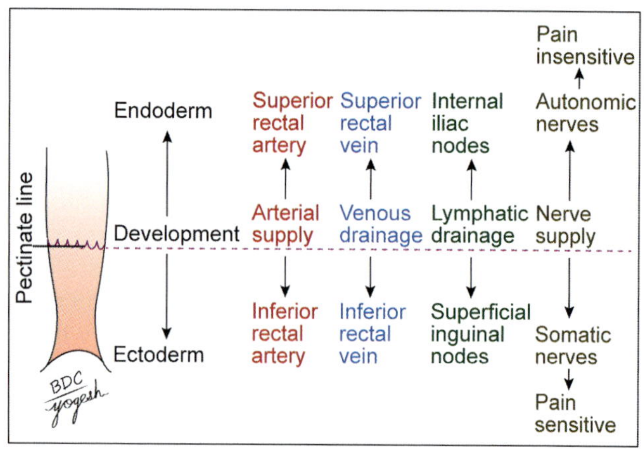

Middle Part or Transitional Zone or Pecten

1. The next 15 mm or so of the anal canal is also lined by mucous membrane, but anal columns are not present here.
2. The mucosa has a bluish appearance because of a dense venous plexus that lies between it and the muscle coat. The mucosa is less mobile than in the upper part of the anal canal. This region is referred to as the ***pecten*** or ***transitional zone*** (Flowchart 33.3).
3. The lower limit of the pecten often has a whitish appearance because of which it is referred to as the ***white line of Hilton***. Hilton's line is situated at the level of the interval between the subcutaneous part of external anal sphincter and the lower border of internal anal sphincter.
4. It marks the lower limit of pecten or stratified squamous epithelium which is thin, pale and glossy and is devoid of sweat glands.

Lower Cutaneous Part

It is about 8 mm long and is lined by true skin containing sebaceous glands. The epithelium of the lowest part resembles that of pigmented skin in which sebaceous glands, sweat glands and hair are present.

Anal Sphincters

The anal canal has powerful sphincters. The anal sphincters are divided into external and internal anal sphincters.

Internal Anal Sphincter

The *internal anal sphincter* is involuntary in nature. It is formed by the thickened circular muscle coat of this part of the gut. It surrounds the upper 3/4th of the anal canal extending from the upper end of the canal to the white line of Hilton.

External Anal Sphincter

The *external anal sphincter* is under voluntary control. It is made up of a striated muscle and is supplied by the inferior rectal nerve and the perineal branch of the fourth sacral nerve. It surrounds the whole length of the anal canal and has three parts: Subcutaneous, superficial and deep (Figs 33.13 and 33.14).

Contrary to earlier view, the external anal sphincter forms a single functional and anatomic entity.

1. *Uppermost fibres* blend with fibres of puborectalis. Anteriorly, some fibres decussate with superficial transversus perinei muscle and posterior fibres get attached to anococcygeal raphe.
2. *Middle fibres* surround lower part of internal anal sphincter. These are attached to perineal body anteriorly and to coccyx via anococcygeal ligament posteriorly. Some fibres of each side decussate to form a commissure in the midline.
3. *Lower fibres* lie below the level of internal anal sphincter and are separated from anal epithelium by submucosa. (*Reference*: Gray's Anatomy, 42nd edition)

In males, transverse perinei and bulbospongiosus end in central point of perineum, so that there is a surgical plane of cleavage between urogenital triangle and anal canal.

In females, the puborectalis is separate from external anal sphincter. Its anterior portion is thinner and shorter.

In addition, in females, transverse perinei and bulbospongiosus fuse with external anal sphincter in lower part of perineum.

Note:

Conjoint Longitudinal Coat: It is formed by fusion of the puborectalis with the longitudinal muscle coat of the rectum at the anorectal junction. It lies between the external and internal sphincters. When traced downwards, it becomes fibroelastic and at the level of the white line, it breaks up into a number of fibroelastic septa which spread out an-wise, pierce the subcutaneous part of the external sphincter, and are attached to the skin around the anus called corrugator cutis ani. The most lateral of these septa forms the perianal fascia. The most medial septum forms, the ***anal intermuscular septum***, which is attached to the white line. In addition, some strands pass obliquely through the internal sphincter and end in the submucosa below the anal valves.

Anorectal Ring: This is a muscular ring present at the anorectal junction. It is formed by the fusion of the puborectalis, uppermost fibres of external sphincter and the internal sphincter. It is easily felt by a finger in the anal canal. Surgical division of this ring results in rectal incontinence. The ring is less marked anteriorly where the fibres of the puborectalis are absent (Fig. 33.14).

Surgical Spaces Related to the Anal Canal

There are spaces containing fat surrounding the anal canal. These spaces include two ischioanal fossae, a perianal space, and a subcutaneous space of anal canal (Fig. 33.15).

1. ***Ischioanal space*** or fossa lies on each side of the anal canal (For details, *see* Chapter 28, page 284).
2. ***Perianal space*** surrounds the anal canal below the white line. It contains the lower fibres of external sphincter, the external rectal venous plexus, and the terminal branches of the inferior rectal vessels and nerves.

   Note: Pus in this space tends to spread to the anal canal at the white line or to the surface of the perineal skin rather than to the ischioanal space.
3. ***Submucous space*** of the canal lies above the white line between the mucous membrane and the internal sphincter. It contains the internal rectal venous plexus and lymphatics.

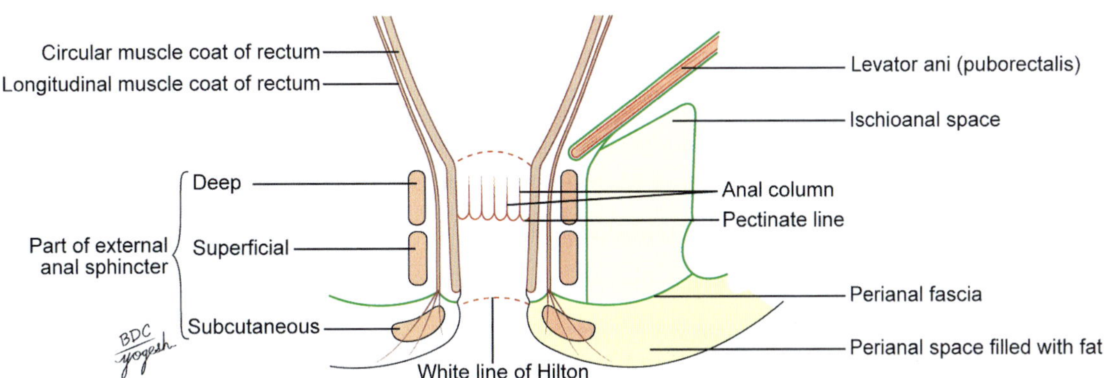

Fig. 33.13: Anal canal and external anal sphincters (coronal section)

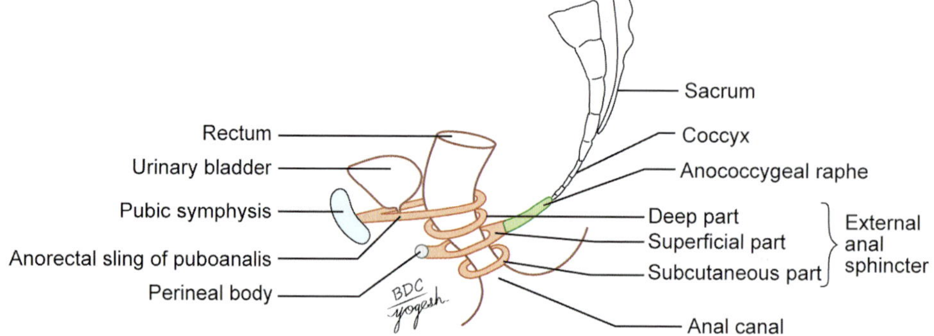

Fig. 33.14: External anal sphincter

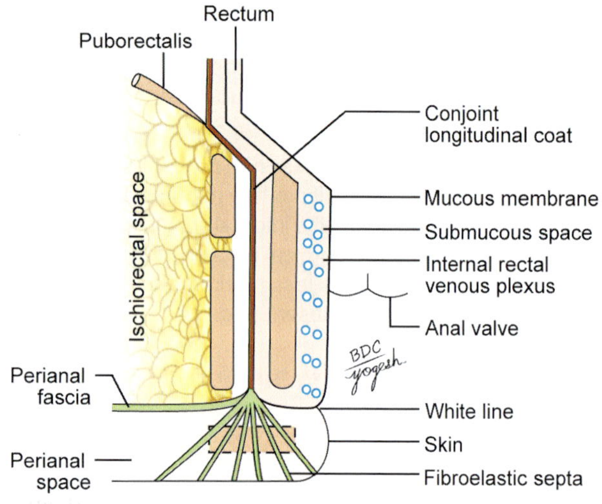

Fig. 33.15: Coronal section through the anal canal (magnified) showing surgical spaces around it

Arterial Supply

The part of the anal canal above the pectinate line is supplied by the superior rectal artery.

The part below the pectinate line is supplied by the inferior rectal arteries (Fig. 33.6).

Venous Drainage

1. The part of anal canal above the pectinate line is drained into the portal venous system by the superior rectal veins.
2. The part of anal canal below the pectinate line is drained into the systemic veins by the inferior rectal veins.

Note:

1. The ***internal rectal venous plexus*** or haemorrhoidal plexus lies in the submucosa of the anal canal. It drains mainly into the superior rectal vein, but communicates freely with the external plexus and thus with the middle and inferior rectal veins. The internal plexus is, therefore, an important site of communication between the portal and systemic veins. The internal plexus is in the form of a series of dilated pouches connected by transverse branches around the anal canal (Fig. 33.7).

   Veins present in the three anal columns situated at 3, 7 and 11 o'clock positions as seen in the lithotomy position are large and constitute potential sites for the formation of primary internal piles (Fig. 33.15).
2. The ***external rectal venous plexus*** lies outside the muscular coat of the rectum and anal canal, and communicates freely with the internal plexus. The lower part of the external plexus is drained by the inferior rectal vein into internal pudendal vein; the middle part by middle rectal vein into internal iliac vein; and the upper part by superior rectal vein, which continues as the inferior mesenteric vein.
3. The ***anal veins*** are arranged radially around the anal margin. They communicate with the internal rectal plexus and with the inferior rectal veins. Excessive straining during the defaecation may rupture one of these veins, forming a subcutaneous perianal haematoma known as external piles.

Lymphatic Drainage

1. The part of anal canal above the pectinate line drains into internal iliac nodes.
2. The part of anal canal below the pectinate line drains into superficial inguinal nodes. Thus, pectinate line forms ***watershed line*** of the anal canal.

Nerve Supply

1. *Above the pectinate line*, the anal canal is supplied by autonomic nerves—both sympathetic (inferior hypogastric plexus—L1, 2) and parasympathetic (pelvic splanchnic—S2, 3, 4). Pain sensations are carried by both of them.
2. *Below the pectinate line*, it is supplied by somatic (inferior rectal—S2, 3, 4) nerves.
3. *Sphincters*: The internal sphincter is caused to contract by sympathetic nerves and is relaxed by parasympathetic nerves. The external sphincter is supplied by the inferior rectal nerve and by the perineal branch of the fourth sacral nerve.

DISSECTION

Identify the relations of the anal canal in both male and female. Examine the lining of the anal canal. Strip the mucous membrane and skin from a sector of the anal canal. Identify the thickened part of the circular muscle layer forming the internal sphincter of the anus. Locate the external anal sphincter with its parts, partly overlapping the internal sphincter. The anal canal is the terminal part of the large intestine.

Competency:

AN49.5 Explain the anatomical basis of perineal tear, episiotomy (p-431), perianal abscess and anal fissure.

CLINICAL ANATOMY

- ***Piles/haemorrhoids*** are dilated veins in the lower part of the anal canal. According to the locations, the haemorrhoids are classified as internal or true piles and external or false piles.

  Internal piles or ***true piles*** are saccular dilatations of the internal rectal venous plexus. They occur above the pectinate line and are, therefore, painless. They bleed profusely during straining at stool.

  1. The ***primary piles*** occur in 3, 7 and 11 o'clock positions of the anal wall when viewed in the lithotomy position. They are formed by enlargement of the three main radicles of the superior rectal vein which lie in the anal columns, which occupy the left lateral, right posterior, and right anterior positions (Fig. 33.16).
  2. Varicosities in other positions of the lumen are called ***secondary piles***. The various *factors* responsible for causing internal piles are:

  External piles or ***false piles*** occur below the pectinate line and are, therefore, very painful. They do not bleed on straining at stool.

  Anatomically each pile consists of a fold of mucosa and submucosa containing a dilated tributary (radicle) of the superior rectal vein with a branch of superior rectal artery.
- ***Fissure in ano:*** Anal fissure is caused by the rupture of one of the anal valves, usually by the passage of dry hard stool in a constipated person. Each valve is lined with mucous membrane above, and with skin below. Because of the involvement of skin, the condition is extremely painful and is associated with marked spasm of the anal sphincters.
- ***Fistula in ano:*** It is a fistula in the anal canal. It is an abnormal tract connecting cavity of abscess to the interior of the anal canal or with the exterior on the skin. It is caused by spontaneous rupture of abscess around the anus. The low-level anal fistula passing through the lower part of superficial anal sphincter is the most common fistula in ano.
- Table 33.1 shows comparison of upper and lower parts of anal canal.

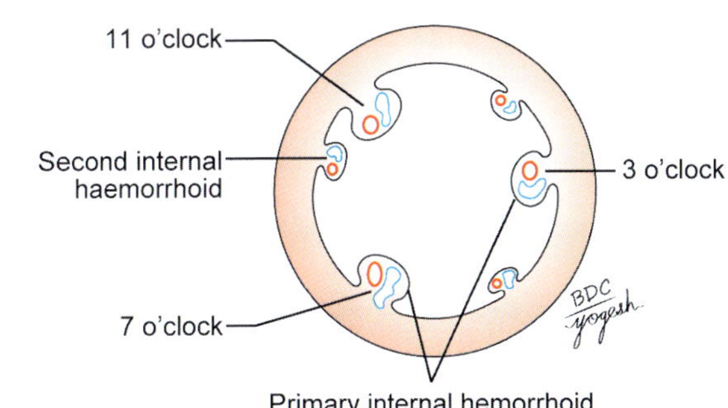

Fig. 33.16: Position of primary and secondary piles/haemorrhoids as seen in lithotomy position

TABLE 33.1: Comparison of upper (15 mm) and lower (23 mm) parts of anal canal

	Upper part (15 mm)	*Lower part (15 + 8 mm)*
Development	Hindgut (endoderm)	Proctodaeum (ectoderm)
Lining	Simple columnar epithelium squamous	Stratified columnar and stratified
Arterial supply of mucosa	Mainly superior rectal	Mainly inferior rectal
Venous drainage	Chiefly into portal vein	Chiefly into systemic veins
Lymph drainage	Internal iliac lymph nodes	Superficial inguinal lymph nodes
Nerve supply	Autonomic nerves: Sympathetic (L1, 2) Parasympathetic (S2, 3, 4)	Inferior rectal (somatic) nerves (S2, 3, 4)
Sensory to	Ischaemia, distension and spasm	Pain, touch, temperature and pressure
Type of piles	Internal painless piles	External painful piles

Competency:

AN52.6 Describe the development of hindgut.

DEVELOPMENT

Rectum

- The distal part of hindgut known as cloaca is divided by urorectal septum into primitive anorectal canal posteriorly and vesicourethral canal anteriorly.
- Primitive anorectal canal forms the lower part of rectum and proximal part of anal canal. Its distal part of anal canal is formed by the proctodeum.
- Upper part of rectum, i.e. part above the third transverse fold of rectum, develops from endoderm of hindgut. This part is related to peritoneum. Lower part, below the third transverse fold, is formed from the dorsal part of the cloaca. It is devoid of peritoneum.

Anal Canal

- Upper 15 mm develops from the primitive anorectal canal.
- Lower part below the pectinate line (lower 15 + 8 mm) is formed from ectodermal invagination, i.e. proctodeum (Greek *on the way to*). Non-continuity of the two parts results in imperforate anus.

Facts to Remember

- Chief vessels of rectum are superior rectal artery and superior rectal vein.
- Perineal body and levator ani form the main supports of rectum.
- Most of the anal canal is surrounded by internal and external anal sphincters.
- Only middle fibres of external anal sphincter have a bony attachment.
- Proximal 15 mm of anal canal develops from anorectal canal (endoderm) and distal 23 mm develops from the proctodaeum (ectoderm).
- Primary piles appear at 3, 7, 11 o'clock positions.

BDC's Anatomy *e*-book

1. Histology of rectum and anal canal
2. Factors responsible for internal piles
3. Further reading
4. Viva voce questions.

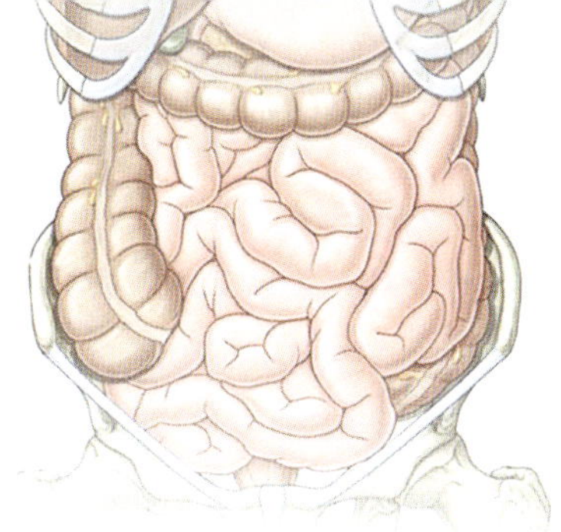

Chapter

34

Walls of Pelvis

All the pelvic viscera, i.e. terminal parts of digestive and urinary systems; and components of genital system are located in the pelvis. These organs are provided due to protection and nutrition by the bones, muscles, fascia, blood vessels, lymphatics and nerves of the pelvis. The posterior superior iliac spine, seen as a dimple (mostly covered), lies opposite the middle of the sacroiliac joint.

In this chapter the vessels, nerves, muscles, fascia and joints of the pelvis will be considered (Fig. 34.1).

PELVIC FASCIA

The pelvic fasciae are divided into two following groups (Figs 34.2 and 34.3):

A. *Parietal pelvic fascia:* It lines the pelvic muscles.
B. *Visceral pelvic fascia:* It covers the pelvic organs and neurovascular bundles.

Parietal Pelvic Fascia

It is a strong layer that covers the pelvic muscles. It includes:

1. *Obturator fascia* that covers the pelvic surface of obturator internus
2. Fascia over piriformis
3. Fascia over upper surface of levator ani muscle or pelvic diaphragm
4. Presacral fascia that lies on the anterior aspect of sacrum.

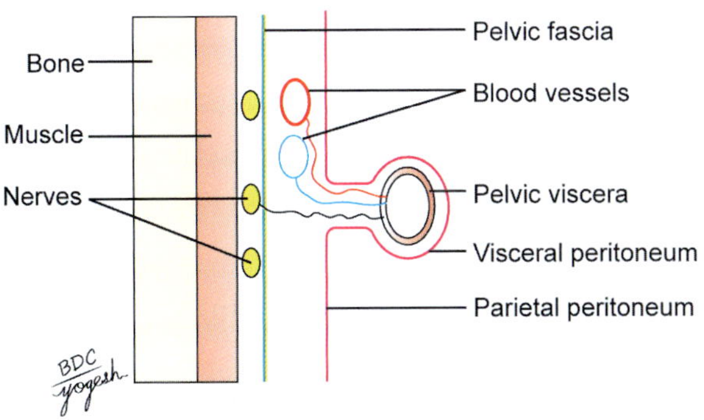

Fig. 34.1: Schematic representation showing arrangement of structures on the pelvic walls

Visceral Fascia (Endopelvic Fascia)

It is also called endopelvic fascia. It consists of loose areolar tissue and fat. The endopelvic fascia condenses to form the following ligaments and structures:

1. *Cardinal* or Mackenrodt's ligament
2. *Uterosacral ligament*
3. *Vesicosacral fold*
4. *Pubourethral ligament*
5. *Rectovesical septum* in male and *rectovaginal septum* in female
6. *Parametrium*
7. *Paracolpium.*

Note:

***Obturator fascia*:** It covers the pelvic surface of obturator internus muscle. Superiorly, it is attached to the arcuate line of ileum. Further, the obturator fascia is attached to the bones along the margin of origin of obturator internus muscle.

Tendinous arch of levator ani (arcus tendinous musculi levatores ani) or *white line* is an arched line or thickening of obturator fascia that gives origin to iliococcygeus part of the levator ani. The origin of iliococcygeus divides obturator fascia into two parts: Upper part forms the lateral pelvic wall and lower part forms the lateral wall of ischioanal fossa.

***Fascia over piriformis*:** It covers the inner aspect of piriformis. It is very thin and has attachments. It fuses with sacrum at the margins of sacral foramina. The ventral primary rami of sacral nerves are covered by this fascia.

***Fascia covering levator ani (pelvic diaphragm)*:** Both the surfaces (superior and inferior) of the levator ani muscle are covered by the fascia. These superior and inferior layers of fascia and sandwiched levator ani form the pelvic diaphragm. *Superior fascia of pelvic diaphragm* is a thick layer. It is attached anteriorly to the body of pubis superior ramus of pubis, and blend with obturator fascia. Posteriorly, it is continuous with the fascia over the piriformis. Medially, it blends with endopelvic fascia. *Inferior fascia of pelvic diaphragm* is thin. It forms the medial wall of ischioanal fossa.

***Presacral fascia*:** It forms a hammock-like fascia behind the rectum and anterior to the sacrum. Laterally, the presacral fascia blends with fascia covering the piriformis and with superior layer of fascia over levator ani and with obturator fascia. Anteriorly, it blends with fascia covering the peri rectal pad of fat (mesorectal fascia). Inferiorly, it blends with mesorectal fascia and iliococcygeal raphe. Superiorly, it is continuous with retroperitoneal connective tissue.

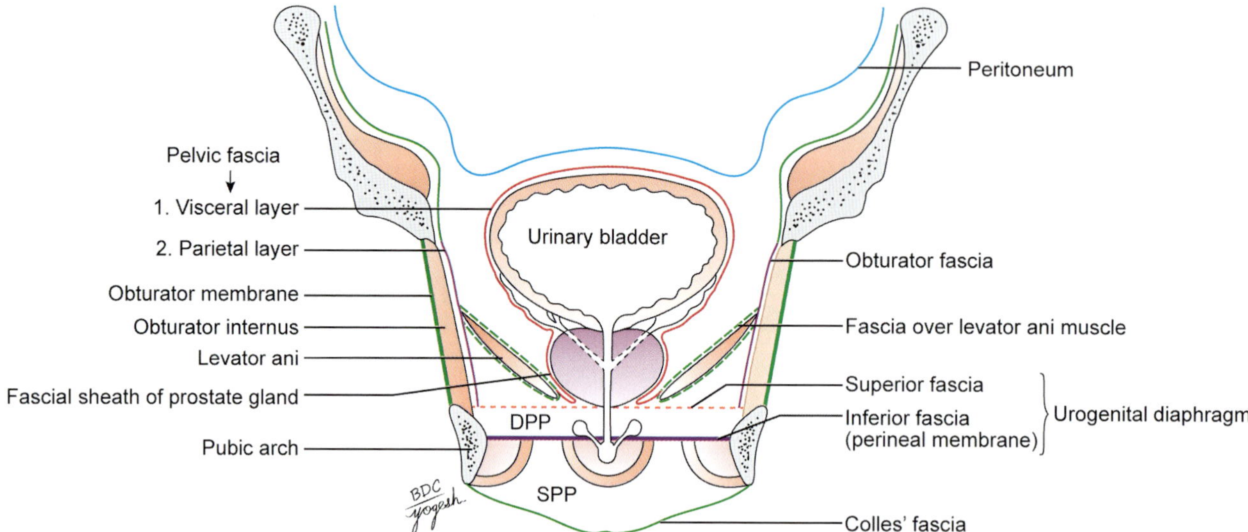

Fig. 34.2: Pelvic fascia (coronal section of the male pelvis, DPP: Deep perineal pouch, SPP: Superficial perineal pouch)

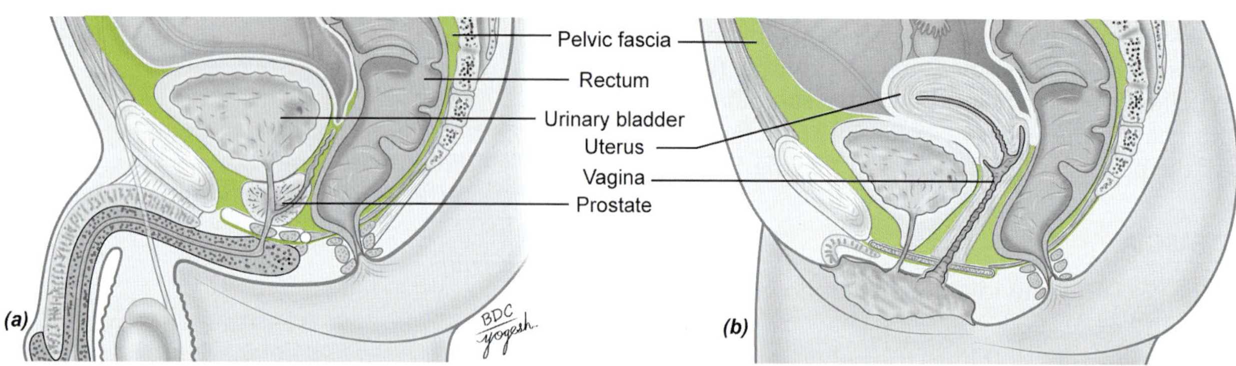

Figs 34.3a and b: Pelvic fascia: (a) In male and (b) in female (midsagittal section through the male and female pelvic cavities viewed from the left)

Details of Endopelvic Fascia

The endopelvic fascia is a *visceral layer of pelvic fascia*. It consists of loose connective tissue and fat. It anchors the pelvic organs to the lateral pelvic wall (Fig. 34.2).

Functions

1. It provides passage to neurovascular bundles from pelvic wall to the pelvic viscera.
2. It holds the pelvic organs in place and prevents their prolapse.
3. It separates adjacent viscera from each other.

Derivatives: Endopelvic fascia condenses to form the following ligaments:

1. *Cardinal ligaments* (Mackenrodt's or lateral cervical or transverse cervical ligament): It is a pair of fan-shaped ligaments that connects the cervix of uterus and upper part of vagina to the lateral pelvic wall.
2. *Uterosacral ligament*: It is a condensation of endopelvic fascia. It connects the cervix of uterus posteriorly to the sacrum.
3. *Vesicosacral fold*: In males, instead of uterosacral ligament, vesicosacral fold is present.
4. *Pubourethral ligament*: It is misnomer. It extends from pelvic surface of pubis bone to the anterior wall of vagina.
5. *Rectovesical septum* in male and *rectovaginal septum* in female: It is a connective tissue that lies between rectum and seminal vesicles in the male and rectum and vagina in the female. It does not connect rectum with seminal vesicle or vagina.

Note: *Parametrium*: It is a part of pelvic fascia that surrounds the uterus. It separates the uterus from urinary bladder. It extends in between the layers of broad ligaments. It gives passage to uterine vessels and ovarian ligament.

Paracolpium: It is a part of pelvic fascia that surrounds the vaginal walls, and pubocervical and rectovaginal septums. It gives passage to the vessels and nerves to the vagina.

Competency:
AN48.1 Describe and identify the muscles of pelvic diaphragms.

PELVIC MUSCLES

The muscles of the pelvic wall are (Plate 34.1):

1. Obturator internus
2. Piriformis
3. Levator ani
4. Coccygeus.

Plate 34.1: Piriformis and obturator internus

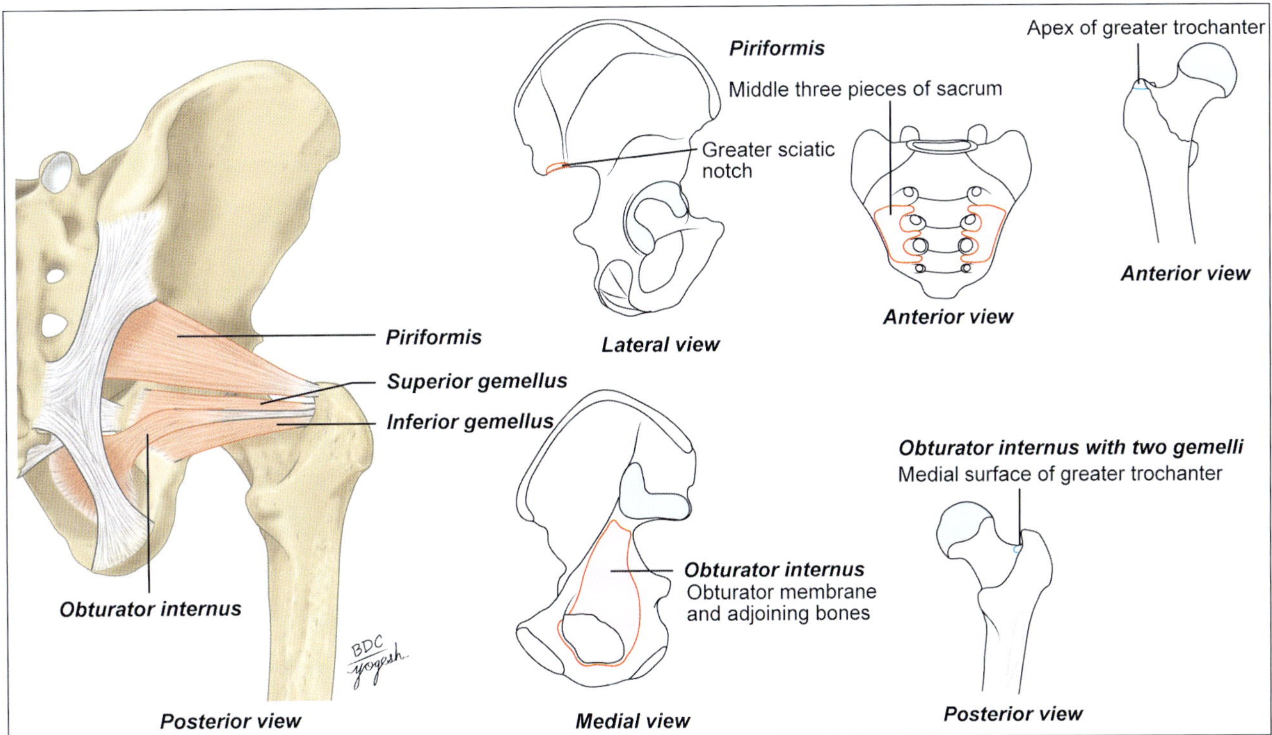

Obturator Internus

It is a fan-shaped muscle. It arises within the pelvis and its tendon leaves the pelvic cavity through lesser sciatic foramen (Plate 34.1, Flowchart 34.1).

Origin: It arises from:

1. Pelvic surface of obturator membrane, and
2. Adjoining bones surrounding the obturator membrane.

Insertion: The tendon of obturator internus turns almost at right angle at the lesser sciatic notch. Further, it crosses the posterior aspect of the hip joint and inserts into the medial surface of the greater trochanter of *femur*.

Nerve supply: Nerve to obturator internus (L5, S1, S2) – a branch of sacral plexus.

Actions: It is a lateral rotator of the hip joint in erect posture and acts as abductor of the hip joint when thigh is flexed. It stabilizes the hip joint.

Pyriformis (Piriformis)

It is pear-shaped muscle that forms the posterolateral wall of true pelvis (Plate 34.1, Flowchart 34.2)

Origin: It arises within the true pelvis from anterior surface of middle three pieces of *sacrum* by three digitations. Few fibres arise from the upper margin of greater sciatic notch. The fibres run downward and laterally to form a tendon. It leaves the true pelvis through greater sciatic notch to enter in the gluteal region. Here, the tendon lies deep to the gluteus maximus muscle.

Insertion: It inserts at the tip of the greater trochanter of femur.

Nerve supply: Ventral primary rami of S1 and S2 nerves.

Flowchart 34.1: Obturator internus

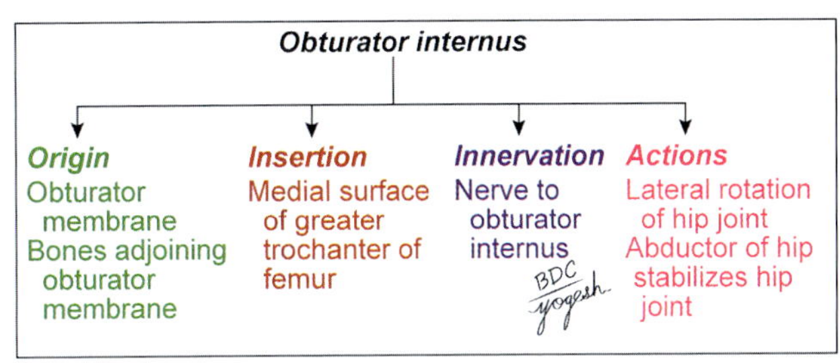

Flowchart 34.2: Piriformis

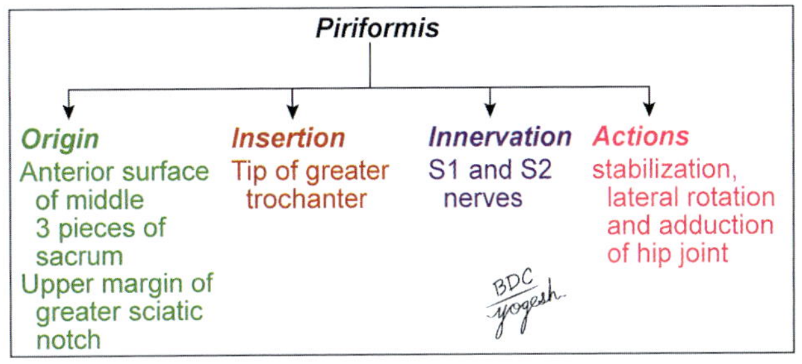

Actions: It stabilizes the hip joint. It acts as lateral rotator of hip when thigh is extended and as adductor when thigh is flexed.

Levator Ani

(Pubococcygeus, Iliococcygeus, and Pubo-analis)

Levator ani is a broad, flat muscle and forms the larger part of the pelvic floor. Levator ani is divisible into three parts: Pubococcygeus, iliococcygeus and pubo-analis (Plate 34.2, Flowchart 34.3) [*Reference*: *Gray's Anatomy*, 42nd edn.].

Plate 34.2: Levator ani muscle and coccygeus muscles

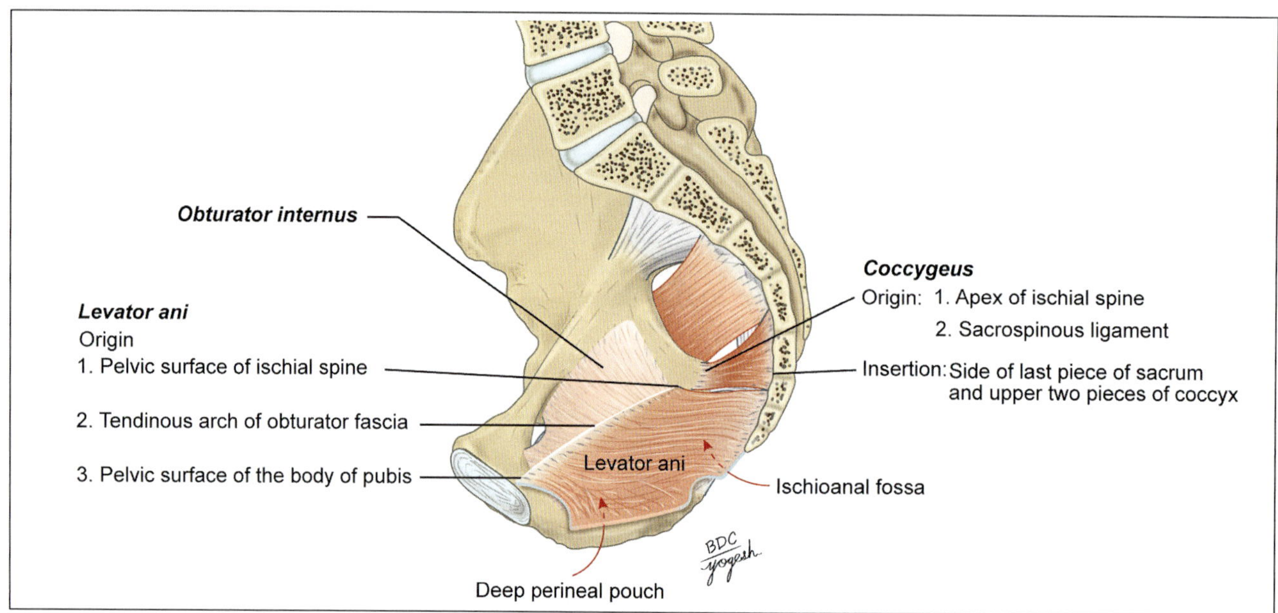

Flowchart 34.3: Levator ani

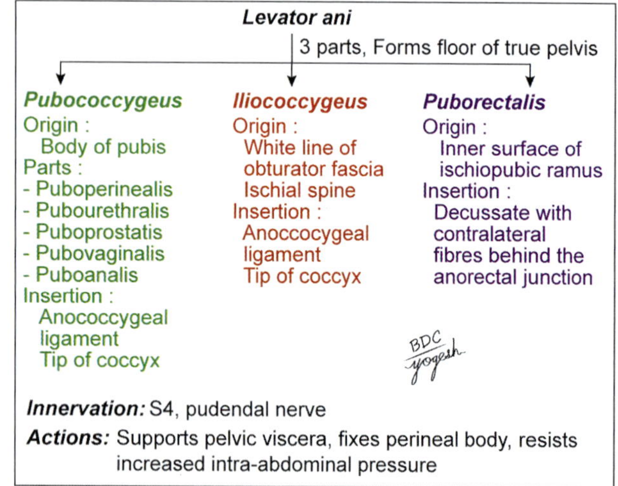

Both the levator ani (right and left) slope from the side wall of the pelvis toward the medial plane where they fuse with each other. Thus, it forms slopping gutter-like floor of the true pelvis and separates it from the ischioanal fossa.

Pubococcygeus

It is subdivided into puboperinealis or pubourethralis, puboprostaticus (levator prostatae), pubovaginalis and puboanalis parts.

Origin: Pubococcygeus originates from posterior aspect of body of the pubis.

Subgroups

1. *Puboperinealis* or *pubourethralis*: These are medial fibres of pubococcygeus that run lateral to the urethra. It has no direct connection with urethra.
2. *Puboprostaticus* (*levator prostatae*): In male, some of the fibres of pubococcygeus lie inferolateral to the prostate. These fibres form puboprostaticus part.
3. *Pubovaginalis*: In female, some of the fibres of pubococcygeus attach to the lateral wall of vagina to form pubvaginalis or *sphincter vaginalis* part.
4. *Puboanalis*: In both sexes, some middle fibres of pubococcygeus decussate and blend with longitudinal muscle coat of rectum to form puboanalis part.

Insertion: Remaining posterior fibres of pubococcygeus insert on the levator raphe (anococcygeal ligament) and tip of coccyx.

Iliococcygeus

Origin

1. Posterior part of tendinous arc of levator of ani (white line on the obturator fascia)
2. Inner surface of ischial spine.

Insertion

1. Most of the fibres insert on the median raphe of levator ani and anococcygeal ligament
2. Posterior fibres insert on tip of coccyx.

Pubo-analis

These fibres are not visible from inside the pelvis.

Origin: It originates from inner surface of ischiopubic ramus adjacent to the attachment of perineal membrane.

Insertion: Fibres of puboanalis pass posterior to the rectum at anorectal junction and decussate with contralateral fibres.

Nerve supply

1. Perineal branch of S4 nerve.
2. Perineal branch of pudendal nerve (S2, S3).

Actions

1. *Support*: Both the levator ani form pelvic floor and support the pelvic viscera.

2. *Fixation of perineal body*: Some fibres of levator ani insert on perineal body and they fix the perineal body to support pelvic viscera.
3. *Resistance against increase intra-abdominal pressure*: Levator ani supports the pelvic viscera in increased intra-abdominal pressure during coughing, sneezing, lifting of heavy objects and so on.
4. Relaxation of levator ani assists the micturition and defecation.
5. Reinforcement of external anal sphincter by maintaining anorectal angle by pubo-analis and pubococcygeus. They pull the anorectal junction forward.

Coccygeus (Ischiococcygeus)

It is a small triangular muscle. Some authors consider it as the posterior most part of levator ani and some consider as a separate muscle (Plate 34.2, Flowchart 34.4).

Origin: It originates from pelvic surface and tip of ischial spine.

Insertion: The fibres pass horizontally backward and medially and insert on lateral border of coccyx and lower part of sacrum.

Nerve supply: Ventral primary rami of S4 and S5 nerves.

Actions

1. Assist the actions of levator ani
2. Pulls the coccyx forward after it has been pressed backward during defecation and parturition.

Note: Pubovisceralis = puboperineus + pubovaginalis or puboprostaticus + puboanalis.

Morphology of pelvic diaphragm: Sacrospinous ligament is degenerated aponeurosis of ischiococcygeus muscle. In lower animals, the movement of coccygeal vertebrae and tail is performed by pubococcygeal and iliococcygeal parts.

Flowchart 34.4: Coccygeus

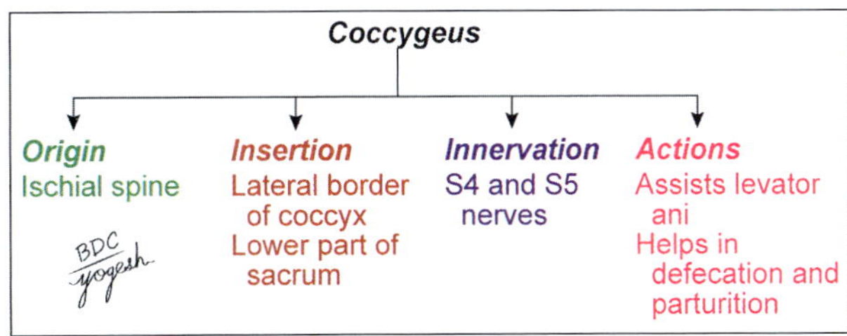

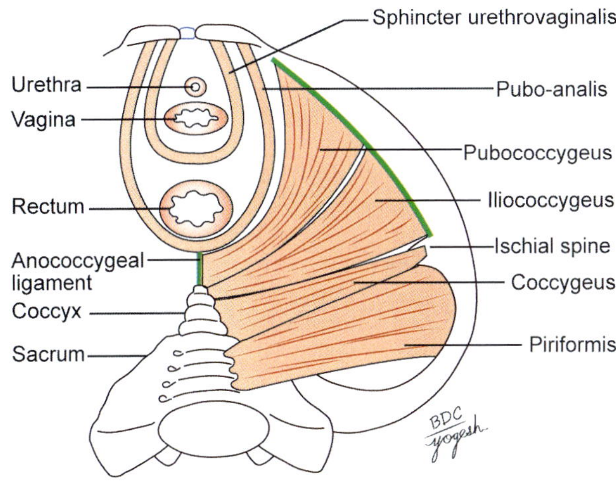

Fig. 34.4: Levator ani, coccygeus, and piriformis muscles (in female, superior view)

PELVIC DIAPHRAGM

It is a muscular partition between the true pelvis and the perineum. It forms a gutter-shaped pelvic floor (Fig. 34.4).

Formation

It is formed by the following components:

1. Most of the pelvic diaphragm is formed by levator ani
2. Posteriorly by the coccygeus
3. Pelvic fascia.

Functions

1. Pelvic diaphragm supports the pelvic viscera and prevents their prolapse.
2. Sphincteric action: Its fibres act as sphincter around the vagina and at anorectal junction.
3. It facilitates defecation, micturition and parturition.

Openings of Pelvic Diaphragm

The pelvic diaphragm has the following openings:

1. *Hiatus urogenitalis*: It is a triangular gap in the anterior fibres of two levator ani muscles. This hiatus transmits urethra in male and urethra and vagina in female. This gap is closed inferiorly by urogenital diaphragm.
2. *Hiatus rectalis*: It is a circular opening in the pelvic diaphragm. It is located between the perineal body and anococcygeal raphe. It gives passage to the anorectal junction.

CLINICAL ANATOMY

- ***Injury to the pelvic diaphragm***: Ruptured perineal body during parturition (childbirth) weakens the pelvic diaphragm. It may result in uterine prolapse and rectal prolapse. Hence, the repair of perineal body should be done after its injuries.
- ***Hiatus of Schwalbe***: It is an abnormal gap between the levator ani and obturator fascia. Pelvic viscera may herniate through this gap.

DISSECTION

Identify the origin of piriformis from the ventral surface of the sacrum. Trace it through the greater sciatic foramen to its insertion into the upper border of greater trochanter of femur.

Feel the ischial spine and trace the fibres of coccygeus and levator ani that arise from it. Trace the origin of levator ani from thickened fascia, i.e. tendinous arch over the middle of obturator internus muscle till the back of body of the pubis. Note that the right and left sheet like levator ani muscles are united and the muscles are inserted into central perineal tendon or perineal body, anal canal, anococcygeal ligament.

Detach the origin of levator ani from obturator fascia. While removing obturator fascia identify pudendal canal with its contents in the lower part of the fascia.

Trace the tendon of obturator internus muscle. This tendon along with superior and inferior gemelli muscles leaves through the lesser sciatic foramen to be inserted into the medial surface of greater trochanter of femur.

VESSELS OF THE PELVIS

Competency:

AN48.3 Describe and demonstrate the origin, course, important relations and branches of internal iliac artery.

INTERNAL ILIAC ARTERY

The internal iliac artery is the smaller terminal branch of the common iliac artery. It supplies (Plate 34.3, Fig. 34.5, Flowchart 34.5):

1. Pelvic organs except those supplied by the superior rectal, ovarian and median sacral arteries.
2. Perineum
3. Greater part of the gluteal region
4. Iliac fossa.

Note: In the foetus, internal iliac artery is double the size of the external iliac artery because it transmits blood to the placenta through the umbilical artery. The umbilical artery with the internal iliac then forms the direct continuation of the common iliac artery. After birth, the proximal part of the umbilical artery persists to form superior vesical artery, and the rest of it degenerates into a fibrous cord, the medial umbilical ligament.

Course

The internal iliac artery begins in front of the sacroiliac joint, at the level of the intervertebral disc between the L5 vertebra and the sacrum. Here, it lies medial to the psoas major muscle. The artery runs downwards and backwards and ends near the upper margin of the greater sciatic notch, by dividing into anterior and posterior divisions or trunks (Plate 34.3).

Flowchart 34.5: Internal iliac artery

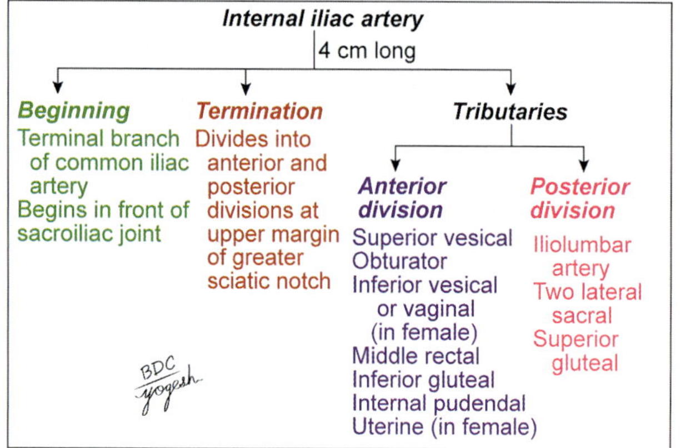

Relations

Anterior: In female, it is related to the ovary and lateral end of the uterine tube and ureter.

Posterior: Internal iliac vein, lumbosacral trunk and the sacroiliac joint

Lateral: External iliac vessels and obturator nerve

Medial: Peritoneum and to a few tributaries of the internal iliac vein.

Branches (Plate 34.4, Fig. 34.5, Flowchart 34.5)

Branches of anterior division

1. Superior vesical artery
2. Obturator artery
3. Inferior vesical in male or vaginal artery in female
4. Middle rectal artery
5. Inferior gluteal artery
6. Internal pudendal artery
7. Uterine artery in female.

Branches of posterior division

1. Iliolumbar artery
2. Two lateral sacral arteries
3. Superior gluteal artery.

Note: ***Details of branches of internal iliac artery***

1. *Inferior gluteal artery:* It is the largest branch of the anterior division of the internal iliac artery. It is the *axial artery* of the lower limb. It supplies chiefly the buttock and the back of the thigh. In the pelvis, it runs downwards in front of the sacral plexus and piriformis. Next, it pierces the parietal pelvic fascia, passes below the first sacral nerve and then between the piriformis and the coccygeus, and enters the gluteal region through the lower part of the greater sciatic foramen (Fig. 34.5). In the pelvis, it supplies:
   a. Muscular branches to nearby muscles.
   b. Vesical branches to the base of the bladder, the seminal vesicles and the prostate.
2. *Obturator artery:* It runs forwards and downwards on the obturator fascia below the obturator nerve and above the obturator vein (NAV). Medially, it is crossed by the ureter and the ductus deferens, and is covered with peritoneum. It passes through the obturator foramen to leave the pelvis and enter the thigh. In the pelvis, it gives off:
   a. Iliac branches to the iliac fossa
   b. A vesical branch to the urinary bladder
   c. A pubic branch to the back of the pubis, which anastomoses with the pubic branch of the inferior epigastric artery and with its fellow of the opposite side (Plate 34.3).
3. *Superior vesical artery:* The proximal 2.5 cm or so of the superior vesical artery represents the persistent part of the umbilical artery. It supplies many branches to the upper part of the urinary bladder. One of these branches gives off the artery to the ductus deferens.
4. *Middle rectal artery:* It is characterized by three features. It is often absent, especially in females. Very little of its blood goes to the rectum, and that too goes only to its muscle coats. Most of its blood goes to the prostate and seminal vesicles.
5. *Inferior vesical artery:* It supplies the trigone of the bladder, the prostate, the seminal vesicles and the lower part of the ureter.
6. *Internal pudendal artery:* It is the smaller terminal branch of the anterior division of the internal iliac artery. It supplies

Plate 34.3: Internal iliac artery

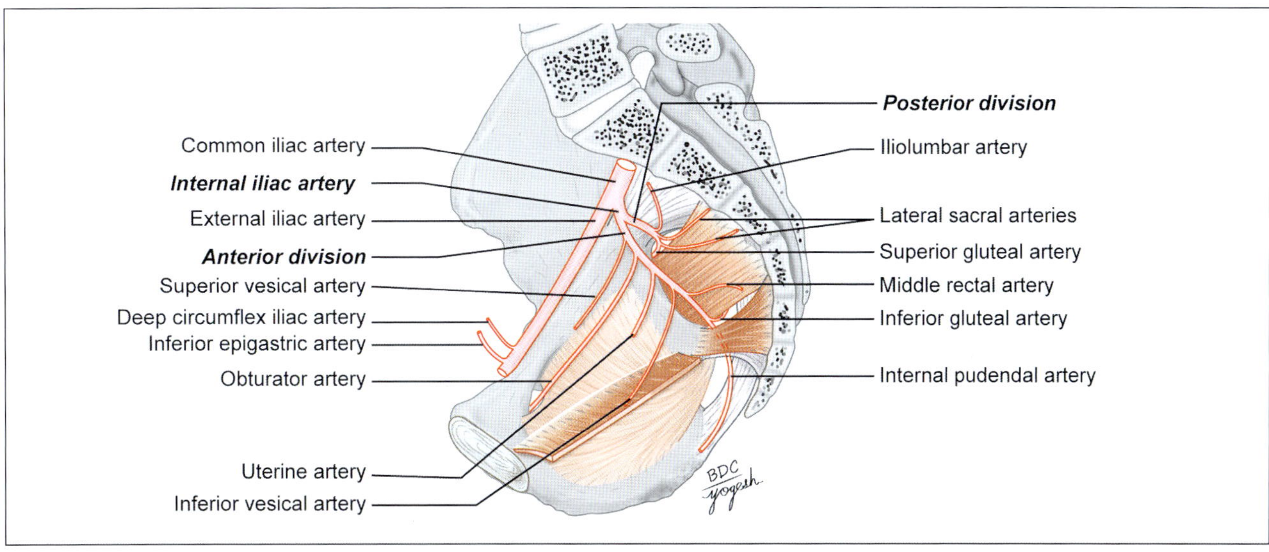

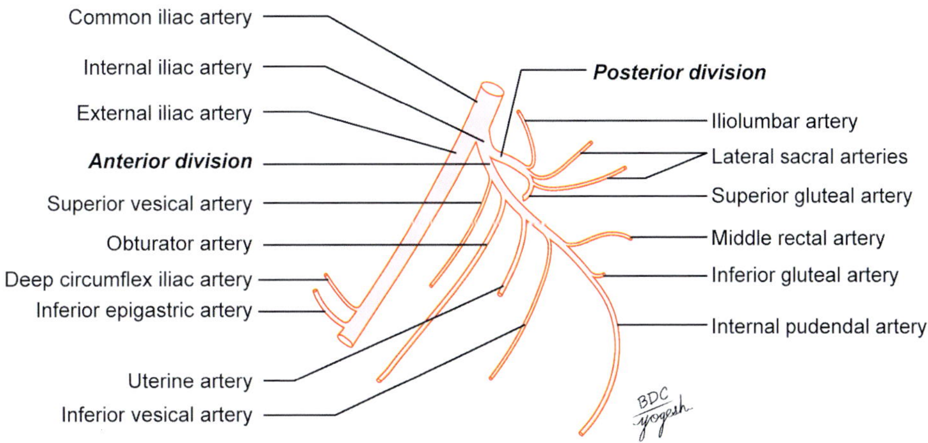

Fig. 34.5: Branches of the right internal iliac artery

the perineum and external genitalia. Its branches are inferior rectal, perineal, artery to bulb, urethral, deep and dorsal arteries. It is described in Chapter 28.

7. *Vaginal artery:* It corresponds to the inferior vesical artery of the male, and supplies the vagina, the bulb of the vestibule, the base of the urinary bladder, and the adjacent part of the rectum
8. *Uterine artery:* It has a tortuous course. Crosses the ureter 2 cm lateral to cervix. Runs along side of uterus. Supplies vagina, cervix uterus, and fallopian tube.
9. *Iliolumbar artery:* It runs upwards in front of the sacroiliac joint and lumbosacral trunk, and behind the obturator nerve and external iliac vessels (Fig. 34.5). Behind the psoas major, it divides into the lumbar and iliac branches.

   The *lumbar branch* represents the fifth lumbar artery, and supplies the psoas, the quadratus lumborum and the erector spinae. Its spinal branch supplies the cauda equina.

   The *iliac branch* supplies the iliac fossa and the iliacus. It participates in the anastomoses around the anterior superior iliac spine.
10. *Lateral sacral arteries:* These are usually two in number—upper and lower. They run downwards and medially over the sacral nerves. Their branches enter the four anterior sacral foramina to supply the contents of the sacral canal. Their terminations pass out through the posterior sacral foramina and supply the muscles and skin on the back of the sacrum (Fig. 34.5).
11. *Superior gluteal artery:* It runs backwards, pierces the pelvic fascia, passes above the first sacral nerve and leaves the pelvis through the greater sciatic foramen above the piriformis (Fig. 34.5). It supplies gluteus maximus muscle. Also takes part in anastomoses around anterior superior iliac spine and in trochanteric anastomoses to supply nearby muscles and overlying skin.

INTERNAL ILIAC VEIN

It ascends posteromedial to the internal iliac artery, and joins the external iliac vein to form the common iliac vein at the pelvic brim, in front of the lower part of the sacroiliac joint. Its tributaries correspond with the branches of the artery, except for the iliolumbar vein which joins the common iliac vein.

Veins arising in and outside the pelvic wall

1. Superior gluteal is the largest tributary
2. Inferior gluteal
3. Internal pudendal

4. Obturator
5. Lateral sacral veins.

Veins arising from the plexuses of pelvic viscera

1. Rectal venous plexus is drained by the superior, middle and inferior rectal veins.
2. Prostatic venous plexus is drained by the vesical and internal iliac veins.
3. Vesical venous plexus is drained by the vesical veins.
4. Uterine venous plexus is drained by the uterine veins.
5. Vaginal venous plexus is drained by the vaginal veins.

LYMPH NODES OF THE PELVIS

The pelvic lymphatics drain into the following lymph nodes, which lie along the vessels of the same name.

1. 4 to 6 ***common iliac nodes*** receive lymphatics from the external and internal iliac nodes, and send their efferents to the lateral aortic nodes.
2. 8 to 10 ***external iliac nodes*** receive lymphatics from the inguinal nodes, the deeper layers of the infraumbilical part of the anterior abdominal wall, the membranous urethra, the prostate, the base of the urinary bladder, the uterine cervix, and part of the vagina. Their efferents pass to the common iliac nodes. The *inferior epigastric* and *circumflex iliac nodes* are outlying members of this group.
3. The ***internal iliac nodes*** receive lymphatics from all the pelvic viscera, the deeper parts of the perineum, and muscles of the buttocks and of the back of the thigh. Their efferents pass to the common iliac nodes. The sacral and obturator nodes are outlying members of this group.

DISSECTION

Remove the viscera from the pelvic wall and the pelvic cavity. Trace the internal iliac artery and its two divisions. Follow the branches of each of its divisions to the position of the viscera and the parieties. Remove the veins and venous plexuses as these obstruct the view of the arteries. Clean the hypogastric plexus.

NERVES OF THE PELVIS

The nerves of the pelvis include:

1. Lumbosacral trunk
2. Sacral and coccygeal plexuses
3. Autonomic nerves
4. Pelvic parts of sympathetic and parasympathetic system.

Competency:
AN48.4 Describe the branches of sacral plexus.

Lumbosacral Trunk (L4, L5)

It is a thick cord-like nerve formed by the fibres from ventral primary ramus L4 and entire ventral primary ramus of L5 spinal nerve (Fig. 34.6).

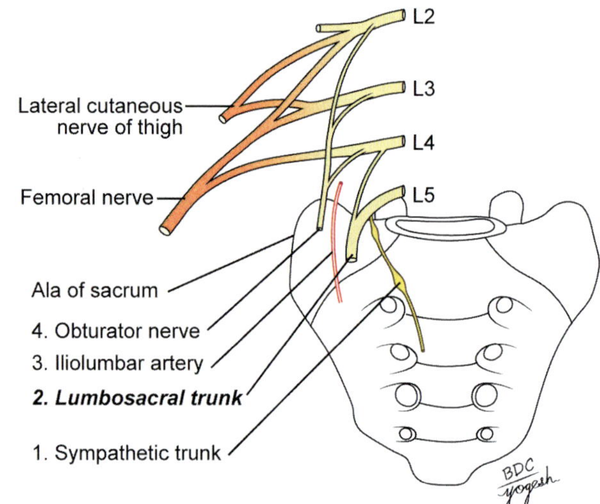

Fig. 34.6: Relations of lumbosacral trunk

It descends over the ala of the sacrum. It crosses the pelvic brim in front of the sacroiliac joint. It joins with 1st sacral nerves to form the sacral plexus.

Sacral Plexus

Sacral plexus is the plexus of the nerves that lies in front of the piriformis, on the posterior wall of the pelvis (Fig. 34.7, Flowchart 34.6).

Root Value

L4, L5, S1, S2, S3 and S4.

Formation

The sacral plexus is formed by the following nerves:

1. Lumbosacral trunk
   a. Part of primary ramus of L4 spinal nerve
   b. Entire ventral primary ramus of L5 spinal nerve.
2. Entire ventral primary ramus of S1 to S3 spinal nerves.
3. Part of ventral primary ramus of S4 spinal nerve.

Relations

The sacral plexus lies in front of the piriformis, deep to the pelvic fascia on the posterior pelvic wall. It lies posterior to internal iliac vessels, ureter and sigmoid colon.

Note: The L4 spinal nerve contributes to both lumbar and sacral plexuses. The S4 spinal nerve contributes to both sacral and coccygeal plexuses.

The superior gluteal vessels pass between the lumbosacral trunk and ventral primary ramus of S1 nerve. The inferior gluteal vessels pass between the ventral primary rami of S1 and S2 nerves.

Branches of Sacral Plexus (Fig. 34.7)

Branches arising from roots of plexus

1. Muscular branches to
   - Piriformis (S1, S2)
   - Levator ani (S3, S4)
   - Coccygeus (S3, S4)
2. Pelvic splanchnic nerves or nervi erigentes (S2, S3, S4).

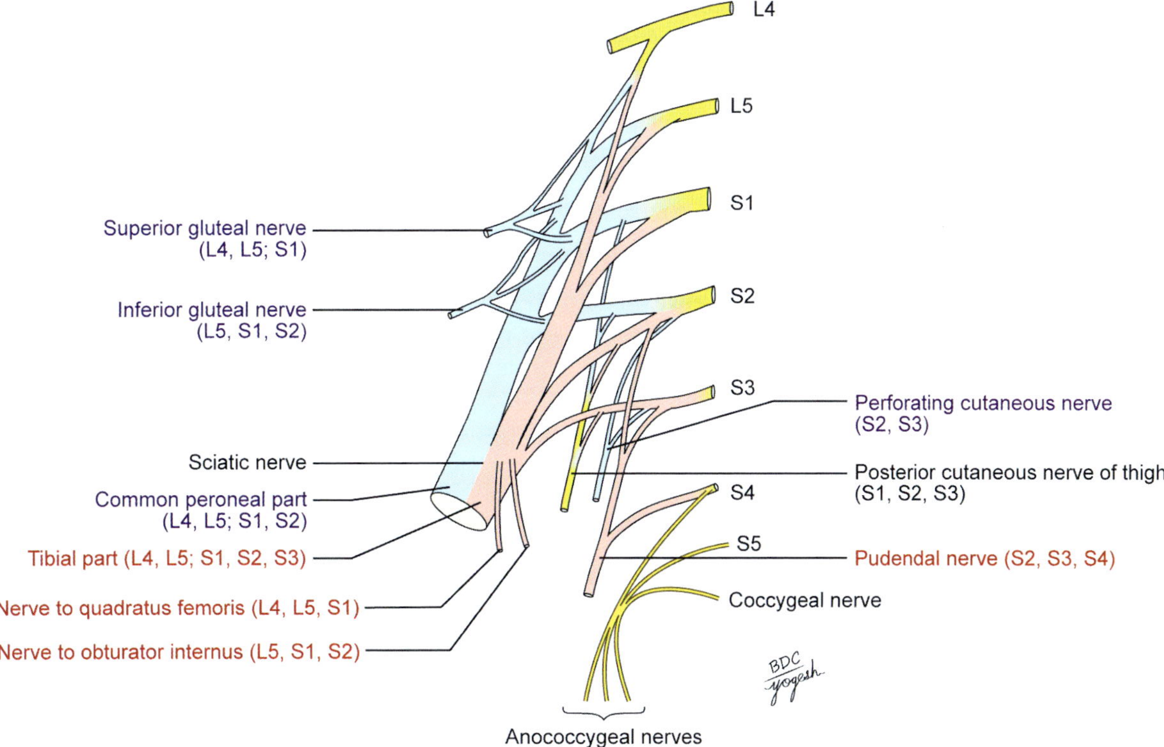

Fig. 34.7: Anterior view of the right sacral and coccygeal plexuses. Dorsal divisions (DDs) are shown by blue colour and ventral divisions (VDs) are shown by pink colour

Flowchart 34.6: Sacral plexus

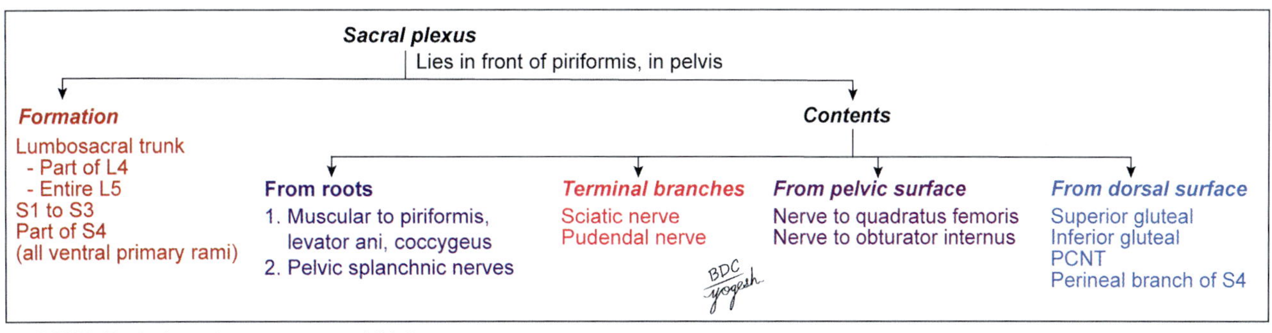

PCNT: Posterior cutaneous nerve of thigh

Terminal branches

1. Sciatic nerve (L4, L5, S1–S3)
2. Pudendal nerve (ventral divisions of S2, S3, S4).

Branches from pelvic surface of the plexus

1. Nerve to quadratus femoris (ventral division of L4, L5; S1).
2. Nerve to obturator internus (ventral divisions of L5; S1, S2).

Branches from the dorsal surface of the plexus

1. Superior gluteal nerve (dorsal divisions of L4, L5, S1)
2. Inferior gluteal nerve (dorsal divisions of L5, S1, S2)
3. Posterior cutaneous nerve of thigh (S1, S2, S3)
4. Perforating cutaneous nerves (dorsal divisions of S2, S3)
5. Perineal branch of S4 nerve.

Note:

1. *Muscular branches for piriformis* directly arise from the ventral primary rami of 1st and 2nd sacral nerves. Twigs for levator ani and coccygeus arise from the ventral primary rami of S3 and S4 nerves.
2. *Pelvic splanchnic nerves or nervi erigentes* (S2, S3, S4): These are preganglionic parasympathetic fibres arising as thin filaments from the ventral primary rami of S2, S3, and S4 nerves. They are motor for the sphincter vesicae and external urethral sphincter. They dilate the arteries of erectile tissue of the penis and clitoris during erection.
3. *Sciatic nerve* (L4, L5, S1–S3): It consists of two components:
   a. *Tibial component* is derived from ventral branches of ventral primary rami of L4, L5, S1–S3.
   b. *Common peroneal component* is derived from dorsal branches of ventral primary rami of L4, L5, S1, S2. Sciatic nerve is the thickest nerve of the body (2 cm wide). It is formed on the pelvic surface of the piriformis and leaves the pelvis below the piriformis.

4. *Pudendal nerve* (S2, S3, S4): It arises from ventral divisions of S2, S3 and S4. It is formed just above the sacrotuberous ligament in the true pelvis. It leaves the true pelvis through the greater sciatic notch below the piriformis. It crosses posterior surface of ischial spine in the gluteal region along with internal pudendal vessels and nerve to obturator internus. All these structures enter the pelvis through lesser sciatic notch. Here, the pudendal nerve runs in pudendal canal to supply perineum.
5. *Nerve to quadratus femoris* (L4, L5, S1): It is formed by the ventral branches of L4, L5, and S1 nerves. It leaves the pelvis through greater sciatic notch below the piriformis. In the gluteal region, it descends on the gemelli and obturator internus tendon. It supplies quadratus femoris, inferior gemellus, and hip joint.
6. *Nerve to obturator internus* (L5, S1, S2): It arises from ventral branches of ventral rami of L5, S1 and S2. It follows the course of pudendal nerve. It supplies superior gemellus in the gluteal region and obturator internus from its pelvic surface.
7. *Superior gluteal nerve* (L4, L5, S1): It arises from the dorsal branches of L4, L5, S1. It leaves the greater sciatic foramen above the piriformis. It supplies gluteus medius, gluteus minimus, and tensor fascia latae.
8. *Inferior gluteal nerve* (L5, S1, S2): It arises from dorsal branches of ventral primary rami L5, S1 and S2. It leaves the pelvis through greater sciatic foramen below the piriformis. It supplies the gluteus maximus.
9. *Posterior cutaneous nerve of thigh* (S1, S2, S3): It arises from dorsal branches of S1 and S2 and ventral branches of S2 and S3 ventral primary rami. It leaves the pelvis through greater sciatic foramen below the piriformis. It supplies skin of gluteal region, back of thigh and leg, and posterior part of scrotum or labia majora.
10. *Perforating cutaneous nerve* (L4, L5, S1): It arises from dorsal branches of ventral primary rami of L4, L5 and S1 nerves. It pierces sacrotuberous ligament, curves round the inferior border of gluteus maximus, and supplies skin over inferomedial aspect of gluteal region.
11. *Perineal branch of S4 nerve*: It pierces coccygeus to enter the ischioanal fossa by the side of the tip of coccyx. It supplies sphincter ani externus and adjoining skin.

Coccygeal Plexus

Formation

It is formed by (Fig. 34.7):

1. Small descending branch from ventral primary ramus of S4 nerve
2. Ventral primary ramus of S5 nerve
3. Ventral primary ramus of coccygeal nerve.

Branches

Anococcygeal nerves – pierce sacrotuberous ligament and supplies the skin in the region of coccyx.

CLINICAL ANATOMY

The lumbosacral trunk (L4, 5) and the ventral ramus of nerve S1 cross the pelvic surface of the joint and may be involved in disease of the joint, causing pain in the area of their distribution below the knee. L4 supplies medial aspect of leg and sole. S1 supplies lateral aspect of sole.

PELVIC AUTONOMIC NERVES

Pelvic Sympathetic System

The autonomic nerves of the true pelvis include:

1. Pelvic part of sympathetic trunk
2. Presacral nerve
3. Inferior hypogastric plexus
4. Pelvic splanchnic nerves or nervi erigentes.

Sacral Sympathetic Chain

The right and left sympathetic trunks descend in the pelvis between the bodies of sacral vertebrae and pelvic sacral foramina (Fig. 34.8). Inferiorly, both the trunks join in front of the coccyx to form unpaired *ganglion impar*. The sacral or pelvic part of sympathetic trunk consists of four ganglia. These chains are connected with sacral and coccygeal spinal nerves through the grey rami communicantes that carry postganglionic sympathetic fibres.

Ganglions: Four pairs of sacral ganglia and unpaired ganglion impar.

Branches

1. Grey rami communicantes to ventral primary rami of sacral and coccygeal nerve.
2. Sacral splanchnic nerves to the inferior hypogastric plexus and rectum.
3. Branches to the median sacral artery.
4. Branches from ganglion impar to the coccygeal body.

Presacral Nerve or Superior Hypogastric Plexus

It lies in front of bifurcation of abdominal aorta at the level of L5 vertebra.

Inferior Hypogastric Plexus

There are two inferior hypogastric plexuses (right and left) that lie in the extraperitoneal connective tissue of the pelvis, by the sides of the rectum.

Coccygeal Body or Glomus Coccygeum

It is a small oval body situated in front of coccyx near the ganglion impar. It contains chromaffin cells derived from neural crest cells. It is also called Luschka's gland.

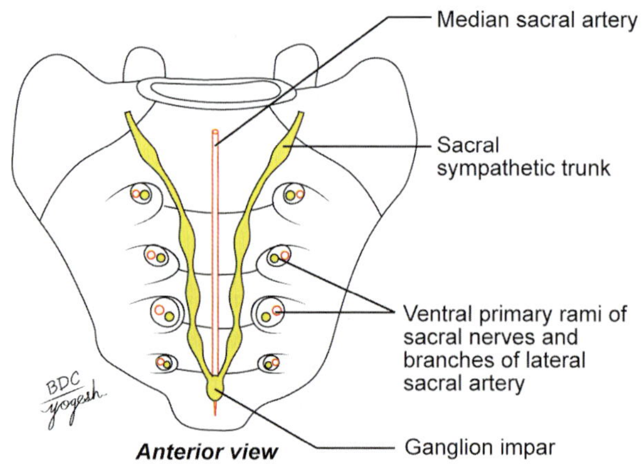

Fig. 34.8: Sacral sympathetic trunks

Pelvic Splanchnic Nerves

Nervi Erigentes

The nervi erigentes represent the sacral outflow of the parasympathetic nervous system. The nerves arise as fine filaments from the ventral rami of S2, 3, 4. They join the inferior hypogastric plexus and are distributed to the pelvic organs. Some parasympathetic fibres ascend with the hypogastric nerve to the superior hypogastric plexus and thence to the inferior mesenteric plexus. Others ascend independently and directly to the part of the colon derived from the hindgut.

DISSECTION

Expose the lumbosacral trunk and ventral rami of sacral one to sacral five nerves. Lift the sacral plexus forwards and expose its terminal branches, the sciatic and pudendal nerves.

Find the nerves arising from the dorsal surface of plexus, e.g. superior gluteal, inferior gluteal, perforating cutaneous and perineal branch of fourth sacral nerve.

Trace the two branches, e.g. nerve to quadratus femoris and nerve to obturator internus arising from the pelvic surface of the plexus.

Trace the sympathetic trunks in the pelvis till these terminate in the single *ganglion impar* on the coccyx.

Trace the large grey rami communicantes from the ganglia to the ventral rami of the sacral nerves.

Find the inferior hypogastric plexus around the internal iliac vessels. In addition, trace the pelvic splanchnic nerves reaching the inferior hypogastric plexus from the ventral rami of S2, S3 and S4 nerves.

JOINTS OF PELVIS

The pelvis is support with the following joints (Plate 34.4):
1. Lumbosacral joints
2. Sacrococcygeal joint
3. Intercoccygeal joints
4. Sacroiliac joints with vertebropelvic ligaments
5. Pubic symphysis.

Lumbosacral Joints

It includes median and lateral lumbosacral joints. It is the articulation between the L5 vertebra and the base of the sacrum (body of S1 vertebra) (Plate 34.5). It is similar to other typical intervertebral joints.

Type

It is symphysial joint that includes large intervertebral disc. Laterally, inferior articular facets of L5 vertebra articulate with the superior articular processes of S1 vertebra.

Articular Surfaces

Anterior intervertebral joint: Inferior surface of body of L5 vertebra and superior surface of body of S1 vertebra.

Plate 34.4: Joints supporting pelvis

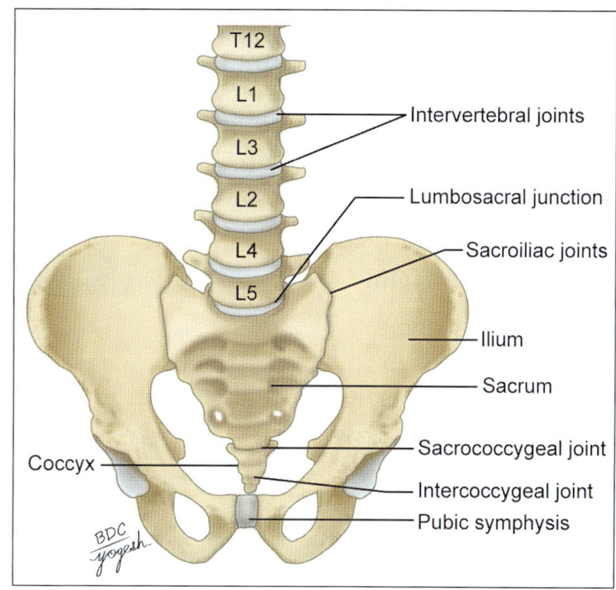

Plate 34.5: Lumbosacral joints (midsagittal section, medial view)

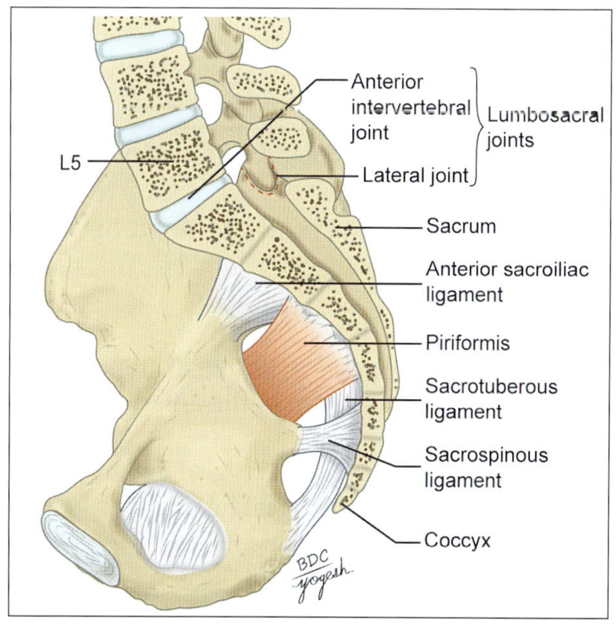

Facet joints: Superior articular processes of S1 vertebra and inferior articular processes of L5 vertebra.

Ligaments

Lumbosacral joint is stabilised by the following ligaments:
1. *Iliolumbar ligament* (strong ligament) extends from the apex of the transverse process of L5 vertebra to the inner lip of the iliac crest.
2. *Lateral lumbosacral ligament* extends from the lower margin of transverse process of L5 vertebra to the ala of the sacrum.

Nerve Supply

Anterior and posterior primary rami from L5 and S1 spinal nerves.

Movements

Flexion and extension in about 18°, whereas lateral flexion at 7° can take place at lumbosacral joint. Flexion is produced by psoas major and muscles of anterior abdominal wall. Extension is produced by interspinalis, multifidus, longissimus lumborum, and iliocostalis lumborum. Lateral flexion is produced by unilateral contraction of the above-mentioned muscles.

CLINICAL ANATOMY

- Lumbosacral angle
- Sacralisation of L5 vertebra
- Lumbarisation of S1 vertebra
- Spondylolisthesis

Sacrococcygeal Joint

It is a joint between the apex of the sacrum and the base of the coccyx.

Type

It is a secondary cartilaginous (symphysis) joint.

Articular Surfaces

1. Apex of sacrum
2. Base of coccyx
3. Fibrocartilaginous articular disc – may be ossified in old age.

Both the articular surfaces are lined by hyaline cartilage.

Ligaments

1. *Anterior sacrococcygeal ligament*: It extends from anterior surface of sacrum to the anterior surface of coccyx.
2. Superficial posterior sacrococcygeal ligament
3. Deep posterior sacrococcygeal ligament
4. Lateral sacrococcygeal ligament
5. Intercornual ligament.

Nerve Supply

S4–S5 spinal nerves and coccygeal nerve.

Movements

- Only slight degree of passive flexion and extension is possible.
- These movements occur during defecation and labour.
- There is no muscle directly acting on the joint.

Intercoccygeal Joints

The intercoccygeal joints are present only in young subjects. They are symphyseal joints with thin discs of fibrocartilage between coccygeal segments. Fusion of coccygeal segments begins at the age of 20 years and is complete by about 30 years.

Competency:

AN50.2 Describe and demonstrate the type, articular ends, ligaments and movements of intervertebral joints, sacroiliac joints and pubic symphysis.

Sacroiliac Joint

Sacroiliac joint is the joint between ilium and sacrum. Right and left sacroiliac joints and pubic symphysis together form pelvic girdle articulation (Figs 34.9a to c).

Function: Main function of sacroiliac joint is weight-bearing.

Type

It is a *plane synovial joint*. Some authors consider it as *syndesmosis* as articular bones are connected by fibrous connective tissue.

Articular Surfaces

Auricular surface on the lateral side of sacrum articulates with reciprocal auricular surface on the ilium (Figs 34.9a to c). Both the articular surfaces show irregularities which are reciprocal and congruent to each other. Articular surfaces are covered with hyaline cartilage.

Ligaments (Fig. 34.10)

1. *Fibrous capsule* is attached close to margins of articular surfaces. It is internally lined by synovial membrane.
2. *Anterior sacroiliac ligament* is thickening of anterior part of the capsule. It is attached to preauricular sulcus.
3. *Posterior sacroiliac ligament* consists of three bands.
   a. *Short posterior sacroiliac ligament* extends from ilium to the transverse tubercles of the first two sacral pieces.
   b. *Long posterior sacroiliac ligament* is a vertical band extends from posterior superior iliac spine to the transverse tubercles of 3rd and 4th sacral pieces.
   c. *Interosseous sacroiliac ligament* is massive and very strong ligament that connects the rough area adjacent to the auricular surface of ilium with the sacrum.
4. *Accessory ligaments:* These are ligaments that contribute to the stability of the sacroiliac joint. They include:
   a. *Sacrotuberous ligament*: Flat triangular ligament
   b. *Sacrospinous ligament*: Thin, triangular ligament.

Relations

Posterior: Erector spinae, gluteus maximus, sacrotuberous ligament.

Anterior

- *Abdominal surface*: Psoas major, iliacus, iliolumbar vessels, obturator nerve.
- *Pelvic surface*: Lumbosacral trunk, posterior division of internal iliac artery and internal iliac vein, superior gluteal vessels, S1 nerve, piriformis.

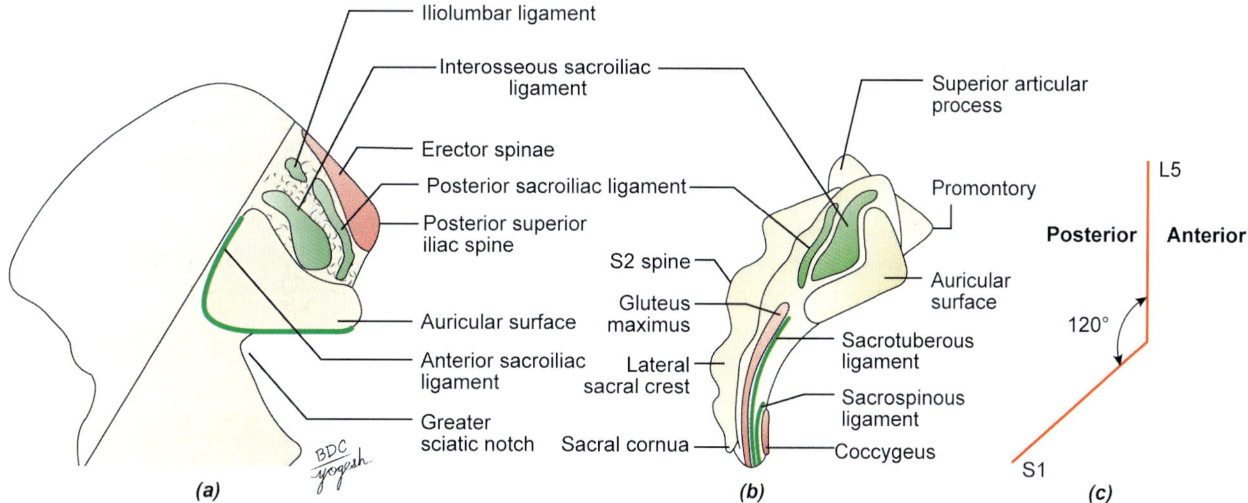

Figs 34.9a to c: Articular surfaces of the right sacroiliac joint: (a) Medial view of the upper part of the right hip bone, (b) right lateral view of the sacrum, and (c) lumbosacral angle is 120° opening backwards

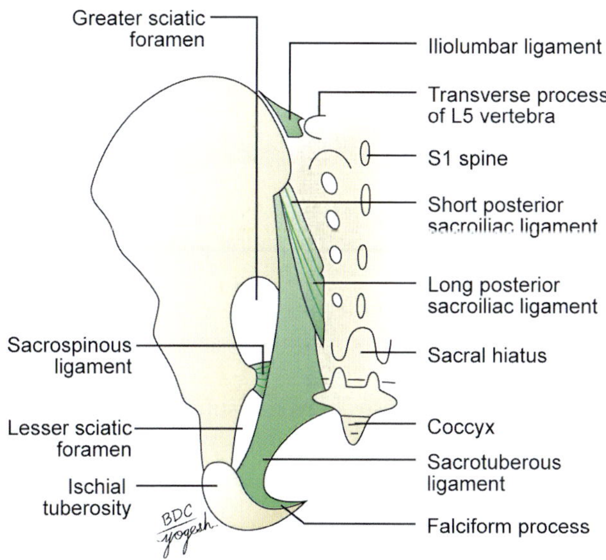

Fig. 34.10: Ligaments of the pelvis as seen from behind

Factors Providing Stability

Stability is the primary requirement of the joint as it transmits body weight from the vertebral column to the lower limbs. Stability is maintained by a number of factors which are as follows:

1. Interlocking of the articular surfaces.
2. Thick and strong interosseous and dorsal sacroiliac ligaments play a very important role in maintaining stability.
3. Vertebropelvic ligaments, i.e. iliolumbar, sacrotuberous and sacrospinous are equally important in this respect.
4. With advancing age, partial synostosis of the joint takes place which further reduces movements.

Blood Supply

Sacroiliac joint is supplied by twigs from all the three branches of posterior division of internal iliac artery, i.e. iliolumbar, lateral sacral and superior gluteal arteries.

Nerve Supply

The joint is supplied by the following nerves.

1. Superior gluteal
2. Ventral rami and the lateral branches of dorsal rami of the first and second sacral nerves.

Movements

During flexion and extension of the trunk, stooping and straightening, i.e. the sacroiliac joint permits a small amount of *anteroposterior rotatory movement* around a transverse axis passing 5 to 10 cm vertically below the sacral promontory. This little movement serves the important function of *absorbing the shocks* of jumping and bearing of loads. The range of movement is increased temporarily in pregnancy in which all the ligaments of the pelvis become loose, under the influence of hormones, to facilitate delivery of the foetus.

Pubic Symphysis

This is a secondary cartilaginous joint between the bodies of the right and left pubic bones. Each articular surface is covered with a thin layer of hyaline cartilage. The fibrocartilaginous disc is reinforced by surrounding ligamentous fibres. The fibres are thickest inferiorly where they form the *arcuate pubic ligament*. Anteriorly, the fibres form the *anterior pubic ligament*.

Functions: Slight movement at pubic symphysis permits shock absorption. During pregnancy, the movements increase at pubic symphysis due to softening of ligaments and cartilages.

DISSECTION

Remove the remains of any muscle of the back or thoracolumbar fascia. Identify the iliolumbar and dorsal sacroiliac ligaments. Remove the dorsal sacroiliac ligament to identify the deeply placed interosseous sacroiliac ligament. Divide this interosseous ligament and open the joint from the posterior aspect.

Define the attachments of ventral sacroiliac ligament. Cut through this thin ligament to open the sacroiliac joint.

CLINICAL ANATOMY

- During pregnancy, the pelvic joints and ligaments are relaxed, so that the range of movement is increased and locking mechanism becomes less efficient. This naturally puts greater strain on the ligaments. The *sacroiliac strain* thus produced may persist even after pregnancy.

  After childbirth, the ligaments are tightened up again, so that the locking mechanism returns to its original efficiency. Sometimes locking occurs in the rotated position of the hip bones adopted during pregnancy. This results in *subluxation* of the joint, causing low backache due to strain on ligaments.
- The *diseases of the lumbosacral and sacroiliac joints can be differentiated* by the following tests:
  a. In lumbosacral lesions, the tenderness is present over the spines and above the dimple of posterior superior iliac spine (over the iliolumbar ligament). In sacroiliac lesions, the tenderness is located inferomedial to the dimple (over the posterior sacroiliac ligament) (Fig. 34.11).
  b. In lumbosacral disease, the movements of vertebral column are restricted in all directions. In sacroiliac disease, the movements are free, except for extreme forward bending, when the tension on hamstrings causes backward rotation of the hip bones, opposite to that of sacrum, producing pain in a diseased joint.

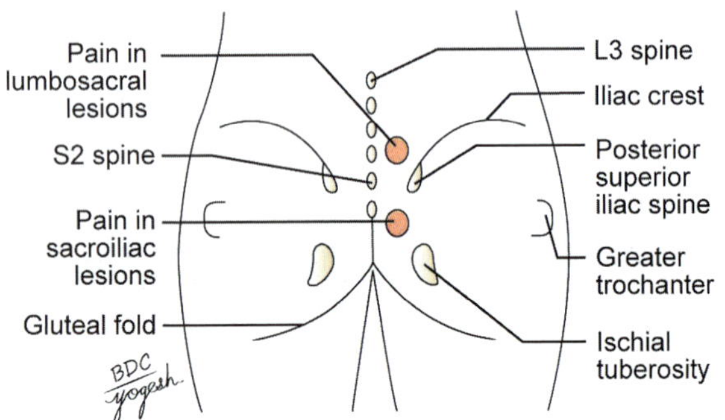

Fig. 34.11: Sites of tenderness in lumbosacral and sacroiliac lesions

- ***Pelvic fracture***: Fractures of the pelvis are one of the most serious injuries. They have a very high mortality and are frequently complicated by associated injuries (pelvic haemorrhage, bladder injury and urethral injury). Common causes include road traffic accidents and falls. They are classified as anterior compression, lateral compression, vertical shear and combined mechanism.

Facts to Remember

- Inferior gluteal artery is the largest branch of anterior division of internal iliac artery. It is also part of the axial artery of lower limb.
- Pelvic viscera are supported by pelvic diaphragm formed by levator ani and coccygeus muscles in the large posterior part of pelvic outlet. In its small anterior part, the muscles of urogenital region support the viscera.
- Inferior vesical is replaced by vaginal artery in female.
- Uterine artery is the additional artery exclusively in the female.
- Ventral ramus of L4 nerve takes part both in formation of lumbar plexus as well as sacral plexus and is called *nervi furcalis*.
- Nerves forming sacral plexus lie outside the parietal layer of pelvic fascia. Blood vessels of the pelvis lie inside the parietal layer.
- The free anastomoses between superior rectal vein of portal and the middle and inferior rectal veins of the caval system explain the metastases in the liver from cancers of the genital organs.
- Interosseous sacroiliac ligament is the strongest ligament of the body.

BDC's Anatomy *e*-book

1. Peritoneum of the pelvis
2. Mechanism of pelvis
3. Further reading
4. Viva voce questions

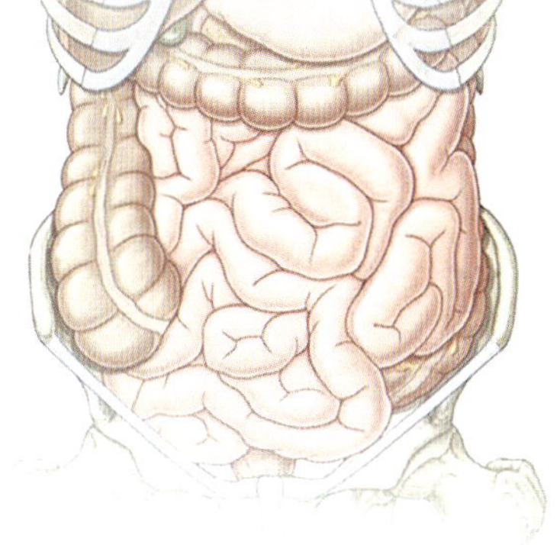

Chapter

35

Surface Marking of Abdomen and Pelvis

PLANES AND REGIONS OF THE ABDOMEN

Two horizontal (transpyloric and transtubercular) and two vertical (right and left lateral) planes divide the abdomen into nine regions (Fig. 35.1). These are described in Chapter 18.

SURFACE MARKING OF VISCERA

Spleen

1. It is marked on the left side of the back, with its long axis corresponding with that of the 11th rib (*Reference*: *Gary's Anatomy*, 42nd edition) (Fig. 35.2).
2. The upper border corresponds to the upper border of the 10th rib, and the lower border to the lower border of the 12th rib (previous concept: 9th to 12th rib).
3. The medial end lies 4 to 5 cm from the posterior midline; and the lateral end 4 cm beyond the left midaxillary line.

Stomach

Cardiac orifice: It is marked by two short parallel lines 2 cm apart, directed downwards and to the left on vii/7th costal cartilage, 2.5 cm to the left of median plane.

Pyloric orifice: It is marked by two short parallel lines 2 cm apart, directed upwards and to the right, on transpyloric plane, 1.2 cm to the right of the median plane (Fig. 35.3).

Lesser curvature: It is marked by joining the right margin of the cardiac orifice with upper margin of the pyloric orifice by a J-shaped curved line. The lowest point of this line reaches a little below the transpyloric plane.

Fundus: This is marked by a line convex upwards drawn from the left margin of the cardiac orifice to the highest point in the left 5th intercostal space just below the nipple.

Greater curvature: This is marked by a curved line convex to the left and downwards, drawn from the fundus to the lower margin of the pyloric orifice. It cuts the left costal margin between the tips of the 9th and 10th costal cartilages and extends down to the subcostal plane, i.e. level of L3 vertebra.

Duodenum

The duodenum is 2.5 cm wide, and lies above the umbilicus. Mark the pylorus, right lateral vertical plane, median plane, transpyloric plane and subcostal plane. Its four parts are marked in the following ways (Fig. 35.4).

1. *First part* is marked by two parallel lines 2.5 cm apart extending from the pyloric orifice upwards and to the right for 5.0 cm (Fig. 35.4).
2. *Second part* is marked by similar lines on the right lateral vertical plane extending from the end of the first part downwards for 7.5 cm.
3. *Third part* is marked by two transverse parallel lines 2.5 cm apart on the subcostal plane, extending from the lower end of the second part towards the left for 10 cm. It crosses the median plane above the umbilicus.
4. *Fourth part* is marked by two lines extending from the left end of the third part to the duodenojejunal flexure, which lies 1 cm below the transpyloric plane, and 3 cm to the left of the median plane. This part is 2.5 cm long.

Caecum

The caecum is marked in the right iliac fossa between inguinal ligament, right lateral plane and intertubercular plane. It is about 6 cm long and 7.5 cm broad. Its axis is directed downwards and slightly medially (Fig. 35.3).

Ileocaecal Orifice or Valve

Ileocaecal orifice is marked on the point of intersection of the right lateral and transtubercular planes (Fig. 35.3).

Appendix

1. The *appendicular orifice* (McBurney's point) is marked at a point 2 cm below the ileocaecal orifice (Fig. 35.3).
2. The *appendix* is marked by two parallel lines 1 cm apart and 7 to 10 cm long, extending from the appendicular orifice usually upwards behind the caecum. However, the position of the appendix is highly variable.

Ascending Colon

Ascending colon is marked by two parallel lines 5 cm apart, immediately to the right of the right lateral

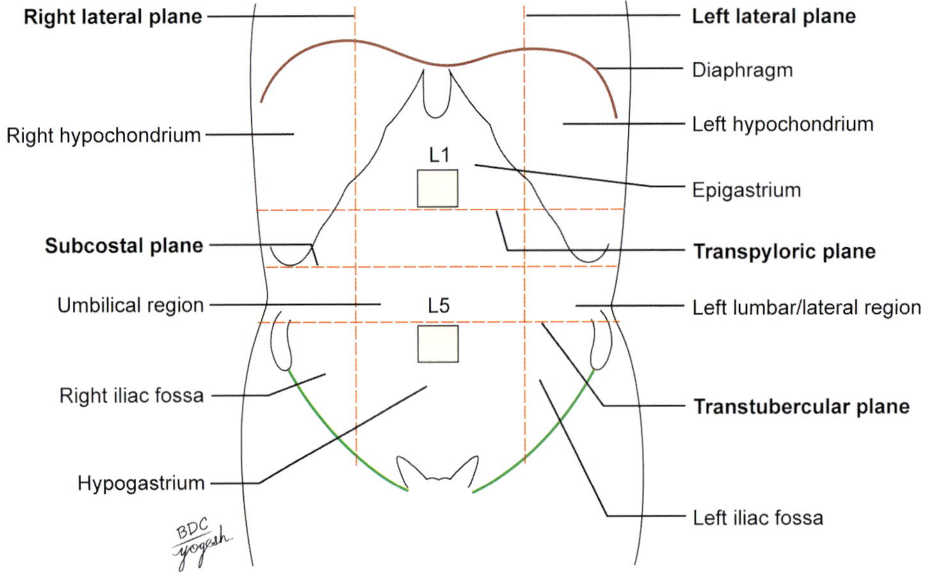

Fig. 35.1: Surface marking of regions of the abdomen

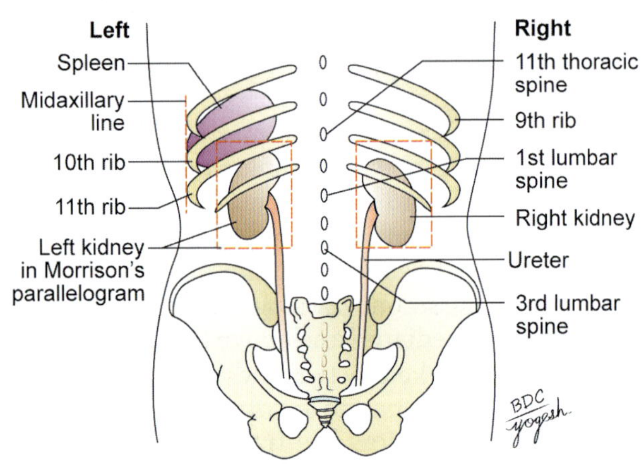

Fig. 35.2: Position of spleen, kidney and ureter from the posterior aspect

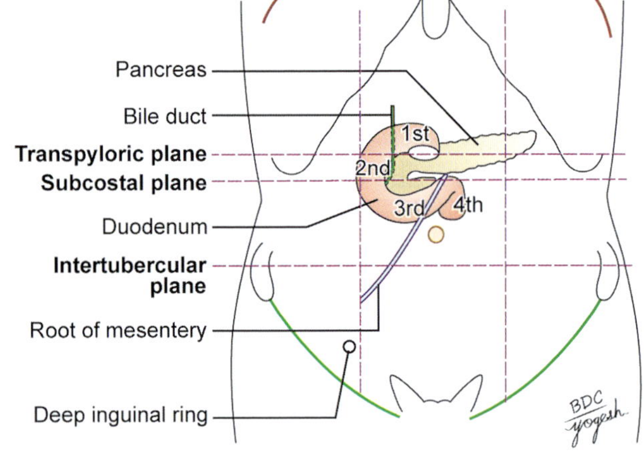

Fig. 35.4: Position of duodenum, pancreas and root of mesentery

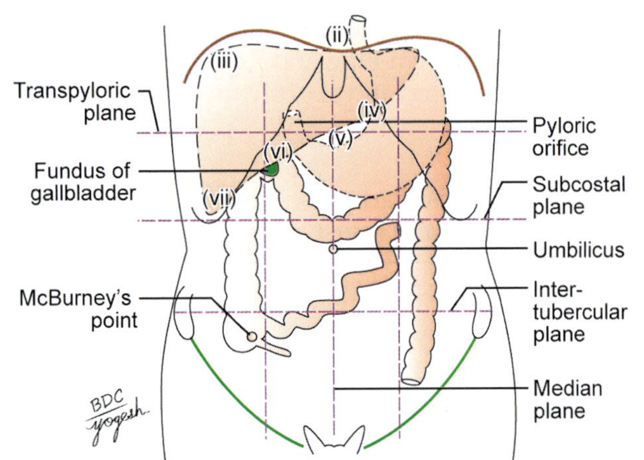

Fig. 35.3: Surface marking of some abdominal organs

vertical plane, from the level of the intertubercular plane (upper end of caecum) to the upper part of the 9th costal cartilage (right colic flexure) (Fig. 35.3).

Transverse Colon

Transverse colon is marked by two parallel lines 5 cm apart. It begins at the upper part of the 9th costal cartilage (right colic flexure), runs downwards and medially to the umbilicus, and then upwards and laterally, crossing the transpyloric plane and also the left lateral vertical plane, to end at the 8th costal cartilage (left colic flexure) (Fig. 35.3).

Descending Colon

Descending colon is marked by two parallel lines 2.5 cm apart. It begins at the 8th costal cartilage (left colic flexure), runs downward immediately lateral to the left lateral vertical plane, and ends at the fold of the groin (inguinal ligament) (Fig. 35.3).

Rectum and Anal Canal

Rectum and anal canal are marked on the back by drawing two lines joining the posterior superior iliac

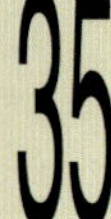

spines to the anus. The lower parts of these lines (from 1 cm below the second sacral spine) represent the rectum and anal canal.

Liver

In surface projection from anterior aspect, the liver is triangular in shape when seen from the front (Fig. 35.5).

a. *Upper border* is marked by joining the following points:
   - First point (i) in the left 5th intercostal space below and medial to left nipple.
   - Second point (ii) at the xiphisternal joint.
   - Third point (iii) at the upper border of the right 5th costal cartilage in the right lateral vertical plane.

b. *Lower border* is marked by a curved line joining the following points:
   - First point (i) in the left 5th intercostal space below and medial to left nipple.
   - Fourth point (iv) at the tip of the 8th costal cartilage on the left costal margin.
   - Fifth point (v) at the transpyloric plane in the midline.
   - Sixth point (vi) at the tip of the 9th costal cartilage on the right costal margin.
   - Seventh point (vii) 1 cm below the right costal margin at the tip of the 10th costal cartilage.

c. *Right border* is marked on the front by a curved line convex laterally, drawn from a point little below the right nipple to a point 1 cm below the right costal margin at the tip of the 10th costal cartilage (points iii and vii).

Gallbladder

The fundus of the gallbladder (Fig. 35.3) is marked by a small convex area at the tip of the right 9th costal cartilage.

Bile Duct

Bile duct is marked by a line 7.5 cm long. The line is vertical in its upper half and inclines to the right in its lower half. The line extends from a point 5 cm above the transpyloric plane and 2 cm to the right of the median plane, to the middle of the medial border of the second part of the duodenum (Fig. 35.4).

Pancreas

First draw duodenum.

1. *Head* is marked within the concavity of the duodenum (Fig. 35.4).
2. *Neck* passes upwards and to the left behind the pylorus in the transpyloric plane.
3. *Body* is marked by two parallel lines 3 cm apart, drawn upwards and to the left for 10 cm from the neck, occupying the upper two-thirds of the space between the transpyloric and subcostal planes.

Kidney

The kidney measures 11 × 5 cm. It can be marked both on the back as well on the front (Fig. 35.6).

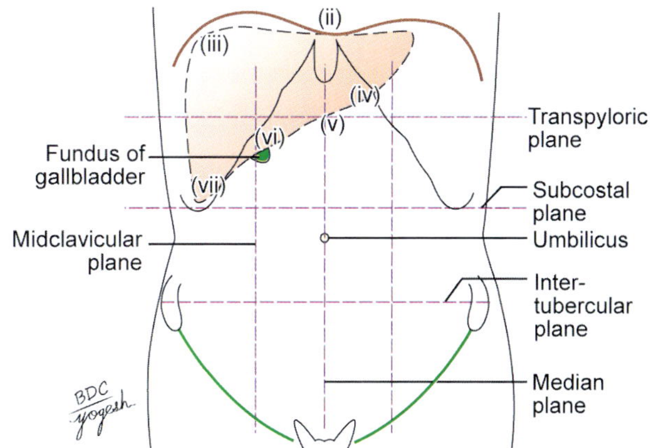

Fig. 35.5: Surface marking of liver

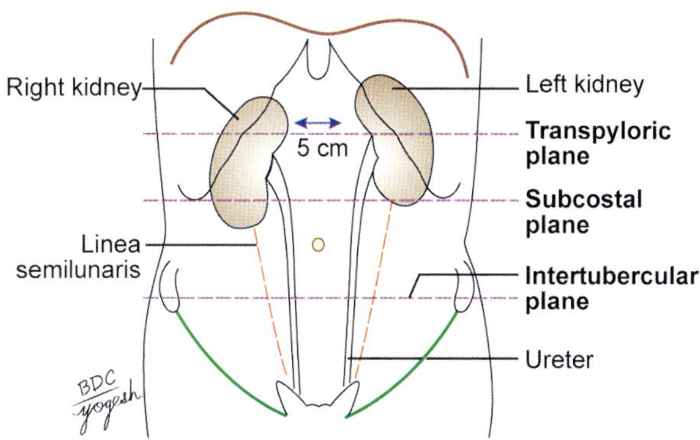

Fig. 35.6: Surface marking of kidneys from anterior aspect

On the back: It is marked within *Morrison's parallelogram* which is drawn in the following ways: Two horizontal lines are drawn, one at the level of the 11th thoracic spine and the other at the level of the 3rd lumbar spine. Two vertical lines: Medial vertical line 2.5 cm from median plane; lateral vertical line 7.5 cm from median plane.

On the front: The bean-shaped kidney is marked with the following specifications.

a. On the right side, the *centre of the hilum* lies 5 cm from the median plane a little below the transpyloric plane; and on the left side, it lies 5 cm from the median plane a little above the transpyloric plane, just medial to the tips of the 9th costal cartilages.
b. The *upper pole* lies 4 to 5 cm from the midline, half way between the xiphisternum and the transpyloric plane (right one, a little lower).
c. The *lower pole* lies 6 to 7 cm from the midline on the right side at the umbilical plane and on the left side at subcostal plane.

Ureter

The ureter can also be marked both on the front as well as on the back.

On the front: It is marked by a line running downwards and slightly medially from the tip of the 9th costal cartilage to the pubic tubercle. The upper 5 cm of this line represents the renal pelvis (Fig. 35.6).

On the back: It is marked by a line running vertically upwards from the posterior superior iliac spine to the level of the second lumbar spine. The lower end of the renal hilum lies at this level (Fig. 35.6).

SURFACE MARKINGS OF VESSELS

Abdominal Aorta

Abdominal aorta is marked by two parallel lines 2 cm apart, extending from a point 2.5 cm above the transpyloric plane in the median plane to a point 1.2 cm below and to the left of the umbilicus (level of vertebra L4) (Fig. 35.7).

Common Iliac Artery

Common iliac artery is represented by the upper 1/3rd of a broad line drawn from the lower end of the abdominal aorta to the midinguinal point (midpoint between anterior superior iliac spine and pubic symphysis).

External Iliac Artery

External iliac artery is represented by the lower 2/3rd of a line drawn from the lower end of the abdominal aorta to the midinguinal point.

Coeliac Trunk and its Branches

The coeliac trunk is marked as a point 1 cm below the beginning of the abdominal aorta (Fig. 35.7).

1. The *left gastric artery* is marked by a line passing from the coeliac artery upwards and to the left towards the cardiac end of the stomach.
2. The *splenic artery* is marked by a broad line passing from the coeliac artery towards the left and slightly upwards for about 10 cm.
3. The *common hepatic artery* is marked by a line passing from the coeliac artery towards the right and slightly downwards for 2.5 cm, and then vertically upwards for 3 cm as proper hepatic artery.

Superior Mesenteric Artery

Superior mesenteric artery is marked by a curved line convex to the left, extending from the abdominal aorta just above the transpyloric plane to the point of intersection of the transtubercular and right lateral planes.

Inferior Mesenteric Artery

Inferior mesenteric artery is marked by a curved line slightly convex to the left, extending from the abdominal aorta 4 cm below the transpyloric plane to a point 4 cm below the umbilicus, and about the same distance to the left of median plane (Fig. 35.7).

Inferior Vena Cava

Inferior vena cava is marked by two vertical parallel lines 2.5 cm apart, a little to the right of the median plane. It extends from a point just below the transtubercular plane to the sternal end of the right 6th costal cartilage.

Portal Vein

Portal vein is marked by a broad line extending from a point on the transpyloric plane 1.2 cm to the right of the median plane upwards and to the right for about 8 cm (Fig. 35.7). It is formed behind the neck of pancreas by union of splenic vein and superior mesenteric vein.

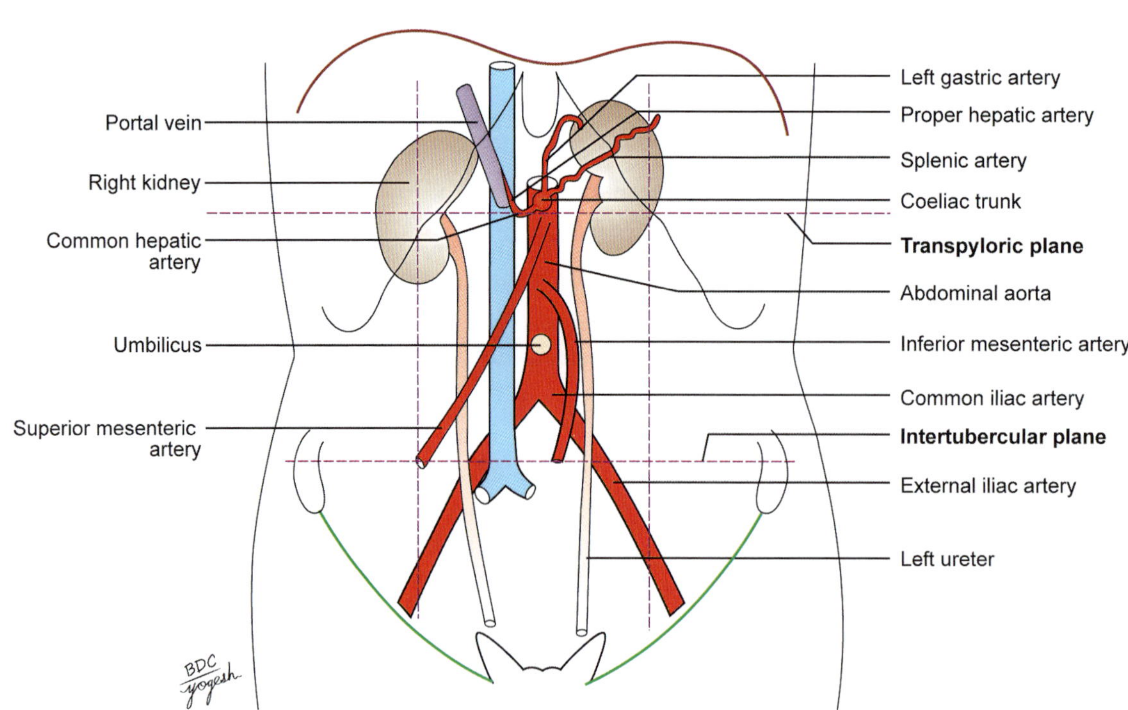

Fig. 35.7: Surface marking of various blood vessels

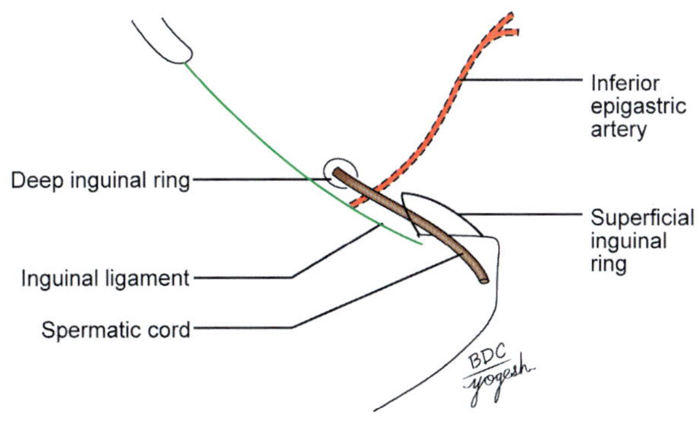

Fig. 35.8: Superficial and deep inguinal rings

MISCELLANEOUS

Inguinal Canal

Inguinal canal is marked by two parallel lines 1 cm apart and about 3.7 cm long, above the medial half of the inguinal ligament, extending from the deep to the superficial inguinal rings.

1. The *deep inguinal ring* is marked 1 cm above the midinguinal point, as a vertical oval ring (Fig. 35.8).
2. *Superficial inguinal ring* lies above and lateral to the pubic crest. Pubic crest forms the base of the triangle; the margins are called the crura. Each crus meets laterally to form an obtuse apex, which lies above and lateral to pubic tubercle. Lateral crus is thicker and curved while medial crus is thinner and oblique (Fig. 35.8).

Root of Mesentery

Root of mesentery is marked by two parallel lines close together, extending from the duodenojejunal flexure to the junction of the right lateral and transtubercular planes. The duodenojejunal flexure lies 1 cm below the transpyloric plane and 3 cm to the left of the median plane (Fig. 35.4).

Chapter

36

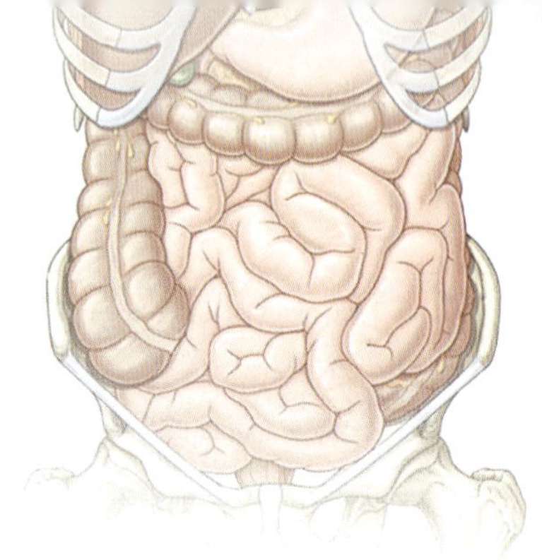

Radiological and Imaging Procedures

The common radiological methods used for the study or investigation of abdomen include the following:

1. Plain radiography
2. Contrast radiography
   a. Barium meal and follow through
   b. Barium enema
   c. Pyelography
   d. Hysterosalpingography for uterus and fallopian tubes.
3. Ultrasonography for the gallbladder, cystic duct, bile duct, pancreas, kidneys, spleen, abdominal vessels, uterus, ovaries and prostate.
4. CT scan
5. Magnetic resonance imaging (MRI).

Competency:
AN54.1 Describe and identify features of plain X-ray abdomen.

PLAIN SKIAGRAM OF ABDOMEN

Nomenclature

Anteroposterior plain skiagram of the abdomen has been variously named, as the straight film, survey film, scout and KUB film. When done in a case of acute abdomen, it is often called a straight film. A scout film is obtained before taking a contrast radiograph. A KUB film is taken primarily for examining the kidney, ureter, and urinary bladder, for which the acronym KUB stands.

Preparation

In cases of emergency, requiring urgent surgical intervention, a straight film is taken without any preparation.

However, in chronic conditions, it is better to prepare the patient to obtain a clear and good picture. The object of preparation is to make the gastrointestinal tract as empty as possible, free from food in the stomach and from gases and faecal matter in the intestines. This may be achieved by:

1. Using antiflatulents for 3 days; antiflatulents like enzyme preparations, charcoal tablets and laxatives.
2. Avoiding oral feeds for about 12 hours before the investigation. Constipated subjects may require an enema to empty their bowels. In a picture taken without any preparation, the shadows of the gases and faecal matter may completely mask the significant findings.

Reading of Skiagram

The plain skiagram of the abdomen can be studied systematically in the following ways.

Bony Shadows

The radiograph (Fig. 36.1) shows:

1. Lower ribs
2. Lumbar vertebrae
3. Upper parts of the hip bones
4. Sacrum with the sacroiliac joints.

However, the whole of the pelvis may have been included in the exposure. The bony shadows are used as landmarks for the assessment of the position of viscera and of existing abnormalities. Any variation in the ribs and vertebrae, if present, may be noted.

Soft Tissue Shadows

The faint shadows of the following structures may be seen.

1. Domes of the diaphragm
2. Psoas major
3. Kidney, made visible by the perirenal fat
4. Liver, beneath the right dome of diaphragm
5. Spleen.

Gas Shadows

Gas shadows are seen as black shadows because gases are radiolucent.

1. Gas in the fundus of stomach appears as a large bubble under the left dome of diaphragm (Fig. 36.3).
2. The scattered intestinal gas shadows are often intermixed with the shadows of faecal matter.

Abnormal Shadows

Various abnormal shadows may be seen in different diseases.

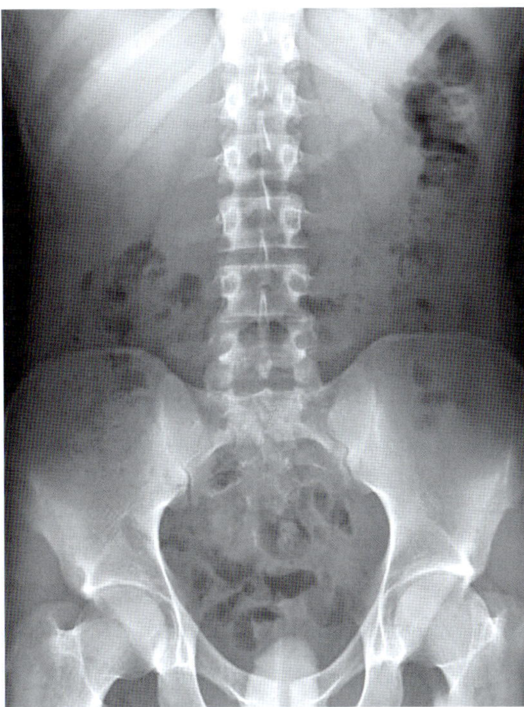

Fig. 36.1: Plain X-ray abdomen

Competency:

AN54.2 Describe and identify the special radiographs of abdominopelvic region (contrast X-ray barium swallow, barium meal, barium enema, cholecystography, intravenous pyelography and hysterosalpingography).

BARIUM STUDIES

Contrast Medium

The alimentary canal can be visualized and examined radiologically by using a suspension of barium sulphate in water. Barium is radio-opaque because of its high molecular weight. Barium sulphate is absolutely harmless to the body and is not absorbed from the gastrointestinal tract. Barium sulphate is not soluble in water and can make only a suspension or emulsion in it.

Principle

The passage of barium through the lumen outlines the mucosal patterns, which can be examined under a screen (fluoroscopy) or radiographed on a film.

Barium Swallow

A 50% suspension of barium sulphate is to be swallowed 2–3 times with patient standing behind fluoroscopic screen. Barium swallow shows the normal position of oesophagus as it lies posterior to aortic arch, left bronchus and the left atrium of heart (Fig. 36.2). Enlargement of left atrium would show narrowed oesophagus.

Barium Meal Examination

Preparation

The subject is instructed not to eat or drink anything for 12 hours before the examination.

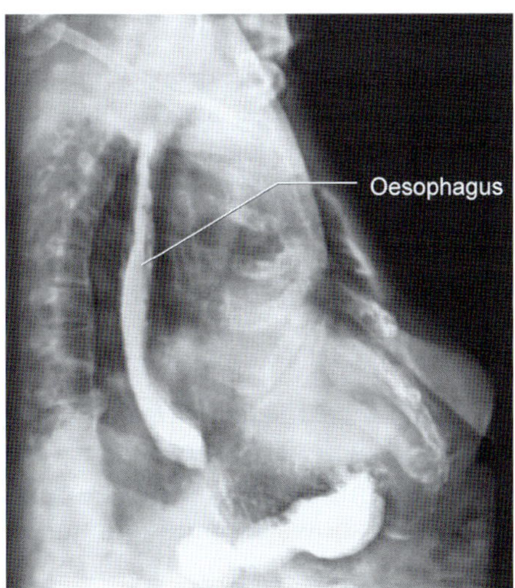

Fig. 36.2: Barium swallow

Administration of Contrast Medium

The patient is made to drink 300 to 400 cc (10 to 15 oz.) of a 5% barium sulphate suspension in water, and then examined under fluoroscopy. Thus, the entire alimentary canal can be examined by following the barium and taking successive radiographs. The stomach and duodenum are visualized immediately after the barium drink (Fig. 36.3). The medium reaches the ileocaecal region in 3 to 4 hours, the hepatic flexure of the colon in about 6 hours, the splenic flexure of the colon in about 9 hours, the descending colon in 11 hours, and the sigmoid colon in about 16 hours. It is usually evacuated in 16 to 24 hours. However, some barium may persist in the large intestine for several days.

Stomach

As barium enters the stomach, it tends to form a triangular mass below the air in the fundus. It then descends in a narrow stream (canalisation) to the pyloric part of the stomach. In addition, the shape, curvatures, peristaltic waves and the rate of emptying of the stomach can also be studied.

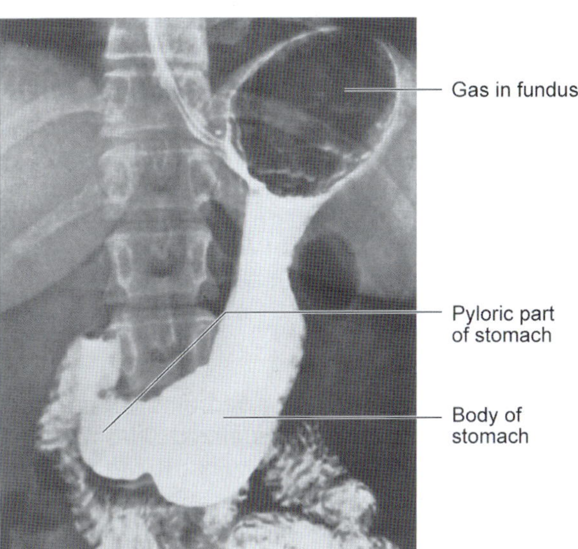

Fig. 36.3: Barium meal follow through

Duodenum

The beginning of the first part of duodenum shows a well-formed *duodenal cap* produced by poorly developed circular folds of mucous membrane and protruding pylorus into it. The rest of the duodenum has a characteristic feathery or floccular appearance due to the presence of well-developed circular folds.

Jejunum and Ileum

The greater part of the small intestine presents a feathery or floccular appearance due to the presence of transverse mucosal folds and their rapid movements.

However, the terminal part of the ileum is comparatively narrow and shows a homogeneous shadow of barium.

Large Intestine

It is identified by its smooth outline marked by characteristic haustra or sacculations, which are the most prominent in the proximal part and may disappear in the distal part. Acute curvatures at the flexures cause superimposition of the shadows. Occasionally, the appendix may also be visible. Diseases of the large intestine are better examined by barium enema, which gives a better filling.

Barium Enema

Preparation

1. A mild laxative is given on two nights before the examination.
2. A plain warm water enema on the morning of the examination.

Contrast Medium

About 2 litres of barium sulphate suspension are slowly introduced through the anus, from a can kept at a height of 2 to 4 feet. The enema is stopped when the barium starts flowing into the terminal ileum through the ileocaecal valve (as seen under the fluoroscopic screen).

Appearance

The rectum and sigmoid colon appear much dilated, and the colon shows characteristic haustrations (Fig. 36.4). The outline of the colon and the haustra may be accentuated by the double-contrast method in which the barium is evacuated and air is injected through the anus to distend the colon. In the background of air, the barium is still lining the mucosa makes it clearly visible.

PYELOGRAPHY

Pyelography (urography) is a radiological method by which the urinary tract is visualized. The radiograph thus obtained is called a *pyelogram*. It can be done in two ways depending on the route of administration of the radiopaque dye. When the dye is injected intravenously, it is called the *excretory* (*intravenous* or *descending*) *pyelography*. When the dye is injected directly

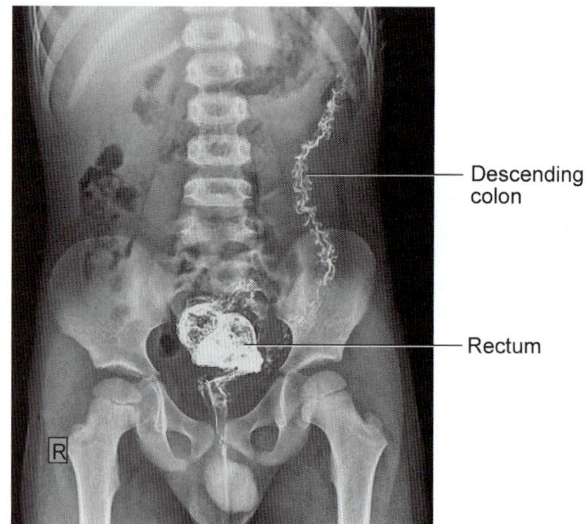

Fig. 36.4: Barium enema

into the ureter, through a ureteric catheter guided through a cystoscope, the technique is called *retrograde* (*instrumental* or *ascending*) *pyelography*.

Excretory (Intravenous or Descending) Pyelography

Preparation

In addition to routine abdomen preparation:

1. For 8 hours before pyelography, the patient is not given anything orally, all fluids are withheld, and diuretics are discontinued.
2. Patient is asked to empty his bladder just before the injection of the dye (Fig. 36.5).

Administration of the Dye

20–40 cc of a warm iodine compound (urograffin 60% or 76% and Conray 420 or Conray 280), which is selectively excreted by the kidneys, is slowly injected intravenously. Care is taken not to push any dye outside the vein because it is an irritant and may cause sloughing.

Exposures

Serial skiagram (excretory pyelograms) are taken at 5, 15 and 30 minutes after the injection of the dye. Maximum concentration is reached in 15 to 20 minutes, and by 30 minutes, the dye fills the urinary bladder.

Reading

Intravenous pyelography is an anatomical as well as a physiological test because it permits not only visualisation of the urinary tract but also helps in assessment of the functional status of the kidney.

Normally:

1. Minor calices are cup-shaped due to the renal papillae projecting into them.
2. Renal pelvis is funnel-shaped.
3. Course of the ureter is clearly seen along the tips of the lumbar transverse processes, the sacroiliac joint and the ischial spine, up to the bladder (*see* Fig. 24.26).
4. Bladder appears oval or triangular in shape.

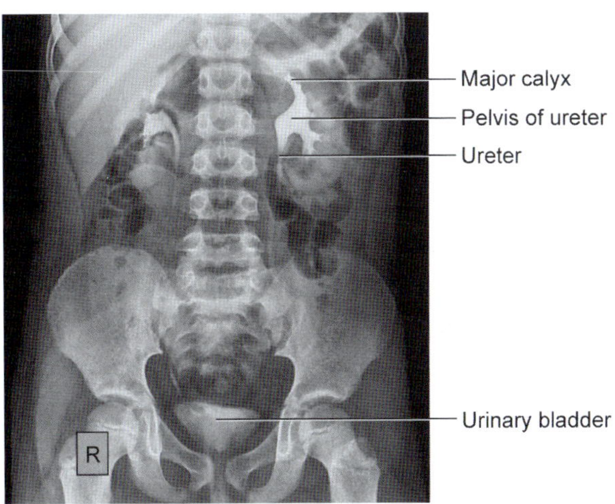

Fig. 36.5: Intravenous pyelogram

Retrograde (Instrumental or Ascending) Pyelography

Preparation

Preparation of the patient is similar to that for descending pyelography.

Injection of Dye

The technique is quite difficult and can be done only by urologists. A cystoscope is passed into the urinary bladder through the urethra. Then the ureteric catheter is guided into the ureteric opening and passed up to the renal pelvis. Through the catheter, 5 to 10 ml of a sterile solution of 6–8% sodium iodide (Conray 280) is injected.

As the renal pelvis is filled to its capacity, the patient begins to complain of pain, when further injection must be stopped. General anaesthesia is, therefore, contraindicated because of the risk of overdistension of the pelvis. If the renal pelvis admits more than 10 ml of the dye, hydronephrosis is suspected.

An ascending pyelogram can be distinguished from a descending pyelogram because:

a. Only one pelvis is outlined.
b. The catheter through which the dye is injected can be seen.

BILIARY APPARATUS (ULTRASONOGRAPHY)

Investigation of Choice

The investigation of choice for gallbladder is *ultrasonography* (Figs 36.6a and b). It can be undertaken on a fasting patient. Gallbladder is seen as a cystic oval shadow with a narrow neck in the right upper quadrant along with visualisation of the bile duct and portal vein.

However, endoscopic retrograde cholangiopancreatography (ERCP) can be carried out to outline the intrahepatic radicals, bile duct, pancreatic duct and gallbladder through the oral route via an endoscope through which a catheter is inserted and the contrast is injected into the common bile duct.

Oral cholecystography is an outdated method for visualising the gallbladder by taking radio-opaque dye, which is exclusively excreted by the liver and concentrated by the gallbladder. The contrast is taken overnight and X-rays are taken 14–16 hours after the intake of the dye when gallbladder, cystic duct and bile duct can be seen. It is, however, dependent on the proper absorption from intestines.

Uterus in the female pelvis is seen by ultrasonography (Figs 36.7a and b).

HYSTEROSALPINGOGRAPHY

This is a radiological method by which the uterus and uterine tubes are visualised and their patency confirmed. The radiograph thus obtained is called a *hysterosalpingogram*.

The investigation is done preferably within the first 5 to 10 days of the menstrual cycle. A tight-fitting cannula is introduced into the internal os of the cervix. The cannula is connected to a syringe through which 5 to 10 ml of an iodized oil (lipiodol) are injected, and the skiagram taken.

The shape and size of the uterus and the uterine tubes are studied. Spilling of the dye into the peritoneal cavity is noted (Fig. 36.8).

Hysterosalpingography is usually done to determine the patency of the uterine tubes in cases of sterility.

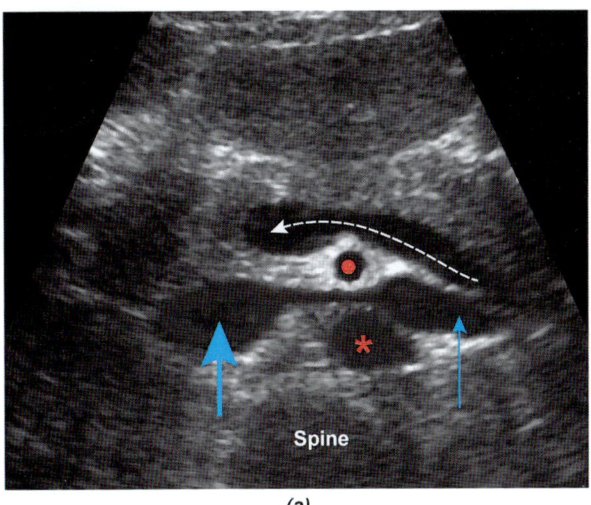

(a)

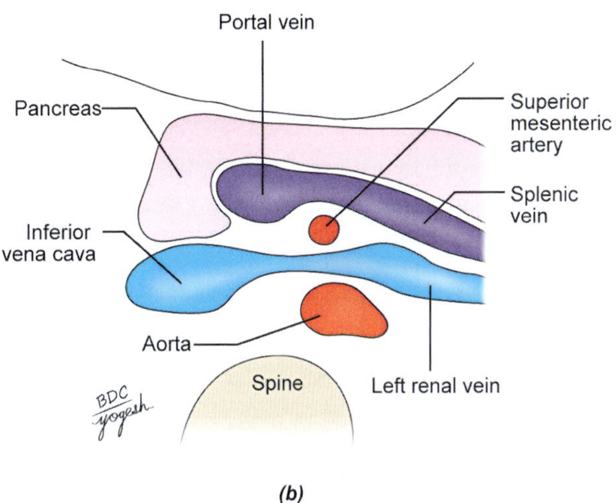

(b)

Figs 36.6a and b: (a) Ultrasound image of pancreas and related structures and (b) diagrammatic representation

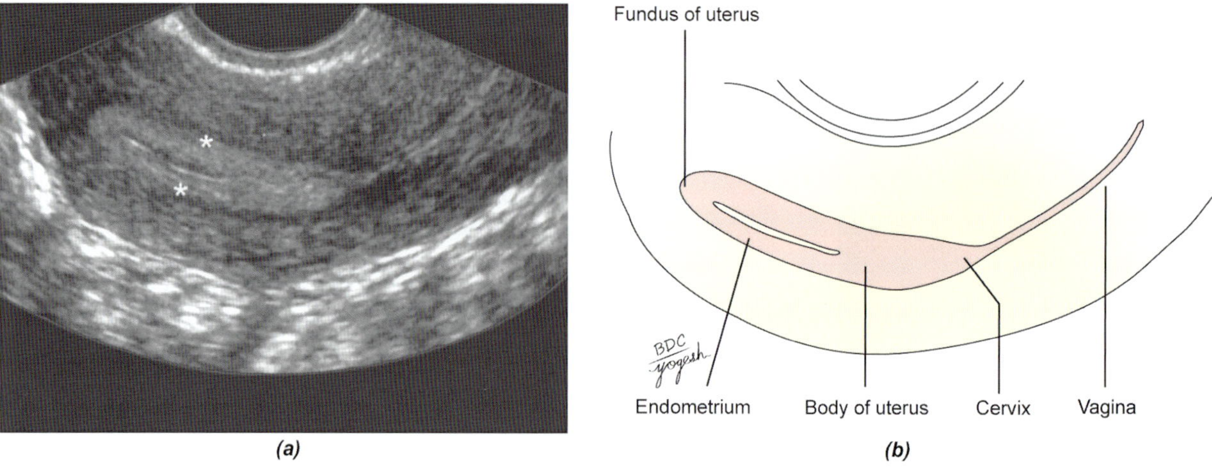

Figs 36.7a and b: (a) Ultrasound image of uterus (marked with *) and cervix and (b) diagrammatic representation

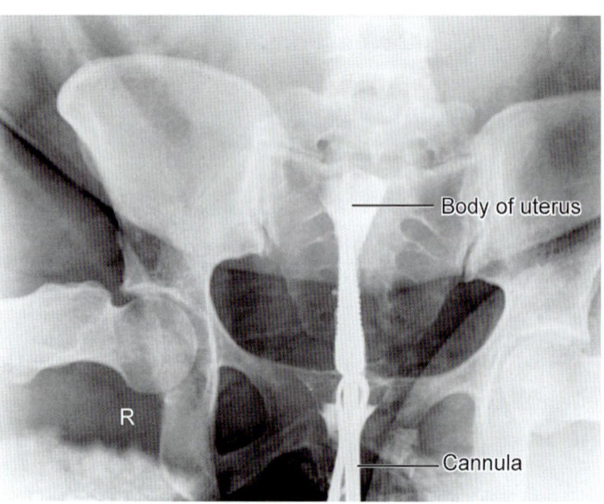

Fig. 36.8: Hysterosalpingogram

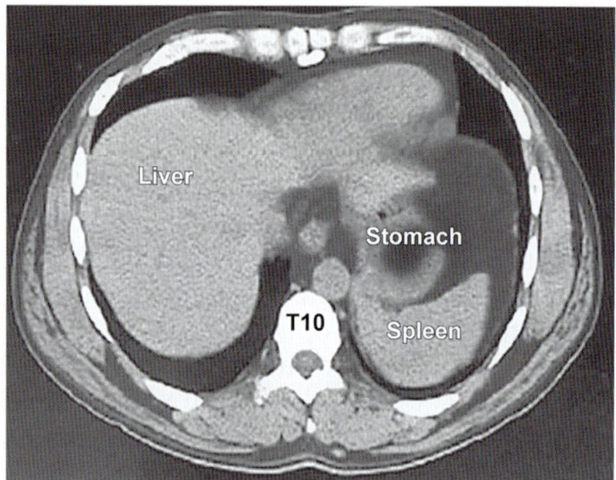

Fig. 36.9: CT scan at level of T10 vertebra

However, it is also of value in the diagnosis of anomalies of the female genital tract. The female pelvic organs can also be seen by ultrasound.

CT SCAN AT T10 AND L1 VERTEBRAE

CT scan at level of T10 vertebra shows mainly stomach, liver and spleen (Fig. 36.9). Stomach is intraperitoneal organ and is movable. Liver is connected to anterior and posterior abdominal walls by superior and inferior layers of coronary ligaments. Spleen is connected to stomach by gastrosplenic ligament and to left kidney by lienorenal ligament.

CT scan at level of L1 vertebra depicts liver, gallbladder, spleen, kidneys and pancreas across the abdominal cavity. Kidneys and pancreas are retroperitoneal organs (Fig. 36.10).

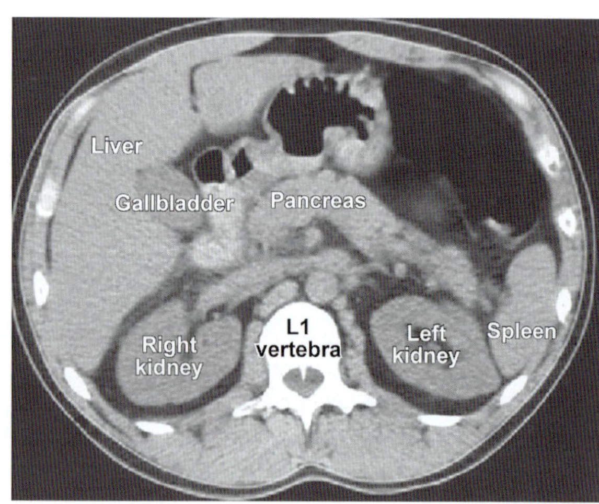

Fig. 36.10: CT scan at level of L1 vertebra

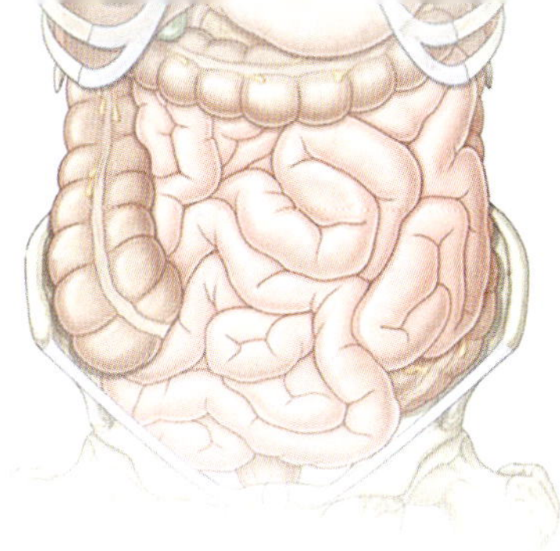

Nerves, Arteries and Clinical Terms

NERVES OF ABDOMEN

The major nerves of the abdomen include (Table A2.1):

1. Lower intercostal nerves
2. Lumbar plexus
3. Sacral plexus
4. Abdominal part of sympathetic trunk
5. Pelvic part of sympathetic trunk
6. Collateral or prevertebral ganglia and plexuses.

TABLE A2.1: Major nerves of the abdomen and pelvis

Nerve/plexus	*Description*	*Branches*
Lower intercostal nerves (T7–T11), subcostal nerve (T12), L1 nerve	Ventral rami of T7–T11	Muscular Intercostal muscles and muscles of anterolateral abdominal wall. (T12 supplies pyramidalis also) Cutaneous Anterior cutaneous branches – supply the skin close to the anterior median line • T10 supplying the skin around umbilicus • T7 – skin of epigastrium • T8, T9 – skin between epigastrium and the umbilicus. • T11, T12 and iliohypogastric (L1) – skin between umbilicus and pubic symphysis Lateral cutaneous branches – divide into anterior and posterior branches to supply the skin of lateral side of abdomen and back.
Lumbar plexus	Ventral rami of L1, 2, 3 and part of L4	Ilioinguinal (L1), genitofemoral (L1, 2), obturator (L2, 3, 4), and accessory obturator (L3, 4) nerves. Lateral cutaneous nerve of thigh (L2, 3), and femoral nerve (L2, 3, 4)
Iliohypogastric	L1	Supply muscles of anterolateral abdominal wall.
Ilioinguinal	L1	Supply internal oblique muscle, transversus abdominis muscle Skin of proximal medial thigh, mons pubis, labium majus and root of the clitoris; anterior scrotum and root of the penis
Genitofemoral	L1 and L2	Femoral branch – skin of the upper part of the front of the thigh Genital branch – supplies the cremaster muscle
Sacral plexus	Ventral rami of part of L4, whole of L5, S1, 2, 3 nerves	*Branches arising from ventral divisions* 1. Nerve to quadratus femoris (L4, 5, S1): Supplies quadratus femoris, inferior gemellus and hip joint. 2. Nerve to obturator internus (L5, S1, 2): Supplies obturator internus and superior gemellus. 3. Pudendal nerve (S2, 3, 4) is described below. 4. Perforating cutaneous nerve (S3, 4): Supplies small area of skin of gluteal region. 5. Tibial part of sciatic nerve (L4, 5, S1, 2, 3): Supplies hamstrings, all muscles of the calf and the sole. 6. Posterior cutaneous nerve of thigh (S1, 2): Supplies skin of back of thigh. *Branches from dorsal divisions* 1. Superior gluteal nerve (L4, 5, S1): Supplies gluteus medius, gluteus minimus and tensor fasciae latae. 2. Inferior gluteal nerve (L5, S1, 2): Supplies only gluteus maximus. 3. Common peroneal part of sciatic nerve (L4, 5, S1, 2): Supplies evertors and foot and dorsiflexors of ankle joint and extensor digitorum brevis.

(Contd.)

TABLE A2.1: Major nerves of the abdomen and pelvis *(Contd.)*

Nerve/plexus	*Description*	*Branches*
Pudendal nerve	Ventral rami of S2, 3, 4	1. Inferior rectal nerve 2. Perineal nerve: Medial and lateral scrotal/labial branches. Muscular branches to deep transversus perinei, compressor urethrae, sphincter urethrovaginalis, ischiocavernosus, bulbospongiosus, external anal sphincter, levator ani, corpus spongiosum, penis and urethra, lower 2.5 cm of vagina. 3. Dorsal nerve of penis/clitoris.
Abdominal part of sympathetic trunk	4 ganglia	1. Grey rami communicates to the lumbar spinal nerves. These pass along the spinal nerves to be distributed to the sweat glands, cutaneous blood vessels and arrector pili muscles (sudomotor, vasomotor and pilomotor). 2. Postganglionic fibres pass medially to the aortic plexus. 3. Postganglionic fibres pass in front of common iliac vessels to form hypogastric plexus, which is also supplemented by branches of aortic plexus.
Aortic plexus	Around the origin branches of abdominal aorta	Coeliac plexus, superior mesenteric plexus, inferior mesenteric plexus, and renal plexus
Coeliac plexus	Two coeliac ganglia	Distributed along the branches of the aorta, namely phrenic, splenic, left gastric, hepatic, intermesenteric, suprarenal, renal, gonadal, superior and inferior mesenteric plexuses, and abdominal aortic plexus.
Superior hypogastric plexus	Lies between the two common iliac arteries	Right and left inferior hypogastric plexus – supply of the pelvic viscera along the branches of the arteries. The plexuses supply gastrointestinal tract and genitourinary tract.
Pelvic part of sympathetic trunk	Ganglion impar	1. Grey rami communicantes to the sacral and coccygeal nerves. 2. Branches to the pelvic plexuses.

ARTERIES OF ABDOMEN AND PELVIS

The major nerves of the abdomen are listed in Table A2.2.

TABLE A2.2: Arteries of the abdomen and pelvis

Ventral Branches of Abdominal Aorta		
Artery	*Origin, course and termination*	*Branches/distribution*
Abdominal aorta	It is a continuation of the descending thoracic aorta at the aortic opening of the diaphragm, opposite to the lower border of T12 vertebra. It descends vertically downward and slightly to the left in front of the vertebral column. It terminates by dividing into two common iliac arteries opposite to the body of L4 vertebra.	1. Coeliac trunk 2. Superior mesenteric artery 3. Inferior mesenteric artery 4. Inferior phrenic artery 5. Middle suprarenal artery 6. Renal artery 7. Gonadal (testicular or ovarian) 8. Four pairs of lumbar arteries 9. Median sacral artery 10. Terminal branches 11. Right common iliac artery 12. Left common iliac artery
Coeliac trunk	It is the artery of foregut and the first ventral visceral branch of abdominal aorta arising at upper border of L1 vertebra. It has a course of 1.25 cm and ends by dividing into left gastric, common hepatic and splenic arteries	1. Left gastric artery 2. Common hepatic artery 3. Splenic artery
Left gastric artery	Smallest branch of coeliac trunk. First it courses upward till the cardiac end of stomach, then it enters lesser omentum to run along lesser curvature of stomach. Ends by anastomosing with right gastric artery	Oesophageal branches Gastric branches
Common hepatic artery	Branch of coeliac trunk. First descends till the upper border of duodenum, where it gives gastroduodenal artery, and continues as proper hepatic artery	1. Gastroduodenal artery i. Right gastroepiploic artery: Gastric and omental branches ii. Superior ancreaticoduodenal artery 2. Right gastric artery 3. Proper hepatic artery

(Contd.)

TABLE A2.2: Arteries of the abdomen and pelvis *(Contd.)*

Proper hepatic artery	It runs upwards in lesser omentum and ends at porta hepatis by dividing into right and left hepatic branches	Right hepatic artery – cystic artery Left hepatic artery
Splenic artery	It is the largest branch of coeliac trunk. Runs sinuously along upper border of pancreas to reach hilum of spleen, where it ends by dividing 5–7 splenic branches	Pancreatic branches Arteria pancreatica magna Arteria pancreatica caudae Short gastric arteries Left gastroepiploic artery – gastric and omental branches.
Superior mesenteric artery	It is the artery of midgut, arising from aorta at lower border of L1 vertebra. Courses downwards and to right to terminate in the right iliac fossa by anastomosing with a branch of ileocolic artery	Inferior pancreaticoduodenal artery – anterior and posterior branches Middle colic artery Right colic artery: Ascending and descending branches Ileocolic artery Jejunal and ileal branches (12–15 in number)
Inferior pancreatico-duodenal artery	First branch of superior mesenteric artery from its right side	Anterior and posterior branches
Middle colic artery	Branch of superior mesenteric artery from its right side. It passes in the transverse mesocolon and divides into right and left branches	Right and left branches
Right colic	Branch of superior mesenteric artery from right side passes to right to reach ascending colon and divides into ascending and descending branches	Ascending and descending branches
Ileocolic artery	Arises from right side of superior mesenteric artery. Runs downwards and to right till the caecum and ends by dividing into superior and inferior branches. Inferior branch ends by anastomosing with superior mesenteric artery	Superior branch Inferior branch: Ascending colic branch, anterior and posterior caecal branches, appendicular artery, and iliac branch.
Inferior mesenteric artery	This is the artery of the hindgut. It is also a ventral branch of abdominal aorta arising at the left, crosses to left at the level of L3 vertebra. It courses downwards crosses common iliac artery and continues in sigmoid mesocolon, by changing its name to superior rectal artery	Left colic artery: Ascending and descending branches Sigmoid arteries (2–4 in number) Superior rectal artery: Right and left branches
Other Branches of Abdominal Aorta		
Inferior phrenic arteries	Right and left inferior phrenic arteries give branches to the respective suprarenal glands and end in the thoracoabdominal diaphragm	Gives branches to suprarenal glands and diaphragm
Middle suprarenal arteries	Right and left arteries run upwards on the muscles of diaphragm to end in the suprarenal glands	Supply suprarenal glands
Renal arteries	These two large arteries arise at the level of L2 vertebra. Reach the hila of respective kidney to supply kidney	Inferior suprarenal artery Anterior and posterior divisions
Gonadal arteries	Arise at level of L2 vertebra. Each artery runs downwards and laterally	Run as ovarian artery in female and as testicular artery in male
Lumbar arteries	Four pairs of lumbar arteries arise from the dorsal aspect of abdominal aorta. These pass laterally and dorsally to supply muscles of posterior abdominal wall. Give branch to the vertebral canal also	Muscular branches Dorsal branch – spinal branch
Median sacral artery	Single artery from back of aorta above its bifurcation. Ends in front of coccyx	Arteriae lumbales image (5th lumbar artery, occasionally present) Lateral branches to the anterior sacral foramina.
Common iliac artery	The two terminal branches of abdominal aorta. Each runs downwards and laterally and ends by dividing into larger external iliac and smaller internal iliac arteries in front of sacroiliac joint at the level of L5 and S1 vertebrae	External and internal iliac arteries

(Contd.)

TABLE A2.2: Arteries of the abdomen and pelvis *(Contd.)*		
External Iliac Artery		
External iliac artery	Larger terminal branch of common iliac artery Courses downwards and laterally till the midinguinal point from where it continues as the femoral artery	Continues as the femoral artery Deep circumflex iliac artery Inferior epigastric artery
Internal Iliac Artery		
Internal iliac artery	Smaller terminal branch of common iliac artery Begins in front of sacroiliac joint, crosses the pelvic brim and ends by dividing into anterior and posterior divisions	**Anterior division** 1. Superior vesical artery 2. Obturator artery 3. Inferior vesical in male or vaginal artery in female 4. Middle rectal artery 5. Inferior gluteal artery 6. Internal pudendal artery 7. Uterine artery in female **Posterior divisions** 1. Iliolumbar artery 2. Two lateral sacral arteries 3. Superior gluteal artery

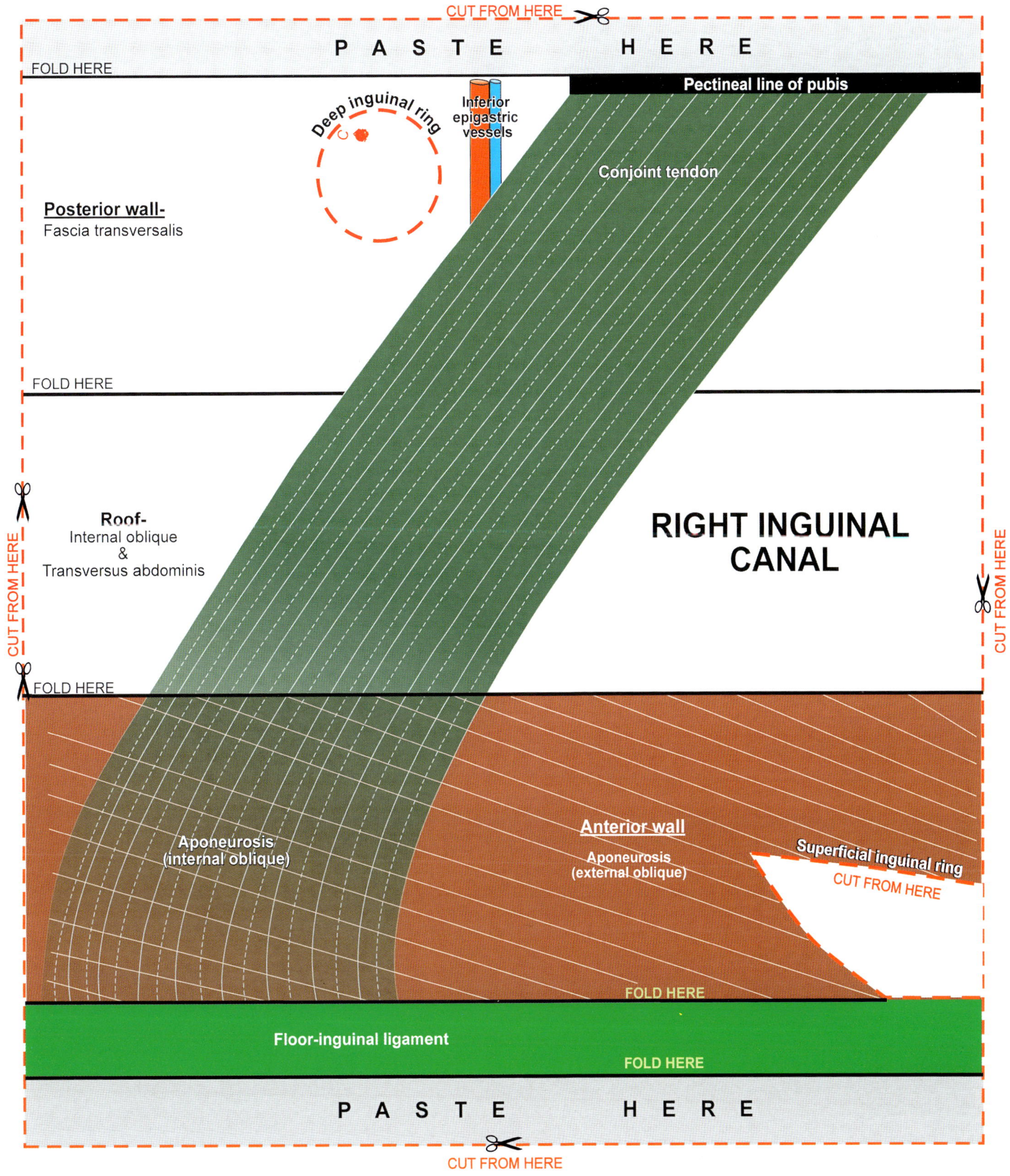

CUT FROM HERE

P A S T E H E R E

FOLD HERE

Pectineal line of pubis

Deep inguinal ring

Inferior epigastric vessels

Posterior wall-

Fascia transversalis

Conjoint tendon

FOLD HERE

Roof-

Internal oblique

&

Transversus abdominis

RIGHT INGUINAL CANAL

CUT FROM HERE

CUT FROM HERE

FOLD HERE

Aponeurosis (internal oblique)

Anterior wall

Aponeurosis (external oblique)

Superficial inguinal ring

CUT FROM HERE

FOLD HERE

Floor-inguinal ligament

FOLD HERE

P A S T E H E R E

CUT FROM HERE

Index

A

G

H

I

J

K

L

M

N

O

P

Q

R

S

T

Free with

BD Chaurasia's

Human Anatomy | Volume 2

Tenth Edition

Workbook of **Human Anatomy**

Learn | Assess | Practice Activity

As per the latest NMC Guidelines | Competency Based Medical Education (CBME) Curriculum under Graduate Medical Education Regulation

Lower Limb

Abdomen and Pelvis

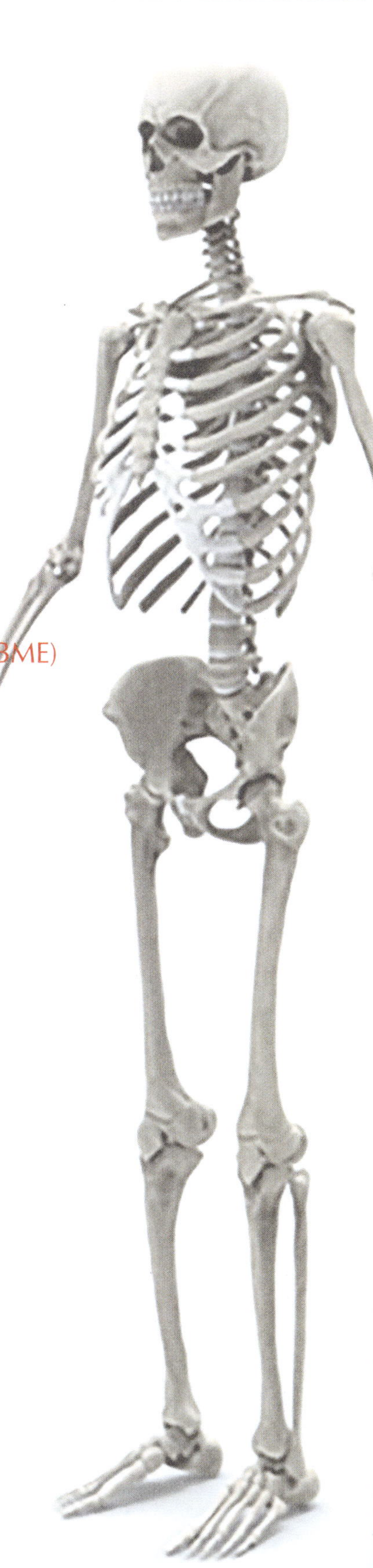

Free with

BD Chaurasia's

Human Anatomy | Volume 2

Tenth Edition

Workbook of

Human Anatomy

Learn | Assess | Practice Activity

As per the latest NMC Guidelines | Competency Based Medical Education (CBME) Curriculum under Graduate Medical Education Regulation

Lower Limb

Abdomen and Pelvis

Executive Editor, BD Chaurasia's *Human Anatomy*, Tenth Edition

Yogesh Ashok Sontakke MBBS MD

Additional Professor

Department of Anatomy

Jawaharlal Institute of Postgraduate Medical Education and Research (JIPMER)

(An Institute of National Importance under the Ministry of Health and Family Welfare, Government of India)

Puducherry, India

CBS Publishers & Distributors Pvt Ltd

New Delhi • Bengaluru • Chennai • Kochi • Kolkata • Lucknow • Mumbai

Hyderabad • Jharkhand • Nagpur • Patna • Pune • Uttarakhand

To accompany BD Chaurasia's Human Anatomy Vol 2

ISBN: 978-93-5466-967-5

Published by Satish Kumar Jain and produced by Varun Jain for

CBS Publishers & Distributors Pvt Ltd
4819/XI Prahlad Street, 24 Ansari Road, Daryaganj, New Delhi 110 002, India
Ph: 011-23289259, 23266838 Website: www.cbspd.com
e-mail: delhi@cbspd.com

Corporate Office: 204 FIE, Industrial Area, Patparganj, Delhi 110 092, India
Ph: 011-4934 4934 Fax: 011-4934 4935 e-mail: publishing@cbspd.com; publicity@cbspd.com

Branches

- **Bengaluru:** Seema House 2975, 17th Cross, K.R. Road, Banasankari 2nd Stage, Bengaluru 560 070, Karnataka, India
  Ph: +91-80-26771678/79 Fax: +91-80-26771680 e-mail: bangalore@cbspd.com
- **Chennai:** 7, Subbaraya Street, Shenoy Nagar, Chennai 600 030, Tamil Nadu, India
  Ph: +91-44-26680620, 26681266 Fax: +91-44-42032115 e-mail: chennai@cbspd.com
- **Kochi:** 42/1325, 1326, Power House Road, Opposite KSEB, Power House, Ernakulum 682018, Kochi, Kerala, India
  Ph: +91-484-4059061–65, 67 Fax: +91-484-4059065 e-mail: kochi@cbspd.com
- **Kolkata:** 147, Hind Ceramics Compound, 1st Floor, Nilgunj Road, Belghoria, Kolkata 700056, West Bengal, India
  Ph: +91-33-25633055/56 e-mail: kolkata@cbspd.com
- **Lucknow:** Basement, Khushnuma Complex, 7 Meerabai Marg (behind Jawahar Bhawan), Lucknow 226001, UP, India
  Ph: +91-522-4000032 e-mail: tiwari.lucknow@cbspd.com
- **Mumbai:** PWD Shed, Gala No. 25/26, Ramchandra Bhatt Marg, Next JJ Hospital Gate No. 2, Opp. Union Bank of India, Noorbaug, Mumbai 400009, Maharashtra, India
  Ph: +91-22-66661880/89 e-mail: mumbai@cbspd.com

Representatives

- **Hyderabad** 0-9885175004
- **Patna** 0-9334159340
- **Jharkhand** 0-9811541605
- **Pune** 0-9664372571
- **Nagpur** 0-8692091830
- **Uttarakhand** 0-9716462459

Printed at: Thomson Press (India) Ltd., Faridabad, Haryana, India

Preface

The *Workbook of Human Anatomy* is prepared after discussions with the students to fulfil the requirements of students for examination preparations. This workbook will help the students to achieve the required levels of the given competencies: Knows (K), knows how (KH) and shows how (SH), with the help of included domains of learning, knowledge (K) and skills (S). To fulfil the need for curriculum, requirements of the students and the field of medicine, it is essential for every learner to convert subject knowledge into presentable format in the examinations.

Students face the problem in revision and focusing on the practice of figures and revising the subject. Each book on the anatomy contains thousands of images. It is very difficult to select the figures to be practised. To solve these students' concerns, this *Workbook* has been prepared to help the students by making them aware about practising selected figures for preparation of theory examinations. The students should keep in mind that while answering the questions in the examination about anatomy, if they support the answer by a selected figure, the explanation will be easy and presentable.

To address these issues of the students, this workbook is facilitated with the following features:

1. Clinicoanatomical problems will help to sensitize the students to Early Clinical Exposure.
2. MCQs will help in analysing the understanding of the subject.
3. Question Bank will help to prepare for upcoming academic examinations.
4. Spotters will help to prepare for practical examinations.
5. Answer Keys will help to cross-check and self-assessments.

Always read a complete textbook for getting better knowledge and generating perfect concepts of the subject. ***Cadavers and dissections are the best teachers of human anatomy***. Due to increasing number of students in the medical colleges and less availability of cadavers, under the expertise of teachers, the students can utilize their spare time in the dissection hall to complete this workbook. It will help in consolidation of the knowledge and better understanding of the structures. Due to space constrain, all practice figures are not included in this Workbook. Students are advised to practice additional images in their practice notebooks.

For any suggestions, please write at dryogeshas@gmail.com

Yogesh Ashok Sontakke
dryogeshas@gmail.com

Instructions to Students

1. Read the theory part from the main textbook before starting to solve the workbook.
2. *Clinicoanatomical problems*: Read these problems carefully. Write precise answers. Use separate sheet of copy for writing in details.
3. *Practice figures*: As we are aware that many students are good in drawings and to avoid difficulty of initial stages of drawings, the workbook is provided with dotted outlines of practice figures. Trace these lines with suitable colour pencils and shade the figures. Refer the main Textbook before colouring the figures. Label the figures with good handwriting.
4. *MCQs*: Tick the single best correct option in the workbook. Some diagram based MCQs are introduced to align with CBME pattern.
5. *Question Bank*: It will give orientation towards upcoming academic examinations. Use separate copy to solve the following questions. Maintain this copy properly so that it can be referred during subject revision.
6. *Spotters*: These will give orientation towards practical examinations. Solve them on a separate sheet.
7. *Answer Keys*: Match your answers with the provided key. Self-evaluation is the best method for progress.
8. *eSmartQuiz – Online MCQ test*: Scan the QR code for online MCQ test. Fill the required details and solve the test.

Always keep in mind *"Practice is essential and integral part of academics. Hard work is the path for success"*.

Yogesh Ashok Sontakke

Contents

eSmartQuiz – Online MCQ Test

After attending the class, students should go through the "*eSmartQuiz* – Online MCQ test" for the following reasons:

- *Reinforcement of Learning*: The "*eSmartQuiz* – Online MCQ test" provides an opportunity to reinforce learning after attending a class or reading a book. It helps to assess understanding and retention of concepts, to solidify knowledge and identify areas that need further revision or clarification.
- *Assessment of Comprehension*: The "*eSmartQuiz* – Online MCQ test" is an effective tool to assess comprehension of the subject matter and to demonstrate the ability to apply the concepts learned in the class.
- *Enhancement of Attention and Critical Thinking*: The "*eSmartQuiz* – Online MCQ test" will help to make students attentive for the class and to enhance critical thinking skills by selecting the most appropriate answer among the given options.

Each *eSmartQuiz* test consists of 10 MCQ, mostly image-based, and the students can see their scores at the end of each test. These questions will be modified after a certain interval. Use the given links or scan the QR code (given in each chapter) for the test. One student can solve each test only one time.

Chapter	*Link for* ***eSmartQuiz***
Lower Limb	
1. Introduction	https://forms.gle/NRD1x2JNDTgRCKP8A
2. Bones of Lower Limb	https://forms.gle/h5Q9mGxpUd6QyGXA6
3. Front of Thigh	https://forms.gle/hDFsJd1Z7Bb2srAYA
4. Medial Side of Thigh	https://forms.gle/SMJp1NN4pEvhjKXAA
5. Gluteal Region	https://forms.gle/fHLmnxN4AQri9yWQA
6. Popliteal Fossa	https://forms.gle/ZWaNVwwx1bSCbmt78
7. Back of Thigh	https://forms.gle/ycdgWXengkHBGf1U6
8. Front of Leg with Dorsum of Foot; Lateral and Medial Sides of Leg	https://forms.gle/MXUuoohUSG78axgC9
9. Back of Leg	https://forms.gle/fQDyryQMFrj8wd367
10. Sole of Foot	https://forms.gle/FNMDK27oq214B5HM9
11. Venous and Lymphatic Drainage; Segmental and Sympathetic Innervation	https://forms.gle/GGerj5QhwaXTHEE79
12. Joints of Lower Limb	https://forms.gle/h1tsJyw7LHPjoorp8
13. Arches of Foot	https://forms.gle/knQU4jRtBTJtZB4q6
14. Surface and Radiological Anatomy of Lower Limb	https://forms.gle/XKF5AnXCuVma6GAK7
Abdomen and Pelvis	
15. Introduction and Osteology of Abdomen	https://forms.gle/Hp4nkwjwCMvj4EzL9
16. Anterior Abdominal Wall	https://forms.gle/EJK7Jfbu98HURPTe7
17. Male External Genital Organs	https://forms.gle/cdzkugyBMuY6Kcgb8
18. Abdominal Cavity and Peritoneum	https://forms.gle/1oFckyZQrFMukRAY8
19. Abdominal Part of Oesophagus and Stomach	https://forms.gle/LEuZcnnGYthhX3X57
20. Small and Large Intestines	https://forms.gle/MLheERXtp6DaKmM27
21. Large Blood Vessels of the Gut	https://forms.gle/wvcrmtfwwRNc6qa78
22. Extrahepatic Biliary Apparatus	https://forms.gle/wqF56B31VuCcmAVf8
23. Spleen, Pancreas and Liver	https://forms.gle/hbBKKRzMGtdgfhej9

(Contd.)

(*Contd.*)

Chapter	*Link for* ***eSmartQuiz***
24. Kidney and Ureter	https://forms.gle/X9ciDTSfZFrSrH8x5
25. Suprarenal Gland and Chromaffin System	https://forms.gle/NQ8NZMHXV6rv4Mgw9
26. Thoracoabdominal Diaphragm	https://forms.gle/hbweRURskHBGxxaT6
27. Posterior Abdominal Wall	https://forms.gle/r5LpaZxDTJttJssQA
28. Perineum	https://forms.gle/T7ubgYmw4sGJZM9o8
29. Preliminary Consideration of Boundaries and Contents of Pelvis	https://forms.gle/gwzfqVVg3ch3MvcM8
30. Urinary Bladder and Urethra	https://forms.gle/WNPbBLGFfAh5GKKd7
31. Female Reproductive Organs	https://forms.gle/XD6GirCZd1g1g2Ht7
32. Male Internal Genital Organs	https://forms.gle/c6RzPMqBkYZHWkg86
33. Rectum and Anal Canal	https://forms.gle/8hcohRy1S84wzVyk7
34. Walls of Pelvis	https://forms.gle/q9NoHXkiZ9SNcASn9
35. Surface Marking of Abdomen and Pelvis	https://forms.gle/dL7zyQVdjdFTXjkHA
36. Radiological and Imaging Procedures	https://forms.gle/mMyvGuXv6pdccaKPA

Lower Limb

Chapter

1

eSmartQuiz

Introduction

MULTIPLE CHOICE QUESTIONS

(Tick the single best correct option)

1. ____________ is the largest sesamoid bone in the human body.
   a. Pisiform b. Patella
   c. Fabella d. Rider's bone
2. Which of the following is a true statement about the line of gravity in the lower limb?
   a. Passes behind the hip joint
   b. Passes anterior to the hip joint
   c. Passes anterior to the knee joint
   d. Passes posterior to the ankle joint
3. The knee joint is formed by all of the following bones, EXCEPT:
   a. Tibia b. Femur
   c. Fibula d. Patella
4. Which of the following bones does not take part in the hip bone formation?
   a. Ilium b. Pubis
   c. Ischium d. Sacrum
5. Out of the 60 kg weight kept on the head, ____________ kg weight will be transmitted to each foot.
   a. 5 b. 15
   c. 25 d. 30
6. Which is the most common site of the intramuscular injections in children?
   a. Gluteal region
   b. Lateral side of arm
   c. Anterolateral aspect of thigh
   d. Cubital fossa
7. Which is the longest muscle?
   a. Plantaris b. Sartorius
   c. Gracilis d. Gluteus maximus
8. Which is the longest vein of the body?
   a. Median cubital vein
   b. Great saphenous vein
   c. Cephalic vein
   d. Basilic vein
9. Which of the following arterial pulsations is commonly felt in the lower limb?
   a. Femoral
   b. Popliteal
   c. Dorsalis pedis
   d. All of the above
10. Ham is ____________.
    a. Superolateral part of gluteal region
    b. Lower part of back of thigh and back of leg
    c. Plantar aspect of foot
    d. Lateral aspect of leg

QUESTION BANK

(Use separate copy to solve the following questions)

1. How does the centre of gravity pass in the human body?
2. Enlist the following:
   a. Parts of the lower limb as regions, bones and joints
   b. Homologous parts of the upper and lower limbs
   c. Differences in lower and upper limbs

Chapter

2

eSmartQuiz

Bones of Lower Limb

CLINICOANATOMICAL PROBLEMS

Clinical Case 1

An 80-year-old woman, living independently, fell at home, experiencing immediate hip pain. On radiological investigation, fracturing of her right femur neck was confirmed. Surgical intervention revealed avascular necrosis of the femoral head.

1. Why fractures are common in old-aged females?
2. On plain radiograph, which line helps for diagnosis of fracture neck femur?
3. Give anatomical basis for avascular necrosis of femur.

Explanation

1. ______________________________

2. ______________________________

3. ______________________________

Clinical Case 2

A 10-year-old boy presented with a painful, swollen right leg following a minor injury while playing. Radiological imaging revealed signs of osteomyelitis in the tibia, evidenced by bone destruction and surrounding soft tissue swelling. Pus accumulation indicated infection.

1. Give anatomical basis for:
   a. Osteomyelitis common in children.
   b. Upper end of tibia is common site for osteomyelitis.
   c. Osteomyelitis is less common in adults.

Explanation

Anatomical basis for:

a. ______________________________

b. ______________________________

c. ______________________________

PRACTICE FIGURES

(Label the practice figures)

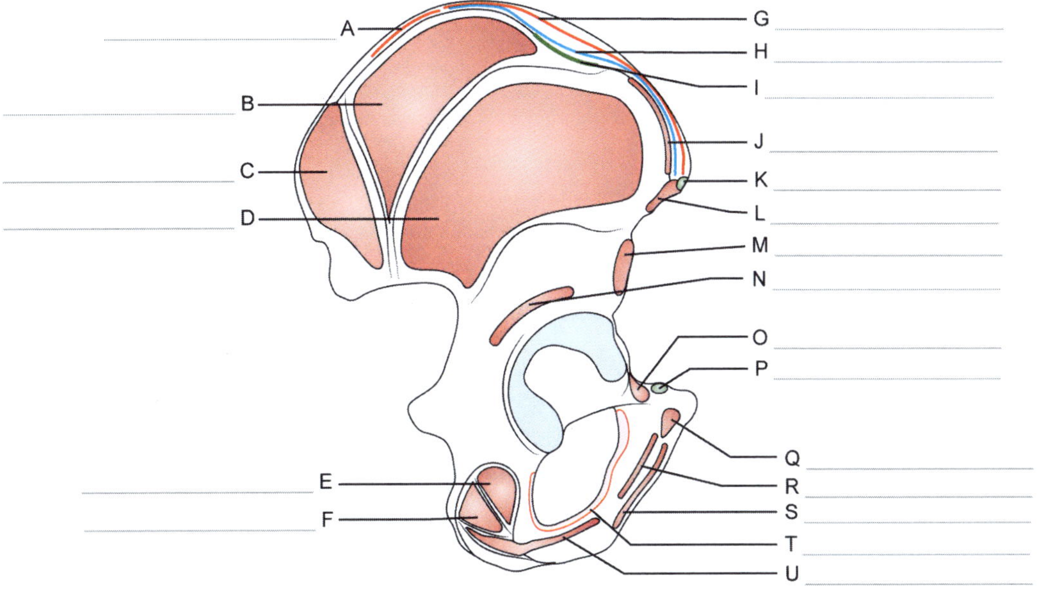

Practice Figure 2.1: Attachments on the outer surface of the right hip bone

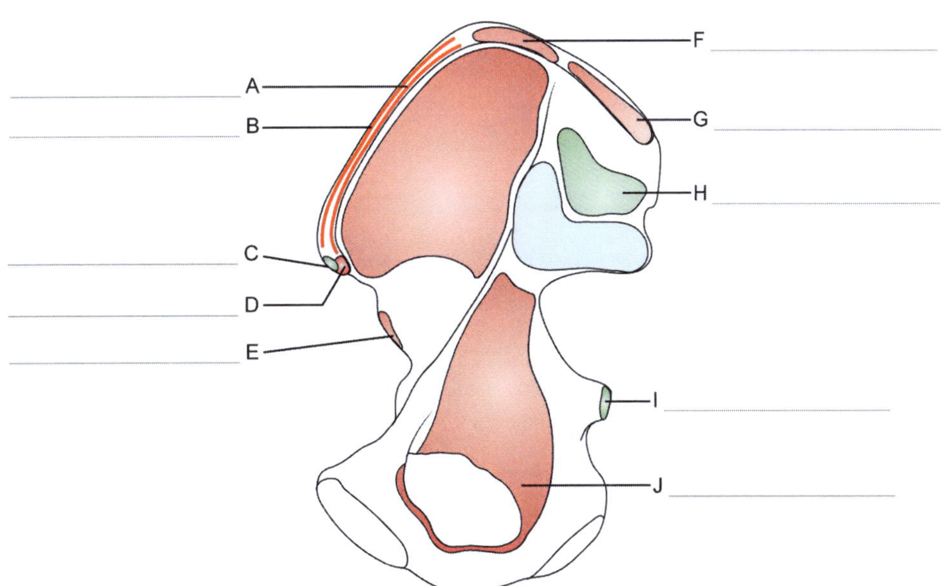

Practice Figure 2.2: Attachments on the inner surface of the right hip bone

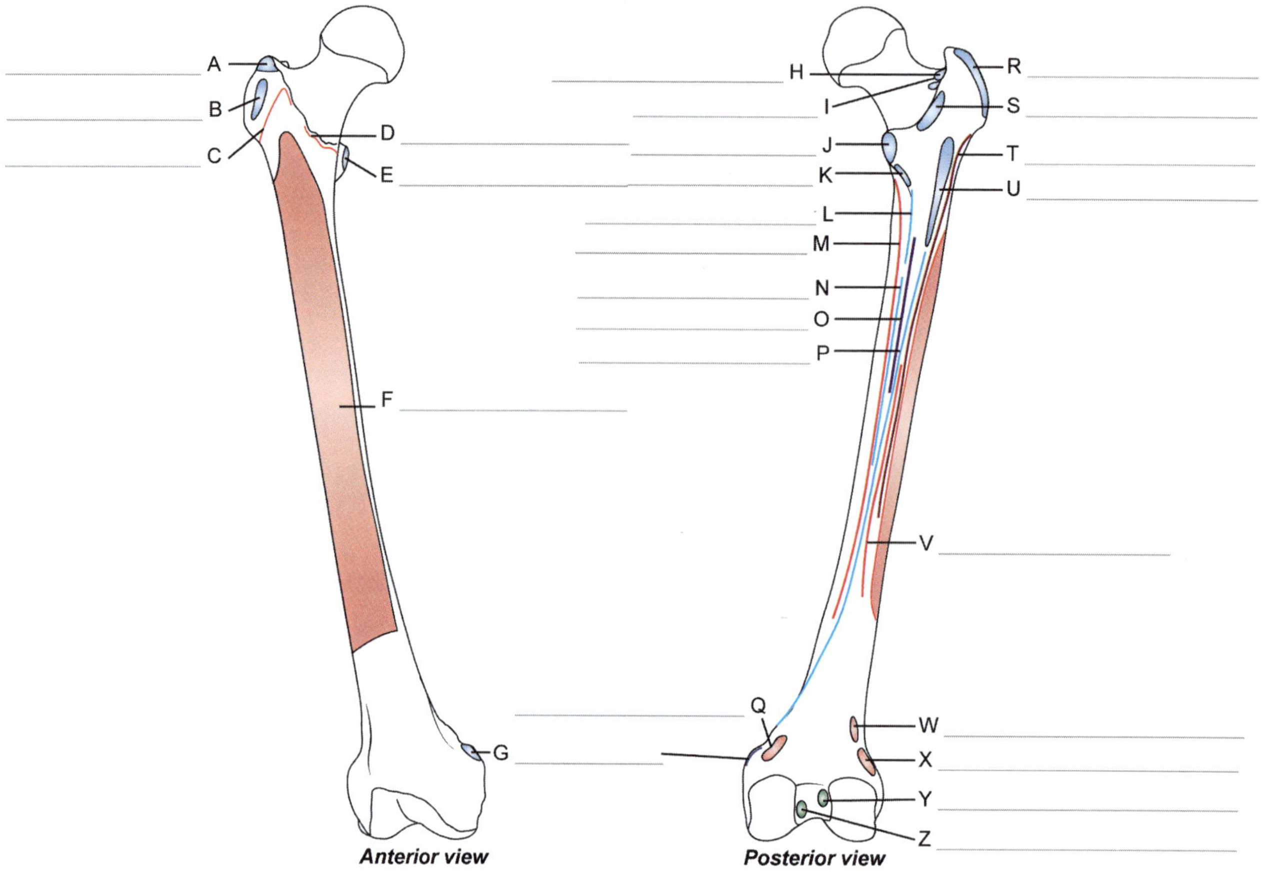

A B C D E F G

Anterior view

H I J K L M N O P Q R S T U V W X Y Z

Posterior view

Practice Figure 2.3: Attachments on the right femur

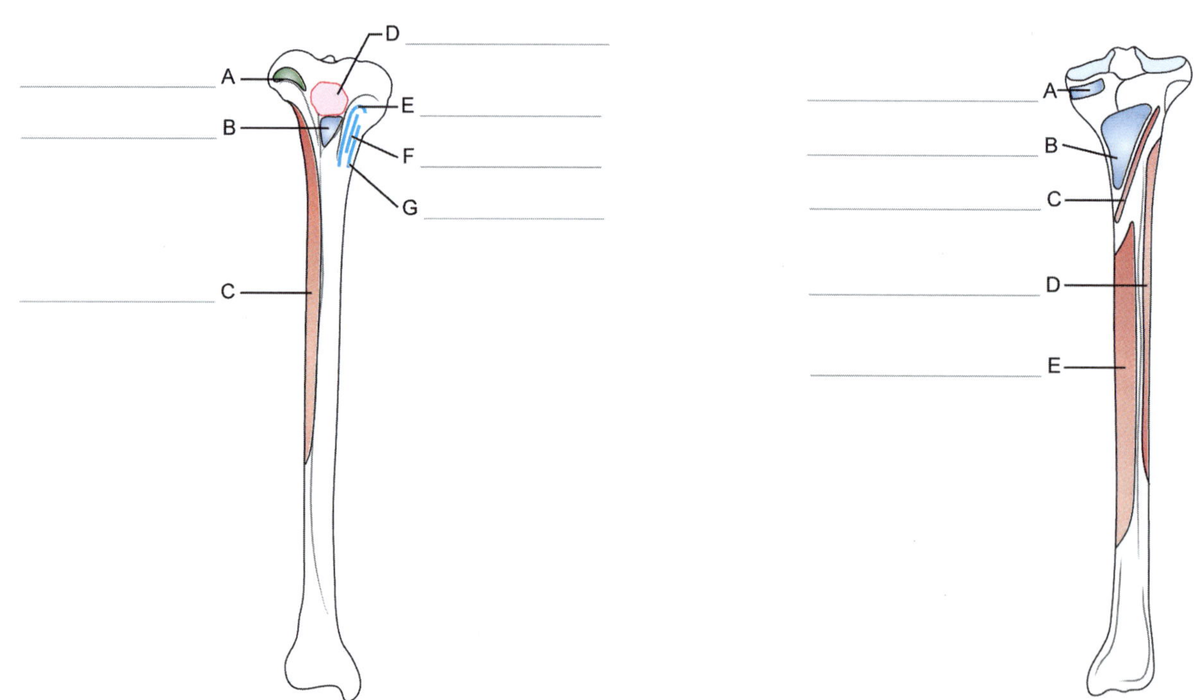

Practice Figure 2.4: Attachments and relations on the anterior aspect of the right tibia

Practice Figure 2.5: Attachments and relations on the posterior aspect of the right tibia

MULTIPLE CHOICE QUESTIONS

(Tick the single best correct option)

1. A 63-year-old female with an accidental fall from stairs came to the emergency room; her X-ray showed a fracture of the neck of femur. What is the most common complication associated with this condition?
   a. Septic arthritis
   b. Avascular necrosis of femoral head
   c. Osteoarthritis
   d. Dislocation of the hip joint
2. What is the procedure done on the X-marked site?
   a. Bone marrow aspiration and biopsy
   b. Lumbar puncture
   c. Bone densitometry
   d. DEXA scan
3. Inguinal ligament extends from ____________.
   a. Anterior inferior iliac spine to pubic tubercle
   b. Posterior superior iliac spine to pubic tubercle
   c. Anterior superior iliac spine to pubic tubercle
   d. Posterior superior iliac spine to ischial tuberosity
4. Which of the following is true about obturator foramen?
   a. It is a large gap in hip bone, lying anterosuperior to acetabulum
   b. No muscular attachments are present
   c. It is triangular in females and oval in males
   d. Femoral vessels pass through this foramen.
5. Weaver's bottom is ____________.
   a. Ischial tuberosity bursitis
   b. Prepatellar bursitis
   c. Trochanteric bursitis
   d. Olecranon bursitis
6. Iliotibial tract is the modification of ____________.
   a. Femoral sheath b. Fascia lata
   c. Cribriform fascia d. Superficial fascia
7. Apex of the greater trochanter gives insertion to________.
   a. Gluteus minimus b. Piriformis
   c. Gluteus medius d. Obturator externus
8. What angle is shown in the below image?
   a. Trochanteric shaft angle
   b. Angle of femoral torsion
   c. Angle of inclination
   d. Femoral condylar angle
9. Which muscle originates from anterior inferior iliac spine?
   a. Tensor fascia lata
   b. Straight head of rectus femoris
   c. Sartorius
   d. Latissismus dorsi
10. Which of the following nerves is injured in the neck of fibula fracture?
    a. Common peroneal nerve
    b. Deep peroneal nerve
    c. Superficial peroneal nerve
    d. Tibial nerve
11. Which of the following statements is true about metatarsal bones?
    a. The head and shaft are prismoid
    b. The shaft tapers proximally
    c. The dorsal surface of the shaft is uniformly convex
    d. The base is irregular
12. What is a bunion?
    a. It is a fungal infection of the great toe
    b. It is an adventitious bursa found on the great toe
    c. It is an inflammation of the Achilles tendon
    d. It is a condition where the arch of the foot collapses
13. Which among the following bones is preferred for bone graft?
    a. Tibia
    b. Lower end of femur
    c. Fibula
    d. Lower end of humerus
14. The largest nutrient artery in the body is ____________.
    a. Nutrient artery to femur
    b. Nutrient artery to humerus
    c. Nutrient artery to tibia
    d. Nutrient artery to ulna
15. ____________ does not provide any muscle attachment.
    a. Calcaneum
    b. Navicular
    c. Talus
    d. Cuboid
16. Identify the clinical condition shown in the following radiographs.
    a. Dislocation of patella
    b. Osteoarthritis
    c. Fracture of patella
    d. Absence of fibula

QUESTION BANK

(Use separate copy to solve the following question)

Q 1. Enlist the following:
   a. Attachment on iliac crest
   b. Attachments on ischial tuberosity
   c. Structures passing through greater sciatic notch
   d. Attachments on linea aspera
   e. Intercondylar structures of tibia/upper end

eSmartQuiz

Front of Thigh

CLINICOANATOMICAL PROBLEM

Clinical Case 1

A 50-year-old woman came to the OPD with a swelling on the upper medial side of her right thigh, exacerbated by coughing. Physical examination revealed a reducible lump consistent with a femoral hernia. Further evaluation and possible surgical interventions are warranted to prevent complications such as bowel incarceration or strangulation.

1. What is the position of the swelling in relation to pubic tubercle?
2. Name the passage through which the hernia has entered into the thigh.
3. What is the direction of femoral hernia?
4. Why does it appear when she coughs?
5. Why the femoral hernia is common in females?

Explanation

1. ____________________
2. ____________________
3. ____________________
4. ____________________
5. ____________________

PRACTICE FIGURES

(Label the practice figures)

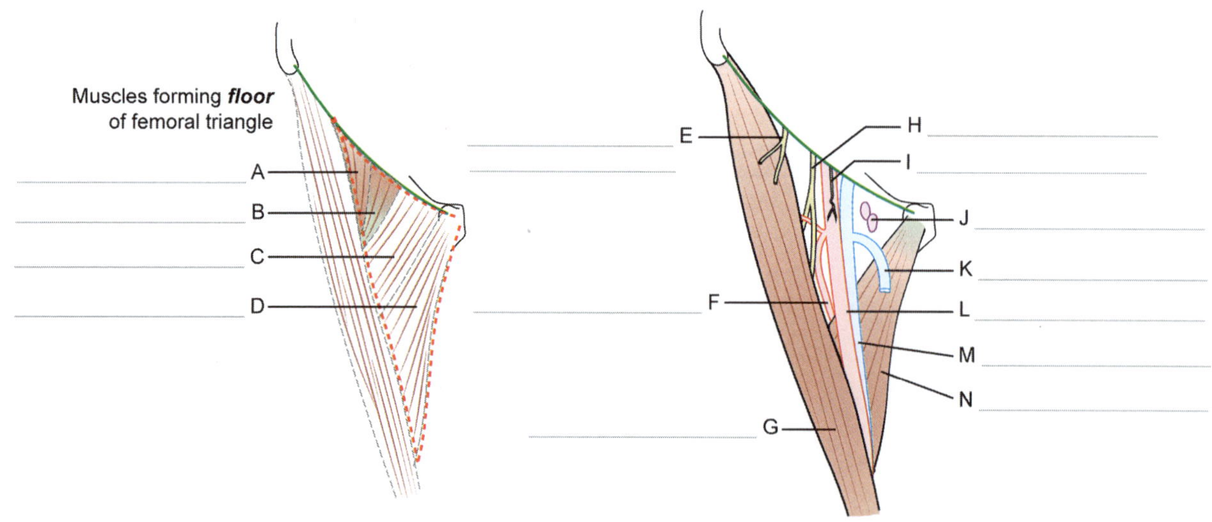

Practice Figure 3.1: Contents of the right femoral triangle

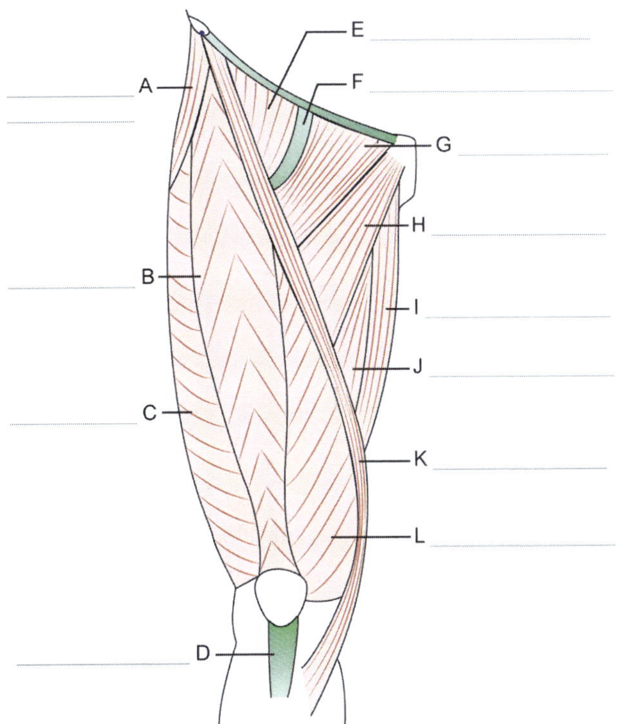

Practice Figure 3.2: Muscles seen on the front of the thigh

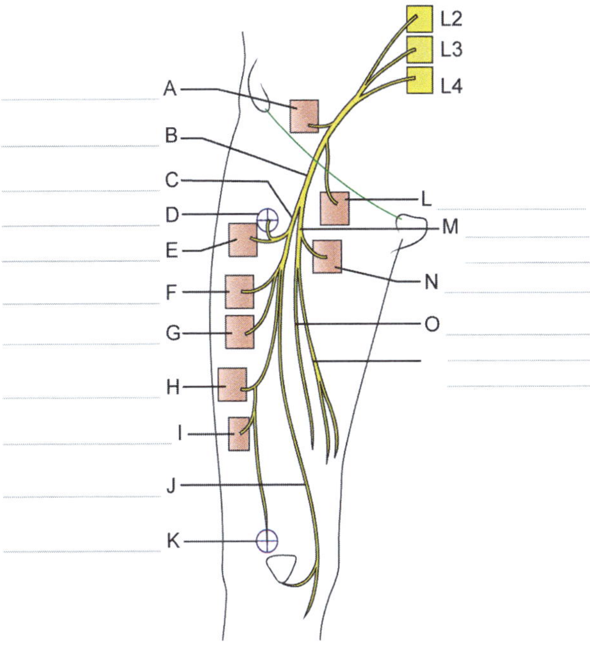

Practice Figure 3.3: The branches and distribution of femoral nerve

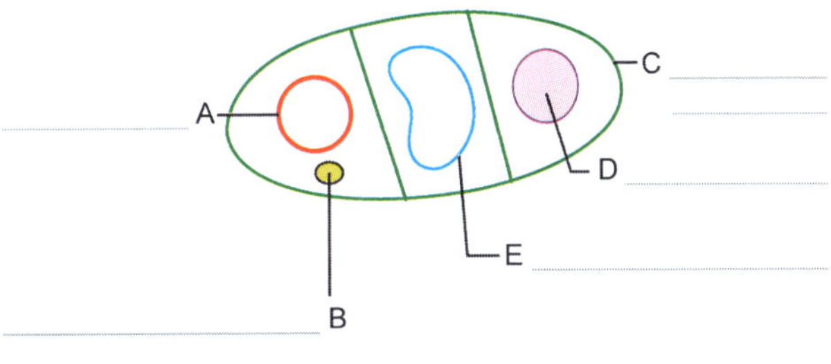

Practice Figure 3.4: Transverse section of the right femoral sheath with its contents

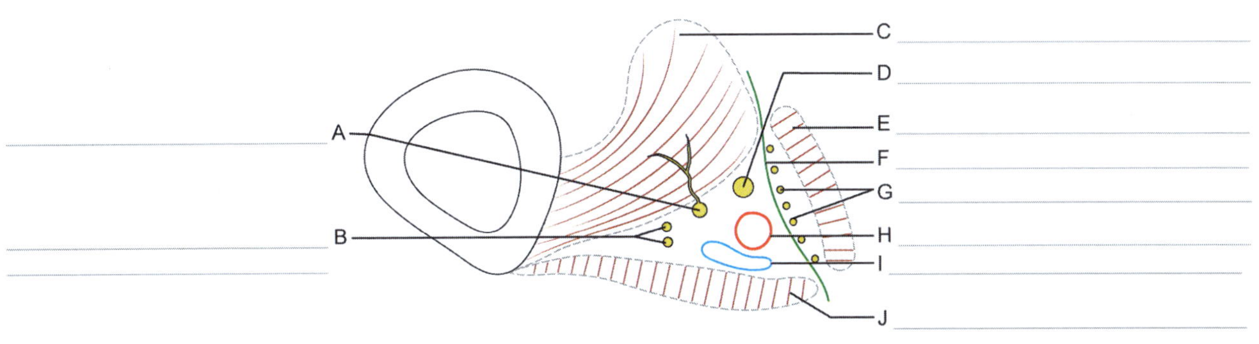

Practice Figure 3.5: Transverse section through the middle of the right adductor canal, seen from above. Note the boundaries and contents of the canal

MULTIPLE CHOICE QUESTIONS

(Tick the single best correct option)

1. Midinguinal point lies midway between ____________.
   a. The anterior superior iliac spine and the pubic symphysis
   b. The anterior superior iliac spine and pubic tubercle
   c. The anterior superior iliac spine and pubic crest
   d. The anterior superior iliac spine and pubic arch
2. The structure marked as X drains ____________.

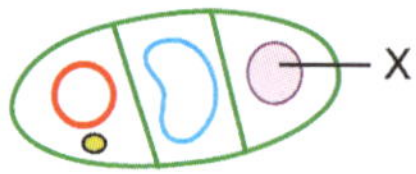

   a. The inner upper thigh area
   b. The glans penis in males and clitoris in females
   c. The scrotum and testis
   d. The labia majora and labia minora
3. Name the structure marked as X in the following picture.

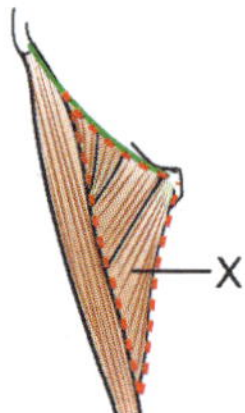

   a. Adductor magnus   b. Adductor longus
   c. Vastus medialis   d. Vastus intermedius
4. Which nerve entanglement causes meralgia paraesthetica?
   a. Ilioinguinal nerve
   b. Lateral cutaneous nerve of thigh
   c. Femoral branch of genitofemoral nerve
   d. Saphenous nerve
5. A Church priest came to ortho outpatient clinic with swelling and redness in the knee joint. What is the likely diagnosis?
   a. Housemaid's knee   b. Baker's cyst
   c. Clergyman's knee   d. Trochanteric bursitis
6. Identify the muscle marked as X.

   a. Gluteus medius   b. Gluteus maximus
   c. Tensor fasciae latae   d. Vastus medialis
7. Saphenous opening is a defect seen in ____________.
   a. Superficial fascia
   b. Medial intermuscular septum
   c. Lateral intermuscular septum
   d. Deep fascia
8. All of the following are contents of the femoral triangle, EXCEPT:
   a. Femoral artery and its branches
   b. Femoral vein and its tributaries
   c. Genital branch of genitofemoral nerve
   d. Deep inguinal lymph nodes
9. Superficial epigastric artery is a branch of ____________.
   a. External iliac artery   b. Profunda femoris
   c. Femoral artery   d. Common iliac artery
10. Which of the following statements is false regarding the femoral canal?
    a. It is conical in shape, wide above and narrow below
    b. It is about 1.5 cm long
    c. The base or upper end of the femoral canal is called the femoral ring
    d. Femoral canal is wider in males
11. What is the root value of the saphenous nerve?
    a. L2, L3   b. L1, L2
    c. L3, L4   d. L4, L5
12. Abnormal obturator artery is a branch of ____________.
    a. Internal iliac artery   b. External iliac artery
    c. Profunda femoris   d. Inferior epigastric artery
13. Identify the muscle marked as X.

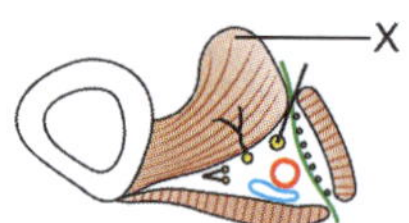

    a. Vastus lateralis   b. Vastus medialis
    c. Vastus intermedius   d. Articularis genu
14. Identify the muscle marked as X.

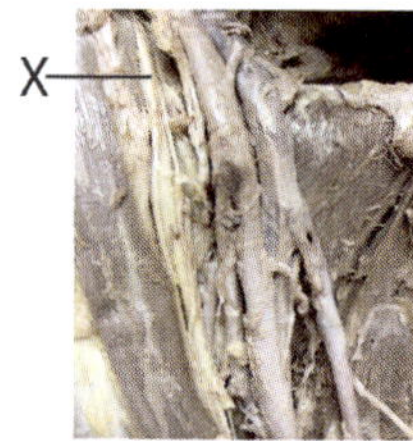

    a. Femoral artery   b. Femoral nerve
    c. Femoral vein   d. Profunda femoris artery

QUESTION BANK

(Use separate copy to solve the following questions)

Q 1. A 45-year-old female patient presented with a swelling in the right groin since 6 months. It increases on coughing, associated with occasional pain. She was diagnosed with the femoral hernia. Describe the anatomical basis of femoral hernia under following headings:
a. Femoral sheath, b. Femoral canal, c. Femoral ring, c. Direction of femoral hernia, d. Complications.

Q 2. Describe the femoral triangle under the following headings: Boundaries, roof, floor, contents, applied aspects.

Q 3. Describe the femoral artery under the following heads: Beginning, course, termination, relations, branches and applied aspects.

Q 4. Describe the adductor canal under the following headings: Boundaries, contents, applied aspects.

Q 5. Write a short note on:
a. Femoral sheath
b. Profunda brachii artery
c. Femoral nerve
d. Iliotibial tract—formation, attachments and importance
e. Saphenous opening

eSmartQuiz

Medial Side of Thigh

CLINICOANATOMICAL PROBLEM

Clinical Case 1

A 65-year-old female came to the OPD with pain in the right knee and difficulty in walking. She was diagnosed as a case of osteoarthritis and suggested physiotherapy. After three months of exercise, she developed right hip pain.

1. What is the nerve supply of the knee joint?
2. What is the nerve supply of the hip joint?
3. What nerve supplies these two joints?
4. What is the reason for development of pain in right hip joint in this case?

Explanation

1. ______________________________
2. ______________________________
3. ______________________________
4. ______________________________

PRACTICE FIGURES

(Label the practice figures)

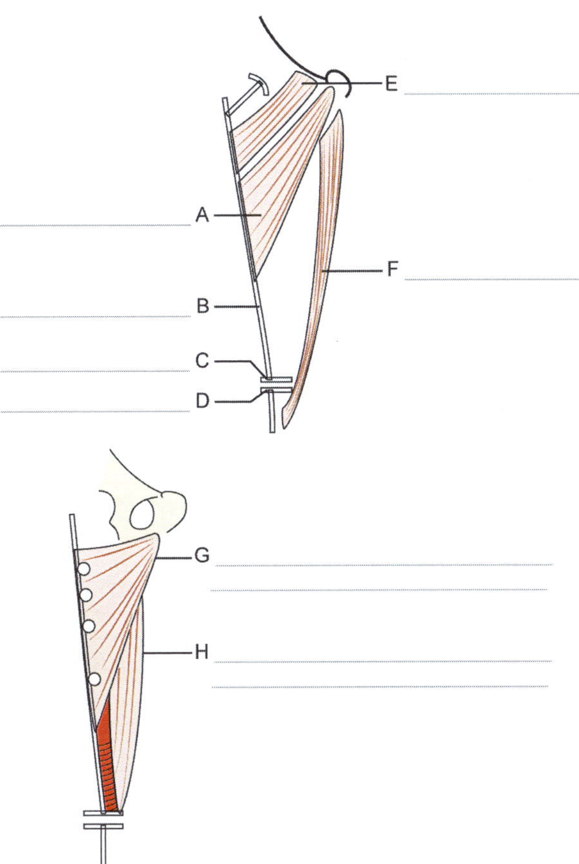

Practice Figure 4.1: Insertion of adductor muscles

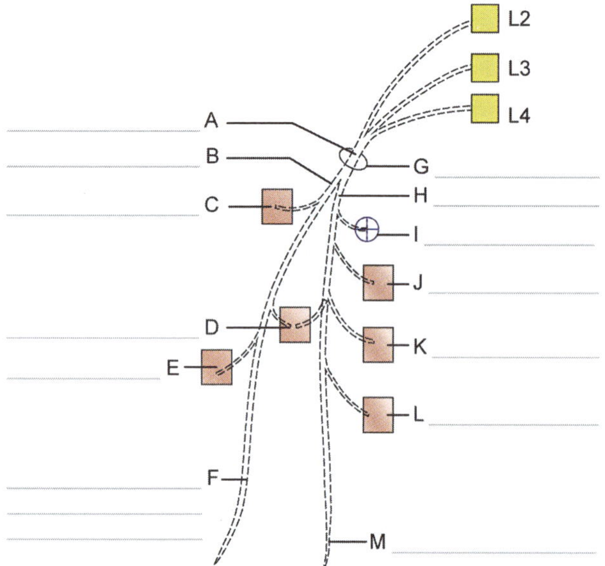

Practice Figure 4.2: Branches of obturator nerve

MULTIPLE CHOICE QUESTIONS

(Tick the single best correct option)

1. A 40-year-old male sustained an injury to the left hip joint; gradually, he developed pain in the left knee joint. What is the likely cause?
   a. Hematoma formation   b. Referred pain
   c. Injury to the tendon   d. Rupture of the muscle
2. Which muscle in the arm acts as a counterpart to the adductor compartment of the thigh?
   a. Biceps brachii
   b. Brachialis
   c. Triceps brachii
   d. Coracobrachialis
3. Which is the largest muscle of the adductor compartment of the thigh?
   a. Adductor brevis
   b. Adductor magnus
   c. Adductor longus
   d. Gracilis
4. Obturator artery is a branch of ____________.
   a. Internal iliac artery
   b. Femoral artery
   c. External pudendal artery
   d. Common iliac artery
5. Which of the following statements is true about the obturator nerve?
   a. Gives branches in abdomen
   b. Emerges at the medial border of the psoas major
   c. Thicker in size
   d. Exits from the abdomen by passing deep to the inguinal ligament.
6. All of the following muscles have insertion in linea aspera, EXCEPT:
   a. Adductor magnus   b. Adductor brevis
   c. Pectineus   d. Gracilis
7. Identify the structure marked with X.

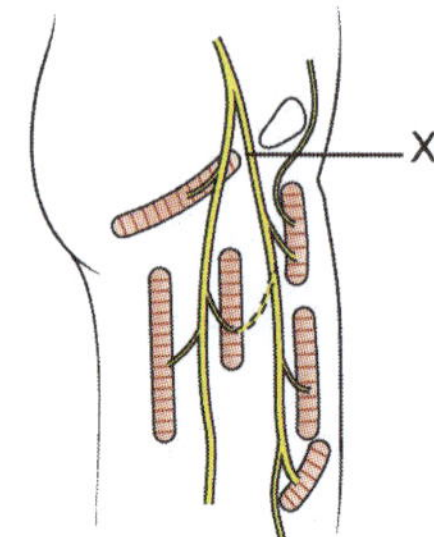

   a. Anterior division of femoral nerve
   b. Posterior division of femoral nerve
   c. Anterior division of obturator nerve
   d. Posterior division of obturator nerve
8. Which of the following is the triangular muscle in the adductor compartment?
   a. Adductor brevis   b. Adductor longus
   c. Adductor magnus   d. Gracilis
9. All of the following muscles are supplied by anterior division of the obturator nerve, EXCEPT:
   a. Pectineus
   b. Adductor brevis
   c. Gracilis
   d. Hamstring part of adductor magnus
10. Pectineus muscle is supplied by ____________ nerve.
    a. Anterior fibres by obturator
    b. A branch from sciatic
    c. Posterior fibres by anterior division of obturator
    d. Accessory obturator
11. Which of the following structures is supplied by accessory obturator nerve?
    a. Pectineus muscle   b. Sacroiliac joint
    c. Obturator internus   d. Gracilis muscle
12. Identify the structure marked by X.

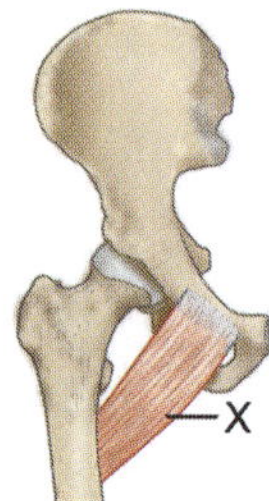

    a. Obturator externus   b. Pectineus
    c. Gracilis   d. Adductor longus

QUESTION BANK

(Use separate copy to solve the following questions)

Q 1. Write a short note on:
   a. Adductor magnus
   b. Obturator nerve
   c. Obturator artery
   d. Peculiarities of adductor muscles.

Q 2. List the differences between the obturator nerve and femoral nerve.

eSmartQuiz

Gluteal Region

CLINICOANATOMICAL PROBLEMS

Clinical Case 1

A 27-year-old boy brought to the emergency department for a penetrating injury in his right buttock. He was treated and discharged. After healing, he came for the stitch removal; the physician noticed a limp during walking and sagging of the left hip while taking steps on the right foot. The physician diagnosed him as a case of superior gluteal nerve injury.

1. Which muscles are supplied by superior gluteal nerve?
2. What clinical signs the physician observed to confirm his findings?

Explanation

1.

2.

Clinical Case 2

The physician decided to start intramuscular multivitamin injections for a 22-year-old man.

1. Which quadrant of the gluteal region needs to be selected for intramuscular injections?
2. Justify your answer.

Explanation

1.

2.

PRACTICE FIGURES

(Label the practice figures)

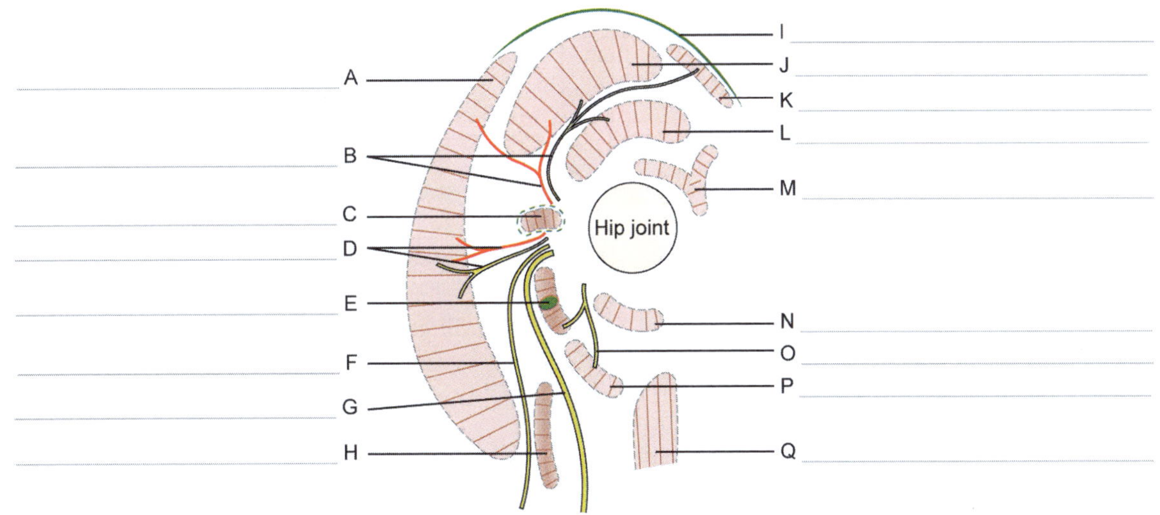

Practice Figure 5.1: Scheme of an oblique vertical section showing structures under cover of the gluteus maximus

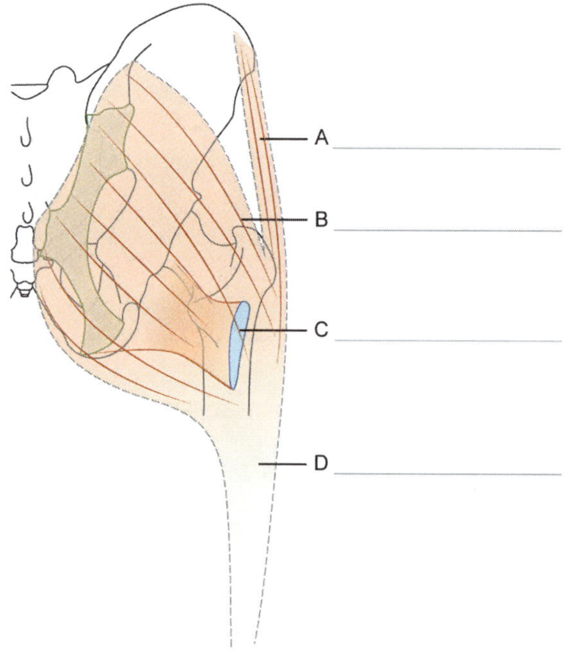

Practice Figure 5.2: Origin and insertion of the gluteus maximus muscle

MULTIPLE CHOICE QUESTIONS

(Tick the single best correct option)

1. Which muscle lies between the gamelli muscles?
   a. Gluteus medius b. Gluteus minimus
   c. Obturator internus d. Tensor fascia lata
2. All of the following are the lateral rotators of the thigh at the hip joint, EXCEPT:
   a. Obturator internus b. Pectineus
   c. Gamellus inferior d. Quadratus femoris
3. Which of the following statements is NOT true about pudendal nerve?
   a. It enters the gluteal region through greater sciatic notch
   b. It is a branch of sacral plexus
   c. It supplies a part of gluteus maximus
   d. It leaves the gluteal region by passing through lesser sciatic notch
4. Name the structure marked by X.

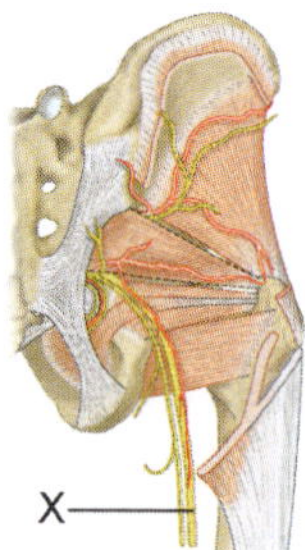

   a. Sciatic nerve b. Pudendal nerve
   c. Femoral nerve d. Obturator nerve
5. Gluteus maximus is supplied by ____________ nerve.
   a. Superior gluteal b. Inferior gluteal
   c. Superior genicular d. Inferior genicular
6. ____________ is known as the gateway of perineal region.
   a. Greater sciatic notch b. Obturator foramen
   c. Acetabular cavity d. Lesser sciatic notch
7. What sign is depicted in the image?

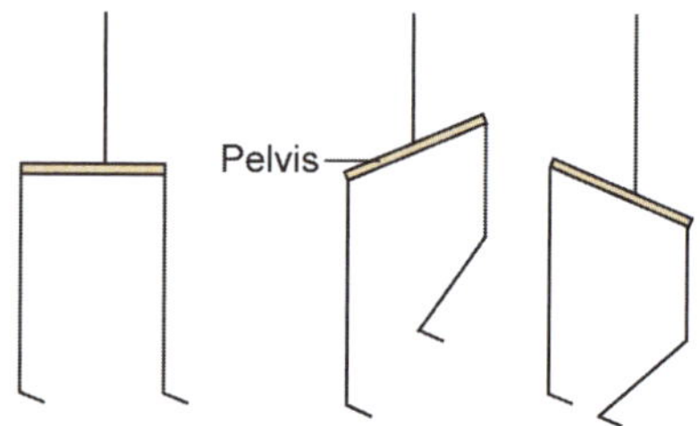

   a. Gower's sign
   b. McMurray's sign
   c. Trendelenburg's sign
   d. Latchman sign
8. Name the structure marked by X.

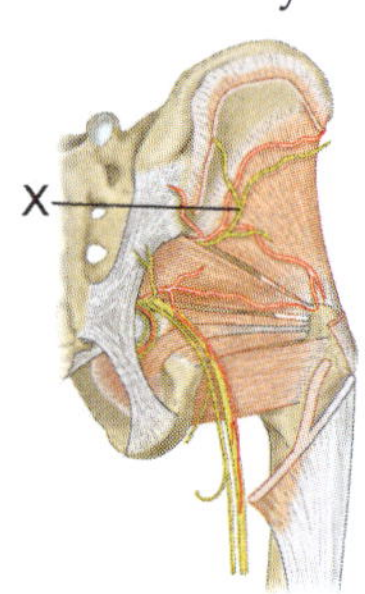

   a. Pudendal nerve
   b. Nerve to quadratus femoris
   c. Superior gluteal nerve
   d. Nerve to obturator externus
9. What is the root value of the pudendal nerve?
   a. S2, S3, S4 b. S3, S4, S5
   c. S1, S2, S3 d. L5, S1, S2
10. The nerve supply of hamstring muscles is primarily by ____________.
   a. Femoral nerve b. Obturator nerve
   c. Sciatic nerve d. Sural nerve
11. ____________ nerve is involved in the piriformis syndrome.
   a. Sciatic b. Obturator
   c. Femoral d. Ilioinguinal
12. Which of the following muscles is NOT a part of the triceps coxae?
   a. Obturator externus b. Obturator internus
   c. Superior gemellus d. Inferior gamellus
13. All the muscles are supplied by the superior gluteal nerve, EXCEPT:
   a. Gluteus maximus b. Gluteus medius
   c. Gluteus minimus d. Tensor fasciae latae

QUESTION BANK

(Use separate copy to solve the following questions)

Q 1. Describe gluteus maximus muscle under following headings: Origin, insertion, actions, structures under cover of this muscle.

Q 2. Write a short note on:
   a. Trendelenburg sign
   b. Piriformis
   c. Trochanteric anastomosis
   d. Cruciate anastomosis
   e. Structures passing through the greater sciatic notch

Popliteal Fossa

CLINICOANATOMICAL PROBLEMS

Clinical Case 1

A 25-year-old male came to the OPD with exertional dyspnoea and fatigue. Physical examination revealed diminished pulses and lower blood pressure in the lower extremities compared to the upper extremities. The physician diagnosed him with the coarctation of the aorta.

1. Which of the lower limb arteries can be palpated?
2. How to measure BP in lower limb?
3. Why there is lower BP in the above-mentioned case?

Explanation

1. ____________________

2. ____________________

3. ____________________

Clinical Case 2

A 55-year-old male smoker presented with a pulsatile midline mass behind his right knee. He complained of intermittent claudication and numbness in the foot. Physical examination revealed a palpable, non-tender mass in the popliteal fossa with a weak dorsalis pedis pulse. The physician diagnosed him as a case of aneurysm of the popliteal artery.

1. What is aneurysm?
2. What may be the cause of aneurysm in this case?
3. Why the swelling was pulsatile in this case?
4. Which are other common swellings in popliteal fossa?
5. How to differentiate between popliteal aneurysm and Baker's cyst?

Explanation

1. ____________________

2. ____________________

3. ____________________

4. ____________________

5. ____________________

PRACTICE FIGURES

(Label the practice figures)

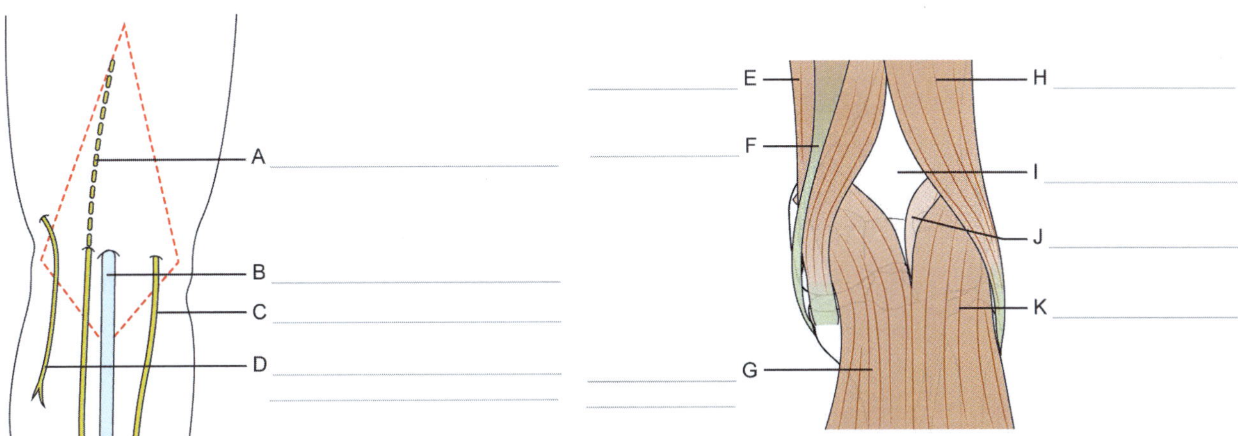

Practice Figure 6.1: Popliteal fossa: Roof and boundaries

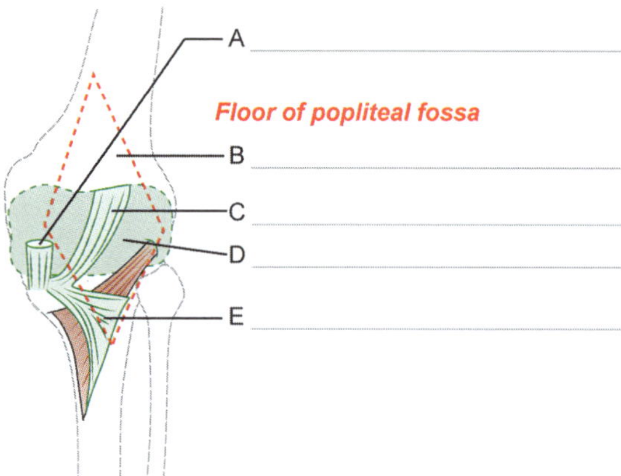

Practice Figure 6.2: Floor of the popliteal fossa

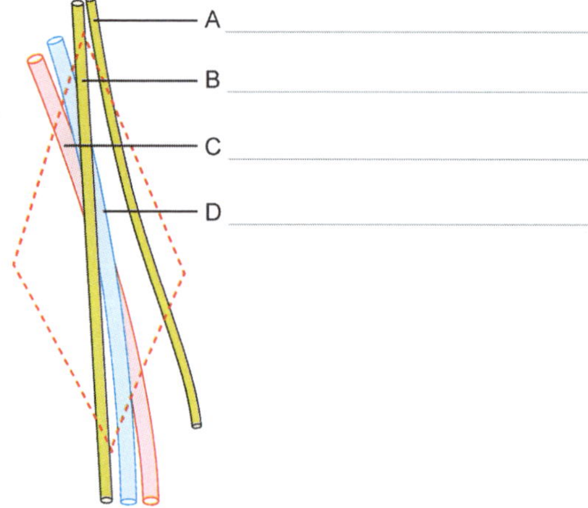

Practice Figure 6.3: The arrangement of the main nerves and vessels in the popliteal fossa

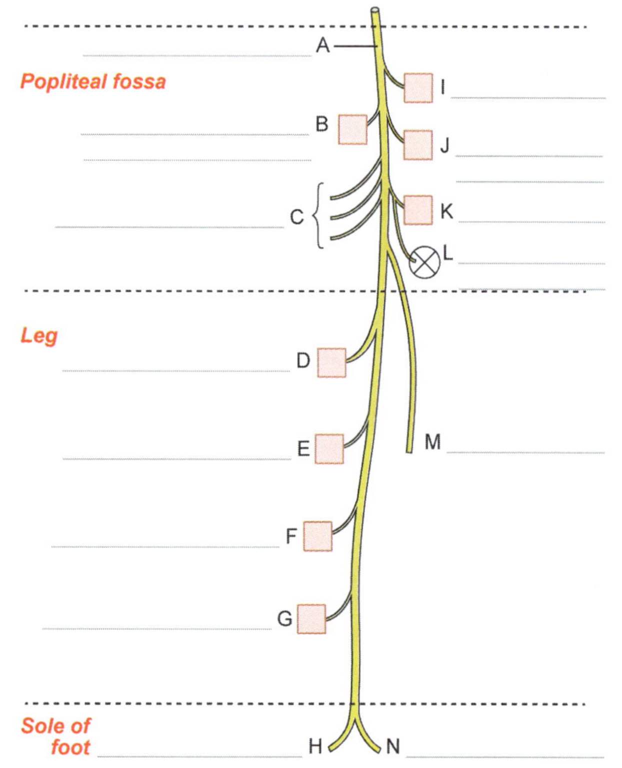

Practice Figure 6.4: Tibial nerve in the popliteal fossa and leg

MULTIPLE CHOICE QUESTIONS

(Tick the single best correct option)

1. Which is the deepest structure in the popliteal fossa?
   a. Tibial nerve
   b. Inferior genicular nerve
   c. Popliteal vein
   d. Popliteal artery
2. The oblique popliteal ligament is pierced by __________ genicular artery.
   a. Superior
   b. Inferior
   c. Middle
   d. Descending
3. The superolateral boundary of the popliteal fossa is formed by __________.

   a. Semimembranosus
   b. Biceps femoris
   c. Semitendinosus
   d. Lateral head of gastrocnemius
4. Name the structure marked by X.

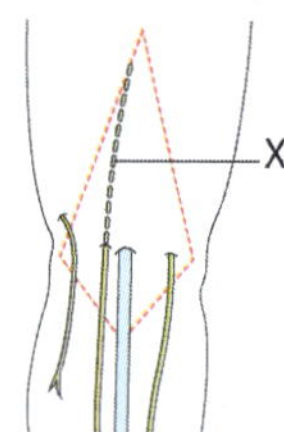

   a. Posterior tibial nerve
   b. Posterior division of medial cutaneous nerve of thigh
   c. Sural nerve
   d. Posterior cutaneous nerve of thigh
5. A 60-year-old male came with a history of dizziness. On examination, blood pressure discrepancy was noted in both the extremities. What is the likely diagnosis?
   a. Aortic dissection
   b. Mitral valve syndrome
   c. Coarctation of aorta
   d. Scaphoid
6. The unlocking of the knee joint is done by which of the following muscles?
   a. Popliteus
   b. Soleus
   c. Gastrocnemius
   d. Biceps femoris
7. All of the following statements about the genicular branch of the obturator nerve are true, EXCEPT:
   a. It is the continuation of the posterior division of the obturator nerve.
   b. It runs on the anterior surface of the popliteal artery.
   c. It pierces the oblique popliteal ligament.
   d. It supplies the capsule of the knee joint.

8. Identify the structure marked as X:

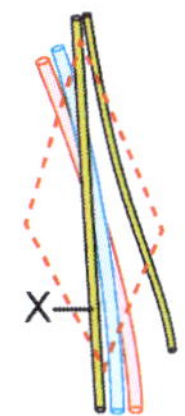

   a. Sciatic nerve
   b. Obturator nerve
   c. Tibial nerve
   d. Sural nerve
9. Which nerve is affected in the below image on the left side?

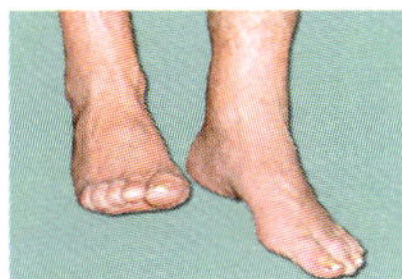

   a. Superficial peroneal nerve
   b. Anterior tibial nerve
   c. Common peroneal nerve
   d. Deep peroneal nerve
10. Popliteal vein continues as ____________.
   a. Saphenous vein
   b. Femoral vein
   c. Internal iliac vein
   d. External iliac vein
11. Root value of the tibial nerve is ____________.
   a. Ventral divisions of ventral rami of L4, 5, S1, 2, 3
   b. Dorsal division of ventral rami of L4, 5, S1, 2, 3
   c. Ventral divisions of ventral rami of L5, S1, 2, 3
   d. Dorsal divisions of ventral rami of L5, S1, 2, 3
12. All of the following are the contents of popliteal fossa, EXCEPT:
   a. Popliteal artery and its branches
   b. Posterior cutaneous nerve of thigh
   c. Deep peroneal nerve
   d. Tibial nerve
13. Middle genicular nerve is a branch of ____________.
   a. Common peroneal nerve
   b. Deep peroneal nerve
   c. Tibial nerve
   d. Femoral nerve
14. True statement about the tibial nerve is ____________.
   a. It is the larger terminal branch of the femoral nerve
   b. Cutaneous nerve is called sural, which originates in the lower part of the fossa
   c. Tibial nerve runs horizontally in the popliteal fossa
   d. Damage to the tibial nerve causes motor and sensory loss
15. Posterior tibial artery is a branch of ____________.
   a. Terminal branch of femoral artery
   b. Terminal branch of obturator artery
   c. Terminal branch of popliteal artery
   d. Terminal branch of inferior genicular artery

QUESTION BANK

(Use separate copy to solve the following questions)

Q 1. Describe the popliteal fossa under the following headings: Boundaries, roof, floor, contents, and clinical aspects.

Q 2. A middle-aged person complained of severe weakness in both the lower limbs. His blood pressure in the lower limbs was quite less than that of upper limb. The physician measured the BP using auscultation over the popliteal fossa. Which artery was auscultated? Describe this artery under the following headings: Beginning, course, termination, branches, and applied aspects. (Key: Popliteal artery).

Q 3. Write a short note on:
   a. Tibial nerve in popliteal fossa
   b. Genicular anastomosis
   c. Popliteal lymph nodes

Chapter 7

eSmartQuiz

Back of Thigh

CLINICOANATOMICAL PROBLEM

Clinical Case 1

A 40-year-old man presented with severe pain radiating from his lower back down the back of his left leg worsened by sitting or standing. Physician noticed that the straight leg raising test elicited pain and diagnosed with sciatica.

1. Which nerve is involved in this case?
2. What is the root value of involved nerve?
3. What is straight leg raising test?
4. Why there is increased pain in straight leg raising test?

Explanation

1. ______

2. ______

3. ______

4. ______

PRACTICE FIGURES

(Label the practice figures)

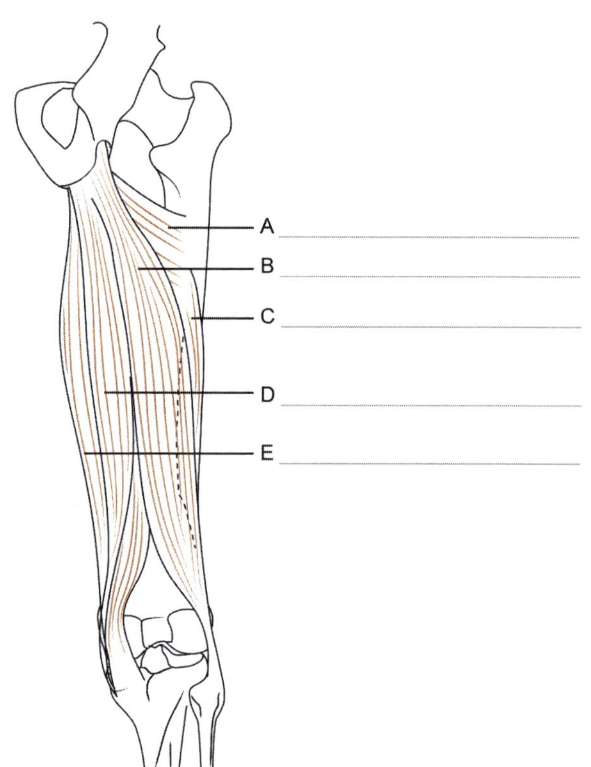

Practice Figure 7.1: Hamstring muscles

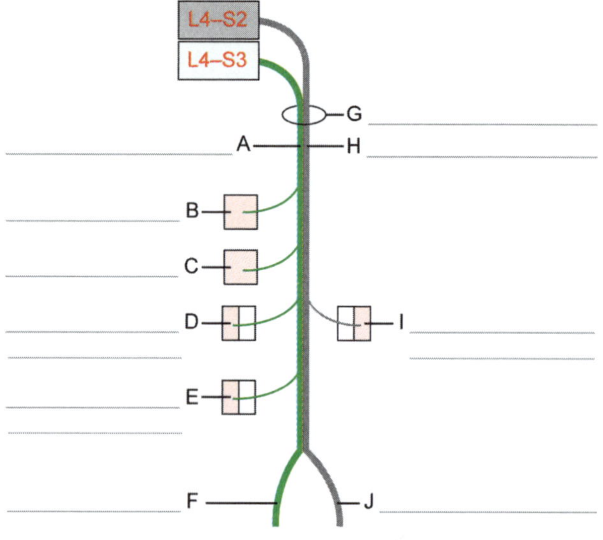

Practice Figure 7.2: Branches of sciatic nerve

MULTIPLE CHOICE QUESTIONS

(Tick the single best correct option)

1. ____________ muscle is a component of both the adductor and flexor compartment of the thigh.
   a. Semimembranosus b. Semitendinosus
   c. Adductor brevis d. Adductor magnus
2. Identify the muscle marked as X, which originates from the superolateral part of ischial tuberosity.

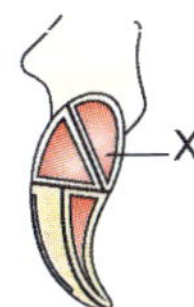

   a. Semimembranosus
   b. Semitendinosus
   c. Gracilis
   d. Long head of biceps femoris
3. Pick out the correct statement about the Hamstring muscle.
   a. All of them are supplied by common peroneal nerve
   b. Insertion into one of the bones of leg
   c. Common origin from the iliac fossa
   d. They act as flexors of the hip joint and extensors of the knee joint.
4. Name the structure marked by X.

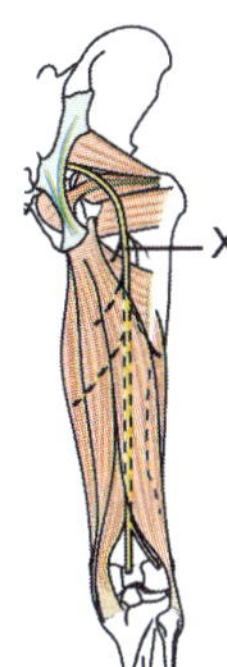

   a. Tibial nerve
   b. Sciatic nerve
   c. Common peroneal nerve
   d. Sural nerve
5. Trochanteric anastomosis is formed by all of the following arteries, EXCEPT:
   a. Branch of superior gluteal artery
   b. Branch of inferior gluteal artery
   c. Ascending branch of medial circumflex artery
   d. Perforating branches from profunda femoris artery
6. Short head of biceps femoris is supplied by ____________ nerve.
   a. Tibial part of sciatic
   b. Common peroneal part of sciatic
   c. Branch from femoral
   d. Posterior cutaneous nerve of thigh
7. Which of the following muscles is a medial rotator of the leg in semiflexed knee?
   a. Long head of biceps femoris
   b. Short head of biceps femoris
   c. Ischial part of adductor magnus
   d. Semimembranosus
8. A 45-year old female came to neurology outpatient service with a history of shooting pain over the gluteal and back of thigh region for 10 days. Which of the following may be the probable diagnosis?
   a. Foot drop b. Myalgia
   c. Sciatica d. Ischaemia of limbs
9. The muscle marked as X crosses the thickest nerve in the body. Identify X.

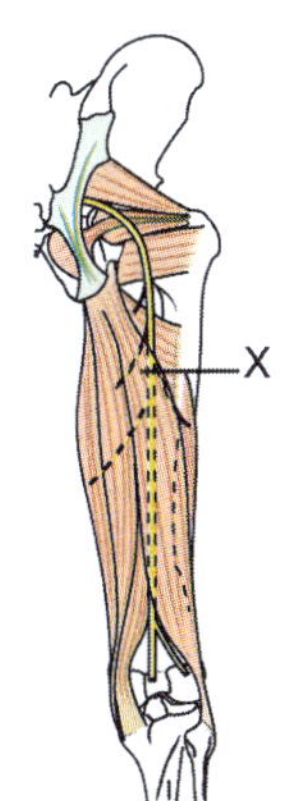

   a. Semimembranosus
   b. Semitendinosus
   c. Long head of biceps femoris
   d. Adductor magnus
10. The degenerated part of the adductor magnus muscle forms ____________.
    a. Fibular collateral ligament
    b. Tibial collateral ligament
    c. Oblique popliteal ligament
    d. Ligamentum patellae
11. The root value of sciatic nerve is:
    a. L4, 5, S1, 2, 3 b. L5, S1, 2, 3
    c. S1, 2, 3 d. L5, S1, 2
12. ____________ is supplied by both common peroneal and tibial components of the sciatic nerve.
    a. Semitendinosus b. Semimembranosus
    c. Biceps femoris d. Adductor magnus
13. Straight leg raising test is performed to assess ____________ nerve.
    a. Sciatic b. Common peroneal
    c. Tibial d. Sural
14. All of the following statements are true about sciatic nerve, EXCEPT:
    a. It enters the back of the thigh at the lower border of the gluteus maximus.
    b. It is accompanied by a small vein.
    c. It begins in the pelvis and terminates at the inferior angle of the popliteal fossa.
    d. It is the thickest nerve in the body.

QUESTION BANK

(Use separate copy to solve the following questions)

Q 1. Describe the sciatic nerve under the following heads: Formation, root value, course, relations, branches and applied aspects.

Q 2. Write a short note on:
   a. Actions of hamstring muscles
   b. Sciatica
   c. Anastomosis

Chapter

8 Front of Leg with Dorsum of Foot; Lateral and Medial Sides of Leg

eSmartQuiz

CLINICOANATOMICAL PROBLEMS

Clinical Case 1

A 35-year-old athlete developed intense pain and swelling in his left lower leg following a marathon. He complained of numbness in the dorsum of his foot and was unable to dorsiflex his ankle, resulting in foot drop. Physical examination revealed tense swelling in the anterior leg compartment. The treating physician diagnosed him with anterior tibial compartment syndrome and suggested emergency fasciotomy.

1. What is anterior tibial compartment syndrome?
2. Why was there intense pain and swelling in the lower leg?
3. Why was there a foot drop?
4. Why did the physician suggested an emergency fasciotomy?

Explanation

1. ______________________________

2. ______________________________

3. ______________________________

4. ______________________________

Clinical Case 2

A 28-year-old construction worker suffered an injury to the lateral side of his left leg after a fall at work. He experienced immediate pain and swelling in the area. Subsequently, he noticed sensory loss on the dorsum of his left foot and loss of eversion of the foot. Examination revealed injury to the superficial peroneal nerve.

1. Why was there a loss of eversion of foot?
2. Why was there a sensory loss on the dorsum of foot?

Explanation

1. ______________________________

2. ______________________________

PRACTICE FIGURES

(Label the practice figures)

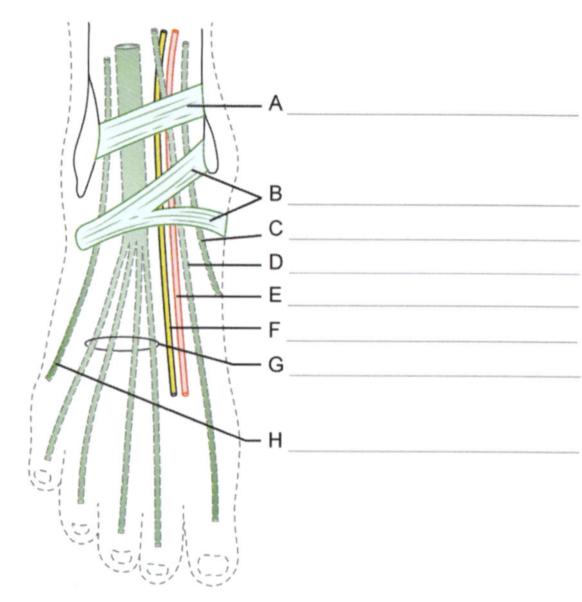

Practice Figure 8.1: Extensor retinacula

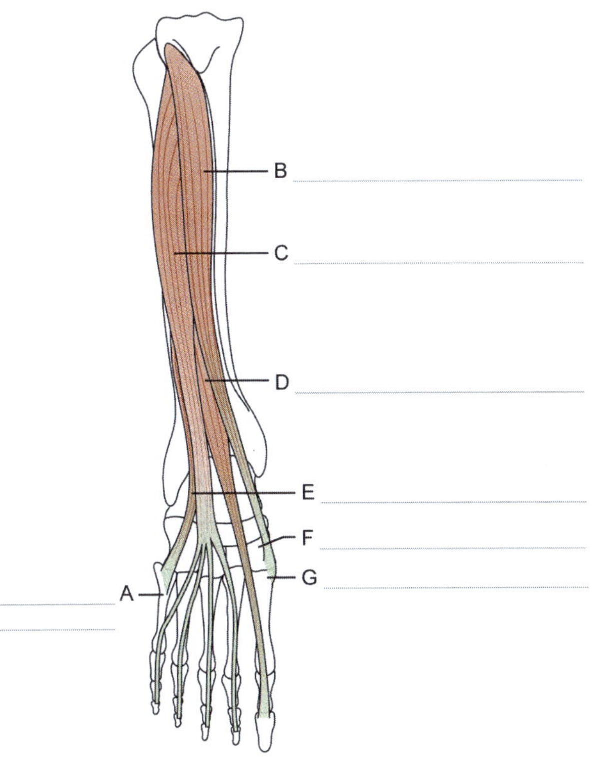

Practice Figure 8.2: Muscles of anterior compartment of leg

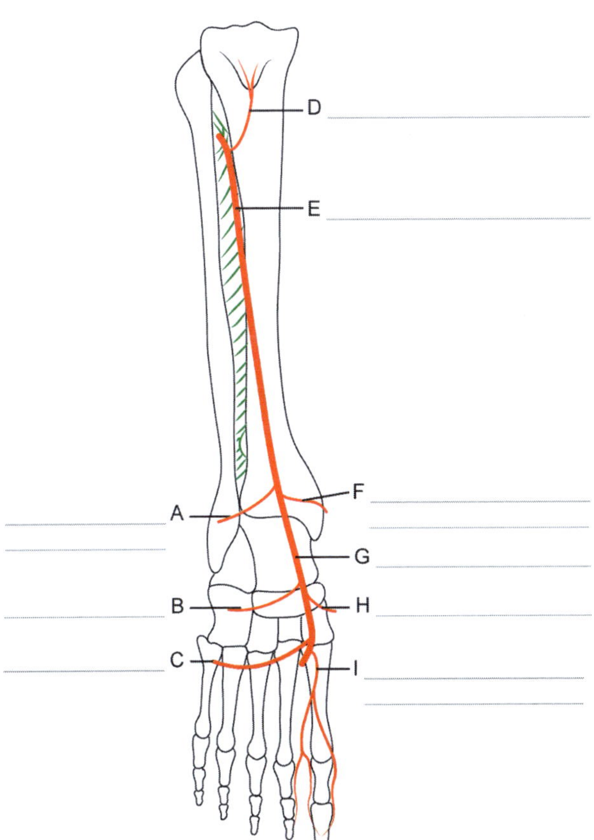

Practice Figure 8.3: Arteries on the front of the leg and dorsum of the foot

MULTIPLE CHOICE QUESTIONS

(Tick the single best correct option)

1. Sural nerve is a branch of ___________.
   a. Femoral nerve
   b. Tibial nerve
   c. Sciatic nerve
   d. Obturator nerve
2. The structure marked by X drains into ___________.

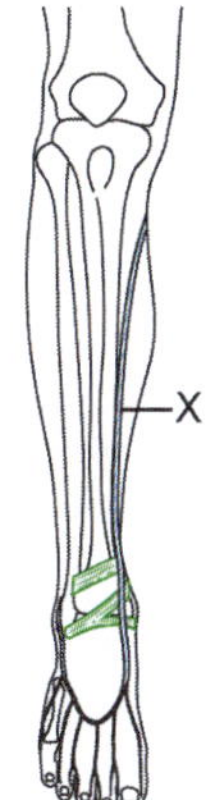

   a. Popliteal vein
   b. Femoral vein
   c. Short saphenous vein
   d. Deep perforating vein
3. Which of the following statements is TRUE about long saphenous vein?
   a. It is accompanied by sural nerve
   b. It is formed by the union of medial end of dorsal venous arch with medial marginal vein
   c. It passes behind the medial malleolus
   d. Not connected with deep veins.
4. A 50-year-old male presented with weakness in his right leg and difficulty lifting his foot. On examination, there was weakness in dorsiflexion and eversion of the right foot, with diminished sensation over the dorsum of the foot. What is the likely nerve injured?
   a. Common peroneal nerve
   b. Superficial peroneal nerve
   c. Deep peroneal nerve
   d. Saphenous nerve
5. Saphenous nerve a branch of ___________.
   a. Anterior division of femoral nerve
   b. Posterior division of sciatic nerve
   c. Anterior division of sciatic nerve
   d. Posterior division of femoral nerve
6. All of the following structure passes under the inferior extensor retinaculum, EXCEPT:
   a. Anterior tibial vessels
   b. Deep peroneal nerve
   c. Extensor digitorum longus
   d. Peroneus longus
7. Peroneus tertius belongs to which compartment of leg
   a. Medial compartment
   b. Lateral compartment
   c. Anterior compartment
   d. Posterior compartment

8. Identify the structure marked as X in the above-mentioned picture.

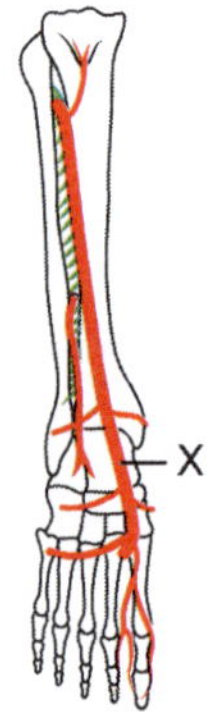

a. First metatarsal artery b. Anterior tibial artery
c. Dorsalis pedis artery d. Perforating branch

9. The lateral compartment of the leg is mainly supplied by which nerve?
a. Common peroneal nerve b. Superficial peroneal nerve
c. Deep peroneal nerve d. Saphenous nerve

10. Which among the following is NOT a part of Guy rope muscles?
a. Semitendinosus b. Semimembranosus
c. Gracilis d. Sartorius

11. A 55-year-old woman presents with pain and swelling on the medial aspect of her right knee. On examination, tenderness present over the medial aspect of the knee, passive stretching of the hamstring muscles exacerbates the pain. Which of the following is the most likely diagnosis?
a. Medial meniscus tear b. Patellar tendinitis
c. Anserine bursitis d. Infrapatellar bursitis

12. The site marked as X is supplied by ________.

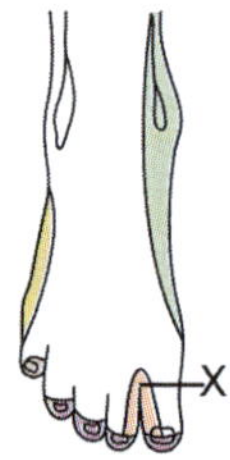

a. Superficial peroneal nerve
b. Saphenous nerve
c. Sural nerve
d. Deep peroneal nerve

13. Which of the following muscles does NOT cause dorsiflexion of foot?
a. Tibialis anterior
b. Extensor digitorum longus
c. Peroneus tertius
d. Peroneus longus

14. Identify the X marked site.

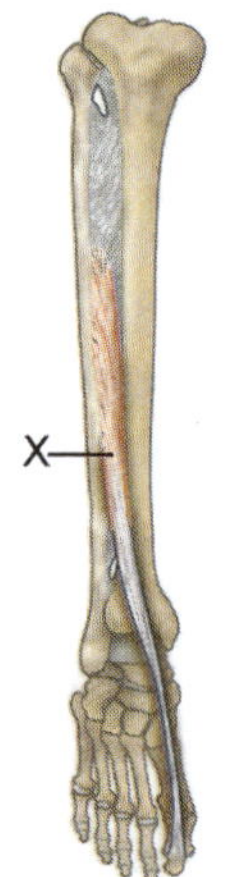

a. Extensor digitorum longus
b. Extensor hallucis longus
c. Extensor digitorum brevis
d. Extensor hallucis brevis

15. A 29-year-old male came with complaints of sudden pain in the anterior compartment of his leg followed by strenuous activity in the gym. What is the likely diagnosis?
a. Tendinitis
b. Anserine bursitis
c. Tarsal tunnel syndrome
d. Fresher's syndrome

QUESTION BANK

(Use separate copy to solve the following question)

Q 1. Write a short note on:
a. Dorsalis pedis artery
b. Tibialis anterior
c. Extensor retinaculum of foot
d. Sensory supply of dorsum of foot
e. Anterior tibial artery
f. Superficial peroneal nerve
g. Deep peroneal nerve

eSmartQuiz

Back of Leg

CLINICOANATOMICAL PROBLEMS

Clinical Case 1

A 45-year-old man experienced sudden, severe pain in his right heel while playing basketball. He recalls feeling a "pop" at the back of his ankle. On examination, there was a palpable defect in the Achilles tendon with inability to plantarflex the foot. The treating physician diagnosed him as a case of ruptured tendo calcaneus.

1. What is tendo calcaneus?
2. What is the action of tendo calcaneus?
3. Why there was feeling of "pop" at the back of ankle?

Explanation

1. ______________________________

2. ______________________________

3. ______________________________

Clinical Case 2

A 38-year-old woman presented with burning pain and numbness in her left foot, radiating to the sole and toes. She experienced worsening symptoms at night and tingling sensations along the medial ankle. On examination, Tinel's sign was positive over the tarsal tunnel. Nerve conduction studies confirmed tarsal tunnel syndrome.

1. What is tarsal tunnel syndrome?
2. What is Tinel's sign?
3. Why is there pain in the foot in this case?

Explanation

1. ______________________________

2. ______________________________

3. ______________________________

PRACTICE FIGURES

(Label the practice figures)

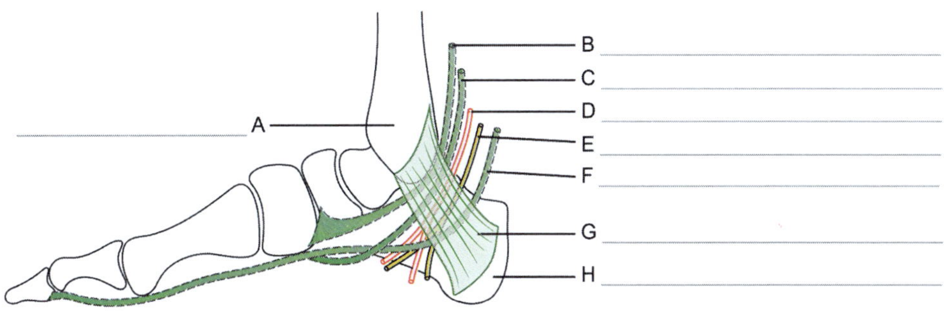

Practice Figure 9.1: Flexor retinaculum of the ankle and the structures passing deep to it

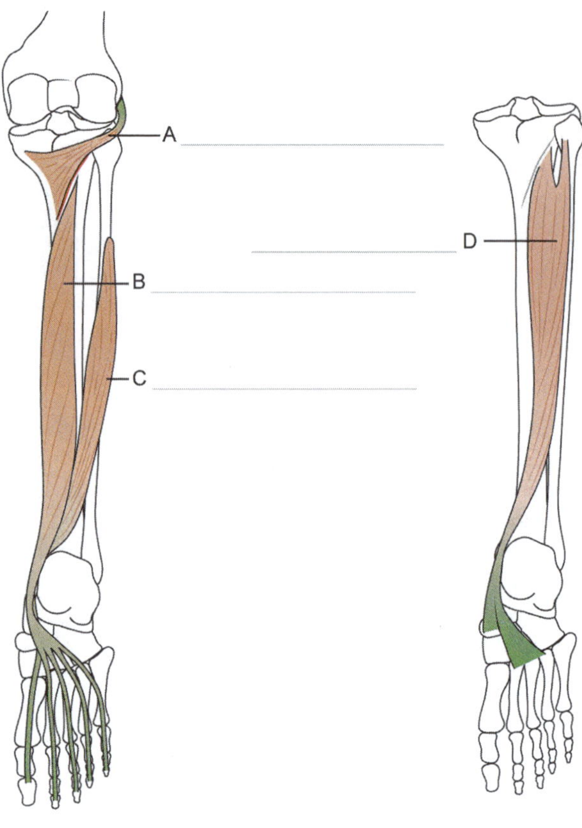

Practice Figure 9.2: Deep muscles of the back of the leg

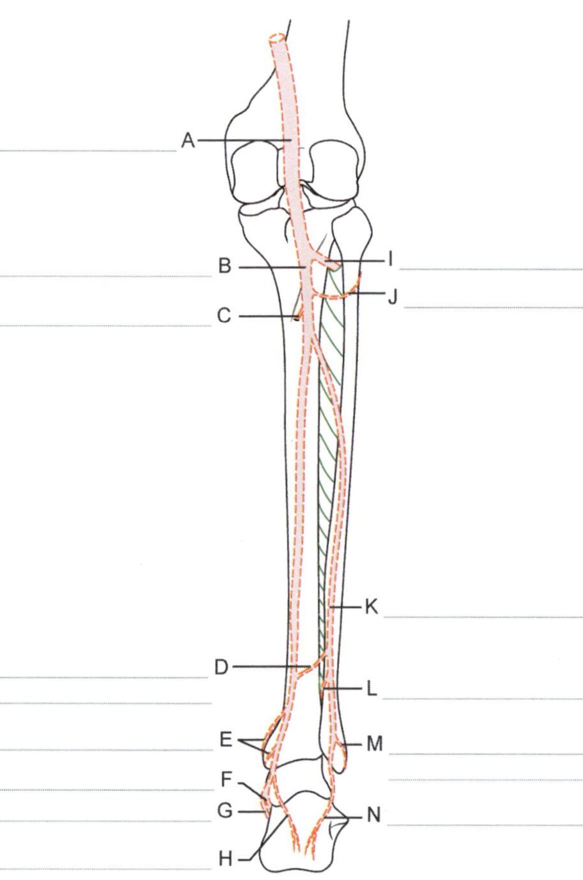

Practice Figure 9.3: Posterior tibial artery

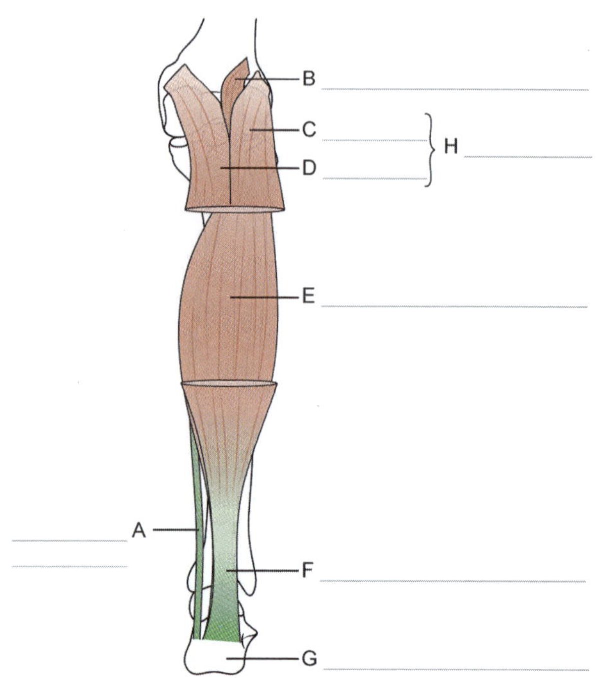

Practice Figure 9.4: Muscles of back of the leg

MULTIPLE CHOICE QUESTIONS

(Tick the single best correct option)

1. Root value of the lateral cutaneous nerve of the calf is ___________.
   a. L4, 5, S1 b. L5, S1, S2
   c. L3, 4, 5 d. S1, 2, 3
2. ___________ is used for grafting purposes.
   a. Saphenous nerve
   b. Sural nerve
   c. Common fibular nerve
   d. Lateral cutaneous nerve of calf
3. Identify X in the following picture.

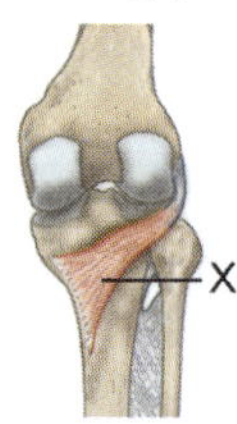

   a. Lateral head of gastrocnemius
   b. Plantaris
   c. Tibialis posterior
   d. Popliteus
4. Which tendon is tested in the following picture?

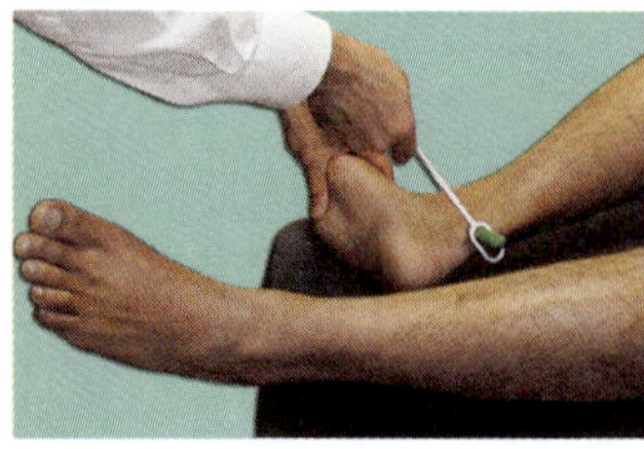

   a. Tendo calcaneus
   b. Extensor hallucis longus
   c. Plantaris tendon
   d. Peroneal retinaculum

5. Brodie's bursa is formed in ____________ muscle.
   a. Semimembranosus
   b. Medial head of gastrocnemius
   c. Plantaris
   d. Soleus
6. Tibial nerve compressed in the flexor retinaculum leads to ____________.
   a. Fresher's syndrome
   b. Sleeping foot syndrome
   c. Tarsal tunnel syndrome
   d. Foot drop
7. A 28-year-old basketball player presents with sudden pain in the left calf. On examination, palpable defect in the tendon in the leg. What is the most likely diagnosis?
   a. Calf muscle weakness
   b. Tenosynovitis
   c. Rupture of Achilles tendon
   d. Plantaris tendon rupture
8. Peroneal artery is a branch of ____________.
   a. Anterior tibial artery
   b. Posterior tibial artery
   c. Popliteal artery
   d. Inferior genicular artery
9. All of the following statements are false about tendo calcaneus, EXCEPT:
   a. It is about 30 cm long
   b. It is the thickest and strongest tendon in the body
   c. It is wide and thin in the middle
   d. It is attached to anterior surface of the calcaneum
10. Tendon transplantation can be done by using ____________ muscle.
    a. Achilles tendon
    b. Tibialis posterior
    c. Plantaris
    d. Flexor digitorum longus
11. An athletic player complains of sharp pain in the calf region during jumping. On examination, tenderness and swelling were present over the calf region. Which of the following movements primarily involves the calf muscles?
    a. Dorsiflexion of the ankle
    b. Inversion of the foot
    c. Eversion of the foot
    d. Plantar flexion of the ankle
12. The deep muscles of the posterior compartment of the leg are supplied by ____________.
    a. Common fibular nerve
    b. Tibial nerve
    c. Deep peroneal nerve
    d. Superficial peroneal nerve
13. Which muscle is primarily involved in walking on the flat surface?
    a. Soleus
    b. Tibialis anterior
    c. Peroneus longus
    d. Peroneus brevis
14. Identify the structure marked with X.

    a. Superior peroneal retinaculum
    b. Inferior peroneal retinaculum
    c. Flexor retinaculum of the ankle
    d. Aponeurosis
15. Navicular tuberosity gives attachment to ____________.
    a. Tibialis posterior
    b. Flexor digitorum brevis
    c. Flexor hallucis longus
    d. Flexor digiti minimi
16. ____________ is regarded as the 'peripheral heart'.
    a. Soleus
    b. Gastrocnemius
    c. Tibialis posterior
    d. Flexor digitorum longus

QUESTION BANK

(Use separate copy to solve the following questions)

Q 1. Describe the tibial nerve under the following headings: Beginning, root value, relations, distribution and branches, and applied aspects.

Q 2. Write a short note on:
   a. Tarsal tunnel syndrome
   b. Ankle reflex
   c. Popliteus muscle
   d. Tendocalcaneus
   e. Flexor retinaculum of foot

Chapter

10

eSmartQuiz

Sole of Foot

CLINICOANATOMICAL PROBLEMS

Clinical Case 1

A 50-year-old woman presented with sharp heel pain, particularly with the first steps in the morning or after prolonged standing. On examination, tenderness was noted over the medial aspect of the heel. Imaging revealed a calcaneal spur and thickening of the plantar fascia. The treating physician diagnosed her as a case of plantar fasciitis with a calcaneal spur.

1. What is plantar fasciitis?
2. What is calcaneal spur?
3. Why there is pain in the plantar fasciitis, particularly with the first steps in the morning?

Explanation

1. ______________________________

2. ______________________________

3. ______________________________

Clinical Case 2

A 30-year-old enthusiastic jogger complained of pain and swelling in his right foot, particularly around the base of the second toe. He noticed difficulty in bearing weight and discomfort while running. On examination, tenderness and redness were noted over the second metatarsophalangeal joint. The treating physician diagnosed him with jogger's foot.

1. What is jogger's foot?
2. Which nerve is involved in Jogger's foot?
3. What is the area of distribution of the nerve involved in jogger's foot?

Explanation

1. ______________________________

2. ______________________________

3. ______________________________

PRACTICE FIGURES

(Label the practice figures)

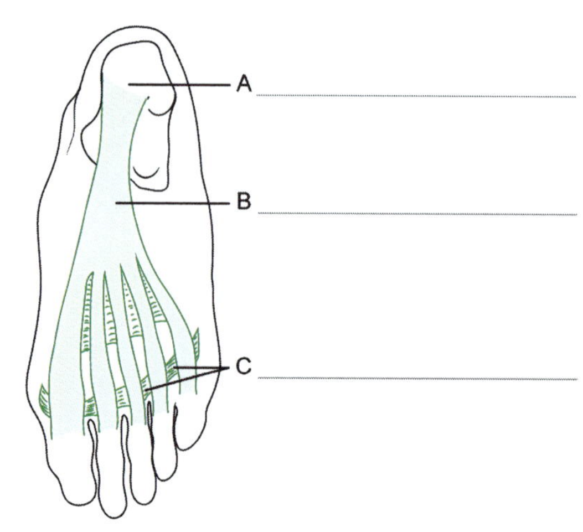

Practice Figure 10.1: Plantar aponeurosis

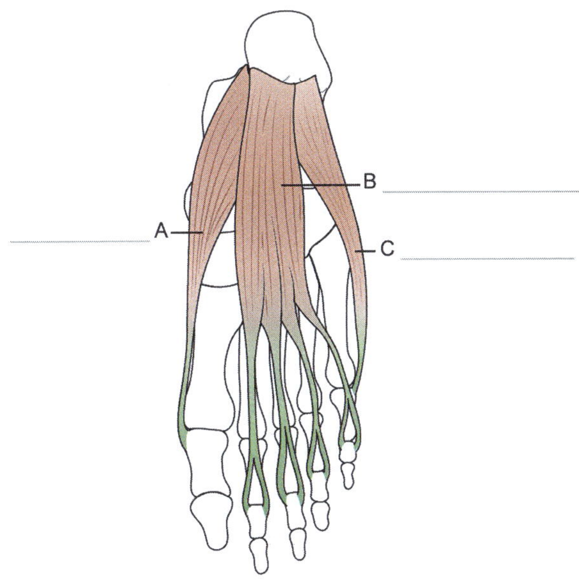

Practice Figure 10.2: Muscles of first layer of sole

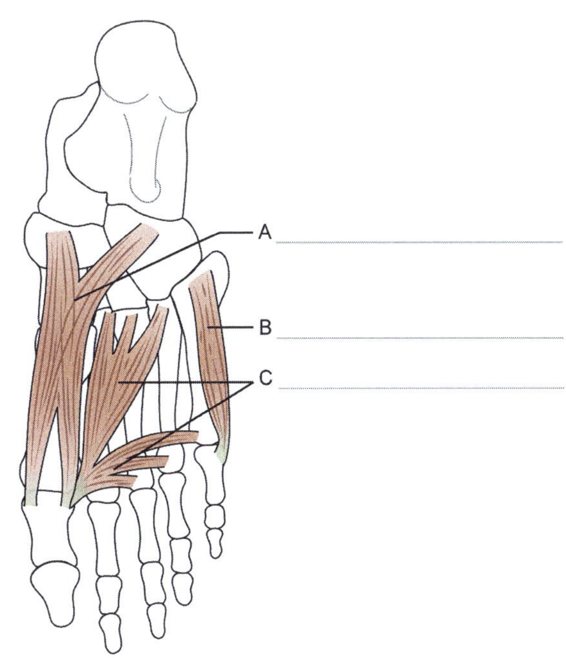

Practice Figure 10.4: Muscles of third layer of the sole

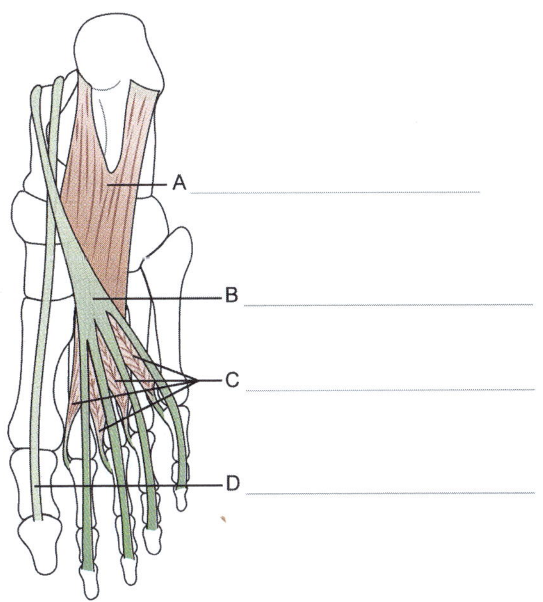

Practice Figure 10.3: Muscles and tendons of second layer of the sole

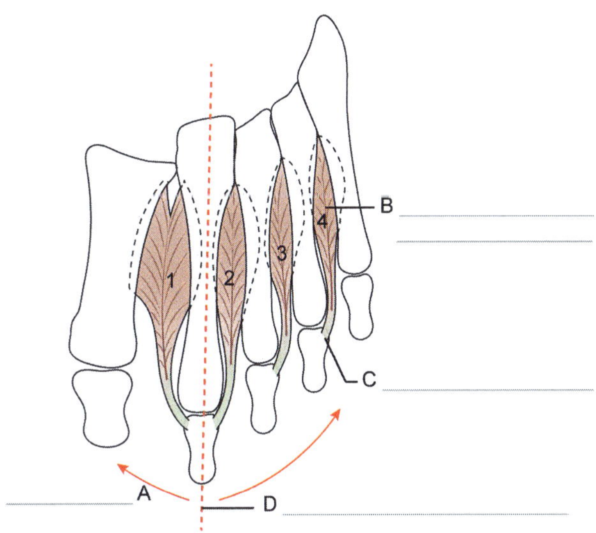

Practice Figure 10.5: The plantar interossei

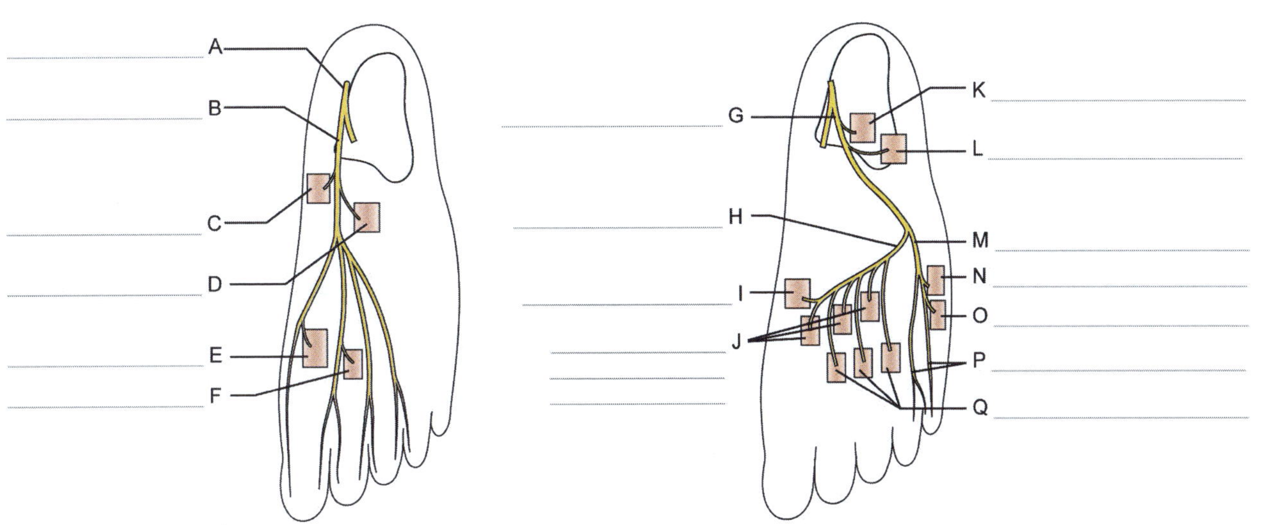

Practice Figure 10.6: Medial and lateral plantar nerves

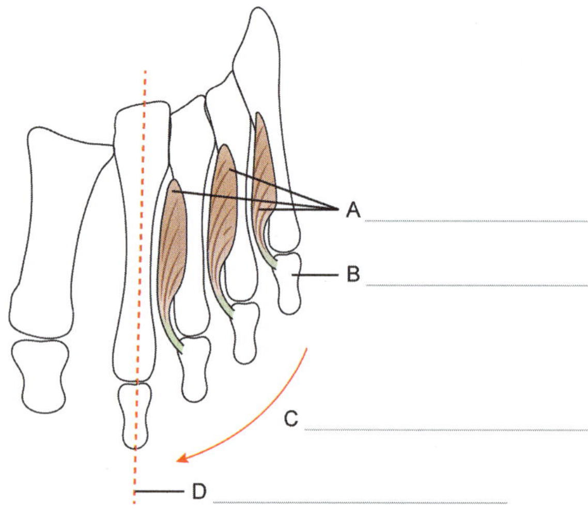

Practice Figure 10.7: The dorsal interossei

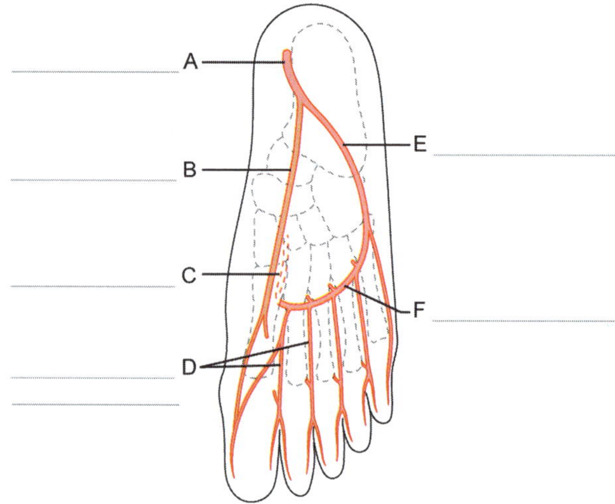

Practice Figure 10.8: Medial and lateral plantar arteries

MULTIPLE CHOICE QUESTIONS

(Tick the single best correct option)

1. Which of the following statements is true about plantar aponeurosis?
   a. It represents the proximal part of the plantaris muscle
   b. It gives origin to third layer of muscles
   c. It maintains the longitudinal arch of the foot
   d. It divides into three processes near head of metatarsal bones
2. A 45-year-old policeman presents with complaints of severe heel pain on prolonged periods of standing; the pain is sharp and stabbing in nature. On examination, there is tenderness on palpation of the medial aspect of the heel. What is the likely diagnosis?
   a. Tarsal tunnel syndrome
   b. Morton's neuroma
   c. Plantar fasciitis
   d. Achilles tendon rupture
3. The first lumbrical is supplied by which nerve?
   a. Superficial branch of lateral plantar nerve
   b. Medial plantar nerve
   c. Deep branch of lateral plantar nerve
   d. Deep peroneal nerve
4. The structure marked as X is derived from ___________.

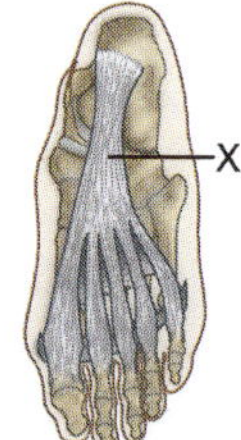

   a. Deep fascia b. Superficial fascia
   c. Deep muscle tendons d. Flexor retinaculum
5. Which of the following nerves supplies the area marked with X?
   a. Lateral plantar nerve
   b. A branch from the tibial nerve
   c. Medial plantar nerve
   d. Sural nerve
6. All of the following muscles belong to the first layer of foot, EXCEPT:
   a. Abductor hallucis b. Flexor digitorum brevis
   c. Abductor digiti minimi d. Flexor digitorum longus
7. What is the function of muscles marked as X?

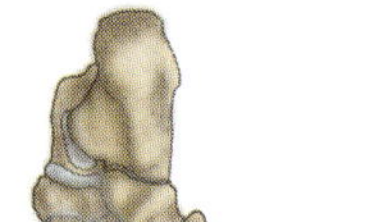

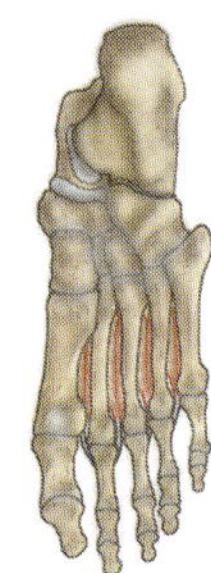

   a. Abduction b. Adduction
   c. Flexion d. Extension
8. Lateral plantar artery is a terminal branch of ___________.
   a. Anterior tibial artery b. Posterior tibial artery
   c. Peroneal artery d. Dorsalis pedis artery
9. A soldier complains of pain over 2nd and 3rd toes. X-ray shows fracture shaft of 2nd and 3rd toes. What is the diagnosis?
   a. Jogger's foot b. Morton's neuroma
   c. March fracture d. Pott's fracture
10. ___________ lumbrical muscle in the sole of foot is not supplied by the lateral plantar nerve.
    a. 1st b. 2nd
    c. 3rd d. 4th
11. All of the following statements are true about plantar arch, EXCEPT:
    a. It is the direct continuation of medial plantar artery
    b. It is accompanied by venae comitantes
    c. The arch is completed by dorsalis pedis artery
    d. It is present between the 1st and 2nd layers of muscle

QUESTION BANK

(Use separate copy to solve the following question)

Q 1. Write a short note on:
   a. Cutaneous innervation of sole of foot
   b. Plantar aponeurosis
   c. Medial and lateral plantar nerve
   d. Plantar arch
   e. Lumbricals of sole
   f. March foot

Chapter

Venous and Lymphatic Drainage; Segmental and Sympathetic Innervation

11

eSmartQuiz

CLINICOANATOMICAL PROBLEM

Clinical Case 1

A 40-year-old woman presented with aching pain and discomfort in her left leg, accompanied by visible bulging veins. She noticed skin discoloration and ulceration around the ankle. On examination, dilated and tortuous veins were noted, along with brownish pigmentation and a venous ulcer on the medial aspect of the ankle. The treating surgeon diagnosed her with varicose veins.

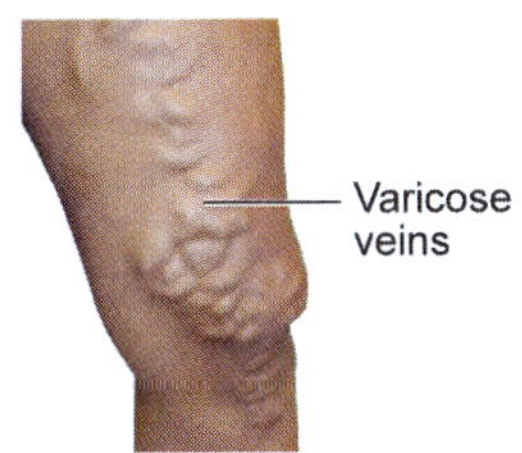

1. What is varicose vein?
2. Name the structure making the appearance shown in the above image.
3. Give the anatomical basis for the development of varicose veins in lower limbs.

Explanation

1. ____

____

____

____

2. ____

____

____

____

____

____

____

3. ____

____

____

____

____

____

____

____

PRACTICE FIGURES

(Label the practice figures)

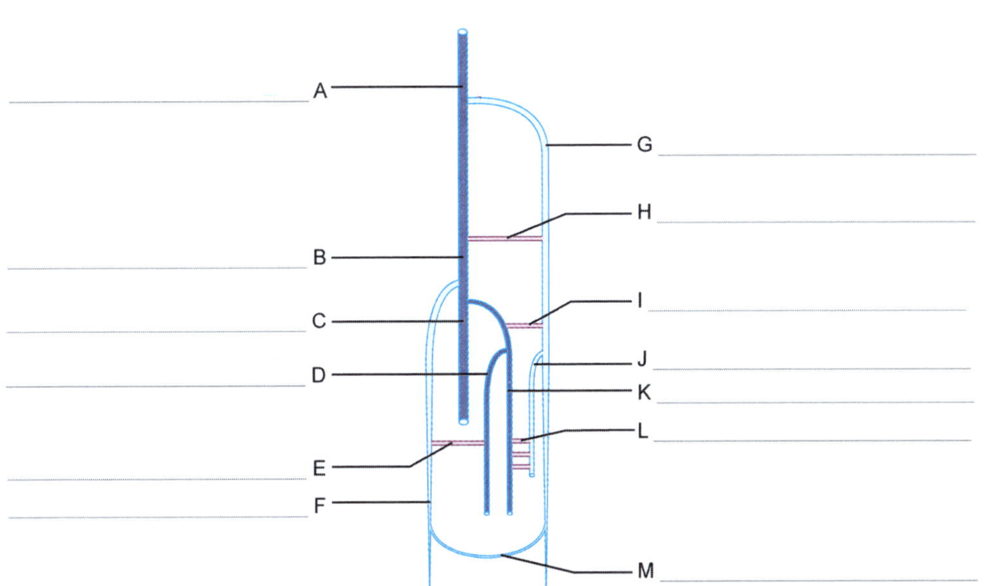

Practice Figure 11.1: Scheme of the veins of lower limb

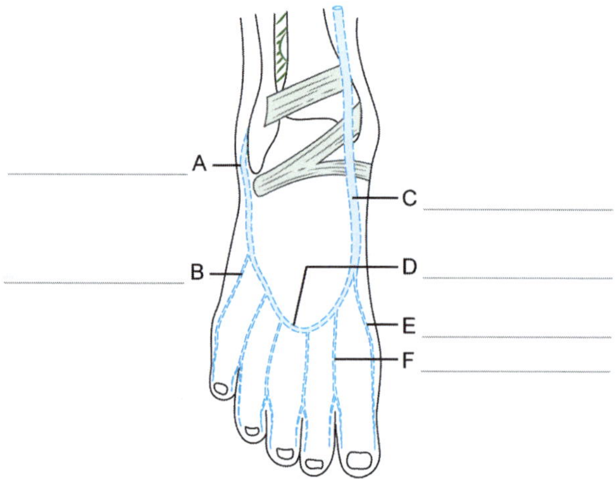

Practice Figure 11.2: Superficial veins of the front of the leg and dorsum of the foot

MULTIPLE CHOICE QUESTIONS

(Tick the single best correct option)

1. Which of the following statements is TRUE about the perforating veins in the lower limb?
   a. It connects the deep veins with the superficial veins.
   b. The valves permit only one-way flow of blood from the superficial to the deep veins.
   c. The great and small saphenous veins are the large indirect perforators.
   d. They are valveless.
2. __________ vein is used for venesection during collapse of peripheral veins.
   a. Femoral vein b. Long saphenous vein
   c. Short saphenous vein d. Popliteal vein
3. Name the structure marked by X.

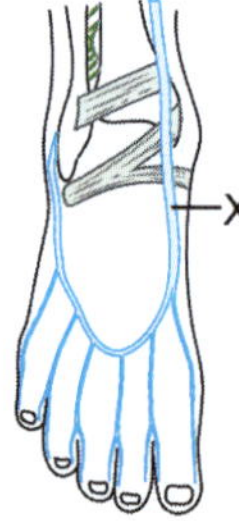

   a. Dorsal venous arch b. Anterior tibial vein
   c. Short saphenous vein d. Great saphenous vein
4. The effect of calf pump on venous return is __________.
   a. Decreases venous return
   b. Increases venous return
   c. Does not affect venous return
   d. Redistributes blood flow within the capillaries
5. Identify the clinical condition shown in the following picture.

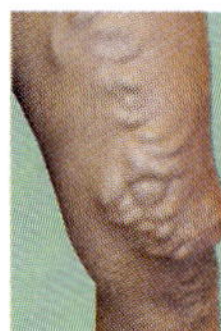

   a. Soft tissue swelling b. Urticaria
   c. Vascular tumour d. Varicose vein
6. A 19-year-old pregnant lady developed dilated veins near her right knee medial aspect during her 7th month of gestation. What is the possible cause?
   a. Genetic inheritance
   b. Increased pressure on iliac veins due to enlarged uterus
   c. Physiological change
   d. Incompetent valves
7. A 60-year-old man came with complaints of swelling in the left upper limb over several months, worsening during day time. On examination, non-pitting pedal oedema present over ankle, non-tender nodules over lymphatic channels present. What is the likely diagnosis?
   a. Deep vein thrombosis
   b. Filariasis
   c. Varicose veins
   d. Neuropathy
8. Pick out the correct statement regarding the superficial inguinal lymph nodes.
   a. The upper medial group drains glans penis
   b. Efferents pierce the cribriform fascia, and terminate in the deep inguinal nodes
   c. The lower vertical group drains buttock and short saphenous territory
   d. Perthes test is employed to test the superficial inguinal nodes.
9. What is the complication shown in the below image marked as X?

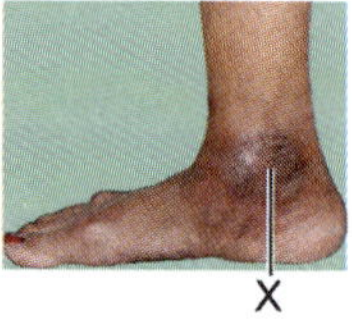

   a. Eczematous lesion
   b. Varicose ulcer
   c. Deep vein thrombosis
   d. Hyperpigmented skin
10. The commonest cause of swelling in the sublingual region is __________.
    a. Inguinal lymphadenopathy
    b. Femoral hernia
    c. Psoas abscess
    d. Filariasis
11. Which of the following statements is TRUE about short saphenous veins?
    a. It terminates as femoral vein
    b. It is accompanied by saphenous nerve
    c. It is located posterior to lateral malleolus
    d. It has 15–20 valves

QUESTION BANK

(Use separate copy to solve the following question)

Q 1. Write a short note on:
   a. Varicose vein
   b. Great saphenous vein
   c. Inguinal lymph nodes
   d. Soleus as a peripheral heart

eSmartQuiz

Joints of Lower Limb

CLINICOANATOMICAL PROBLEMS

Clinical Case 1

A 25-year-old tennis player experienced sudden knee pain and instability after a twisting injury during a match. On examination, anterior drawer sign was positive, indicating anterior translation of the tibia relative to the femur, suggestive of a torn anterior cruciate ligament (ACL). MRI confirmed the diagnosis.

1. What are the attachments of the anterior cruciate ligament?
2. What is drawer sign?
3. What is positive Drawer sing?
4. What is "unhappy triad" of the knee joint?

Explanation

1. ______________________________
2. ______________________________
3. ______________________________
4. ______________________________

Clinical Case 2

A 30-year-old football player experienced sharp knee pain and swelling after a sudden twisting motion during a game. On examination, there was a tenderness along the joint line, and McMurray's test was positive, and the anterior and posterior drawer tests were negative. MRI confirmed an isolated tear of the medial meniscus.

1. What is McMurray's test?
2. Why is the injury of medial meniscus more common than that of a lateral meniscus?
3. Which test differentiates the anterior cruciate ligament tear and medial meniscus injury?

Explanation

1. ______________________________
2. ______________________________
3. ______________________________

Clinical Case 3

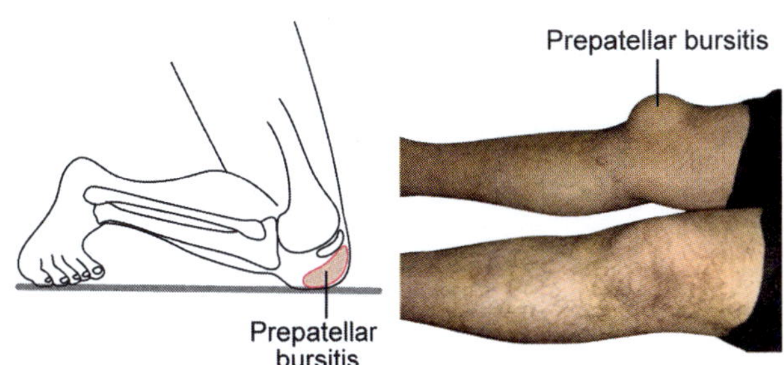

Fig. 12.1: Housemaid knee

A 35-year-old housemaid presented with swelling and tenderness over her left knee. She described worsening pain while kneeling and difficulty performing her daily tasks. On examination, a tender, fluctuant swelling was noted over the anterior aspect of the knee. The treating physician diagnosed her as a case of prepatellar bursitis.

1. What is prepatellar bursitis?
2. Why it is common in housemaids?

Explanation

1.

2.

PRACTICE FIGURES

(Label the practice figures)

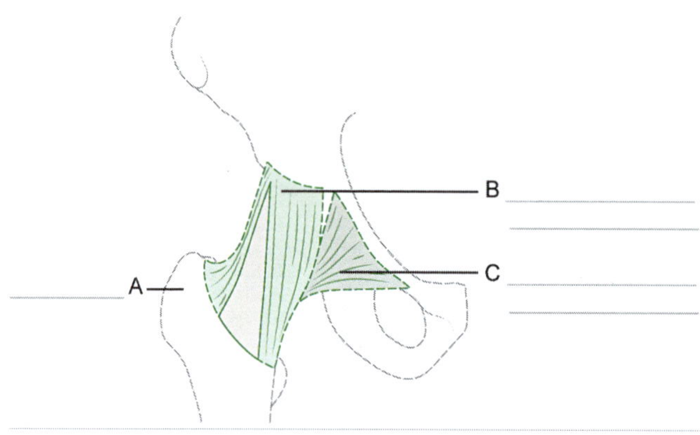

Practice Figure 12.1: The iliofemoral and pubofemoral ligaments

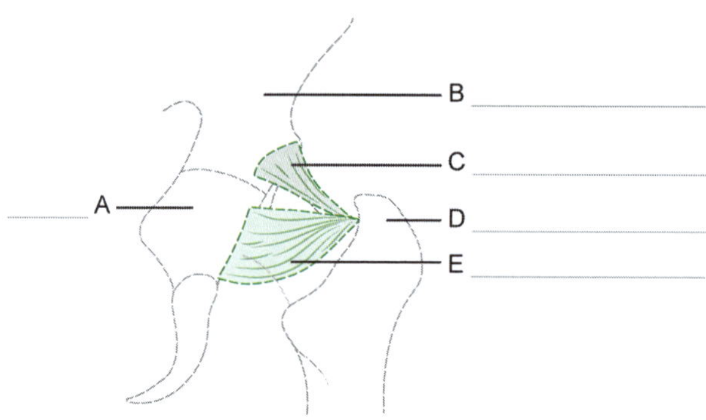

Practice Figure 12.2: Iliofemoral and ischiofemoral ligaments

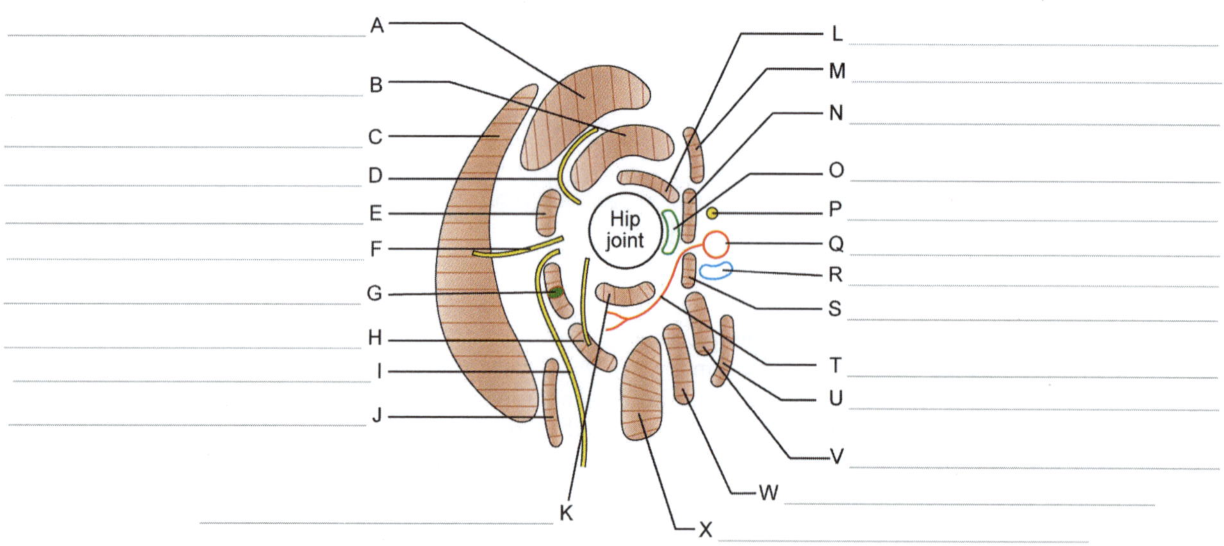

Practice Figure 12.3: Relations of the hip joint

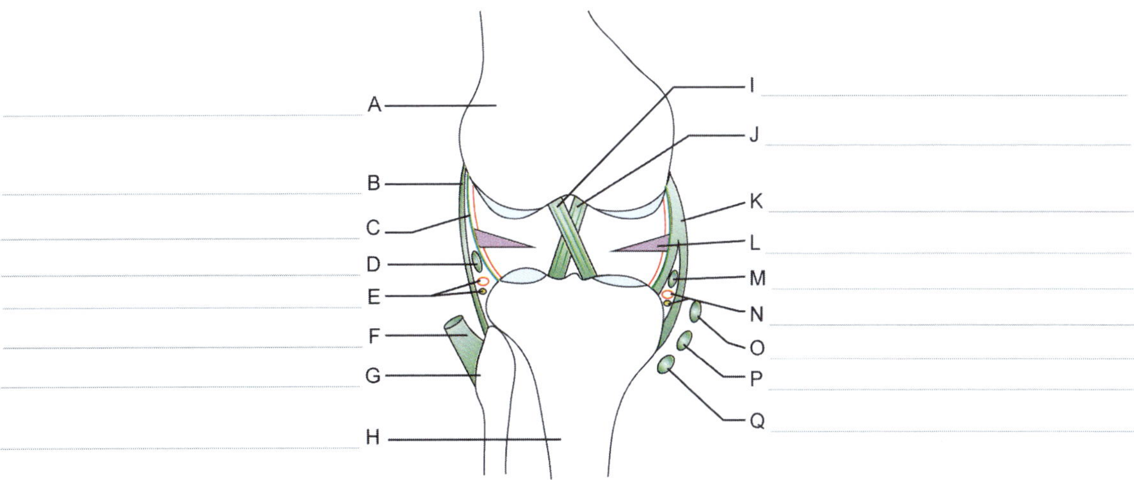

Practice Figure 12.4: Coronal section of knee joint

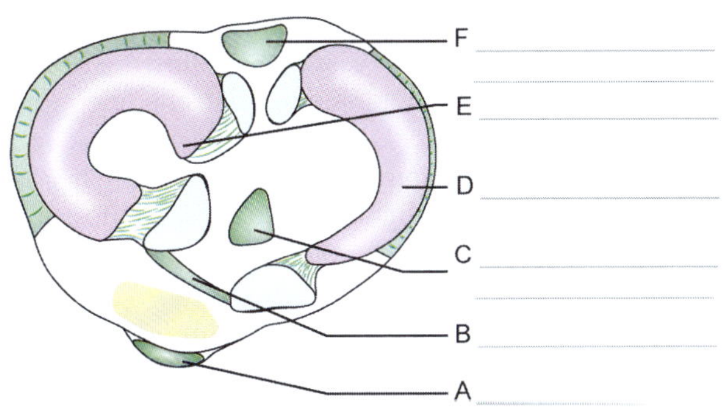

Practice Figure 12.5: Superior view of upper end of the right tibia

MULTIPLE CHOICE QUESTIONS

(Tick the single best correct option)

1. Which of the following is an example of a multiaxial joint?
   a. Knee joint b. Hip joint
   c. Talonavicular joint d. Subtalar joint
2. Pick out the correct statement about the ligament of Bigelow.
   a. It is one of the strongest ligaments in the body.
   b. It prevents the trunk from falling forwards in the standing posture.
   c. The ligament is rectangular in shape.
   d. Its apex is attached to the lower half of the anterior superior iliac spine.
3. Dislocation of the hip is more common in ____________.
   a. Anterior b. Posterior
   c. Central d. Lateral
4. Name the structure marked by X.

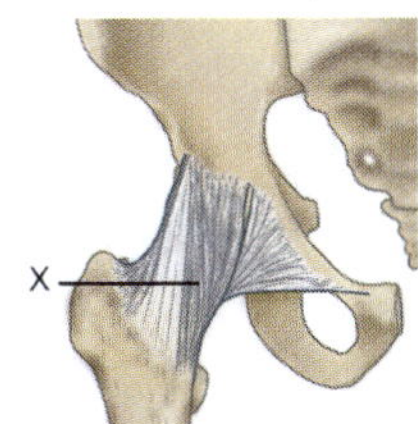

   a. Pubofemoral ligament
   b. Iliofemoral ligament
   c. Transverse acetabular ligament
   d. Ligamentum teres femoris
5. Identify the clinical condition.

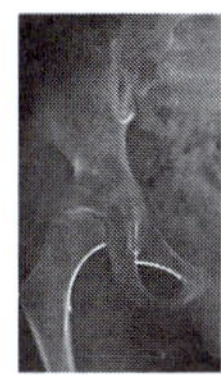

   a. Fracture of head of femur
   b. Osteomyelitis
   c. Dislocation of hip joint
   d. Subluxation of head of femur
6. Identify the structure marked as X.

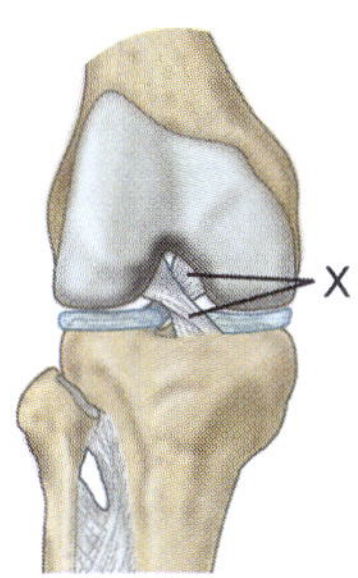

   a. Transverse ligaments b. Cruciate ligaments
   c. Capsular ligaments d. Oblique popliteal ligament
7. Which of the following statements is false about medial collateral ligament?
   a. It is the degenerated tendon of the adductor magnus.
   b. It is crossed by the tendon of semimembranosus.
   c. It has anterior and posterior parts.
   d. It is attached to the medial epicondyle of the femur.
8. Locking of the knee joint is done by which muscle?
   a. Vastus medialis b. Semitendinosus
   c. Biceps femoris d. Popliteus
9. Identify the deformity shown in the following image.

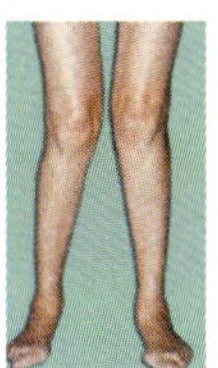

   a. Genu varum b. Genu valgum
   c. Perthes' disease d. Osteoarthritis

10. A 67-year-old female presented with bilateral knee pain for more than 10 months. X-ray shows osteophytes and reduced joint space. What is the likely diagnosis?
    a. Rheumatoid arthritis b. Osteoarthritis
    c. Tenosynovitis d. Meniscal injury
11. Ankle joint is a synovial joint of ____________ variety.
    a. Ball and socket b. Saddle joint
    c. Gliding joint d. Hinge joint
12. ____________ test is done to assess the cruciate ligament.
    a. Trendelenberg's test b. Perthes' test
    c. Drawer's test d. Straight leg raise test
13. A 20-year-old football player sustained an injury over his left knee while playing. On examination, instability of the knee joint present with positive Lachman test. Which ligament is affected in this condition?
    a. Anterior cruciate ligament
    b. Medial collateral ligament
    c. Lateral collateral ligament
    d. Transverse ligament
14. Which of the following muscles is not a dorsiflexor?
    a. Tibialis anterior
    b. Peroneus tertius
    c. Extensor hallucis longus
    d. Flexor hallucis longus
15. ____________ are damaged in the "unhappy triad" of knee injuries.
    a. ACL, tibial collateral, and medial meniscus
    b. PCL, fibular collateral, and lateral meniscus
    c. ACL, fibular collateral, and medial meniscus
    d. PCL, tibial collateral, and lateral meniscus
16. Identify the structure marked with X.

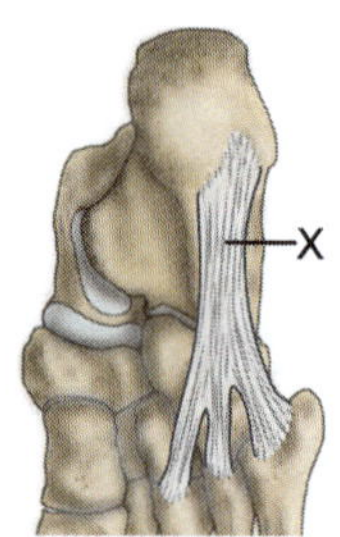

    a. Short plantar ligament b. Plantar aponeurosis
    c. Long plantar ligament d. Spring ligament

QUESTION BANK

(Use separate copy to solve the following questions)

Q 1. Describe the hip joint under the following headings: Articular surfaces, ligaments, relations, movements, applied aspects.

Q 2. Describe the knee joint under the following headings: Articular surfaces, ligaments, relations, movements, applied aspects.

Q 3. Describe the ankle joint under the following headings: Articular surfaces, ligaments, relations, movements, applied aspects.

Q 4. Write as short note on:
1. Deltoid ligament of the ankle joint
2. Inversion and eversion of foot
3. Cruciate ligaments of knee joint
4. Knee Menisci
5. Bursae related to the knee joint

Arches of Foot

CLINICOANATOMICAL PROBLEM

Clinical Case 1

A 22-year-old man aspiring for a military career was disqualified during the medical examination due to flat feet. He reported occasional foot pain and fatigue during physical activities. On examination, both feet exhibited decreased arch height, with the entire sole making contact with the ground. Despite meeting other criteria, his flat feet were deemed incompatible with the physical demands of military service, leading to his disqualification from the recruitment process.

1. What is flat foot?
2. Why the aspirant disqualified for military service?
3. List any two factors maintaining the medial longitudinal arches of foot.

Explanation

1. ____________________
2. ____________________
3. ____________________

PRACTICE FIGURES

(Label the practice figures)

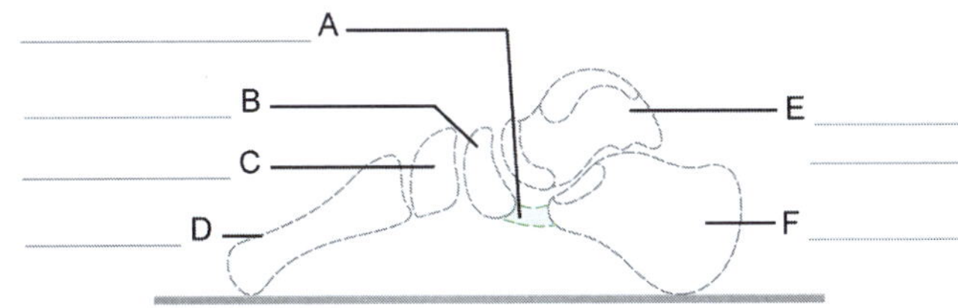

Practice Figure 13.1: Bones forming the longitudinal arch of foot

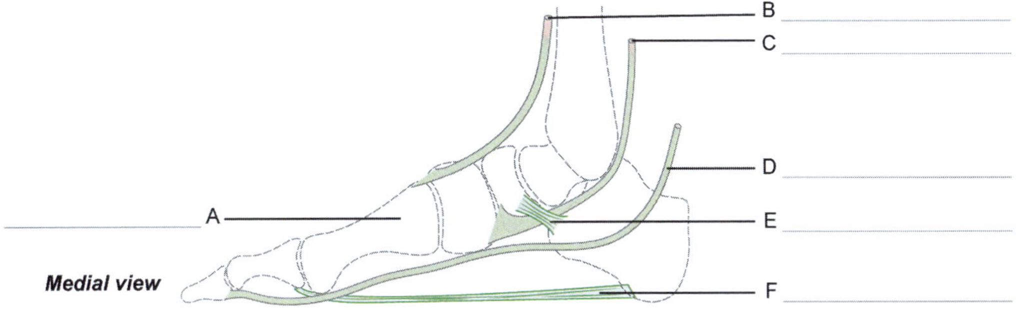

Practice Figure 13.2: Factors maintaining the medial longitudinal arch

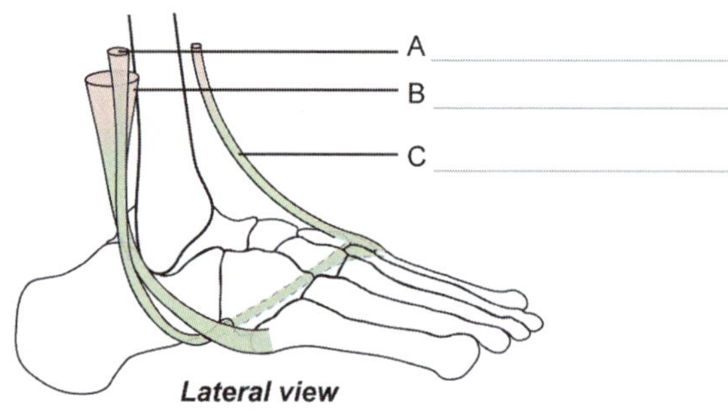

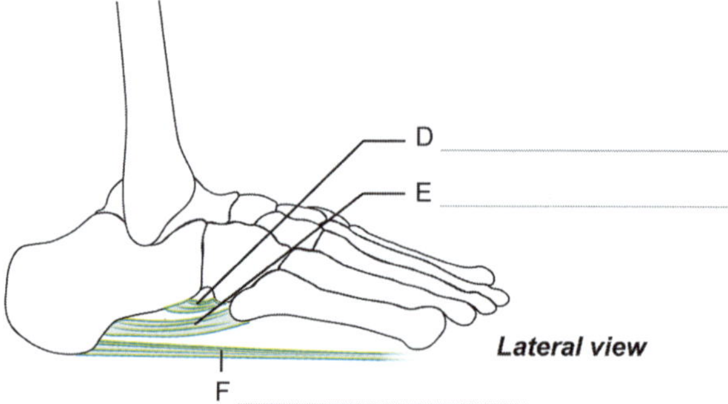

Practice Figure 13.3: Factors maintaining lateral longitudinal arches

MULTIPLE CHOICE QUESTIONS

(Tick the single best correct option)

1. The main joint of the medial longitudinal arch is the ___________.
   a. Intertarsal joint
   b. 1st metatarsal joint
   c. Calcaneocuboid joint
   d. Talocalcaneonavicular joint
2. Insertion of tibialis posterior includes all of the following, EXCEPT:
   a. Calcaneum   b. Cuboid
   c. Cuneiforms   d. Talus
3. Pick out the correct statement about medial longitudinal arch.
   a. The main joint of the arch is the subtalar joint
   b. The anterior pillar is short and strong
   c. The posterior end is formed by the medial tubercle of the calcaneum
   d. Key stone is cuboid
4. Mother of a newborn incidentally noted that the baby's left foot is turned inwards with abnormal posture. Upon examination by orthopaedician the left foot was inverted, adducted and plantar flexed. What is the most likely diagnosis?
   a. Talipes valgus   b. Talipes equinovarus
   c. Pes planus   d. Talipes calcaneus
5. The picture shows bones forming the medial longitudinal arch. Which of the following bones does not take part in the formation of medial longitudinal arch?

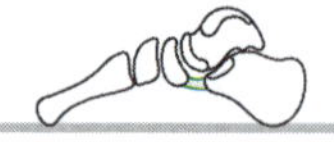

   a. Talus   b. 4th and 5th metatarsals
   c. Cuneiforms   d. Navicular
6. Which bone is the key stone for lateral longitudinal arch?
   a. Talus   b. Navicular
   c. Cuneiform   d. Cuboid
7. Identify the ligament marked as X.

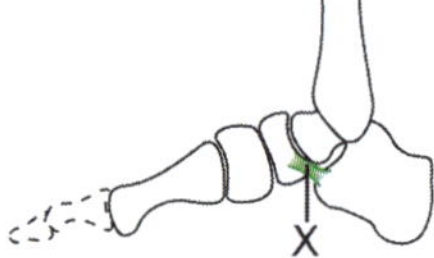

   a. Short plantar ligament   b. Long plantar ligament
   c. Spring ligament   d. Metatarsal ligament
8. Exaggeration of the longitudinal arches of the foot is known as ___________.
   a. Pes planus
   b. Pes cavus
   c. Talipus varus
   d. Hallux valgus
9. The clinical condition shown in the image is due to loss of ___________ arch.

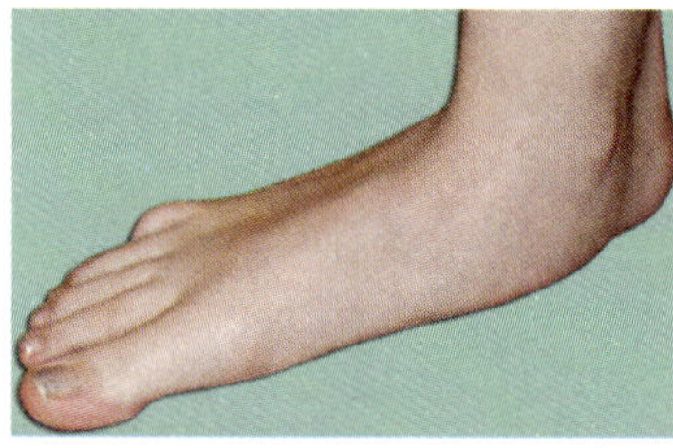

   a. Lateral longitudinal arch
   b. Medial longitudinal arch
   c. Anterior transverse arch
   d. Posterior transverse arch
10. A medical student observed an old man walking on his toes, with the heel raised. What is the condition?
    a. Talipes equinus
    b. Talipes varus
    c. Talipes valgus
    d. Talipes calcaneus

QUESTION BANK

(Use separate copy to solve the following questions)

Q 1. Describe the arches of foot under the following headings: Classification, formation, factors maintaining their stability, applied aspects.

Q 2. List the differences between medial and lateral longitudinal arches.

Q 3. List the differences between anterior and posterior transverse arches.

Q 4. List the factors mainintaning the following arches:
   a. Medial longitudinal arch
   b. Lateral longitudinal arch
   c. Transverse arches

Q 5. Write a short note on:
   a. Londitudinal arches
   b. Pes cavus
   c. Flat foot

Surface and Radiological Anatomy of Lower Limb

eSmartQuiz

PRACTICE FIGURES

(Label the practice figures)

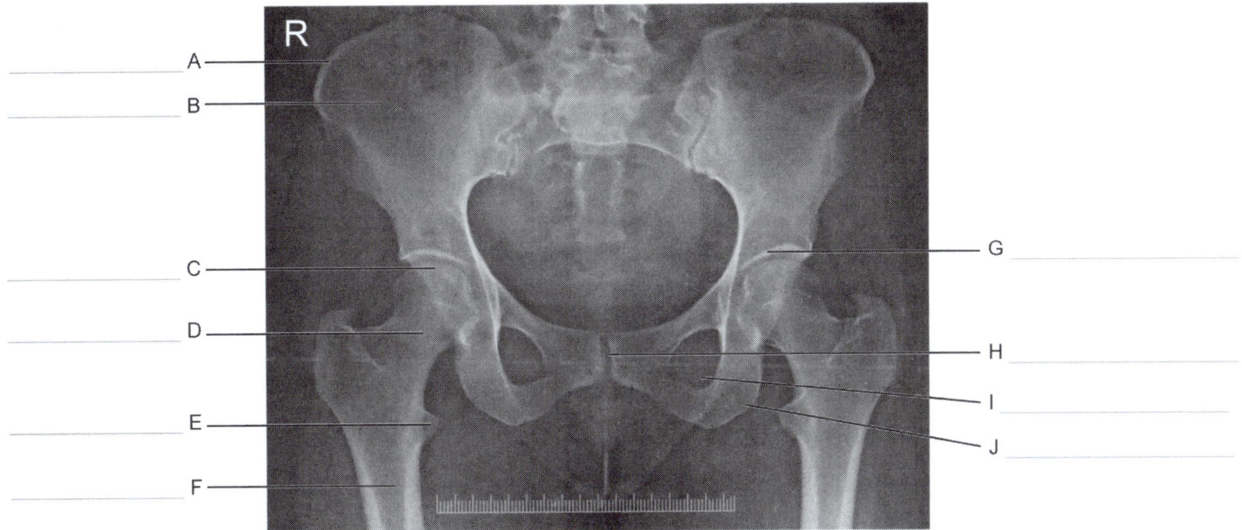

Practice Figure 14.1: Anteroposterior view of the pelvis

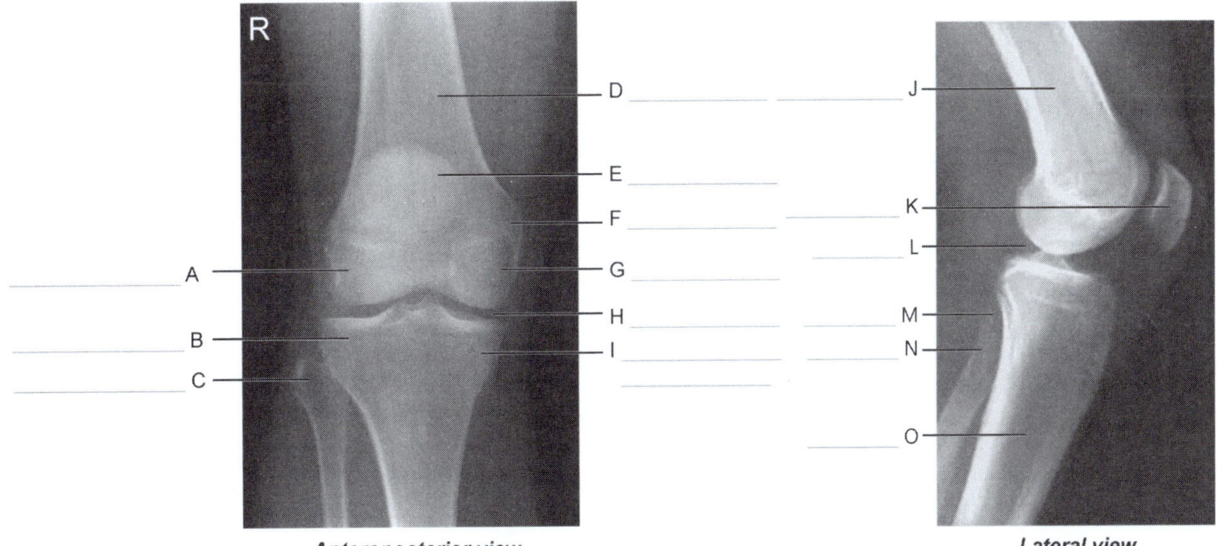

Practice Figure 14.2: Radiograph of the knee joint

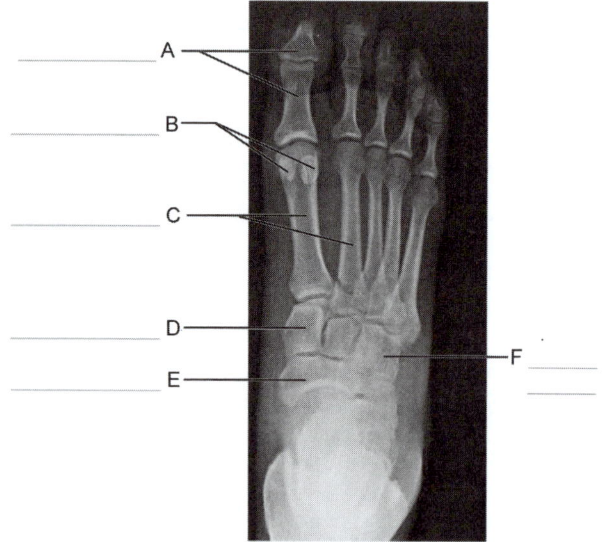

Practice Figure 14.3: Dorsoplantar view of the ankle and foot

MULTIPLE CHOICE QUESTIONS

(Tick the single best correct option)

1. True about saphenous opening is ___________.
   a. Its centre lies 4 cm below and 4 cm lateral to the pubic tubercle
   b. Its long axis is directed upwards and medially.
   c. It is about 5 cm long and 5 cm broad
   d. It is a defect in superficial fascia
2. Os Trigonum is the accessory bone of ___________.
   a. Medial tubercle of talus
   b. Lateral tubercle of talus
   c. Tuberosity of fifth metatarsal bone
   d. Tuberosity of first metatarsal bone
3. Name the structure marked by X.

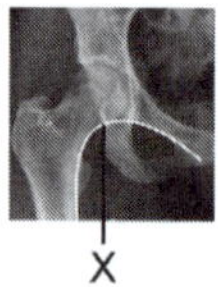

   a. Shoemaker's line b. Shenton's line
   c. Nelaton's line d. Ober's test
4. Ward's triangle is ___________.
   a. Thickened band of compact bone in the neck of femur
   b. Dense wedge cancellous bone in the head of femur
   c. It is radiological triangle formed in fracture neck of femur
   d. It is a portal of exit to obturator vessels.
5. Identify X-marked site.

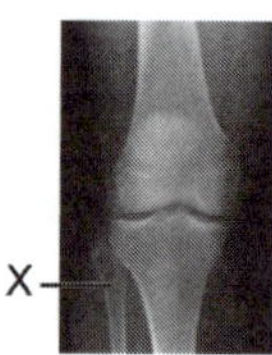

   a. Fibula b. Tibia
   c. Lateral epicondyle d. Femur
6. Identify the X-marked bone

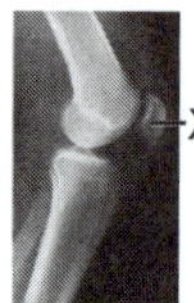

   a. Fibula b. Tibia
   c. Femur d. Patella
7. Identify the site marked as X.

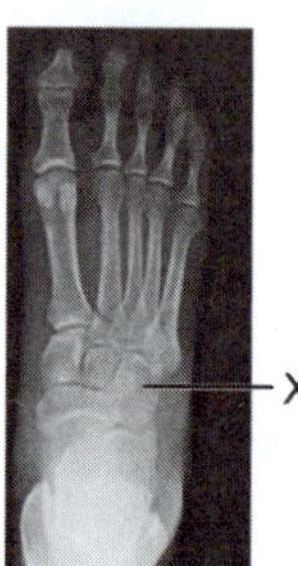

   a. Calcaneum b. Talus
   c. Cuneiform d. Cuboid
8. Identify the site marked as X

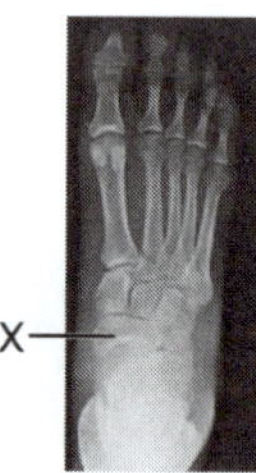

   a. Navicular b. Talus
   c. Cuneiform d. Cuboid

Abdomen and Pelvis

Chapter

15

Introduction and Osteology of Abdomen

eSmartQuiz

CLINICOANATOMICAL PROBLEM

Clinical Case 1

A 40-year-old office worker presented with chronic low back pain exacerbated by prolonged sitting. On examination, there was tenderness over the lumbar spine, and the patient reported occasional numbness and tingling in the lower limbs. Imaging revealed spondylolisthesis, with forward displacement of the L5 vertebra over the sacrum.

1. What is the difference between spondylolysis and spondylolisthesis?
2. What is the reason for low backache in the above-mentioned case?
3. Why the pain was increasing with prolonged sitting?

Explanation

1. ____________________

2. ____________________

3. ____________________

PRACTICE FIGURES

(Label the practice figures)

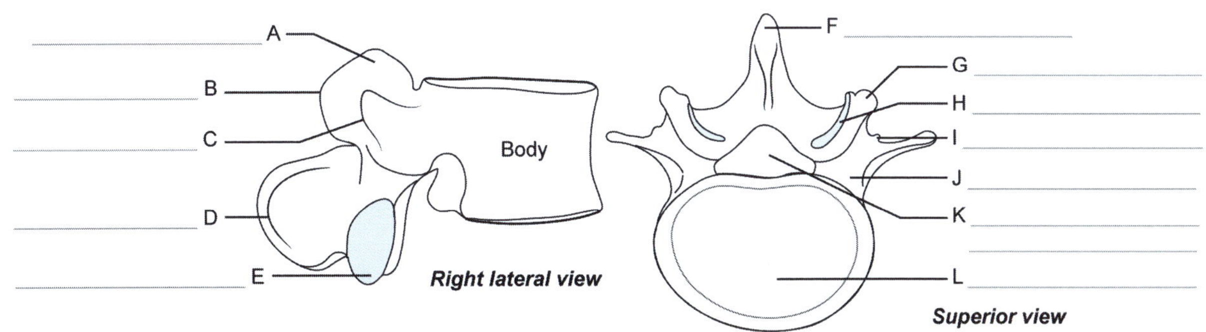

Practice Figure 15.1: Typical lumbar vertebra

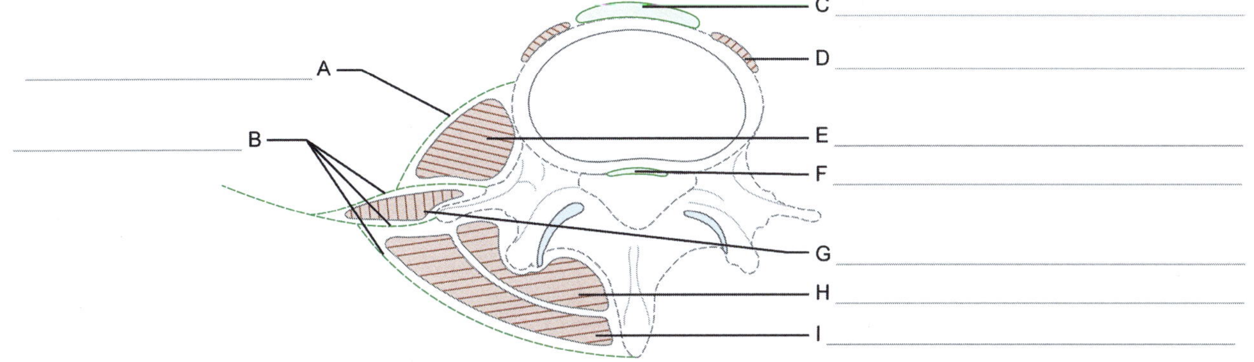

Practice Figure 15.2: Attachments of the lumbar vertebra

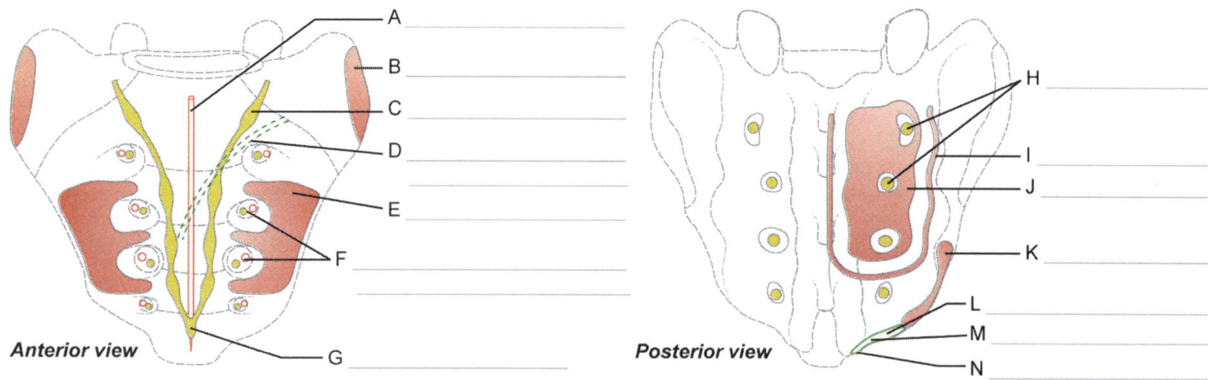

Practice Figure 15.3: Attachments and relations of sacrum

MULTIPLE CHOICE QUESTIONS

(Tick the single best correct option)

1. Identify the clinical condition shown in the following figure.
   a. Lumbarization of sacral vertebra
   b. Sacralisation of lumbar vertebra
   c. First sacral hemivertebra
   d. Transitional vertebra
2. ___________ is the secondary cartilaginous joint.
   a. Metatarsal joint b. Metacarpal joint
   c. Intervertebral joint d. Hip joint
3. A young adult met with a road traffic accident sustained injury in the lumbar region. MRI shows fracture dislocation of lumbar vertebrae. He has flaccid paralysis, saddle anaesthesia, incontinence of urine and faeces. What is the likely diagnosis?
   a. Transverse myelitis
   b. Cauda equina syndrome
   c. Conus medullaris syndrome
   d. Anterior cord syndrome
4. Identify the vertebra shown in the image:
   a. Typical lumbar vertebrae
   b. Atypical lumbar vertebrae
   c. Sacrum
   d. Thoracic vertebrae
5. Diagnose the condition shown in the below image.
   a. Scoliosis b. Kyphosis
   c. Spondylosis d. Lordosis
6. Name the structure marked as X in the following picture.
   a. Supraspinous ligament
   b. Transverse ligament
   c. Interspinous ligament
   d. Posterior layer of thoracolumbar fascia.
7. A 3-day-old infant presents with swelling in the lumbar region covered with a thin membrane. On examination, noticeable defects were noted in the vertebral column. MRI reveals a cystic structure containing cerebrospinal fluid and neural tissue extending from the spinal canal. Which of the following is the most likely diagnosis?
   a. Meningocele
   b. Myelomeningocele
   c. Spina bifida occulta
   d. Arnold-Chiari malformation
8. Name the triangle marked as X.

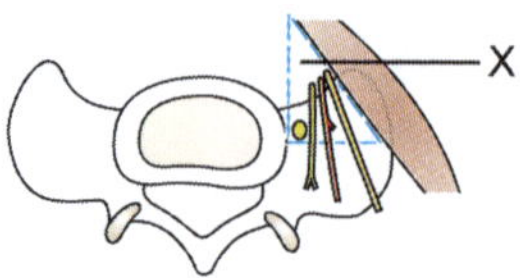

   a. Grynfeltt-Lesshaft triangle
   b. Scarpa's triangle
   c. Petit's triangle
   d. Triangle of Marcille
9. All of the following structures have attachment to the dorsal surface of the coccyx, EXCEPT:
   a. Gluteus maximus
   b. Sphincter ani externus
   c. Dorsal sacrococcygeal ligaments
   d. Sacrotuberous ligaments
10. Which is the most common type of pelvis in females?
   a. Android b. Platypelloid
   c. Gynecoid d. Anthropoid
11. All of the following structures are related to the ala of the sacrum, EXCEPT:
   a. S1 nerve
   b. Sympathetic trunk
   c. Lumbosacral trunk
   d. Obturator nerve
12. The angle between the anterior surface of L5 vertebra and pelvic surface of S1 vertebra (lumbosacral angle) is:
   a. 60° b. 90°
   c. 120° d. 150°
13. All of the following structures emerge at the sacral hiatus, EXCEPT:
   a. Filum terminale
   b. Fifth sacral spinal nerves
   c. Pair of coccygeal nerves
   d. Median sacral artery
14. Subarachnoid space ends at the level of ___________.
   a. L5 vertebra b. S2 vertebra
   c. S5 vertebra d. Coccyx

QUESTION BANK

(Use separate copy to solve the following questions)

Q 1. List the differences between male and female pelvis.
Q 2. List the differences between male and female sacrum.
Q 3. Explain the anatomical basis of sacralisation of lumbar vertebra.
Q 4. List the relations of ala of sacrum.

Anterior Abdominal Wall

CLINICOANATOMICAL PROBLEMS

Clinical Case 1

A 60-year-old male presented with severe abdominal pain, distension, and vomiting for 2 days. On examination, a distended abdomen with hyperactive bowel sounds was noted. Imaging revealed dilated loops of small bowel suggestive of intestinal obstruction. Emergency surgery was performed, and a paramedian supraumbilical incision was made to access the affected bowel segment. Intraoperatively, a strangulated segment of small bowel was found and resected.

1. What is the advantage of paramedian incision over the midline incision?
2. Why the rectus abdominis muscle need to be retracted laterally in the paramedian incision?

Explanation

1. ______

2. ______

Clinical Case 2

A 48-year-old male presented to the emergency department with a one-week history of a painful lump in his right groin that he could not reduce. He complained of nausea and vomiting. Notably, he had a previous history of a reducible lump in the same area. On examination, there was a tender, irreducible mass noted in the right inguinal region. Urinary and bowel functions were normal. A diagnosis of inguinal hernia was made, and the patient was scheduled for surgical repair.

1. What is inguinal hernia?
2. Name the types of inguinal hernia.
3. Name any two of the risk factors associated with the development of inguinal hernias.
4. Explain the difference between a reducible and irreducible inguinal hernia.

Explanation

1. ______

2. ______

3. ______

4. ______

PRACTICE FIGURES

(Label the practice figures)

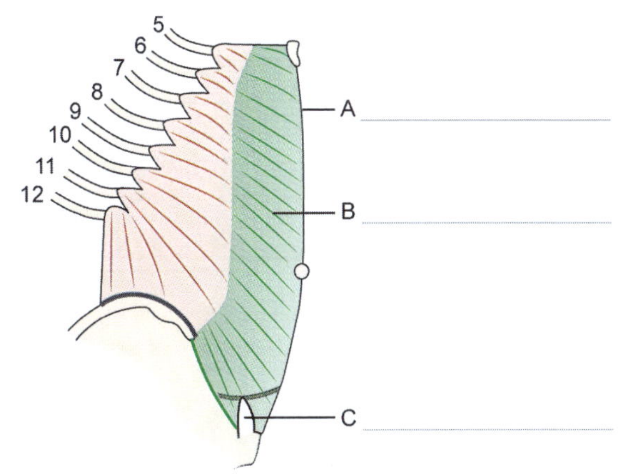

Practice Figure 16.1: External oblique muscle of the abdomen

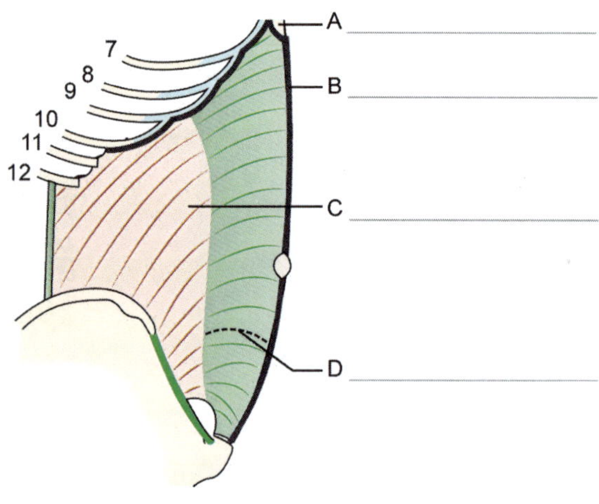

Practice Figure 16.2: Internal oblique muscle of the abdomen

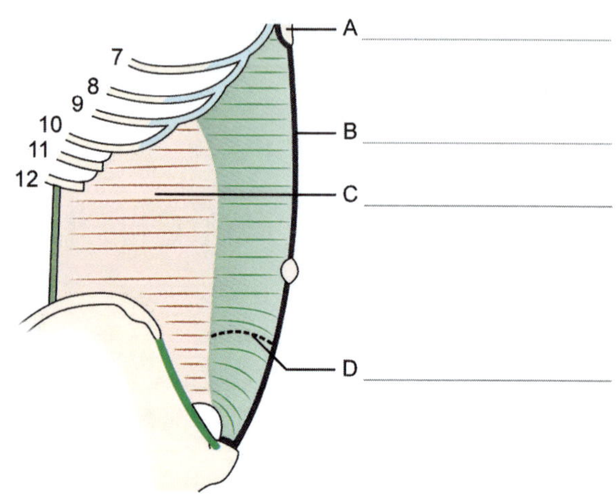

Practice Figure 16.3: Transversus abdominis muscle

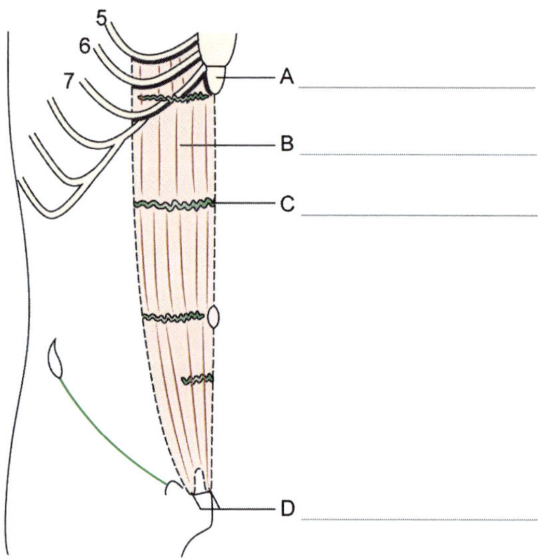

Practice Figure 16.4: Rectus abdominis muscle

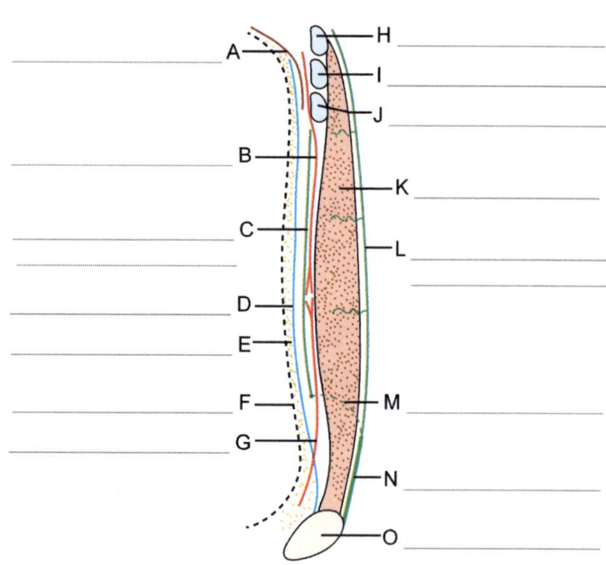

Practice Figure 16.5: Anterior and posterior walls of rectus sheath

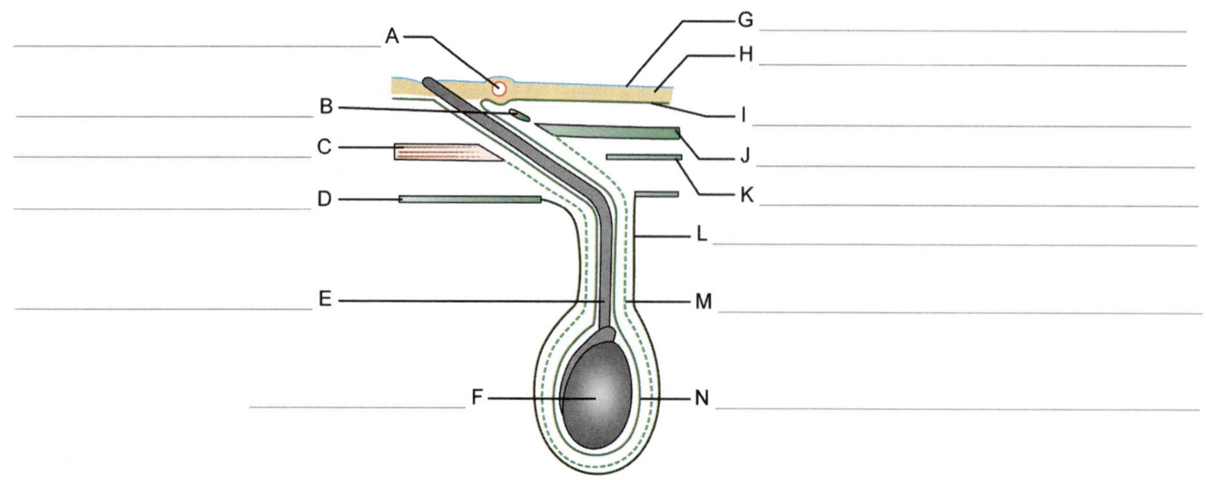

Practice Figure 16.6: Boundaries of the inguinal canal

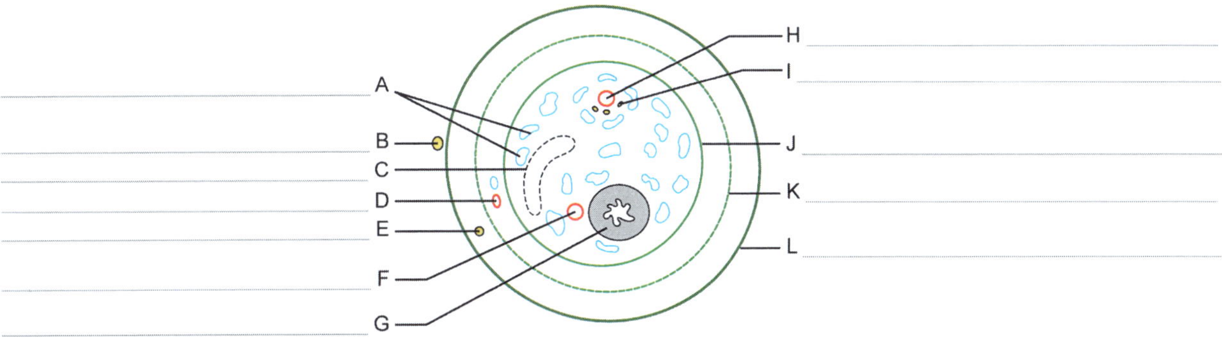

Practice Figure 16.7: Transverse section through the spermatic cord showing coverings and contents

MULTIPLE CHOICE QUESTIONS

(Tick the single best correct option)

1. The conjoint tendon is formed by the fusion of ____________ muscles.
   a. Rectus abdominis and transverse abdominis
   b. Transverse abdominis and external oblique
   c. Internal oblique and transverse abdominis
   d. External oblique and internal oblique
2. Poupart's ligament is derivative of the ____________ muscle.
   a. Rectus abdominis   b. External oblique
   c. Internal oblique   d. Transverse abdominis
3. What is the action of muscle marked as X?

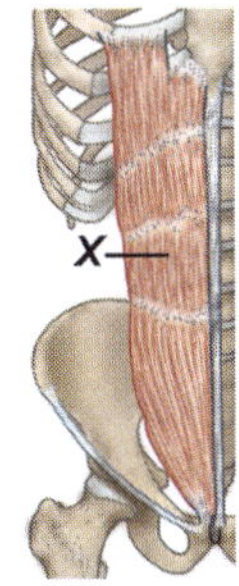

   a. Extension of the trunk
   b. Flexion of the trunk
   c. Lateral flexion of the trunk
   d. Rotation of the trunk
4. The segmental innervation of the X marked site is:

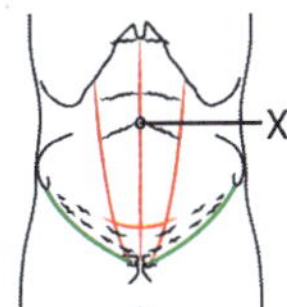

   a. T10   b. T8
   c. T7   d. T6
5. Which structure persistence leads to the following condition?

   a. Vitellointestinal duct
   b. Urachus
   c. Omphalomesenteric artery
   d. Dorsal pancreatic bud
6. Pyramidalis muscle is supplied by ____________ nerve.
   a. Subcostal nerve   b. Genitofemoral nerve
   c. Iliohypogastric nerve   d. Ilioinguinal nerve
7. All of the following are correct about the rectus sheath, EXCEPT:
   a. The rectus abdominis is the chief and largest content.
   b. The anterior wall is incomplete, being deficient below the arcuate line.
   c. It maintains the strength of the anterior abdominal wall.
   d. The anterior and posterior walls extend till linea semilunaris on the lateral side.
8. The following structure marked as X is an opening seen in ____________.

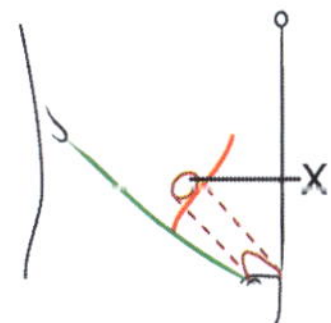

   a. Fascia Scarpa   b. Fascia lata
   c. Fascia transversalis   d. Fascia camphor
9. Pick out the correct statement about the inguinal canal.
   a. It is about 6 cm long and widened medially
   b. It is directed upwards, backward and laterally
   c. It extends from the deep inguinal ring to the superficial inguinal ring.
   d. The floor is formed by the external oblique muscle .
10. A 55-year-old male presented to the surgery outpatient clinic with a painless swelling in his right groin. On examination, a reducible mass is noted in the inguinal region. The swelling increases in size when the patient coughs. What is the most likely diagnosis?
   a. Direct inguinal hernia   b. Indirect inguinal hernia
   c. Femoral hernia   d. Obturator hernia.
11. Identify the clinical condition:

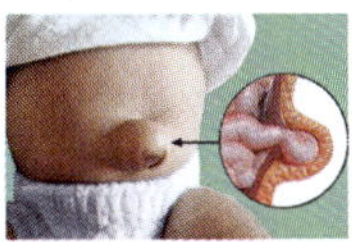

   a. Umbilical hernia   b. Paraumbilical hernia
   c. Oblique hernia   d. Femoral hernia
12. The membranous layer of superficial fascia of anterior abdominal wall has continuity with all of the following, EXCEPT:
   a. Buck's fascia of penis
   b. Dartos muscle of scrotum
   c. Colles' fascia of perineum
   d. Fascia of Gerota

13. The medial wall of the triangle shown in the following figure is formed by:

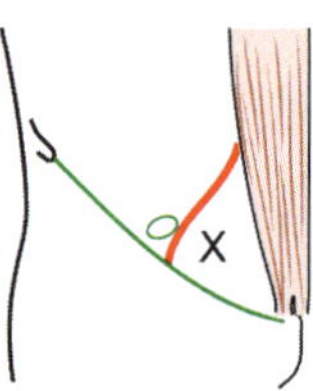

a. Inferior epigastric artery
b. Inguinal ligament
c. Deep inguinal ring
d. Rectus abdominis

14. All are the contents of rectus sheath, EXCEPT:
a. Superior epigastric artery
b. Inferior epigastric artery
c. Cremaster muscle
d. Pyramidalis muscle

QUESTION BANK

(Use separate copy to solve the following questions)

Q 1. Describe the formation and contents of the rectus sheath.

Q 2. Describe the inguinal canal under the following headings: Extent, inguinal rings, walls, content, applied aspects.

Q 3. What is inguinal hernia. What are its different types?

Q 4. Explain the mechanism to maintain the integrity of the inguinal canal.

Q 5. Write a short note on:
a. Umbilicus
b. Rectus abdominis muscle
c. Conjoint tendon of abdomen
d. Inguinal ligament
e. Holden's line

eSmartQuiz

Male External Genital Organs

CLINICOANATOMICAL PROBLEMS

Clinical Case 1

An one-month-old male infant was brought to the paediatrician due to a small swelling noticed in the right inguinal region. Physical examination revealed an absence of the right testis in the scrotum, with a palpable mass in the right inguinal canal. The left testis was present and descended into the scrotum. A diagnosis of undescended testis was made.

1. Why is the right side of scrotal sac empty?
2. What is cryptorchidism?
2. What are the effects of cryptorchidism?
3. Can testis descend naturally after birth?

Explanation

1.
2.
3.
4.

Clinical Case 2

A 22-year-old male came to the emergency department, presenting with a sudden and continuous pain in the right testicle. It was accompanied by a pain that radiated to the abdomen and right inguinal area. He was diagnosed with the testicular torsion.

1. What is testicular torsion?
2. What is the complication of testicular torsion?
3. Why the pain was referred to the abdomen in this case?

Explanation

1.
2.
3.

PRACTICE FIGURE

(Label the practice figure)

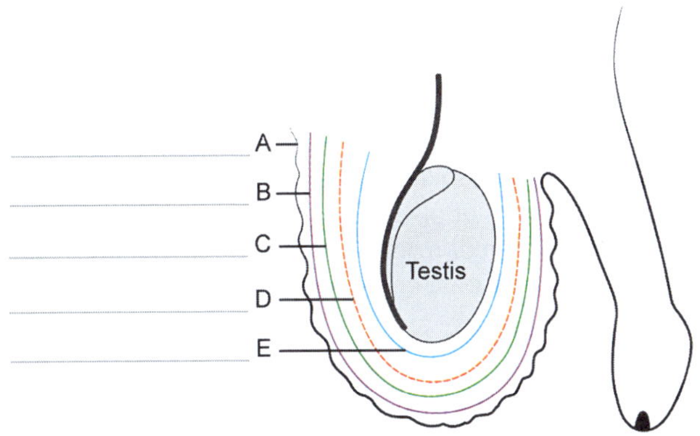

Practice Figure 17.1: Layers of the scrotum

MULTIPLE CHOICE QUESTIONS

(Tick the single best correct option)

1. The root of penis is present in the ________.
   a. Deep perineal pouch b. Superficial perineal pouch
   c. Bulbourethral space d. Urogenital triangle
2. Helicine arteries are derived from ________.
   a. Superficial external pudendal artery
   b. Dorsal artery of penis
   c. Deep artery of penis
   d. Artery of the bulb of the penis
3. Name the structure marked by X.

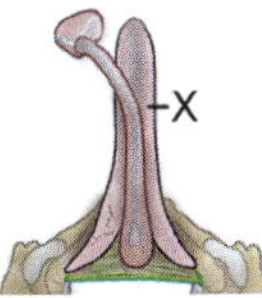

   a. Corpus spongiosum b. Tunica albuginea
   c. Corpus cavernosum d. Deep fascia

4. Identify the structure marked as X in the following picture.

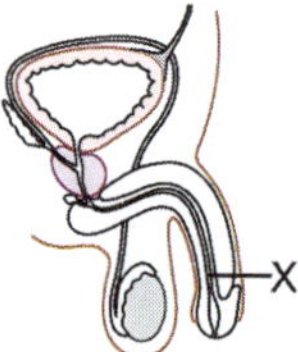

a. Spongy urethra
b. Membranous urethra
c. Prostatic urethra
d. Glans penis

5. A 10-year-old boy was taken to a paediatric clinic with complaints of pain in the tip of penis. On examination, the foreskin is tight and cannot be retracted. What is the most likely diagnosis?
a. Paraphimosis
b. Phimosis
c. Chordee
d. Epispadias

6. Which of the following fasciae covers the masses of erectile tissue in penis?
a. Superficial fascia
b. Cremasteric fascia
c. Buck's fascia
d. Colles fascia

7. Pick out the CORRECT statement about the nerve supply of penis.
a. The sensory nerve supply is derived from iliohypogastric nerve.
b. The parasympathetic nerves are vasoconstrictors.
c. The autonomic fibres are distributed through the branches of the pudendal nerve.
d. The muscles of the root of the penis are supplied by the dorsal nerve of penis.

8. What is the function of the dartos muscle?
a. Contraction to aid in ejaculation
b. Regulation of penile temperature
c. Facilitation of urine flow during micturition
d. Promotion of sperm production

9. Cremasteric fascia is derived from ____________.
a. External oblique muscle
b. Fascia transversalis
c. Cremasteric muscle
d. Internal oblique muscle

10. A 56-year-old male came to surgical outpatient clinic with history of painless swelling in the scrotum, which is gradually increasing in size. On examination, painless, fluid-filled mass in the scrotum that transilluminates on illumination present. What is the most likely diagnosis?
a. Varicocele
b. Hydrocele
c. Epididymitis
d. Spermatocele

11. Identify the structure marked as X.

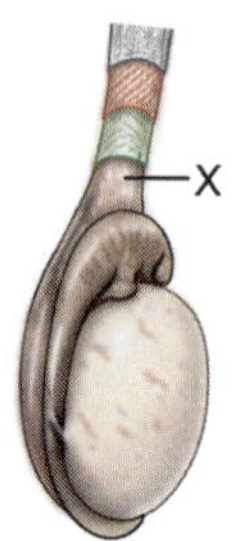

a. Paradidymis
b. Appendix of epididymis
c. Epididymis
d. Vas deferens

12. A 6-month-old male infant is brought to the paediatrician by his parents for a well-child visit. During the physical examination, the paediatrician notices that one of the infant's testicles cannot be palpated in the scrotum. The infant is otherwise healthy. What is the likely diagnosis?
a. Anorchism
b. Cryptorchidism
c. Hydrocele
d. Varicocele

13. Left testicular vein drains into ____________.
a. Left renal vein
b. Inferior vena cava
c. Left external iliac vein
d. Left common iliac vein

14. ____________ lymph nodes drain the lymph from the glans penis.
a. External iliac
b. Internal iliac
c. Deep inguinal
d. Para aortic

15. Testis normally reaches to the lower part of the scrotum by ____________ month of intrauterine life.
a. 6th
b. 7th
c. 8th
d. 9th

16. Helicine arteries are located in ____________.
a. Testis
b. Prostate
c. Corpora cavernosa
d. Spermatic cord

17. A pain from the testis is referred to as the ____________.
a. Scrotum
b. Suprapubic region
c. Umbilical region
d. Epigastric region

QUESTION BANK

(Use separate copy to solve the following questions)

Q 1. Write a short note on:
a. Testis
b. Layers of scrotum
c. Vasectomy
d. Structure of penis
e. Cryptorchidism

Q 2. Why the varicocele being common on left side?

Abdominal Cavity and Peritoneum

eSmartQuiz

CLINICOANATOMICAL PROBLEMS

Clinical Case 1

A 45-year-old man presented to the emergency department with severe abdominal pain, fever, and tachycardia. He reported sudden onset of sharp abdominal pain, accompanied by nausea and vomiting. On examination, his abdomen was tender, rigid, and distended. Laboratory tests revealed leucocytosis and elevated inflammatory markers. A diagnosis of acute peritonitis was made.

1. What is peritonitis?
2. Why there is abdominal pain and tenderness in peritonitis?
3. What are the sources of infection in peritonitis?

Explanation

1. ____________________
2. ____________________
3. ____________________

Clinical Case 2

A 60-year-old man with a history of chronic liver disease presented with abdominal distention and discomfort. He reported a recent increase in abdominal girth, along with weight gain and ankle swelling. On abdominal examination, a fluid wave was appreciated, and shifting dullness was noted. Laboratory investigations revealed hypoalbuminemia and elevated liver enzymes. Imaging confirmed the presence of ascites. The patient was diagnosed with ascites secondary to liver failure.

1. What is ascites?
2. List any two causes of ascites.

Explanation

1. ____________________
2. ____________________

PRACTICE FIGURES

(Label the practice figures)

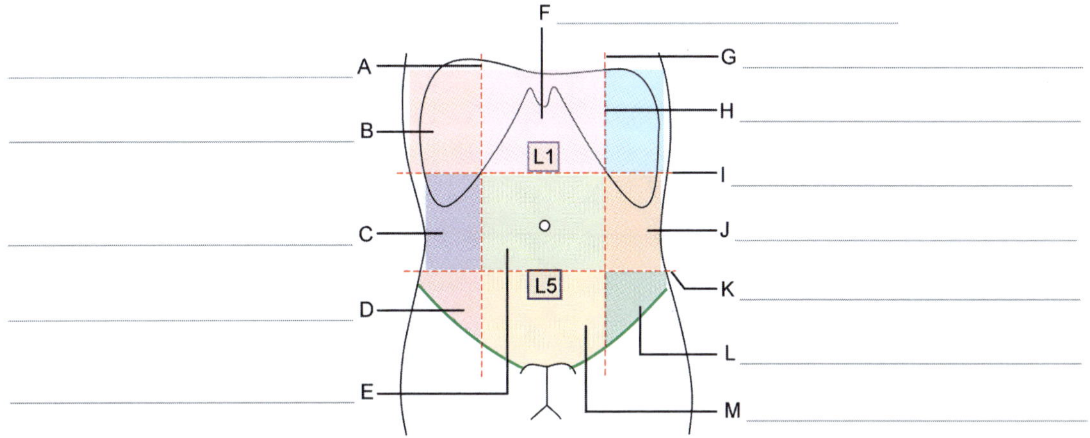

Practice Figure 18.1: Regions of the abdomen

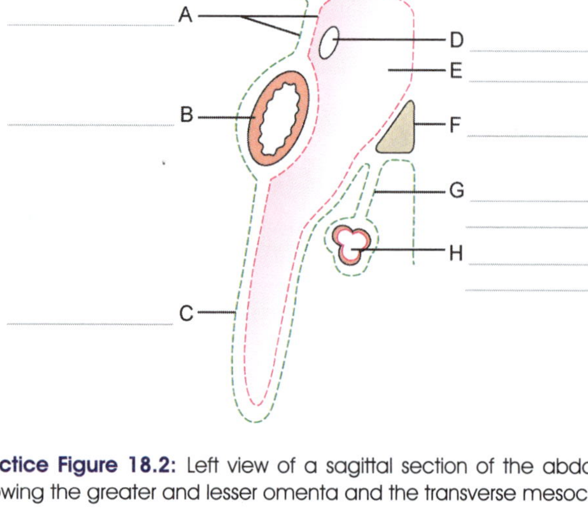

Practice Figure 18.2: Left view of a sagittal section of the abdomen showing the greater and lesser omenta and the transverse mesocolon

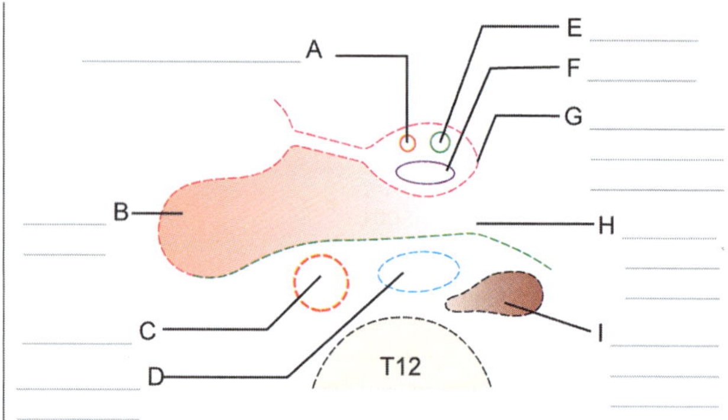

Practice Figure 18.3: Epiploic foramen as seen in a transverse section at the level of the twelfth thoracic vertebra

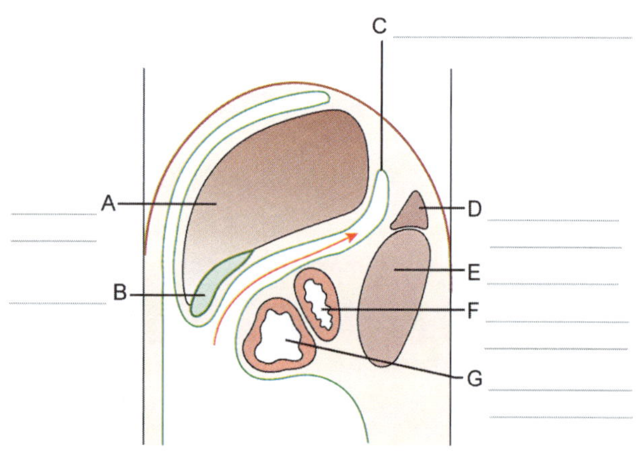

Practice Figure 18.4: Hepatorenal pouch

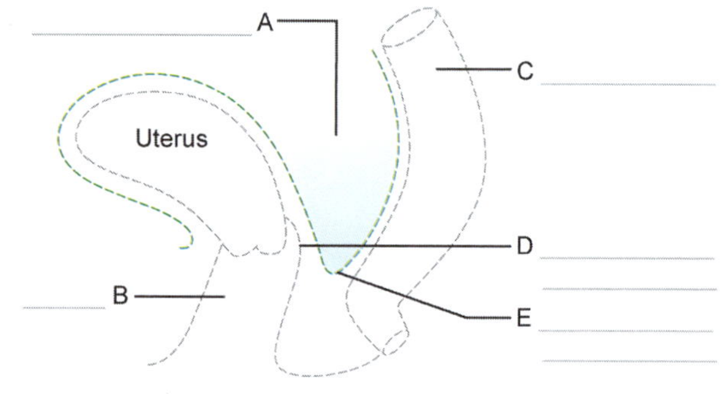

Practice Figure 18.5: Left view of a sagittal section through the recto-uterine pouch

MULTIPLE CHOICE QUESTIONS

(Tick the single best correct option)

1. All of the following organs are retroperitoneal, EXCEPT:
   a. Duodenum b. Pancreas
   c. Appendix d. Ureter
2. Embryologically parietal peritoneum is derived from ___________.
   a. Lateral plate mesoderm
   b. Extraembryonic mesoderm
   c. Paraxial mesoderm
   d. Somatic mesoderm
3. What is the area marked as X?

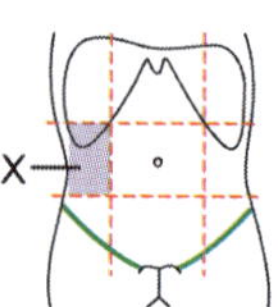

   a. Right hypochondrium b. Right lumbar region
   c. Right iliac fossa d. Hypogastrium
4. All of the following statements are true about the transpyloric plane, EXCEPT:
   a. The transpyloric plane of Addison passes midway between the suprasternal notch and the pubic symphysis.
   b. It lies roughly two hands' breadth below the xiphisternal joint.
   c. Anteriorly, it passes through the tips of the ninth costal cartilage.
   d. Posteriorly it passes through the body of L1 vertebrae near its lower border.
5. Which of the following structures is known as 'Abdominal policeman'?
   a. Greater sac b. Lesser omentum
   c. Lesser sac d. Greater omentum
6. The greater and lesser sacs communicate with each other through ___________.
   a. The foramen of Winslow
   b. The foramen ovale
   c. The foramen magnum
   d. The foramen spinosum
7. A 47-year-old alcoholic male came to the surgical outpatient department with complaints of abdominal distension and discomfort for the past 3 days. On examination, tense and distended abdomen noted, dilated veins are seen around the umbilicus. What procedure is done to relieve the discomfort?
   a. Laparoscopy b. Paracentesis
   c. Laparotomy d. Incision and drainage
8. The artery which supplies the foregut is ___________.

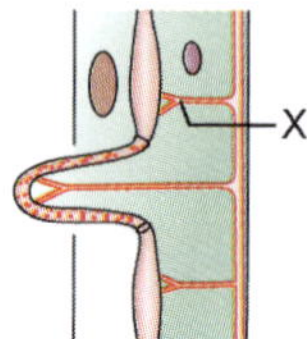

   a. Superior mesenteric artery
   b. Inferior mesenteric artery
   c. Coeliac artery
   d. Right gastric artery

9. Which of the following structures forms the superior margin of the omental foramen?
   a. Caudate process of liver
   b. Inferior vena cava
   c. Right free margin of the lesser omentum
   d. First part of duodenum
10. Which is the most dependent part of the abdominal cavity while the patient is in supine position?
   a. Rectouterine pouch
   b. Right subhepatic space
   c. Rectovesical space
   d. Left subphrenic space.
11. Identify the X-marked site.

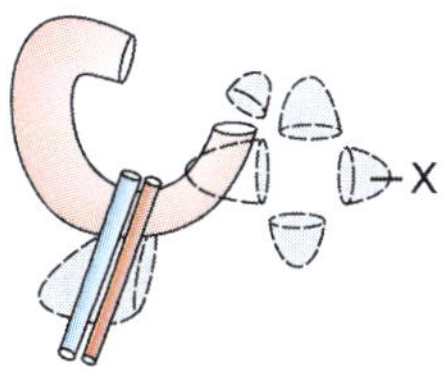

   a. Inferior duodenal recess
   b. Left paracolic gutter
   c. Retroduodenal recess
   d. Paraduodenal recess
12. The root of the mesentery crosses all of the following structures, EXCEPT:
   a. Abdominal aorta
   b. Inferior vena cava
   c. Right ureter
   d. Inferior mesenteric artery
13. Identify the area marked by red arrow.

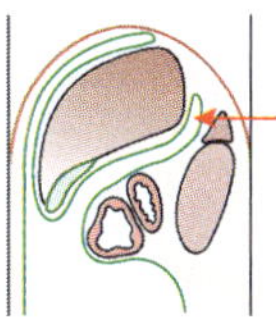

   a. Hepatorenal pouch b. Lesser sac
   c. Epiploic foramen d. Retroperitoneum
14. Identify the area marked by X.

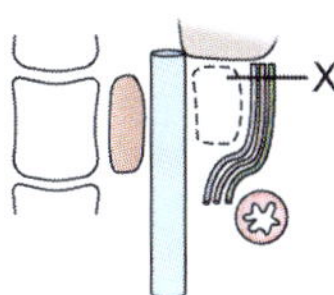

   a. Hepatorenal pouch b. Greater sac
   c. Epiploic foramen d. Retroperitoneum

QUESTION BANK

(Use separate copy to solve the following question)

1. Write a short note on:
   a. Greater omentum
   b. Lesser omentum
   c. Root of mesentery
   d. Lesser sac
   e. Epiploic foramen
   f. Hepatorenal pouch
   g. Rectouterine pouch

Chapter

19

eSmartQuiz

Abdominal Part of Oesophagus and Stomach

CLINICOANATOMICAL PROBLEMS

Clinical Case 1

A 30-year-old IT company worker complained of recurrent epigastric pain exacerbated by spicy food and job stress. He reported occasional heartburn and bloating. Physical examination was unremarkable. Upper gastrointestinal endoscopy revealed a well-defined ulcer with a clean base in the gastric antrum. Biopsy confirmed the diagnosis of gastric ulcer.

1. What is nerve supply of stomach?
2. Why the pain is referred to epigastric region in this case?
3. Why the pain is aggravated by spicy food and stress?

Explanation

1. ______________________________

2. ______________________________

3. ______________________________

Clinical Case 2

A 58-year-old male presented with a six-month history of unexplained weight loss, persistent abdominal discomfort, and loss of appetite. On examination, enlarged left supraclavicular lymph nodes were palpable. He reported occasional episodes of nausea, vomiting, and dysphagia for solid foods. Upper gastrointestinal endoscopy revealed a large ulcerated mass in the stomach. Biopsy confirmed poorly differentiated adenocarcinoma. Imaging showed metastasis to the supraclavicular lymph nodes. The patient was diagnosed with advanced gastric cancer.

1. What is the common site for gastric carcinoma?
2. Which is precancerous condition for gastric carcinoma?
3. What is sex and blood group preponderance in gastric carcinoma?
4. What the left supraclavicular nodes enlarge in this case?

Explanation

1. ______________________________

2. ______________________________

3. ______________________________

4. ______________________________

PRACTICE FIGURES

(Label the practice figures)

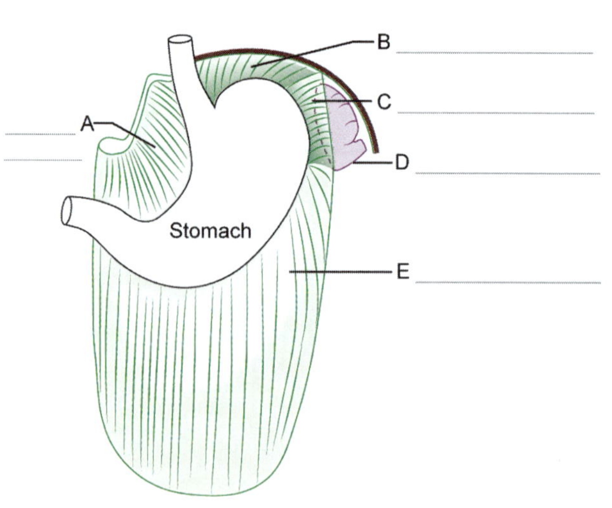

Practice Figure 19.1: Peritoneal relations of stomach

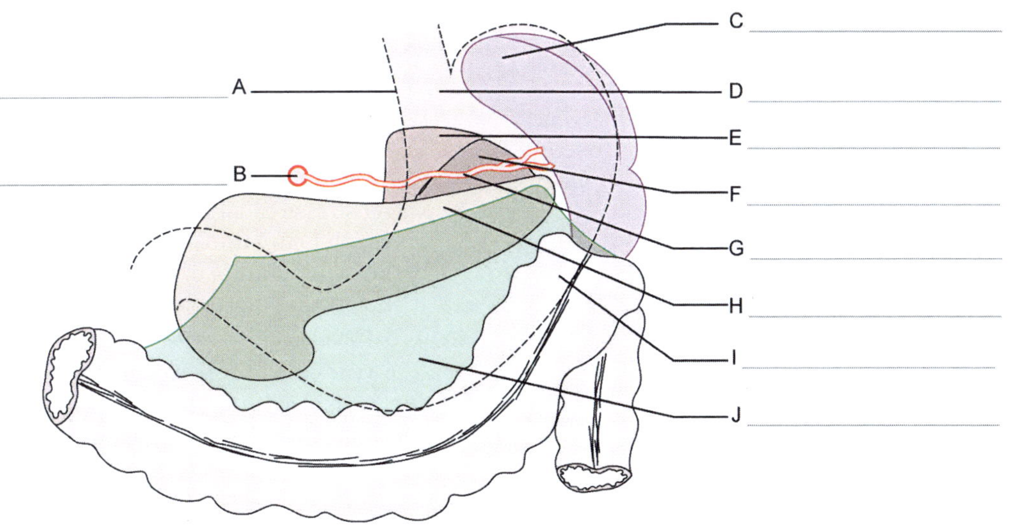

Practice Figure 19.2: The stomach bed

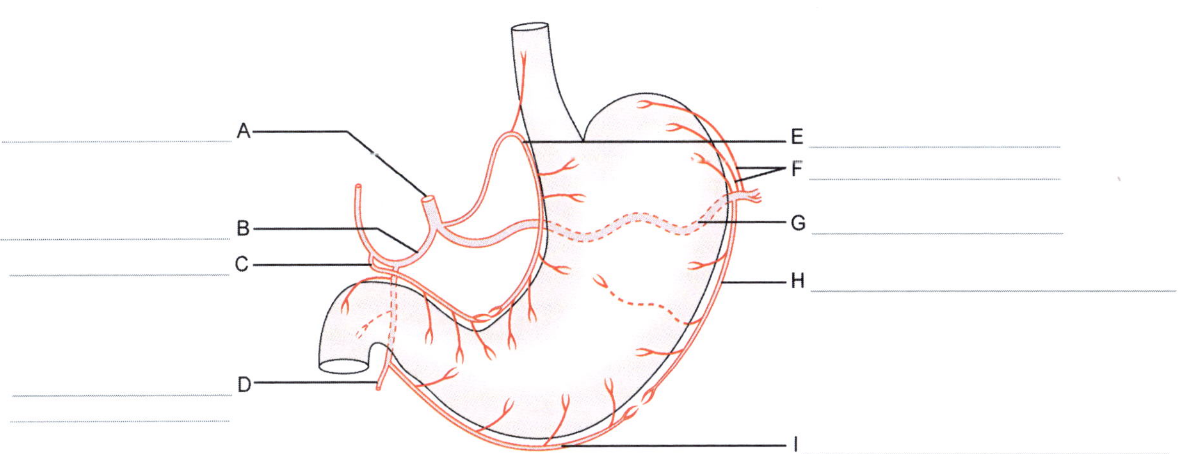

Practice Figure 19.3: Arteries supplying the stomach

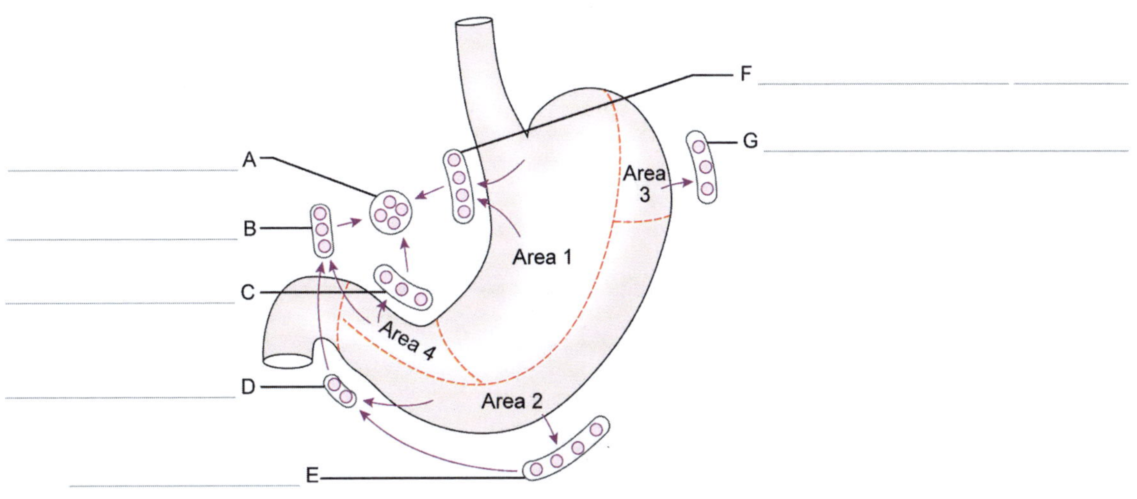

Practice Figure 19.4: Lymphatic drainage of the stomach

MULTIPLE CHOICE QUESTIONS

(Tick the single best correct option)

1. A 37-year-old alcoholic male presented to the emergency department with blood vomiting. His endoscopy shows tortuous veins in the lower end of oesophagus ________.
   a. Oesophageal ulcer
   b. Oesophageal carcinoma
   c. Oesophageal varices
   d. GERD
2. Oesophageal opening is situated at the level of ______.
   a. T8 b. T10
   c. T11 d. L1
3. Identify the clinical condition in the following radiograph of barium sallow.

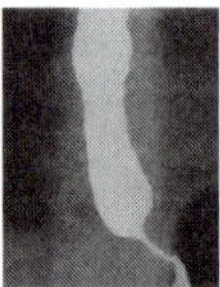

   a. Oesophagitis
   b. Achalasia cardia
   c. Gastroesophageal reflux disease
   d. Oesophageal carcinoma
4. All the structures form the stomach bed, EXCEPT:
   a. Left kidney
   b. Left suprarenal gland
   c. Left colic flexure
   d. Duodenum
5. The stomach bed is formed by all of the following, EXCEPT:
   a. Splenic artery b. Diaphragm
   c. Left kidney d. Spleen
6. Right gastric artery is a branch of ________.
   a. Splenic artery
   b. Coeliac trunk
   c. Common hepatic artery
   d. Gastroduodenal artery
7. The marked site X is drained by which group of lymph nodes?
   a. Subpyloric nodes
   b. Right gastroepiploic nodes
   c. Pancreaticoduodenal nodes
   d. Coeliac nodes
8. Magenstrasse canal is present in ________.
   a. Greater curvature of stomach
   b. Lesser curvature of stomach
   c. Lower end of oesophagus
   d. Upper end of oesophagus
9. A 26-year-old IT professional presented to the emergency department with a history of chest pain and burning sensation over the chest. His ECG study-normal. What is the likely diagnosis?
   a. Peptic ulcer disease b. Oesophagitis
   c. Intestinal obstruction d. Perforation
10. A 75-year-old man complains of recurrent attacks of pain in the region of left shoulder radiating to sternum and pit of stomach. He was diagnosed with angina pectoris. Here, the pain from the heart is carried by ________ nerve.
    a. Superior cervical cardiac
    b. Middle and inferior cervical cardiac
    c. Thoracic splanchnic
    d. Vagus
11. Auerbach's plexus are seen in ________.
    a. Mucosa b. Submucosa
    c. Muscularis externa d. Serosa

QUESTION BANK

(Use separate copy to solve the following questions)

Q 1. Describe the stomach under following headings: Presenting parts and relations, blood supply, lymphatic drainage.

Q 2. Write a short note on:
   a. Peritoneal relations of stomach
   b. Stomach bed
   c. Lymphatic drainage of stomach
   d. Interior of stomach

Chapter

20

Small and Large Intestines

eSmartQuiz

CLINICOANATOMICAL PROBLEM

Clinical Case 1

A 25-year-old man presented to the emergency department with sudden-onset abdominal pain, initially periumbilical, which later migrated to the right lower quadrant. On examination, there was tenderness and guarding at McBurney's point. The psoas sign was positive. Laboratory tests revealed leucocytosis. A diagnosis of acute appendicitis was made, and the patient underwent an emergency appendicectomy.

1. What is appendicitis?
2. What is McBurney's point?
3. Why the pain initially located in the periumbilical region in this case?
4. What is psoas test?

Explanation

1. ______

2. ______

3. ______

4. ______

PRACTICE FIGURES

(Label the practice figures)

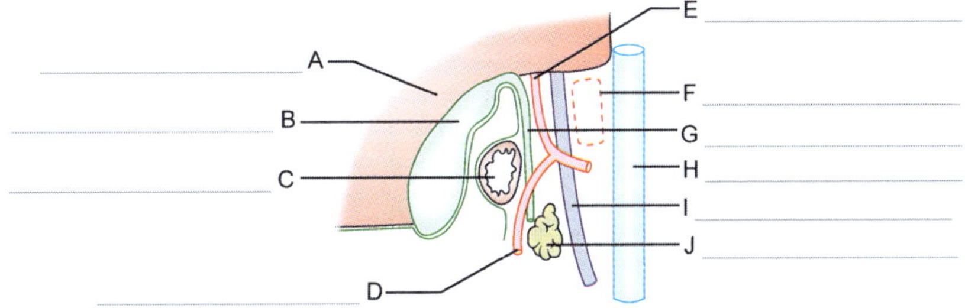

Practice Figure 20.1: Relations of the first part of the duodenum

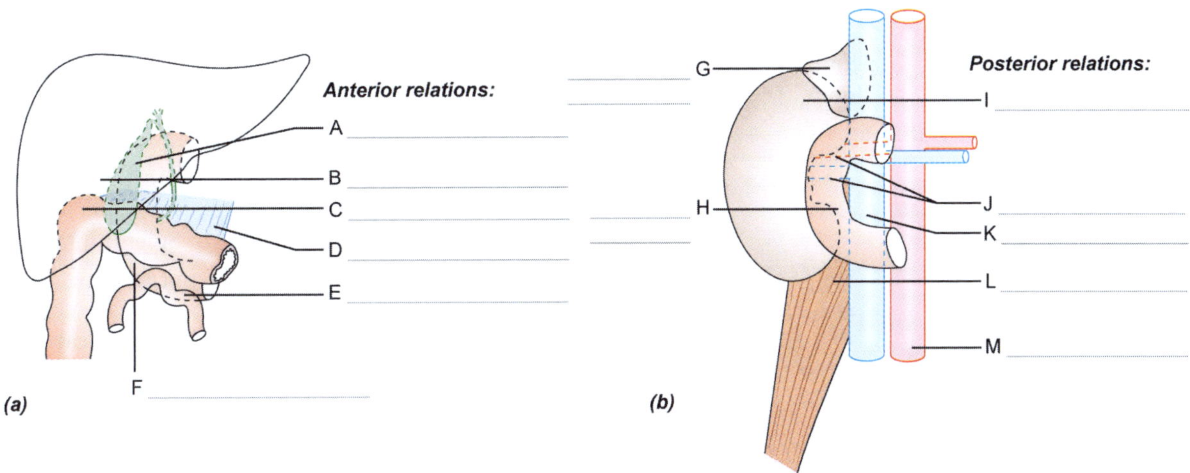

Practice Figures 20.2a and b: Relations of the second part of the duodenum: (a) Anterior relations; (b) Posterior relations

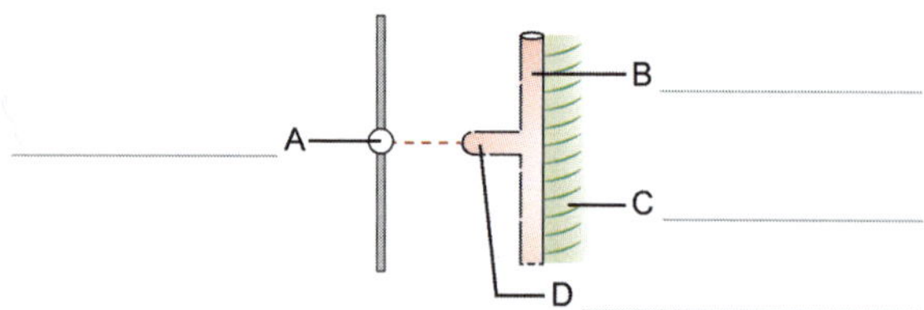

Practice Figure 20.3: Meckel's diverticulum

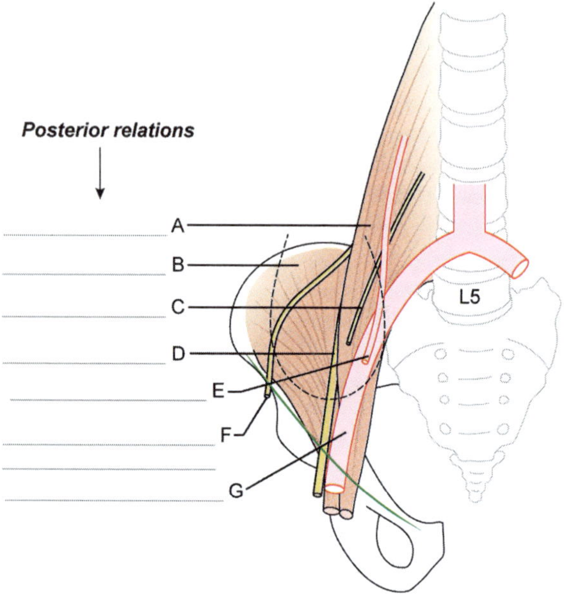

Practice Figure 20.4: Relations of caecum

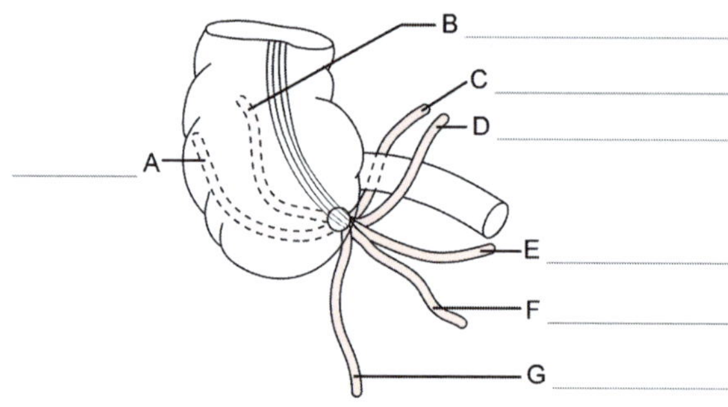

Practice Figure 20.5: Positions of vermiform appendix (after Treves)

MULTIPLE CHOICE QUESTIONS

(Tick the single best correct option)

1. Submucosal glands of Brunner's are present in ________.
   a. Jejunum b. Stomach
   c. Duodenum d. Ileum
2. Name the structure marked as X.

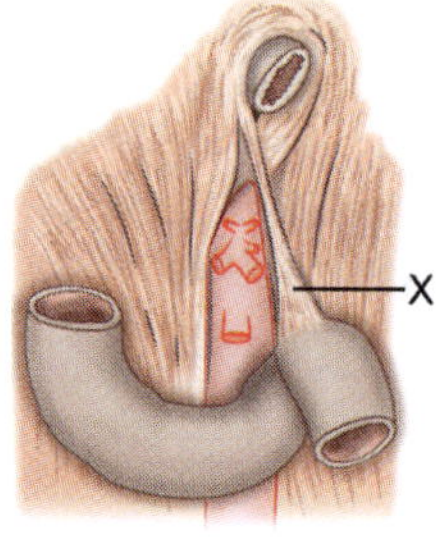

   a. Hepatoduodenal ligament
   b. Ligamentum teres
   c. Falciform ligament
   d. Ligament of Treitz
3. Which part of the duodenum shows 'duodenal cap' in barium meal study?

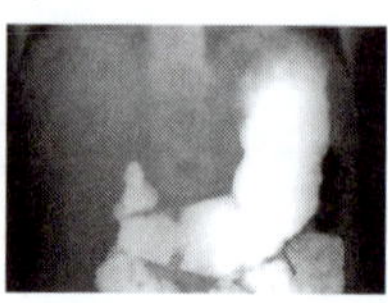

   a. Third part b. Fourth part
   c. First part d. Second part
4. Which of the following statements is true about jejunum?
   a. Vasa recta shorter and more numerous
   b. Villi are short, thin and less abundant
   c. The arterial arcades are 1–2 in number
   d. Peyer's patches are more compared to ileum
5. Pick out the correct statement about the clinical condition shown in the image.

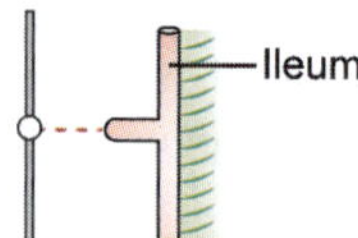

   a. It is attached to the mesenteric border of the ileum
   b. It is the persistent distal part of the vitellointestinal duct
   c. It is situated about 2 inches proximal to the ileocaecal valve
   d. Occasionally, ectopic pancreatic or gastric mucosa can be seen
6. All of the following are features of large intestine, EXCEPT:
   a. Appendices epiploicae b. Taeniae coli
   c. Villi d. Sacculations
7. The valve of Gerlach is located in ________.
   a. Jejunum b. Ileum
   c. Appendix d. Caecum
8. Which position of the tip of the appendix is considered a dangerous type?
   a. Postileal b. Pelvic
   c. Preileal d. Subcaecal
9. A 24-year-old male presents to the emergency department complaining of severe abdominal pain, which initially appeared around the umbilicus moved to the right lower quadrant eventually. What is the most likely diagnosis?
   a. Appendicular mass
   b. Acute appendicitis
   c. Mucocele of appendix
   d. Appendicular diverticulitis
10. A 24-year-old female feels pain in periumbilical region since last night. She started feeling pain in the right iliac fossa in the morning. It may be due to:
   a. Cholecystitis b. Appendicitis
   c. Ureteric calculi d. Splenic infarction
11. Most common position of vermiform appendix is ________.
   a. Pelvic b. Retrocaecal
   c. Preileal d. Postileal
12. All of the following organs have dual blood supply, EXCEPT:
   a. Pancreas b. First part of duodenum
   c. Kidney d. Stomach

13. All of the following are the cardinal features of the large intestine, EXCEPT:
    a. Appendices epiploicae b. Sacculations
    c. Taenia coli d. Villi
14. __________ is present in the appendix.
    a. Appendices epiploicae b. Taenia coli
    c. Sacculations d. Mesentery

QUESTION BANK

(Use separate copy to solve the following questions)

Q 1. Describe the vermiform appendix under the following headings: Location, positions, blood supply, nerve supply, applied aspects.

Q 2. Describe the relations of the 1st part, 2nd part, and 3rd parts of duodenum.

Q 3. Name the arteries and veins supplying duodenum.

Q 4. Name the openings in the 2nd part of duodenum.

Q 5. Describe the internal features of the 2nd part of duodenum.

Q 6. Write a short note on:
   a. Suspensory muscle of duodenum or ligament of Treitz
   b. Differences between jejunum and ileum
   c. Meckel's diverticulum
   d. Interior of second part of duodenum
   e. Differences between small and large intestine
   f. Caecum

21

eSmartQuiz

Large Blood Vessels of the Gut

CLINICOANATOMICAL PROBLEM

Clinical Case 1

A 55-year-old male with a history of chronic alcohol abuse presented with abdominal distension, dull pain. He had intermittent bouts of haematemesis for last one week. On examination, prominent dilated abdominal veins resembling caput medusae were observed. Further investigation revealed massive ascites. Radiological investigation confirmed portal hypertension.

1. What is caput medusae?
2. What is haematemesis and why it occurred in this case?
3. Why there was ascites in this case?

Explanation

1. ______________________________

2. ______________________________

3. ______________________________

PRACTICE FIGURES

(Label the practice figures)

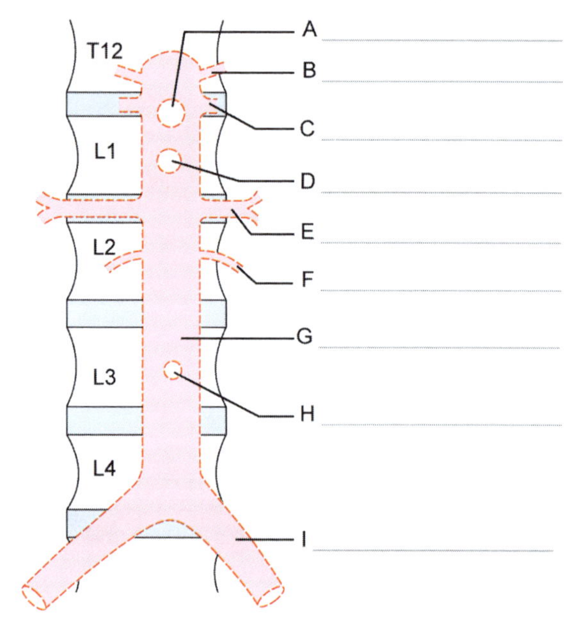

Practice Figure 21.1: Ventral and lateral branches of the abdominal aorta with their levels of origin

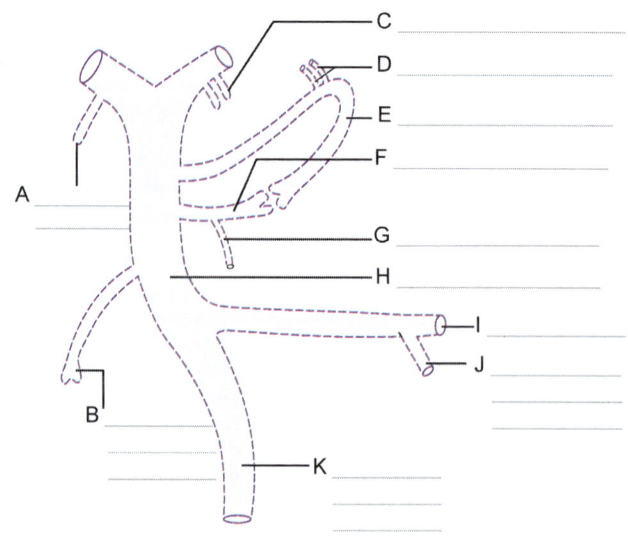

Practice Figure 21.2: Formation and tributaries of portal vein

MULTIPLE CHOICE QUESTIONS

(Tick the single best correct option)

1. Right gastric artery is a branch of ___________.
   a. Common hepatic artery
   b. Coeliac trunk
   c. Right gastroduodenal artery
   d. Right gastroepiploic artery
2. Which of the following arteries is not a branch from the coeliac trunk?
   a. Cystic artery
   b. Common hepatic artery
   c. Left gastric artery
   d. Splenic artery
3. Name the structure marked by X.

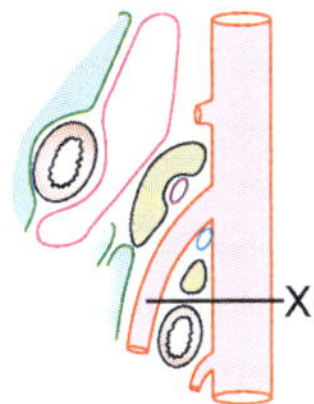

   a. Superior mesenteric artery
   b. Inferior mesenteric artery
   c. Right gastroduodenal artery
   d. Left gastroduodenal artery
4. Pick out the INCORRECT statement about superior mesenteric artery.
   a. It is the artery of the midgut
   b. It originates at the level of L2 vertebra
   c. It terminates by anastomosing with ileocolic artery
   d. It crosses third part of the duodenum
5. Inferior pancreaticoduodenal artery is a branch of ___________.
   a. Splenic artery
   b. Superior mesenteric artery
   c. Inferior mesenteric artery
   d. Short gastric artery
6. A young male presented to the emergency department with a history of sudden diffuse abdominal pain for 4 hr. His vitals show hypotension and tachycardia. CT abdomen shows gangrenous necrosis of the small intestine. Which of the following would be the cause?
   a. Acute appendicitis
   b. Intestinal perforation
   c. Intestinal obstruction
   d. Superior mesenteric artery embolism
7. Paraduodenal recess is crossed by which of the following structures?
   a. Inferior mesenteric artery
   b. Superior mesenteric artery
   c. Inferior mesenteric vein
   d. Superior mesenteric vein
8. Identify the vessel marked as X.

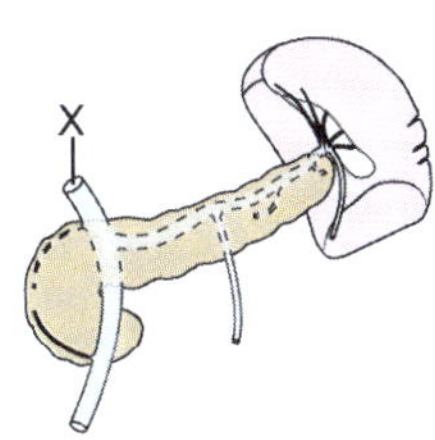

   a. Superior mesenteric vein
   b. Portal vein
   c. Inferior mesenteric vein
   d. Inferior vena cava
9. All of the following statements regarding the portal vein are true, EXCEPT:
   a. The portal vein carries nutrient-rich blood from the gastrointestinal tract to the liver.
   b. It is formed by the union of the splenic vein and the superior mesenteric vein.
   c. The portal vein is a part of the systemic circulation.
   d. It is a low-pressure vessel compared to the systemic arteries.
10. The major blood supply to the liver is by ___________.
    a. Hepatic artery
    b. Portal vein
    c. Cystic artery
    d. Hepatoduodenal artery
11. All of the following are the sites of portocaval anastomoses, EXCEPT:
    a. Umbilicus
    b. Lower end of oesophagus
    c. Appendix
    d. The bare area of liver
12. Appendicular artery is a branch of ___________ artery.
    a. Middle colic
    b. Right colic
    c. Left colic
    d. Ileocolic

QUESTION BANK

(Use separate copy to solve the following questions)

Q 1. Describe the portal vein under the following headings: Formation, course, termination, relations, tributaries. Add a note on portacaval anastomosis.

Q 2. Write a short note on:
   a. Coeliac trunk and its branches
   b. Sites of portocaval anastomosis and veins involved
   c. Marginal artery of Drummond
   d. Portal hypertension

Q 3. Enlist the following:
   a. Branches of superior mesenteric artery
   b. Branches of inferior mesenteric artery

22

eSmartQuiz

Extrahepatic Biliary Apparatus

CLINICOANATOMICAL PROBLEM

Clinical Case 1

A 40-year-old fertile female with fair complexion presented with severe right hypochondrium pain radiating to the right shoulder. She reported a history of fatty food indulgence. On examination, Murphy's sign was positive. Further investigation revealed gallbladder inflammation consistent with cholecystitis. The patient underwent cholecystectomy, with subsequent resolution of symptoms.

1. Give anatomical basis for
   a. Pain in right hypochondrium.
   b. Radiating pain to the right shoulder.
2. What is Murphy's sign?

Explanation

1. ______________________________

PRACTICE FIGURE

(Label the practice figure)

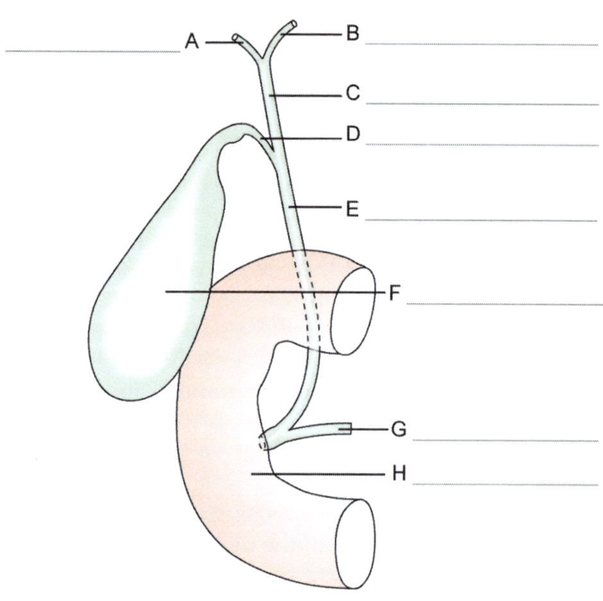

Practice Figure 22.1: Parts of the extrahepatic biliary apparatus

MULTIPLE CHOICE QUESTIONS

(Tick the single best correct option)

1. Name the structure marked as X in the below image.

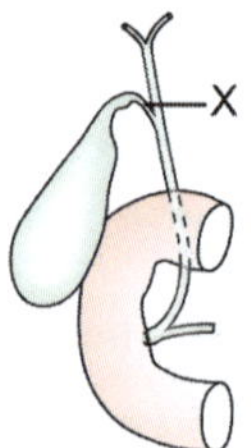

   a. Cystic duct
   b. Common hepatic duct
   c. Left hepatic duct
   d. Right hepatic duct

2. State the TRUE statement about the cystic duct.
   a. It is about 8 cm in length.
   b. It is guarded by valve of Heister.
   c. Along with left hepatic duct, it forms the common bile duct.
   d. It begins at the neck of the gallbladder, runs upwards and forwards.

3. What is the content of the triangle marked as X?

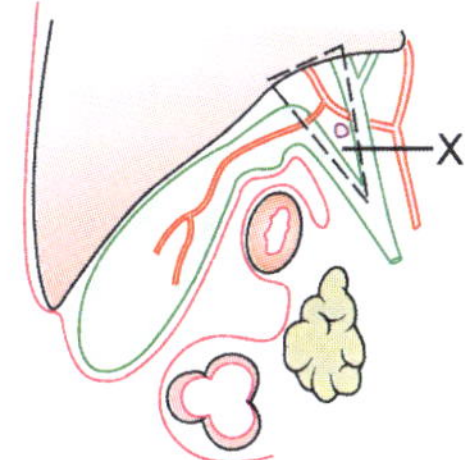

a. Common hepatic artery
b. Cystic duct
c. Node of Lund
d. Left hepatic artery

4. Ampulla of Vater is situated in ____________ of the duodenum.
a. First part
b. Second part
c. Third part
d. Fourth part

5. Identify the clinical condition shown in the image.

a. Cholesterolosis
b. Cholelithiasis
c. Cholecystitis
d. Cholangiocarcinoma

6. What is the clinical sign elicited below?

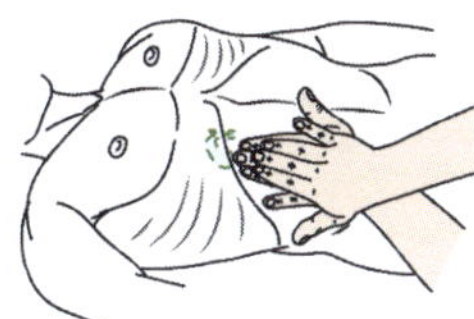

a. Aaron's sign
b. Murphy's sign
c. Puddle sign
d. Fox sign

7. A 43-year-old obese female presented to a medical outpatient clinic with a history of right upper quadrant pain and tenderness. On examination, tenderness present over the right hypochondrium. Laboratory tests showed leucocytosis and normal liver function tests. What is the most likely diagnosis?
a. Acute cholecystitis
b. Chronic cholecystitis
c. Biliary colic
d. Choledocholithiasis

8. Which of the following is correct regarding the arrangement of structures in porta hepatis from anterior to posterior?
a. Hepatic duct, portal vein, hepatic artery
b. Hepatic duct, hepatic artery, portal vein
c. Portal vein, hepatic duct, hepatic artery
d. Hepatic artery, portal vein, hepatic duct

9. The gallbladder is lined by:
a. Stratified columnar epithelium
b. Stratified cuboidal epithelium
c. Brush border epithelium
d. Squamous epithelium

10. Referred pain from the gallbladder is present over all of the following areas, EXCEPT:
a. Tip of right shoulder
b. Epigastric region
c. Crus of the right diaphragm
d. Inferior angle of right scapula

QUESTION BANK

(Use separate copy to solve the following questions)

Q 1. Describe the extrahepatic biliary apparatus under the following headings: Components, relations, blood supply, nerve supply and applied aspects.

Q 2. Write a short note on:
a. Murphy's sign
b. Gallbladder
c. Bile duct
d. Calot's triangle
e. Sphincter of pancreaticobiliary junction
f. Courvoisier's law

Chapter

23

eSmartQuiz

Spleen, Pancreas and Liver

CLINICOANATOMICAL PROBLEMS

Clinical Case 1

A 30-year-old male presented to the emergency room after a motor vehicle accident. He complained of left upper quadrant abdominal pain and reported fainting spells post-accident. On examination, he was hypotensive and tachycardic. Abdominal examination revealed tenderness with guarding. Ultrasound examination confirmed ***splenic rupture*** with internal bleeding. The patient underwent emergent splenectomy and received blood transfusions, resulting in stabilisation.

1. Which anatomical structure damages the spleen in motor vehicle accidents?
2. Why there is hypotension in patients with splenic rupture?

Explanation

1. ______________________

2. ______________________

Clinical Case 2

A 65-year-old male presented with jaundice, weight loss, and fatigue. On examination, yellowing of the skin and sclerae was evident. Abdominal examination revealed a palpable mass in the epigastric region. Ultrasound examination showed a mass at the head of the pancreas, causing biliary obstruction. Biopsy confirmed ***adenocarcinoma of the pancreatic head***.

1. Give anatomical basis for a jaundice in case of carcinoma of head of pancreas.
2. Name any other two structures located in epigastric region which may form palpable mass in pathological conditions.
3. Name the two major vessels related posteriorly to the head of pancreas.

Explanation

1. ______________________

2. ______________________
3. ______________________

Clinical Case 3

A 50-year-old obese male presented with fatigue, abdominal discomfort, and yellowing of the skin and sclerae. Physical examination revealed hepatomegaly. Laboratory tests showed elevated liver enzymes and bilirubin levels. Ultrasound examination and CT scan confirmed fatty liver changes with hepatomegaly. The patient denied alcohol consumption. Further evaluation excluded viral hepatitis and autoimmune liver diseases. Diagnosis of ***non-alcoholic fatty liver disease*** (NAFLD) with associated ***hepatomegaly*** and jaundice was made. Lifestyle modifications and dietary changes were recommended to manage the condition.

1. What is the direction of liver enlargement?
2. Why there was jaundice in this case?

Explanation

1. ______________________

2. ______________________

PRACTICE FIGURES

(Label the practice figures)

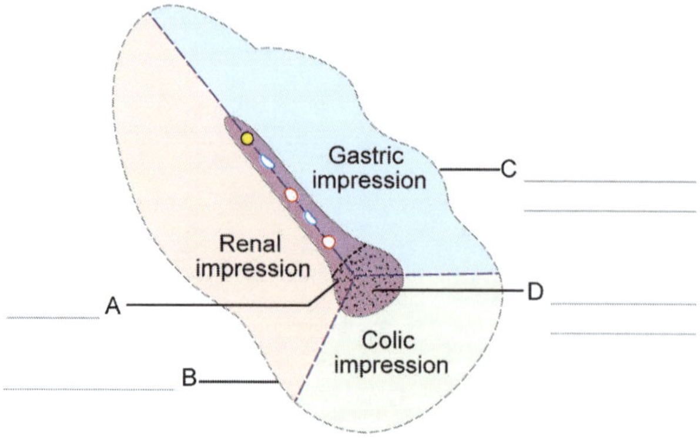

Gastric impression
Renal impression
Colic impression
A
B
C
D

Practice Figure 23.1: Visceral relations of the spleen

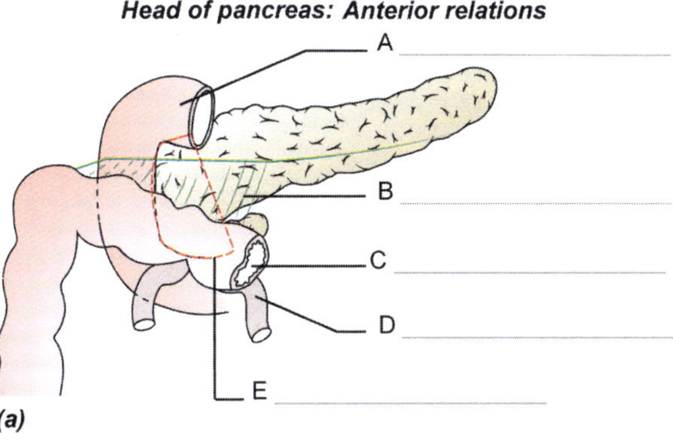

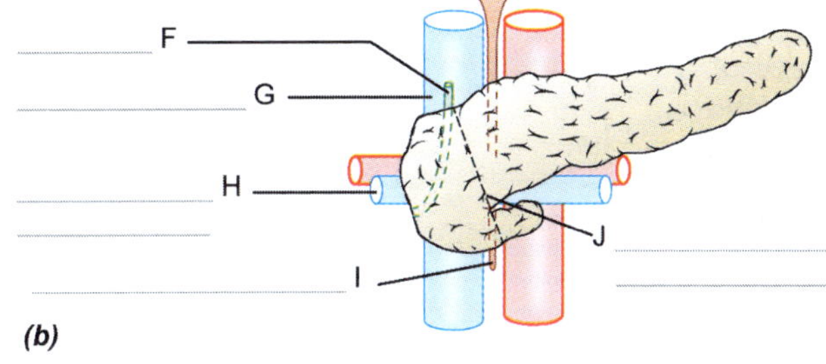

Practice Figures 23.2a and b: Relations of head of the pancreas: (a) Anterior; (b) Posterior

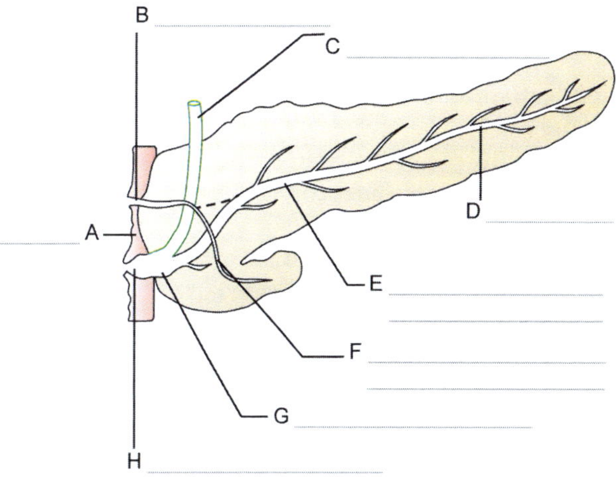

Practice Figure 23.3: The pancreatic ducts

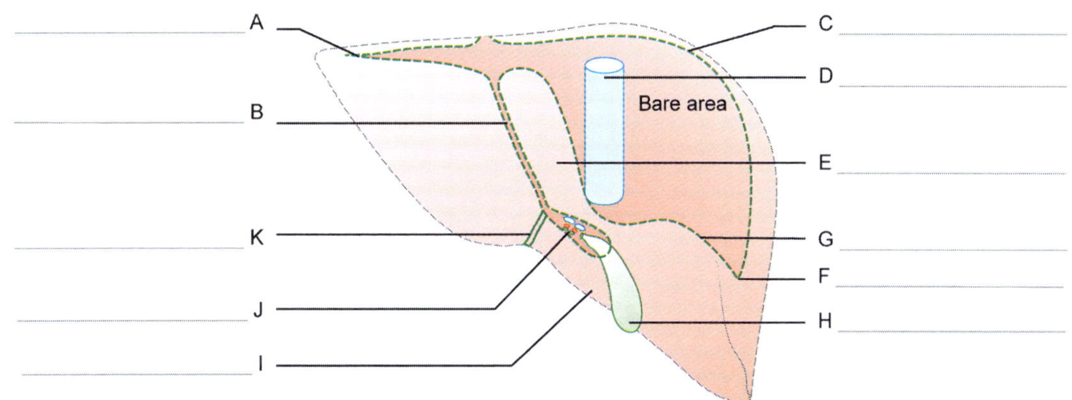

Practice Figure 23.4: Liver: Seen from behind

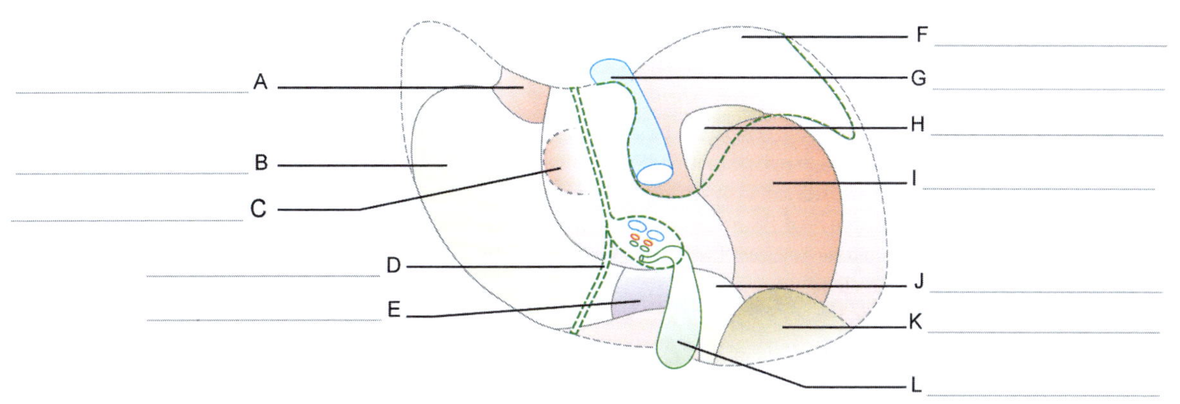

Practice Figure 23.5: Relations of the inferior surface of the liver

MULTIPLE CHOICE QUESTIONS

(Tick the single best correct option)

1. Which of the following statements is TRUE about spleen?
   a. It is highly vascular and dark red in colour.
   b. It lies opposite to 9th, 10th and 11th ribs behind midaxillary line under the diaphragm.
   c. It has two ends, three borders, and two surfaces.
   d. The inferior border is characteristically notched near the anterior end.
2. Which of the following ligaments contains the tail of pancreas?
   a. Gastrosplenic ligament
   b. Phrenicocolic ligament
   c. Lienorenal ligament
   d. Gastrophrenic ligament
3. Malphigian corpuscle is present in:
   a. White pulp
   b. Red pulp
   c. Splenic capsule
   d. Sinusoidal space
4. Identify the part of the pancreas marked as X.

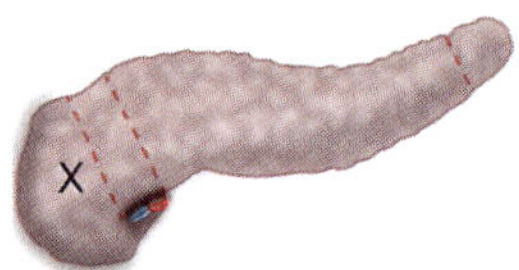

   a. Head b. Uncinate process
   c. Body d. Tail
5. Duct of Wirsung opens into:
   a. Minor duodenal papilla
   b. Bile duct
   c. Major duodenal papilla
   d. Accessory pancreatic duct
6. All of the following structures form the posterior relation to the head of the pancreas, EXCEPT:
   a. Inferior vena cava
   b. Portal vein
   c. Right crus of the diaphragm
   d. Bile duct
7. A 10-year-old boy presented to the surgical out patient department with a history of hit over the left hypochondrium while playing. USG shows rupture of spleen. Splenectomy was done. Histopathology showed the tail of the pancreas along with spleen. What is the most likely complication expected in a patient?
   a. Diabetes mellitus
   b. Diabetes insipidus
   c. Somatostatinoma
   d. Cushing's syndrome
8. A 39-year-old male known alcoholic presented to the casualty department with severe epigastric pain radiating to the back. He also had complaints of vomiting. On examination, he has a temperature of 38.5°C, and his abdomen is tender in the epigastric region. Laboratory tests show elevated serum amylase and lipase levels. What is the most likely diagnosis?
   a. Peptic ulcer disease
   b. Acute pancreatitis
   c. Acute gastrointestinal bleeding
   d. Perforation
9. Which of the following best suits about the area marked with X?

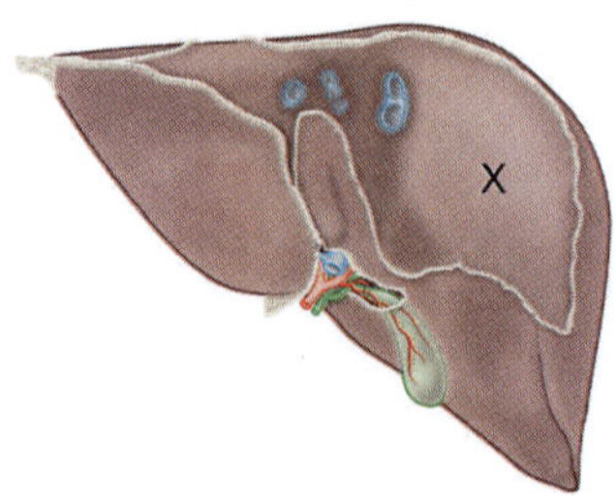

   a. It serves as a site for lymphatic drainage
   b. It is a common location for liver abscesses
   c. It provides access to surgical procedures on the liver
   d. It helps in maintaining hepatic blood supply
10. All of the following organs move with respiration, EXCEPT:
   a. Gallbladder b. Pancreas
   c. Spleen d. Liver
11. The Couinaud's segmental nomenclature is based on the position of the:
   a. Hepatic veins and portal vein
   b. Hepatic veins and biliary ducts
   c. Portal vein and biliary ducts
   d. Portal vein and hepatic artery
12. Factors keeping the liver in position include all, EXCEPT:
   a. Hepatic veins
   b. Intra-abdominal pressure
   c. Ligaments of liver
   d. Proper hepatic artery
13. Which of the following is most commonly associated with the caput medusae?
   a. Cirrhosis
   b. Pancreatitis
   c. Gastric ulcers
   d. Cholecystitis
14. The total number of hepatic segments is ___________.
   a. 3 b. 5
   c. 7 d. 9

QUESTION BANK

(Use separate copy to solve the following questions)

Q 1. Describe the spleen under the following headings: Gross features, peritoneal and visceral relations, blood supply, nerve supply and applied aspects.

Q 2. Describe the liver under the following headings: Gross features, peritoneal and visceral relations, blood supply, nerve supply and applied aspects.

Q 3. Describe the head of pancreas under the following headings: Gross features, peritoneal and visceral relations, ducts, blood supply, nerve supply and applied aspects.

Q 4. Write a short note on:
   a. Visceral relations of spleen
   b. Clinical angle of spleen
   c. Relations of neck and body of pancreas
   d. Blood supply of pancreas
   e. Ducts of pancreas
   f. Bare areas of liver
   g. Lobes of liver

eSmartQuiz

Kidney and Ureter

CLINICOANATOMICAL PROBLEMS

Clinical Case 1

A 35-year-old male presented with severe left flank pain. Later, the pain started radiating to the groin and scrotum. Physical examination revealed tenderness in the left flank. Imaging confirmed a calculus lodged in the left ureter, causing obstruction. The patient experienced episodic renal colic with worsening pain. Conservative management with hydration and analgesics was initiated, followed by spontaneous passage of the stone with relief of symptoms.

1. Give anatomical basis for:
   a. Pain in the left flank
   b. Radiating pain in groin and scrotum
2. Which radiological imaging technique will help to find urinary stone?
3. Which radiological examination will help to find the obstruction in the urinary tract?

Explanation

1. ______

2. a. ______

   b. ______

3. ______

Clinical Case 2

A 55-year-old male with a history of diabetes and hypertension presented with fatigue decreased urine output, and swelling in the legs. Laboratory tests revealed elevated creatinine and urea levels, indicating kidney failure. Despite medical management, renal function continued to decline, necessitating dialysis. The patient was evaluated for kidney transplantation due to ***end-stage renal disease***. A suitable donor was identified, and the patient underwent successful kidney transplantation, leading to improved renal function and quality of life.

1. Why left kidney of donor was selected for transplantation?
2. Where will the new kidney be placed? be put?
3. Where will the new ureter and blood vessels be connected?
4. What are the types of dialysis?

Explanation

1. ______

2. ______

3. ______

4. ______

PRACTICE FIGURES

(Label the practice figures)

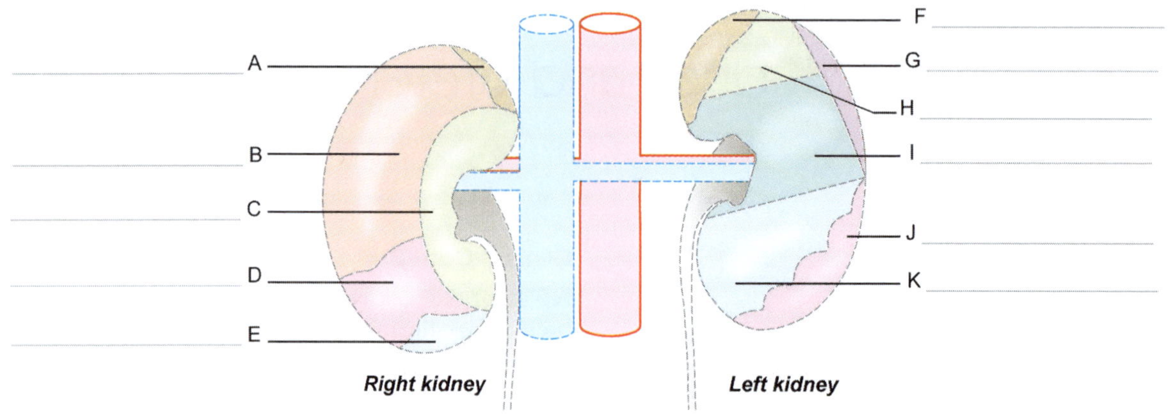

Practice Figure 24.1: Anterior relations of the kidneys. Areas covered by peritoneum are shaded

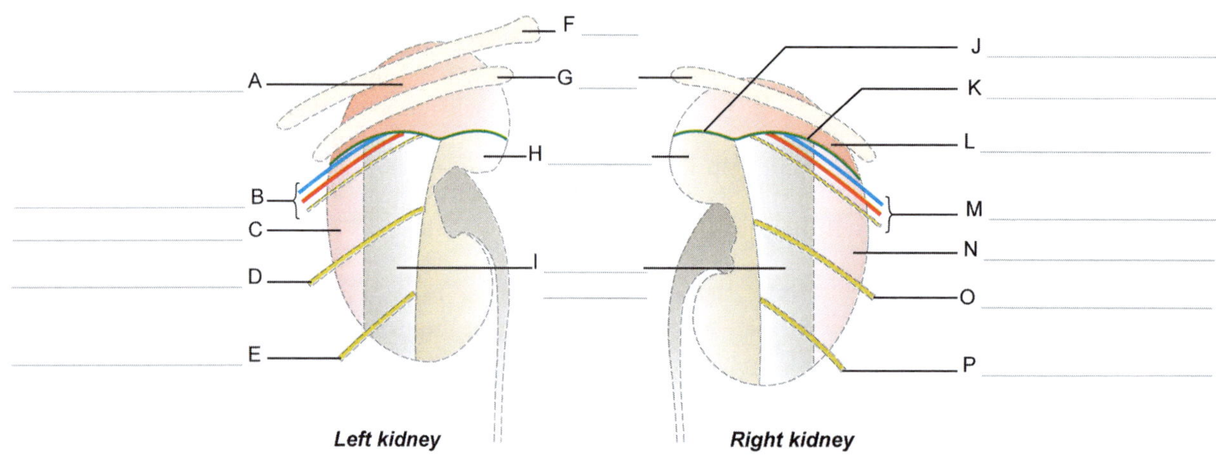

Practice Figure 24.2: Posterior relations of the left kidney and right kidney

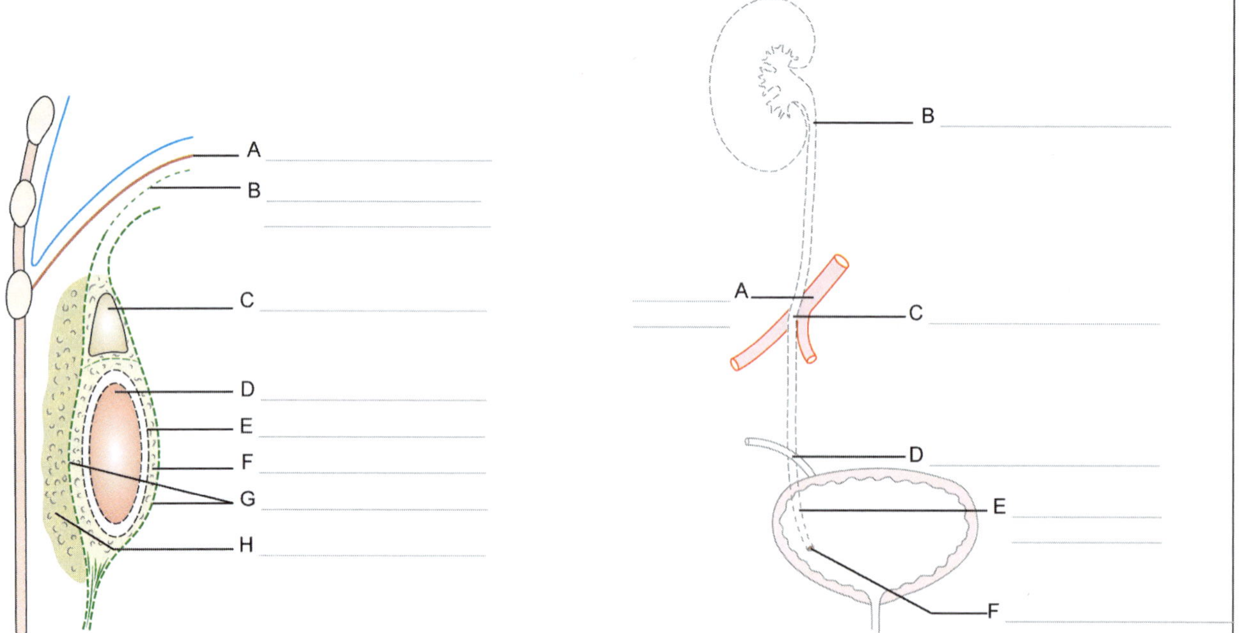

Practice Figure 24.3: Vertical section showing coverings of the kidney

Practice Figure 24.4: Sites of anatomical constrictions of ureter (in male)

MULTIPLE CHOICE QUESTIONS

(Tick the single best correct option)

1. Name the structure marked as X in the following picture.

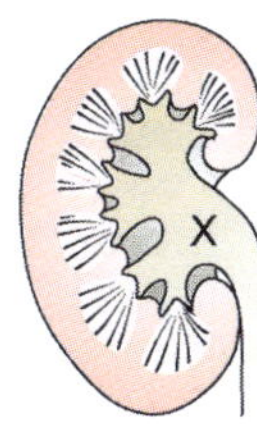

 a. Major calyx b. Ureter
 c. Renal pelvis d. Hilum

2. A 30-year-old female presented to the medicine outpatient department with new onset of dizziness and headache. On examination, her BP—160/100 mmHg. Ultrasound shows enlarged kidney. She underwent nephrectomy. What is the likely diagnosis?
 a. Renal cell carcinoma
 b. Polycystic kidney disease
 c. Multicystic renal dysplasia
 d. Medullary cystic disease.

3. Pick out the TRUE statement about the renal angle.
 a. It is the angle between the lower border of 11th rib and the outer border of the erector spinae muscle.
 b. It overlies the upper part of the kidney.
 c. This angle corresponds to the hilar structures.
 d. Tenderness is elicited at this angle.

4. Identify the artery marked as X.

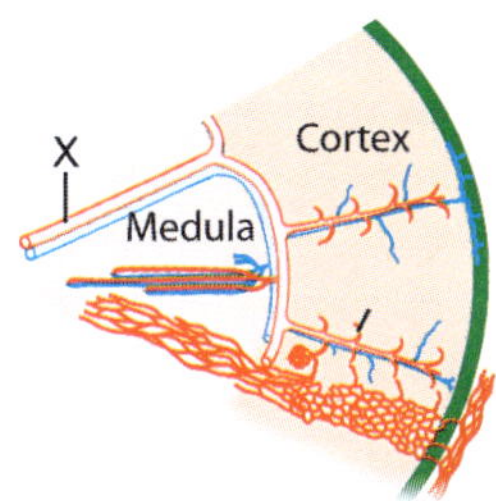

 a. Interlobar b. Interlobular
 c. Arcuate d. Renal

5. All of the following structures form the anterior relations of the right kidney, EXCEPT:
 a. Liver b. Second part of duodenum
 c. Hepatic flexure of colon d. Pancreas

6. Which of the following is the correct order of reflection of the kidney from behind?
 a. Skin, superficial fascia, posterior layer of thoracolumbar fascia, latissimus dorsi muscle
 b. Skin, superficial fascia, posterior layer of thoracolumbar fascia, erector spinae muscle.
 c. Skin, posterior layer of thoracolumbar fascia, erector spinae muscle, middle layer of thoracolumbar fascia
 d. Skin, superficial fascia, erector spinae muscle, middle layer of thoracolumbar fascia

7. The lining epithelium of ureter is:
 a. Brush border epithelium
 b. Ciliated columnar epithelium
 c. Simple squamous epithelium
 d. Transitional epithelium

8. All of the following statements about ureter true, EXCEPT:
 a. Sympathetic innervation of the ureter is from T10 to L1 segments.
 b. Ductus deferens crosses the ureter superiorly from lateral to medial side.
 c. The ureter is slightly constricted at the brim of the greater pelvis.
 d. The ureter is 25–30 cm in length.

9. Which among the following vessels crosses the pelvic part of the ureter?
 a. Common iliac artery b. Left colic artery
 c. Uterine artery d. Inferior mesenteric artery

10. A 56-year-old male presented to the medical outpatient clinic with severe pain over the right loin extending to groin region. Ultrasound showed a 3 mm of stone in the pelviureteric junction. Which nerve is involved in causing the referred pain to the groin in this patient?
 a. Genitofemoral b. Iliohypogastric
 c. Ilioinguinal d. Pudendal nerve

11. Identify the clinical condition shown in the following figure.

 a. Renal cell carcinoma
 b. Polycystic kidney disease
 c. Multicystic renal dysplasia
 d. Medullary cystic disease.

12. Identify the clinical condition shown in the following radiograph.

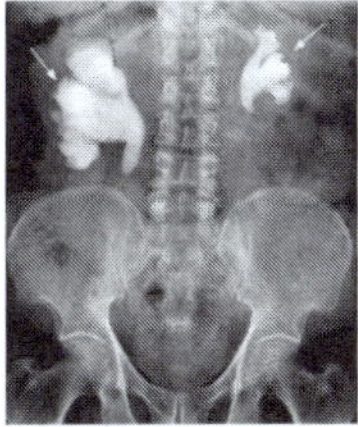

 a. Staghorn renal stone b. Gallstone
 c. Stone in ureter d. Descending pyelography

13. The length of each ureter is about:
 a. 15 cm b. 25 cm
 c. 35 cm d. 40 cm

QUESTION BANK

(Use separate copy to solve the following questions)

Q 1. Describe kidneys (left and right) under the following headings: Location and gross anatomy, supports, relation, blood supply and applied anatomy

Q 2. Write a short note on:
 a. Coverings of kidney
 b. Constrictions of ureter
 c. Juxtaglomerular apparatus
 d. Vascular segment of kidney

Q 3. Draw a well-labelled diagram of:
 a. Anterior and posterior relations of kidney

Chapter

25

Suprarenal Gland and Chromaffin System

CLINICOANATOMICAL PROBLEMS

Clinical Case 1

A 45-year-old female presented with weight gain, hypertension, and uncontrolled diabetes. Laboratory tests revealed elevated cortisol levels. Abdominal ultrasound showed a right adrenal mass. Further investigations confirmed adrenal cortical adenoma causing ***Cushing's syndrome***. The patient underwent surgical removal of the adenoma. Postoperatively, cortisol levels normalised, and symptoms resolved.

1. What causes Cushing syndrome?
2. What is the venous drainage of adrenal gland?

Explanation

1. ______________________________

2. ______________________________

Clinical Case 2

A 40-year-old male presented with episodic headaches, palpitations, and sweating. Blood pressure readings fluctuated significantly during episodes. Laboratory tests revealed elevated catecholamine levels. Abdominal imaging showed a unilateral adrenal mass. Further investigation confirmed ***pheochromocytoma***.

1. What is pheochromocytoma?
2. Why there is hypertension in pheochromocytoma?

Explanation

1. ______________________________

2. ______________________________

PRACTICE FIGURES

(Label the practice figures)

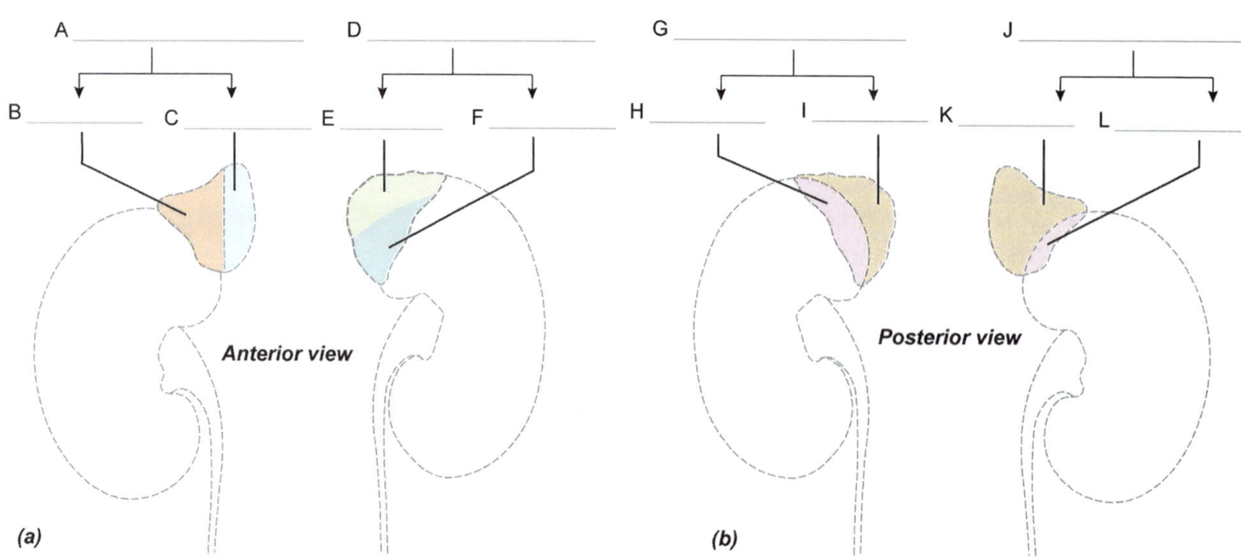

Practice Figures 25.1a and b: Relations of the suprarenal glands: (a) Anterior view of right suprarenal gland and anterior view of left suprarenal gland; (b) Posterior view of left suprarenal gland and posterior view of right suprarenal gland

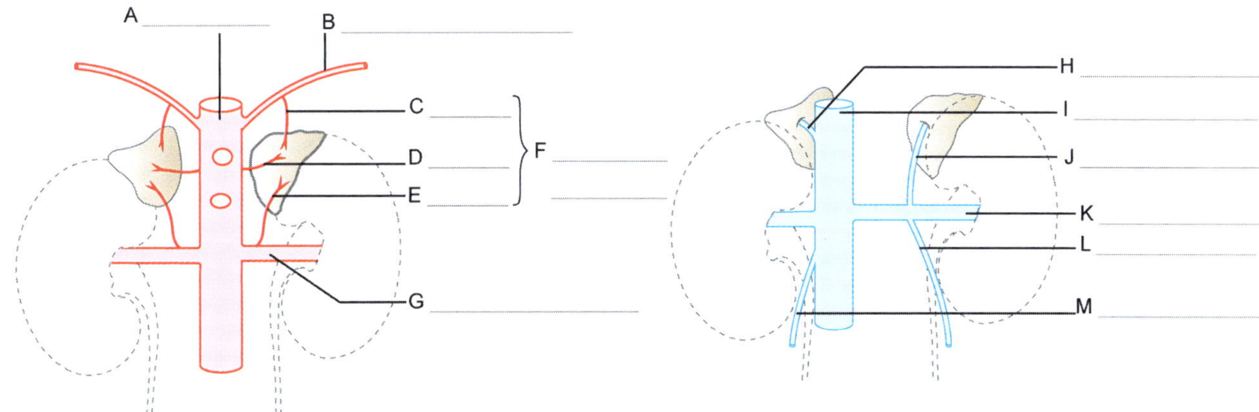

Practice Figure 25.2: Blood supply of the suprarenal glands

MULTIPLE CHOICE QUESTIONS

(Tick the single best correct option)

1. All of the following vessels supply the suprarenal gland, EXCEPT:
   a. Abdominal aorta
   b. Inferior phrenic artery
   c. Renal artery
   d. Intercostal artery
2. Pick out the incorrect statement about the left suprarenal gland.
   a. It is semilunar in shape
   b. The medial border is formed by liver
   c. The posterior surface is formed by left crus of diaphragm
   d. One of its blood supplies is from the direct branch of abdominal aorta.
3. Inferior suprarenal artery is a branch of:
   a. Abdominal aorta
   b. Inferior phrenic artery
   c. Renal artery
   d. Intercostal artery
4. A 35-year-old male came in with frequent headache, raised blood pressure, palpitation and excessive sweating. Ultrasound shows suprarenal mass. What is the most likely diagnosis?
   a. Adrenal adenoma
   b. Adrenal metastasis
   c. Pheochromocytoma
   d. Adrenal tuberculosis
5. The right suprarenal vein drains into:
   a. Right renal vein
   b. Inferior vena cava
   c. Right gonadal vein
   d. External iliac vein
6. The outermost part of the adrenal cortex is known as:
   a. Zona fasciculata
   b. Zona glomerulosa
   c. Zona reticularis
   d. Zona pellucida
7. Left suprarenal veins drain into:
   a. Left gonadal vein
   b. Left renal vein
   c. External iliac vein
   d. Inferior vena cava
8. The adrenal medulla is derived from:
   a. Surface ectoderm
   b. Extraembryonic coelomic epithelium
   c. Neural crest cells
   d. Germinal epithelium
9. Which of the following statement is true about the suprarenal gland?
   a. The lymphatics are drained into lateral aortic nodes
   b. It is supplied by middle suprarenal artery, branch from the renal artery
   c. The right suprarenal gland is semilunar in shape
   d. Left suprarenal vein drains into inferior vena cava.
10. Identify the structure marked as 'X' lining the suprarenal gland.

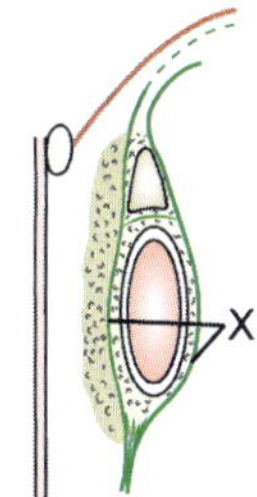

   a. Fibrous capsule
   b. Renal fascia
   c. Gerota's fascia
   d. Zuckerkandl fascia

QUESTION BANK

(Use separate copy to solve the following questions)

Q 1. Describe the adrenal glands under the following headings: gross features, relations, blood supply, nerve supply, applied aspects.

Q 2. Write a short note on:
   a. Blood supply of adrenal glands
   b. Comparison of right and left adrenal glands.

Chapter

26

Thoracoabdominal Diaphragm

CLINICOANATOMICAL PROBLEM

Clinical Case 1

A 55-year-old obese male presented with chronic acid reflux, regurgitation, and epigastric discomfort. Upper gastrointestinal endoscopy revealed a ***sliding hiatal hernia,*** with the gastroesophageal junction displaced into the thoracic cavity. Radiological imaging confirmed the diagnosis. Conservative management with lifestyle modifications and proton pump inhibitors (antacids) was initiated to alleviate symptoms.

1. What is sliding hiatal hernia?
2. Why does this hernia occur?
3. What factors prevent sliding hiatal hernia?

Explanation

1. ______________________________

2. ______________________________

3. ______________________________

PRACTICE FIGURE

(Label the practice figure)

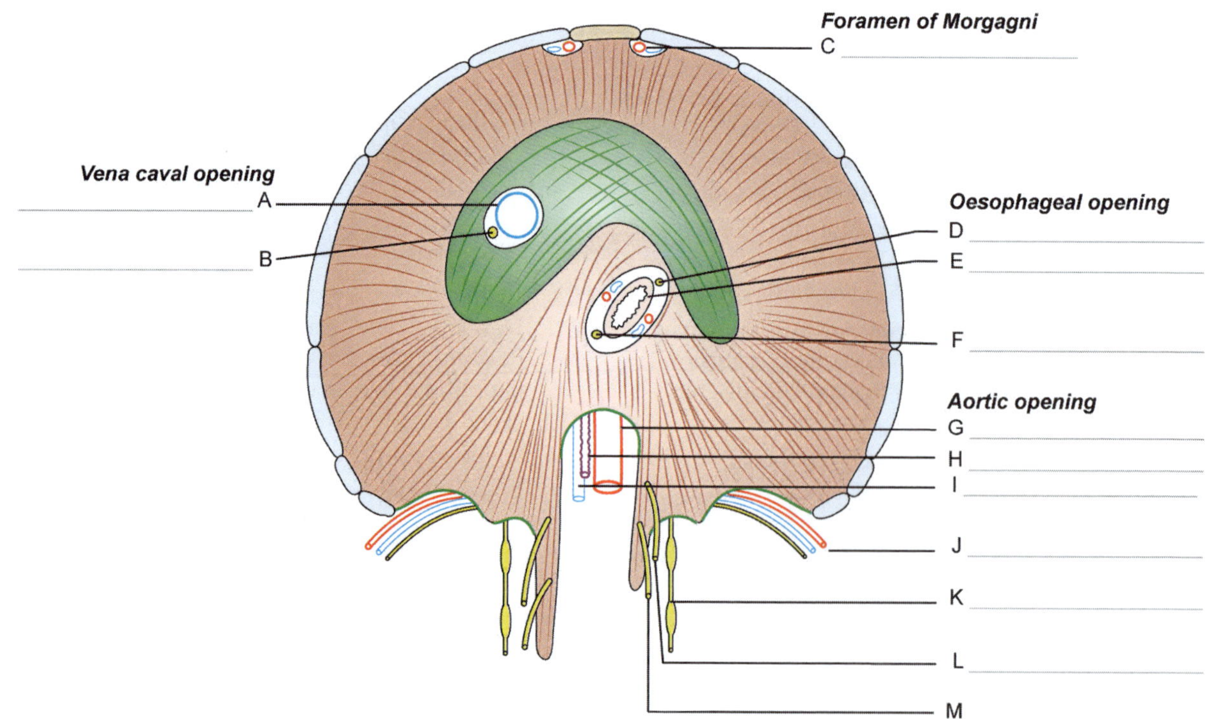

Practice Figure 26.1: The thoracoabdominal diaphragm: Openings in the diaphragm and structures passing through these openings

MULTIPLE CHOICE QUESTIONS

(Tick the single best correct option)

1. What is the vertebral level of oesophageal opening in the diagram?
   a. T8   b. T10
   c. T12   d. T11
2. The median arcuate ligament is derived from ________.
   a. Medial margin of both crura
   b. Lateral margin of both crura
   c. Psoas major muscle
   d. Quadratus lumborum
3. Name the structure marked by X.

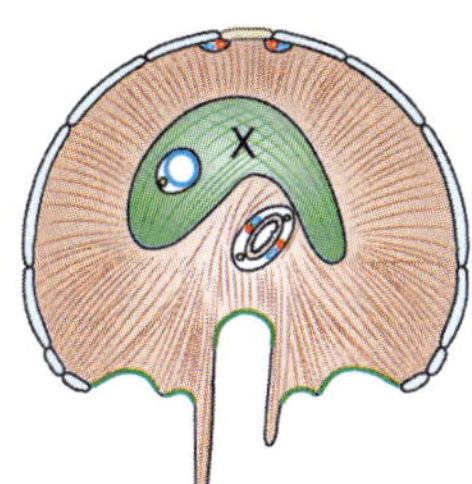

   a. Medial arcuate ligament
   b. Central tendon
   c. Median arcuate ligament
   d. Lateral arcuate ligament
4. T12 vertebral level corresponds to which of the following openings?
   a. Oesophagus   b. Aorta
   c. Inferior vena cava   d. Trachea
5. What is the structure marked as X.

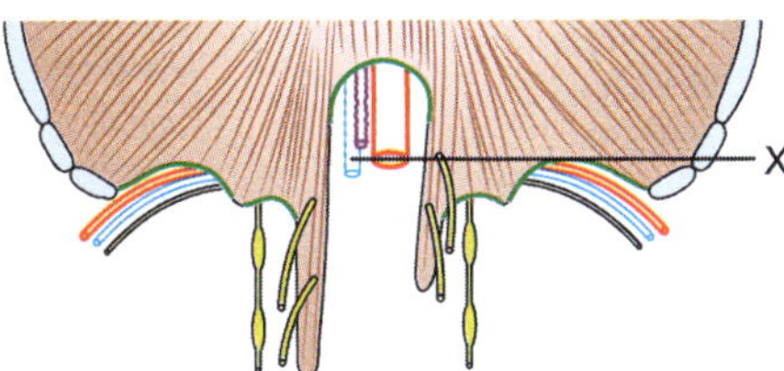

   a. Azygos vein   b. Hemiazygos vein
   c. Right intercostal vein   d. Right lumbar vein
6. A newborn baby presents with severe respiratory distress shortly after birth. Physical examination reveals diminished breath sounds on the left side with a scaphoid abdomen. Chest X-ray shows bowel loops in the left hemithorax and mediastinal shift to the right. What is the most likely diagnosis?
   a. Pneumothorax
   b. Pulmonary hypoplasia
   c. Congenital diaphragmatic hernia
   d. Diaphragmatic rupture
7. Which is the most common organ to herniate in congenital diaphragmatic hernia?
   a. Intestine
   b. Stomach
   c. Liver
   d. Gallbladder
8. All of the following structures pass through T8 vertebral opening, EXCEPT:
   a. Inferior vena cava
   b. Right phrenic nerve
   c. Lymphatic vessel
   d. Azygos vein
9. The space between the xiphoid and costal origins of the thoracoabdominal diaphragm is known as ________.
   a. Space of Larrey
   b. Foramen of Bochdalek
   c. Lumbar triangle
   d. Coastal arch
10. Foramen of Bochdalek is situated at the ________.
    a. Posterior
    b. Central
    c. Posterolateral
    d. Retrosternal

QUESTION BANK

(Use separate copy to solve the following questions)

Q 1. Describe the major openings of the diaphragm.
Q 2. What is hiatal hernia? What are the types?

Chapter

27

Posterior Abdominal Wall

CLINICOANATOMICAL PROBLEM

Clinical Case 1

A 45-year-old male presented with fever and swelling in the right femoral triangle. Physical examination revealed tenderness and swelling, but no signs of hernia. Ultrasound imaging confirmed the presence of a ***psoas abscess*** extending into the inguinal region.

1. What is psoas abscess?
2. What are the anatomical structures that act as a source of infection for pasos abscess?
3. How does the psoas abscess extend into the thigh?

Explanation

1. ______________________________
2. ______________________________
3. ______________________________

PRACTICE FIGURES

(Label the practice figures)

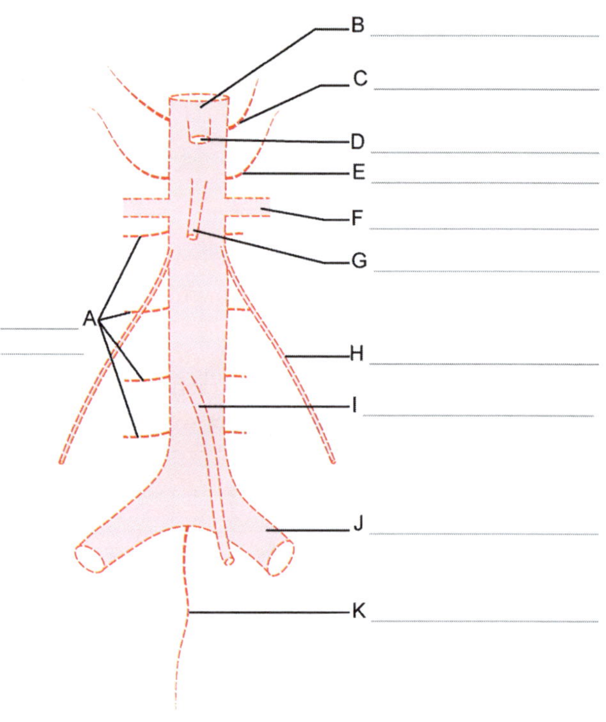

Practice Figure 27.1: Branches of abdominal aorta

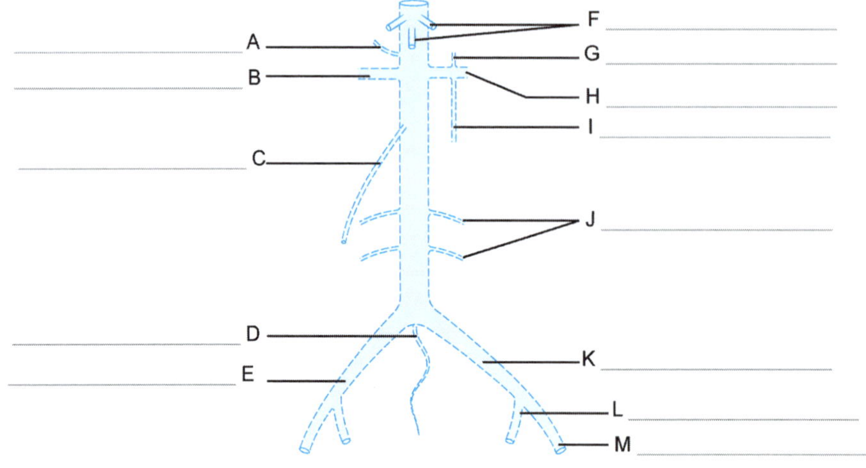

Practice Figure 27.2: Tributaries of the inferior vena cava

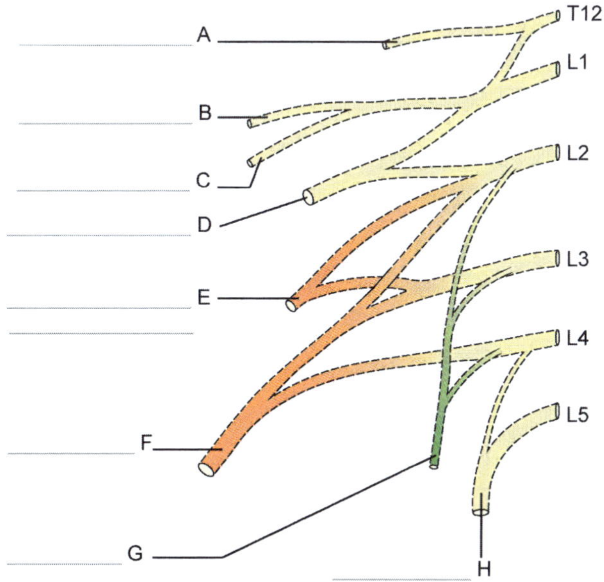

Practice Figure 27.3: Right lumbar plexus of nerves

MULTIPLE CHOICE QUESTIONS

(Tick the single best correct option)

1. Median sacral artery is a branch of ____________.
   a. Abdominal aorta
   b. Common iliac artery
   c. Internal iliac artery
   d. External iliac artery
2. The azygos vein is formed by the union of which veins?
   a. Left renal vein and inferior vena cava
   b. Superior vena cava and inferior vena cava
   c. Right subclavian vein and right internal thoracic vein
   d. Right ascending lumbar vein and right subcostal vein
3. Which of the following is NOT a tributary of inferior vena cava?
   a. Iliac veins
   b. Azygos vein
   c. Lumbar veins
   d. Suprarenal veins
4. Name the muscle marked by X.

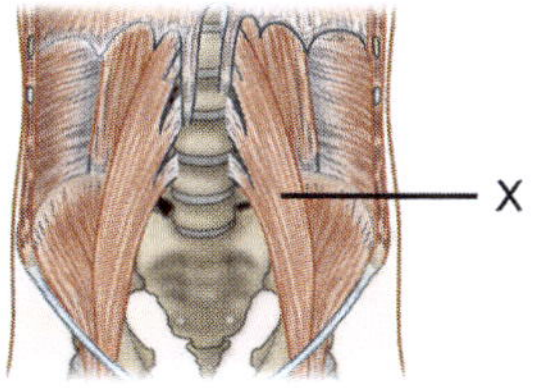

   a. Quadratus lumborum
   b. Iliacus
   c. Psoas major
   d. Latissimus dorsi
5. Inferior phrenic artery is a branch of ____________.
   a. Internal iliac artery
   b. Common iliac artery
   c. Abdominal aorta
   d. External iliac artery
6. Pick out the correct statement about the course of inferior vena cava.
   a. It is formed by the union of the right and left common iliac veins on the right side of the L4 vertebra.
   b. The renal veins join the inferior vena cava above the transpyloric plane.
   c. It opens into the lower and posterior part of the left atrium.
   d. The azygos vein arises from the posterior surface of the inferior vena cava near the renal veins.
7. All of the following vessels take part in collateral venous circulation, EXCEPT:
   a. Superficial epigastric vein
   b. Right lumbar vein
   c. Lateral thoracic vein
   d. Thoracoepigastric vein
8. Which among the following group of lymph nodes does NOT belong to the posterior abdominal wall?
   a. Common iliac
   b. External iliac
   c. Deep inguinal
   d. Aortic group
9. Presacral nerve is ____________.
   a. Inferior hypogastric plexus
   b. Superior hypogastric plexus
   c. Superior mesenteric plexus
   d. Abdominal aortic plexus
10. Identify the structure marked as X.

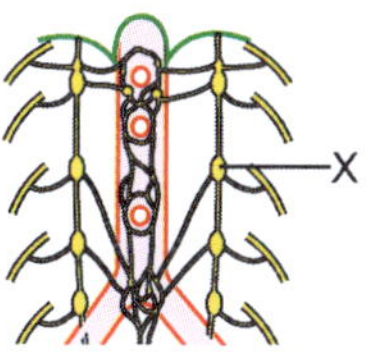

   a. Lumbar sympathetic ganglion
   b. Parasympathetic ganglion
   c. Presacral plexus
   d. Abdominal aortic plexus

QUESTION BANK

(Use separate copy to solve the following questions)

Q 1. Describe the abdominal aorta under the following headings: Beginning, course, termination, relations, branches and applied aspects.

Q 2. Describe the inferior vena cava (IVC) under the following headings: Formation, course, termination, relations, tributaries and applied aspects.

Q 3. Write a short note on:
   a. Quadratus lumborum
   b. Lumbosacral triangle of Marcille
   c. Psoas fascia
   d. Thoracolumbar fascia (lumbar fascia)

Chapter

28

Perineum

CLINICOANATOMICAL PROBLEMS

Clinical Case 1

A 55-year-old male presented with severe pain and swelling in the perianal region. He reported difficulty in sitting and discomfort during defecation. Physical examination revealed a tender, fluctuant swelling near the anus. A digital rectal examination confirmed the presence of an ***abscess in the ischiorectal fossa***. Incision and drainage were performed under local anaesthesia, with subsequent antibiotic therapy.

1. What is ischioanal fossa?
2. What is fistula in ano?
3. Why the infections of the ischioanal fossa are common?

Explanation

1. ______________________________
2. ______________________________
3. ______________________________

PRACTICE FIGURES

(Label the practice figures)

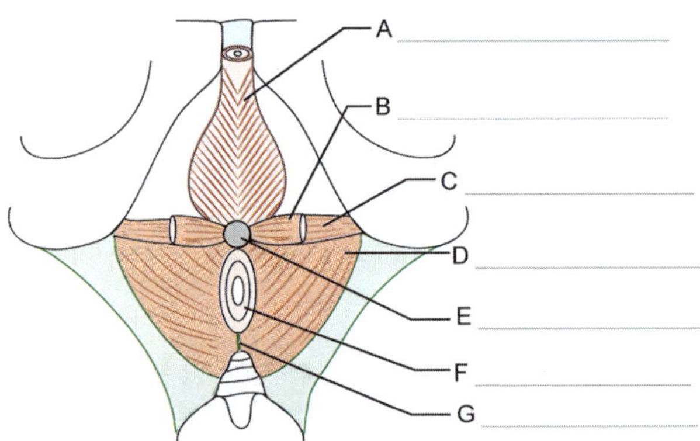

Practice Figure 28.1: Muscles attached to perineal body (in male)

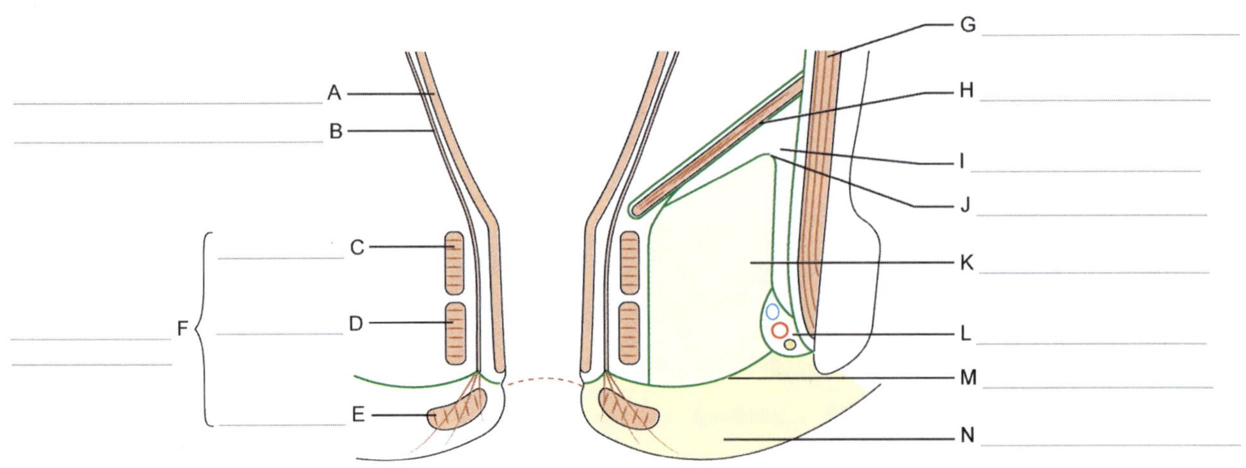

Practice Figure 28.2: Ischioanal fossa (coronal section through the anal triangle)

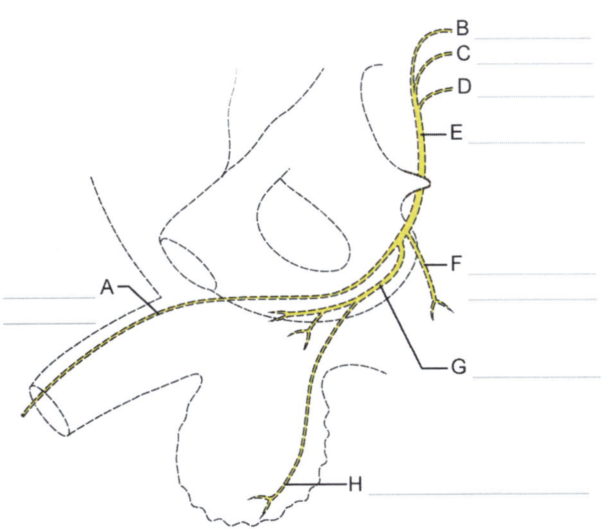

Practice Figure 28.3: Course and branches of pudendal nerve

MULTIPLE CHOICE QUESTIONS

(Tick the single best correct option)

1. Identify the triangle marked as X.

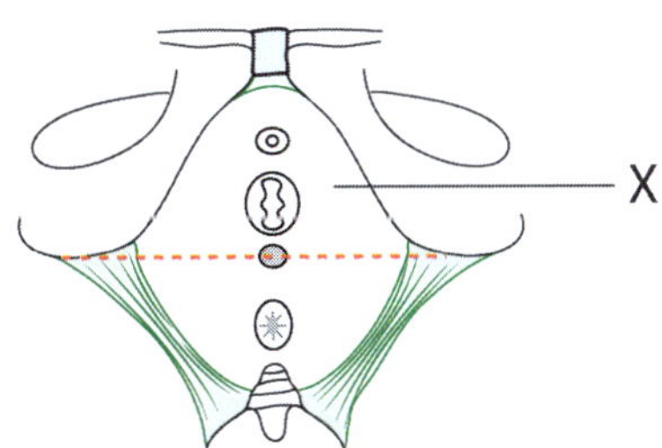

   a. Urogenital triangle
   b. Anal triangle
   c. Deep perineal space
   d. Superficial perineal space

2. The external anal sphincter is supplied by ______________.
   a. Superior rectal nerve
   b. Pudendal nerve
   c. Inferior rectal nerve
   d. Genital branch of the genitofemoral nerve.

3. Name the structure marked by X.

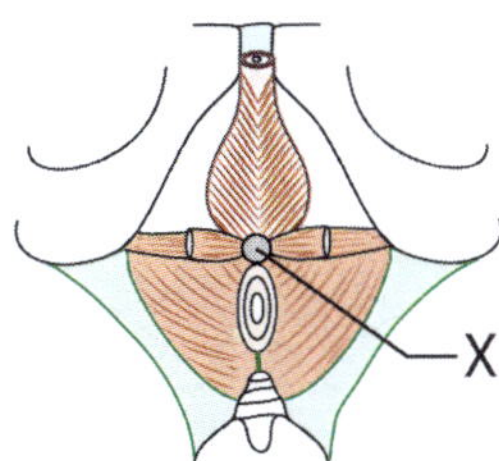

   a. Superficial anal sphincter
   b. Perineal body
   c. Bulbospongiosus
   d. Deep transversus perinei

4. The occasional gap between the tendinous origin of levator ani and the obturator fascia is known as ______________.
   a. Superficial perineal space
   b. Ischioanal fossa
   c. Hiatus of Schwalbe
   d. Deep perineal space

5. A 35-year-old male presented to the surgical outpatient clinic with the history of recurrent perianal discharge and intermittent pain. On examination, there was an external opening near the anal verge with induration along a tract leading to the anal canal. What is the most likely diagnosis?
   a. Haemorrhoids
   b. Anal fissure
   c. Fistula in ano
   d. Rectal prolapse

6. The structure marked as X is pierced by all of the following, EXCEPT:

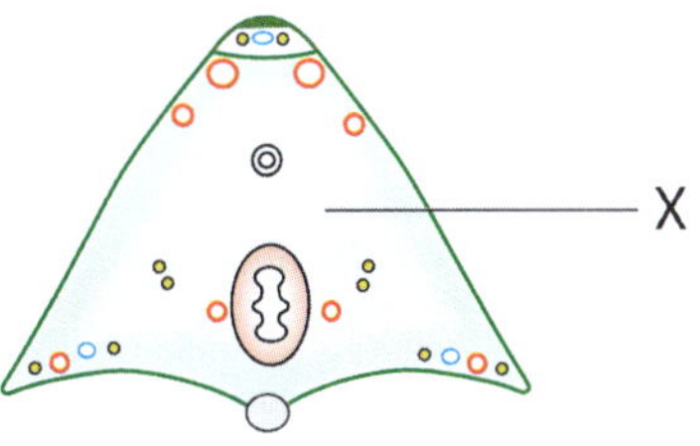

   a. Vagina
   b. Deep artery of clitoris
   c. Dorsal arteries and nerves of clitoris
   d. Internal pudendal artery

7. All of the following structures are contents of deep perineal space, EXCEPT:
   a. Dorsal nerve of penis
   b. Muscular branches from perineal nerve
   c. Artery of penis
   d. Ducts of bulbourethral glands

8. Where is the Alcock's canal located?
   a. Posterior pelvic wall
   b. Anterior pelvic wall
   c. Lateral pelvic wall
   d. Pelvic floor

9. ______________ muscle helps in ejecting the last drop of urine in males.
   a. Bulbospongiosus
   b. Superficial transversus perinei
   c. Ischiocavernosus
   d. Deep transversus perinei

10. What is the root value of the pudendal nerve?
    a. S2, S3, S4
    b. S3, S4, S5
    c. S4, S5
    d. S1, S2, S3

QUESTION BANK

(Use separate copy to solve the following questions)

Q 1. What are the boundaries and contents of superficial perineal pouch?

Q 2. What are the boundaries and contents of deep perineal pouch?

Q 3. Describe the ischioanal fossa under the following headings: Boundaries, content, recesses, spaces and applied aspects.

Q 4. Write a short note on:
   a. Pudendal nerve
   b. Alcock's canal
   c. Structures piercing perineal membrane in female
   d. Perineal body
   e. Perineal membrane.

Chapter

29 Preliminary Consideration of Boundaries and Contents of Pelvis

eSmartQuiz

CLINICOANATOMICAL PROBLEM

Clinical Case 1

During childbirth, a 30-year-old primigravida requested pain relief. After obtaining informed consent, the anaesthesiologist gave ***pudendal nerve block***. Using a specialised needle, local anaesthetic was injected near the pudendal nerve to block sensation in the perineum. The patient experienced effective pain relief during the second stage of labour, facilitating a smoother delivery process with reduced discomfort.

1. What is the root value of the pudendal nerve?
2. What is the site for pudendal nerve block?

Explanation

1. ______________________________

2. ______________________________

PRACTICE FIGURE

(Label the practice figure)

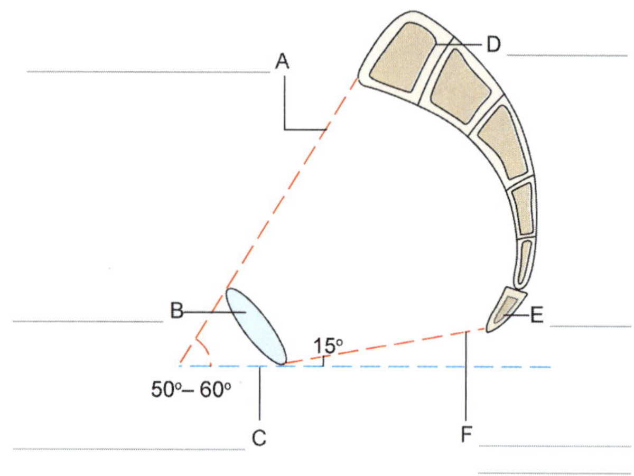

Practice Figure 29.1: Sagittal section of the pelvis showing the planes of its inlet and outlet and their axes. The axis of the pelvic cavity is J-shaped

MULTIPLE CHOICE QUESTIONS

(Tick the single best correct option)

1. Pelvic diaphragm is formed by __________.
   a. Iliococcygeus and pubococcygeus
   b. Levator ani and coccygeus
   c. Gluteus maximus and piriformis
   d. Obturator internus and piriformis
2. The plane of the pelvic inlet passes from the __________.
   a. Sacral promontory to the pubic symphysis
   b. Iliac crest to the ischial tuberosity
   c. Anterior superior iliac spine to the coccyx
   d. Acetabulum to the greater trochanter
3. Name the structure marked by X in the following picture.

   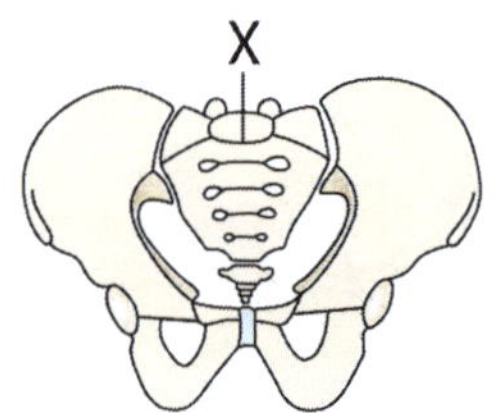

   a. Ala of sacrum b. Sacral promontory
   c. Sacral foramina d. Coccyx
4. All of the following are true about the superior aperture of the pelvis, EXCEPT:
   a. It is oval-shaped in the males and heart-shaped in females.
   b. It is an oblique plane making an angle of 50° to 60° with the horizontal plane.
   c. It is bounded anteriorly by the upper margin of the pubic symphysis.
   d. It is divided into greater and lesser pelvis.
5. Name the bony landmark marked by X in the following picture

   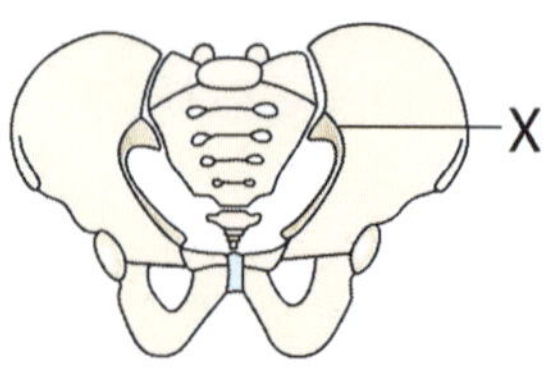

   a. Linea semilunaris b. Linea aspera
   c. Linea terminalis d. Linea nigra
6. A 25-year-old female admitted to the labour ward with labour pain. Per vaginal examination shows head at the introitus. What procedure is done to avoid perineal tears?
   a. Colposcopy b. McRoberts manoeuvre
   c. Rubin's manoeuvre d. Episiotomy

7. The pubic arch is formed by __________.
   a. Ischium and sacrum
   b. Sacrum and coccyx
   c. Pubic symphysis and ilium
   d. Pubic symphysis and ischium
8. What type of joint is pubic symphysis?
   a. Ball-and-socket joint
   b. Hinge joint
   c. Synovial joint
   d. Cartilaginous joint
9. Identify the structure marked as X.

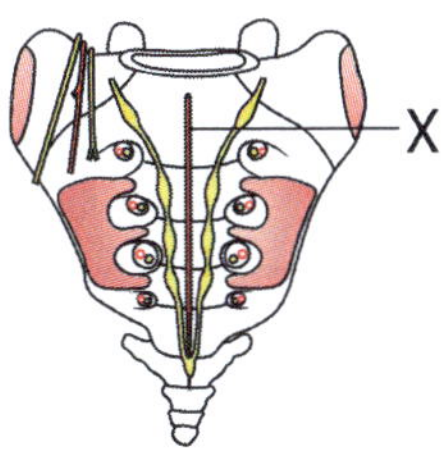

   a. Lateral sacral artery
   b. Median sacral artery
   c. Medial sacral artery
   d. Iliolumbar artery
10. All of the following structures cross the brim of the pelvis, EXCEPT:
   a. Full urinary bladder
   b. Superior gluteal nerve
   c. Ureter
   d. Obturator nerve

QUESTION BANK

(Use separate copy to solve the following question)

Q 1. Write a short note on:
   a. Pelvic inlet
   b. Structures crossing the pelvic inlet/brim of the pelvis
   c. Structures at the ala of the sacrum.

Chapter

30

eSmartQuiz

Urinary Bladder and Urethra

CLINICOANATOMICAL PROBLEM

Clinical Case 1

A 40-year-old male was brought to the emergency room after a motor vehicle accident. He complained of severe lower abdominal pain and inability to pass urine. Physical examination revealed distended abdomen and tenderness on palpation. Diagnostic imaging confirmed ***rupture of the urinary bladder***. Immediate surgical intervention was performed to repair the bladder and address associated injuries.

1. What are the types of rupture of urinary bladder?
2. Where would the extravasated urine go from the ruptured urinary bladder?

Explanation

1. ____

2. ____

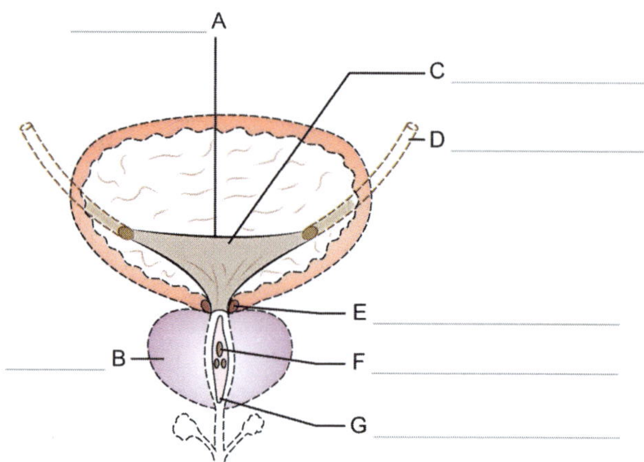

Practice Figure 30.2: Coronal section through the bladder and prostate to show the interior of the bladder

PRACTICE FIGURES

(Label the practice figures)

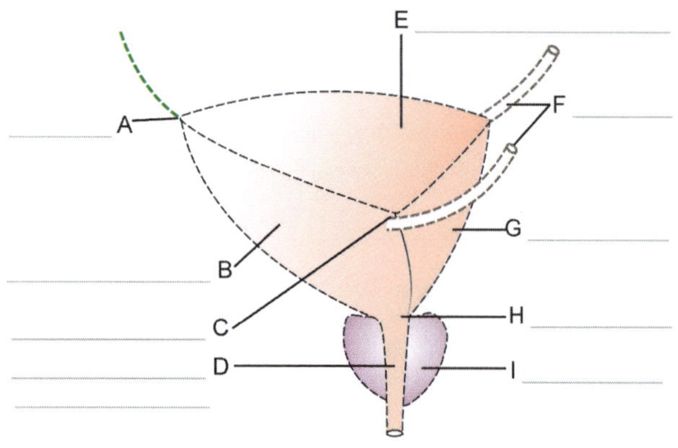

Practice Figure 30.1: The shape of the urinary bladder

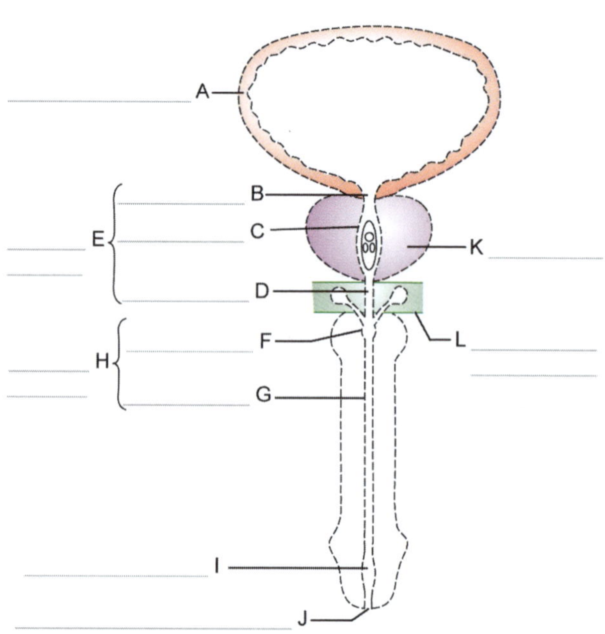

Practice Figure 30.3: Parts of male urethra (anterior view of the male urethra straightened and cut open)

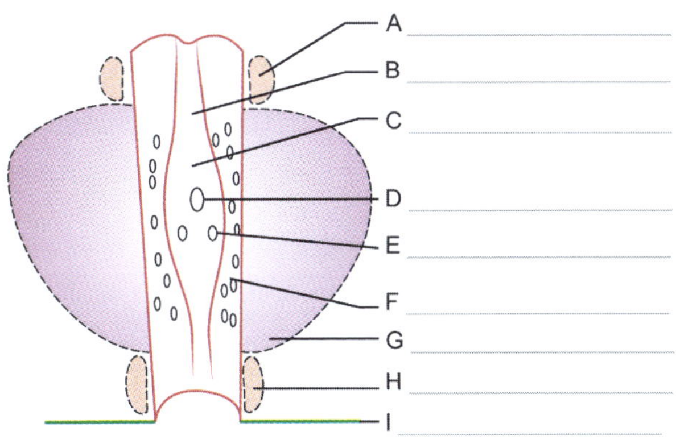

Practice Figure 30.4: Features of the posterior wall of the prostatic urethra (anterior view, coronal section)

MULTIPLE CHOICE QUESTIONS

(Tick the single best correct option)

1. Pick out the incorrect statement about the urinary bladder.
   a. An empty bladder is tetrahedral in shape
   b. It has three surfaces superior, right and left inferolateral surfaces
   c. The apex is connected to the umbilicus by the medial umbilical ligament
   d. The neck is the lowest and most fixed part of the bladder.
2. Uvula vesicae is produced by __________ lobe of the prostate gland.
   a. Anterior b. Posterior
   c. Median d. Lateral
3. Name the structure marked by X.

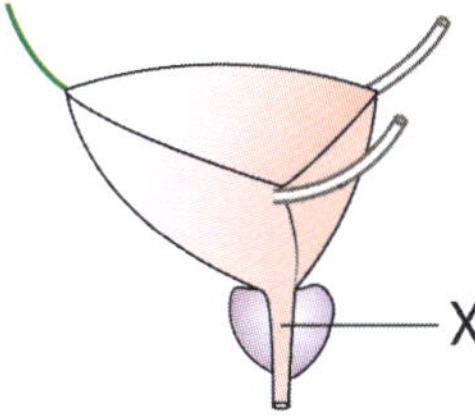

   a. Internal urethral orifice
   b. Prostatic urethra
   c. Membranous urethra
   d. Neck of the bladder
4. Name the structure marked by X.

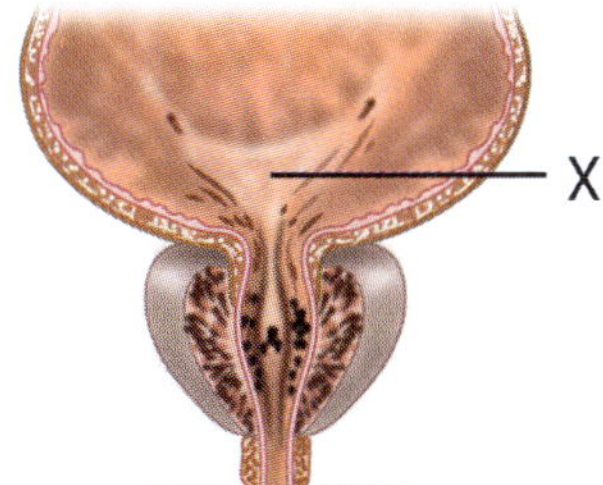

   a. Trigone
   b. Interureteric ridge
   c. Uvula vesicae
   d. Urethral crest
5. A 25-year-old male presented to the casualty department with a road traffic accident. On examination he is conscious and complains of severe lower abdominal pain and an inability to urinate, bleeding is noted in the urethral meatus. What is the most likely diagnosis?
   a. Prostate injury b. Urethral injury
   c. Penile injury d. Scrotal injury
6. Match the following shape of different parts of male urethra.

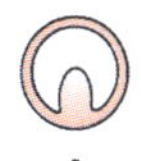   

A B C D

   a. A-Membranous, B-External urethral orifice, C-penile, D- Prostatic
   b. A-Prostatic, B-Membranous, C-penile, D-External urethral orifice
   c. A-Prostatic, B-External urethral orifice, C-penile, D-Membranous
   d. A-Membranous, B-External urethral orifice, C- penile, D- Prostatic
7. Which of the following is the false ligament of the urinary bladder?
   a. Lateral puboprostatic ligament
   b. Lateral true ligament
   c. Median umbilical ligament
   d. Median umbilical fold
8. Which is the most fixed part of the urinary bladder?
   a. Apex b. Base
   c. Neck d. Inferolateral surface
9. State the true statement about the nerve supply of the urinary bladder.
   a. Parasympathetic efferent fibres S2, S3, S4 are sensory to the detrusor muscle
   b. The somatic pudendal nerve supplies the sphincter urethrae
   c. Pain sensation to the urinary bladder is through the anterior spinothalamic tract
   d. The vesical plexus of nerves are made up of fibres derived from the superior hypogastric plexus
10. In which condition does the urethra open on the under-surface of the penis?
   a. Hypospadias
   b. Epispadias
   c. Urethral duplication
   d. Imperforate urethra

QUESTION BANK

(Use separate copy to solve the following questions)

Q 1. Describe the urinary bladder under following headings: Presenting parts and relations, blood supply, nerve supply and applied aspects.

Q 2. A 6-month-old boy presents to hospital with opening of the urethra is located on the underside of the penis instead of at the tip. What is the clinical condition. Describe the parts and features of male urethra.

Q 3. Write a short note on:
   a. Trigone of bladder
   b. Mechanism of micturition
   c. Prostatic urethra
   d. Female urethra

Chapter

31

eSmartQuiz

Female Reproductive Organs

CLINICOANATOMICAL PROBLEMS

Clinical Case 1

During preoperative counselling for tubectomy, a 32-year-old female expressed concerns about the permanence of the procedure and its impact on her sexual health. She inquired about the following concerns:

1. What is tubectomy?
2. Is tubectomy done on one or both sides?
3. How is tubectomy done?
4. Does the patient need hospitalisation?

Explanation

1. ______________________________

2. ______________________________

3. ______________________________

4. ______________________________

Clinical Case 2

A 45-year-old woman presented with vaginal bleeding. She reported intermittent bleeding between periods, accompanied by post-coital bleeding and pelvic pain. Physical examination revealed a friable, ulcerative lesion on the cervix. Further investigation, including colposcopy and biopsy, confirmed the diagnosis of ***carcinoma of the cervix***.

1. What are the anatomical parts of cervix?
2. Which virus is a known causative agent for cervical cancer?
3. Is there any vaccine available for prevention of cervical cancer?
4. What is the sensory nerve supply of the cervix?

Explanation

1. ______________________________

2. ______________________________

3. ______________________________

4. ______________________________

Note: Also study the clinicoanatomical problem of *uterine prolapse* from Chapter 34.

PRACTICE FIGURES

(Label the practice figures)

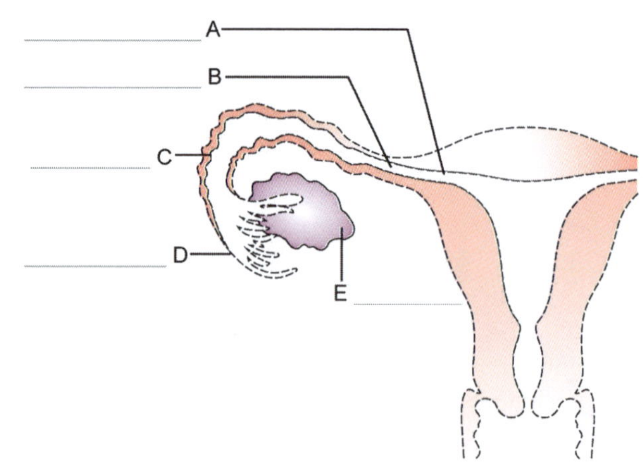

Practice Figure 31.1: Parts of uterine tube

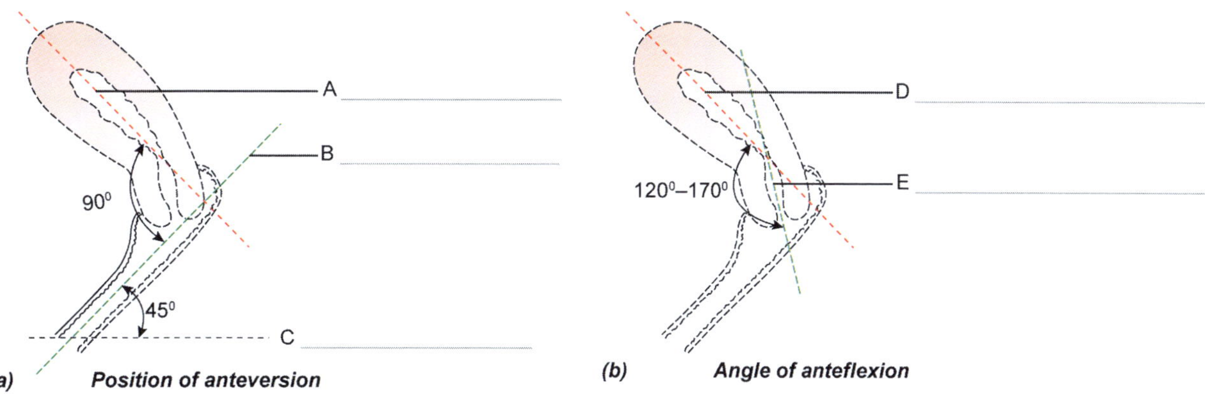

Practice Figures 31.2a and b: (a) Angulations of the uterus and vagina and their axes; (b) Angle of anteversion

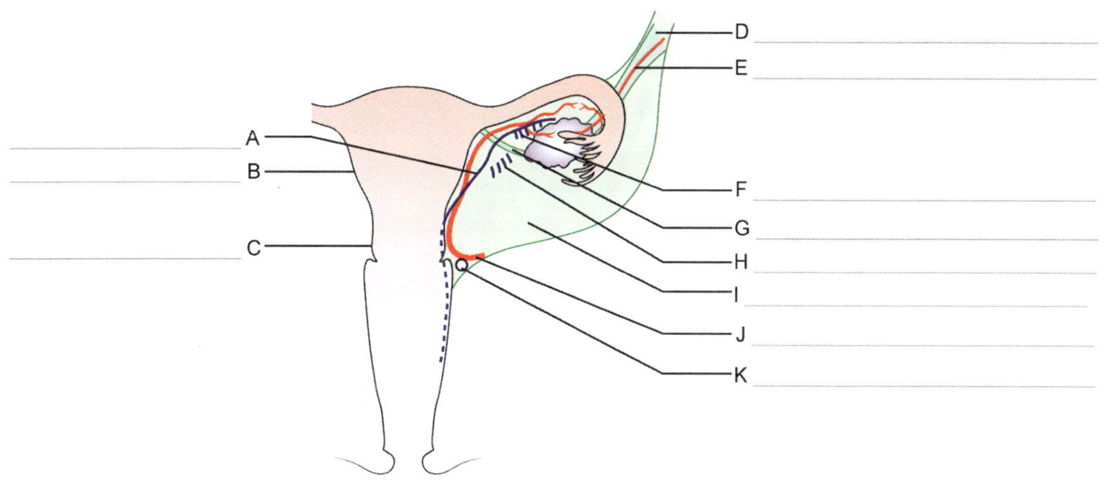

Practice Figure 31.3: Contents of the broad ligament (posterosuperior view of the right broad ligament of the uterus)

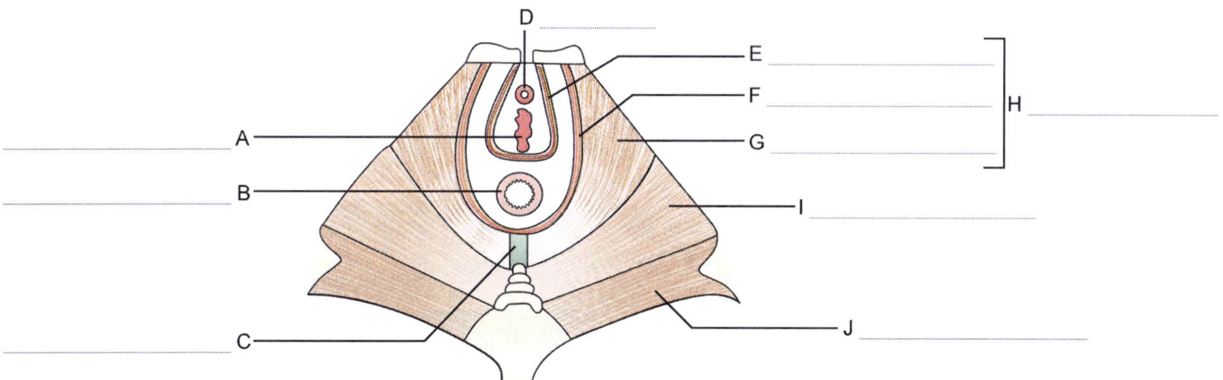

Practice Figure 31.4: Superior view of the pelvic diaphragm (the levator ani and coccygeus)

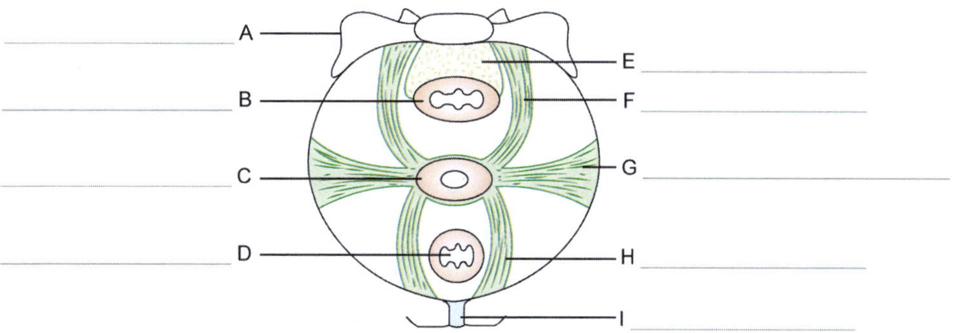

Practice Figure 31.5: Ligamentous (fibromuscular) supports of the uterus (superior view)

MULTIPLE CHOICE QUESTIONS

(Tick the single best correct option)

1. Right ovarian vein drains into ___________.
   a. Inferior vena cava
   b. Right renal vein
   c. Common iliac vein
   d. External iliac vein
2. Which of the following structure secretes progesterone ___________.
   a. Corpus albicans
   b. Corpus haemorrhagicus
   c. Corpus luteum
   d. Zona pellucida
3. From the image shown below the posterior boundary of ovarian fossa is formed by:

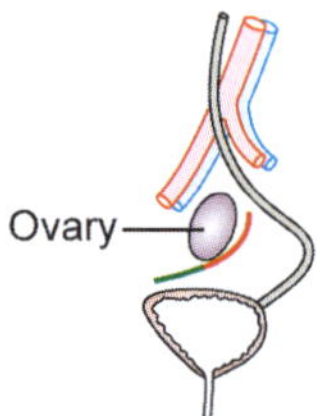

   a. Obliterated umbilical artery.
   b. Ureter and the internal iliac artery
   c. Uterine tubes
   d. Obturator nerve and vessels
4. A 22-year-old woman presented to the emergency department with a sudden onset of severe, right lower abdominal pain for the past 6 hours and has also reported nausea and vomiting. No history of fever. On examination, she has tenderness in the right lower quadrant. Ultrasound reveals an enlarged right ovary with decreased blood flow on Doppler imaging. What is the likely diagnosis?
   a. Appendicitis
   b. Ovarian torsion
   c. Ectopic pregnancy
   d. Pelvic inflammatory disease
5. Name the structure marked by X.

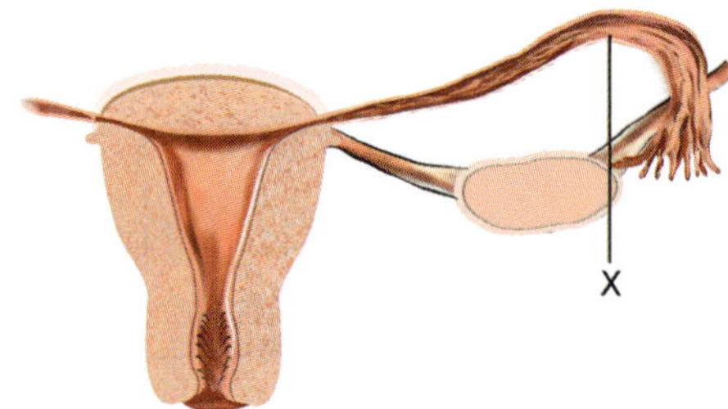

   a. Ampulla
   b. Infundibulum
   c. Isthmus
   d. Intramural part
6. What is the procedure performed in the image shown below.

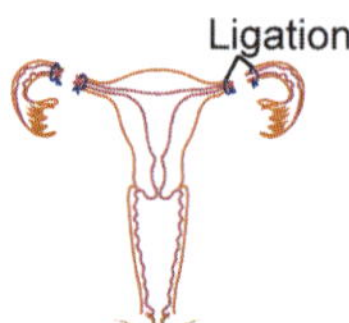

   a. Tubectomy b. Hysteroscopy
   c. Salpingogram d. Colposcopy
7. What is the angle formed in the image shown below?

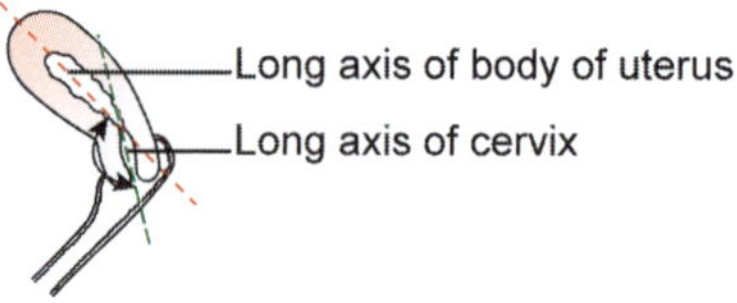

   a. Angle of anteflexion
   b. Angle of anteversion
   c. Reflex angle
   d. Angle of inclination
8. All of the following are contents of the broad ligament of the uterus, EXCEPT:
   a. Uterine tube
   b. Round ligament of uterus
   c. Ovarian artery
   d. Suspensory ligament of ovary
9. Fallopian tubes are lined by which type of epithelium
   a. Simple ciliated columnar epithelium
   b. Stratified columnar epithelium
   c. Pseudostratified ciliated columnar epithelium
   d. Stratified squamous epithelium
10. Identify the structure marked as X.

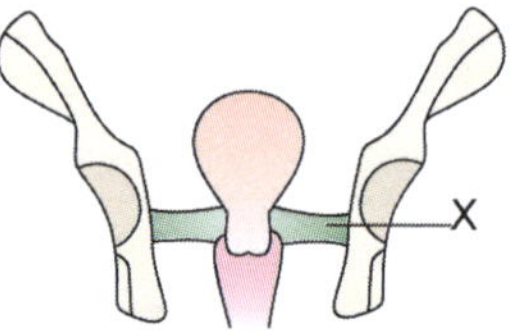

   a. Round ligament b. Cardinal ligament
   c. Uterosacral ligaments d. Broad ligament

QUESTION BANK

(Use separate copy to solve the following questions)

Q 1. Describe the uterus under the following headings: Parts, relations, supports, blood supply, nerve supply and applied aspects.

Q 2. Write a short note on:
   a. Fallopian tube
   b. Broad ligament
   c. Ovary
   d. Uterine prolapse

Chapter

32

Male Internal Genital Organs

eSmartQuiz

CLINICOANATOMICAL PROBLEMS

Clinical Case 1

A 60-year-old male presented with lower urinary tract symptoms, including urinary frequency, urgency and hesitancy. Digital rectal examination revealed a palpable, symmetrically enlarged prostate gland with a smooth surface, consistent with ***benign hypertrophy of prostate (BHP)***. Further evaluation, including serum prostate-specific antigen (PSA) levels and imaging studies, ruled out prostate carcinoma.

1. What is benign hypertrophy of prostate?
2. Which part of the prostate commonly gets involved in BHP?
3. Why there is urinary hesitancy in BHP?
4. Name the two capsules of prostate.

Explanation

1.

2.

3.

4.

Clinical Case 2

A 65-year-old male presented with lower back pain and difficulty in walking. He reported urinary symptoms, including hesitancy and frequency. Physical examination revealed tenderness over the lumbar spine. Imaging studies showed lytic lesions in multiple vertebral bodies. Further evaluation, including prostate-specific antigen (PSA) testing and biopsy, confirmed the diagnosis of metastatic ***prostatic carcinoma***. Management involved hormone therapy and palliative care for pain relief.

1. How do prostate cancer cells spread to lumbar vertebrae?
2. What are the other sites of metastasis (spread)?

Explanation

1.

2.

Clinical Case 3

During preoperative counselling for vasectomy as a part of family planning operation, a 40-year-old man expressed concerns about the permanence of the procedure and its impact on his sexual health. He inquired about the following concerns:

1. What is vasectomy?
2. Is vasectomy done on one or both sides?
3. How is vasectomy done?
4. Does the patient need hospitalisation?

Explanation

1.

2.

3.

4.

PRACTICE FIGURES

(Label the practice figures)

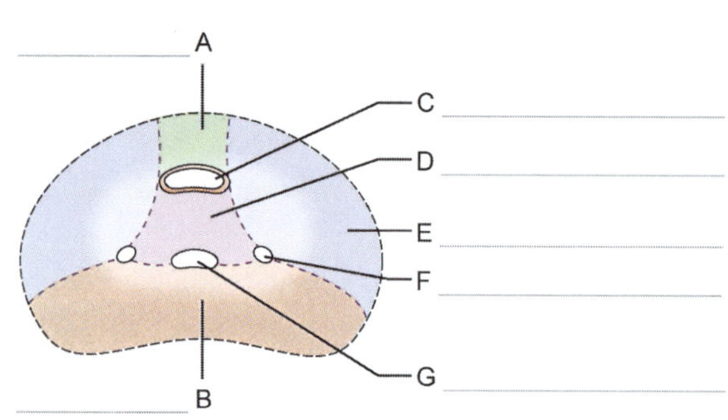

Practice Figure 32.1: Lobes of the prostate gland (transverse section)

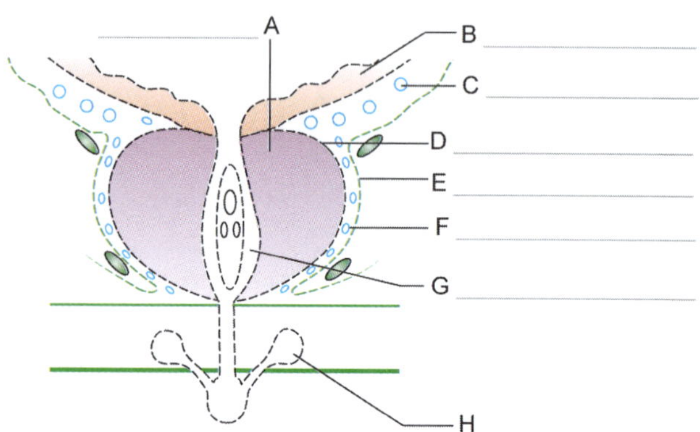

Practice Figure 32.2: Capsules, ligaments and venous plexus of the prostate gland

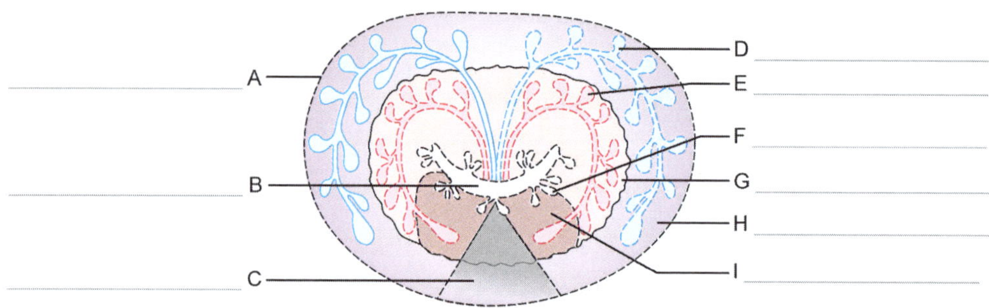

Practice Figure 32.3: Horizontal section through the prostate gland showing the histological zones and the glands in them

MULTIPLE CHOICE QUESTIONS

(Tick the single best correct option)

1. Which fascia separates the prostate from rectum posteriorly?
   a. Denonvilliers' fascia b. Buck's fascia
   c. Scarpa's fascia d. Colles' fascia
2. Pick out the correct statement about vas deferens.
   a. The ductus deferens is about 25 cm long when straightened.
   b. It runs downwards to the superficial inguinal ring and then passes behind the inguinal canal.
   c. Veins from the ductus join the vesical venous plexus which opens into the internal iliac vein.
   d. The mucosa is lined by cuboidal epithelium with stereocilia.
3. Name the structure marked by X.

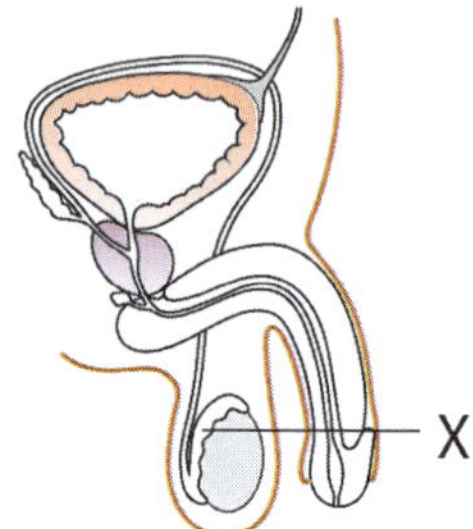

   a. Vas deferens b. Epididymis
   c. Ejaculatory duct d. Bulbourethral gland
4. Name the structure marked by X.

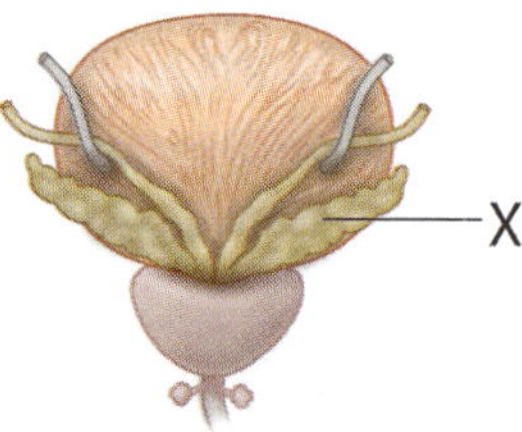

   a. Seminal vesicle
   b. Ejaculatory duct
   c. Vas deferens
   d. Bulbourethral glands
5. Identify the structure marked as X.

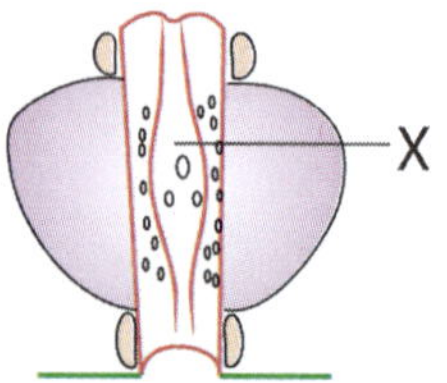

   a. Opening of ejaculatory duct
   b. Prostatic utricle
   c. Colliculus seminalis
   d. Urethral crest
6. A 54-year-old male presented to the surgical outpatient clinic with a history of frequent urination more during

night, incontinence and difficulty in starting urination. What is the most likely diagnosis?
a. Prostate cancer
b. Urinary tract infection
c. Benign prostatic hyperplasia
d. Bladder stones

7. Which lobe of prostate is most commonly affected in carcinoma?
a. Median
b. Posterior
c. Anterior
d. Lateral

8. Which structure is ligated in the procedure shown below?

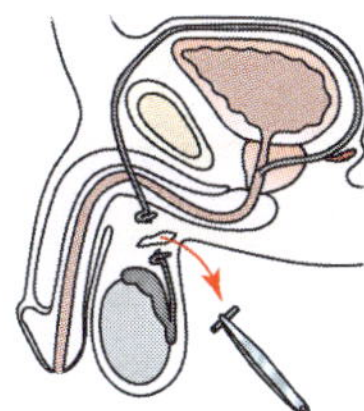

a. Ejaculatory duct
b. Bulbourethral duct
c. Ductus deferens
d. Epididymis

9. Where does the venous plexus lie in the prostate?
a. Within the false capsule
b. Outside the false capsule
c. Inside the true capsule but outside the false capsule
d. Between the true capsule and the false capsule.

10. Cowper's glands are located in ___________.
a. Superficial perineal pouch
b. Deep perineal pouch
c. Membranous urethra
d. Embedded in prostate

QUESTION BANK

(Use separate copy to solve the following questions)

Q 1. Describe the prostate gland under the following headings: Gross features, capsules, zones, lobes, supports, blood supply and nerve supply and applied aspects.

Q 2. Write a short note on:
a. Age changes in prostate
b. Vas deferens

Chapter

33

eSmartQuiz

Rectum and Anal Canal

CLINICOANATOMICAL PROBLEM

Clinical Case 1

A 35-year-old male presented with painless rectal bleeding and occasional discomfort during bowel movements. He complaint of some mass coming out of anus at the time of defaecation. Physical examination revealed ***internal haemorrhoids***.

1. What are haemorrhoids?
2. What is the difference between internal and external haemorrhoids?
3. What are the locations of the internal haemorrhoids seen on proctoscopy?

Explanation

1. __________

2. __________

3. __________

PRACTICE FIGURES

(Label the practice figures)

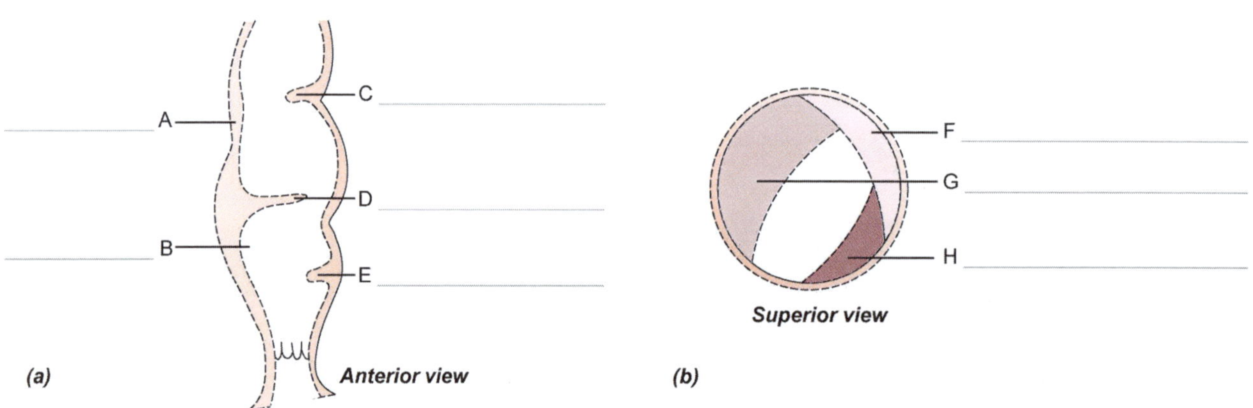

Practice Figures 33.1a and b: Superior view of the transverse mucosal folds of the rectum

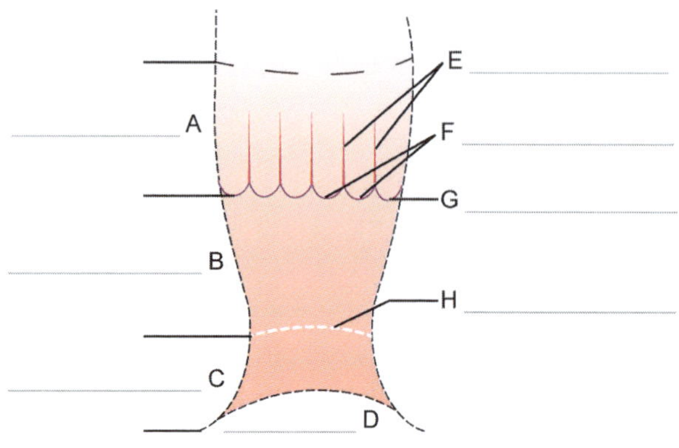

Practice Figure 33.2: Interior of the anal canal

MULTIPLE CHOICE QUESTIONS

(Tick the single best correct option)

1. Which among the following lacks the three cardinal features of the large intestine?
   a. Caecum b. Appendix
   c. Rectum d. Ascending colon
2. At which level of vertebrae does the rectum begin?
   a. S2 b. S3
   c. S4 d. S1
3. Name the structure marked by X in the following picture.

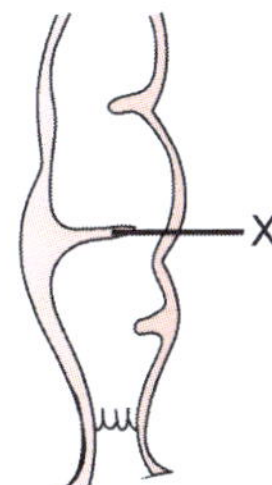

   a. Plica Fimbriata b. Houston's valves
   c. Plica Semilunaris d. Longitudinal folds
4. Which part of the rectum lacks peritoneum?
   a. Upper rectum b. Middle rectum
   c. Lower rectum d. Sigmoid colon
5. A 29-year-old female presented to the surgical clinic with complaints of difficulty in passing stools and bleeding during passing stools for the past three months. She also reports a sensation of swelling around her anus. On examination when the patient strains mass bulges out of the anus and regresses spontaneously. What is the likely diagnosis?
   a. Anal fissure b. Internal haemorrhoids
   c. Anal carcinoma d. Anal polyp
6. Identify the site marked as X in the below-shown image.

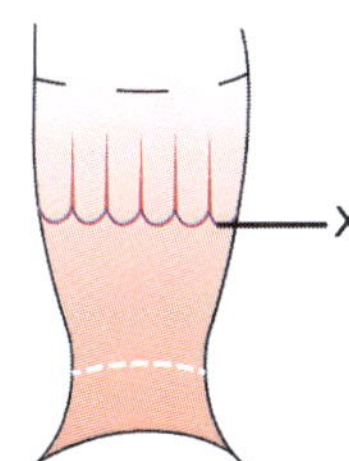

   a. Pectinate line b. Hilton's line
   c. Houston's valve d. Anal columns
7. Which group of nodes drains below the pectinate line?
   a. Superficial inguinal lymph nodes
   b. Internal iliac lymph nodes
   c. External iliac lymph nodes
   d. Inferior mesenteric lymph nodes
8. Inferior rectal artery is a branch of ___________.
   a. Internal iliac artery
   b. Inferior mesenteric artery
   c. Internal pudendal artery
   d. Inferior vesicular artery
9. State the true statement about anal canal anatomy.
   a. Below the pectinate line anal canal is supplied by superior rectal nerve
   b. Hilton's line is the lower limit of pecten or stratified squamous epithelium.
   c. Anal columns of Morgagni are temporary longitudinal mucosal folds.
   d. The anus is the surface opening of the anal canal situated about 1 cm below and in front of the tip of the coccyx.
10. Anorectal sling is formed by all of the following, EXCEPT:
   a. Puborectalis muscle
   b. External anal sphincter
   c. Internal anal sphincter
   d. Levator ani muscle

QUESTION BANK

(Use separate copy to solve the following questions)

Q 1. Describe the rectum under the following headings: Location, extent, curvatures, relations, blood supply and nerve supply lymphatic draining and applied aspects.

Q 2. Describe the anal canal under the following headings: Location, extent, relations, blood supply and nerve supply lymphatic draining and applied aspects.

Q 3. Differences above and below pectinate line of the anal canal.

Q 4. Write a short note on:
   a. Pectinate line
   b. Ischioanal fossa
   c. Hilton's line

Chapter

34

eSmartQuiz

Walls of Pelvis

CLINICOANATOMICAL PROBLEM

Clinical Case 1

A 45-year-old multiparous female presented with a sensation of pelvic pressure and bulging in the vaginal area. She reported worsening symptoms after prolonged standing and lifting heavy objects. Physical examination revealed descent of the uterus into the vaginal canal, consistent with ***uterine prolapse***. Further evaluation indicated ***damage to the pelvic diaphragm***, likely resulted from previous.

1. What is uterine prolapse?
2. Which structures form pelvic diaphragm?
3. Why is uterine prolapse common in multiparous women?

Explanation

1. ______________________________

2. ______________________________

3. ______________________________

PRACTICE FIGURES

(Label the practice figures)

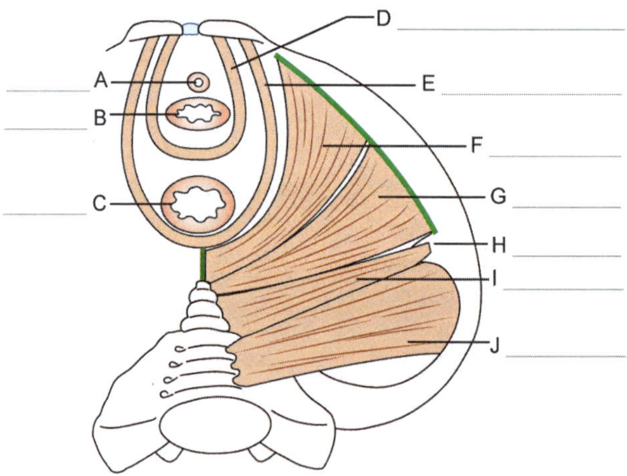

Practice Figure 34.1: Levator ani, coccygeus and piriformis muscles (in female, superior view)

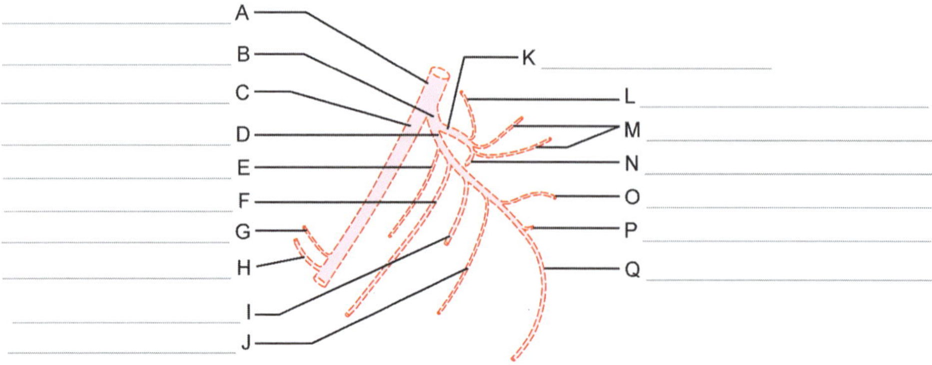

Practice Figure 34.2: Branches of the right internal iliac artery

MULTIPLE CHOICE QUESTIONS

(Tick the single best correct option)

1. All of the following are derivatives of endopelvic fascia, EXCEPT:
   a. Mackenrodt's ligament
   b. Uterosacral ligament
   c. Obturator fascia
   d. Pubourethral ligament
2. Levator ani is formed by all, EXCEPT:
   a. Pubococcygeus
   b. Iliococcygeus
   c. Pubo-analis
   d. Iliacus
3. Coccygeus originates from ___________.
   a. Ischial spine
   b. Sacral promontory
   c. Sacral foramina
   d. Coccyx
4. Which is the strongest ligament in the body?
   a. Sacrotuberous ligament
   b. Interosseous sacroiliac ligament
   c. Sacrospinous ligament
   d. Iliolumbar ligament
5. Name the muscle marked as X.

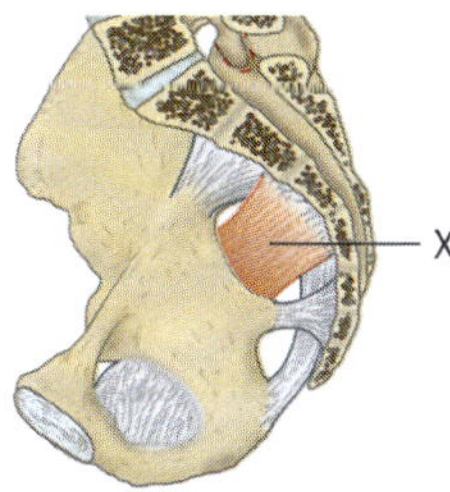

   a. Obturator internus
   b. Obturator externus
   c. Piriformis
   d. Superior gamelli
6. A 28-year-old female delivered a male baby at home. No support to the perineum was given during labour. What is the long-term complication you can expect in this case?
   a. Rupture urethra
   b. Uterine prolapse
   c. Vaginal cyst
   d. Rupture uterus
7. Internal iliac artery is a branch of ___________.
   a. Abdominal aorta
   b. Common iliac artery
   c. Femoral artery
   d. External iliac artery
8. Name the structure marked as X.

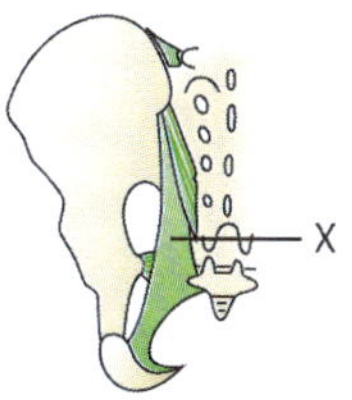

   a. Sacrospinous ligament
   b. Sacrotuberous ligament
   c. Sacroiliac ligament
   d. Iliolumbar ligament
9. Identify the muscle marked as X.

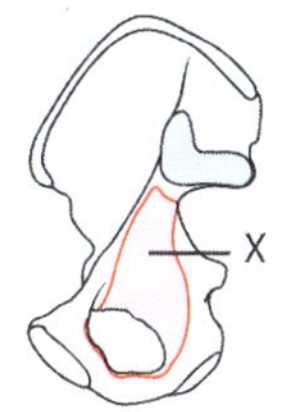

   a. Obturator internus
   b. Obturator externus
   c. Piriformis
   d. Superior gamelli
10. All of the following are branches of anterior division of internal iliac artery, EXCEPT:
    a. Middle rectal artery
    b. Superior gluteal artery
    c. Uterine artery
    d. Superior vesical artery

QUESTION BANK

(Use separate copy to solve the following question)

Q 1. Write a short note on:
   a. Pelvic diaphragm
   b. Endopelvic diaphragm
   c. Levator ani muscle
   d. Internal iliac artery
   e. Sacroiliac artery.

Chapter

35

Surface Marking of Abdomen and Pelvis

MULTIPLE CHOICE QUESTIONS

(Tick the single best correct option)

1. Identify the line marked as X.

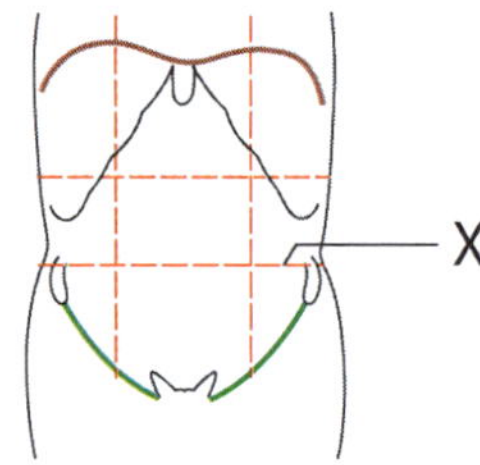

   a. Transpyloric plane b. Transtubercular plane
   c. Subcostal plane d. Right lateral plane

2. Where does the portal vein formation take place?
   a. Behind second part of duodenum
   b. At the level of gastric antrum
   c. Behind the neck of pancreas
   d. Near ampulla of Vater

3. From the below-shown image, where does the fundus of the gallbladder lie?

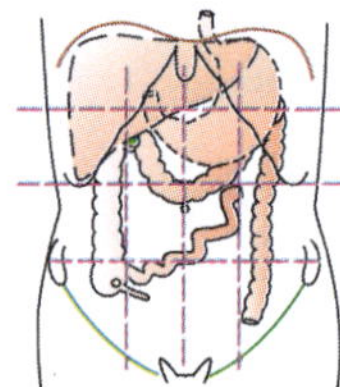

   a. Tip of the right 8th costal cartilage
   b. Tip of the right 9th costal cartilage
   c. Tip of the 10th right costal cartilage
   d. Tip of the 11th costal cartilage

4. What is the surface marking of the superficial inguinal ring?

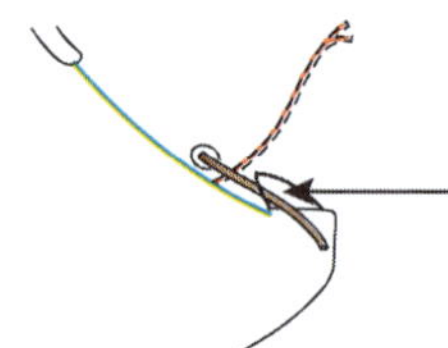

   a. Lies above and lateral to the pubic crest
   b. Lies below and medial to the pubic crest
   c. Lies above and medial to the pubic tubercle
   d. Lies below and lateral to the pubic tubercle

5. A 50-year-old male was admitted with chest pain, he was scheduled for a coronary angiogram. Where does the cardiologist pass the catheter?
   a. Midpoint of the inguinal ligament
   b. Midinguinal point
   c. Above the midinguinal point
   d. Lateral to the pubic crest.

6. Identify the vessel marked as X in the following image.

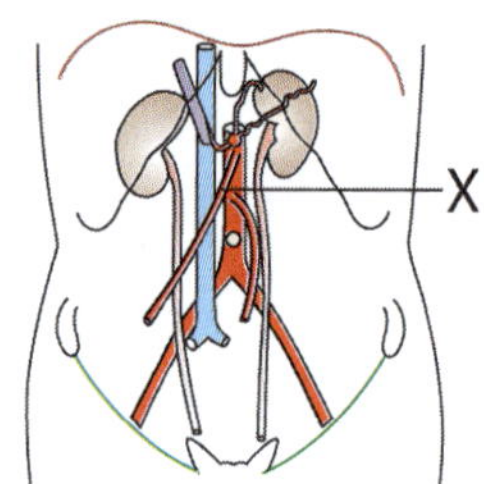

   a. Inferior mesenteric artery
   b. Coeliac artery
   c. Common iliac artery
   d. Superior mesenteric artery

7. The root of mesentery ____________.
   a. Extends from the falciform ligament spleen
   b. Extends from the duodenojejunal flexure to the junction between transtubercular planes
   c. Extends from the pancreas to the transtubercular plane
   d. Extends from the gastrosplenic ligament to the colon

8. Morrison's parallelogram is drawn for which of the following organs?
   a. Kidney b. Spleen
   c. Liver d. Pancreas

9. Which of the following statements is true about the point marked as X in the below diagram?

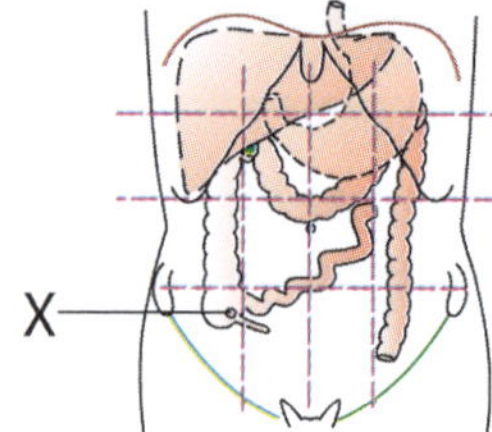

   a. The midpoint between the umbilicus and the xiphoid process
   b. The intersection of the midclavicular line and the umbilical line
   c. It is one-third of the distance from the anterior superior iliac spine to the umbilicus
   d. The lateral border of the rectus abdominis muscle.

10. Kidneys lie at which vertebral level?
   a. T10–L1 vertebral levels b. T12–L3 vertebral levels
   c. L1–L4 vertebral levels d. T12–L2 vertebral levels

Chapter 36

Radiological and Imaging Procedures

eSmartQuiz

PRACTICE FIGURES

(Label the practice figures)

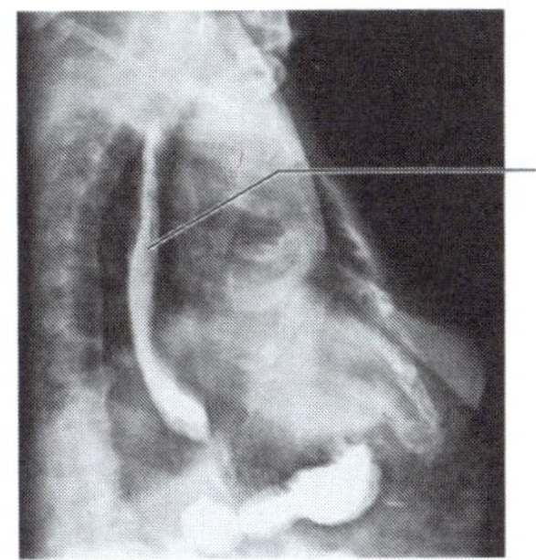

Practice Figure 36.1: Barium swallow

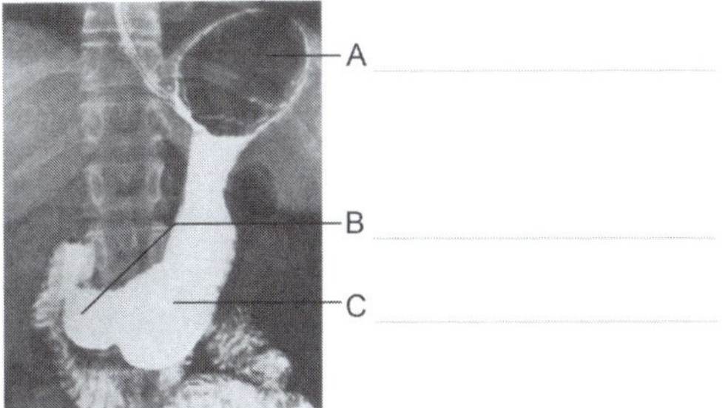

Practice Figure 36.2: Barium meal follow through

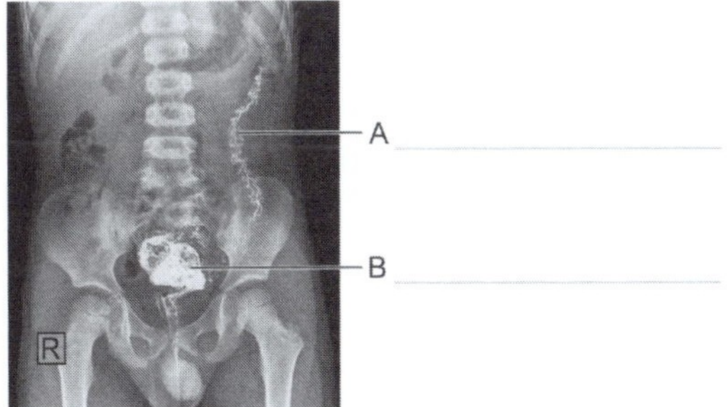

Practice Figure 36.3: Barium enema

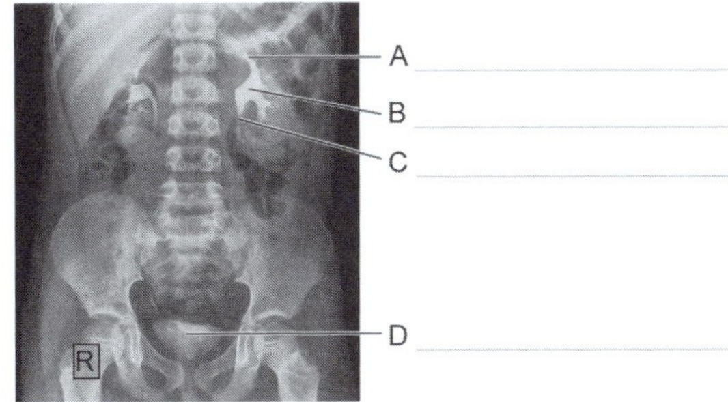

Practice Figure 36.4: Intravenous pyelogram

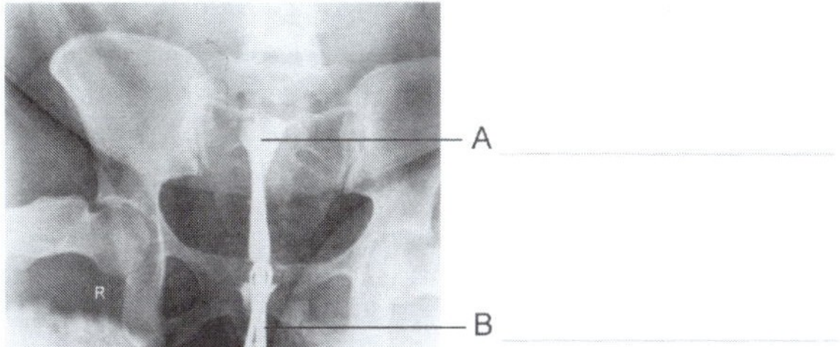

Practice Figure 36.5: Hysterosalpingogram

MULTIPLE CHOICE QUESTIONS

(Tick the single best correct option)

1. What investigation is shown in the image?

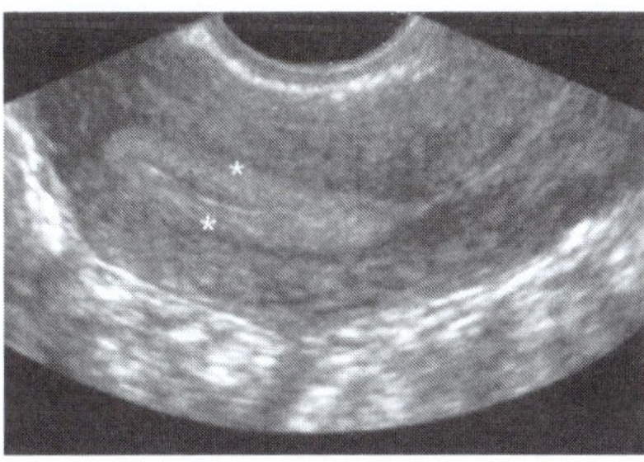

   a. Computerised tomography
   b. Ultrasonogram
   c. MRI scan
   d. X-ray

2. Pick out the incorrect statement about the barium studies.
   a. The beginning of the first part of duodenum shows a duodenal cap.
   b. It is a harmful substance to use in malabsorption syndrome patients.
   c. Barium is radio-opaque because of its high molecular weight.
   d. 50% suspension of barium sulphate is to be swallowed during the study.

3. Which vertebral level shows all of the marked structures?

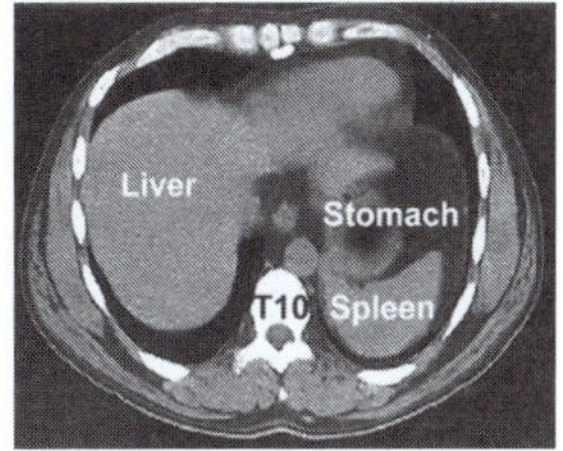

   a. T8 b. T9
   c. T10 d. T11

4. Name the procedure performed in the below image.

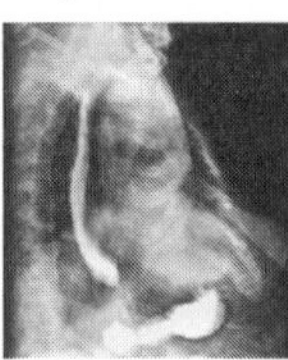

a. Barium enema
b. Barium follow through
c. Barium meal
d. Barium swallow

5. A 63-year-old patient presents with a history of change in bowel habits, occasional rectal bleeding and generalised abdominal pain. On examination patient has tenderness in the left lower quadrant. What is the further investigation we can do on this patient?
a. X-ray abdomen
b. CT scan with oral contrast
c. Barium enema
d. Upper gastroendoscopy

6. All of the following organs are visualised by CT scan at the level of L1 vertebrae, EXCEPT:
a. Stomach　b. Gallbladder
c. Spleen　d. Liver

7. Which is the investigation of choice for gallbladder pathology?
a. CT scan　b. MRI scan
c. Ultrasonography　d. Plain skiagram

8. What procedure is performed in the below image?

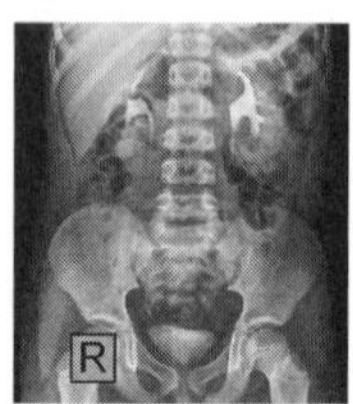

a. Intravenous pyelogram
b. Fluoroscopy
c. Retrograde pyelography
d. Hysterosalpingography

9. Hysterosalpingography is usually done to determine ____________.
a. Volume of endometrial cavity
b. Patency of the uterine tubes
c. Vaginal wall thickness
d. Length of the cervical canal

10. Which part of the stomach shows a gas bubble in the below image?

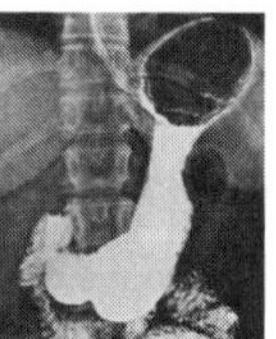

a. Pylorus　b. Antrum
c. Body　d. Fundus

Spotters in Lower Limb, Abdomen and Pelvis

Answer the Questions for the given Spotters or Objective Structured Practical Examination (OSPE).

Note: The purpose of the spotters given here is to orient the students for the practical examination pattern. However, numerous other questions may come for spotters as well. For bone, side determination is important. For muscles, nerve supply and actions are important. For arteries and nerves, their branches are important for spotter examination.

Spotter 1

a. Name the two structures attached to the part of the bone marked green.

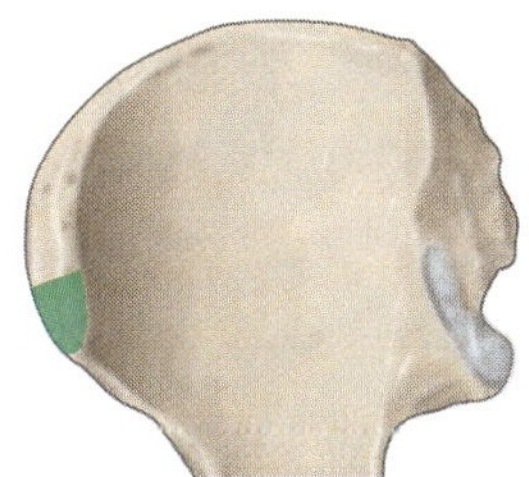

(*Other possible spotters*: Attachments of iliacus, pubic tubercle, anterior inferior iliac spine, ischial spine, ischial tuberosity)

Spotter 2

a. Name the structure attached to the part of the bone marked green.
b. What is its nerve supply?

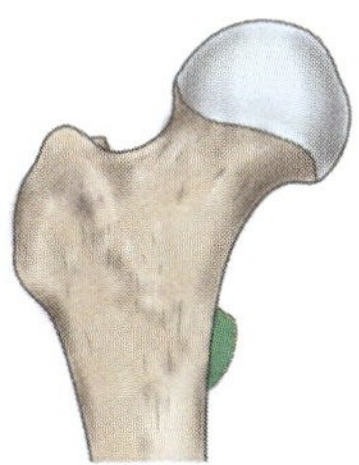

(*Other possible spotters*: Side identification, attachments of the greater trochanter, adductor tubercle, gluteal tuberosity, popliteus. For patella: Side identification, attachments)

Spotter 3

a. Name the structure attached to the part of the bone marked green.
b. What is its action?

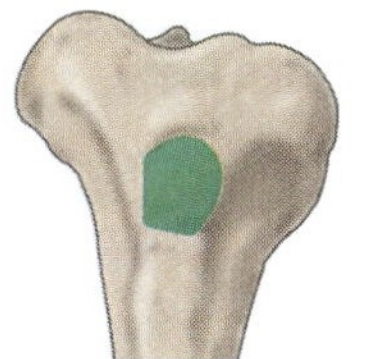

(*Other possible spotters*: Tibia: Side determination, attachments of soleal line, popliteus, relations of the lower end and medial malleolus. Fibula: side determination, attachments of head, relations of malleolus)

Spotter 4

a. Name the part of the bone marked green.
b. Name the tendon passing below it.

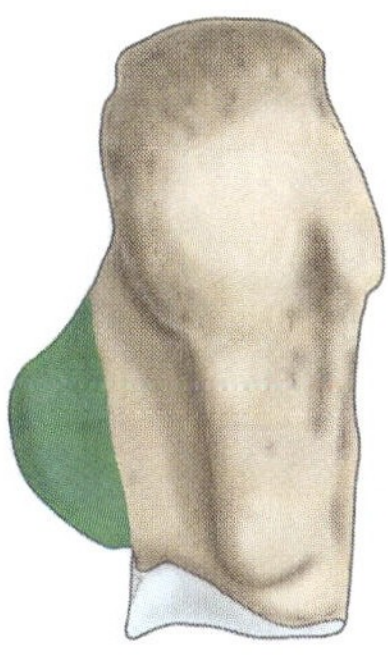

(*Other possible spotters*: Attachments of calcaneal tubercles, navicular, tibialis anterior, tibialis posterior, relations of groove of the cuboid)

Spotter 5

a. Identify the muscle marked with X.
b. Name its nerve supply.

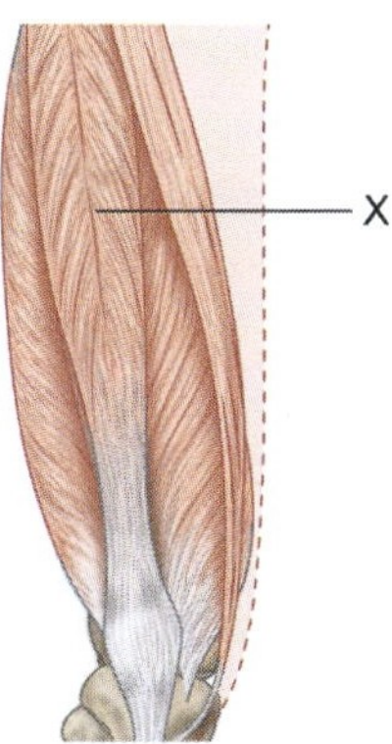

(*Other possible spotters*: Sartorius, vastus medialis and lateralis, femoral nerve, femoral artery, adductor muscles, tendocalcaneus)

Spotter 6

a. Identify the muscle marked with X.
b. Name its nerve supply.

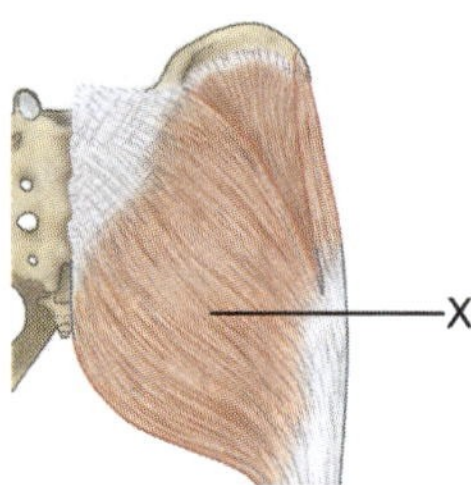

(*Other possible spotters*: Gluteus medius, gluteus minimus, sciatic nerve, pyriformis, semitendinosus, semimembranosus, biceps femoris, tibial nerve, popliteal artery)

Spotter 7

a. Identify the structure marked with X.
b. Write its actions.

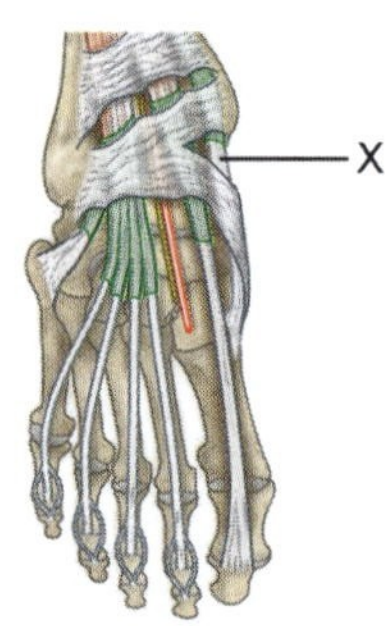

(*Other possible spotters*: Extensor hallucis longus, peroneus tertius, anterior tibial artery, dorsalis pedis artery, deep peroneal nerve)

Spotter 8

a. Name the nerve supplying the area marked with X.
b. What is the effect of its injury on foot.

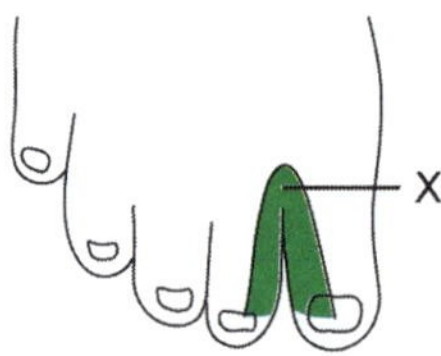

Spotter 9

a. Identify the structure marked with X.
b. Write its actions.

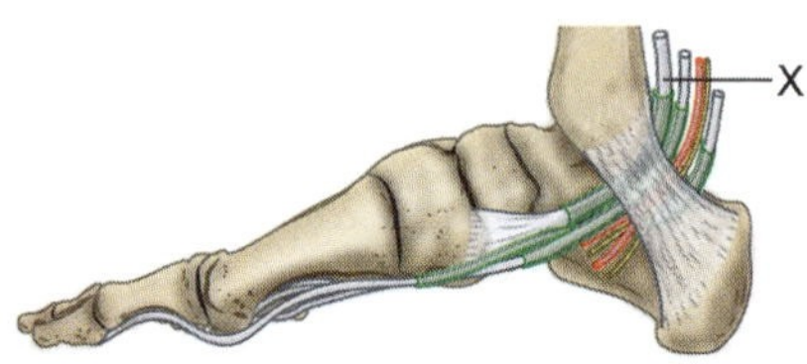

(*Other possible spotter*: Soleus, gastrocnemius, plantaris, tibial nerve, posterior tibial artery, long and short saphenous veins)

Spotter 10

a. Identify the structure marked with X.
b. What is its nerve supply?

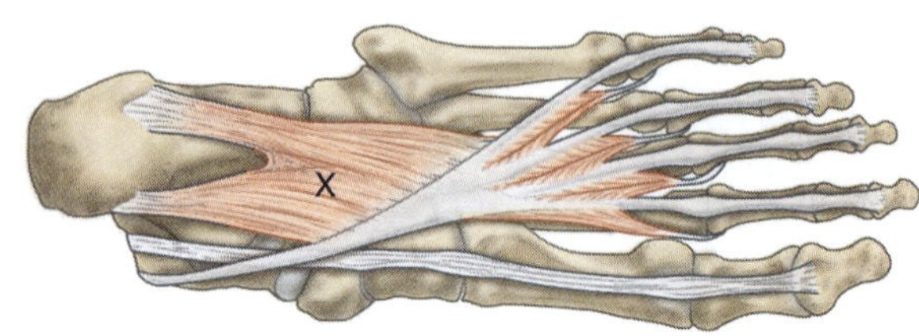

(*Other possible spotters*: Muscles of all layers of sole, medial and lateral plantar arteries and nerves)

Spotter 11

a. Identify the part of the bone marked green.
b. Name the structures related to it.

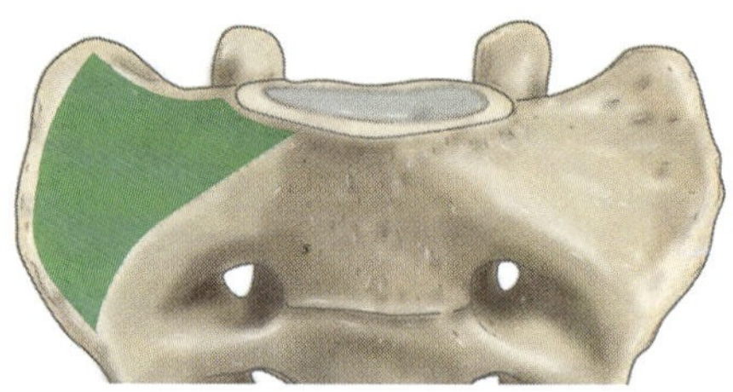

(*Other possible spotters*: Sacrum: The origin of pyriformis, relations of anterior surface, sacral hiatus, sex determination. Lumbar vertebra: identification, 5th lumbar vertebra identification, Pelvis: sex determination)

Spotter 12

a. Identify the muscle.
b. Name its nerve supply.

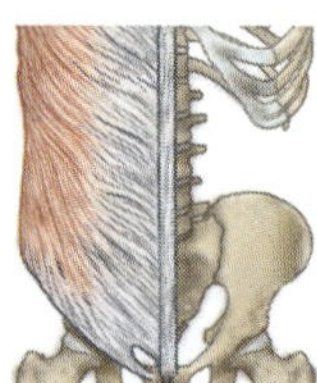

(*Other possible spotters*: Internal oblique, transverse abdominis rectus abdominis, rectus sheath, inguinal canal, spermatic cord)

Spotter 13

a. Identify the viscera marked with X.
b. Name its coverings.

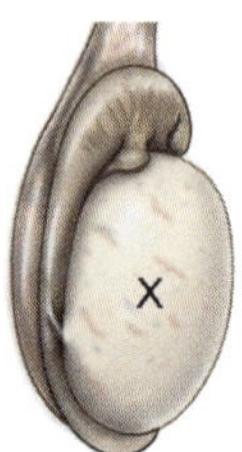

(*Other possible spotters*: Epididymis, side determination)

Spotter 14

a. Identify the viscera.
b. Name its parts.

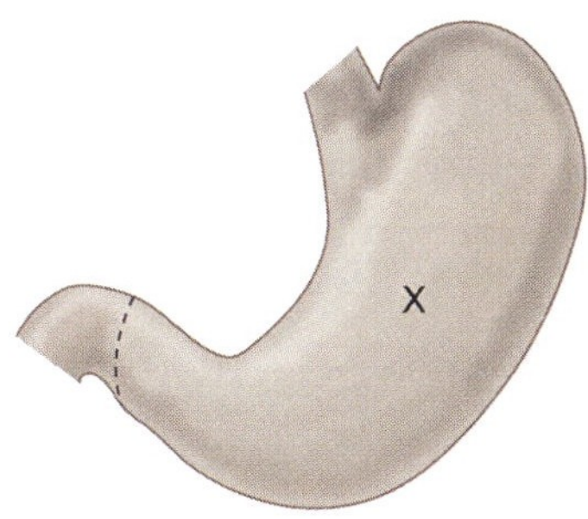

(*Other possible spotters*: Interior of stomach, blood supply, nerve supply of stomach, attachments of greater and lesser curvatures)

Spotter 15

a. Identify the part of the viscera marked with X.
b. Name the structures opening in it.

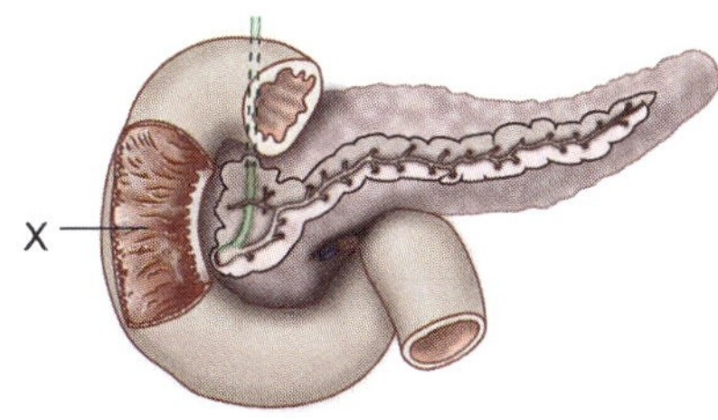

(*Other possible spotters*: Difference between small intestine and large intestine, appendix: position and blood supply, caecum. Abdominal aorta and its branches, inferior vena cava and its tributaries, portal vein)

Spotter 16

a. Identify the viscera.
b. Name its parts.

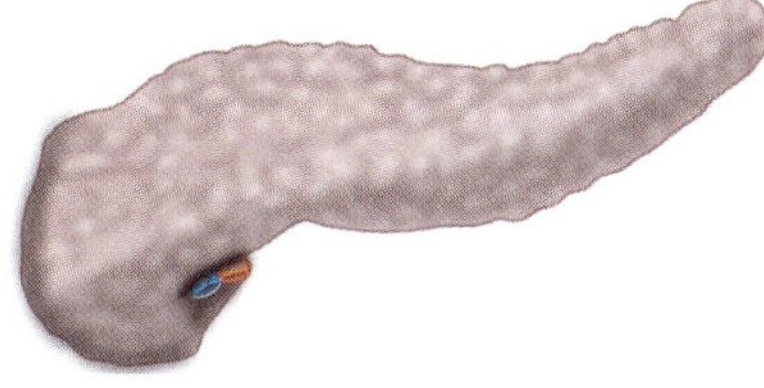

(*Other possible spotters*: Blood supply, ducts and their openings)

Spotter 17

a. Identify the area marked with X.
b. Write its boundaries.

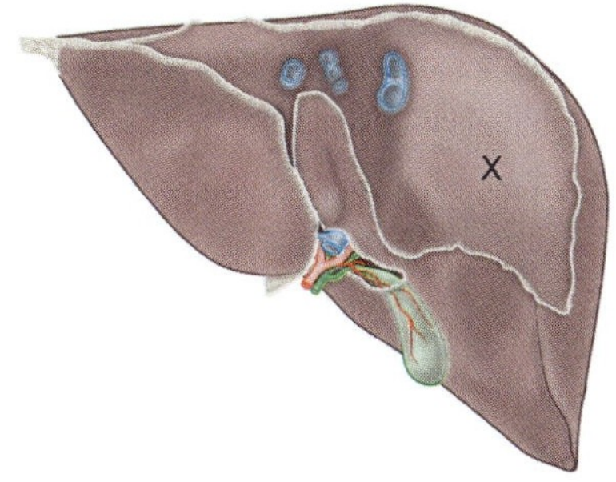

(*Other possible spotters*: Live: Caudate and quadrate lobes. Fissure for ligamentum venosus, ligamentum teres, porta hepatis. Gallbladder: Capacity, blood supply. Pancreas: Parts, ducts. Spleen: Visceral relations, blood supply)

Spotter 18

a. Identify the area marked with X.
b. Name the structures passing through its hilus.

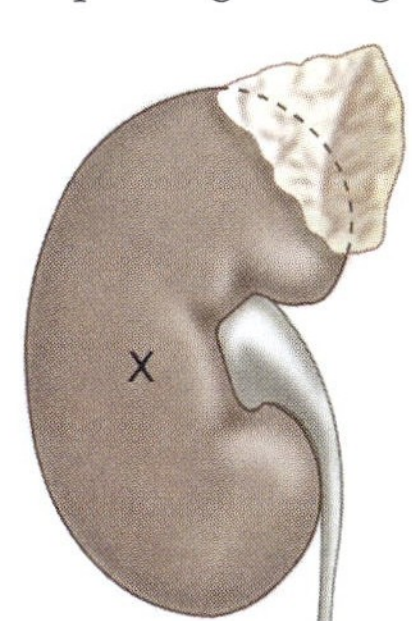

(*Other possible spotters*: Relations, blood supply, vascular segments. Ureter: constrictions, blood supply. Suprarenal glands: Relations, blood supply, functions. Diaphragm: Openings, structures passing, vertebral levels)

Spotter 19

Identify the area marked with X and Y.

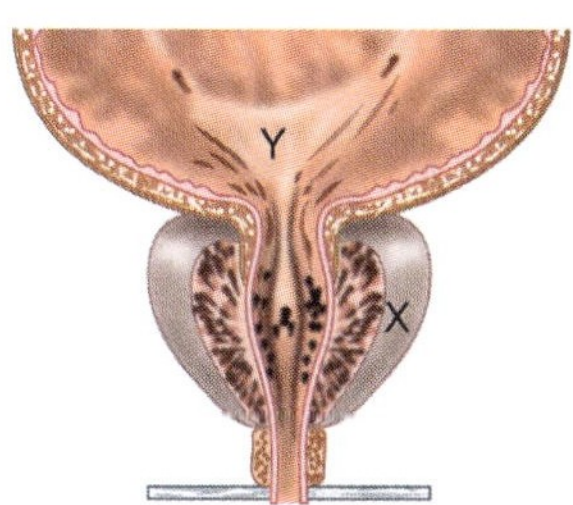

(*Other possible spotters*: Parts of male urethra, lobes of prostate, capsules of prostate, openings of ureters)

Spotter 20

a. Identify the area marked with X.
b. Name its any two contents.

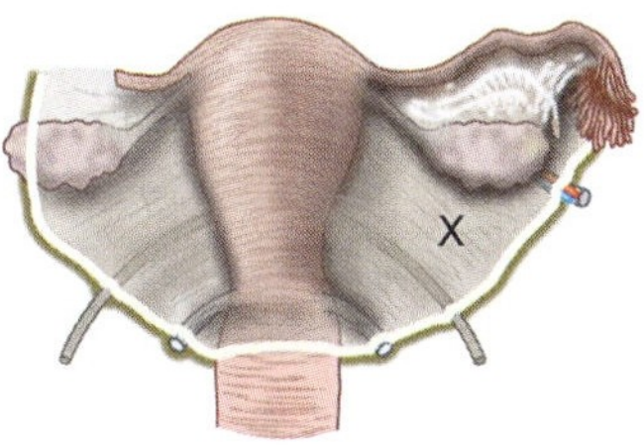

(*Other possible spotters*: Ovary, uterus: Blood supply and supports, cervix, fallopian tube and its parts, fornix of vagina)

Answers

LOWER LIMB

Chapter 1

Key to MCQs

1. b 2. a 3. c 4. d 5. d 6. c 7. b
8. b 9. d 10. b

Chapter 2

Key to Clinicoanatomical Problems

Clinical Case 1

1. Fractures are common in elderly females due to age-related factors such as osteoporosis, decreased bone density, and increased risk of falls.
2. Shenton's line, formed by the medial border of the femoral neck and the inferomedial border of the superior pubic ramus, is a reference line used to assess hip joint integrity on plain radiographs.
3. Avascular necrosis of the femur occurs as the femoral head receives its blood supply primarily from the medial circumflex femoral artery through the retinacular arteries.

Clinical Case 2

Anatomical basis for:

a. In children, osteomyelitis commonly occurs due to the spread of bacteria from nearby soft tissues or skin wounds. In typical young bones, due to hairpin bends of arteries in the metaphysis, circulating bacteria get trapped, resulting in osteomyelitis.
b. The upper end of the tibia is vulnerable due to its thinner cortex and less soft tissue coverage, making it prone to trauma and infection.
c. In adult long bones, the absence of hairpin bends in arteries at the metaphysis reduces susceptibility to infection, making osteomyelitis less common than in children.

Key to Practice Figures

Practice Figure 2.1

A. Latissimus dorsi, B. Gluteus medius, C. Gluteus maximus, D. Gluteus minimus, E. Semimembranosus, F. Semitendinosus + long head of biceps femoris, G. Internal oblique, H. External oblique, I. Iliotibial tract, J. Tensor fascia lata, K. Inguinal ligament, L. Sartorius, M. Straight the head of rectus femoris, N. Reflected head of rectus femoris, O. Pectineus, P. Inguinal ligament, Q. Adductor longus, R. Adductor brevis, S. Gracilis, T. Obturator externus, U. Adductor magnus

Practice Figure 2.2

A. Transverse abdominis, B. Internal oblique, C. Inguinal ligament, D. Sartorius, E. Straight head of rectus femoris, F. Quadratus lumborum, G. Erector spinae, H. Interosseous sacroiliac ligaments, I. Sacrospinous ligament, J. Obturator internus

Practice Figure 2.3

A. Piriformis, B. Gluteus minimus, C. Vastus lateralis, D. Vastus medialis, E. Psoas major, F. Vastus intermedius, G. Adductor magnus, H. Obturator internus and gemelli, I. Obturator externus, J. Psoas major, K. Iliacus, L. Pectineus, M. Vastus medialis, N. Adductor longus, O. Adductor brevis, P. Adductor magnus, Q. Medial head of gastrocnemius, R. Gluteus medius, S. Quadratus femoris, T. Vastus lateralis, U. Gluteus maximus, V. Biceps femoris (short head), W. Plantaris, X. Lateral head of gastrocnemius, Y. Anterior cruciate ligament, Z. Posterior cruciate ligament

Practice Figure 2.4

A. Iliotibial tract, B. Ligamentum patellae, C. Tibialis anterior, D. Deep infrapatellar bursa, E. Sartorius, F. Gracilis, G. Semitendinosus

Practice Figure 2.5

A. Semimembranosus, B. Popliteus, C. Soleus, D. Tibialis posterior, E. Flexor digitorum longus

Key to MCQs

1. b 2. a 3. c 4. c 5. a 6. b 7. b
8. c 9. b 10. a 11. c 12. b 13. c 14. c
15. c 16. c

Chapter 3

Key to Clinicoanatomical Problem

Clinical Case 1

1. The femoral hernia is located below and lateral to the pubic tubercle.
2. Femoral hernia enters the thigh through the femoral ring and femoral canal.
3. The direction of femoral hernia is downward, forward, and upward.
4. The swelling is the femoral hernia that appears at saphenous opening when she coughs due to raised intra-abdominal pressure.
5. The femoral hernia is more common in females due to wider pelvis, larger femoral canal and smaller femoral vessels.

Key to Practice Figures

Practice Figure 3.1

A. Iliacus, B. Psoas major tendon, C. Pectineus, D. Adductor longus, E. Lateral cutaneous nerve of thigh, F. Profunda femoris artery, G. Sartorius, H. Femoral nerve, I. Femoral branch of genitofemoral nerve, J. Deep inguinal lymph nodes, K. Great saphenous vein, L. Femoral artery, M. Femoral vein, N. Adductor longus

Practice Figure 3.2

A. Tensor fasciae latae, B. Rectus femoris, C. Vastus lateralis, D. Ligamentum patellae, E. Iliacus, F. Tendon of psoas major, G. Pectineus, H. Adductor longus, I. Gracilis, J. Adductor magnus, K. Sartorius, L. Vastus medialis

Practice Figure 3.3

A. Iliacus, B. Main trunk, C. Posterior division, D. Hip joint, E. Rectus femoris, F. Vastus lateralis, G. Vastus medialis, H. Vastus intermedius, I. Articularis genu, J. Saphenous nerve, K. Knee joint, L. Pectineus, M. Anterior division, N. Satorius, O. Intermediate and Medial cutaneous nerves of thigh

Practice Figure 3.4

A. Femoral artery, B. Femoral branch of genitofemoral nerve, C. Femoral sheath, D. Lymph node, E. Femoral vein

Practice Figure 3.5

A. Nerve to vastus medialis, B. Branches of anterior and posterior divisions of obturator nerve, C. Vastus medialis, D. Saphenous nerve, E. Sartoris, F. Subsartorial fascia, G. Subsartorial nerve plexus, H. Femoral artery, I. Femoral vein, J. Adductor longus

Key to MCQs

1. a 2. b 3. b 4. b 5. c 6. c 7. d
8. c 9. c 10. d 11. c 12. d 13. b 14. b

Chapter 4

Key to Clinicoanatomical Problem

Clinical Case 1

1. Knee joint — branches from the femoral, obturator, and sciatic nerves.
2. Hip joint — branches of the femoral nerve, obturator nerve, and accessory obturator nerve.
3. Both the knee and hip joints are supplied by the femoral and obturator nerves.
4. The development of hip pain in this case could be attributed to referred pain due to common segmental supply by two nerves: Femoral nerve (L2–L4) and obturator nerve (L2–L4).

Key to Practice Figures

Practice Figures 4.1

A. Adductor longus, B. Shaft of femur, C. Condyles of femur, D. Condyles of tibia, E. Pectineus, F. Gracilis, G. Adductor part of adductor magnus, H. Hamstring part of adductor magnus

Practice Figure 4.2

A. Obturator nerve, B. Posterior division, C. Obturator externus, D. Adductor brevis, E. Adductor magnus, F. Genicular branch (to cruciate ligament, knee joint), G. Obturator foramen, H. Anterior division, I. Hip joint, J. Pectineus, K. Adductor longus, L. Gracilis, M. To subsartorial plexus

Key to MCQs

1. b 2. d 3. b 4. a 5. b 6. d 7. c
8. b 9. d 10. c 11. a 12. b

Chapter 5

Key to Clinicoanatomical Problems

Clinical Case 1

1. Gluteus medius, gluteus minimus, and tensor fasciae latae
2. Trendelenburg's sign: Normally, when the foot is off the ground, the tilting of the pelvis on that side is prevented by the contraction of gluteus medius and minimus of the opposite side. In case of paralysis of these muscles, the pelvis sags on the opposite healthy side if that foot is off the ground. It occurred due to injury to the superior gluteal nerve in this case.

Clinical Case 2

1. Upper lateral quadrant of the gluteal region.
2. To avoid injury to the sciatic nerve, which lies in the lower and medial quadrants.

Key to Practice Figures

Practice Figure 5.1

A. Gluteus maximus, B. Superior gluteal artery and nerve, C. Piriformis, D. Inferior gluteal artery and nerve, E. Obturator internus with gamelli, F. Posterior cutaneous nerve of thigh, G. Sciatic nerve, H. Biceps femoris, I. Deep fascia, J. Gluteus medius, K. Tensor fascia latae, L. Gluteus minimus, M. Rectus femoris, N. Obturator externus, O. Nerve to quadratus femoris, P. Quadratus femoris, Q. Adductor magnus

Practice Figure 5.2

A. Tensor fascia lata, B. Gluteus maximus, C. Gluteal tuberosity, D. Iliotibial tract

Key to MCQs

1. c 2. b 3. c 4. a 5. b 6. d 7. c
8. c 9. a 10. c 11. a 12. a 13. a

Chapter 6

Key to Clinicoanatomical Problems

Clinical Case 1

1. Femoral artery, popliteal artery, dorsalis pedis artery, and posterior tibial artery.
2. A blood pressure cuff is then wrapped around the thigh just above the knee, and the popliteal artery is auscultated over the popliteal fossa. The cuff is inflated and then slowly deflated, and the pressure is recorded based on auscultatory sounds.
3. Coarctation (narrowing) of the aorta restricts blood flow to the lower body, resulting in decreased blood pressure and pulses in the lower extremities compared to the upper extremities.

Clinical Case 2

1. Aneurysm is a localised dilation of an artery due to weakening of the vessel wall.
2. Smoking might have triggered atherosclerosis.
3. Pulsatile swelling indicates swelling arising from the popliteal artery or any other swelling overlying the artery.
4. Aneurysm of the popliteal artery, Baker's cyst, lymphadenopathy, malignancies.
5. The popliteal aneurysms typically present as pulsatile midline masses, while Baker's cysts are cystic and located on the medial side of the popliteal fossa.

Key to Practice Figures

Practice Figure 6.1

A. Posterior cutaneous nerve of thigh, B. Short saphenous vein, C. Sural communicating nerve, D. Posterior division of medial cutaneous nerve of thigh, E. Semimembranosus, F. Semitendinosus, G. Medial head of gastrocnemius, H. Biceps femoris, I. Popliteal fossa, J. Plantaris, K. Lateral head of gastrocnemius

Practice Figure 6.2

A. Semimembranosus, B. Popliteal surface of femur, C. Oblique popliteal ligament, D. Capsule of knee joint, E. Fascia covering popliteus

Practice Figure 6.3

A. Common peroneal nerve, B. Tibial nerve, C. Popliteal artery, D. Popliteal vein

Practice Figure 6.4

A. Tibial nerve, B. Medial head of gastrocnemius, C. Genicular branches, D. Soleus, E. Tibialis posterior, F. Flexor digitorum longus, G. Flexor hallucis longus, H. Medial plantar nerve, I. Plantaris, J. Lateral head of gastrocnemius, K. Popliteus, L. Superior tibiofibular joint, M. Sural nerve, N. Lateral plantar nerve

Key to MCQs

1. d 2. c 3. b 4. d 5. c 6. d 7. b
8. c 9. c 10. b 11. a 12. c 13. c 14. d
15. c

Chapter 7

Key to Clinicoanatomical Problems

Clinical Case 1

1. Sciatic nerve
2. L4 to S3
3. During the straight leg raising test (Lasegue's sign), the patient lies on their back, and the examiner lifts the patient's straightened leg while keeping the knee extended. If pain is elicited in the lower back or down the back of the leg, particularly below the knee, it suggests irritation or compression of the sciatic nerve, indicating a positive test result.

4. Increased pain during the straight leg raising test occurs due to stretching of the sciatic nerve, exacerbating the existing irritation or compression, leading to radiating pain down the back of the leg.

Key to Practice Figures

Practice Figure 7.1

A. Adductor magnus, B. Long head of biceps femoris, C. Short head of biceps femoris, D. Semitendinosus, E. Semimembranosus

Practice Figure 7.2

A. Tibial part, B. Semitendinosus, C. Semimembranosus, D. Long head of biceps femoris, E. Hamstring part of adductor magnus, F. Tibial nerve, G. Sciatic nerve, H. Common peroneal part, I. Short head of biceps femoris, J. Common peroneal nerve

Key to MCQs

1. d	2. a	3. d	4. b	5. d	6. b	7. d
8. c	9. c	10. b	11. a	12. c	13. a	14. a

Chapter 8

Key to Clinicoanatomical Problems

Clinical Case 1

1. Anterior tibial compartment or fresher's syndrome is a condition characterised by increased pressure within the anterior compartment of the lower leg, leading to compression of structures and subsequent ischaemia and tissue damage.
2. The intense pain and swelling in the lower leg were likely caused by decreased blood flow to the muscles and nerves in the compartment, causing pain and swelling.
3. Weakness or paralysis of the muscles due to compression or injury to the deep peroneal nerve.
4. Emergency fasciotomy was suggested to relieve pressure and restore blood flow, thereby resolving the foot drop and preventing further ischaemic damage to the muscles and nerves.

Clinical Case 2

1. Injury to the superficial peroneal nerve causes paralysis of the peroneus longus and peroneus brevis muscles that results into loss of eversion of foot.
2. Sensory loss on the dorsum of foot is resulting from the sensory innervation provided by the superficial peroneal nerve to most of the dorsum of the foot, with the exception of the first webspace, which is supplied by the deep peroneal nerve.

Key to Practice Figures

Practice Figure 8.1

A. Superior extensor retinaculum, B. Inferior extensor retinaculum, C. Tibialis anterior, D. Extensor hallucis longus, E. Anterior tibial artery, F. Deep peroneal nerve, G. Extensor digitorum longus, H. Peroneus tertius

Practice Figure 8.2

A. 5th metacarpal, B. Tibialis anterior, C. Extensor digitorum longus, D. Extensor hallucis longus, E. Peroneus tertius, F. Medial cuneiform, G. Base of 1st metatarsal

Practice Figure 6.3

A. Anterior lateral malleolar artery, B. Lateral tarsal artery, C. Arcuate artery, D. Anterior tibial recurrent artery, E. Anterior tibial artery, F. Anterior medial malleolar artery, G. Dorsalis pedis artery, H. Medial tarsal artery, I. First dorsal metatarsal artery

Key to MCQs

1. b	2. b	3. b	4. a	5. d	6. d	7. c
8. c	9. b	10. a	11. c	12. d	13. d	14. b
15. d						

Chapter 9

Key to Clinicoanatomical Problems

Clinical Case 1

1. Tendocalcaneus is a combined tendon of gastrocnemius and soleus. It is attached to the middle area of posterior surface of calcaneum.
2. The primary action of the Achilles tendon is plantar flexion of the foot in walking, running, and jumping.
3. Feeling of "pop" occurred due to tendon tears or ruptures, which is caused by excessive force or overloading, leading to the sudden onset of pain and dysfunction.

Clinical Case 2

1. Tarsal tunnel syndrome is a condition resulting from compression of the tibial nerve as it passes through the tarsal tunnel, located on the medial side of the ankle, deep into the flexor retinaculum.
2. Tinel's sign is a physical examination technique where tapping over a nerve elicits a tingling sensation or pain in the distribution of the nerve.
3. The pain in the foot is due to compression of the tibial nerve within the tarsal tunnel. Most of the skin of sole is supplied by medial and lateral plantar branches of tibial nerve.

Key to Practice Figures

Practice Figure 9.1

A. Medial malleolus, B. Tibialis posterior, C. Flexor digitorum longus, D. Posterior tibial artery, E. Tibial nerve, F. Flexor hallucis longus, G. Flexor retinaculum, H. Calcaneum

Practice Figure 9.2

A. Popliteus, B. Flexor digitorum longus (FDL), C. Flexor hallucis longus (FHL), D. Tibialis posterior

Practice Figure 9.3

A. Popliteal artery, B. Posterior tibial artery, C. Nutrient artery of tibia, D. Communicating branch for peroneal artery, E. Medial malleolar branch, F. Medial plantar artery, G. Lateral plantar artery, H. Medial calcaneal branch, I. Anterior tibial artery, J. Circumflex fibular branch, K. Peroneal artery, L. Perforating branch, M. Lateral malleolar branch, N. Lateral calcaneal branch

Practice Figure 9.4

A. Tendon of plantaris, B. Plantaris, C. Lateral head, D. Medial head, E. Soleus, F. Tendo calcaneus, G. Calcaneum, H. Gastrocnemius

Key to MCQs

1. a	2. b	3. d	4. a	5. b	6. c	7. c
8. b	9. b	10. c	11. d	12. b	13. a	14. c
15. a	16. a					

Chapter 10

Key to Clinicoanatomical Problems

Clinical Case 1

1. Plantar fasciitis is the inflammation of the plantar aponeurosis, often caused by repeated minor trauma.
2. Calcaneal spur is ossified proximal part of the plantar aponeurosis at its attachment with the calcaneum.
3. Due to the sudden stretching and microtears of the tight plantar fascia during weight-bearing after periods of rest, exacerbating inflammation and sensitivity in the affected area.

Clinical Case 2

1. Jogger's foot or metatarsalgia: It is a compression of the medial plantar nerve deep to the flexor retinaculum, leading to symptoms such as burning, numbness, and tingling on the medial side of the sole.

2. Medial plantar nerve.
3. Medial plantar nerve gives:
   a. Muscular branches to abductor hallucis, flexor digitorum brevis, first lumbrical and flexor hallucis brevis.
   b. Branches to adjacent sides of medial 3½ toes, including their nail beds and distal phalanges on the dorsum of foot.

Key to Practice Figures

Practice Figure 10.1

A. Medial tubercle of calcaneum, B. Plantar aponeurosis, C. Superficial transverse metatarsal ligaments

Practice Figure 10.2

A. Abductor hallucis, B. Flexor digitorum brevis, C. Abductor digiti minimi

Practice Figure 10.3

A. Flexor digitorum accessories, B. Tendon of flexor digitorum longus, C. Lumbricals, D. Tendon of flexor hallucis longus

Practice Figure 10.4

A. Flexor hallucis brevis, B. Flexor digiti minimi brevis, C. Adductor hallucis

Practice Figure 10.5

A. Abduction, B. Dorsal interossei (1–4), C. Proximal phalanx, D. Axis of movement

Practice Figure 10.6

A. Tibial nerve, B. Medial plantar nerve, C. Abductor hallucis, D. Flexor digitorum brevis, E. Flexor hallucis brevis, F. First lumbrical, G. Lateral plantar nerve, H. Deep branch, I. Adductor hallucis, J. Interossei of 1st, 2nd, and 3rd spaces, K. Flexor digitorum accessories, L. Abductor digiti minimi, M. Superficial branch, N. Flexor digiti minimi brevis, O. Interossei of 4th space, P. Plantar digital nerve, Q. 2nd–4th lumbricals

Practice Figure 10.7

A. Palmar interossei, B. Proximal phalanx, C. Adduction, D. Axis of movement

Practice Figure 10.8

A. Posterior tibial artery, B. Medial plantar artery, C. Dorsalis pedis artery, D. Plantar metatarsal arteries, E. Lateral plantar artery, F. Plantar arch

Key to MCQs

1. c 2. c 3. b 4. a 5. c 6. d 7. a
8. b 9. c 10. a 11. a

Chapter 11

Key to Clinicoanatomical Problem

Clinical Case 1

1. Varicose veins are enlarged, swollen, and twisted veins.
2. These structures are the varicose veins in the lower limbs.
3. Factors causing varicose veins in the lower limbs: Weak or damaged valves in the veins, increased pressure within the veins, often due to prolonged standing, obesity, or pregnancy, weakening of the vein walls over time, and reduced elasticity of the veins, impairing their ability to return blood to the heart efficiently.

Key to Practice Figures

Practice Figure 11.1

A. Femoral vein, B. Popliteal vein, C. Anterior tibial vein, D. Peroneal vein, E. Lateral ankle perforator, F. Short saphenous vein, G. Long saphenous vein, H. Adductor canal (Hunterian) perforator, I. Boyd's perforator or knee perforator, J. Posterior arch vein, K. Posterior tibial vein, L. Medial perforators of Cockett, M. Dorsal venous arch

Practice Figure 11.2

A. Short saphenous vein, B. Lateral marginal vein, C. Long saphenous vein, D. Dorsal venous arch, E. Medial marginal vein, F. Dorsal metatarsal vein

Key to MCQs

1. b 2. b 3. d 4. b 5. d 6. b 7. b
8. b 9. b 10. b 11. c

Chapter 12

Key to Clinicoanatomical Problems

Clinical Case 1

1. Anterior cruciate ligament extends from anterior part of intercondylar area of tibia, runs upwards, backwards and laterally and is attached to the posterior part of medial surface of lateral condyle of femur.
2. The drawer sign assesses the integrity of the anterior cruciate ligament, involving attempting to move the tibia forward (anterior translation) relative to the femur.
3. A positive drawer sign indicates excessive forward movement of the tibia compared to the femur, suggesting a tear or laxity of the ACL.
4. It is a combination of injury to the tibial collateral ligament, medial meniscus, and the anterior cruciate ligament, commonly occurring together, particularly in sports-related knee injuries.

Clinical Case 2

1. McMurray's test assesses for meniscal injuries in the knee joint by flexing and extending the knee while applying rotational stress. A positive test indicates clicking, popping, or pain along the joint line, suggestive of a meniscal tear.
2. The medial meniscus is firmly attached to the medial collateral ligament and the joint capsule, making it less mobile and more susceptible to injury during rotational movements.
3. McMurray's test is more specific for detecting medial meniscus injuries, while the anterior drawer test is more specific for assessing anterior cruciate ligament integrity.

Clinical Case 3

1. Prepatellar bursitis is inflammation of the prepatellar bursa, characterised by swelling and tenderness over the anterior aspect of the knee.
2. Housemaids often spend prolonged periods of time kneeling while performing household chores such as scrubbing floors, cleaning, and gardening. This repetitive kneeling places excessive pressure on the prepatellar bursa, leading to irritation and inflammation.

Key to Practice Figures

Practice Figure 12.1

A. Greater trochanter, B. Iliofemoral ligament (Y-shaped), C. Pubofemoral ligament

Practice Figure 12.2

A. Ischium, B. Ilium, C. Iliofemoral ligament, D. Greater trochanter, E. Ischiofemoral ligament

Practice Figure 12.3

A. Gluteus medius, B. Gluteus minimus, C. Gluteus maximus, D. Superior gluteal nerve, E. Pyriformis, F. Inferior gluteal nerve, G. Obturator internus with gemelli, H. Quadratus femoris, I. Sciatic nerve, J. Biceps femoris, K. Obturator externus, L. Reflected head of rectus femoris, M. Straight head of rectus femoris, N. Tendon of iliopsoas, O. Synovial bursa, P. Femoral nerve, Q. Femoral artery, R. Femoral vein, S. Pectineus, T. Medial circumflex femoral artery, U. Gracilis, V. Adductor longus, W. Adductor brevis, X. Adductor magnus

Practice Figure 12.4

A. Femur, B. Fibular collateral ligament, C. Capsular ligament, D. Tendon of popliteus, E. Inferior lateral genicular artery and nerve, F. Tendon of biceps femoris, G. Fibula, H. Tibia, I. Anterior cruciate ligament,

J. Posterior cruciate ligament, K. Tibial collateral ligament, L. Meniscus, M. Tendon of semimembranosus, N. Inferior medial genicular artery and nerve, O. Sartorius, P. Gracilis, Q. Semitendinosus

Practice Figure 12.5

A. Ligamentum patellae, B. Transverse ligament, C. Anterior cruciate ligament, D. Medial meniscus, E. Lateral meniscus, F. Posterior cruciate ligament

Key to MCQs

1. b	2. a	3. b	4. b	5. a	6. b	7. b
8. d	9. a	10. b	11. d	12. c	13. a	14. d
15. a	16. c					

Chapter 13

Key to Clinicoanatomical Problems

Clinical Case 1

1. In flat feet, the feet do not show the normal upward concavity along the medial border of foot.
2. Due to concerns about their ability to withstand the physical demands and rigours of military training and operations. Flat feet may lead to increased risk of stress fractures, plantar fasciitis, and shin splints, especially during activities involving prolonged standing, marching, and running.
3. Factors maintaining medial longitudinal arch of the foot are:
   a. Proper shape of the bones, e.g. talus, calcaneum
   b. Ligaments like spring ligaments, deltoid ligaments

Key to Practice Figures

Practice Figure 13.1

A. Spring ligament, B. Navicular, C. Medial cuneiform, D. 1st metatarsal, E. Talus (keystone), F. Calcaneum, G. Calcaneum, H. Cuboid (keystone), I. 5th metatarsal

Practice Figure 13.2

A. 1st metatarsal, B. Tibialis anterior, C. Tibialis posterior, D. Flexor hallucis longus, E. Spring ligament, F. Plantar aponeurosis

Practice Figure 13.3

A. Peroneus longus, B. Peroneus brevis, C. Tibialis anterior, D. Short plantar ligament, E. Long plantar ligament, F. Plantar aponeurosis

Key to MCQs

1. d	2. d	3. c	4. b	5. b	6. d	7. c
8. b	9. b	10. a				

Chapter 14

Key to Practice Figures

Practice Figure 14.1

A. Iliac crest, B. Ilium, C. Femoral head, D. Neck of femur, E. Lesser trochanter, F. Femur, G. Acetabulum, H. Pubic symphysis, I. Obturator foramen, J. Ischial tuberosity

Practice Figure 14.2

A. Lateral condyle of femur, B. Lateral condyle of tibia, C. Head of fibula, D. Femur, E. Patella, F. Medial epicondyle, G. Medial condyle of femur, H. Knee joint, I. Medial condyle of tibia, J. Femur, K. Patella, L. Knee joint, M. Head of fibula, N. Neck of fibula, O. Tibia

Practice Figure 14.3

A. Phalanges, B. Sesamoid bones, C. Metatarsals, D. Cuneiforms, E. Navicular, F. Cuboid

Key to MCQs

1. a	2. b	3. b	4. b	5. a	6. d	7. d
8. a						

ABDOMEN AND PELVIS

Chapter 15

Key to Clinicoanatomical Problem

Clinical Case 1

1. In spondylolysis, there is a separation of body of L5 vertebra from vertebral arch. Spondylolisthesis is the forward slipping of L5 vertebra over the sacrum. Normally, this is prevented by inferior articular processes of L5 vertebra.
2. The forward displacement of the L5 vertebra over the sacrum causes compression of sciatic nerve roots, resulting in chronic lower back pain.
3. Prolonged sitting exacerbates the pain due to increased pressure on the lumbar spine and sacrum.

Key to Practice Figures

Practice Figure 15.1

A. Superior articular process, B. Mamillary process, C. Transverse process, D. Spine, E. Inferior articular process, F. Spine, G. Mamillary process, H. Superior articular process, I. Accessory process, J. Pedicle, K. Vertebral foramen (triangular), L. Body (kidney-shaped)

Practice Figure 15.2

A. Psoas fascia, B. Thoraco-lumbar fascia, C. Anterior longitudinal ligament, D. Crus of diaphragm, E. Psoas major, F. Posterior longitudinal ligament, G. Quadratus lumborum, H. Multifidus, I. Erector spinae

Practice Figure 15.3

A. Median sacral artery, B. Iliacus, C. Sympathetic trunk, D. Attachment of transverse mesocolon, E. Piriformis, F. Ventral primary rami of sacral nerves and branches of lateral sacral artery, G. Ganglion impar, H. Dorsal primary rami, I. Erector spinae, J. Multifidus, K. Gluteus maximus, L. Sacrospinous ligament, M. Sacrotuberous ligament, N. Sacrococcygeal ligament

Key to MCQs

1. a	2. c	3. b	4. b	5. a	6. a	7. b
8. d	9. d	10. c	11. a	12. c	13. d	14. b

Chapter 16

Key to Clinicoanatomical Problems

Clinical Case 1

1. Though the median incision is relatively bloodless, it tends to leave a postoperative weakness through which a ventral hernia may develop.
2. In paramedian incision, rectus abdominis muscle is retracted laterally to protect the thoracic nerves. The nerves enter the rectus muscle from lateral side.

Clinical Case 2

1. Protrusion of the loop of intestine through the inguinal wall or inguinal canal is called inguinal hernia.
2. Types of inguinal hernia: Indirect and direct (medial and lateral). In indirect inguinal hernia, abdominal content enters into inguinal canal through deep inguinal ring, whereas in direct inguinal hernia, abdominal content protrudes into inguinal canal by pushing its posterior wall.
3. Risk factors: Male gender, advancing age, obesity, heavy lifting or straining, and a family history of hernias.
4. A reducible inguinal hernia can be pushed back into the abdomen, while an irreducible hernia cannot be manually reduced.

Key to Practice Figures

Practice Figure 16.1

A. Linea alba, B. External oblique muscle, C. Superficial inguinal ring

Practice Figure 16.2

A. Xiphoid process, B. Linea alba, C. Internal oblique muscle, D. Arcuate line

Practice Figure 16.3

A. Xiphoid process, B. Linea alba, C. Transversus abdominis, D. Arcuate line

Practice Figure 16.4

A. Xiphoid, B. Rectus abdominis, C. Tendinous intersection, D. Two heads of origin

Practice Figure 16.5

A. Diaphragm, B. Superior epigastric artery, C. Posterior wall of rectus sheath, D. Fascia transversalis, E. Extraperitoneal fat, F. Parietal peritoneum, G. Inferior epigastric artery, H. 5th Costal cartilages, I. 6th Costal cartilages, J. 7th Costal cartilages, K. Rectus abdominis, L. Anterior wall of rectus sheath, M. Arcuate line, N. Conjoint tendon, O. Pubis

Practice Figure 16.6

A. Inferior epigastric artery, B. Interfoveolar ligament, C. Internal oblique, D. External oblique aponeurosis, E. Spermatic cord, F. Testis, G. Peritoneum, H. Extraperitoneal connective tissue, I. Fascia transversalis, J. Conjoint aponeurosis, K. Reflected ligament, L. External spermatic fascia, M. Cremasteric fascia, N. Internal spermatic fascia

Practice Figure 16.7

A. Pampiniform plexus of veins, B. Ilioinguinal nerve, C. Remains of processus vaginalis, D. Cremasteric artery, E. Genital branch of genitofemoral nerve, F. Artery to ductus deferens, G. Ductus deferens, H. Testicular artery, I. Sympathetic nerves, J. Internal spermatic fascia, K. Cremasteric fascia, L. External spermatic fascia

Key to MCQs

1. c	2. b	3. b	4. a	5. a	6. a	7. b
8. c	9. c	10. b	11. a	12. d	13. d	14. c

Chapter 17

Key to Clinicoanatomical Problems

Clinical Case 1

1. Right testis failed to descent to the scrotum.
2. Cryptorchidism is a condition in which the testis fails to reach the scrotum.
3. Effects of cryptorchidism: Spermatogenesis may fail to occur and a malignant tumour may develop.
4. Yes, testis may descend on its own within first 6 months of life.

Clinical Case 2

1. Testicular torsion is a urological/surgical emergency characterised by the twisting of the spermatic cord, which leads to compromised blood flow to the testicle.
2. It may result into ischaemia and irreversible damage to the testicle, hence it is surgical emergency.
3. While the testicles are innervated by the ilioinguinal and genital branches of the genitofemoral nerve, which originate from the T10 spinal segment, the pain is often felt in the lower abdomen.

Key to Practice Figure

Practice Figure 17.1

A. Skin, B. Dartos muscle, C. External spermatic fascia, D. Cremasteric fascia, E. Internal spermatic fascia

Key to MCQs

1. b	2. c	3. c	4. a	5. b	6. c	7. c
8. b	9. d	10. b	11. d	12. b	13. a	14. c
15. c	16. c	17. c				

Chapter 18

Key to Clinicoanatomical Problems

Clinical Case 1

1. Peritonitis is inflammation of the peritoneum.
2. Parietal peritoneum is supplied by the somatic nerves that supply the abdominal wall; hence, in peritonitis, the abdominal pain and tenderness occur.
3. Sources of infection in peritonitis can include trauma, perforation of abdominal organs (such as the stomach or intestines), ruptured appendix, infected ascites, or postoperative complications.

Clinical Case 2

1. Ascites is the abnormal accumulation of fluid in the peritoneal cavity, leading to abdominal distention.
2. Causes of ascites: liver cirrhosis (the most common cause) and congestive heart failure.

Key to Practice Figures

Practice Figure 18.1

A. Right lateral plane, B. Right hypochondrium, C. Right lumbar/lateral region, D. Right iliac fossa/right inguinal, E. Umbilical region, F. Epigastrium, G. Left lateral plane, H. Left hypochondrium, I. Transpyloric plane, J. Left lumbar/lateral region, K. Transtubercular plane, L. Left iliac fossa/left inguinal, M. Hypogastrium/suprapubic

Practice Figure 18.2

A. Lesser omentum, B. Stomach, C. Greater omentum, D. Epiploic foramen, E. Lesser sac, F. Pancreas, G. Transverse mesocolon, H. Transverse colon

Practice Figure 18.3

A. Hepatic artery, B. Lesser sac, C. Aorta, D. Inferior vena cava, E. Bile duct, F. Portal vein, G. Right free margin of lesser omentum, H. Epiploic foramen, I. Right suprarenal gland

Practice Figure 18.4

A. Right lobe of liver, B. Gallbladder, C. Inferior layer of coronary ligaments, D. Right suprarenal gland, E. Right kidney, F. 2nd part of duodenum, G. Hepatic flexure of colon

Practice Figure 18.5

A. Rectouterine pouch, B. Vagina, C. Rectum, D. Posterior fornix of vagina, E. Rectovaginal fold of peritoneum

Key to MCQs

1. c	2. a	3. b	4. b	5. d	6. a	7. b
8. c	9. a	10. b	11. d	12. d	13. a	14. c

Chapter 19

Key to Clinicoanatomical Problems

Clinical Case 1

1. The stomach is primarily innervated by the vagus nerve (parasympathetic) and sympathetic fibres from the celiac plexus, not directly from the spinal segments T6–T9.
2. Stomach pain is referred to the epigastric region through T6–T9 fibres.
3. Spicy food and stress can exacerbate gastric ulcer symptoms by increasing gastric acid secretion and impairing the protective mucosal barrier of the stomach.

Clinical Case 2

1. The common site for gastric carcinoma is the pyloric antrum along the greater curvature.
2. Precancerous conditions: Chronic gastritis or ulcers, intestinal metaplasia, and gastric adenomas or polyps.

3. Gastric carcinoma is more common in males than females, and individuals with blood type A have a higher risk.
4. Left supraclavicular lymph (Virchow's) node enlarges due to metastasis through lymphatic root.

Key to Practice Figures

Practice Figure 19.1

A. Lesser omentum, B. Gastrophrenic ligament, C. Gastrosplenic ligament, D. Spleen, E. Greater omentum

Practice Figure 19.2

A. Stomach (dotted outline), B. Coeliac trunk, C. Spleen, D. Diaphragm, E. Left suprarenal gland, F. Left kidney, G. Splenic artery, H. Pancreas, I. Left colic flexure, J. Transverse mesocolon

Practice Figure 19.3

A. Coeliac trunk, B. Common hepatic artery, C. Right gastric artery, D. Superior pancreaticoduodenal artery, E. Left gastric artery, F. Short gastric arteries, G. Splenic artery, H. Left gastroepiploic artery, I. Right gastroepiploic artery

Practice Figure 19.4

A. Coeliac nodes, B. Hepatic nodes, C. Right gastric nodes, D. Pyloric nodes, E. Right gastroepiploic nodes, F. Left gastric nodes, G. Pancreaticosplenic nodes

Key to MCQs

1. c 2. b 3. b 4. d 5. d 6. c 7. b
8. b 9. a 10. c 11. c

Chapter 20

Key to Clinicoanatomical Problem

Clinical Case 1

1. Appendicitis is an inflammation of appendix.
2. McBurney's point is the site of maximum tenderness in appendicitis. The point lies at the junction of lateral 1/3rd and medial 2/3rd of line joining the right anterior superior iliac spine to umbilicus.
3. In case of appendicitis, the pain initially referred to the periumbilical region as T10 spinal segment supplies both of these structures.
4. Psoas test: In retrocaecal position of appendix, its inflammation may irritate the right psoas major muscle. In these patients, forced extension of the right thigh induces pain in the right iliac fossa.

Key to Practice Figures

Practice Figure 20.1

A. Quadrate lobe of liver, B. Gallbladder, C. 1st part of duodenum, D. Gastroduodenal artery, E. Hepatic artery proper, F. Epiploic foramen, G. Bile duct, H. IVC, I. Portal vein, J. Head of pancreas

Practice Figure 20.2

A. Gallbladder, B. Right lobe of liver, C. Transverse colon, D. Transverse mesocolon, E. Coils of small intestine, F. 2nd part of duodenum, G. Right suprarenal gland, H. 2nd part of duodenum, I. Right kidney, J. Right renal vessels, K. IVC, L. Right psoas major, M. Aorta

Practice Figure 20.3

A. Umbilicus, B. Ileum, C. Mesentery, D. Meckel's diverticulum

Practice Figure 20.4

A. Psoas major, B. Iliacus, C. Genitofemoral nerve, D. Femoral nerve, E. Right gonadal vessels, F. Lateral cutaneous nerve of thigh, G. External iliac artery

Practice Figure 20.5

A. Paracolic, B. Retrocolic, C. Post-ileal, D. Pre-ileal, E. Promonteric, F. Pelvic, G. Midinguinal

Key to MCQs

1. c 2. d 3. c 4. c 5. d 6. c 7. c
8. c 9. b 10. b 11. b 12. c 13. d 14. d

Chapter 21

Key to Clinicoanatomical Problem

Clinical Case 1

1. Caput medusae are prominent dilated veins radiating from the umbilicus (resembling the appearance of the head of Medusa from Greek mythology). It is typically seen in patients with portal hypertension.
2. Haematemesis is the vomiting of blood, indicating bleeding from the upper gastrointestinal tract. In this case, haematemesis occurred due to the presence of oesophageal varices, which are dilated veins in the lower oesophagus.
3. Ascites is the accumulation of fluid within the peritoneal cavity. In this case, the portal hypertension leads to increased pressure within the portal vein system, causing the fluid to accumulate in the abdominal cavity and result in ascites.

Key to Practice Figures

Practice Figure 21.1

A. Coeliac trunk, B. Inferior phrenic artery, C. Middle suprarenal artery, D. Superior mesenteric artery, E. Renal artery, F. Gonadal artery, G. Abdominal aorta, H. Inferior mesenteric artery, I. Common iliac artery

Practice Figure 21.2

A. Cystic Vein, B. Superior pancreaticoduodenal vein, C. Paraumbilical vein, D. Oesophageal veins, E. Left gastric vein, F. Right gastric vein, G. Prepyloric vein, H. Portal vein, I. Splenic vein, J. Inferior mesenteric vein, K. Superior mesenteric vein

Key to MCQs

1. a 2. a 3. a 4. b 5. b 6. d 7. c
8. b 9. c 10. b 11. c 12. d

Chapter 22

Key to Clinicoanatomical Problem

Clinical Case 1

1. Anatomical basis for:
   a. The epigastric region is supplied by T7–T9 nerves. The gallbladder also receives the innervation through T7–T9 sympathetic ganglia. Hence, visceral pain of gallbladder is referred to as the epigastric region.
   b. Inflamed gallbladder irritates the diaphragm which is supplied by the phrenic nerve (C3–C5). The supraclavicular nerves (C3, C4) supply the shoulder region. Hence, pain in cholecystitis radiates to the right shoulder due to same segmental innervation.
   c. Murphy's sign is elicited by asking the patient to take a deep breath while the examiner palpates the right subcostal area below the liver margin. If the patient abruptly stops breathing in (due to pain) when pressure is applied over the gallbladder as it descends during inspiration, the test is considered positive for Murphy's sign, indicating inflammation of the gallbladder.

Key to Practice Figure

Practice Figure 22.1

A. Right hepatic duct, B. Left hepatic duct, C. Common hepatic duct, D. Cystic duct, E. Common bile duct, F. Gallbladder, G. Main pancreatic duct, H. Second part of duodenum

Key to MCQs

1. a 2. b 3. c 4. b 5. b 6. b 7. a
8. b 9. c 10. c

Chapter 23

Key to Clinicoanatomical Problems

Clinical Case 1

1. The spleen's position adjacent to the lower ribs on the lateral surface indeed makes it vulnerable to damage in motor vehicle accidents, particularly from broken ribs that can penetrate or compress the spleen.
2. Hypotension in patients with splenic rupture is primarily due to the significant internal bleeding resulting from the injury, which leads to a decrease in circulating blood volume and subsequent hypotension.

Clinical Case 2

1. Jaundice in carcinoma of the head of the pancreas occurs due to obstruction of the common bile duct by the tumour mass.
2. Gastric tumours, liver cancers
3. Inferior vena cava, and abdominal aorta

Clinical Case 3

1. The liver enlarges downward toward the right iliac fossa.
2. In this case, liver dysfunction resulted in increased bilirubin levels that produced jaundice. This excess bilirubin then manifests as yellowing of the skin and sclerae, characteristic of jaundice.

Key to Practice Figures

Practice Figure 23.1

A. Hilum, B. Inferior border, C. Superior border, D. Pancreatic impression

Practice Figures 23.2a and b

A. 1st part of duodenum, B. transverse mesocolon, C. transverse colon, D. Jejunum, E. Head of pancreas (red dotted line), F. bile duct, G. inferior vena cava, H. terminal part of renal veins, I. right crus of diaphragm, J. Head of pancreas (black dotted line)

Practice Figure 23.3

A. Duodenum, B. Minor duodenal papilla, C. Common bile duct, D. Herringbone pattern, E. Main pancreatic duct (duct of Wirsung), F. Accessory pancreatic duct (duct of Santorini), G. Hepatopancreatic ampulla (of Vater), H. Major duodenal papilla

Practice Figure 23.4

A. Left triangular ligament, B. Fissure for ligamentum venosum, C. Superior layer of coronary ligament, D. Inferior vena cava, E. Caudate lobe, F. Right triangular ligament, G. Inferior layer of coronary ligament, H. Gallbladder, I. Quadrate lobe, J. Porta hepatis, K. Fissure for ligamentum teres hepatis

Practice Figure 23.5

A. Oesophageal impression, B. Gastric impression, C. Tuber omentale, D. Fissure for ligamentum teres, E. Pyloric impression, F. Bare area of liver, G. Inferior vena cava, H. Right suprarenal impression, I. Right renal impression, J. Duodenal impression, K. Colic impression, L. Gallbladder

Key to MCQs

1. c	2. c	3. a	4. a	5. c	6. b	7. a
8. b	9. c	10. b	11. a	12. d	13. a	14. c

Chapter 24

Key to Clinicoanatomical Problems

Clinical Case 1

1. a. Pain in the left flank due to left ureteric colic is referred from the T10–L1 spinal nerve fibres, which also innervate the left flank.
   b. Radiating pain in the groin and scrotum occurs due to referred pain from the sympathetic nerves that supply the ureter, which are also derived from the T10–L1 spinal nerve segments.
2. KUB — a plain radiograph of abdomen to examine kidney, ureter and urinary bladder; and non-contrast CT scan of the abdomen and pelvis.
3. Renal ultrasound or intravenous pyelogram (IVP)

Clinical Case 2

1. The left kidney of the donor was selected for transplantation because the left renal vein is longer than the right, which helps for surgical anastomosis with the recipient's blood vessels.
2. The new kidney will be placed in the recipient's iliac fossa. This location allows for optimal vascular access and ureteral implantation.
3. The new ureter is connected to the urinary bladder. The renal blood vessels are connected to internal iliac vessels.
4. Peritoneal dialysis and haemodialysis.

Key to Practice Figures

Practice Figure 24.1

A. Right suprarenal gland, B. Right lobe of liver, C. Second part of duodenum, D. Right colic flexure, E. Jejunum, F. Left suprarenal gland, G. Spleen, H. Stomach, I. Pancreas, J. colic (splenic flexure), K. Jejunum

Practice Figure 24.2

A. Diaphragm, B. Subcostal vessels and nerve, C. Transverse abdominis, D. Iliohypogastric nerve, E. Ilioinguinal nerve, F. 11th rib, G. 12th rib, H. Psoas major, I. Quadratus Lumborum, J. Medial arcuate ligament, K. Lateral arcuate ligament, L. Diaphragm, M. Subcostal vessels and nerve, N. Transverse abdominis, O. Iliohypogastric nerve, P. Ilioinguinal nerve

Practice Figure 24.3

A. Diaphragm, B. Diaphragmatic fascia, C. Suprarenal gland, D. Kidney, E. Fibrous capsule, F. Perirenal fat, G. Renal fascia, H. Pararenal fat

Practice Figure 24.4

A. Common iliac artery, B. At the pelviureteric junction, C. At the pelvic brim, D. At crossing by ductus deferens, E. At the oblique passage through bladder wall, F. At ureteric opening

Key to MCQs

1. c	2. b	3. d	4. a	5. d	6. a	7. d
8. c	9. c	10. c	11. b	12. a	13. b	

Chapter 25

Key to Clinicoanatomical Problems

Clinical Case 1

1. Cushing's syndrome is caused by excess cortisol hormone. May be due to adrenal adenoma, pituitary adenomas producing adrenocorticotropic hormone (ACTH), ectopic ACTH-secreting tumours, or prolonged use of corticosteroid medications.
2. The right adrenal vein drains directly into the inferior vena cava, while the left adrenal vein drains into the left renal vein.

Clinical Case 2

1. Pheochromocytoma is a neuroendocrine tumour of adrenal medulla. It produces excess catecholamines (epinephrine and norepinephrine).
2. Hypertension in pheochromocytoma occurs due to the excessive release of catecholamines by the tumour.

Key to Practice Figures

Practice Figures 25.1a and b

A. Right suprarenal gland, B. Liver, C. Inferior vena cava, D. Left suprarenal gland, E. Stomach, F. Pancreas, G. Left suprarenal gland, H. Kidney, I. Diaphragm, J. Right suprarenal gland, K. Diaphragm, L. Kidney

Practice Figure 25.2

A. Aorta, B. Inferior phrenic artery, C. Superior, D. Middle, E. Inferior, F. Suprarenal arteries, G. Renal artery, H. Right suprarenal vein, I. Inferior vena cava, J. Left suprarenal vein, K. Renal vein, L. Left gonadal vein, M. Right gonadal vein

Key to MCQs

1. d 2. b 3. c 4. c 5. b 6. b 7. b
8. c 9. a 10. b

Chapter 26

Key to Clinicoanatomical Problem

Clinical Case 1

1. A sliding hiatal hernia is a type of hernia where the upper part of the stomach, along with the gastro-oesophageal junction, protrudes upward into the chest cavity through the oesophageal hiatus of the diaphragm.
2. Sliding hiatal hernia occurs due to weakness of the diaphragm, increased intra-abdominal pressure (such as obesity or pregnancy), or chronic straining (such as heavy lifting or chronic coughing).
3. Integrity of the oesophageal hiatus and the supportive structures surrounding the gastroesophageal junction, such as the phreno-oesophageal ligament.

Key to Practice Figure

Practice Figure 26.1

A. Inferior vena cava, B. Right phrenic nerve, C. Superior epigastric vessels, D. Left vagus (anterior), E. Oesophagus, F. Right vagus (posterior), G. Aorta, H. Thoracic duct, I. Azygos vein, J. Subcostal vessels and nerve, K. Sympathetic trunk, L. splanchnic nerve, M. Lesser splanchnic nerve

Key to MCQs

1. b 2. a 3. b 4. b 5. a 6. c 7. b
8. d 9. a 10. c

Chapter 27

Key to Clinicoanatomical Problem

Clinical Case 1

1. A psoas abscess is a collection of pus within the psoas muscle or its surrounding sheath.
2. Psoas abscesses can indeed be formed by the spread of infection from adjacent structures such as the kidneys (hematogenous spread) or vertebral bodies (direct extension).
3. Inferiorly, psoas fascia continues with fascia covering iliacus muscle. Hence, the psoas abscess may track down through the sheath into the thigh.

Key to Practice Figures

Practice Figure 27.1

A. Lumbar arteries, B. Abdominal aorta, C. Inferior phrenic artery, D. Coeliac trunk, E. Suprarenal artery, F. Renal artery, G. Superior mesenteric artery, H. Gonadal artery, I. Inferior mesenteric artery, J. Common iliac artery, K. Median sacral artery

Practice Figure 27.2

A. suprarenal vein, B. Right renal vein, C. Right gonadal vein, D. Median sacral vein, E. Right common iliac vein, F. Hepatic veins, G. Left suprarenal vein, H. Left renal vein, I. Left gonadal vein, J. Lumbar veins, K. Left common iliac vein, L. Left internal external iliac vein, M. Left external external iliac vein

Practice Figure 27.3

A. Subcostal nerve, B. Iliohypogastric nerve, C. Ilioinguinal nerve, D. Genitofemoral nerve, E. Lateral cutaneous nerve of thigh, F. Femoral nerve, G. Obturator nerve, H. Lumbosacral trunk

Key to MCQs

1. a 2. d 3. b 4. c 5. c 6. d 7. b
8. c 9. b 10. a

Chapter 28

Key to Clinicoanatomical Problem

Clinical Case 1

1. The ischioanal fossa is a wedge-shaped space located on each side of the anal canal and rectum.
2. A fistula in ano is an abnormal tract between the anal canal and the skin around the anus.
3. Infections of the ischioanal fossa are common due to the presence of numerous sweat glands and hair follicles in the perianal region.

Key to Practice Figures

Practice Figure 28.1

A. Bulbospongiosus, B. Superficial transverse perinei, C. Deep transverse perinei, D. Levator ani, E. Perineal body, F. Sphincter ani externus, G. Anococcygeal raphe

Practice Figure 28.2

A. Circular muscle coat of rectum, B. Longitudinal muscle coat of rectum, C. Deep, D. Superficial, E. Subcutaneous, F. Parts of external anal sphincter, G. Obturator internus muscle, H. Levator ani, I. Suprasegmental space, J. Fascia lunata, K. Ischioanal space, L. Pudendal canal, M. Perianal fascia, N. Perianal space filled with fat

Practice Figure 28.3

A. Dorsal nerve of penis, B. S2, C. S3, D. S4, E. Pudendal nerve, F. Inferior rectal nerve, G. Perineal nerve, H. Posterior scrotal nerves

Key to MCQs

1. a 2. c 3. b 4. c 5. c 6. d 7. d
8. c 9. a 10. a

Chapter 29

Key to Clinicoanatomical Problem

Clinical Case 1

1. The root value of the pudendal nerve is the ventral rami of S2, S3 and S4 segments of the spinal cord.
2. The site for pudendal nerve block is above the ischial tuberosity, where the pudendal nerve passes through Alcock's canal (also known as the pudendal canal) within the pelvis.

Key to Practice Figure

Practice Figure 29.1

A. Plane of inlet, B. Pubic symphysis, C. Horizontal plane, D. Sacrum, E. Coccyx, F. Plane of outlet

Key to MCQs

1. b 2. a 3. b 4. a 5. c 6. d 7. d
8. d 9. b 10. b

Chapter 30

Key to Clinicoanatomical Problem

Clinical Case 1

1. Two types: Intraperitoneal and extraperitoneal.
2. In the case of intraperitoneal rupture, the extravasated urine would spread within the peritoneal cavity. In extraperitoneal rupture, the extravasated urine would be confined to the extraperitoneal space.

Key to Practice Figures

Practice Figure 30.1

A. Apex, B. Inferolateral surface, C. Posterolateral angle, D. Prostatic part of urethra, E. Superior surface, F. Ureters, G. Base, H. Neck, I. Prostate

Practice Figure 30.2

A. Interureteric ridge (bar of Mercier), B. Prostate, C. Trigone of bladder, D. Ureter, E. Internal urethral sphincter, F. Seminal colliculus, G. Urethral crest

Practice Figure 30.3

A. Urinary bladder, B. Preprostatic, C. Prostatic, D. Membranous, E. Posterior urethra, F. Bulbar urethra, G. Penile urethra, H. Anterior urethra, I. Navicular fossa, J. External urethral meatus, K. Prostate, L. Urogenital diaphragm

Practice Figure 30.4

A. Internal urethral sphincter, B. Urethral crest, C. Colliculus seminalis, D. Opening of prostatic utricle, E. Opening of ejaculatory duct, F. Prostatic sinus, G. Prostate gland, H. External urethral sphincter, I. Perineal membrane

Key to MCQs

1. c 2. c 3. b 4. a 5. b 6. b 7. d
8. c 9. b 10. a

Chapter 31

Key to Clinicoanatomical Problems

Clinical Case 1

1. Tubectomy is indeed a surgical procedure for permanent contraception in women, involving the cutting and ligating of the fallopian tubes.
2. Bilateral tubectomy is commonly performed for family planning to ensure complete sterilisation.
3. Tubectomy can be performed as a minimally invasive laparoscopic procedure or laparotomy under general anaesthesia.
4. Hospitalisation is generally not required for laparoscopic tubectomy, but a few days of hospitalisation may be necessary for laparotomy.

Clinical Case 2

1. Cervix has external os, endocervical canal, supravaginal and vaginal parts.
2. Human papillomavirus (HPV) is a known causative agent for cervical cancer.
3. Yes, vaccines against HPV infection are more effective against cervical cancers if given before exposure to the virus, typically during adolescence.
4. The cervix receives sensory nerve supply from branches of the pelvic plexus, including the pelvic splanchnic nerves (parasympathetic) and the sacral spinal nerves (somatic).

Key to Practice Figures

Practice Figure 31.1

A. Intramural part, B. Isthmus, C. Ampulla, D. Infundibulum, E. Ovary

Practice Figures 31.2a and b

A. Long axis of body of uterus, B. Long axis of vagina, C. Horizontal plane, D. Long axis of body of uterus, E. Long axis of cervix

Practice Figure 31.3

A. Gartner's duct, B. Body of uterus, C. Cervix of uterus, D. Infundibulopelvic ligament, E. Ovarian artery, F. Epoöphoron, G. Round ligament of ovary, H. Paroöphoron, I. Broad ligament of uterus, J. Uterine artery, K. Ureter

Practice Figure 31.4

A. Vagina, B. Rectum, C. Anococcygeal ligament, D. Urethra, E. Pubovaginalis, F. Puborectalis, G. Pubococcygeus proper, H. Pubococcygeus, I. Iliococcygeus, J. Coccygeus

Practice Figure 31.5

A. Sacrum, B. Rectum, C. Cervix, D. Urinary bladder, E. Fascia of Waldeyer, F. Uterosacral ligament, G. Transverse cervical ligament, H. Pubocervical ligament, I. Pubic symphysis

Key to MCQs

1. a 2. c 3. b 4. b 5. a 6. a 7. a
8. d 9. c 10. b

Chapter 32

Key to Clinicoanatomical Problems

Clinical Case 1

1. It is a non-cancerous enlargement of the prostate gland that commonly occurs in older men.
2. The periurethral (transition) zone of the prostate, which surrounds the urethra, is the part most commonly involved in BHP.
3. Urinary hesitancy in BHP occurs due to mechanical obstruction of the urethra by the enlarged prostate gland.
4. The prostate gland is surrounded by two capsules: The inner true capsule, derived from the condensation of the peripheral part of the gland, and the outer false capsule, derived from the endopelvic fascia.

Clinical Case 2

1. Prostate cancer cells can spread to the lumbar vertebrae by direct extension or haematogenous spread via the prostatic venous plexus and through the Batson's vertebral venous plexus.
2. Other sites of metastasis: Pelvic lymph nodes, bones, liver and lungs, cranial cavity.

Clinical Case 3

1. Vasectomy is a surgical procedure for male sterilisation that involves cutting the vas deferens.
2. Vasectomy is done on both sides for family planning operations to ensure complete sterilisation.
3. Vasectomy is commonly performed as an outpatient procedure under local anaesthesia. The surgeon makes small incisions in the scrotum to access and cut the vas deferens.
4. For vasectomy, hospitalisation is not typically required. It is an outpatient procedure.

Key to Practice Figures

Practice Figure 32.1

A. Anterior lobe (Isthmus), B. Posterior lobe, C. Prostatic urethra, D. Median lobe, E. Lateral lobe, F. Opening of ejaculatory duct, G. Opening of prostatic utricle

Practice Figure 32.2

A. Prostate gland, B. Bladder, C. Vesical venous plexus, D. True capsule, E. False capsule, F. Prostatic venous plexus, G. Prostatic urethra, H. Bulbourethral gland

Practice Figure 32.3

A. True capsule, B. Prostatic urethra, C. Isthmus, D. Main prostatic glands, E. Submucosal glands, F. Mucosal glands, G. Central zone, H. Peripheral zone, I. Transitional zone

Key to MCQs

1. a 2. c 3. b 4. a 5. c 6. c 7. b
8. c 9. d 10. b

Chapter 33

Key to Clinicoanatomical Problem

Clinical Case 1

1. Haemorrhoids or piles, are swollen and inflamed veins in the rectum and anus.
2. Internal haemorrhoids develop inside the rectum and may cause painless rectal bleeding and protrude through the anal canal during bowel movements. External haemorrhoids form under the skin around the anus and are often painful.

3. The proctoscopic examination revealed three pink-coloured swellings located at 3, 7 and 11 o'clock positions with the patient in lithotomy position.

Key to Practice Figures

Practice Figures 33.1a and b

A. Wall of rectum, B. Rectal ampulla, C. First transverse fold, D. Second transverse fold, D. Third transverse fold, F. First transverse fold, G. Second transverse fold, H. Third transverse fold

Practice Figure 33.2

A. Upper part, B. Area of pecten, C. Lower part, D. Anal orifice, E. Anal columns, F. Anal valves, G. Pectinate line, H. White line of Hilton

Key to MCQs

1. c 2. b 3. b 4. c 5. c 6. a 7. a
8. c 9. b 10. d

Chapter 34

Key to Clinicoanatomical Problem

Clinical Case 1

1. In uterine prolapse, the uterus descends from its normal position in the pelvis and protrudes into the vaginal canal.
2. The pelvic diaphragm is formed by levator ani muscles (puborectalis, pubococcygeus and iliococcygeus), coccygeus muscles and their associated fascia.
3. Because of damage and weakness of pelvic diaphragm and ligament of uterus during childbirth.

Key to Practice Figures

Practice Figure 34.1

A. Urethra, B. Vagina, C. Rectum, D. Sphincter urethovaginalis, E. Pubo-analis, F. Pubococcygeus, G. Iliococcygeus, H. Ischial spine, I. Coccygeus, J. Piriformis

Practice Figure 34.2

A. Common iliac artery, B. Internal iliac artery, C. External iliac artery, D. Anterior division, E. Superior vesical artery, F. Obturator artery, G. Deep circumflex iliac artery, H. Inferior epigastric artery, I. Uterine artery, J. Inferior vesical artery, K. Posterior division, L. Iliolumbar artery, M. Lateral sacral arteries, N. Superior gluteal artery, O. Middle rectal artery, P. Inferior gluteal artery, Q. Internal pudendal artery

Key to MCQs

1. c 2. d 3. a 4. b 5. c 6. b 7. b
8. b 9. a 10. b

Chapter 35

Key to MCQs

1. b 2. c 3. b 4. a 5. b 6. d 7. b
8. a 9. c 10. d

Chapter 36

Key to Practice Figures

Practice Figure 36.1

A. Oesophagus

Practice Figure 36.2

A. Gas in fundus, B. Pyloric part of stomach, C. Body of stomach

Practice Figure 36.3

A. Descending colon, B. Rectum

Practice Figure 36.4

A. Major calyx, B. Pelvis of ureter, C. Ureter, D. Urinary bladder

Practice Figure 36.5

A. Body of uterus, B. Canula

Key to MCQs

1. b 2. b 3. c 4. d 5. c 6. a 7. c
8. a 9. b 10. d

Appendix

Key to Spotters

Spotter 1

Sartorius, inguinal ligament.

Spotter 2

a. Iliacus, b. Femoral nerve

Spotter 3

a. Ligamentum patellae, b. Extension of knee joint

Spotter 4

a. Sustentaculum tali.; b. Tendon of the flexor hallucis longus muscle

Spotter 5

a. Rectus femoris, b. Posterior division of the femoral nerve.

Spotter 6

a. Rectus femoris, b. Posterior division of the femoral nerve.

Spotter 7

a. Tibialis anterior, b. Dorsiflexion, inversion.

Spotter 8

a. Deep peroneal nerve. b. Foot drop.

Spotter 9

a. Tibialis posterior, b. Plantar flexion, inversion of foot, maintain medial longitudinal arch

Spotter 10

a. Flexor digitorum accessories, b. Lateral plantar nerve

Spotter 11

a. Ala of the sacrum. b. Sympathetic chain, lumbosacral trunk, iliolumbar artery and obturator nerve

Spotter 12

a. External oblique muscle, b. Lower six thoracic nerves

Spotter 13

a. Right testis, b. Tunica vaginalis, albuginea, vasculosa

Spotter 14

a. Stomach, b. Fundus, body, pyloric antrum and pyloric canal

Spotter 15

a. Second part of duodenum, b. Common bile duct and minor pancreatic duct.

Spotter 16

a. Pancreas, b. Head, neck, body, tail.

Spotter 17

a. The bare area of the liver, b. Its boundaries

Spotter 18

a. Right kidney, b. Renal vein, renal artery and renal pelvis.

Spotter 19

X: Prostate Y: Trigone of urinary bladder

Spotter 20

a. Broad ligament, b. Its contents.